INDUSTRIAL RESEARCH SERVICE'S

SUPPLEMENT II

TO THE
1953 EDITION
OF

HANDBOOK OF
MATERIAL TRADE NAMES

INDUSTRIAL RESEARCH SERVICE'S

Supplement II
TO THE
1953 EDITION
OF

Handbook of
MATERIAL TRADE NAMES

By

O. T. ZIMMERMAN, Ph.D.,
*Professor of Chemical Engineering
and Chairman of the Department
University of New Hampshire*

and

IRVIN LAVINE, Ph.D.,
*Professor of Chemical Engineering
University of New Hampshire*

INDUSTRIAL RESEARCH SERVICE INC.
DOVER, NEW HAMPSHIRE
1957

COPYRIGHT 1946, 1953, 1956, 1957, BY
INDUSTRIAL RESEARCH SERVICE INC.

All rights reserved. This book, or any part thereof, may not be reproduced in any form without written permission from the publishers.

Printed in the United States of America

Preface

Supplement II to the 1953 Edition of *Handbook of Material Trade Names*, like Supplement I which was published a year ago, is designed to bring "Handbook of Material Trade Names" up-to-date.

Although only a year has elapsed since *Supplement I* made its appearance, thousands of new products have been placed on the market, and many products have been withdrawn. Furthermore, some companies have gone out of business, others have changed their names, and many have lost their company identity through mergers.

Supplement II brings to our readers descriptions of many thousands of new products, including products of many companies which were not listed in either the Handbook or Supplement I. It also points out changes in trademark registration or company name.

Supplement II is based on the same style used in the 1953 Edition and in Supplement I. Like the previous volumes, it has three major sections:

1. The *Trade Name Section* in which the products are listed alphabetically and described.

2. The *Classification Section* in which all of the products described in the Trade Name Section are classified according to their major uses or composition.

3. The *Directory Section* which gives the address of each manufacturer or distributor whose products are described, and a list of each company's products for which information is given.

In addition to these major sections, Supplement II, like Supplement I, has a section entitled *Products Withdrawn From the Market*. In this section, all products described in the 1953 Edition or in Supplement I but which are no longer available are listed alphabetically for ready reference.

Another section has been added to Supplement II. In this section, entitled *Company Name and Address Changes*, are listed the old and new company names and the old and new addresses of any company whose products are described in either the 1953 Edition or Supplement I.

In Supplement II, as in the previous volumes, trademarks registered in the U. S. Patent Office are designated by the symbol ®; unregistered trademarks by the symbol ^{NR}; and generic and common names by the symbol $^{\triangle}$. Furthermore, trademarks registered in Canada, Germany, and Great Britain are identified by the symbols $®^{Can.}$, $®^{Ger.}$, and $®^{Brit.}$, respectively.

As in the preparation of the previous volumes we have taken every precaution to insure accuracy in compiling the information from the original sources. Nevertheless, we realize that in spite of our efforts some errors may have crept in; and we will not be responsible for errors or omissions. However, we would appreciate it if errors or omissions are called to our attention so that we can make the necessary corrections in Supplement III.

Durham, New Hampshire O. T. ZIMMERMAN
September, 1957 IRVIN LAVINE

Contents

	PAGE
Preface	v
Abbreviations	ix
Symbols	x
Alphabetical System	x
Trade Names Beginning with Letters	1
Trade Names Beginning with Numbers	246
Products Withdrawn from the Market	251
Classification Section	257
Directory Section	315
Company Name or Address Changes	351

Abbreviations

abbrev.	abbreviation	gr.	grain
abs.	absolute	HBMTN	Handbook of Material Trade Names
A.C.S.	American Chemical Society		
A.I.S.I.	American Iron & Steel Institute	hr.	hour
		I.A.C.S.	International Annealed Copper Standard
A.M.S.	Aeronautical Material Specifications		
		I.C.C.	Interstate Commerce Commission
A.O.A.C.	Association of Official Agricultural Chemists		
		i.d.	inside diameter
A.P.I.	American Petroleum Institute	in.	inch
		Inc.	Incorporated
approx.	approximate; approximately	I.P.S.	iron pipe size
		I.U.	International Unit
A.S.A.	American Standards Association	kc.	kilocycles
		kg.	kilogram
A.S.T.M.	American Society for Testing Materials	l	laevo
		Labs.	Laboratories
atm.	atmosphere	lb.	pound
av.	average	Ltd.	Limited
A.W.S.	American Welding Society	m	meta
Bé.	Baumé	max.	maximum
b.p.	boiling point	mcg.	micrograms
Brit.	British	mfg.	manufacture; manufacturing
B.t.u.	British thermal unit		
C.	Centigrade	mfg'd.	manufactured
cal.	calorie	mg.	milligram
Can.	Canadian	MIL	military
c.c.	cubic centimeter	min.	minute; minimum
cm.	centimeter	mm.	millimeter
Co.	Company	mmu.	millimicrons
C.O.C.	Cleveland Open Cup	mol. wt.	molecular weight
coef. *or* coeff.	coefficient	m.p.	melting point
		mu.	micron
comp.	compound	N	normal
conc.	concentration; concentrated	N.E.M.A.	National Electrical Manufacturers Association
Corp.	Corporation	N.F.	National Formulary
C.P.	chemically pure	no.	number
cps.	centipoises	N.P.A.	National Petroleum Association
cu.	cubic		
d	dextro	o	ortho
d.c.	direct current	ORD	ordnance
deg.	degree	oz.	ounce
Dept.	Department	pH	hydrogen ion concentration
diam.	diameter	p	para
dist'd.	distributed	p.p.m.	parts per million
emf.	electromotive force	press.	pressure
equip.	equipment	psi.	pounds per square inch
equiv.	equivalent	rpm.	revolutions per minute
F.	Fahrenheit	S.A.E.	Society of Automotive Engineers
F.D.A.	Food and Drug Administration		
		sec.	second
flex.	flexible; flexibility	specs.	specifications
f.p.	freezing point	sp.gr.	specific gravity
ft.	foot	sq.	square
g.	gram	std.	standard
gal.	gallon	Supp. I	Supplement I to the 1953 Edition of Handbook of Material Trade Names
Ger.	German		
G-H	Gardner-Holdt		
Govt.	Government	S.U.S.	Saybolt Universal Seconds

Tag.	Tagliabue
T.C.C.	Tagliabue Closed Cup
teasp.	teaspoonful
tech.	technical
temp.	temperature
uhf.	ultra high frequency
U.S.	United States
U.S.P.	United States Pharmacopoeia
vhf.	very high frequency
V.M.&P.	Varnish makers' & painters'
vol.	volume
vs.	versus
wt.	weight

Symbols

Ⓒ	Generic or common name
NR	Trade-mark not registered in U.S. Patent Office
®	Trade-mark registered in U.S. Patent Office
® Brit.	Trade-mark registered in Great Britain
® Can.	Trade-mark registered in Canada
® Ger.	Trade-mark registered in Germany.

Alphabetical System

All names are listed in alphabetical order regardless of spacing between letters or words, periods, commas, hyphens, number sign (#) or abbreviation (No.), or the ampersand (&). For example:

Ahcowet® SDS
AHT-28®Can.
Aircomb®
Air-Cub NR

Air Curtain NR
Air Dryette, Jr.®
Airfil®
Airkem 10-39®

Furthermore, a name with a number designation after it precedes the same name followed by a letter designation or another word, as illustrated below:

Aerosol® 18
Aerosol® 22
Aerosol® AY

Aerosol Insekil®
Aerosol® MA-80%
Aerosol® OS

A

a-3. See AIRKEM a-3®.

A-118[NR]. (*Supp.* I p. 1). Now a product of THE BORDEN CO., CHEMICAL DIV., successor to PIONEER LATEX & CHEMICAL CO.

AAF®. Registered trade name for air filters, dust collectors, and other products mfg'd by the AMERICAN AIR FILTER CO., INC.

AA Quality® Fertilizers. The trademark of THE AMERICAN AGRICULTURAL CHEMICAL CO. for an extensive line of fertilizer materials.

AA Quality® Phosphate Rock. A finely-ground, Florida pebble phosphate rock fertilizer material. It is used to build up the phosphorus content of soil for the growing of legumes such as alfalfa, sweet clover, red clover, ladino clover, lespedeza, etc.
AMERICAN AGRICULTURAL CHEMICAL CO.

Abbocillin®. A parenteral penicillin preparation composed of PENICILLIN G PROCAINE and buffered PENICILLIN G POTASSIUM for aqueous injection.
ABBOTT LABORATORIES

Abboject®. The trademark for a plastic disposable syringe designed for the administration of penicillin.
ABBOTT LABORATORIES

Abbo-Liter®. The trademark for a special container designed to hold infusion solutions for intravenous injection. ABBOTT LABORATORIES

Abbo-Vac®. The trademark for a blood bottle with vacuum. ABBOTT LABORATORIES

Abco-Gel[NR]. A gelling agent for water systems. It is a smooth-flowing, fine, off-white powder; insoluble in water and organic liquids. Available in two grades, both of which serve special purposes and find wide latitude in plastogels, as thickeners for vegetable oils, aromatic solvents, glycols, alcohols, lubricants, etc. Especially useful in emulsion paints, cleaners and polishes, oil-in-water emulsions, textile-processing aids, cosmetics, and various household products.
ABCO CHEMICAL CO.

A-B-C Phenothiazine[NR]. A dewormer for cattle, sheep, goats, horses, mules, swine, and poultry. It can be mixed with feed or salt, or applied as a slurry with drench syringe or bottle, or as tablets with a balling gun or blow gun.
ATOMIC BASIC CHEMICAL CORP.

ABDEC® Drops. A multiple vitamin dietary supplement, in a non-alcoholic liquid, for infants.
PARKE, DAVIS & CO.

ABDEC® Kapseals®. A multiple vitamin dietary supplement of 10 vitamins. PARKE, DAVIS & CO.

Abesto® Fibrated. Incorrectly listed as ASBESTO® FIBRATED (*HBMTN* p. 66).
ABESTO MANUFACTURING CO.

Absto® Liquid. Incorrectly listed as ASBESTO® LIQUID (*HBMTN* p. 67).
ABESTO MANUFACTURING CO.

Abesto® Lumiclad®. Incorrectly listed as ASBESTO® LUMICLAD® (*HBMTN* p. 67).
ABESTO MANUFACTURING CO.

Abesto® Quick-Setting Plastic. Incorrectly listed as ASBESTO® QUICK-SETTING PLASTIC (*HBMTN* p. 67).
ABESTO MANUFACTURING CO.

Abesto® Sealer. Incorrectly listed as ASBESTO® SEALER (*HBMTN* p. 67).
ABESTO MANUFACTURING CO.

Abesto® Semi-Plastic. Incorrectly listed as ASBESTO® SEMI-PLASTIC (*HBMTN* p. 67).
ABESTO MANUFACTURING CO.

Abitol®. Technical hydroabietyl alcohol derived from rosin by reducing the carboxyl group of the rosin acids to hydroxyl. It is a sparkling-clear, almost colorless, extremely tacky liquid. ABITOL is used extensively in adhesives. It is misable with paraffin wax, and such mixtures are used for laminating paper to foil, or foil to plastic sheeting. It is a good vehicle for grinding pigments as in inks or protective coatings. Also used as a plasticizer for synthetic resins; and as a chemical intermediate in the mfg. of nonionic synthetic detergents and for making simple esters. HERCULES POWDER CO.

Able-Stick. A line of self-sticking labels and tape that can be secured on any hard, clean surface without glue, water, or any processing. The labels are coated with a pressure-sensitive adhesive covered with a protective paper backing which is removed either manually or mechanically before the labels are pressed into place. ABLE-STICK tape is available without the backing for immediate application.
ALLEN HOLLANDER CO.

Abrac Resins 22 and 22A. All-purpose resins for the surface-coating industry. They can be used in most complex varnish formulations. They are soluble in a wide range of raw, heat-treated, and blown drying oils and in aliphatic and aromatic hydrocarbon solvents. RESIN 22A differs from RESIN 22 in that it is slightly darker, has a slightly lower m.p., and yields somewhat less viscous solutions, thus permitting the formulation of finishes of higher total solids content. RESIN 22: color, N-WG; acid value, 15–20 (max.); melting range, 125–135°C. Resin 22A: color N-WG; acid value, 15–20 (max.); melting range, 120–130°C.
BAIRD CHEMICAL CORP.

Absolute Filters. A line of air filters that will remove more than 99.95% of atmospheric dust, bacteria, pollen, and molds. They are very effective for the removal of radioactive particles, and were developed specifically for this purpose. Available in models which can withstand 100% humidity and temps. up to 1,000°F. CAMBRIDGE FILTER CORP.

Absorbent Cotton△. See COTTON△.

A-C®. The trademark for a local anesthetic and iodine troches. ABBOTT LABORATORIES

Acacia Gum△. Same as GUM ARABIC△.

Acaroid Resin△. *Also known as* YACCA GUM△ *and* GUM ACCROIDES△. The gum resin obtained from the base of the tufted trunk leaves of various species of *Xanthorrhoea* trees found in Australia and Tasmania. The resins contain from 80–85% resinotannol with coumaric acid and some cinnamic acid. Has the property, unique among natural resins, of thermosetting to a hard, insoluble, chemical-resistant film.

Treated with nitric acid, it yields picric acid; with sulfuric acid, it yields fast brown to black dyes. Soluble in alcohols and aniline; slightly soluble in chlorinated compounds; insoluble in coal-tar hydrocarbons. Has some of the physical properties of shellac, but is difficult to bleach. *Uses:* For spirit varnishes and metal lacquers, coatings, paper sizing, in inks and sealing waxes, binders, for blending with shellac, production of picric acid, and in catarrhal medicine. (*See also* RED ACAROID, *and* BLACK BOY RESIN).

Accelerator 1033 *and* **1033-A.** *See* TOOLCAST 1000 RESIN.

Accelerator P-70. *See* TOOLCAST 1000 RESIN.

Accobound® 3900, Cellulosic Film Resin. An aqueous, cationic melamine-formaldehyde resin syrup that is soluble in all proportions in water. It is a superior agent for bonding coatings and printing to cellulosic films. ACCOBOND 3900 confers unusually strong adhesion between such films and subsequently applied topcoats, as measured by hot-water-immersion, heat-seal, and wax streak tests. It can be used over a wide range of pH.   AMERICAN CYANAMID CO.

ACCO[NE] Calcium Caseinate. (*HBMTN* p. 2). No longer available.   AMERICAN CYANAMID CO.

Accolade Oleomargarine[NE]. A margarine made of hydrogenated soybean and cottonseed oils, nonfat dry milk, water, salt, LECITHIN, 0.1% sodium benzoate added as a preservative, artificial coloring, and 15,000 units of VITAMIN A per lb.
ANDERSON, CLAYTON & CO. FOODS DIV.

ACCO® Rosin Sizes. The trademark for a series of dry and liquid rosin sizes for the paper industry.
AMERICAN CYANAMID CO.

Accosperse®. The trademark for a series of aqueous dispersions of chemically manufactured pigments. These dispersions, shipped in polyethylene lined containers of 30 gal.-capacity, find use in latex paints and other aqueous systems.   AMERICAN CYANAMID CO.

ACCO® Streptomycin D. A proprietary product containing not less than 45% active streptomycin as the sulfate salt. It is a light tan powder, soluble in water. Supplied in 12½-lb. cans. Designed for the control of plant diseases.   AMERICAN CYANAMID CO.

Ace-Flex®. A lightweight, plasticized, flexible polyvinyl chloride thermoplastic compound available in a number of different colors. Non-toxic, odorless, and tasteless; resistant to acids, alkalis, and solvents. Sp.gr. 1.24–1.35; tensile strength, 1,900–3,000 lb./sq.in. It is an excellent material for general-purpose flexible tubing.   AMERICAN HARD RUBBER CO.

Ace-Hide®. An impact-resistant, resin-reinforced rubber compound that lends itself to mass production of molded parts, such as trays, water or acid containers, chair arm pads, refrigerator storage-doors and tracks, beverage cooler lids, etc. It is not as rigid as HARD RUBBER but it has higher impact strength. It has good resistance to strong inorganic acids and alkalis and salt solutions, good electrical properties, low heat conductivity, and excellent aging properties. Tensile strength, 1,000–2,500 lb./sq. in.; sp.gr. 1.20–1.40; heat distortion temp. 110–120°F. Available in black, green, brown, red and gray.
AMERICAN HARD RUBBER CO.

Acele®. (*HBMTN* p. 2). No longer available.
E. I. DU PONT DE NEMOURS & CO.

Ace® Parene®. A methyl methacrylate molding compound characterized by its high transparency and resistance to sun and weather. It is flexible yet shatter resistant and rigid. Sp.gr. 1.16–1.20; tensile strength, 6,000–10,000 lb./sq.in.; heat distortion temp. 145°–195°F.; attacked by oxidizing acids; soluble in aromatic hydrocarbons, ketones and esters. Available in an unlimited number of colors.
AMERICAN HARD RUBBER CO.

Ace® Parian®. An odorless, tasteless, flexible, polyethylene compound that is resistant to corrosive chemicals, and has excellent resistance to moisture and excellent electrical properties. Sp.gr. 0.92–1.10; tensile strength, 1,800–3,000 lb./sq.in.; heat distortion temp. 115°–122°F. at 66 lb./sq.in. Available in an unlimited number of colors, and in form of flexible tubing, pipe and fittings, rods, and sheets.
AMERICAN HARD RUBBER CO.

Ace® Parith®. An ethyl cellulose molding compound characterized by its outstanding toughness and low-temp. impact resistance, and good dimensional stability and heat resistance. Sp.gr. 1.07–1.18; tensile strength, 2,000–10,000 lb./sq.in.; heat distortion temp. 100°–190°F. Soluble in organic solvents. Available in an unlimited number of colors.
AMERICAN HARD RUBBER CO.

Ace® Parlan®. A cellulose acetate-butyrate molding compound characterized by its toughness, high impact strength at low temps., and good machining and fabricating properties. Sp.gr. 1.15–1.24; tensile strength, 1,400–6,600 lb/sq.in.; heat distortion temp. 120°–210°F.; soluble in esters and ketones; affected very little by hydrocarbons. Available in an unlimited number of colors.
AMERICAN HARD RUBBER CO.

Ace® Parnal®. A cellulose acetate molding compound characterized by its toughness, high impact strength, flexibility, and good machining and fabricating properties. Sp.gr. 1.27–1.37; tensile strength, 1,500–8,200 lb./sq.in.; heat distortion temp. 115°–235°F.; soluble in esters and ketones; affected very little by hydrocarbons. Available in an unlimited number of colors.   AMERICAN HARD RUBBER CO.

Ace® Parsan®. A polystyrene molding compound that is odorless and tasteless, has excellent electrical properties, is resistant to corrosive chemicals, has low water absorption, and has good dimensional stability. Sp.gr. 1.05–1.08; tensile strength, 3,000–9,000 lb./sq.in.; heat distortion temp. 155°–210°F. Available in an unlimited number of colors.
AMERICAN HARD RUBBER CO.

Ace® Riviclor®. A rigid, unplasticized polyvinyl chloride molding compound that is equal to or slightly superior to SARAN in chemical resistance. It is resistant to almost all inorganic and organic chemicals and solvents; has excellent impact strength, even at low temps; and very good aging properties. Sp.gr. 1.35–1.45; tensile strength, 6,000–8,500 lb./sq.in.; heat distortion temp., 140°–180°F. Avail-

able in a number of different colors, and in the form of tubing, pipe and fittings, rods, sheets, etc.
AMERICAN HARD RUBBER CO.

Ace-Sil®. A special porous rubber material that combines the chemical resistance of hard rubber with unusual porosity and moisture absorption. It is made by mixing processed rubber with silica-hydrogel, which, when calendered and vulcanized, forms a thermosetting material with uniform cellular structure. It is semi-hard, and is available in stiff sheets or plates which may be plain, ribbed, or corrugated. Storage battery separators are presently the principal use for this material. It permits the free flow of acid ions between plates while preventing the passage of lead particles. It does not dry out, split or warp. AMERICAN HARD RUBBER CO.

Acetest®. A diagnostic reagent for determining the presence of acetone bodies in urine. AMES CO.

Ace-Tex®Can.. (*Supp.* I p. 1). The name ACE-TEX is registered in the Canadian Patent Office.
CANADA ROOF PRODUCTS LTD.

Ace-Tuf®. An impact-resistant, resin-reinforced, rubber compound that has better molding characteristics than either ACE-HIDE® or RIJI-TUF®, but does not have quite as high a gloss. It is a fairly rigid material, with impact resistance higher than that of hard rubber, but not as high as that of ACE-HIDE® or RIJI-TUF®. Its chemical resistance is excellent. Tensile strength, 1,700–2,000 lb./sq.in.; sp.gr. 1.28–1.38; heat distortion temp. 120–130°F. Available in black only. It is an extremely economical material for molding such items as automotive battery cases, beverage cooler lids, etc.
AMERICAN HARD RUBBER CO.

Acetycol®. A medicinal for the relief of pain and rehabilitation of patients with arthritis, osteoarthritis, lumbago, bursitis, fibrositis, or chronic gouty arthritis. Each tablet contains: 325.0 mg. ASPIRIN, 162.0 mg. para-aminobenzoic acid, 0.25 mg. colchicine (salicylated), 20.0 mg. ascorbic acid, 5.0 mg. THIAMINE hydrochloride, 15.0 mg. NIACIN.
WARNER-CHILCOTT LABORATORIES

Acidit. See KLINGER-ACIDIT®Brit..

Acidogen®. (*HBMTN* p. 3). No longer available.
ABBOTT LABORATORIES

Acidoride®. Glutamic acid hydrochloride, COOH·-CH$_2$·CH$_2$·CH(NH$_2$)·COOH·HCl. A white, crystalline powder that is readily decomposed in water with liberation of free hydrochloric acid. A medicinal used in the treatment of achlorhydria due to pernicious anemia or other causes, and in hypochlorphydria. ABBOTT LABORATORIES

AcidprufNE. A protective suit of NEOPRENE-FAIRPRENE fabric used for protection against light concentrations of acid. It offers complete body protection.
MINE SAFETY APPLIANCES CO.

Acidsil CementNE. A silicate type, acid-proof mortar, consisting of a liquid binder and a finely divided, pure porcelain filler, which form an insoluble silica gel upon reaction. It resists spalling and vitrification at operating temps. as high as 1,800°F., and is not subject to crazing or growth in the joints. It is resistant to all acids and salts except those containing fluorine; it is unaffected by strong oxidizing agents; and is inert to all organic solvents.
MAURICE A. KNIGHT

Acidulum®. (*HBMTN* p. 3). Now a registered trademark. SERVICE INDUSTRIES

A*C*M®. A mixture of 4.8% ascorbic acid, 67.2% citric acid and 28% lactose; used to prevent the formation of undesirable browning and off-flavors when canning and freezing fruits, vegetables, fish and meat. CHAS. PFIZER & CO.

Acme®. The trademark for spring wire.
UNITED STATES STEEL CORP.

Acme® Grade 4-L-10. (*HBMTN* p. 3). No longer available. HANSON-VAN WINKLE-MUNNING CO.

Acme Polyfluoron® Liquid Dispersion. A 50% by weight dispersion of a polymer of chlorotrifluoroethylene in POLYFLUORON® DISPERSANT A—a liquid which boils at approx. 275°C. The dispersion may be thinned with methyl isobutyl ketone. It can be applied to any metal surface by spraying, casting, dipping, or painting; and, after evaporation of the solvent, it is fused at a high temp. to form a tightly-adhered, continuous, protective film. The fused film has the same chemical resistance and electrical properties as articles molded from ACME POLYFLUORON® MOLDING POWDER. *Uses:* As a corrosion-resisting lining for tanks, drums, pipes, and valves; coating for metal objects; general maintenance finishes; moisture seals; magnet wire insulation; and as a dielectric for high frequency coils. ACME RESIN CORP.

Acme Polyfluoron® Molding Powder. A high polymer of chlorotrifluoroethylene available either as crystal granules or as low density powder. The granules are recommended for extrusion and injection molding; the powder is often more suitable for compression molding since it makes good preforms. POLYFLUORON® is tough, strong, chemically inert, and flame resistant; and has good electrical properties and a wide operating range (−320°F. to +390°F.). It is stable indefinitely at a temp. of 150°C., and will stand much higher temps. for short periods of time without decomposition. It is completely unaffected by inorganic acids, alkalis, or salts in any conc.; and no known solvent will dissolve it at temps. below 100°C., and only a few halogenated solvents will appreciably attack it above this temp. Typical properties: sp.gr. 2.12; tensile strength (77°F.), 5,890 lb./sq. in.; elongation, 25–87%; dielectric strength, 600 volts/mil; impact strength (Izod), 1.52 ft.-lb./in. notch; water absorption, zero. *Uses:* For wire insulation and jackets; tubing; molded parts; laminates; electrical tape; condenser insulation and slot insulation; gaskets; and pipe wrapping. ACME RESIN CORP.

Acme-Stick®. (*Supp.* I p. 2). Now a registered trademark. ACME WIRE CO.

Acobyte. An asphaltic concrete for filling holes in floors, cushioning spalled areas, and retopping concrete floors and stairs. It consists of a mixture of mastic, Portland cement, aggregate, gravel, and sand; and is mixed on the job. ACORN REFINING CO.

Acolite. An all-purpose, industrial BAKELITE resin-base enamel for use on all types of interior industrial machines and equipment. It is resistant to acids and alkali fumes, salt brine, and abrasion.
ACORN REFINING CO.

Acousti-Celotex® Varitex®. (*Supp.* I p. 3). The trade name VARITEX® should have been listed as a registered trademark. CELOTEX CORP.

Acousti Lock Board®. A screw-holding gypsum board. It is a composite panel. CELOTEX CORP.

Acousti-Lux®. Translucent, sound-absorbing units used in building construction. CELOTEX CORP.

Acoustolight®. (*HBMTN* p. 4). No longer available. BARRELED SUNLIGHT PAINT CO.

Acraglas®. A room-temp.-curing plastic gunstock-bedding compound. After it is mixed with the catalyst, ACRAGLAS does not set up for 2 hr. if chilled before using. At 65–75°F., hardening does not start for 15–30 min. At 90–100°F. hardening occurs in 5–6 min., but at room temp. it requires 24–48 hr. It is waterproof and weatherproof, and resistant to acids and alkalis. Shrinkage is less than 1%. ACRAGLAS can be used for bonding wood to wood, wood to plastic, wood to metal, or metal to plastic. BOB BROWNELL'S

Acra-Kleen[NE]. A cleaner for plastics, especially for acrylic windows of aircraft and boats. It is a powder which is sprinkled on a damp cloth and rubbed over the plastic surface to remove foreign matter, haze, and minute scratches. SCHWARTZ CHEMICAL CO.

Acrol®. (*HBMTN* p. 5). No longer available. EASTMAN KODAK CO.

Acrylastic. A line of odorless, fast-drying, waterproof and mildew-resistant acrylic resin-base emulsion paints, for wet or dry masonry, stucco, concrete, and plaster. For use on exterior walls, and interior walls in basements, locker rooms, shower rooms, cold storage rooms, etc. KLEE WATERPROOFING CORP.

Acrylic Frosting Lacquer 158A. A special lacquer that produces a sand-blasted or frosted effect on LUCITE, PLEXIGLAS, and some other materials. The degree of opacity can be easily controlled by the amount of lacquer applied. A very dense treatment is best obtained by applying several thin coats. Articles can be treated by dipping, brushing or spraying. It dies in 3 to 5 min. at room temp., and produces a smooth coating which is less inclined to hold dirt than a sand-blasted finish. Unlike sand-blasting, this is a surface treatment, and thick sheets are not necessary. DEVCON CORP.

Acrylic Resin[△]. Synthetic resins prepared from acrylic acid ($CH_2=CHCOOH$) or from a derivative of acrylic acid. Solid acrylic polymers are characterized by crystal clarity, high impact strength, good resistance to weathering and to most chemicals, and good formability. In the military field, sheet ACRYLIC is the standard transparent material for cockpit canopies, windows, instrument panels, and searchlight and landing light covers on aircraft. In the civilian field, ACRYLIC is widely used for faces and letters of indoor and outdoor signs, counter dividers, display fixtures and cases, transparent demonstration models of household appliances and industrial machines, industrial window glazing, safety shields, machine covers, pump components, dome skylights, plating barrels, diffusing medium in lighting fixtures and luminous ceiling areas, shower enclosures, decorative partitions, etc. In molding powder form, ACRYLIC is used for the mfg. of automotive parts such as tail light and stop light lenses, medallions, name plates, dials, instrument panels, and signal lights; for control knobs, dials and handles on all types of home appliances; and for pen and pencil barrels, hairbrush backs, chemical pump parts, jukebox panels, covers for fluorescent street lights, etc. Extruded ACRYLIC sheet is used in such applications as lighting, glazing, signs, partitions and shower enclosures. In the textile field, ACRYLIC fibers are being produced commercially in large quantities. ACRYLICS are established materials for sizing of fibers. In the coating field, ACRYLIC emulsion paints are finding increased use because of their durability, lack of odor, speed of drying, and ease of application. Both emulsion and compounded paints for interior and exterior use in pigmented formulations are available. ACRYLIC dispersions find use in the mfg. of paper as a coating for clear and greaseproof paper, as heat-sealing adhesives, and as a binder for clay coatings. In the adhesive field, acrylic monomers find application as components of copolymers used in making pressure-sensitive tapes and bonding agents. In leather mfg., acrylic dispersions are used as a base coat for cellulose nitrate and polyvinyl chloride finishes, and as a component of water finishes.

Acrylite[NE]. Decorative and colorful embedments permanently cast into sheets of WASCOLITE acrylic. Available in flat sheets in various thicknesses with embedments of natural leaves, butterflies, straw and metallics. WASCO PRODUCTS, INC.

Acrysol® G-110. An ammonium polyacrylate solution for thickening rubber latex. In concentrations of 1% or less it is 3 to 20 times as effective as conventional thickeners. The thickened latices have good storage stability and do not undergo phase separation or creaming. Viscosity is unaffected by high pH or temps. ACRYSOL G-110 functions in the presence of sodium, calcium, or magnesium salts.
ROHM & HAAS CO.

Actaloy®. The trademark for a radioactive alloy used in radiation therapy. ABBOTT LABORATORIES

Acterol-D. Capsules of 50,000 units Vitamin D.
TESTAGAR & CO.

ACTH[△]. Adrenocorticotropin. The adrenocorticotropic hormone of the pituitary gland. It is a protein material of high mol.wt., approx. 20,000, that occurs in the anterior lobe of the pituitary gland. It is extracted from the whole pituitary gland of swine, sheep and ox. It is a white powder; freely soluble in water; appreciably soluble in 60–70% alcohol or acetone; partially precipitated at the isoelectric point (pH, 4.65–4.80); almost completely precipitated in 2.5% trichloroacetic acid solution. It is a medicinal stimulant of adrenal cortex; an anti-inflammatory, anti-allergic and anti-fibroplastic agent in diseases such as acute inflammatory and allergic diseases of the eye, skin, and mucosa; bronchial asthma, rheumatoid arthritis and rheumatic fever; psoriasis, pemphigus and gout; in post-operative collapse; and thermal burns.

Activ-8[NB]. A solution of ortho-phenanthroline in butanol and octoic acid, containing 38% solids. *Use:* In paints, to accelerate and stabilize drying.
R. T. Vanderbilt Co.

Actophene[NB]. An active chemical ingredient for use as a pesticide. Hercules Powder Co.

Ad-A-Switch®. The trademark for a line of electrical controls and switches and parts thereof. (Registration No. 590,358; Class 21; June 1, 1954).
Clarostat Mfg. Co.

Ad-Dri®. A commercial laundry bleach for the bleaching of Cottons and Linens. It is added in dry form to the laundry washer.
Olin Mathieson Chemical Corp.

Adelphi Met-L-Kote Machinery Enamel[NB]. A synthetic enamel formulated to produce a fast-drying, hard, mar-resistant, high gloss finish for the protection of all types of machinery and equipment exposed to interior or exterior conditions. Can be applied by brush, dip, or spray methods. Available in a number of colors. Adelphi Paint & Color Works

Adhesive 701. An adhesive for attaching paper or labels permanently to metal. Carl H. Biggs Co.

Adomite®. A petrochemical product which is added to crude oils to make an oil-well fracturing fluid and to control fluid loss in other fracturing fluids such as gelled or thickened oils. To make a fracturing fluid, a max. of $1/10$ lb. of Adomite is added per gal. of crude. In fracturing treatment, the formation is first broken down, then 200–1,000 gal. of Adomite-treated oil, without sand, is injected and then sand—up to 8 lb. per gal.—is added and the mixture is pumped down. Continental Oil Co.

Adrephine®. (*HBMTN* p. 8). No longer available.
Parke, Davis & Co.

Adsol[NB]. (*HBMTN* p. 8). No longer available.
F. E. Anderson Oil Co.

Adsorbit®. A series of activated charcoals for solvent recovery, gas purification, gas masks, liquid purification, water treatment, catalysis, chemical separations, waste disposal, and pollution elimination.
Barnebey-Cheney Co.

Advacide®. A line of fungicides used to impart mildew-resisting properties to paint films. The line includes:

Advacide MN-70%. A concentrated mercury napthenate solution containing 25% mercury as metal. Sp.gr. @ 75°F., 1.18; color (Gardner), 15 (max.); viscosity (Gardner-Holdt), A—; solids, 70%.

Advacide PMN. A phenyl mercury napthenate solution offered in two concentrations: Concentrate (10% mercury), and 10% solution (3.5–3.6% mercury). Properties of concentrate: sp.gr. 0.920–0.960; color (Gardner), 5 (max.); viscosity, (Gardner-Holdt), A—. Properties of 10% solution: sp.gr. 0.842; color (Gardner), 4+; viscosity, (Gardner-Holdt), A—.

Advacide PMO. A phenyl mercury oleate available as a 28% concentrate (10% mercury), and as a 10% solution (3.5–3.6% mercury). Properties of 28% concentrate: sp.gr. 0.88–0.93; color (Gardner), 4 (max.); viscosity (Gardner-Holdt), A—. Properties of 10% solution: sp.gr. 0.825; color (Gardner), 2; viscosity (Gardner-Holdt), A—.
Advance Solvents & Chemical

Advastab®. A line of heat and light stabilizers for vinyl plastics. The line includes the following:

Advastab No.	Description	Form	Sp.gr.	Color (G-H)	Viscosity, cps
BC-74	Liquid barium-cadmium compound with auxiliary stabilizing materials	Clear liquid	1.08	7	375–400
BC-105	Liquid barium-cadmium system, including auxiliary stabilizers	Clear liquid	1.13–1.15	7 (max.)	125
C-77	Liquid cadmium compound with auxiliary stabilizers	Clear, thin liquid	1.04–1.07	6 (max.)	50
E-82	Epoxy type stabilizer	Clear, viscous liquid	1.06–1.07	3 (max.)	1,070
L	White, 50% dispersion of organic barium salt in plasticizer	Uniform, finely dispersed paste	1.09–1.14	—	—
SN	Liquid strontium compound in plasticizer carrier	Clear, amber liquid	1.05–1.08	12 (max.)	1,760
T-50-LT	Organo-tin compound containing no plasticizer or diluent	Clear, viscous liquid	1.32–1.35	5 (max.)	1,000
T-52	Complex organo-tin compound in plasticizer carrier	Clear liquid	1.09–1.12	7 (max.)	50
XBC-147	Co-precipitated barium-cadmium compound	Free-flowing, white powder	—	—	—

ADVASTAB No.	Description	Form	Sp.gr.	Color (G-H)	Viscosity, cps
XBZ-51	Liquid barium-zinc compound with auxiliary stabilizers	Clear liquid	1.03–1.04	8 (max.)	400
XBZ-155	Co-precipitated barium-zinc soap	Free-flowing, white powder	—	—	—
XC-79	Liquid cadmium compound containing auxiliary stabilizers	Clear liquid	1.13–1.14	5 (max.)	50
XCH-201	Complex polymeric phosphite	Clear liquid	1.030	1	225
XZN-15	Concentrated liquid zinc compound	Clear, viscous liquid	1.07–1.08	6 (max.)	15,000
Z-6	Liquid zinc compound containing auxiliary stabilizers	Clear, amber, thin liquid	0.970–0.985	9 (max.)	100

ADVANCE SOLVENTS & CHEMICAL

Advawet® NA-6. (*HBMTN* p. 10). No longer available. ADVANCE SOLVENTS & CHEMICAL CORP.

AE® Board. (*HBMTN* p. 10). AE® is now a registered trademark. OWENS-CORNING FIBERGLAS CORP.

AE-F® Board. (*HBMTN* p. 10). AE-F® is now a registered trademark. OWENS-CORNING FIBERGLAS CORP.

"Aero"® Ammonium Sulfate. The trademark for a 21% nitrogen fertilizer for mfg. of mixed fertilizers, and for direct application to the soil. AMERICAN CYANAMID CO.

Aer-O-Buoy®. A line of rigid and flexible polyvinyl chloride plastic foam materials for a wide variety of industrial and consumer applications, including low-temp. insulation, gaskets and seals, flotation equipment, contact padding, and dielectric equipment housings. Among the many products made from AER-O-BUOY are aircraft crash padding, athletic equipment, industrial pads and mats, life rafts, net floats, life rings and vests, tank floats, weatherstripping, aircraft and automotive gaskets, lightweight doors. etc. It is resistant to water, gasoline, oils, acids, corrosion, rot, and fire; and has high tensile strength and electrical resistance. The buoyancy material weighs 3.8 lb./cu.ft.; the thermal insulation material has a thermal conductivity of 0.27 B.t.u. inch/hr. x sq.ft. x °F. ROBINSON MOULDED PRODUCTS LTD.

Aerocat®. A group of synthetic cracking catalysts designed for use in the refining of petroleum in fluid catalytic cracking units. They are essentially alumina on silica gel, and are characterized by their high degree of chemical purity, high surface area, and high catalytic efficiency. They are available in the following grades and particle size distributions:

AEROCAT FLUID CRACKING CATALYST 60/70, 75/85, *and* 80/90. These contain 13% alumina on silica and are spheroidal-shaped particles characterized by improved flow characteristics, high resistance to attrition, and a closely controlled particle-size distribution. They contain a minimum amount of fines, and attain maximum catalytic efficiency.

AEROCAT TRIPLE A HIGH ALUMINA CRACKING CATALYST 60/70, 75/85, *and* 80/90. These contain 25% alumina on silica, and are spheroidal-shaped particles characterized by improved flow characteristics, high resistance to attrition, and a closely controlled particle-size distribution. They contain a minimum amount of fines, and attain maximum catalytic efficiency. AMERICAN CYANAMID CO.

Aero® Cyanamid. A line of calcium cyanamide products for fertilizer and other agricultural uses. Available in the following grades:

Aero Cyanamid designation	Calcium cyanamide, %	Nitrogen, %	Lime equivalent, %	Uses
Granular	46	21	70	For direct application or in fertilizer mixtures; for killing weed seeds in plant beds and certain crops, and controlling certain soil borne diseases.
Pulverized	57	22	70	As a conditioning agent in mixed fertilizers.
Special Grade	57	22	70	As a defoliant for cotton and soybeans; as a vine killer for potatoes and tomatoes.
Lawn and Garden Cyanamid	46	21	70	For the preparation of new lawns to aid in establishing a practically weed-free turf; in the repair of bare and weedy spots in established lawns; in the compost pile to accelerate decomposition, to produce humus in the annual garden, and to control azalea blight.

AMERICAN CYANAMID CO.

Aero® Cyanide. The trademark for calcium cyanide sold in the form of black flakes and used primarily for leaching of gold and silver ores. It is also used as a chemical intermediate.
American Cyanamid Co.

Aero® Depressants. The trade name for a group of flotation reagents suitable for depression of talcose, micaceous or carbonaceous gangue minerals.
American Cyanamid Co.

Aeroflo® 40. (*HBMTN* p. 11.) No longer available. American Cyanamid Co.

Aerofloat® Flotation Reagents. (*HBMTN* p. 11). Now marketed under the name Aerofloat® Promoters. American Cyanamid Co.

Aerofloat® Promoter 211. A dry, water-soluble reagent containing the active promoting constituent of the liquid Aerofloat Promoters. It is a strong zinc sulfide promoter. Extensively used in flotation of gold, silver, and copper sulfide minerals in the presence of pyrite, which it does not actively promote.
American Cyanamid Co.

Aerofloat® Promoter 249. A stronger promoter than other dry Aerofloat Promoters. Used extensively for copper flotation. American Cyanamid Co.

Aerofloat® Promoters. Formerly marketed as Aerofloat® Flotation Reagents (*HBMTN* p. 11).
American Cyanamid Co.

"Aerofloc"® Reagents. The trade name for a group of synthetic, water-soluble polymers used as flocculating agents to improve solid-liquid separations by thickening and filtration. American Cyanamid Co.

Aeroform®. A group of catalysts used in the petroleum industry for the reforming of petroleum to obtain premium octane gasoline. The following two types are available:

Aeroform® MS-1. A fluid hydroforming catalyst of the micro-spheroidal, molybdena-alumina type. Has excellent resistance to attrition, highest available activity, controlled particle size, and high surface area.

Aeroform® PHF. A pelleted, highly-refined platinum-promoted alumina-base catalyst. Designed to incorporate the outstanding features of high selectivity, easy regenerability, good stability and high octane-barrel rating.
American Cyanamid Co.

Aerofroth® Frothers. The trade name for a group of surface-active agents used primarily as foaming agents or frothers in flotation processing of ores and minerals. American Cyanamid Co.

Aerohaler®. The trademark for a plastic inhalation device for administering penicillin and other dry solid aerosols. Abbott Laboratories

Aero® HDS Catalyst. A catalyst designed for use by the petroleum-refining industry to promote hydrogenation reactions. It is an extruded cobalt-molybdena-on-alumina catalyst. Has the outstanding characteristics of high volume activity, high pore volume, excellent mechanical properties, and low bulk density. American Cyanamid Co.

Aeroheat® 1100. A new member of American Cyanamid Co.'s line of neutral heat-treating salts (*HBMTN* p. 12). Aeroheat 1100 is a chloride-carbonate mixture for annealing low-carbon metals and non-ferrous metals such as brass and bronze. M.p. 1,085°F.; operating range, 1,125–1,650°F.
American Cyanamid Co.

Aeroheat® 1200R. A member of American Cyanamid Co.'s line of heat-treating salts (*HBMTN* p. 12). Aeroheat 1200R is a rectifying agent briquetted for separate addition to Aeroheats, 1000, 1200, or 1400. American Cyanamid Co.

Aeromatic De-Odor Mist. A non-toxic, non-flammable deodorant in an aerosol dispenser. Used for destroying offensive odors in rooms.
J. I. Holcomb Mfg. Co.

Aeromet®. The trademark for a metallurgical additive used in steel making where nitrogen content is desired. It may be also used in iron and steel for desulfurization. American Cyanamid Co.

"Aeromine"® Promoters. The trade name for a group of cationic flotation reagents used in froth-flotation processing of ores and minerals, especially for the flotation of silica and silicates.
American Cyanamid Co.

Aeronox®. A series of lubricating and industrial oil additives used to increase resistance to oxidation.
American Cyanamid Co.

Aeropan SR-1[NB]. (*HBMTN* p. 12). No longer available. American Cyanamid Co.

Aero® Promoter 404. A powerful, water-soluble promoter, possessing some frothing properties, especially adapted to the flotation of fine, free gold and auriferous pyrite as well as oxidized lead ores.
American Cyanamid Co.

Aero® Promoter 708. A fatty acid reagent useful for the flotation of non-metallic ores. It is capable of replacing more expensive reagents in many applications. American Cyanamid Co.

Aero® Promoter 712. A soap-type flotation frother. It possesses certain promoter characteristics. It is a valuable secondary promoter for some non-metallic types of ores and locked sulfide middlings.
American Cyanamid Co.

Aero® Promoters 801 *and* 825. Flotation promoters developed principally for beneficiating iron ores and washery wastes. They are also useful for reducing iron impurities associated with glass sands and ceramic raw materials, and for the flotation of garnet, rhodochrosite, spodumene, barite and kyanite.
American Cyanamid Co.

Aeroseal® Q. (*HBMTN* p. 13). No longer available. American Cyanamid Co.

Aero Soap T[NB]. (*HBMTN* p. 13). No longer available. American Cyanamid Co.

Aero Sodium Cyanamid, Dust[NB]. (*HBMTN* p. 13). No longer available. American Cyanamid Co.

Aerosol® 18. N-octadecyl disodium sulfosuccinamate. Mol.wt. 493. A light cream-colored paste containing 35% active ingredient, 65% water. It is readily dispersible in water yielding pearly, opalescent dispersions that become clear when heated. Stable in acid and alkali. AEROSOL 18 is notable for its emulsifying, dispersing and foaming powers, detergency, and solubilizing action on soaps and other surface-active agents. AMERICAN CYANAMID CO.

Aerosol® 22. Tetrasodium N-(1,2-dicarboxyethyl)-N-octadecyl sulfosuccinamate. Mol.wt. 653. A clear liquid containing 35% active ingredient. AEROSOL 22 has excellent salt tolerance and is an excellent solubilizing agent, even in saturated salt solutions. It is recommended for the emulsion polymerization of vinyl-type monomers in general and acrylate monomers in particular. It is used in shoe polishes and other wax polishes to improve texture and to disperse pigments, silicones, and ultra-violet light absorbers in such systems. It lowers the surface tension of writing and drawing inks. AMERICAN CYANAMID CO.

Aerosol® AS. (*HBMTN* p. 13). No longer available. AMERICAN CYANAMID CO.

Aerosol® AY. Diamyl sodium sulfosuccinate. Mol. wt. 360. A surface-active agent similar to AEROSOL OT, supplied in the form of a solid containing 100% active ingredient. It is used as an emulsifier in emulsion polymerization and as a wetting agent in relatively concentrated solutions of salts. It dissolves very rapidly in water at room temp.; it is somewhat soluble in polar organic liquids, but almost insoluble in non-polar liquids. AMERICAN CYANAMID CO.

Aerosol® C-61. An ethanolated alkyl guanidine-amine complex. A new type of cationic surface-active agent containing approx. 80% active ingredient in isopropyl alcohol and water. Its appearance varies from a soft tan paste to a clear brown liquid, depending upon the temp. It is effective in acid, alkaline or neutral solutions. AEROSOL C-61 is recommended as a pigment dispersing agent, as a wetting agent in acid fluxes, and as a frothing agent in acid cleaning solutions. Its applications have not been fully explored as yet, but its properties suggest its evaluation as a process aid and auxiliary in a variety of uses. AMERICAN CYANAMID CO.

Aerosol® IB. (*HBMTN* p. 13). No longer available. AMERICAN CYANAMID CO.

Aerosol® Insekil®. An insecticide, in an aerosol bomb dispenser, for killing flies, mosquitoes, gnats, etc. It contains PYRETHRINS plus piperonyl butoxide for quick knock-down. J. I. HOLCOMB MFG. CO.

Aerosol® MA-80%. Dihexyl sodium sulfosuccinate. Mol.wt. 388. An aqueous solution containing 80% active ingredient. This form is convenient for storage, handling and mixing. AEROSOL MA is used chiefly in emulsion polymerization and as a wetting agent in dilute solutions of salts. It possesses a powerful penetrating action. Its excellent calcium tolerance makes it a valuable auxiliary to AEROSOL OT in hard water areas where OT gives turbid solutions. AMERICAN CYANAMID CO.

Aerosol® OS. Isopropyl naphthalene sodium sulfonate. Available as a light tan, hygroscopic powder containing approx. 75% active ingredient, the remainder being sodium sulfate. Its usefulness depends principally on its stability, solubility and effectiveness in relatively high concentrations of acids and alkalis. In such solutions where many agents are salted out or decomposed, AEROSOL OS becomes even more effective than it is in plain water. AMERICAN CYANAMID CO.

Aerosol® OT-75%. A convenient, economical form of AEROSOL OT, well suited to most AEROSOL OT applications, except those in anhydrous systems. Contains 75% AEROSOL OT, the remainder being water and approx. 5% of a lower alcohol to provide fluidity. Less concentrated solutions may be prepared by adding the AEROSOL OT-75% directly to the required amount of water, with sufficient agitation to gain uniformity. Clear, fluid solutions may be obtained by addition of a mutual solvent, together with water. AMERICAN CYANAMID CO.

Aerosol® OT-100%. Dioctyl sodium sulfosuccinate. Mol.wt. 444. A waxy solid, designed primarily for use in anhydrous systems. One of the most powerful wetting agents and surface-tension depressants available commercially. Its solubility in water is relatively low, although it forms stable, gel-like dispersions at nearly all concentrations. It is readily soluble in most organic solvents, both polar and non-polar. Solubility in oils, fats, waxes and the like can usually be achieved by heating above 75°C. AEROSOL OT remains in solution when cooled to room temp. AMERICAN CYANAMID CO.

Aerosol® OT-B. A free-flowing surface-active agent. It is a white powder containing 85% AEROSOL OT and 15% sodium benzoate. The sodium benzoate is considered to be essentially inert, and should not interfere with most uses. The bulk particle size of AEROSOL OT-B is 15-150 microns. Because of the particle size and because of the influence of sodium benzoate, AEROSOL OT-B dissolves almost instantaneously in water up to its solubility limit (0.6% at 30°C.). At higher concentrations, it disperses readily, providing uniform suspensions more quickly than either of the other two forms of AEROSOL OT. AEROSOL OT-B can be dry-blended with other powders, as in the mfg. of wettable dusts and powdered detergents. AMERICAN CYANAMID CO.

Aerosolve Filters. A line of air filters of high efficiency at low pressure drop. Efficiencies range from 35 to 95%. They will remove pollen, tobacco smoke and other substances. An AEROSOLVE FILTER consists of a heavily cadmium-plated permanent metal frame and a replaceable cartridge. Not affected by high humidity. CAMBRIDGE FILTER CORP.

Aero® Specialty Catalysts. A series of catalysts mfg'd. in rings, pellets, and granular form for use in various chemical syntheses. Typical of these are: (1) AERO CATALYST FM, which is a granular, fused magnetite catalyst for use in the synthetic ammonia process; (2) AERO CATALYST HI, which is a promoted iron oxide catalyst in pellet form for use in the oxidation of CO to CO_2; (3) AERO CATALYST NR and extruded nickel oxide catalyst used in the reforming of methane, ethane, or natural gas. AMERICAN CYANAMID CO.

Aerosyn®. The trademark for a line of air-dry synthetic finishes. FIDELITY CHEMICAL PRODUCTS CORP.

Aerotex Accelerator 187[NR]. An ammoniacal salt recommended as an accelerator with thermosetting resins on NYLON for durable stiff finishes. AMERICAN CYANAMID CO.

Aerotex Accelerator AS[NE]. An ammoniacal salt particularly recommended as an accelerator with PERMEL RESIN B. AMERICAN CYANAMID CO.

Aerotex Accelerator MX[NE]. An inorganic salt accelerator for general use with thermosetting resins. It increases the efficiency of melamine-formaldehyde resins and reduces chlorine retention.
AMERICAN CYANAMID CO.

Aerotex Accelerator NF[NE]. An ammoniacal salt accelerator designed specifically for use with PYROSET FIRE RETARDANT N-2. AMERICAN CYANAMID CO.

Aerotex Accelerator S[NE]. An accelerator for use with silicone water-repellent emulsions only.
AMERICAN CYANAMID CO.

Aerotex Accelerator T[NE]. (HBMTN p. 14). No longer available. AMERICAN CYANAMID CO.

Aerotex Accelerator UTX[NE]. A hydroxy-alkylamine-hydrochloride accelerator for urea and melamine-formaldehyde resins. AMERICAN CYANAMID CO.

Aerotex Antistatic[NE]. A condensate which provides a retreatable antistatic finish for WOOL and for hydrophobic synthetic fabrics. AMERICAN CYANAMID CO.

Aerotex Buffer 190-A[NE]. An organic nitrogen-containing compound similar in use to AEROTEX BUFFER DCY, and recommended where the limited solubility of AEROTEX BUFFER DCY is a factor.
AMERICAN CYANAMID CO.

Aerotex Buffer DCY[NE]. An organic, nitrogen-containing compound which is added to thermosetting-resin baths to prevent the formation of amine odors due to improper processing of resin finishes, to reduce formaldehyde odor, and to help maintain tensile and tear strength through resin finishing.
AMERICAN CYANAMID CO.

Aerotex Cream 450[NE]. A urea-formaldehyde condensate, the major use of which is the production of wrinkle-resistant finishes on RAYON and mixed synthetic fiber fabrics. AMERICAN CYANAMID CO.

Aerotex Fire Retardant NDC[NE]. A water-soluble phosphate mixture for use as a non-durable fire retardant for cellulosic fabrics. It gives a non-hygroscopic finish that is resistant to tensile strength loss when exposed to high temps.
AMERICAN CYANAMID CO.

Aerotex Fire Retardant NDS[NE]. A phosphate mixture similar to AEROTEX FIRE RETARDANT NDC. However, it is more soluble than the latter and produces a softer hand. May be applied by padding or spraying. AMERICAN CYANAMID CO.

Aerotex Purifying Agent No. 1[NE]. A durable finish for textiles, designed to reduce the development of body odor. AMERICAN CYANAMID CO.

Aerotex Resin 110[NE]. A thermoplastic resin emulsion for modifying thermosetting resin finishes.
AMERICAN CYANAMID CO.

Aerotex Resin 120[NE]. A thermoplastic resin emulsion useful as a durable finish for cellulose fabrics to increase abrasion resistance and improve hand.
AMERICAN CYANAMID CO.

Aerotex Resin 121[NE]. A thermoplastic resin emulsion useful as a durable finish for cellulosic fabrics to increase abrasion resistance and improve hand.
AMERICAN CYANAMID CO.

Aerotex Resin 133[NE]. A thermoplastic resin particularly useful when combined with melamine-formaldehyde resins to produce a durable finish on cotton with high wrinkle recovery and high tensile strength retention. AMERICAN CYANAMID CO.

Aerotex Resin 134[NE]. A thermoplastic resin that is particularly useful when combined with melamine-formaldehyde resins for finishing cotton. It produces a durable finish having high wrinkle recovery and excellent tensile strength retention.
AMERICAN CYANAMID CO.

Aerotex Resin 140, 160, 301, 625[NE]. (HBMTN p. 14). No longer available. AMERICAN CYANAMID CO.

Aerotex Resin 159[NE]. A thermoplastic resin dispersion used primarily for stiffening textile fabrics.
AMERICAN CYANAMID CO.

Aerotex Resin 180[NE]. A resin product used in combination with reactive starches as a binder for pigments. AMERICAN CYANAMID CO.

Aerotex Resin 390[NE]. A resin product designed to improve the bonding strength of coatings on a variety of fabrics. AMERICAN CYANAMID CO.

Aerotex Resin 801[NE]. An exceptionally stable modified urea-formaldehyde condensate for durable resin finishing, antislippage and shrinkage control, particularly for RAYON. AMERICAN CYANAMID CO.

Aerotex Resin 802[NE]. A modified urea-formaldehyde condensate textile finishing agent. It is a liquid having exceptional storage and application stability. Useful for producing a durable finish with excellent wrinkle recovery. Also useful in glazed and embossed finishes. AMERICAN CYANAMID CO.

Aerotex Resin 803[NE]. A modified urea-formaldehyde condensate syrup for producing a durable, stiff finish on fabrics of all kinds.
AMERICAN CYANAMID CO.

Aerotex Resin 7513[NE]. A thermoplastic resin emulsion used as a body builder on COTTON and synthetic fabrics. AMERICAN CYANAMID CO.

Aerotex Resin EU[NE]. An ethylene-urea formaldehyde condensate textile-finishing agent which provides excellent wrinkle recovery, stabilization, and resistance to damage due to chlorine bleaching on COTTONS and other types of fabric. AMERICAN CYANAMID CO.

Aerotex Resin M-3[NE]. A textile-finishing, melamine-formaldehyde condensate used to provide durable wrinkle recovery, shrinkage control, and durable mechanical finishes on COTTONS. Durable finishes are also obtained on RAYON, NYLON and synthetic fiber blends. AMERICAN CYANAMID CO.

Aerotex Resin MW[NE]. A modified melamine-formaldehyde condensate textile-finishing agent which reduces chlorine retention. It also provides durable wrinkle recovery, mechanical finishes and shrinkage control. AMERICAN CYANAMID CO.

Aerotex Resin P-114[NE]. A solution of a resin in mineral spirits. Used in resin-bonded pigment applications as a pigment binder.
AMERICAN CYANAMID CO.

Aerotex Resin P-116[NB]. A solution of a resin in mineral spirits used to prepare printing emulsions for resin-bonded pigments. AMERICAN CYANAMID CO.

Aerotex Resin P-117[NB]. A solution of resin in xylol, used to prepare printing emulsions for resin-bonded pigments. AMERICAN CYANAMID CO.

Aerotex Resin P-200[NB]. A solvent-soluble resin that is added to resin-bonded pigment formulations to improve scrub resistance. AMERICAN CYANAMID CO.

Aerotex Resin UM[NB]. A melamine-formaldehyde condensate producing a durable finish for cellulosic fibers. It provides durable wrinkle recovery, shrinkage control, luster and crispness while maintaining a soft, full hand. AMERICAN CYANAMID CO.

Aerotex Softener H[NB]. A cationic textile softener used to soften the hand of textiles when used alone or with thermosetting resin finishes. Exceptionally durable on WOOL, COTTON or synthetic fibers. Used as an antistatic agent on all types of fibers.
AMERICAN CYANAMID CO.

Aerotex Softener W[NB]. An anionic wax emulsion which acts as a softening agent and as a lubricant for thermosetting resin textile finishes, both mechanical and non-mechanical. Used as a plasticizing agent for AEROTEX RESIN 159. AMERICAN CYANAMID CO.

Aerotex Syrup 55[NB]. A modified urea-formaldehyde condensate which is used either alone or with other thermosetting resins to produce durable stiffness on textile fabrics. AMERICAN CYANAMID CO.

Aerotex Syrup 250 Conc.[NB]. A high-solids urea-formaldehyde condensate used as a stiffener alone or with thermosetting resins on both cellulosic and synthetic fabrics. AMERICAN CYANAMID CO.

Aerotex Thickener 37[NB]. A water-soluble polymer, in flake form, which is used as a thickener and as an additive to warp sizes to improve the abrasion resistance, flexibility, and size adhesion. Useful also as a hand-modifying agent with resins.
AMERICAN CYANAMID CO.

Aerotex Water Repellent S[NB]. A durable textile water-repellent emulsion of the silicone type. Especially useful on RAYONS and synthetics. Also used as a hand modifier with thermosetting resins.
AMERICAN CYANAMID CO.

Aerowrap®. A thin flexible blanket of fibrous glass used as an insulation on pipes and conduits.
OWENS-CORNING FIBERGLAS CORP.

Aero® **Xanthate 301.** A powerful, xanthate-type, water-soluble, non-frothing promoter for sulfide minerals. It is effective for use in bulk flotation of all types of sulfide ores, and for the oxidized base-metal ores after sulfidizing. It is widely used in the flotation of pyritic ores, in combination with AEROFLOAT PROMOTERS. AMERICAN CYANAMID CO.

Aero® **Xanthates 322, 325,** *and* **343.** A group of xanthate-type, water-soluble, non-frothing promoters for sulfide minerals. They are commonly used where a non-selective promoter of less strength than AERO XANTHATE 301 or 350 is applicable.
AMERICAN CYANAMID CO.

Aero® **Xanthate 350.** A very powerful xanthate promoter for mineral flotation, made from amyl alcohol. AMERICAN CYANAMID CO.

Afko-Carb[NB]. An effervescent and palatable antacid used to neutralize gastric hyperacidity. Contains sodium bicarbonate, potassium bicarbonate, citric acid, tartaric acid, magnesium sulfate, sodium phosphate, calcium lactate, and sodium chloride.
AMERICAN PHARMACEUTICAL CO.

Afko Ear Oil[NB]. A medicinal for softening ear wax. Contains benzocaine, thymol, camphor, oil sassafras, oil cajuput in isopropyl myristate.
AMERICAN PHARMACEUTICAL CO.

Afko-Hist[NB]. An antihistamine, in tablet form, for the relief of symptoms of colds and hay fever. Each tablet contains 25 mg. pyrilamine maleate.
AMERICAN PHARMACEUTICAL CO.

Afko Rub[NB]. An athletic rub and general liniment for muscular stiffness, minor aches and pains, bruises of the muscles, mosquito and innocuous insect bites, simple ringworm of toes and feet, and athlete's foot. Contains oil of wormwood, thymol iodide, menthol, methyl salicylate, camphor, echinacea and calendula.
AMERICAN PHARMACEUTICAL CO.

Afko-Sal[NB]. A medicinal for the temporary relief of headaches and minor muscular aches and pains. Each tablet contains 5 gr. salicylamide.
AMERICAN PHARMACEUTICAL CO.

Afko Syrup[NB]. A medicinal for the treatment of coughs due to colds. Recommended to loosen phlegm and soothe irritated throat membranes. Contains ephedrine sulfate and saccharated extract of thyme in 9% alcohol. AMERICAN PHARMACEUTICAL CO.

Afko-Thricin Cream[NB]. An antibiotic ointment containing 0.5 mg. tyrothricin per g. in a special emollient, non-irritant washable base. *Use:* For the prevention and treatment of minor skin injuries—cuts, burns, abrasions. AMERICAN PHARMACEUTICAL CO.

Afko-Thricin Lozenges[NB]. A pink, flavored antibiotic-anesthetic for the relief of minor throat and mouth irritations. Each lozenge contains 2 mg. tyrothricin, and 5 mg. benzocaine.
AMERICAN PHARMACEUTICAL CO.

African Honeywood[NB]. A species of plywood made from African wood. UNITED STATES PLYWOOD CORP.

Afta. A line of cleaners, including: (1) AFTA FABRIC AND LEATHER CLEANING FLUID, a non-flammable spot remover; (2) AFTA SURFACE CLEANER, a tar and grease remover for cleaning automobile finishes, Venetian blinds, painted walls, and furniture; (3) AFTA CARBON TETRACHLORIDE. AFTA SOLVENTS CORP.

Aftalene. A non-flammable dry-cleaning fluid for fabrics, upholstery, carpets, linoleum, walls, and woodwork. AFTA SOLVENTS CORP.

Aftite. A cleaner for removing chewing gum. Used by theaters, airlines, and transportation companies. Can also be used as a spot remover, and for cleaning upholstery, carpets, leather, suede, furs, linoleum, marble, and chromium trim. AFTA SOLVENTS CORP.

Agar-Agar△. A gelatinous extract obtained from various species of seaweed, *Algae*, principally from the Pacific and Indian Oceans, although some AGAR-AGAR is produced in the United States, Great Britain, and Australia. Made by boiling the dry seaweed and straining out the insoluble matter. The extract is then dried and bleached. Commercial AGAR-AGAR is marketed in strips, blocks or shredded; it is colorless, yellowish, or pink to black. When dissolved in water, it forms a transparent jelly. *Uses:* For fixing bacteria for counts; as a stabilizer in toilet lotions and medicines; in foods; etc.

Aggrecoat®. (*HBMTN* p. 17). Now a registered trademark. MINNESOTA MINING & MFG. CO.

Agilene®-F. An expanded polyethylene foam with uniform small-sized closed-cell structure. The cells contain an inert, non-toxic gas. The density can be varied from 10 to 50 lb./cu.ft. Tensile strength, 500–600 lb./sq.in. Available in semi-finished molded components as rings, blocks, rods, and sheets. It is easily worked with common wood- and metal-working tools. Resistant to fungus growth, flaking, dusting, inorganic salts, most inorganic acids except oxidizing acids, and caustic solutions. *Uses:* For gaskets, low-temp. insulation, sandwich cores, shock absorbers, life floats, radiation shielding, packaging, radomes, cap linings, etc. AMERICAN AGILE CORP.

Agilon[NR]. A modified NYLON resin used for coating automotive parts such as distributor gears, speedometer gears, fuse holders, insulation bushings, timing gears, windshield-wiper gears, and other parts; electrical equipment such as wire connectors, switch components, gears, etc.; and misc. articles such as drafting-equipment parts, saddle bearings, egg beater gears, and washing machine and fan parts. For application, AGILON is preheated to 750–780°F., and the articles immersed in the fluidized bed of the resin until the desired thickness is attained. The coating is strong, tough, and chemical and abrasion resistant.
AMERICAN AGILE CORP.

Agoral®. A medicinal for the relief of acute or temporary constipation; in debilitating disorders complicated by inadequate bowel action; in bed-ridden or elderly patients; in post-operative cases; in hypertensive or chronic cardiac disorders where forcing of stool must be avoided. It contains phenolphthalein and mineral oil in a thoroughly homogenized emulsion containing agar-gel, TRAGACANTH, egg albumen, ACACIA, glycerin and water.
WARNER-CHILCOTT LABORATORIES

Agrico®. The trademark of the AMERICAN AGRICULTURAL CHEMICAL CO., for an extensive line of fertilizer materials.

Agrinite®. An all-organic plant food for use on lawns, shrubs, flowers and vegetables. It is a carefully processed, high nitrogen, organic fertilizer containing over 8% organic nitrogen. It provides the plant food gradually in a highly acceptable form; it adds humus and increases the moisture-holding capacity of the soil; it can be applied at any time; it does not burn plants or grasses; and it is easy to handle.
AMERICAN AGRICULTURAL CHEMICAL CO.

Agron®. A line of water-soluble chelates of heavy metals with non-toxic sugar derivatives. (Patent applied for.) AGRON®-15 contains 15% ferric iron in chelated form. It is soluble in both acidic and alkaline waters over the complete pH range. *Uses:* For spray application to foliage of ornamental plants and field crops for the prevention of chlorosis, and in the enrichment of animal foods.
PFANSTIEHL LABORATORIES, INC.

Agrox®. A seed disinfectant containing 6.70% phenyl mercury urea (equivalent to 4% metallic mercury). It is in powder form, for application as dust or slurry *Use:* For the seed treatment of small grains, cotton, rice and flax, to control certain seedborne diseases.
CHIPMAN CHEMICAL CO.

Ahcobase Oil W-200[NR]. (*HBMTN* p. 17). No longer available. ARNOLD, HOFFMAN & CO.

Ahcofix® **134** *and* **Ahcofix**® **S**. (*Supp*. I p. 6). No longer available. ARNOLD, HOFFMAN & CO.

Ahcowet® **SDS**. A sulfonated alkyl ester. It is a very powerful anionic wetting and rewetting agent for the dyeing and finishing of textiles. Also used for wall paper removal; cleaning windows, mirrors, glassware, etc.; laying dust; washing coal; metal cleaning; rinsing photographic film; and cleaning of automobile radiators. It is a clear, light, straw-colored, viscous solution, readily soluble in water up to 3–4%; soluble in many organic solvents; moderately stable in dilute acid solutions. ARNOLD, HOFFMAN & CO.

AHT-28®[Can.]. A machinery steel designed to supplement ULTIMO®[Can.]-4 for intricately designed applications requiring an air-hardening hardness greater than about 375 Brinell. Typical analysis, %: 0.30 carbon, 0.50 manganese, 0.30 phosphorus (max.), 0.030 sulfur (max.); 0.25 silicon, 1.40 chromium, 4.00 nickel, and 0.20 molybdenum. ATLAS STEELS LTD.

Aircomb®. A honeycomb structure of paper impregnated with a phenolic-type resin. In use it is sandwiched between faces of thin materials such as aluminum, plywood, magnesium, wood, and stainless steel to form lightweight high-strength structural panels. DOUGLAS AIRCRAFT CO.

Air-Cub[NR]. A name used to designate a self-contained air-breathing apparatus, of relatively short service time, for use in poisonous or oxygen-deficient atmospheres. MINE SAFETY APPLIANCES CO.

Air Curtain[NR]. A device for effecting an air flow which is used to provide eye and face protection against sprayed paint or similar liquid preparations.
MINE SAFETY APPLIANCES CO.

Air Dryette, Jr.®. (*HBMTN* p. 18 and *Supp*. I p. 7). No longer available. SOLVAY PROCESS DIV.,
ALLIED CHEMICAL & DYE CORP.

Airfil®. A filter oil designed specifically for impregnating air filters of the impingement type used in diesel locomotives and in certain industrial equipment. It is a light-colored oil that has excellent anti-foam properties and can be used at temps. of 180–200°F. Flash point, 435°F.; S.U.S. viscosity: 155 at 210°F., and 3,500 at 100°F. ESSO STANDARD OIL CO.

Airkem 10-39®. A concentrated deodorant-sanitizer that eliminates odors at their source through a two-phase assault on odors. As a deodorant, it contains proven AIRKEM deodorant components that counteract odors and defend against their return; and as a

sanitizer, it contains a quaternary ammonium compound that kills odor-generating bacteria and fungi. It is non-toxic, non-flammable, and will not bleach or stain; phenol coefficient, 3.0 (*S. typhosa*) and 4.5 (*S. aureus*); effective against odors imbedded in, or adhering to, floors, walls, or other surfaces. Available in single gallons, or 5, 15, 30 and 55 gallon drums.
AIRKEM INC.

Airkem a-3®. A detergent composition having a combined detergent, deodorant, and sanitizer action. It contains a true odor counteractant chemical for deodorizing, a non-ionic synthetic detergent (not a soap) for cleaning, and a quaternary ammonium compound with a phenol coefficient of 7.5 (*S. typhosa*) 9.2 (*M. aureus*) for sanitizing. It functions equally well in hot or cold, hard or soft water. It is designed as a medium-duty cleaner for washing and deodorizing any hard surface, such as walls, floors and similar surfaces. It may be safely used on wood, linoleum, VINYL, tile, marble, metal, and other hard surfaces. Available in 1, 5, 15, 30, and 55 gallon containers.
AIRKEM INC.

Airkem Aerosol Insecticide[NR]. An insecticide that contains STROBANE and proven odor counteractants that leave a pleasant odor trace in the treated area. Effective against both flying and crawling insects; has high knock-down rating and long lasting residual effect; does not deteriorate with age. When used as directed, this insecticide does not leave a crystalline residue or in any way stain or harm fabrics, upholstery or other materials. Packaged in handy-sized 12 oz. aerosol bombs.
AIRKEM INC.

Airkem® Blue Label. A special formulation designed to counteract the odors of live animals in indoor areas. It is effective against the smells peculiar to both domestic and caged animals. Correctly applied, AIRKEM BLUE LABEL kills animal odors without leaving any objectionable odor trace of its own. It is non-toxic and non-flammable, and it has absolutely no harmful effect on animals. BLUE LABEL is packaged in pint wick-bottles, or bulk. It is suitable for use in all standard types of AIRKEM dispensing equipment for either air-conditioned or non-air-conditioned space.
AIRKEM INC.

Airkem Deoterge®. A deodorant-detergent that gets rid of dirt and odors that ordinary cleaners won't touch. It is a concentrated, non-toxic deodorant-detergent powder containing 97.5% active ingredients. Designed for both medium- and heavy-duty hard surface cleaning, it is more effective and milder than common alkaline cleaners. It is non-toxic, non-flammable, and non-corrosive; leaves wall surfaces and floors sparkling clean and free of all odor trace; will not bleach or stain, and is safe to use on food handling equipment. Available in 5, 25, 50, and 100 lb. spiral-wrap fiber containers.
AIRKEM INC.

Airkem® Green Label. A non-toxic, non-flammable space deodorant designed to kill common airborne odors and at the same time add an air-freshened effect to the stale indoor air. It does not act as an allergen nor does it anesthetize the sense of smell. It is suitable for the widest possible range of odor conditions. Air treatment can be secured through wick-bottle evaporation or through the use of AIRKEM-designed dispersing equipment. It is available in pint wick-bottles or in bulk.
AIRKEM INC.

Airkem Non-Toxic Insecticide[NR]. An aerosol product that makes use of a dual synergist system that increases the lethal properties of pyrethrins against flying and crawling insects. This insecticide can be safely used around humans or warm-blooded animals. It meets the specifications of Meat Inspection Division Memo #52, Insect Sprays, and can be used wherever food is grown, processed or stored, as in cafes, restaurants, food-processing plants and storage warehouses. Available in single 1-lb. aerosol packages or in case lots of 12 cans per case; also available in bulk for use in electrical vaporizers or standard pressure spraying equipment.
AIRKEM INC.

Airkem® Red Label. A heavy-duty odor counteractant that contains the same basic elements as AIRKEM GREEN LABEL plus selected compounds for counteracting the high-level odors encountered in rest rooms, autopsy rooms, and in hospital areas where body-drainage cases and terminal carcinoma or incontinency create a severe odor condition. It is non-toxic, non-flammable, and contains no anesthetizing agents. Its high concentration of active ingredients results in greater efficiency and economy of operation when used against odors of high intensity. Special ingredients add a pleasant air-freshened effect to the air. It eliminates completely the problem of heavy chemical odors normally associated with other products used to combat high-level odors. AIRKEM RED LABEL is sold in 15½ oz. wick bottles, or bulk.
AIRKEM INC.

Airkem® Red Label Mist. A product designed to provide quick relief from high-level odors. A single burst of this highly concentrated product will instantly knock out the most unpleasant odor. It has the same odor counteractant properties as AIRKEM RED LABEL LIQUID, but in aerosol form offers even quicker relief for the emergency treatment of severe odor problems. It is the ideal product for use in rest rooms, sick rooms, or wherever high-level odor concentrations are likely to occur. It is non-toxic and non-flammable and has absolutely no effect as an allergen. It may be used with complete confidence in the nursery or sick room where it provides quick and complete relief from temporary but highly distressing odor conditions. RED LABEL MIST is sold in large 12 oz. aerosol containers. Also available in case lots—one dozen cans per case.
AIRKEM INC.

Air-Mask[NR]. A self-contained, demand-type air-breathing apparatus for use in poisonous or oxygen deficient atmospheres. *Use:* To supply air, on demand, under the worst respiratory conditions.
MINE SAFETY APPLIANCES CO.

Airmat®. The registered trademark for: (1) mechanical, dry-type dust arrestors or collectors; (2) mechanical, dry-type, ventilating air filters; and (3) media for dust arrestors and air filters, including: (a) pre-fabricated pockets of woven glass and cloth; (b) sheets of fiber glass, paper, cloth, and synthetic fibers; (c) fiber glass and paper having di-electric properties. (*See also* AUTO-AIRMAT®) AMERICAN AIR FILTER CO.

Airtron®. A line of ducts, sleeves and couplings, fabricated of rubber-impregnated fiberglass cloth. They are noiseless under vibration; fire resistant; resistant to salt spray, fungi, mildew, and other corrosive agents; remain flexible and serviceable at continuous operating temps. from −65° to +450°F.;

and can be made resistant to most vapors and liquids including aromatic fuels, alcohol, lubricating and hydraulic oils, kerosene, and many acids and alkalies. Available in various pressure ranges up to 200 lb./sq.in. positive and 10 lb./sq.in. negative. AIRTRON is made in the following types:

TYPE "A." Fully convoluted, extremely flexible. For low positive pressures only.

TYPE "AE." The same as TYPE "A" with the addition of wire rings between convolutions. Can be used for higher pressures than "A" and for negative pressures.

TYPE "AX." Flexible, with plies of material supported on a wire helix.

TYPE B. Semi-flexible straight sleeving with any combination of convolutions spaced at intervals for added rigidity.

TYPE C. Straight sleeve sections and couplings, with no convolutions; semi-rigid or stiff depending on material and coating.

TYPE D. Any of the above types in irregular shape or construction. Made to specifications.

Uses: For cold and hot air ducts, blower systems, heater connections, fume and dust collectors, solids conveyors; radiator, pneumatic, and spray hoses; etc.
ARROWHEAD RUBBER CO.

Ajax #2[NR]. (*HBMTN* p. 19). No longer available.
UNIVERSAL-CYCLOPS STEEL CORP.

Aji-Ac'cent[NR]. Food savoring powders comprising monosodium glutamate.
INTERNATIONAL MINERALS & CHEMICAL CORP.

Ajonjoli[△]. *See* SESAME OIL[△].

Aker-Tuba[△]. *Same as* DERRIS ROOT[△].

Akoustikos Felt[NR]. An acoustical material made of asbestos fiber and selected hair. It is used where a flexible sound-absorbent is necessary. Especially suited for the internal lining of high-velocity air ducts which might be subject to salt spray, such as fan inlets on ships. Supplied in 180 sq.ft. rolls of ¼", ½", ¾" and 1" thicknesses.
JOHNS-MANVILLE SALES CORP.

Akrode[NR]. A vapor-pressure-type corrosion inhibitor used for protection, in packaging and storage, of machinery, tools, and similar articles made of ferrous metals. *Mfg'd by* HOWARDS OF ILFORD LTD.
Sole U. S. Distributor, BAIRD CHEMICAL CORP.

Aladdin® Galvanizing Compound. A compound for regalvanizing parts that are demaged by welding. Available in powder and stick forms.
ALADDIN ROD & FLUX MFG. CO.

Aladdin® Soapstone Pencil. A refillable, mechanical pencil made of plastic and holding a soapstone "lead." Used for marking metal, etc.
ALADDIN ROD & FLUX MFG. CO.

Alase®. An enzyme preparation of fungal origin used for the conversion of starch to soluble dextrines and simple sugars in the mfg. of foods.
TAKAMINE LABORATORIES

Albaloy® Plating Process. (*Supp.* I p. 8). No longer available. HANSON-VAN WINKLE-MUNNING CO.

Albatex PO®. (*HBMTN* p. 22). *Now known as* ALBATEX® POK. CIBA CO.

Albatex® POK. *Formerly known as* ALBATEX PO® (*HBMTN* p. 22). CIBA CO.

Albigen® A. A non-ionic polymerization product with pronounced affinity for dyestuffs, for use as a dye stripper. It is a viscous, pale yellowish liquid with a neutral reaction, and it can be diluted with water in all proportions. It is unaffected by hard water, acids and alkalis in the concentrations normally employed in the textile industry. It cannot be used, however, in mercerizing liquors.
Mfg'd by BADISCHE ANILIN-U. SODA-FABRIK AG.
Dist'd by NOVA CHEMICAL CORP.

Albion®. The trademark for a line of kaolin clays for refractories, pottery, and other industrial uses.
INTERCHEMICAL CORP., ALBION KAOLIN DIV.

Alcojet®. A detergent for use in dishwashing machines. ALCONOX INC.

Alcolo®. The trademark for a rubbing alcohol compound. ABBOTT LABORATORIES

Alcolube. (*HBMTN* p. 26). No longer available.
PARKER APPLIANCE CO.

Alcophate Paste[NR]. A sulfated alcohol paste used as a detergent for removing foreign materials from all types of natural and synthetic fibers. It is made from ethyl and oleic alcohol waxes, and contains a powerful solvent and pine oil as a binder. It is easily dissolved in water, requires no additives, and is easily rinsed out. MAC CHEMICAL CO.

Alcophobin[NR]. A medicinal for the treatment of alcoholism. Supplied in the form of tablets, each of which contains 250 mg. tetraethylthiuram disulfide.
CONSOLIDATED MIDLAND CORP.

Alcotabs®. A detergent in tablet form.
ALCONOX INC.

Aldarsone®. (*HBMTN* p. 26). No longer available.
ABBOTT LABORATORIES

Aldex®. The trademark for a line of 15 imitation fruit flavors. S. B. PENICK & CO.

Aldox®. A metal-cleaning and -pickling composition primarily adapted for use with aluminum.
PENNSYLVANIA SALT MFG. CO.

Aldrin[△]. *Also known as* COMPOUND 118. A potent and persistent insecticidal compound recommended for the control of cotton pests, grasshoppers, soil pests, etc. Chemically, it is 1,2,3,4,10,10-hexachloro-1, 4,4a,5,8,8a-hexahydro-1,4-*endo*, exo-5,8-dimethanonaphthalene. $C_{12}H_8Cl_6$; mol.wt. 364.94. The technical product is a brown, waxy solid containing about 78% of the above compound and perhaps about 5% of other insecticidally active compounds, and has a m.p. not less than 90°C. Insoluble in water; moderately soluble in mineral oils; readily soluble in acetone, benzene, xylene; stable to alkalis and mild acids; oxidizing agents and strong acids attack the unchlorinated ring. ALDRIN is readily absorbed through the skin; contact with the skin, inhalation, and food contamination should be avoided. Compatible with most fertilizers, herbicides, fungicides, and insecticides. Can be formulated as an emulsifiable concentrate, wettable powder, oil solution, and dust,

Alexall Tape. A splicing compound for electrical repairs. It has high resistance to water and electricity.
BOSTON WOVEN HOSE & RUBBER CO.

Alfco® Crystals. (*HBMTN* p. 26). Now known as AMERICAN LAFRANCE® CRYSTALS.
AMERICAN LAFRANCE CORP.

Algin△ or Alginic Acid△. A protein gelatin obtained from seaweed either directly or as a by-product in the mfg. of iodine and potash. It is a colorless mass resembling gelatin, and has the empirical formula, $C_{21}H_{27}O_{20}$. Dry seaweed contains from 20–30% algin. Commercially, ALGIN is used principally in the form of sodium alginate, made by dissolving ALGIN in sodium carbonate and neutralizing with hydrochloric acid. It is used as a stabilizer in ice cream and other foods; in textile printing; as an emulsifier and stabilizer in medicinals, and as a laxative; in water paints, boiler compounds, polishes; and in meat packing. Sodium alginate is also used for making a synthetic fiber: the sodium alginate is forced through spinnerets into a calcium chloride bath and then treated with a beryllium acetate solution to insolubilize the fibers, which are used for non-flammable fabrics. However, these fabrics must be dry cleaned and not washed with soap and water since the fiber is soluble in sodium soaps.

Alglyn® Tablets. An antacid for the treatment of hyperacidity and peptic ulcer. A brand of dihydroxy aluminum aminoacetate, N.N.R. Small, pleasant-tasting tablets, with 46% less aluminum than dried aluminum hydroxide gel.
BRAYTON PHARMACEUTICAL CO.

Algol®. A group of vat dyes for dyeing and printing COTTON and RAYON. These dyes are of lesser all-round fastness properties than INDANTHRENE® dyes.
GENERAL DYESTUFF CO.

Algosol®. A group of water-soluble leuco esters of vat dyes for dyeing and printing COTTON, RAYON, SILK, WOOL and some of the newer synthetic fibers. The resultant dyeing on the fiber is the same as that which would be produced from the vat dye from which the leuco ester was derived in the first place and has the same fastness properties.
GENERAL DYESTUFF CO.

Alkabar®. (*HBMTN* p. 29). No longer available.
TRUSCON LABORATORIES

Alkanet△. Also known as ORCANNETTE△, ANCHUSA△, and ALKANNA△. The root of the plant *Alkanna tinctoria* found in the Mediterranean countries, Hungary, and Western Asia. The roots are used to obtain a dark red, amorphous, slightly acid, powdered extract which is used as a coloring principle. The extract, known as ALKANNIN, is soluble in alcohol, benzene, ether, and in oils. *Uses:* For coloring fats and oils in pharmaceuticals and in cosmetics, for producing an even-red color in wines, for coloring waxes, and as a chemical indicator. ALKANNIN PAPER, which is also known as BOETTGER'S PAPER, is a white paper that has been impregnated with an alcohol solution of ALKANNIN. The red color of the paper is turned to shades of green to blue by alkalis.

Alkanex®. A polyester resin possessing outstanding electrical properties and particularly suitable for use as a Class B wire enamel but which may also be used for impregnating or other insulating applications.
GENERAL ELECTRIC CO.

Alkanna△. Same as ALKANET△.

Alkannin△. See ALKANET△.

Alka-Seltzer®. An effervescent analgesic alkalizing preparation comprising aspirin, mono-calcium phosphate, sodium bicarbonate, and citric acid.
MILES LABORATORIES, INC.

Alk-A-Sol®. Incorrectly listed as ALK-S-SOL® (*Supp.* I p. 10).
WHITFIELD CHEMICAL CO.

Alka-Zane®. A medicinal for the relief of acidosis. Each heaping teaspoonful provides 2.7 g. sodium citrate, 1.6 g. sodium bicarbonate, 0.50 g. potassium citrate, 0.25 g. calcium phosphate, 0.25 g. magnesium phosphate, 0.11 g. calcium glycerophosphate. It contains no sodium chloride, lactate, sulfate or tartrate.
WARNER-CHILCOTT LABORATORIES

Alk-Li-Pruf Cement[NE]. (*HBMTN* p. 30). No longer available.
ELECTRO-CHEMICAL SUPPLY & ENGINEERING CO.

Alkontrol[NE]. An addition agent for use in metal-cleaning and cyanide copper baths. It reduces the troublesome hexavalent forms of chrome contamination to harmless ones. In a copper strike it improves the deposition of copper, making for better covering of casting patterns; it improves plating in low-current-density areas; and eliminates some causes of blistering.
NORTHWEST CHEMICAL CO.

Alk-S-Sol®. (*Supp* I p. 10). Should have been listed as ALK-A-SOL®.
WHITFIELD CHEMICAL CO.

Alkyd Resins△. Synthetic resins prepared by the interaction of acids and alcohols. The reaction product derived from a polyhydric alcohol and a polybasic acid is properly termed a polyester resin. However, it is common practice to always refer to an oil-modified polyester resin as an alkyd or an alkyd coating resin. Furthermore, certain polyester resins that are capable of cross-linking can be properly compounded with fillers and catalysts to form thermosetting molding compounds, which are generally known as alkyd molding compounds. Some of the important characteristics of alkyd coating resins and alkyd molding compounds are as follows:

ALKYD COATING RESINS. The predominant group of alkyd resins used in the mfg. of surface coatings employ phthalic anhydride as the principal polybasic acid constituent and glycerol or pentaerythritol as the polyhydric alcohol constituent. When special resin properties are desired, other polyhydric alcohols can be used in place of glycerol or pentaerythritol. These include di- or tri-pentaerythritol, sorbitol or trimethylolethane. Furthermore, alkyd resins for protective coatings are modified with oxidizing or non-oxidizing fatty acids derived from vegetable, and in some cases, marine oils. Alkyds generally contain from 30 to 70% oil and are frequently classified as follows: short-oil, 30–46% oil content; medium-oil 46–56% oil content; and long oil, 56–70% oil content. Short-oil alkyds contain fewer of the aliphatic, solvent-tolerant, fatty acid chains in their molecular structure and, therefore, are generally incompatible with aliphatic solvents. These alkyds are supplied as solutions in aromatic solvents, such as benzene or toluene.

Short-oil alkyds that are modified with non-oxidizing oils, such as coconut or castor oil, are used as plasticizers in cellulose nitrate formulations to provide improved adhesion, flexibility, durability, and color retention to modern automotive and other fast-drying industrial lacquer finishes. They are also used extensively with urea and melamine resins in baking enamels to provide exceptionally hard, tough finishes for refrigerators, washing machines, home freezers, etc. Short-oil, oxidizing alkyds based on soya, dihydrated castor, or cotton-seed oils find wide application in forced-dry, wood furniture finishes that are superior in abrasion resistance, impact strength and durability to oleoresinous varnishes or cellulose nitrate lacquers. Medium- and long-oil alkyds that are soluble in mineral spirits are modified most frequently with oxidizing oils and are used in brushing-type, air-drying finishes. Most of the commonly used household paint products, such as alkyd, flat wall paint, 4-hour high-gloss enamel, and porch, floor and deck paints are manufactured at present from either medium- or long-oil alkyd resins. Odorless interior alkyd-based flat paints and gloss enamels are finding increased use. These finishes are formulated with medium- and long-oil alkyd resins and odorless and low-odor mineral spirits. Long-oil and extra-long-oil alkyds of 100% solids are used as modifiers for various water-dispersed lattices and as components for exterior house paints. Highly thixotropic alkyds have been developed by modification with polyamide resin. Paint products produced from polyamide-modified alkyds are jelly-like in appearance but are quickly reduced to ordinary consistency by mechanical agitation.

ALKYD MOLDING COMPOUNDS. Thermosetting molding compounds with rather unique properties are obtained by compounding suitable polyester resins with fillers, pigments and catalysts. These alkyd compounds are fast curing and they may be made to flow around delicate inserts in intricate shapes. Molding temps. are usually in the range of 300°–315°F. with pressures of 800 to 1,500 lb./sq.in. The moldings exhibit excellent dimensional stability and electrical characteristics, and have good moisture and solvent resistance. The compounds may be filled with a mineral filler or reinforced with fibrous glass. The mineral-filled products are available in putty and in granular forms. The putty form is especially useful for encapsulating small electrical resistors and capacitors. The granular types are free flowing and are readily adaptable for automatic molding operations. The fibrous glass-reinforced materials are usually supplied in mat form and are characterized by their high strength and good electrical properties. They are used for the mfg. of insulating brackets and braces, rocker rings, circuit breaker cases, and coil forms.

Alkylene A[NE]. A low-foaming anionic phosphated organic alcohol, stable in strongly alkaline solutions. *Use:* As a dye leveling and dispersing agent.
HART PRODUCTS CORP.

All-Dust®. A line of respirators and filters. *Use:* For protection against inhalation of dusts.
MINE SAFETY APPLIANCES CO.

Allegheny® 47-50, 88X, *and* Magnet Steels. (*HBMTN* p. 31). Now known as ALLEGHENY LUDLUM® 47-50, 88X, *and* MAGNET STEELS.
ALLEGHENY LUDLUM STEEL CORP.

Allegheny Ludlum® 47-50, 88X, *and* Magnet Steels. Incorrectly listed as ALLEGHENY® 47-50, 88X, *and* MAGNET STEELS (*HBMTN* p. 31).
ALLEGHENY LUDLUM STEEL CORP.

Allegheny Ludlum® Clad Steel, Corrosion Resisting Castings, *and* Stainless Steel Alloys. Incorrectly listed as ALLEGHENY METAL® CLAD STEEL, CORROSION RESISTING CASTINGS, *and* STAINLESS STEEL ALLOYS (*HBMTN* pp. 31, 32).
ALLEGHENY LUDLUM STEEL CORP.

Allegheny Ludlum® Mumetal®, Ohmaloy®, Sealmet®, *and* Silicon Steels. Incorrectly listed as ALLEGHENY® MUMETAL®, OHMALOY®, SEALMET®, *and* SILICON STEELS.
ALLEGHENY LUDLUM STEEL CORP.

Allegheny Metal® Clad Steel, Corrosion Resisting Castings, *and* Stainless Steel Alloys. (*HBMTN* pp. 31, 32). Now known as ALLEGHENY LUDLUM® CLAD STEEL, CORROSION RESISTING CASTINGS, *and* STAINLESS STEEL ALLOYS.
ALLEGHENY LUDLUM STEEL CORP.

Allegheny® Mumetal®, Ohmaloy®, Sealmet®, *and* Silicon Steels. (*HBMTN* p. 34). Now known as ALLEGHENY LUDLUM® MUMETAL®, OHMALOY®, SEALMET®, *and* SILICON STEELS.
ALLEGHENY LUDLUM STEEL CORP.

Allis-Chalmers®. Registered trademark for all goods mfg'd by the ALLIS-CHALMERS MFG. CO.

Allisite®. A special abrasion-resisting iron alloy used for such applications as casings and stuffing boxes of solids-handling pumps. ALLIS-CHALMERS MFG. CO.

All Purpose Gear Lubricant[NE]. An SAE 140 lubricant for all types of gears, including hypoid gears, in cars, trucks, etc. (*See also* KEYSTONE ALL PURPOSE HYPOID LUBRICANT.) KEYSTONE LUBRICATING CO.

All-Service®. A gas mask canister. *Use:* For protection against poisonous gases and vapors, including carbon monoxide. U. S. Bureau of Mines approved.
MINE SAFETY APPLIANCES CO.

Alluracel[NE]. The trade name for a line of fabrics made wholly or partially of cellulose derivatives.
CELANESE CORP. OF AMERICA

All-Vision®. Wide-angle vision facepieces. *Use:* For masks or full facepiece respirators.
MINE SAFETY APPLIANCES CO.

Allwall[NE]. A vinyl emulsion, interior, flat paint for walls, ceilings, and trim. Usually, only one coat is required to give a hard, tough, scrubbable surface in brilliant deep or pastel colors. It is odorless, non-toxic, and fast drying.
CALIFORNIA STUCCO PRODUCTS OF N. E., INC

All-Weather[NE]. A name used to designate a line of unit-type first-aid kits. MINE SAFETY APPLIANCES CO.

Allyl Plastics[△]. A group of clear, water-white casting plastics made by polymerizing the ester of allyl alcohol or allyl chloride. Allyl ester is a clear, syrupy liquid which polymerizes with a peroxide catalyst; the liquid monomer can be poured into molds and hardened by polymerization. ALLYL PLASTICS have a sp.gr. of 1.34–1.40, dielectric strength of about 1,275 volts per mil, a refractive index of 1.57, a Rockwell M hardness of 116, and a compressive strength of 19,600 psi. *Uses:* For lenses, prisms, reflectors, and mechanical and electrical parts.

Alminate® Tablets. A medicinal—dehydroxy aluminum aminoacetate—which offers prompt and prolonged antacid action. Used in the management of peptic ulcer or gastric hyperacidity.
BRISTOL LABORATORIES INC.

Alpha®. The trademark for a line of brass pipe.
CHASE BRASS & COPPER CO.

Alphanol®. A line of dyestuffs midway in properties between acid and direct dyes. Used for dyeing wool-cotton unions and for dyeing level shades on chrome leather.
GENERAL DYESTUFF CO.

"Alpha"® Protein. An industrial isolated soybean protein used in latex paints, paper coatings, emulsions, paper and insulating board.
GLIDDEN CO.

Alpiste△. *See* CANARY SEED△.

Alracompt®. Incorrectly listed as ALRARCOMPT® (*HBMTN* p. 37).
REED & CARNRICK

Alrarcompt®. (*HBMTN* p. 37). Should have been listed as ALRACOMPT®.
REED & CARNRICK

Alsibronz®. The trademark for Muscovite mica, $H_2KAl_3(SiO_4)_3$ prepared as a pigment by the wet or water-ground method. It is a highly delaminated product, washed free from foreign matter, and carefully graded for size. Sp.gr. 2.8–3.0; bulk density, 10 lb./cu.ft. Available in various types and grades, including:

No. 12 ALSIBRONZ. A 325-mesh mica extender for latex emulsion paints.

No. 20 ALSIBRONZ. Surface-coated with aluminum silicate to make it water repellent. For use in low-loss insulating varnishes and encapsulating agents.

No. 21 LEAFY ALSIBRONZ.

No. 30 ALSIBRONZ. Surface coated with a stearate film.

No. 40 ALSIBRONZ. Surface coated with an oil film.

No. 45 ALSIBRONZ. Surface coated with a resin film.

No. 46 ALSIBRONZ. Surface coated with a resin. For use in aluminum paints.

No. 50 ALSIBRONZ. Surface coated with a silicone.
FRANKLIN MINERAL PRODUCTS CO.

Aluma Block®. A cold chemical coating for aluminum. Applied by dip, spray, or with rag or brush, it gives either a soft or high gloss finish.
BIRCHWOOD CHEMICAL CO.

Alumel®. (*HBMTN* p. 40). Now a registered trademark.
HOSKINS MFG. CO.

Alumicone. An aluminum-silicone paint that withstands 1,500°F. For use on aircraft and automobile exhaust systems, furnaces, stoves, heater doors, and smoke stacks.
ATECH, INC.

Aluminacrete. *See* R & I ALUMINACRETE®.

Aluminoid[NB]. (*HBMTN* p. 40). No longer available.
CHATHAM PHARMACEUTICALS, INC.

Aluminum Brightener I-2767-C[NB]. A heavy-duty fast-acting phosphoric acid-type brightener for cleaning and brightening exterior aircraft surfaces and large aluminum equipment in a single operation. Removes oxides, traffic film, oil deposits, and exhaust stains, leaving a clean, brightened surface. It is a heavy, white liquid of mild odor. Acidity, as H_3PO_4, 5.1–5.3%.
WYANDOTTE CHEMICALS CORP.,
J. B. FORD DIV.

Alumiprep®. A chemical preparation for etching, cleaning, and treating aluminum alloy surfaces prior to painting.
NEILSON CHEMICAL CO.

Alumitee®. An acoustical tile suspension system.
CELOTEX CORP.

Alutone®. A liquid for cleaning and brightening exterior aircraft surfaces and other large aluminum equipment, in one single operation. It removes oxides, traffic film, oil deposits, and exhaust stains, leaving a clean, brightened surface. It is non-corrosive and non-hazardous; and will not harm acrylic-based plastics.
WYANDOTTE CHEMICALS CORP.,
J. B. FORD DIV.

A-M 14. A casein-type, interior plywood patching and assembly glue.
AMERICAN-MARIETTA CO.,
ADHESIVE RESIN & CHEMICAL DIV.

A-M 150. A partly proteinaceous extender for use in exterior plywood adhesives. Designed for use with AMRES 580, 5531 and 5570.
AMERICAN-MARIETTA CO.,
ADHESIVE RESIN & CHEMICAL DIV.

A-M 160. An organic-inorganic extender for use in exterior plywood resin glues. Designed for use with AMRES 5570.
AMERICAN-MARIETTA CO.,
ADHESIVE RESIN & CHEMICAL DIV.

A-M 188. A soy-type, cold press, clamp and no clamp, interior grade plywood adhesive. It can also be used for laminating hardboards.
AMERICAN-MARIETTA CO.,
ADHESIVE RESIN & CHEMICAL DIV.

A-M 302. A blood-soy type, hot-press interior grade plywood adhesive.
AMERICAN-MARIETTA CO.,
ADHESIVE RESIN & CHEMICAL DIV.

A-M 414-T. A toxic, casein-type, interior plywood patching and assembly glue.
AMERICAN-MARIETTA CO.,
ADHESIVE RESIN & CHEMICAL DIV.

A-M 580. An inorganic-organic extender for exterior plywood resin glues. Designed for use with AMRES 580.
AMERICAN-MARIETTA CO.,
ADHESIVE RESIN & CHEMICAL DIV.

A-M 604. A blood-soy type, hot-press, interior plywood adhesive.
AMERICAN-MARIETTA CO.,
ADHESIVE RESIN & CHEMICAL DIV.

A-M 620. A catalyst-extender for urea plywood glues. Designed for use with AMRES 54.
AMERICAN-MARIETTA CO.,
ADHESIVE RESIN & CHEMICAL DIV.

A-M 3720. A proteinaceous extender for interior plywood resin glue. Designed for use with AMRES 580.
AMERICAN-MARIETTA CO.,
ADHESIVE RESIN & CHEMICAL DIV.

A-M 4620. A proteinaceous extender for interior plywood resin glues. Designed for use with AMRES 580 and AMRES 5570.
AMERICAN-MARIETTA CO.,
ADHESIVE RESIN & CHEMICAL DIV.

A-M 5531. An organic-inorganic extender for use in exterior and interior plywood resin glues. Designed for use with Amres 5531. American-Marietta Co., Adhesive Resin & Chemical Div.

A-M 5602. An anti-foam agent for use with blood-soy glues, soy glues, and urea glues.
American-Marietta Co., Adhesive Resin & Chemical Div.

A-M 6701. A casein-type, non-toxic glue for general assembly use. American-Marietta Co., Adhesive Resin & Chemical Div.

A-M 6712. A casein-type, low-temp.-setting, water-resistant adhesive for bench, joint, assembly and timber-laminating work. It is a toxic-type glue with a low water requirement. American-Marietta Co., Adhesive Resin & Chemical Div.

A-M 6720. A toxic, casein-type, low-temp.-setting, water-resistant adhesive for bench, joint, assembly, and timber-laminating work.
American-Marietta Co., Adhesive Resin & Chemical Div.

Amaizo® "400" Stabilizer. (*Supp.* I p. 12). The name Amaizo® should have been listed as a registerd trademark. American Maize Products Co.

Amaizo® 721A Starch. A precooked, waxy maize corn starch which has been scientifically modified to produce cold-water gelation. It is pure white, fluffy, free-flowing, odorless, and tasteless.
American Maize Products Co.

Amanitine△. Same as Choline△.

Amanol® Nitrogen Solutions. The trademark for nitrogen fertilizers containing 41%, 44%, 45% and 49% nitrogen in the form of aqua ammonia and ammonium nitrate. Supplied in bulk tank cars and trucks. *Uses:* For direct applications, and in fertilizer mixtures. American Cyanamid Co.

A-M AP 30. A blood-type, high quality, interior grade plywood hot-press adhesive.
American-Marietta Co., Adhesive Resin & Chemical Div.

A-M AP 30R. A resin-fortified, blood-type, mold-proof, interior-grade plywood hot-press adhesive.
American-Marietta Co., Adhesive Resin & Chemical Div.

Amarine®. The trademark for moisture-resistant electrical wire and cable. United States Steel Corp.

Amasize®. A textile size for warps of spun Rayon and blends with Cotton and Wool. A dry, white powder which disperses easily in cold water.
Stein, Hall & Co.

Amazite[NE]. A corrosion-resistant floor topping designed to protect concrete floors and other surfaces from chemical attack. Hallemite Mfg. Co.

Amber△. A fossil resin used for ornaments and in the mfg. of varnishes and lacquers. Found buried along the Baltic Sea and in Madagascar. It is hard, brittle, and tasteless, but has an aromatic odor; it is frequently transparent, but is generally semi-transparent or opaque with a glossy surface, yellow or orange in color. The Amber from Madagascar is semi-transparent, wave-streaked, and honey-colored, and is used especially for necklaces and pipe mouthpieces. (*See also* Amberoid, *and* Amber Oil.)

Amberoid△. Scrap Amber pieces that are reclaimed by being compressed into a solid mass; sometimes the Amber pieces are mixed with Copal or other resins. Used for the same purposes as Amber.

Amber Oil△. An oil that is obtained by distilling scrap Amber. Consists of a mixture of terpenes. Used in the mfg. of varnish.

AmBridge®. The trademark for a line of specially-constructed steel joists for floor and roof construction in light-occupancy structures.
United States Steel Corp., American Bridge Div.

AMC[NE]. (*HBMTN* p. 41). Should have been listed as Milne AMC[NE]. A. Milne & Co.

Amco-Goggle[NE]. A line of welder's and chipper's goggles. Eastern Equipment Co.

Amcohood[NE]. A line of welding helmets.
Eastern Equipment Co.

Amdelate®. (*HBMTN* p. 41). No longer available.
Abbott Laboratories

Amerbestos®. The trademark for asbestos-insulated electrical wire and cable. United States Steel Corp.

Amerbus[NE]. The trade name for an electrical, loom-covered portable cable. United States Steel Corp.

Amerclad®. The trademark for rubber-sheathed electrical wire and cable. United States Steel Corp.

AMER-clone®. A centrifugal dust separator or concentrator of the cyclone type.
American Air Filter Co.

Amer-Construction[NE]. A galvanized soft steel construction wire. United States Steel Corp.

Amercord[NE]. The trade name for insulated electrical cords. United States Steel Corp.

Amercut®. The trademark for cold finished steel bars. United States Steel Corp.

Amerductor®. The trademark for electrical transmission lines. United States Steel Corp.

Amerfine[NE]. The trade name for a fine wire.
United States Steel Corp.

Amergard®. The trademark for a highway guard cable. United States Steel Corp.

AMER-glas®. Mechanical viscous-impingement ventilating air filters of the disposable type.
American Air Filter Co.

Amerglass®. The trademark for glass-insulated electrical wire and cable. United States Steel Corp.

Amergraph®. The trademark for oil-field electrical wire and cable. United States Steel Corp.

Amerhead®. The trademark for a steel heading wire.
United States Steel Corp.

Americaine®. (*HBMTN* p. 43). Now a product of Arnar-Stone Laboratories, Inc., formerly Americaine, Inc.

Americaine with Neomycin®. A combination of 20% dissolved benzocaine, for the relief of pain, with 5 mg. of neomycin, for the prevention and control of surface infections. ARNAR-STONE LABORATORIES, INC.

American®. The trademark for welded and woven wire fence, barb wire, trellis wire, wire netting, fence posts, fence post drivers and driving caps, fence gates, fence stretchers, fence wire crimpers, fence wire splicers, spiral fence stays, bale ties, tie wire, wire hoops, nails, brads, tacks, staples, woven-wire corn cribs and cribbing, corn-crib ventilators, welded wire fabric, springs, valve spring wire, high-tensile wire for pre-stressed concrete, wire rope, wire clothes lines, and electrical wires, cables and cords.
UNITED STATES STEEL CORP.,
AMERICAN STEEL & WIRE DIV.

American LaFrance® Crystals. Formerly known as ALFCO® CRYSTALS. AMERICAN LAFRANCE CORP.

American Storax△. See STORAX△.

Americore®. The trademark for rubber-insulated electrical building wire and cable.
UNITED STATES STEEL CORP.

Amering®. The trademark for annular ring nails.
UNITED STATES STEEL CORP.

Ameripol®. (*HBMTN* p. 43). Formerly mfg'd by B. F. GOODRICH CO.; now a product of GOODRICH-GULF CHEMICALS, INC.

Amerite®. The trademark for rubber-insulated electrical wire and cable. UNITED STATES STEEL CORP.

AMERjet®. Self-cleaning mechanical dust collectors of the dry, tubular stocking type.
AMERICAN AIR FILTER CO.

Amerled[NE]. The trade name for lead-bearing carbon and alloy steels. UNITED STATES STEEL CORP.

Amerloy[NE]. An alloy spring wire.
UNITED STATES STEEL CORP.

Amerlum®. The trademark for an aluminum-coated wire. UNITED STATES STEEL CORP.

Amerotol®. (*HBMTN* p. 43). Now a product of ARNAR-STONE LABORATORIES, INC., formerly AMERICAINE, INC.

Amer-Plate® Plain. (*Supp.* I p. 14). Now a registered trademark. AMERCOAT CORP.

Amer-Plate T-Lock[NE]. (*Supp.* I p. 14). Should have been listed as T-LOCK AMER-PLATE®.
AMERCOAT CORP.

Amerprene[NE]. A NEOPRENE-sheathed electrical wire and cable. UNITED STATES STEEL CORP.

Amerse®. An odorless, non-corrosive germicide for food utensils and equipment. VESTAL, INC.

Amerseal®. A non-metallic electrical parkway cable.
UNITED STATES STEEL CORP.

Amersheath®. A non-metallic electrical parkway cable. UNITED STATES STEEL CORP.

Amersteel®. The trademark for electrical transmission lines. UNITED STATES STEEL CORP.

Amerstitch®. The trademark for a round stitching wire. UNITED STATES STEEL CORP.

Amerstrand®. The trademark for an electrical wire and steel strand. UNITED STATES STEEL CORP.

Amerstrip®. The trademark for a cold-rolled steel strip. UNITED STATES STEEL CORP.

Amertel®. The trademark for a telephone and telegraph and tie wire. UNITED STATES STEEL CORP.

Amervent®. A forced-draft cooling, heating, and ventilating unit of the cabinet type.
AMERICAN AIR FILTER CO.

Amerzone®. The trademark for an ozone- and corona-resisting rubber-insulated electrical cable.
UNITED STATES STEEL CORP.

Ametallic®. The trademark for a flat steel taped electrical parkway cable. UNITED STATES STEEL CORP.

Amethyst△. A transparent quartz with a violet or purple color due to the presence of manganese and iron oxides. Found principally in Brazil and Uruguay. Sp.gr. 2.65; hardness on Moh scale, 7; breaks with rippled fracture instead of conchoidal fracture of ordinary quartz. *Uses:* For making pivot bearings for instruments, needles for recording machines, etc. The deep and uniformly-colored stones are used as gems.

Amex®. The trade name for a low-density, ammonia-type dynamite. It is used for blasting tough ores in mines and quarries. AMERICAN CYANAMID CO.

Amgal®. The trademark for a drawn galvanized wire. UNITED STATES STEEL CORP.

Aminet®. An antiasthmatic-diuretic composition comprising aminophylline, sodium pentobarbital, and benzocaine. AMES CO.

Aminonat®. (*HBMTN* p. 43). No longer available.
NATIONAL DRUG CO.

Aminoso®. Modified fibrin hydrolysate for intravenous or subcutaneous administration. It is a sterile, pyrogen-free hydrolysate containing the "essential" amino acids. Used in a variety of medical and surgical conditions in which protein of the body is being or has been depleted without the possibility of restoring it by feeding. ABBOTT LABORATORIES

Aminotriazole[NE]. A proprietary product sold as a weed killer. 3-Amino-1,2,4-triazole. Particularly effective for control of noxious perennial weeds, defoliation, and plant growth inhibition. A white crystalline solid; m.p. 150–153°C.; soluble in water; slightly soluble in ethanol; insoluble in ether or acetone. *Uses:* As a weed killer, defoliant, and plant growth inhibitor. Particularly effective for control of perennial weeds such as poison ivy, poison oak, Canada thistle, quack grass, and aquatic weeds. Also effective as a defoliant for COTTON and other plants with additional advantage of inhibiting regrowth of new foliage. AMERICAN CYANAMID CO.

Aminovite®. (*HBMTN* p. 43). No longer available.
NATIONAL DRUG CO.

Amioca®. (*HBMTN* p. 43). Should have been listed as a registered trademark.
AMERICAN MAIZE PRODUCTS CO.

Amisate®. (*HBMTN* p. 44). No longer available.
SHARP & DOHME, INC.

Amizyme®. An amylolytic enzyme product. *Use:* In the paper industry for conversion of starch for tub and calender sizes and for coatings and laminations.
PABST BREWING CO., INDUSTRIAL PRODUCTS DIV.

Ammoniated Speedsope®. (*Supp.* I p. 14). Now a registered trademark.
FRANKLIN RESEARCH CO.

Amoco®. The trademark of AMOCO CHEMICALS CORP. for their line of products, including sulfonates, detergent alkylates, isoctyl alcohol, decyl alcohol, etc.

Amo-Dex. Medicinal tablets, each of which contains 5 mg. dextro amphetamine HCl and 20 mg. AMOBARBITAL.
TESTAGAR & CO.

Amoebicon®. An amebicide for the treatment of intestinal amebiasis. Supplied in the form of tablets, each of which contains 0.25 g. bismuth glycolylarsanilate.
CONSOLIDATED MIDLAND CORP.

Ampave®. (*Supp.* I p. 14). No longer available.
SHARP & DOHME DIV., MERCK & CO.

Amperox®. The trademark for a heat-resistant electrical wire and cable.
UNITED STATES STEEL CORP.

A-M P.O.E. An anti-foam agent especially suitable for blood-soy glues.
AMERICAN-MARIETTA CO.,
ADHESIVE RESIN & CHEMICAL DIV.

Ampolene®. The trademark for a synthetic resin-insulated weatherproof wire and cable.
UNITED STATES STEEL CORP.

Ampolite®. A machine dishwashing compound.
DIVERSEY CORP.

Ampulbex®. (*HBMTN* p. 45). No longer available.
ABBOTT LABORATORIES

Ampyrol®. The trademark for a synthetic resin-insulated electrical wire and cable.
UNITED STATES STEEL CORP.

Amres 54. A general-purpose, urea-type, plywood adhesive resin. Suitable for a variety of uses depending upon the catalyst and extender used.
AMERICAN-MARIETTA CO.,
ADHESIVE RESIN & CHEMICAL DIV.

Amres 118. A phenolic resin used as a binding agent in the mfg. of wet process hardboard.
AMERICAN-MARIETTA CO.,
ADHESIVE RESIN & CHEMICAL DIV.

Amres 136, 580, 4565, 5531, 5570 *and* 5580. A group of phenolic resins for hot-press exterior and interior plywood adhesives. They can also be used for veneering with hardboards, hardwoods, and other surfacing materials.
AMERICAN-MARIETTA CO.,
ADHESIVE RESIN & CHEMICAL DIV.

Amres 200. A urea-formaldehyde resin used for wet-strengthening paper.
AMERICAN-MARIETTA CO.,
ADHESIVE RESIN & CHEMICAL DIV.

Amres 210. A highly cationic, urea-formaldehyde, wet-strengthening, paper resin.
AMERICAN-MARIETTA CO.,
ADHESIVE RESIN & CHEMICAL DIV.

Amres 225. A urea-formaldehyde resin used to produce water resistance in starch and dextrin adhesives used in corrugated board, solid fiber board, paper laminates, and bag seams; for producing water resistance in starch coatings for paper, insulation board, and acoustical tile; and as a binder for chip and core boards.
AMERICAN-MARIETTA CO.,
ADHESIVE RESIN & CHEMICAL DIV.

Amres 250. A general-purpose, urea-type, plywood adhesive resin suitable for such applications as panel and veneer patching, edge gluing, etc.
AMERICAN-MARIETTA CO.,
ADHESIVE RESIN & CHEMICAL DIV.

Amres 255. A general-purpose urea-formaldehyde plywood adhesive resin that can also be used as a binder for chip and core boards.
AMERICAN-MARIETTA CO.,
ADHESIVE RESIN & CHEMICAL DIV.

Amres 275. A multi-purpose, urea-formaldehyde resin adhesive used primarily for radio-frequency gluing, special bench work, and door mfg. It has an almost colorless glue line which makes it especially useful in applications where the glue line is exposed and appearance is important.
AMERICAN-MARIETTA CO.,
ADHESIVE RESIN & CHEMICAL DIV.

Amres 1400. A phenolic-type overlay adhesive and glue line resin.
AMERICAN-MARIETTA CO.,
ADHESIVE RESIN & CHEMICAL DIV.

Amres 1420. A phenolic resin used to impart stiffness and to improve the dry- and wet-strength of special papers.
AMERICAN-MARIETTA CO.,
ADHESIVE RESIN & CHEMICAL DIV.

Amres 1430. A phenolic resin used as a beater additive in the mfg. of special papers.
AMERICAN-MARIETTA CO.,
ADHESIVE RESIN & CHEMICAL DIV.

Amres 1910. A resorcinal-type, room or high-temp. setting, waterproof adhesive for plywood panel-patching and scarfing.
AMERICAN-MARIETTA CO.,
ADHESIVE RESIN & CHEMICAL DIV.

Amres 1920. A resorcinal-type, room temp.-setting, waterproof adhesive for plywood panel patching, scarfing, and edge bonding.
AMERICAN-MARIETTA CO.,
ADHESIVE RESIN & CHEMICAL DIV.

Amres 2612. A resorcinol-type, timber-laminating adhesive that produces a waterproof bond. Recommended for boat building and other gluing applications.
AMERICAN-MARIETTA CO.,
ADHESIVE RESIN & CHEMICAL DIV.

Amres 2620. A resorcinol-type, exterior adhesive used for same applications as AMRES 2612.
AMERICAN-MARIETTA CO.,
ADHESIVE RESIN & CHEMICAL DIV.

Amres 2670 *and* Amres 2670B. A two-part, room-temp., resorcinal-type, quick-setting, waterproof adhesive for use on wood and other materials.
AMERICAN-MARIETTA CO.,
ADHESIVE RESIN & CHEMICAL DIV.

Amres 3710B. A phenolic resin used for bonding overlay papers. AMERICAN-MARIETTA CO., ADHESIVE RESIN & CHEMICAL DIV.

Amres 3910. An alcohol-soluble, phenolic resin for impregnating canvas and COMPREG paper; and binding COTTON, hardboard, and insulation board.
AMERICAN-MARIETTA CO., ADHESIVE RESIN & CHEMICAL DIV.

Amres 4050C. A phenolic resin binder for rockwool batts. AMERICAN-MARIETTA CO., ADHESIVE RESIN & CHEMICAL DIV.

Amres 4070A. A phenolic resin binder for rock-wool batts. AMERICAN-MARIETTA CO., ADHESIVE RESIN & CHEMICAL DIV.

Amres 4511. A resorcinol-type, room-temp. or radio-frequency setting, waterproof adhesive for various types of wood assemblies and for adhering other materials. AMERICAN-MARIETTA CO., ADHESIVE RESIN & CHEMICAL DIV.

Amres 6110. A phenolic resin designed for the surface treatment of hardboard. AMERICAN-MARIETTA CO., ADHESIVE RESIN & CHEMICAL DIV.

Amres 6120 and 6120A. Phenolic resin binders for dry-formed, particle-type hardboard.
AMERICAN-MARIETTA CO., ADHESIVE RESIN & CHEMICAL DIV.

Amres 6121. A phenolic resin used as a binder for smooth-two-side, dry-formed hardboard.
AMERICAN-MARIETTA CO., ADHESIVE RESIN & CHEMICAL DIV.

Amres 6130. A phenolic resin binder for dry-formed hardboard. AMERICAN-MARIETTA CO., ADHESIVE RESIN & CHEMICAL DIV.

Amres 6131. A phenolic resin binder for screen back, dry-formed hardboard. AMERICAN-MARIETTA CO., ADHESIVE RESIN & CHEMICAL DIV.

AMS 35. An inhibited acid cleaner for use on metals. J. F. HENRY CHEMICAL CO.

Amvar®. The trademark for a magnet wire. UNITED STATES STEEL CORP.

AN-10[NE]. A readily emulsifiable processed castor oil. BAKER CASTOR OIL CO.

Anabasine[△]. Also known as NEONICOTINE. An insecticidal compound similar in properties to nicotine. Chemically, it is 2-(3′-pyridyl) piperidine; $C_{10}H_{14}N_2$; mol.wt. 162.24. A colorless, viscous liquid; b.p. 280.9°C; miscible with water; soluble in most organic solvents; darkens on exposure to air and light. Marketed as an aqueous solution of the sulfate (40% alkaloids, of which 70% is ANABASINE).

Analeptine®. (*HBMTN* p. 46). Should have been listed as ANALEPTONE®. REED & CARNRICK

Analeptone®. Incorrectly listed as ANALEPTINE® (*HBMTN* p. 46). REED & CARNRICK

Anayodin®. An intestinal amebacide consisting of chiniofon, 7-iodo-8-hydroxyquinoline-5-sulfonate.
AMES CO.

Anchusa[△]. Same as ALKANET[△].

Aneskreme[NE]. (*HBMTN* p. 46). No longer available. ABBOTT LABORATORIES

Anespray[NE]. (*HBMTN* p. 46). No longer available. ABBOTT LABORATORIES

Anesthesin®. Incorrectly listed as ANETHESIN® (*HBMTN* p. 46). ABBOTT LABORATORIES

Anethesin®. (*HBMTN* p. 46). Should have been listed as ANESTHESIN®. ABBOTT LABORATORIES

Angitet. A brand of pentaerythritol tetranitrate for prolonged coronary vasodilation in the prevention of angina pectoris. G. F. HARVEY CO.

Anilox®. The trademark for a line of flexographic inks. INTERCHEMICAL CORP., PRINTING INK DIV.

Animi Gum[△]. Also known as GUM ZANZIBAR[△]. A gum resin obtained from the stem of the plant *Hymenaca courbarii* of Zanzibar and East Africa. It is a member of the group of East African COPALS, but it differs from the regular COPALS in its ease of solubility in alcohol. Sp.gr. 1.062–1.068; m.p. 245°C.

Anise Oil[△]. The oil distilled from ANISE SEED[△]. Contains choline, (3-hydroxyethyl) triammonium hydroxide; $HOCH_2CH_2N(CH_3)_3OH$. Used in perfumes, soaps, and certain liqueurs; and in medicine as a carminative and expectorant.

Anise Seed[△]. The seeds of the annual plant *Pimpinella anisum*, grown in the Mediterranean countries and in India. Used as a flavoring material in the baking industry.

Annatto[△]. Also known as BIXINE[△], and, in West Africa, as ROCOU[△]. A salmon-colored dye made from the pulp of the seeds of the tree *Bixa orellana* of the West Indies and tropical America and Africa. Contains bixin, $C_{25}H_{30}O_4$, a dark-red, crystalline material, and bixol, a dark-green oily alcohol. Soluble in oils and in alcohol. It is a commercially important certified food color. In paste form, it is used to color such food products as butter, cheese, and margarine. It is also used as a wood stain and a silk dye.

AN Oils[NE]. (*HBMTN* p. 47). Only member of series now available is AN-10[NE]. BAKER CASTOR OIL CO.

Anozinc®. (*HBMTN* p. 47). Now a product of METAL & THERMIT CORP., successor to UNITED CHROMIUM, INC.

ANP®. Spectacles and lenses for welder's and chipper's goggles and helmets. EASTERN EQUIPMENT CO.

Anstac 2-M. Same as ANSTAC M but slower drying. Approved for use on PLEXIGLAS®. DEVCON CORP.

Anstac CA. A highly effective, easy-to-apply, clear anti-static and cleaning solution for the elimination of static and dust on cellulose acetate sheeting. It is fast drying, and easily applied by dipping, spraying, or with a cloth dampened in the solution. Used on cellulose acetate boxes, film and many other articles. DEVCON CORP.

Anstac CN. A highly effective, easy-to-apply, clear anti-static and cleaning solution for the elimination of static and dust on cellulose nitrate sheeting. It is fast drying, and easily applied by dipping, spraying, or with a cloth dampened in the solution. DEVCON CORP.

Anstac M. An anti-static and cleaning solution for acrylic plastics and polystyrene. It is a clear liquid that effectively removes gums and dirt and leaves a thin, transparent, and odorless film which prevents static accumulation and dust. Applied by spray or dip, or by wetting the article with a cloth dampened with the solution. Used by aircraft, optical, sign, novelty and other manufacturers. DEVCON CORP.

Anstac N. An anti-static and cleaning solution for NYLON filaments, sheeting, and molded articles. Easily applied by dipping or by wetting with a cloth dampened with the solution. This thin, transparent treatment quickly eliminates static accumulations and dust attraction. DEVCON CORP.

Anstac P. A highly effective, colorless, odorless, non-flammable solution for eliminating static on polyethylene film, tubing and molded articles. Eliminates or reduces blocking and "wildness", and simplifies winding, cutting, printing, wrapping, sewing and other operations which are troublesome and sometimes dangerous. Prevents dust attraction. For extrusion, this material is added to the water in the quench tank. DEVCON CORP.

Anstac P-1. Same as ANSTAC P except that it is very fast drying. Usually applied with a felt wick; does not interfere with regular production speeds. Only a microscopic amount is necessary to eliminate all static charges. DEVCON CORP.

Anstac V. A highly effective, clear anti-static and cleaning solution for preventing static accumulations and dust on rigid vinyl sheets, unsupported film, and molded products. Easily applied by spray, dip, or by a cloth or wick previously dampened with the solution. Prevents blocking and many other problems during cutting, winding, printing, and similar operations. Can be applied directly after the calender stack or extruder without interfering with machine speeds. DEVCON CORP.

Anthosine®. A line of water-soluble azo dyestuffs from which red barium-aluminum-hydrate lakes of high tinctorial value, good brightness, moderate light fastness, and very good fastness to water, oil, alcohol, and heat are prepared for use in coloring printing inks, paints, lacquers, rubber, and vinyl thermoplastics. GENERAL DYESTUFF CO.

AnthraAid. A filter aid, consisting principally of carbon, made from anthracite coal. Because of its chemical inertness, particularly its insolubility in alkalis, it can be used for almost any operation in which suspended solids are to be removed. ANTHRACITE EQUIPMENT CORP.

Anthracyanine®. A line of level-dyeing acid dyes for WOOL. They have good light fastness. GENERAL DYESTUFF CO.

Anthrafilt®. A filter medium made from selected Pennsylvania anthracite, low in ash, high in anthraxylon, low in friability, and carefully shaped and sized. *Uses:* In gravity filters, pressure filters, alkali and acid filters, revolving screen filters, sewage sludge beds, etc. ANTHRACITE EQUIPMENT CORP.

Anthrasol®. A group of water-soluble leuco esters of vat dyes for dyeing and printing COTTON, RAYON, SILK, WOOL and some of the newer synthetic fibers. GENERAL DYESTUFF CO.

Anti-Block QP[NE]. A non-ionic synthetic, anti-blocking agent, designed to eliminate takiness or blocking tendencies in polyvinyl acetate or similar textile resin formulations, and prevent all types of finishes from sticking on cans or frames. Resistant to high temps. COLLOIDS, INC.

Anti-Cementite. A patented anti-carburising compound, in paste and powdered forms, for the selective hardening of steel. KASENIT CO.

Anti-Foam 60[NE]. A silicone anti-foam emulsion designed specifically for the prevention or suppression of foam in aqueous systems. The low viscosity and ready dispersability of this agent, even in cold water, results in improved defoaming and anti-foaming action, eliminates difficulties in the preparation of working dilutions and permits easy handling in manufacturing operations. It is a gray-white liquid with a silicone solids conc. of 30%; wt. per gal. 8.3–8.5 lb.; sp.gr. 1.01–1.05; instantly dispersable, even in cold water. *Uses:* In adhesive mfg., pulp and paper mfg. and coating, textile finishing, latex processing and handling, leather finishing, fermentation processes, and metal reclaiming; and in adhesives, anti-freeze solutions, cutting oils, water-base paints, detergents and disinfectants. GENERAL ELECTRIC CO.

Antifoam AF. See ORCO ANTIFOAM AF[NE].

Anti Foam Extra S[NE]. A highly active defoaming agent. It is a water-dispersible product which is stable in alkaline and acid baths. Used for suppressing foam in operations such as textile finishing and printing. TEX-CHEM CO.

Antilepto[NE]. Leptosphira Pomona Bacterin. A killed culture of Leptospira pomona which is injected subcutaneously into adult cattle and calves to confer active immunity against Bovin Leptospiroses. MERCK SHARP & DOHME

Antioxidant 2246®. The proprietary name for 2,2'-methylene bis (4-methyl-6-tertiary butyl phenol). A powerful antioxidant for white or light-colored rubber products where minimum staining or discoloration is desired. AMERICAN CYANAMID CO.

Anti Seize[NE]. (*HBMTN* p. 50). No longer available. PARKER APPLIANCE CO.

Antistat[NE]. A water-soluble organic polyoxyethylene alkyl amino compound for use in eliminating the formation of static charges during the processing of synthetic fibers. Applied with conventional mill equipment. W. F. FANCOURT CO.

Antistatic Agent[NE] A, PCO, 8, 12, 20 *and* 27. (*Supp.* I p. 17). Now known as VICTOR ANTISTATIC AGENT[NE] A, PCO, 8, 12, 20 *and* 27. VICTOR CHEMICAL WORKS

Antistine®-Privine®. An antihistamine-vasoconstrictor consisting of 5% ANTISTINE® hydrochloride and 0.025% PRIVINE® hydrochloride in an isotonic aqueous solution buffered at a pH compatible with nasal fluids. Designed for prolonged relief of nasal congestion. CIBA PHARMACEUTICAL PRODUCTS INC.

Antrenyl®. An anticholinergic medicinal preparation for the relief of pain, spasm, and acidity in peptic ulcer and other gastro-intestinal disorders. Available in tablet and syrup forms.
CIBA PHARMACEUTICAL PRODUCTS INC.

Anusol®. A medicinal for the treatment of uncomplicated hemorrhoids; simple anorectal inflammations and irritations caused by, or associated with, proctitis, papillitis, or cryptitis. It may also be used pre- and post-operatively in hemorrhoidectomy and repair of fistula-in-ano as well as after incision of thrombosed or sclerosed anorectal veins. Supplied in the form of suppositories containing 2.25% bismuth subgallate, 1.75% bismuth resorcin compound, 3% Nicaraguan balsam (medicinal), 11% zinc oxide, 18% boric acid, and incorporated in a cacao butter ointment base.
WARNER-CHILCOTT LABORATORIES

A-O-K[NE]. A liquid metal polish.
CENTRAL O-B PRODUCTS CO.

Apamide®. An analgesic antipyretic composition having as its active ingredient N-acetyl-*p*-aminophenol.
AMES CO.

Apamide-Vess®. An effervescent analgesic-antipyretic composition containing N-acetyl-*p*-aminophenol and a citrate-carbonate effervescent base. AMES CO.

Apco. A flexible, shock-resistant, and adhesive neoprene protective paint which can be applied to metal, wood, or ceramic surfaces to provide a chemical-resistant rubber film. ADHESIVE PRODUCTS CORP.

Apco 360[NE]. A petroleum solvent consisting of 11.6% aromatics, 41.9% naphthenes, and 46.5% paraffins. Initial b.p., 305–315°F.; end point, 340–350°F.; flash point (TCC), 100°F. (min.); color, water-white; sp.gr. (60°F.), 0.779; odor, mild; viscosity (60°F.), 0.98 cps. *Use:* As a solvent for paints, varnishes, lacquers, enamels, and adhesives.
ANDERSON-PRICHARD OIL CORP.

AP Core and Mold Wash[NE]. A wash characterized by the following important properties: (1) radical color change upon drying, (2) high permeability to facilitate quick drying of the mold surface; (3) high refractory value—up to 3,150°F.—; and (4) miscible with alcohol in all portions, a property which is of value for applications requiring high penetration and fast dry. M. A. BELL CO.

Apco-Sol 42[NE]. (*HBMTN* p. 51). No longer available. ANDERSON-PRICHARD OIL CORP.

Apco Vaportite No. 100®. An anti-corrosion weathercoating for thermal insulation, roofs, structural steel, sheet metal, and masonry surfaces. It is a light mastic suitable for application by spraying with conventional heavy-duty equipment or pressure pot; but it can also be applied by brush, broom, or spreader.
ANDERSON-PRICHARD OIL CORP.

Apex[NE]. (*HBMTN* p. 53). No longer available.
BETHLEHEM STEEL CO.

Apex 417. An aluminum-magnesium base alloy characterized by its high strength, excellent dimensional stability, and excellent corrosion resistance and machinability. Composition: 0.10% (max.) copper, 0.15% (max.) silicon, 6.5–7.5% magnesium, 0.05% (max.) zinc, 0.20 (max.) iron, 0.10–0.25% manganese, 0.10–0.25% titanium, and the balance aluminum. Ultimate strength, 40,000 lb./sq.in.; Brinell hardness, 70; sp.gr. 2.62. *Uses:* For agricultural implements, cast furniture, outdoor and marine hardware, machine-tool equipment, etc. APEX SMELTING CO.

Apex Rich Hardeners. (*HBMTN* p. 53). No longer available. APEX SMELTING CO.

A-P-N®. An analgesic and anti-pyretic composition containing aspirin, N-acetyl-*p*-aminophenol, caffeine, and VITAMIN C. MILES LABORATORIES, INC.

Apolarthron. (*HBMTN* p. 53). No longer available. J. B. ROERIG & CO.

Apresoline®. A relatively safe, antihypertensive agent designed to reduce blood pressure and at the same time increase blood flow through the kidneys.
CIBA PHARMACEUTICAL PRODUCTS INC.

Apromal®. An analgesic antipyretic sedative which comprises N-acetyl-*p*-aminophenol and acetylcarbromal. AMES CO.

Aquacal®. A 45% aqueous dispersion of calcium stearate. It is a white, thixotropic paste, of neutral odor, and pH of 8.5–9.0. Wt., 7.4 lb./gal. It is readily dilutable to any concentration. *Uses:* In paper coatings; in stucco and cement paints; and in other applications where calcium stearate is indicated.
BEACON CHEMICAL INDUSTRIES, INC.

Aqualox®. The trademark for a line of flexographic inks and varnishes. INTERCHEMICAL CORP., PRINTING INK DIV.

Aquapel®. A series of alkylketene dimers for use as surface or internal sizing agents for paper, including containers and drinking-cup stock, soap labels, bag paper, boxboard, etc. It requires no alum, and can be applied in acid or alkaline conditions.
HERCULES POWDER CO.

Aquaprint®. The trademark for a line of resin-bonded pigment colors for printing and for dyeing.
INTERCHEMICAL CORP., TEXTILE COLORS DIV.

Aquaresin GB[NE]. (*HBMTN* p. 55). No longer available. GLYCO PRODUCTS CO.

Aquestrol®. The trademark for bulk estrogenic materials. S. B. PENICK & CO.

Aquet[NE]. A highly-effective liquid detergent that is especially useful for cleaning laboratory glassware and utensils. Available in 1 pt. polyethylene dispenser bottles and in 1 gal. containers. EMIL GREINER CO.

Arapahoe®. The trade name for an extensive line of organic chemicals, analytical reagents, organic compounds for liquid and plastic scintillation counting, solvents, Grignard reagents, intermediates, etc.
ARAPAHOE CHEMICALS, INC.

Aratron®. A miticide in the form of a wettable powder and as an emulsifiable solution of ARAMITE®. It is stable, and compatible with most commonly used spray materials. AMERICAN POTASH & CHEMICAL CORP.

Arcodol®. (*Supp.* I p. 19). No longer available.
SHARP & DOHME DIV., MERCK & CO.

Arco Flex®. Incorrectly listed as ARCO® FLEX (*HBMTN* p. 56). ARCO CO.

Arco Non-Shrinking Dum Dum Calk[NE]. A 100%-solids material for caulking around doors, flashings, wallboard joints, masonry joints and cracks, or similar openings that require sealing and where non-shrinking is required. Has good adhesion to masonry, glass, wood, and metal. It is a creamy white product prepared from a DUM DUM® vehicle, asbestos fibers, and inert pigments. Available in bulk and cartridge forms. ARCO CO.

Arcopel[NE]. A rubberized masonry paint of the "breathing" type. It is a decorative and water-repellent paint for exterior brick, concrete, stucco, and other masonry surfaces; interior basement walls; and asbestos-cement boards and shingles. Resists fungi and mildew, and alkalis. Contains titanium and zinc oxide pigments. ARCO CO.

Arco Rays®. Incorrectly listed as ARCO® RAYS (*HBMTN* p. 56). ARCO CO.

Arcotone[NE]. A washable, flat, alkyd finish for interior masonry, wood, metal, and wallboard surfaces. Particularly adaptable for ceilings where good light diffusion is desired. Available in white and several colors. Unpainted masonry should be primed with ARCOTONE ALKYD WALL PRIMER or ARCOTONE PVA SEALER. ARCO CO.

Arco Top®. Incorrectly listed as ARCO® TOP (*HBMTN* p. 56). ARCO CO.

Arco Zon®. Incorrectly listed as ARCO® ZON (*HBMTN* p. 56). ARCO CO.

Arcturus Red®. A yellowish-red pigment suitable for use in all types of printing inks, especially flexographic inks, and in plastics and rubber. Available in two grades: a non-resinated (GRADE CP 1270) and a resinated (GRADE CP 1275). SHERWIN-WILLIAMS CO.

Argyn®. (*HBMTN* p. 57). No longer available. ABBOTT LABORATORIES

Aridye®. The trademark for: (1) a line of resin-bonded pigment colors for printing and dyeing; and (2) pigmented dispersions for solution dyeing of viscose. INTERCHEMICAL CORP., TEXTILE COLORS DIV.

Arigen®. The trademark for a line of azoic COTTON dyes, in powder and solution forms. INTERCHEMICAL CORP., TEXTILE COLORS DIV.

Arilan[NE]. A line of metalized acid dyes for textiles. INTERCHEMICAL CORP., TEXTILE COLORS DIV.

Arilite[NE]. A line of fast-to-light direct dyes for COTTON and RAYON. INTERCHEMICAL CORP., TEXTILE COLORS DIV.

Aristoclean®. The trademark for a spirit hectograph. INTERCHEMICAL CORP., AULT & WIBORG CARBON & RIBBON DIV.

Aristocrat®. A heavy-duty asphalt shingle. CELOTEX CORP.

Aristocrat®. The trademark for a line of: (1) carbon paper; and (2) inked ribbons. INTERCHEMICAL CORP., AULT & WIBORG CARBON & RIBBON DIV.

Aristomaster®. The trademark for a spirit hectograph. INTERCHEMICAL CORP., AULT & WIBORG CARBON & RIBBON DIV.

Arlacel®. (*Supp.* I p. 20). This product is also mfg'd in England, Germany, and Canada, and the trademark is registered in these countries.
ATLAS POWDER CO.
HONEYWILL-ATLAS, LTD.
ATLAS-GOLDSCHMIDT G.M.B.H.
ATLAS POWDER CO., CANADA, LTD.

Armaflex®. A flexible foamed plastic thermal-insulation material for use on pipe and tubing in the temp. range of 32°–200°F. Available in ⅜" and ½" wall thicknesses, and from ½" to 3⅛" i.d. ARMSTRONG CORK CO.

Armaglas®. A glass-fiber thermal-insulation and duct-lining material available in various forms:

Duct linings for heating and air-conditioning systems, available in densities from ½ to 6 lb./cu.ft. ARMAGLAS PF DUCT INSULATION is uncoated; ARMAGLAS COATED DUCT INSULATION is the PF INSULATION coated with NEOPRENE rubber on one or both sides; ARMAGLAS VAPOR-SEAL DUCT INSULATION has a vapor barrier of asphalt and KRAFT paper on one surface; ARMAGLAS FLEXIBLE DUCT INSULATION (density, ½ to 1 lb./cu.ft.) is available either plain or with various types of coatings including NEOPRENE, laminated KRAFT paper, aluminum foil, and aluminum pigmented vinyl.

Boards with densities from 3¼ to 9 lb./cu.ft. used for insulation of walls, floors, ceilings, and roofs. ARMAGLAS PF INSULATION is not surface coated; ARMAGLAS AE BOARD and AE-F BOARD are coated with asphalt; and ARMAGLAS AR BOARD is coated on the top surface with asphalt, and a strong KRAFT paper is imbedded in the asphalt and lapped around the ends of the board.

Pipe coverings made from glass fiber bonded with resins. Types include lightweight blankets either plain or with wire mesh on one side; and molded sections, both uncoated and coated with vapor-barrier jackets. ARMSTRONG CORK CO.

Armalite[NE]. (Trademark registration pending). A rigid foamed plastic thermal-insulation material for use at temps. from −50° to +160°F. Although it weighs only 1.25 lb./cu.ft. it is exceptionally strong. Thermal conductivity, 0.24 B.t.u.-inch/hr.×sq.ft.×°F. Available as boards 12" × 36" in size and 2", 3", and 4" thick. ARMSTRONG CORK CO.

Armaturo Asbestos Tape[NE]. An asbestos electrical insulating tape for use in such units as electrical heaters and thermal operating devices. This tape is 1-inch wide, and has a nominal thickness of 0.015 inch. It can be used at temps. up to 500°F.
JOHNS-MANVILLE SALES CORP.

Armite® Anti-Seize Compound. (*Supp.* I p. 20). The name ARMITE® is now a registered trademark. ARMITE LABORATORIES

Armite® Joint-Seal Compound No. 411. (*Supp.* I p. 21). The name ARMITE® is now a registered trademark. ARMITE LABORATORIES

Armorhide. A textured plastic finish resembling leather and characterized by very high abrasion and chemical resistance. It is a polyvinyl chloride resin dispersion that is sprayed on metal surfaces and then fused at 350°F. Spray concentration is 60% solids; and a film of 5 mils can be applied with a single pass

of the spray gun. Available in 12 standard colors, and in other colors on special order. ARMORHIDE PRIMER and ARMORHIDE TEXTURE AGENT are also available. The latter, either clear or in color, is sprayed over ARMORHIDE coating, before baking, to produce a morocco grained leather effect.
JOHN L. ARMITAGE & CO.

Armorlokt[NE]. The trade name for a steel tape-armored electrical wire and cable.
UNITED STATES STEEL CORP.

Armstrong Adhesives[NE]. (*HBMTN* p. 64). Now known as ARMSTRONG EPOXY RESIN ADHESIVES[NE].
ARMSTRONG PRODUCTS CO.

Armstrong Epoxy Resin Adhesives[NE]. Formerly known as ARMSTRONG ADHESIVES[NE] (*HBMTN* p. 64).
ARMSTRONG PRODUCTS CO.

Armstrong F-1402 Wall Tile Cement[NE]. (Trademark registration pending). An adhesive that remains permanently resilient, shrinks less than 1% upon setting, remains workable as long as 4 to 6 hr., and does not change appreciably in consistency between temps. of 35° to 100°F. For use on both plastic and metal tile.
ARMSTRONG CORK CO.

Armstrong LT Cork Coverings. A line of pipe coverings fabricated from cut segments of corkboard cemented to a laminated asbestos and aluminum foil paper. Included in the line are:
 LT-THIRTY®. For use on dual temp. lines in air-conditioning systems and on chilled-water and other lines where service conditions are moderate. This covering is 0.8″ thick, for use where line temp. is 30°F. or above.
 LT-ZERO®. For cold lines at temps. as low as 0°F. It is 1½″ thick.
 LT-MINUS THIRTY®. Mfg'd in 1½″ thickness for pipe sizes up to 1¼″, in 2″ thickness for pipes up to 8″, and in 2¼″ thickness for pipes above 8″. For use at temps. to −30°F.
ARMSTRONG CORK CO.

Arosol. (*HBMTN* p. 65). No longer available; Company liquidated as of Oct. 1, 1955.
GENERAL DRUG CO.

Arresto-Moth®. The trademark for an insecticide.
PENNSYLVANIA SALT MFG. CO.

Arrolime[NE]. (*HBMTN* p. 66). No longer available.
HANSON-VAN WINKLE-MUNNING CO.

A. R. Roof Putty. See SPECIAL A. R. ROOF PUTTY[NE].

Arrow®. The trademark for a line of galvanized steel sheets.
UNITED STATES STEEL CORP.

"AR" Soybean Oil[NE]. An alkali-refined, bleached soybean oil especially manufactured for industrial use. It is low in free fatty acids and will not form a precipitate under severe kettle conditions. The maximal specifications are: acid no., 0.3; free fatty acids, 0.15%; Gardner color, 5; heat-bleach color (600°F.), 3. Physical and chemical data: iodine value (Wijs), 128–136; saponification value, 186–196; viscosity (Gardner-Holdt), A; refractive index at 25°C., 1.4728–1.4734; unsaponifiable matter, 0.1–1.5%. *Uses:* It is used extensively in the mfg. of protective coatings of all types because of its non-yellowing and color-retention properties. It is used particularly in alkyd resins for color and gloss retention, flexibility, elasticity, and durability.
A. E. STALEY, MFG. CO.

A-R Steel[NE]. See U.S.S.® A-R STEEL[NE].

Artistain[NE]. A series of quick-drying, non-grain raising stains for furniture.
SHERWIN-WILLIAMS CO.

Art Lace[NE]. Coating materials systems, either of nitrocellulose or synthetic-resin base, that produce a web or lace-like pattern.
MAAS & WALDSTEIN CO.

Art Weave®. A line of rubber sundries—fountain syringes and combination syringes—for sale by druggists.
ARMSTRONG CORK CO.

Asarinin△. See SESAMIN△.

Asbestoboard[NE]. (*HBMTN* p. 66). No longer available.
JOHNS-MANVILLE SALES CORP.

Asbesto® Fibrated. (*HBMTN* p. 66). Should have been listed as ABESTO® FIBRATED.
ABESTO MANUFACTURING CO.

Asbestol Filler[NE]. (*HBMTN* p. 66). No longer available.
WITCO CHEMICAL CO.

Asbesto® Liquid. (*HBMTN* p. 67). Should have been listed as ABESTO® LIQUID.
ABESTO MANUFACTURING CO.

Asbesto® Lumiclad®. (*HBMTN* p. 67). Should have been listed as ABESTO® LUMICLAD®.
ABESTO MANUFACTURING CO.

Asbestoment S[NE]. A powdered refractory material which is mixed with water and applied as an outer protective coating, ½″ to ⅜″ thick, over NIAGARITE asbestos felted tape. The NIAGARITE-ASBESTOMENT S combination is used as an electrical cable insulation and fireproofing coating. ASBESTOMENT S possesses high arch resistance, excellent workability and adhesive qualities. It is very low in alkalinity.
JOHNS-MANVILLE SALES CORP.

Asbestone®. (*HBMTN* p. 67). Now a product of NATIONAL GYPSUM CO., successor to ASBESTONE CORP.

Asbestone® "Economy 250". A lightweight roofing and siding material made of asbestos fibers and portland cement and corrugated under very high hydraulic pressure. It is used on barns, warehouses, garages, patios, houses, etc., and as a fencing material.
NATIONAL GYPSUM CO.

Asbestone® Standard "400". A heavy-duty, durable, roofing and siding made of asbestos fibers and portland cement. These natural cement-gray sheets come in a standard width of 42″ containing 10 corrugations, 4.2″ pitch. The overall depth of each sheet is 1½″. Standard lengths are 1′-0″ to 12′-0″ inclusive in 6″ increments. Thickness is approx. ⅜″ at crests and vales, and ⁵⁄₁₆″ at flanks. It is especially suited for industrial and commercial construction.
NATIONAL GYPSUM CO.

Asbesto® Quick-Setting Plastic. (*HBMTN* p. 67). Should have been listed as ABESTO® QUICK-SETTING PLASTIC.
ABESTO MANUFACTURING CO.

Asbestos△. The commercial name for a number of fibrous silicate minerals that are characterized by their heat-resistant and chemical-resistant properties. Today, most commercial asbestos is obtained principally from the mineral chrysotile, a hydrated silicate of magnesia, $2SiO_2 \cdot 3MgO \cdot 2H_2O$, which is mined primarily in Vermont and Arizona in the U.S.A., and in Quebec, Turkey, and Rhodesia. Chrysotile produces a strong, silky fiber that can be spun and woven into fabrics. ASBESTOS is made into a variety of important commercial products, including fabrics, paper, insulation board, insulating cements, etc. ASBESTOS fabrics are often woven mixed with some cotton. For brake linings and clutch facings ASBESTOS is woven with fine metallic wire. ASBESTOS wick, used for caulking, is made of strands of carded long asbestos fiber, twisted in the form of a soft rope. ASBESTOS felt, used for insulation, is made by saturating felted ASBESTOS with asphalt, synthetic rubber, or other binders. ASBESTOS shingles are generally made of a mixture of ASBESTOS fibers and Portland cement.

Asbesto® Sealer. (*HBMTN* p. 67). Should have been listed as ABESTO® SEALER.
ABESTO MANUFACTURING CO.

Asbesto® Semi Plastic. (*HBMTN* p. 67). Should have been listed as ABESTO® SEMI-PLASTIC.
ABESTO MANUFACTURING CO.

Asbestos Firetard Jacket[NR]. A jacketing for outdoor pipe insulation, consisting of one sheet of asphalt-saturated asbestos felt over which has been cemented an unsaturated felt for an outer surface. This material will not drip asphalt, carry flame, or support combustion. Furnished in rolls of 108 sq.ft., 32" wide, and weighing approx. 55 lb.
JOHNS-MANVILLE SALES CORP.

Asbesto-Sorb®. (*HBMTN* p. 67). No longer available.
PHILIP CAREY MFG. CO.

Asbestos Roll Fire-Felt®. A soft felt of asbestos fiber that may be bent, folded or wrapped around pipes and heated surfaces. Adaptable to a wide variety of uses because of its great flexibility and its insulating and heat-resisting properties. Especially adapted, in roll or strip form, for use in furnace expansion joints. Also used to wrap pipes where space does not permit the application of sectional insulation. Serviceable for temps. up to 1,000°F. Furnished in thicknesses of $3/32"$, $1/8"$, $3/16"$ and $1/4"$, in rolls, 36" wide, containing about 100 sq.ft.
JOHNS-MANVILLE SALES CORP.

Ascoloy. *See* GREEK ASCOLOY®.

Ascorbacaine. Medicinal capsules, each of which contains 250 mg. procaine HCl and 150 mg. ascorbic acid.
TESTAGAR & CO.

A-SEE®. (*Supp.* I p. 22). No longer available.
EASTERN REFRACTORIES CO.

Aseptisil®. A detergent for washing bottles. It has decided bactericidal properties.
PENNSYLVANIA SALT MFG. CO.

Aseptoforms®. (*HBMTN* p. 67). No longer available.
TRUSCON LABORATORIES

ASP®. A line of aluminum silicate pigments.
MINERALS & CHEMICALS CORP. OF AMERICA

Aspidosperma△. *Same As* QUEBRACHO△.

Astrol®. A line of level-dyeing acid blues of good light fastness. Designed for general use on WOOL.
GENERAL DYESTUFF CO.

Astrotone® BR. A synthetic fixative for perfumes. It is a macro-cyclic compound chemically similar to those found in the musk-like materials of natural origin. It is used in perfumes and colognes; face powders, suntan products, dusting powders, and other cosmetics; and industrial products.
RHODIA, INC.

Atarax®. A fast-acting tranquilizing medicinal, with minimum side effects. It calms emotionally tense individuals, yet leaves them mentally alive and alert.
J. B. ROERING & CO.

Atco GS-14[NR]. A 20% active emulsion of 2.2 dihydroxy dichloro diphenyl methane. It is an extremely effective fungicide. The product is compatible with all of the common wax-base water repellents and it can be applied in combination with these materials to produce water-repellent and mildew-resistant effects in a one bath application. It is supplied as a free-flowing emulsion which can be mixed with other finishing ingredients with a minimum of agitation and heat.
METRO-ATLANTIC INC.

Atco Rezsoft JA[NR]. A cationic softener for all textiles. It is particularly effective when used in combination with thermosetting resin formulations. It is a soft, free-flowing slurry which is readily soluble in warm water. It does not discolor whites, and the soft hand imparted by ATCO REZSOFT JA is durable to repeated laundering and dry cleaning.
METRO-ATLANTIC INC.

Atlantic Neutrazoic® Dyestuffs. A line of naphthol-salt colors that are stabilized through the use of compounds which develop almost instantaneously in a Riegel Flash-Acid Ager. These dyestuffs are available in standard strengths and azoic shades as solutions, double solutions, and powders. With these colors, a material can be printed, can dried, Riegel Flash-Acid aged, and swung into boxes at full speed, in one continuous operation.
ATLANTIC CHEMICAL CORP.

Atlas®. The trademark for a line of hydraulic or portland cements.
UNIVERSAL ATLAS CEMENT CO.

Atlas Chippewa®Can.. A mining steel analyzing 0.33% carbon, 0.60% manganese, 0.020% phosphorus, 0.020% sulfur, 0.25% silicon, 0.40% chromium, 3.00% nickel, and 0.25% molybdenum. It is a hollow shank steel designed especially for detachable bit shanks.
ATLAS STEELS LTD.

Atlas®Can, **CM.** A machinery steel that can be used without further heat treatment. Has a tensile strength of 90,000–105,000 lb./sq.in. in sections up to 10" in diam., which makes it especially suitable for shafts for steam shovels, gas engines, crushers, etc. Typical analysis, %: 0.40 carbon, 1.10 manganese, 0.030 phosphorus (max.), 0.080 sulfur (max.), 0.20 silicon, and 0.05 molybdenum.
ATLAS STEELS LTD.

Atlas Core Wash[NR]. A powdered, carbon-base core wash. It has high insulating qualities which afford excellent protection for the core or mold at an economical level. It can be used for all gray iron work. On very heavy castings, it is sometimes advisable to add a portion of high-grade PLUMBAGO.
M. A. BELL CO.

Atlas HW-7[NE]. A hot-work steel that supplements CRODI[®Can.] for tools and dies that will be subjected to temps. of 700°–1,100°F. and where high red hardness, hot strength and wear resistance are required. Typical analysis, %: 0.45 carbon, 0.75 manganese, 1.00 silicon, 5.00 chromium, 3.75 tungsten, 1.00 molybdenum, 0.50 vanadium, and 0.50 cobalt. *Uses:* For headers for rivets and bolts, trimmers, punches, coining dies, shear blades, forging-die inserts, tools for die casting and extrusion of aluminum and magnesium, shear blades, chipper knives, clutch dogs, headers, heavy-duty punches, etc. ATLAS STEELS LTD.

Atlas[®Can.] **KK.** *Also known as* SIOUX. A machinery steel designed especially for applications requiring a file-hard wearing surface with reasonable toughness or for parts that must have a Rockwell C hardness greater than 53 in sections up to about 6″ in thickness or diameter. Typical analysis, %: 1.10 carbon, 0.40 manganese, 0.030 phosphorus (max.), sulfur, 0.030 (max.), 0.20 silicon, 1.40 chromium, and 0.40 molybdenum. ATLAS STEELS LTD.

Atlas Nushank[NE]. A mining steel analyzing 0.43% carbon, 0.60% manganese, 0.020% phosphorus, 0.020% sulfur, 0.25% silicon, 0.40% chromium, 3.00% nickel, and 0.25% molybdenum. It is a hollow shank steel designed to supplement ATLAS CHIPPEWA[®Can.] for detachable bits where higher strength and stiffness is required. ATLAS STEELS LTD.

Atlasol Ag[NE]. A retarding agent, particularly useful with the new fast acid-type colors. It retards and levels these dyes on WOOL and WOOL-synthetic blends. When used with ammonia on over-dyed shades, it levels and brings the shade down without destroying brightness and without harshening the fibers.
ATLAS COLOR & CHEMICAL CO.

Atlas Ottawa[®Can.]. A mining steel analyzing 0.8% carbon, 0.25% manganese, 0.018% phosphorus, 0.018% sulfur and 0.15% silicon. It is a high quality, carbon hollow drill steel designed for conventional drilling in mines, quarries, and excavation projects. Can also be used as a detachable bit shank. ATLAS STEELS LTD.

Atlas Vibresist[®Can.]. A mining steel analyzing 0.95% carbon, 0.30% manganese, 0.020% phosphorus, 0.020% sulfur, 0.25% silicon, 1.00% chromium, and 0.25% molybdenum. It is a hollow drill steel designed to supplement ATLAS OTTAWA[®Can.] for conventional drilling where higher strength, stiffness and wear resistance are required. It is also suitable as a shank steel for tungsten carbide detachable bits. ATLAS STEELS LTD.

Atlox®. (*Supp.* I p. 22). This product is also mfg'd in England and Germany, and the trademark is also registered in these countries. ATLAS POWDER CO.
HONEYWILL-ATLAS, LTD.
ATLAS-GOLDSCHMIDT G.M.B.H.

Atmos®. (*HBMTN* p. 69). This product is also mfg'd in Canada, and the trademark is registered in that country. ATLAS POWDER CO.
ATLAS POWDER CO., CANADA, LTD.

Atmul®. (*Supp.* I p. 22). This product is also mfg'd in Canada, and the trademark is registered in that country. ATLAS POWDER CO.
ATLAS POWDER CO., CANADA, LTD.

Atom-Arc®. A line of iron powder, low-hydrogen electrodes for all-position welding of steels. Available in various alloy compositions. ALLOY RODS CO.

Atom-Ix. *See* BELL'S ATOM-IX.

Atophan®. An antiarthritic medicinal for symptomatic relief in gout, arthritis and certain rheumatoid disorders. It is a brand of cinchophen (phenyl cinchoninic acid), in tablet form.
WARNER-CHILCOTT LABORATORIES

Atpet®. (*Supp.* I p. 22). This product is also mfg'd in England, Germany, and Canada. Trademark is registered in Germany and Canada, but not in England. ATLAS POWDER CO.
HONEYWILL-ATLAS, LTD.
ATLAS-GOLDSCHMIDT G.M.B.H.
ATLAS POWDER CO., CANADA, LTD.

Atrinal®. (*Supp.* I p. 22). No longer available.
HOFFMANN-LA ROCHE INC.

Atrobar-M. Medicinal tablets, each of which contains 0.001 g. atropine and ⅛ g. phenobarbital.
TESTAGAR & CO.

Attaclay®. (*HBMTN* p. 70). Now mfg'd by MINERALS & CHEMICALS CORP. OF AMERICA, successor to ATTAPULGUS CLAY CO.

Attasol®. (*HBMTN* p. 70). Now mfg'd by MINERALS & CHEMICALS CORP. OF AMERICA, successor to ATTAPULGUS CLAY CO.

Attasorb®. A light-weight, free-flowing, highly adsorptive powder derived from the mineral attapulgite, a hydrated magnesium aluminum silicate. Available in three grades designated as HVM, RVM, and LVM (high, regular, and low volatile matter). All are ground to a fineness of 90–95% less than 10 microns; and are composed of agglomerates of needle-like particles, which accounts for the thixotropic properties of ATTASORB. *Uses:* As thixotropic thickeners and emulsion stabilizers in aqueous and organic systems; as anti-caking and anti-blocking agents and grinding aids; as mildly abrasive, highly adsorptive powders for use in cleaners and polishes; and as thixotropic thickeners for reinforced plastics.
MINERALS & CHEMICALS CORP. OF AMERICA

Auflex®. A synthetic resin finish.
INTERCHEMICAL CORP., FINISHES DIV.

Aulspar®. A spar varnish.
INTERCHEMICAL CORP., FINISHES DIV.

Aulta®. The trademark for a line of: (1) accounting, teletype and adding machine rolls; (2) carbon paper; (3) inked ribbons; and (4) stencils.
INTERCHEMICAL CORP.,
AULT & WIBORG CARBON & RIBBON DIV.

Aulta Clean®. The trademark for a spirit hectograph.
INTERCHEMICAL CORP.,
AULT & WIBORG CARBON & RIBBON DIV.

Aultalith®. A line of inked ribbons.
INTERCHEMICAL CORP.,
AULT & WIBORG CARBON & RIBBON DIV.

Aultamaster®. The trademark for a spirit hectograph.
INTERCHEMICAL CORP.,
AULT & WIBORG CARBON & RIBBON DIV.

Aulta Special®. The trademark for a line of inked ribbons. INTERCHEMICAL CORP., AULT & WIBORG CARBON & RIBBON DIV.

Aultone®. A pyroxylin-base lacquer. INTERCHEMICAL CORP., FINISHES DIV.

Aurocoloid[NE]. The trademark for Radio-Gold (Au-198) Colloid, for radioactive therapy. ABBOTT LABORATORIES

Auroseed®. The trademark for Radio-Gold (Au-198) wire enclosed in gold tubing, for radioactive therapy. ABBOTT LABORATORIES

Australian Pine Gum△. *Same as* SANDARAC△.

Auto-AIRMAT®. An automatic self-cleaning, mechanical dry-type lint filter or condenser. AMERICAN AIR FILTER CO.

A. V. S. Rust Preventive[NE]. A semi-solid petroleum product for preventing rust on iron and steel equipment. It dries after application, forming a semi-dry coating which will not crack or peel. It may be diluted with kerosene to any desired consistency for brush or spray application. KEYSTONE LUBRICATING CO.

A & W®. The trademark for: (1) a line of carbon paper; (2) duplicating fluid; and (3) inked ribbons. INTERCHEMICAL CORP., AULT & WIBORG CARBON & RIBBON DIV.

Award[NE]. An anti-slip floor finish for asphalt title, vinyl, rubber or linoleum surfaces. It leaves a clear, colorless film that is resistant to scuffing, water and dirt penetration in addition to providing anti-slip safety. FRANKLIN RESEARCH

Azo Acid®. The trademark for a group of acid dyes for WOOL. GENERAL DYESTUFF CO.

Azo Fuchsine®. A line of level-dyeing, bluish-red acid dyes of good light fastness, very good tinctorial value, and fair dischargeability. Designed for general use on WOOL. GENERAL DYESTUFF CO.

Azo Gantrisin®. A medicinal for the treatment of urinary tract infections. It consists of GANTRISIN®, a sulfonamide, and phenylazo-diamino-pyridine HCl, for relief of the distressing symptoms characteristic of urogenital infections. Available in tablet form. HOFFMANN-LA ROCHE INC.

Azolitmin△. *See* LITMUS△.

Azonamide. A medicinal, in tablet form, for the treatment of urinary tract infections. Each tablet contains 250 mg. sulfacetamide and 75 mg. 2,6-diamino-3-phenylazopyridine hydrochloride. G. F. HARVEY CO.

Azonine®. The trademark for a group of amino bases. GENERAL DYESTUFF CO.

Azo Phloxine®. A line of bright, very level-dyeing, red acid dyes of good light fastness and fair dischargeability. Designed for general use on WOOL. GENERAL DYESTUFF CO.

Azophor®. A group of stabilized diazotized amino bases for use in printing and dyeing cellulosic textiles. GENERAL DYESTUFF CO.

Azurine. *See* SULPHON AZURINE®.

B

B (in diamond)®. The trademark for a line of steel pipes, tubes, casings and couplings. UNITED STATES STEEL CORP.

Babassu Oil△. An oil, similar to coconut oil, obtained from the kernels of the nut of the palm tree *Attalea orbignya*, vast quantities of which grow in Brazil. The oil has a sp.gr. of 0.868, iodine value of 15, a saponification value of 246–250, and a m.p. of 22–26°C. It has a high lauric acid content, and is used as a substitute for coconut oil in the mfg. of soaps, as an edible oil, and as a source of lauric, capric, and myristic acids.

Baby Jumbo®. A hot water bottle for children. ARMSTRONG CORK CO.

Bacigro®. (*Supp.* I p. 24). This trademark is no longer the property of COMMERCIAL SOLVENTS CORP.

Bacillets®. Medicinal troches containing PENICILLIN G potassium and bacitracin in a lime-flavored, hard candy base. ABBOTT LABORATORIES

Bactine®. A pharmaceutical preparation possessing germicidal, fungicidal, and deodorizing properties. It contains, as active ingredients, alcohol, di-isobutyl cresoxy ethoxy ethyl dimethyl benzyl ammonium chloride, polyethylene glycol mono-iso-octyl phenyl ether, and chlorothymol. MILES LABORATORIES, INC.

Bagasse△. The residue from sugar cane after extraction of the juice. This residue has long cellulosic fibers that can be matted together and formed into a strong, tough, lightweight board that is used for wallboard, paneling, acoustical tile, etc.

Bahama Blues®. (*Supp.* I p. 24). Now a registered trademark. STANDARD ULTRAMARINE AND COLOR CO.

Baker Perfect®. The trademark for a galvanized 2-pont (flat point) barbed wire spaced 4″ apart. UNITED STATES STEEL CORP.

Baktak Gum[NE]. An envelope back-seam adhesive. STEIN, HALL & CO.

Balata△. A non-elastic rubber obtained principally from the tree *Manilkara bidentata* of Venezuela, Brazil, and the Guianas. This rubber is used as a substitute material for GUTTA PERCHA. It contains a higher percentage of gums and is more tacky than natural rubber. It can be vulcanized in the same manner as rubber. It is used principally for transmission and conveyor belts. For conveyor belts a heavy duck material is impregnated with a BALATA gum solution and vulcanized.

Balloon Cloth△. A plain-woven, cotton fabric used as a base material for the coated fabrics employed in making balloons and numerous industrial products.

Balsam of Peru△. *Same as* BLACK BALSAM△.

Balsa Wood△. The wood of the trees of the genus *Ochroma* that grow in the area from southern Mexico to Ecuador and in northern Brazil. It is the lightest of the commercial woods, characterized by good strength, stiffness and workability. The commercial BALSA WOOD is obtained principally from the tree *O. grandiflora* of Ecuador; BARRIOS BALSA, *O. concolor*, grown in southern Mexico, Guatemala and Honduras; LIMON BALSA is obtained from the tree *O. limonesis* of Costa Rica and Panama; Santa Marta Balsa is from the tree *O. obtusa* of Colombia; and Red Blasa is from the *O. velutina* trees that grow on the Pacific Coast of Central America. Balsa Wood, because of its peculiar cellular structure, is used as an insulating material for refrigeration systems; it is also used for life preservers, buoys, floats, paneling, vibration isolators, insulating partitions, etc.; Balsa sawdust is used as a lightweight filler for plastics.

Bamboosteel®. The trademark for a line of steel bars. United States Steel Co.

Banacoustic Blankets[NE]. Fireproof acoustical blankets made from mineral wool, felted and held between various types of binders, ranging from 1″ wire mesh on both sides to No. 12 mesh fly-screen wire on both sides. It is usually covered with flame-proofed Muslin or placed behind ornamental grilles.
Johns-Manville Sales Corp.

Bancroft Clay®. (*HBMTN* p. 74). No longer available. United Clay Mines Corp.

Barbasco. See Lonchocarpus[△].

Barbita®. (*HBMTN* p. 75). Now a registered trademark. Chicago Pharmacal Co.

Barbonate® Tablets. A medicinal used for the symptomatic management of gastrointestinal irritability, hyperacidity and spasm. Each tablet contains 0.5 g. dihydroxy aluminum aminoacetate, 8.0 phenobarbital, U.S.P., 0.16 mg. belladonna alkaloids.
Bristol Laboratories Inc.

Barca® 10. A heat and light stabilizer for vinyl resins. It is a liquid containing both barium and cadmium; it can be added to the batch at any stage of the mixing process; it is characterized by excellent heat and light resistance, low initial color, and long life; and it acts as a secondary plasticizer. It does not produce cloudiness or haze in either plastisols or mill-processed compounds. Deecy Products Co.

Bardamp. (*HBMTN* p. 75). No longer available.
Acorn Refining Co.

Baron®. A weed-killing composition containing Erbon [2-(2,4,5-trichlorophenoxy)ethyl-2,2-dichloropropionate]. Dow Chemical Co.

Bar-Ox®. A metal-protective system consisting of Bar-Ox Kromokote Primer 57 and Bar-Ox Metal Protective Finish. This paint system is composed of weather-resisting oils fortified with alkyd resins and inhibitive pigments, and combined into a durable finish coat of good gloss retention and color stability.
Truscon Laboratories

Basa®. A hammer with replaceable, interchangeable faces. Among the faces available are rawhide; plastic; copper; and Babbitt; and Basa®, a molded composition material. Greene, Tweed & Co.

Basalt[△]. A dense, hard, dark-brown to black igneous rock, consisting of feldspar and augite and frequently containing crystals of green olivine. It is extremely hard and has a sp. gr. of 2.87 to 3. Masses of Basalt are frequently found in columns or prisims. *Uses:* As a crushed stone material for paving; as a building stone; and as a raw material for the mfg. of rock wool.

BASF. The trade name for dyestuffs and other products of Badische Anilin-U. Soda-Fabrik AG.
Dist'd by Nova Chemical Corp.

Basolan. A line of acid colors for dyeing textiles.
Mfg'd by Badische Anilin-U. Soda-Fabrik AG.
Dist'd by Nova Chemical Corp.

Basopal NH Conc. Powder. A fat-free, foaming-type synthetic detergent for all kinds of textiles. It is a yellowish powder, readily soluble in water, stable against hardwater and metallic salts, acids and alkalis. Can be used in hot and cold baths; and has excellent fat- and dirt-dissolving power, and strong pigment-washing action. Nova Chemical Corp.

Bayflex®. The trademark for a line of baking lacquers. Interchemical Corp., Finishes Div.

Bayol® N-300. A highly refined mineral oil containing a selected emulsifier and designed for the control of tobacco suckers. It mixes readily with water to form a stable emulsion.
Esso Standard Oil Co.

B-B-L. Trade name of the Baltimore Biological Laboratory, Inc., for microbiological laboratory supplies and equipment including culture media, stains, miscellaneous chemicals pipetting machines, etc.
Baltimore Biological Laboratory, Inc.

Beachanese®. The trademark for a line of fabrics made wholly or partially of cellulose derivatives.
Celanese Corp. of America

Bear®. The trademark for line of smokeless rifle powder. Hercules Powder Co.

Beautafilm. A plastic yard good made of Velon®, available in a variety of patterns and colors.
Firestone Plastics Co.

Beautiflor®. A liquid floor wax consisting of solvent and waxes, made especially for use on wood and cork. It will remove dirt, crayon, lipstick, oil, tar, etc., and leaves a wax film which buffs to a rich luster. It can also be used on vinyl, print and inlaid linoleum, concrete and terrazzo, and leather tile.
S. C. Johnson & Son

Beautiflor Traffic Wax®. A solvent-dispersion-type buffing wax which cleans and waxes floors in one operation. It will remove dirt, oil, tar, grease and other stains not readily removed with soap and water. Recommended for maintenance of wood, cork, linoleum, sealed concrete and terrazzo.
S. C. Johnson & Son

Beautiflor Waxer®. A heavy-duty applicator for applying liquid polishing waxes. It has a heavily ribbed plastic head and comes with washable chenille pads and steel wool. It is also used for polishing.
S. C. Johnson & Son

Beauty-Lok[NE]. A series of interior finishes for wood panelling, etc. Can be tinted to obtain any effect.
Sherwin-Williams Co.

Beaver Clay[NE]. (*HBMTN* p. 78). No longer available. United Clay Mines Corp.

Becco®. A line of "active oxygen" chemicals, including the following:

HYDROGEN PEROXIDE. A clear, colorless liquid, available in three grades with 27.5%, 35.0% and 50.0% by wt. of H_2O_2, respectively. It is an oxidizing agent of very wide applicability. Its many commercial uses are based on its ability to bleach, to oxidize, to release gas, to form free radicals, and to kill micro-organisms. It is used as a bleaching agent for textiles, fur, straw, paper, pulp, wood, sugar, soap, oils, lecithin, etc.; an oxidizing agent in the mfg. of synthetic organic chemicals; an agent for modification of cellulose, starch, gums, and proteins; in metal finishing and plating operations; a developing agent for dyestuffs, blue prints, etc.; a foaming agent in mfg. of foam rubber, foam plastics, porous gypsum and other building materials; a free radical source to promote polymerization reactions, especially in emulsion polymerization; a disinfectant for the control of micro-organisms; and as a source of pure oxygen gas.

HYDROGEN PEROXIDE 90%. A clear, colorless liquid containing 90% by wt. of H_2O_2. It is an exceedingly powerful oxidizing agent; has high heat of decomposition and simultaneously releases large gas volumes. *Uses:* As an oxidizing agent in organic synthesis; in preparation of peracids; as a source of oxygen or high-temp. gases useful for propulsion purposes, etc.

HYDROGEN PEROXIDE, FORMULA F. A special grade of hydrogen peroxide designed for use in food processing. A clear, colorless liquid containing 35.0% by wt. of H_2O_2. Similar to other grades of hydrogen peroxide but is of exceptionally high purity; contains no organic material; neutral to methyl orange; free of heavy metals; total non-volatile content less than 50 ppm. *Uses:* For control of micro-organisms in food processing; for de-sugaring of egg products; as a replacement for yeast in baking; for bleaching food products; for sterilization of edible starch and gelatin.

HYDROGEN PEROXIDE, FORMULA D. A grade of hydrogen peroxide specifically designed for use by consumers who prepare and bottle dilute hydrogen peroxide solutions. Contains 35.0% by wt. of H_2O_2. It is of high purity and, when properly used, produces stable, dilute solutions which will meet U.S.P. XIV specifications.

UREA PEROXIDE. An anhydrous addition compound of urea with hydrogen peroxide. $CO(NH_2)_2 \cdot H_2O_2$; mol.wt. 84.059; white crystals or tablets; active oxygen, 16.0% by wt.; freely soluble in water and quite soluble in many alcohols; aqueous solutions have pH of about 2.6. *Uses:* As a starch modifier; oxidizer in hair-dyeing and cold-waving preparations; as topical disinfectant in the form of ointments or alcohol solution; hypo eliminator and blue print developer; source of water-free hydrogen peroxide, useful in preparing nonaqueous hydrogen peroxide solutions.

SODIUM CARBONATE PEROXIDE. An addition compound of hydrogen peroxide and sodium carbonate. $2Na_2CO_3 \cdot 3H_2O_2$; mol.wt. 348.050; white powder; active oxygen, 14.0% by wt.; solubility, 13.3 g. in 100 g. of water at 20°C. *Uses:* For modification of starch; in compounding denture cleaners, and detergents for household and laundry use.

SODIUM PYROPHOSPHATE PEROXIDE. An addition compound of hydrogen peroxide and sodium pyrophosphate. $Na_2P_4O_7 \cdot 2H_2O_2$; mol.wt. 349.95; white powder; active oxygen, 9.0% by wt.; solubility, 8.3 g. per 100 g. water at 20°C. *Uses:* For compounding denture cleaners, dentifrices, and detergents for household and laundry use.

SODIUM PERBORATE. A stable, mildly alkaline oxidizing agent. $NaBO_3 \cdot 4H_2O$; mol.wt. 153.875; white, crystalline powder; solubility, 3.4 g. in 100 g. water at 25°C. *Uses:* For dyestuff development; neutralizer in cold-wave preparations; compounding of detergents for household and laundry use; compounding of tooth powder, denture cleaners, etc.; mild bleaching agent for dry cleaning and laundry use.

CALCIUM PEROXIDE. A very stable peroxide that loses active oxygen only at elevated temps. Although nearly insoluble in water, an aqueous slurry hydrolyzes slowly, releasing hydrogen peroxide. CaO_2; mol.wt. 72.08; white to yellowish powder; active oxygen, 13.3% by wt. *Uses:* As a dough conditioner for the baking industry; for bleaching of oils; as a modifier of starches; in compounding medicated chewing gums, antacid drug preparations, etc.; in high-temp. oxidation reactions.

MAGNESIUM PEROXIDE. A very stable peroxide similar to CALCIUM PEROXIDE in its properties. MgO_2; mol.wt. 56.32; a yellowish-white powder supplied in 3 grades with 14.2%, 7.1% and 4.3%, respectively, of active oxygen by wt. Insoluble in water; soluble in acid solutions. *Uses:* In soapless shaving stick preparations; and in anti-fermentive, antacid and laxative medical preparations.

ZINC PEROXIDE. A very stable peroxide similar to CALCIUM PEROXIDE in its properties. ZnO_2; mol.wt. 97.38; a yellowish-white powder; active oxygen, 9.0% by wt.; insoluble in water; soluble in acid solutions. *Uses:* As a disinfectant and deodorant in dusting powders, ointments, etc.; as a vulcanizing agent; in high-temp. oxidation reactions.

POTASSIUM PERSULFATE. $K_2S_2O_8$; mol.wt. 270.326; active oxygen content, approx. 5.9% by wt.; white crystals; solubility in water, 5 g. per 100 g. water at 20°C. *Uses:* For modifying starch; as a promoter for emulsion polymerization reactions; as a flour maturing agent; as an oxidizing agent in organic synthesis; for defiberizing wet strength paper; for bleaching of soap; for desizing of textiles; for development of dyestuffs.

AMMONIUM PERSULFATE. A technical grade of ammonium persulfate containing up to 15% POTASSIUM PERSULFATE. White crystals; active oxygen content, 6.6% by wt.; very soluble in water. *Uses:* Same as for POTASSIUM PERSULFATE.

PERACETIC ACID. A stable solution of peracetic acid. CH_3COOOH; mol.wt. 76.034; active oxygen content, 8.6% by wt. A colorless liquid with a strong odor; similar to acetic acid in its solubility. *Uses:* For bleaching of ACETATE, NYLON, etc.; as a promoter for bulk and emulsion polymerization reactions; for modification of starch; in organic synthesis; for epoxidation, hydroxylation, and ring splitting; as a germicide and enzyme inactivator, especially in food processing; as an equipment sanitizing agent; in sanitizing washes for fruits, vegetables, seeds, grains, etc.

ACETYL PEROXIDE IN DIMETHYL PHTHALATE. A solution of a highly reactive organic peroxide in an inert solvent which makes possible a practical way to utilize the valuable properties of diacetyl peroxide, which is extremely difficult to handle in solid form because of its shock sensitivity. Composed of 25% by wt. of diacetyl peroxide and 75% dimethyl phthalate. Active oxygen, 3.4% by wt.; sp.gr. 1.18; soluble in most organic solvents. *Uses:* As a freely soluble catalyst for bulk polymerization; as an oxidizing agent in non-aqueous media; for preparation of dicarboxylic acids. FOOD MACHINERY & CHEMICAL CORP., BECCO CHEMICAL DIV.

Beclysyl®. A VITAMIN B preparation for parenteral administration. Available in aqueous solution or in isotonic sodium chloride solutions containing 5% or 10% dextrose. ABBOTT LABORATORIES

Beechwood®. (*Supp.* I p. 25). No longer available. HANSON-VAN WINKLE-MUNNING CO.

Beesix. A VITAMIN B$_6$ preparation, containing 100 mg. pyridoxine HCl per 10 cc. vial, or 1 mg. per 1 cc. ampul. TESTAGAR & CO.

Beeswax△. The wax formed and deposited by the honey bee, *Apis mellifica*. The new wax is light yellow in color, but it turns brown with age. It is composed principally of myricyl palmitate, $C_{15}H_{31}COO$-$C_{20}H_6$ (mol.wt. 621.80) and cerotic acid, $C_{25}H_{51}COOH$ (mol.wt. 396.70). Sp.gr. 0.965–0.969; m.p. 63°C. *Uses:* In the mfg. of polishes, candles, leather dressings, adhesives, cosmetics, etc.

Behr-Disker®. A sanding pad assembly. It is a pile pad mounted on a metal plate and used with paper and cloth abrasive discs for feather-edging and fine paint removal. BEHR-MANNING CO.

Bejectal®. An injectable solution of B complex vitamins. ABBOTT LABORATORIES

Belamine Fast Blue Bluc[NE]. A direct dyestuff for COTTON and RAYON having excellent all-around fastness. Especially recommended for the production of full shades or bright navies of excellent light and wash fastness when after-treated with urea-formaldehyde resin or urea-formaldehyde and copper complex. Shade change on after-treatment is very slight, and ACETATE and NYLON are unstained. BELLE CHEMICAL CO.

Belastraw®. A rayon yarn spun in an inflated form with straw-like qualities suitable for weaving, braiding, and knitting of fabrics for shoes, millinery, handbags, belts, placemats, etc. MAJESTIC RAYON CORP.

Belglyn® Tablets. A combination of the antacid, ALGLYN®, with 1/500 grain Belladonna alkaloids. Used for the treatment of peptic ulcer and hyperacidity. BRAYTEN PHARMACEUTICAL CO.

Belgrade Glue[NE]. (*HBMTN* p. 80). No longer available. HANSON-VAN WINKLE-MUNNING CO.

Bellefast Colors[NE]. A line of direct dyestuffs for COTTON and RAYON. Designed especially for the production of full shades having very good fastness to light and exceptional fastness to washing when after-treated with BELLEFIX CN or BELLEFIX VS, either alone or in conjunction with urea-formaldehyde resin. BELLE CHEMICAL CO.

Bellefix CN[NE] **and Bellefix VS**[NE]. Clear viscous solution of resinous condensation products for after-treatment of direct colors on COTTON and viscose to improve wash fastness. They can be employed as straight fixatives or in conjunction with urea-formaldehyde resin, and can be used on practically all dyeing and finishing machines. BELLE CHEMICAL CO.

Bellefix N-100[NE]. A cationic fixing agent for after-treatment of selected colors on NYLON to obtain extreme fastness to washings. BELLE CHEMICAL CO.

Bell's Atom-Ix. A fuel-oil additive that provides cleaner, more complete combustion of the fuel; keeps fire boxes, nozzles, tanks, fuel lines, and filter screens clean; reduces smoke and soot; prevents water and other impurities in the oil from settling out as sludge, and emulsifies sludge already present. It can be used with every type of petroleum heating fuel. BELL LABORATORY, INC.

Bemibrite®. A special goods for fabric bags. BEMIS BROTHERS BAG CO.

Bemis Ripp-Tabb®. A quick-opening means for pasted bags. BEMIS BROTHERS BAG CO.

Ben-A-Gel®. A highly purified magnesium montmorillonite used as a thickening, gelling, and emulsion stabilizing agent for water systems. Supplied as a soft, milky-white, granular powder of very fine ultimate particle size. Industrial particles of BEN-A-GEL, which have been fully hydrated and separated in aqueous dispersion, have an ultimate particle size of less than one micron. Sp.gr. 2.4; apparent density, about 4 lb./gal. When properly dispersed, as little as 1% of BEN-A-GEL will produce a stable body in commercial preparations which have originally shown poor viscosity stability. Such preparations can be thickened to a thixotropic gel by incorporating 2 to 2.5% BEN-A-GEL. Incorporating 5% or more of this agent yields unusually firm, solid gels that do not thin out upon heating. Hard settling of finely divided insoluble solids in aqueous systems is eliminated by the use of 1/4 of 1% of BEN-A-GEL. In concentrations of 1% or less, BEN-A-GEL acts as an excellent mechanical emulsion stabilizer for emulsions of oils or other immiscible organic liquids in water. It will not affect the efficiency of the normal types of surface-active agents used in these systems. Aqueous systems containing BEN-A-GEL are compatible with a range of polar organic liquids. *Uses:* In the mfg. of creams, lotions, oil-in-water emulsions, shampoos, emulsion paints, cleaners and polishes, textile finishes, ceramics, buffing compounds, etc. BAROID DIV., NATIONAL LEAD CO.

Bender Process[NE]. A process for sweetening light hydrocarbons by converting mercaptans to disulfides by oxidation. It is used for sweetening gasoline, kerosene, jet fuel, and No. 2 fuel. To effect sweetening, sulfur, a small amount of alkali, and air are added to the distillate and the mixture is passed over a catalyst consisting of pebbles impregnated with lead salts. Catalyst life is normally about 1 yr. before regeneration is required, although in some instances catalyst life is as long as 5 yr. Installation cost is about $10 to $20 per barrel per day throughput; chemical cost is about 0.5 cents per barrel. This process is offered by PETRECO under license by SINCLAIR REFINING CO.

Benne Oil△. *See* SESAME OIL△.

Bennett Clay[NE]. (*HBMTN* p. 81). No longer available. UNITED CLAY MINES CORP.

Ben Oil△. A colorless to yellow oil obtained from the seeds of the trees of the genus *Moringa*, especially *M. aptera, M. oleifera,* and *M. pterygosperma,* of

Arabia, Egypt, India and the Sudan. The seeds contain from 25–34% oil. Sp.gr. 0.898–0.902; saponification no. 179–187; iodine no. 72–113. *Uses:* In cosmetics; and as a lubricant for fine mechanisms.

Bentone®. The trademark for a class of products resulting from cation exchange reactions between organic bases and bentonite or its clay mineral component, montmorillonite, the individual products being identified by a number following the name BENTONE. BAROID DIV., NATIONAL LEAD CO.

Bentone® 18-C. A finely divided, cream-colored powder composed of an organic ammonium cation attached by an electrovalent linkage to the mineral montmorillonite as a result of a base-exchange reaction. The organic modification provides a material capable of swelling in and gelling organic systems. It is chemically inert and it will not react with the organic systems in which it gels. It is resistant to the action of dilute inorganic acids and alkalis, but prolonged contact with strong acids or alkalis may cause decomposition with reduction of gel strength. Dry BENTONE 18-C, due to its organophilic character, is not easily wetted with water. This provides the obvious advantage of increasing the water resistance of coatings in which it is included. Sp.gr. 1.85; bulking value, 15.4 lb./gal. BENTONE 18-C is a companion and supplementary product to BENTONE 34. The choice between these two products is governed by the systems in which they are used. BENTONE 18-C is properly applied to liquids and liquid mixtures containing high proportions of polar constituents. Liquids of these types include ketones, esters, CELLOSOLVES, epoxy and vinyl resin coating solvents, polyester solutions, lacquer solvents, certain industrial paint vehicles, chlorinated solvents, and low-mol.-wt. plasticizers. Whenever it is desired to gel aliphatic or aromatic hydrocarbons or other relatively non-polar materials, or mixtures which are primarily non-polar, BENTONE 34 rather than BENTONE 18-C should be used. BAROID DIV., NATIONAL LEAD CO.

Bentone® 34. A finely divided, light cream-colored powder which has the property of swelling in liquid organic systems. Chemically, it is dimethyldioctadecyl ammonium bentonite. Sp.gr. 1.80; bulking value, 15.0 lb./gal.; fineness, less than 5% on 200-mesh screen; water content, less than 3.0%. *Uses:* In the mfg. of paints, shoe stains, mastic compounds, printing inks, plastisols, organosols, plastigels, synthetic resin adhesives, drawing compounds, hydraulic fluids, etc. BAROID DIV., NATIONAL LEAD CO.

Bentone® 38. An organic derivative of a special magnesium montmorillonite that is used for thickening and gelling organic liquids. It produces thixotropic gels with high efficiency and very light color. Supplied as a fine, creamy-white powder; sp.gr. 1.80; bulking value, 15.0 lb./gal. BENTONE 38 is suitable for a wide range of polar and non-polar liquids. It provides uniform body, controlled flow and penetration, improved color uniformity and good particle suspension. It is especially useful where these properties are desired with minimum quantities of gelling agent, since it is extremely efficient. For best results, the BENTONE 38 powder should be pre-wetted with 25–40% of its weight of methyl or ethyl alcohol before incorporation. Typical applications where its efficiency and good color are desirable include paints, epoxy and polyester resins, cosmetics, waxes, and adhesives. BAROID DIV., NATIONAL LEAD CO.

Benzo Black®. A group of black direct dyes of commercial fastness for use on COTTON, RAYON, paper, and leather. GENERAL DYESTUFF CO.

Benzo Black Blue®. A group of blackish-blue direct dyes of commercial fastness for use on COTTON, RAYON, paper, and leather. GENERAL DYESTUFF CO.

Benzo Brown®. A group of brown direct dyes of commercial fastness for use on COTTON, RAYON, paper, and leather. GENERAL DYESTUFF CO.

Benzofix®. A group of direct dyes for use on COTTON and RAYON. They are considerably improved in light and washing fastness upon aftertreatment with BENZOFIX® CWF. GENERAL DYESTUFF CO.

Benzoform®. A group of direct dyes for use on COTTON and RAYON. They are considerably improved in wet fastness by aftertreatment with formaldehyde. Practically all of them have good-to-excellent dischargeability. GENERAL DYESTUFF CO.

Benzo Grey®. A group of gray direct dyes of commercial fastness for use on COTTON, RAYON, paper, and leather. GENERAL DYESTUFF CO.

Benzylets®. (*Supp.* I p. 26). No longer available. SHARP & DOHME DIV., MERCK & CO.

Be Square® Special Waxes. (*HBMTN* p. 83). Should have been listed as a registered trademark. BARECO WAX CO.

Besta-Monia[NE]. Incorrectly listed as BESTO-MONIA[NE]. (*Supp.* I p. 27). JOHNS-MANVILLE SALES CORP.

Besto-Monia[NE]. (*Supp.* I p. 27). Should have been listed as BESTA-MONIA[NE]. JOHNS-MANVILLE SALES CORP.

Be-Tabs[NE]. (*HBMTN* p. 83). No longer available. ABBOTT LABORATORIES

Betalco V-P 728. A nutritional supplement containing the alcohol-soluble factors from beet molasses, mineral factors from sugar-cane juice, tillandsia, and the specific lipoproteins of the chromatin of beef liver. VITAMIN PRODUCTS CO.

Betamene®. Lipotropic agents containing principally betaine, used in the treatment of fatty infiltration and cirrhosis of the liver, atherosclerosis, disturbed fat metabolism; and treatment of high blood cholesterol, myocardial infarction, and coronary sclerosis. INTERNATIONAL MINERALS & CHEMICAL CORP.

Beta® Protein. An industrial isolated soybean protein used in latex paints, paper coatings, emulsions, paper and insulating board. GLIDDEN CO.

Betaris V-P 727. A nutritional supplement containing the components of green beet leaf juice dehydrated in high vacuum to conserve the betaine content. VITAMIN PRODUCTS CO.

Betasyamine®. A composition of glycocyamine and a methylating agent such as betaine hydrate, in liquid form, useful in the treatment of muscular deficiencies. INTERNATIONAL MINERALS & CHEMICAL CORP.

Bethlehem Alloy Hollow Drill®. (*HBMTN* p. 84). Now known as BETHLEHEM SUPERALLOY HOLLOW DRILL®. BETHLEHEM STEEL CO.

Bethlehem Superalloy Hollow Drill®. Formerly known as BETHLEHEM ALLOY HOLLOW DRILL (*HBMTN* p. 84). BETHLEHEM STEEL CO.

Betula Oil△. *Also known as* SWEET BIRCH OIL△. An oil distilled from the steeped bark of sweet birch, *B. lenta*. It is a lighter volatile oil than BIRCH OIL, and contains methyl salicylate. *Uses:* As a flavoring agent; in perfumes; in cleaning solutions and soaps; and as a deodorant for organic compounds.

Bevidox®. Vitamin B_{12} available for parenteral or for oral administration. ABBOTT LABORATORIES

BHC△. 1,2,3,4,5,6-Hexachlorocyclohexane. Generally, but incorrectly, called benzene hexachloride. $C_{10}H_{14}N_2$; mol.wt. 290.85. Manufactured by the chlorination of benzene in the presence of ultraviolet light. The crude product is a grayish or brownish amorphous solid, with a very characteristic musty odor, which begins to melt at 65°C. and consists of a mixture of six chemically distinct isomers and one or more heptachlorocyclohexanes and octachlorocyclohexanes produced by additive chlorination of monochloro- and dichlorobenzenes formed during the reaction. The important isomers are:

  ALPHA. Crystalline material with a persistent acrid odor; m.p. 159–160°C.; insoluble in water; soluble in 22.8 parts of chloroform at 15°C., and in 15.4 parts of benzene at 18°C.; volatile with steam.

  BETA. Crystals with a m.p. of 309–310°C.; sublimes after melting; not volatile with steam; soluble in 775 parts of chloroform at 20°C., and 213 parts of benzene at 18°C.

  GAMMA. This is the insecticidal isomer of BHC, exhibiting extreme stomach poison action, persistent contact toxicity, and fumigant action against a wide variety of insects. Colorless crystals with a m.p. of 112–113°C.; practically insoluble in water; slightly soluble in petroleum oils; soluble in acetone, aromatic and chlorinated solvents. Present in an amount of about 12% in technical grades of BHC. The gamma isomer of 99% or higher purity has become an important insecticide under the name LINDANE.

  DELTA. Crystalline material with a m.p. of 138–139°C.

  EPSILON. Crystalline material with a m.p. of 219–220°C.

BHC has proved to be very valuable in the control of grasshoppers, cotton insects, wireworms, and other soil insects.

BHC Base. (*HBMTN* p. 84). No longer available. GENERAL CHEMICAL DIV., ALLIED CHEMICAL & DYE CORP.

Bibiru△. *Same as* GREENHEART△.

Bi-Cap®. Vitamin and mineral mixtures designed for the enrichment of flour, corn meal, rice, macaroni and noodles. These mixtures supply the THIAMINE (hydrochloride or mononitrate), RIBOFLAVIN, NIACIN and iron (as reduced iron or iron pyrophosphate), which are lost during the milling process. CHAS. PFIZER & CO.

Bicut®. *See* TANNATE.

Bidco®. Trademark for paper products, including toilet seat covers, paper napkins, and paper towels. The name BIDCO® is used for toilet seat covers made for Federal, State, County, and City Governments. CONSOLIDATED COVER CO.

Bilineurine△. *Same as* CHOLINE△.

Bilt-Rex[NE]. Long chain resins of a styrene-copolymer type, containing a number of carboxyl or acid anhydride groups. *Use:* For surface application to paper and paperboard. R. T. VANDERBILT CO.

Bilt-Wax[NE]. Paraffin and microcrystalline wax emulsions. *Use:* As wax sizes for paper and paperboard. R. T. VANDERBILT CO.

Bi-Met. An insulated furnace wall for high-temp. applications. It is designed to reduce the cost of suspended furnace enclosures. Consists of two different types of castings: (1) an alloy clip embedded in the tile where temps. are highest, and (2) a cast-iron support fastened to the alloy clip. BIGELOW-LIPTAK CORP.

Binder P-812[NE]. An acrylic binder for glass mats and molding preforms. Forms hard, tightly adhesive, colorless polymers that resist discoloration at usual drying and curing temp.—450°F.—for 5 min. Insoluble in styrene and other organic solvents; is flow resistant at high temp. ROHM & HAAS CO.

Biomydrin®. A nasal spray for treatment of upper respiratory tract involvements. It contains 0.05% thonzonium bromide, 0.1% neomycin sulfate, 0.005% gramicidin, 1.0% thonzylamine HCl, and 0.25% phenylephrine HCl. NEPERA CHEMICAL CO.

Biostat®. An antibiotic preparation used to inhibit or prevent the growth of micro-organisms in foods and thus effectively extend the storage life of fresh foods. CHAS. PFIZER & CO.

Biostat®-PA. A broad-spectrum antibiotic preparation, containing oxytetracycline, effective against many gram-positive and Gram-negative organisms, both aerobic and anaerobic. It is designed for specific application in commercial poultry processing. CHAS. PFIZER & CO.

Biost Tablets V-P 733. Nutritional tablets, each of which contains 150 mg. extract from fresh veal bone, and sea salt, milk solids, and cereal germ. VITAMIN PRODUCTS CO.

Biost V-P 730. A biologically active, fresh dehydrated veal bone, with cereal germ and raw sugar. This nutritional supplement is used in place of gelatin and other bodifiers in milk shakes, malted milks, fruit juices, ice cream, and other food products. VITAMIN PRODUCTS CO.

Birchcraft®. The trademark for a line of casual modern living room, dining room, bedroom, and occasional furniture including beds, tables, chairs, sofas, bureaus, chests, buffets, and closets. (Registration No. 627,835; Class 32; May 29, 1956). T. BAUMRITTER CO.

Birch Oil△. *Also known as* OIL OF WHITE BIRCH△. A yellowish, poisonous, viscous oil with a characteristic birch odor; obtained in the distillation of the tar that is produced in the destructive distillation of white birch wood. The oil contains phenols, cresol and xylenol, and has a sp.gr. of 0.956. Used in disinfectants and in pharmaceuticals. (*See also* BETULA OIL).

Bismarsen®. (*HBMTN* p. 85). No longer available.
ABBOTT LABORATORIES

Bismol®. (*HBMTN* p. 85). No longer available.
NATIONAL DRUG CO.

Bitter Ash△. *Same as* QUASSIA△.

Bitterwood△. *Same as* QUASSIA△.

Biwax. The trade name for a line of insulating compounds, waxes, and sealing compounds for the electrical and electronics industries. Available in various group classifications, including:
  1. The "X" group, a bituminous mineral-filled group used for average heat conductivity potting.
  2. The "500" group, a non-filled bituminous group of potting compounds used where heat is not involved.
  3. The "700" group, an impregnating group of wax compounds characterized by low viscosity and average melting point.
  4. The "800" group, which comprises the hard resinous materials used for sealing screw terminals and small recesses.
  5. The "1100" group, which includes those mineral-filled, low viscosity compounds used where small volumes are potted with average heat conductivity requirements.
  6. The "1300" group, a high-heat-conductive group of free-pouring characteristics, used for power transformer potting
  7. The "1600" group, a mineral-filled potting compound group of higher cold-flow requirements.
  8. The "2000" group, which is identified as a higher temp.-resistant group with a hard glossy surface.
  9. The "5900" group, an impregnating group of wax compounds characterized by low viscosity and accompanying high-melt-point and high-cold-flow characteristics.
  10. The "6600" group, a wax modification characterized by excellent electrical properties.
  11. The "7700" group, which is characterized by low temp. resistance coupled with high melting point.
BIWAX CORP.

Bixine△. *Same as* ANNATTO△.

B-K Bacili-Kil®. A preparation used for the prevention and treatment of germ diseases.
PENNSYLVANIA SALT MFG. CO.

B-Kleer®. A general-purpose industrial detergent composition for cleaning bottles, cans, and the like.
PENNSYLVANIA SALT MFG. CO.

Black Balsam△. *Also known as* BALSAM OF PERU△. A reddish-brown, viscous, aromatic liquid obtained from the bark of the tree *M. pereirae*, of El Salvador. *Uses:* In cough medicines; in skin ointments; as an extender for vanilla; and as a fixative for perfumes.

Blackbird®. A rubbermaker's grade of ground crude sulfur with 0.5% carbon black added.
OLIN MATHIESON CHEMICAL CORP.

Black Boy Resin△. An ACAROID RESIN in the form of small, hollow, yellow to reddish pieces, and obtained from the tree *X. preissii* of Western Australia.

Black Fish Oil△. A pale-yellow, waxy oil extracted from the pilot whale, Porpoise, or Blackfish, *Globicephala mela,* found off the North Atlantic Coast as far south as New Jersey, and the *G. ventricosa* of other seas. Sp.gr. 0.929; saponification no. 290; iodine no. 27. Used as a fine lubricant, in cutting oils, for treating leather, etc.

Black Magic®. Activated charcoals and purification equipment for domestic, commercial, industrial, and military adsorption problems. BARNEBEY-CHENEY CO.

Black Magic[NE]. A brand of charcoal.
CHARCOAL CORP. OF AMERICA

Black Magic®. (*HBMTN* p. 86). Now a registered trademark. OIL BASE, INC.

Black Magic "Supermix"®. A low-viscosity oil-base drilling fluid that can be weighted to extremely high weights yet remain stable under high temp. and pressure. It is delivered in bulk by tank truck or tank car from plants in Compton, Calif.; Houston, Odessa, and Alice, Texas; Duncan, Lafayette, and Harvey Louisiana; either unweighted—7.55 lb./gal.—or weighted with either limestone or barite to any desired weight up to 21.4 lb./gal. Also available in powdered form, in 44-lb. sacks. One sack mixed with oil, water and Chemical "V"®, makes one barrel of liquid "SUPERMIX". OIL BASE, INC.

Black Pearls®. (*HBMTN* p. 87). Should have been listed as a registered trademark.
GODFREY L. CABOT, INC.

Blancal®. (*HBMTN* p. 87). No longer available.
WITCO CHEMICAL CO.

Blanchardized®. (*Supp.* I p. 29). Formerly a product of UNITED STATES PLYWOOD CORP. Now mfg'd by BLANCHARD BRO. & LANE.

Blandets[NE]. (*Supp.* I p. 29). No longer available.
SHARP & DOHME DIV., MERCK & CO.

Bleachette® **Laundry Blue.** (*HBMTN* p. 88). No longer available. AMERICAN CYANAMID CO.

Bleachit I. A bleaching agent supplied as a stable white powder, easily soluble in water. The aqueous solutions, which react weakly alkaline shortly after being prepared, are stable. The action is due to its strong reducing power, whereby it combines with oxygen and forms bisulfite. Many natural colors are destroyed by reduction, others are converted into a more easily soluble form and then can easily be rinsed out of the goods. It also destroys hypochlorite residues and removes iron salts from the fiber.
NOVA CHEMICAL CORP.

Bleachit IA. A product for bleaching and brightening animal, vegetable, and synthetic fibers. It is supplied as a stable, yellowish powder, which is readily soluble in water. The aqueous, slightly opalescent solutions of BLEACHIT IA react alkaline shortly after they have been prepared, and have good stability. The effect of BLEACHIT IA is based upon its strong reducing properties and its power of imparting to the treated material the property of converting the ultra-violet rays of daylight into visible blue rays, and reflecting them in this form. As a result of this fluorescent effect, BLEACHIT IA gives a bleaching and brightening effect which is additional to, and surpasses, a mere reduction bleaching effect. In this manner, an exceptionally pure and brilliant white is achieved. NOVA CHEMICAL CORP.

Blem®. A blend of fine abrasives, lubricant and coloring matter in semipaste form designed for aiding in the restoration of scratched or marred furniture. It comes in two colors: light and dark. Will remove or improve white milk spots, water marks from wet glasses, and heat marks; and improve the appearance of burns and other stains caused by alcohol, nail polish, medicine, etc. S. C. JOHNSON & SON

Blend-Eze®. The trademark for a wetting agent. GERING PRODUCTS INC.

Blok-Joint^NE. A control joint used in erecting masonry walls, designed to allow for any slight wall movement resulting from contraction and other stresses, and to relieve the strain in the control joint section of the wall. The units are molded of rubber and have a "cross shape" design. CARTER-WATERS CORP.

Bloomingdale Adhesive FM-47. A heat-curing structural adhesive for bonding highly-stressed structural components. In many cases it can replace more expensive bonding devices such as rivets, spot welds, heat welds, etc. It forms high strength bonds with aluminum and magnesium alloys, iron, steel, copper, brass, plastic laminate, glass, ceramics, wood, leather, and fabrics. It is composed of thermoplastic and thermosetting ingredients in a solvent mixture with a boiling range of 78° to 110°C.; sp.gr. 0.982; solids content, 21%; storage life, indefinite. BLOOMINGDALE RUBBER CO.

Bloomingdale Adhesive FM-47 Film. A fibrous glass-supported film of BLOOMINGDALE ADHESIVE FM-47. It is used for the same purposes as FM-47, but is particularly useful in the mfg. of sandwich panels with honeycomb cores. BLOOMINGDALE RUBBER CO.

Blowing Agent No. 15^NE. (*HBMTN* p. 88). No longer available. SHERWIN-WILLIAMS CO.

Blu-Chek®. (*Supp.* I p. 29). No longer available. GENERAL CHEMICAL DIV., AMERICAN CHEMICAL & DYE CORP.

Blue Bonnet®. The trademark for a single-loop, wire bale tie annealed or galvanized. UNITED STATES STEEL CORP.

Blue Flag^NE. (*Formerly known as* VITRON® PIPE WRAP.) A glass fiber reinforcing, undergrown pipe wrap material. It is made of a special inert glass which is capable of withstanding the damaging effect of soil chemicals. L. O. F. GLASS FIBERS CO.

Blue Flash®. A line of reinforced resinoid abrasive wheels including disc-wheels for portable grinders, and cut-off wheels. Available in various diameters and various thicknesses, and with aluminum oxide and silicon carbide grits. BAY STATE ABRASIVE PRODUCTS CO.

Blue Foam Upholstery Cleaner. *See* PARKO® BLUE FOAM UPHOLSTERY CLEANER.

Blue Label. *See* AIRKEM® BLUE LABEL.

Blutene®. An antimenorrhagic agent consisting of tolonium chloride. Used in the treatment and prevention of abnormal uterine bleeding of functional origin. ABBOTT LABORATORIES

Boettger's Paper△. *See* ALKANET△.

Bolting Cloth△. A fine, strong SILK fabric made principally in France and Switzerland, for screening finely pulverized materials, such as flour. Available in various meshes.

Bombay Black®. Black japans for use on metal household appliances and other metal products. GLIDDEN CO.

Bomb-Lube. *See* SUPER KING BOMB-LUBE.

Bonadur^NE. A trade designation for a series of acid azo red pigments which are made by diazotizing and coupling a substituted toluidine sulfonic acid with beta-oxynaphthoic acid and forming a metallic salt with an appropriate metal compound. This class, ranging from light yellowish red to dark bluish red, are bright and tinctorially strong. They show varying degrees of bleed resistance to acid, alkali and paraffin. Although of relatively good light permanency, the BONADUR REDS are not especially recommended for exterior work. They are often used for shading other types, *e.g.* MOLYBDATE ORANGE, to produce inexpensive yellow shade reds in the range of toluidines. *Uses:* In inks for cartons, food wrappers and waxed papers; for coloring plastics, rubber, and floor coverings; and in metal-decorating lacquers and enamels. AMERICAN CYANAMID CO.

Bond #28. *See* CASPRO®.

Bondco. (*Supp.* I p. 30). Should have been listed as BONDCOR®. STEIN, HALL & CO.

Bondcor®. A series of starches for use in making corrugated board. [Listed incorrectly as BONDCO (*Supp.* I p. 30).] STEIN, HALL & CO.

Bonding Agents R-313, R-314, R-318, R-363, R-385, *and* **R-390.** *See* HELIX BONDING AGENTS.

Bondrez^NE. A series of textile printing binders for metallic powders and white prints. STEIN, HALL & CO.

Bondrite®. (*Supp.* I p. 31). Now a registered trademark. A product of UBS CHEMICAL CORP., successor to UNION BAY STATE CHEMICAL CO.

Bone Oil△. A chemically complex oil, with a disagreeable, pungent odor, obtained as a by-product in the destructive distillation of bones. It contains pyrroles, pyridene, nitrides, and aniline. Used in the formulation of sheep dips, disinfectants, fungicides, insecticides, etc.

Bordeaux Mixture△. A general protective fungicide for foliage application. Made by mixing 5 parts of copper sulfate, 5 parts of calcium oxide (quicklime) and 400 parts of water. This results in an aqueous suspension of a flocculent, blue, slowly-settling, amorphous precipitate which, on standing, tends to become crystalline and assume a purplish color. The precipitate consists of cupric hydroxide stabilized by adsorbed calcium sulfate. When freshly prepared,

BORDEAUX MIXTURE has high tenacity. Its use is limited to crop plants at stages of growth on which its phytotoxic action is small.

Borerkil®. An insecticidal paste, containing 2% gamma ester of BENZENE HEXACHLORIDE. Packed in 2-oz. tubes with applicator tip. *Use:* For injection into borer openings in plants, to control most borers in trees, shrubs and flowers. LETHELIN PRODUCTS CO.

Borneo Tallow△. *Also known as* GREEN BUTTER△. A hard, brittle, yellowish-green fat obtained from the seed nuts of trees of the family *Dipterocarpaceae* of Borneo, Java, Sumatra and Malaya. The kernels of the nuts contain up to 60% fat, which is used chiefly as a substitute for cocoa butter. Sp.gr. 0.852–0.860; saponification no. 185–200; iodine no. 29–38; m.p. 34°–39°C.; contains about 39% stearic acid, 38% oleic acid, 22% palmitic acid and 1.5% myristic acid.

Boscel[NE]. A line of urethane foam polymers and catalysts. The prepolymer and catalyst are mixed to form a foam. B. B. CHEMICAL CO.

Bosfilm®. A patching material for vinyl plastics. To repair vinyl plastic articles such as inflatable toys, wading pools, raincoats, shower curtains, etc., a piece of BOSFILM of the proper size is cemented over the area to be repaired with a fusing liquid. BOSFILM, itself, is a vinyl plastic, and resists water, oil, and heat.
B. B. CHEMICAL CO.

Boston®. The trademark for a steel casing.
UNITED STATES STEEL CORP.

Boston All-Purpose. An all-synthetic, oil-resistant hose for handling air, water, oil, and many other materials. It is reinforced with braided cotton yarn.
BOSTON WOVEN HOSE & RUBBER CO.

Boston Bay State. The trade name for: (1) an air hose for heavy construction work in mines, quarries, tunnels, or other jobs where large-size hose is used; and (2) a rubber-cotton duck elevator belt for moderately severe applications.
BOSTON WOVEN HOSE & RUBBER CO.

Boston Bull Dog. A rubber-and-cotton duck conveyor belt designed to withstand the most abusive conditions that frequent impact loadings of severely abrasive or heavy lump materials can inflict—ore, cement, coal, cork, granite, glass, coke and salt. Tensile strength of covers, 3,500–4,000 lb./sq.in.
BOSTON WOVEN HOSE & RUBBER CO.

Boston Bull Dog Acid Discharge. A rubber-fabric hose for conducting acids or chemicals under pressure or gravity in chemical plants, steel mills, tanneries, bleacheries, chemical plants, etc.
BOSTON WOVEN HOSE & RUBBER CO.

Boston Bull Dog Acid Suction. A rubber-fabric hose for handling acids and other chemicals by suction, gravity, or siphoning.
BOSTON WOVEN HOSE & RUBBER CO.

Boston Bull Dog Cord. A rubber- or NEOPRENE- and-cotton tire-cord fabric transmission belt for tough duty drives where installations have minimum take-up facilities. BOSTON WOVEN HOSE & RUBBER CO.

Boston Bull Dog Gold Edge. A natural rubber- or NEOPRENE-and-cotton duck transmission belt for severe requirements.
BOSTON WOVEN HOSE & RUBBER CO.

Boston Bull Dog Neoprene. A conveyor belt, similar to BOSTON BULL DOG except that the cover is made of NEOPRENE and, therefore, is resistant to petroleum-base oil. BOSTON WOVEN HOSE & RUBBER CO.

Boston Bull Dog Rotocord. A rubber-and-fabric conveyor belt particularly suited for high belt tensions encountered in long-center hauls. The carcass combines two plies of specially woven duck and tire-cord fabric to give both flexibility and strength. Tensile strength of covers, 3,500–4,000 lb./sq.in.
BOSTON WOVEN HOSE & RUBBER CO.

Boston Colliery King. A rubber-and-cotton duck conveyor belt designed for rugged underground service encountered in conveying bituminous and anthracite coal. Tensile strength of covers, 2,500–3,000 lb./sq.in.
BOSTON WOVEN HOSE & RUBBER CO.

Boston Concord Yellow Jack. An air hose for the severest air drill and pneumatic tool services in mines, quarries, and construction jobs. Max. working press varies from 250 lb./sq.in. for the 2½" hose to 2,000 lb./sq.in. for the ⅜" size.
BOSTON WOVEN HOSE & RUBBER CO.

Boston Cyclops. A rubber- or NEOPRENE-and-cotton duck transmission belt that is the same as BOSTON BULL DOG GOLD EDGE except that the edges are folded.
BOSTON WOVEN HOSE & RUBBER CO.

Boston Damascus. A line of conveyer and elevator belts for the handling of grain. Available with natural rubber covers and with vegetable-oil-resistant butyl rubber. Tensile strength of covers, 800–1,000 lb./sq.in. BOSTON WOVEN HOSE & RUBBER CO.

Boston Flameout. A line of fire-resistant conveyor belts with a NEOPRENE covering and with piles of COTTON, RAYON, or combinations of COTTON and NYLON. Tensile strength of covers, 2,500–3,000 lb./sq.in. BOSTON WOVEN HOSE & RUBBER CO.

Boston Flexer. A lightweight, high-strength transmission belt made from RAYON duck and natural rubber or NEOPRENE.
BOSTON WOVEN HOSE & RUBBER CO.

Boston Granger. A rubber-covered conveyor and elevator belt for grain where the service is not so severe as to require the higher quality BOSTON DAMASCUS. Tensile strength of covers, 800–1,000 lb./sq.in. BOSTON WOVEN HOSE & RUBBER CO.

Boston Haul King. A rubber-and-fabric conveyor belt for long-center, high unit tension conveyors where loading impact and abrasion are average. Tensile strength of covers, 2,500–3,000 lb./sq.in.
BOSTON WOVEN HOSE & RUBBER CO.

Boston Heat King. A line of conveyor belts for applications where extreme heat—up to 350°F.—is the primary problem. Available in various types of construction—COTTON and synthetic ducks, glass fabric, etc. BOSTON WOVEN HOSE & RUBBER CO.

Boston Herringbone. A conveyor belt with a ribbed top rubber cover, designed to counteract the tendency

of wet or round materials (sand, gravel, etc.) to wash back down the belt on steep inclines.
BOSTON WOVEN HOSE & RUBBER CO.

Boston High Load. A line of high-tensile-strength rubber-and-synthetic fabric conveyor belts for heavy loads on conveyors where impact loading of severely abrasive and heavy lump material is encountered. Tensile strength of covers, 3,500–4,000 lb./sq.in.
BOSTON WOVEN HOSE & RUBBER CO.

Boston Iron Clad. A rubber-and-cotton duck conveyor belt for average applications, especially for sand and small gravel, portable coal loaders, package conveyors, etc. Tensile strength of covers, 800–1,000 lb./sq.in. BOSTON WOVEN HOSE & RUBBER CO.

Boston Mucker. A superior type of rubber-cotton duck conveyor belt designed specifically for use on EIMCO and CONWAY MUCKERS and EUCLID and SIERRA LOADERS. BOSTON WOVEN HOSE & RUBBER CO.

Boston New Utah. Elevator belts, with rubber or NEOPRENE covers, for the most rugged service requirements, such as for mine and smelter use. Tensile strength of covers, 3,500–4,000 lb./sq.in.
BOSTON WOVEN HOSE & RUBBER CO.

Boston Perfection Cord. A rubber- or NEOPRENE- and-fabric transmission belt designed for use in the woodworking, oil, and sugar industries.
BOSTON WOVEN HOSE & RUBBER CO.

Boston Rough Top. A rubber-cotton duck conveyor belt for package conveyors, sorting conveyors, or wherever a non-skid surface is required. Tensile strength of cover, 3,000 lb./sq.in.
BOSTON WOVEN HOSE & RUBBER CO.

Boston Service. A rubber, 32 oz.-cotton duck elevator belt for light service such as for small sand and gravel plant applications. Tensile strength of covers, 800–900 lb./sq.in. BOSTON WOVEN HOSE & RUBBER CO.

Boston Silver King. A rubber-and-cotton duck conveyor belt for rugged service applications but where conditions are not severe enough to justify the use of BOSTON BULL DOG. Tensile strength of covers, 2,000–3,000 lb./sq.in. BOSTON WOVEN HOSE & RUBBER CO.

Boston Silver King Rotocord. A rubber-and-fabric conveyor belt for conditions where high abrasion resistance is not required, but where centers on head and tail pulleys are long and belt tensions are high. Tensile strength of covers, 2,500–3,000 lb./sq.in.
BOSTON WOVEN HOSE & RUBBER CO.

Boston Speed-Lite. A line of rubber- or NEOPRENE- and-cotton duck transmission and conveyor belts for use in the textile, woodworking, paper, canning and other industries. BOSTON WOVEN HOSE & RUBBER CO.

Boston Tiger. (1) A lightweight, flexible hose for general industrial and medium air service, available in sizes from 3/8" to 3/4" i.d.; and (2) a rubber-covered friction-surface conveyor belt for heavy-duty farm applications. It is made from 32 oz. duck. Friction between plies, 12–15 lb.
BOSTON WOVEN HOSE & RUBBER CO.

Boston Vim. An oil- and heat-resistant air hose for general contractors and industrial service, stationary and portable compressor lines, and pneumatic tool service. Available in sizes from 1/4" to 1 1/2" i.d.
BOSTON WOVEN HOSE & RUBBER CO.

Boston Warrior. A general-purpose industrial transmission belt, made from rubber and 32-oz. duck, for constant pull and speeds where shock and impact loads are not important factors.
BOSTON WOVEN HOSE & RUBBER CO.

Bouncing Bet[△]. *Same as* SAPONARIA[△].

Bovigen®. A triple antigen for immunizing cattle, sheep and goats against blackleg, malignant edema, and hemorrhagic septicemia. Contains the following organisms plus the soluble antigens produced during their growth: clostridium chauroei, clostridium septicum, and Pasteurella multocida.
MERCK SHARP & DOHME

Bowlette[NE]. A pleasantly scented cleaner for toilets and urinals. Free of corrosive fumes; shipped in unbreakable plastic bottles equipped with sponge spouts which serve as dispensers. BRULIN & CO.

Boyco®. The trademark for a line of farm and garden tools, wheelbarrows, baskets, bins, boxes, buckets, cans, canteens, cuspidors, drums, pails, pans, tanks, tubs, funnels, rubbish burners, sprinkling cans, water receptacles, mop wringers, stools, tub stands and orchard torches. UNITED STATES STEEL CORP.

Braddock Clay. (*HBMTN* p. 91). No longer available. UNITED CLAY MINES CORP.

Bradsol OR[NE]. A product designated for use in textile-finishing operations where the removal of oil and grease is desired. It removes oil and rust stains in the same operations without the use of oxalic acid or similar chemicals. When used on NYLON lace, it readily facilitates the removal of troublesome graphite.
ORIGINAL BRADFORD SOAP WORKS, INC.

Bradsyn J Softener[NE]. A substantive, cationic softener for use in textile-finishing operations where improved tear strength, better abrasion resistance, improved sensibility, and a pleasing hand are desired. It has excellent resistance to scorching, yellowing, and water spotting; good wash resistance, dry-cleaning resistance, and antistatic properties; and is compatible with most resins, starches, gums, and other finishing agents. ORIGINAL BRADFORD SOAP WORKS, INC.

Bradsyn Lining Softener[NE]. A softener developed primarily for finishing synthetic piece goods. It imparts a silky smoothness and full-bodied drape to the fabric without affecting color values or wearing qualities. It does not discolor, deteriorate, or develop odor on aging. ORIGINAL BRADFORD SOAP WORKS, INC.

Bradsyn N Softener[NE]. A nonionic finishing agent, compatible with most chemicals used in textile-finishing operations. It has excellent resistance to scorching, yellowing and water spotting, and negligible effect on dye shades. It dissolves readily in 5 times its weight of warm water, and the solution can be diluted to any desired concentration.
ORIGINAL BRADFORD SOAP WORKS, INC.

Bradsyn Plasticizer A-2[NE]. A water-soluble product for use in many textile-finishing operations and especially in resin finishes where it plasticizes the action of the resin and gives improved tear strength.

It has excellent resistance to yellowing and water spotting. Used on natural and synthetic fibers to improve hand, reduce soil pick-up, reduce static, and plasticize the harshening effect of other finishing agents. ORIGINAL BRADFORD SOAP WORKS, INC.

Bradsyn Softener S[NR]. A softening agent for use in finishing fine COTTON fabrics. It does not yellow the goods on aging; has excellent resistance to scorching and water spotting; imparts a desirable luster; and provides inter-fiber lubrication to give a pleasing hand to the finished goods.
ORIGINAL BRADFORD SOAP WORKS, INC.

Bradtone B[NR]. A substantive, cationic compound designed to aid the final finish on woolens and worsteds. It is attracted to and adheres to the fibers, forming a protective film which resists spotting from soils, both liquid and solid; reduces static that may be developed; acts as an inter-fiber lubricant which aids in increasing the tensile strength of the fibers while imparting a pleasing hand to the finished goods; and acts as a lubricant for many mechanical operations of the finishing process. It has excellent stability on aging; resistance to yellowing, water spotting, soil spotting, washing, and dry cleaning; and improves the tear and tensile strength.
ORIGINAL BRADFORD SOAP WORKS, INC.

Bramblcide® 4 *and* **Bramblcide® 5.** (*Supp.* I pp. 31–32). The name BRAMBLCIDE® should have been listed as a registered trademark.
THOMPSON CHEMICALS CORP.

Bramble-Weedicide® 4, 5, *and* **32.** (*Supp.* I p. 32). The name BRAMBLE-WEEDICIDE® should have been listed as a registered trademark.
THOMPSON CHEMICALS INC.

Braze[NR]. A bonding agent consisting of halogenated rubber derivations and selected modifiers in a solvent solution. *Use:* Applied as a thin coating to the surface of properly prepared steel and other metals, it produces a strong bond to adjacent natural rubber, GR-S or NEOPRENE when the assembly is vulcanized under pressure. R. T. VANDERBILT CO.

Braze Cover Cements[NR]. Agents for bonding elastomers to metals. They are dispersions of specially compounded elastomers in appropriate solvents. There are three types, specific for use with elastomers designated by their names. *Uses:* BRAZE COVER CEMENTS are applied over BRAZE BONDING AGENT to facilitate factory handling, and to improve bond strength and uniformity of adhesion after vulcanization. A single coat over the bonding agent produces the desired results. When bonding to brass, the BRAZE COVER CEMENT alone produces the desired results. R. T. VANDERBILT CO.

Brazil Wax△. *Same as* CARNAUBA WAX△.

Brij®. (*HBMTN* p. 92). This product is also mfg'd in England and Germany. The trademark is registered in Germany but not in England.
ATLAS POWDER CO.
HONEYWILL-ATLAS, LTD.
ATLAS-GOLDSCHMIDT G.M.B.H.

Brilliant Toning Red[NR]. A series of red color pigments with good heat resistance, good light resistance, and non-bleeding properties. Available in dry form and dispersed in various organic vehicles. Grades: resinated and non-resinated; yellowish-red and medium red shades. Recommended for paints, enamels, printing inks, plastics, rubber, etc.
SHERWIN-WILLIAMS CO.

Briskeat®. A line of flexible electric heating tapes. The tapes are supplied complete with lead wires, made of heat-resistant nickel-clad coppered wire, that are silver soldered to the heater. Available in the following styles:
  STANDARD INSULATED. Made of stranded resistance wires covered with 2 layers of braided fiber glass insulation, with a connecting lead wire. For continuous operation at about 800°–900°F., and intermittent operation at about 1,000°F.
  HEAVY INSULATED. Same as the STANDARD INSULATED but with a heavy glass, braided yarn covering, for added insulation.
  WIDE HEAVY INSULATED. For widths greater than 1 inch. In this style, STANDARD INSULATED tapes are enclosed inside two layers of heavy fiber glass cloth. Available in widths of 1¾″, 2½″, and 3¼″.
  SILICONE RUBBER EMBEDDED. These tapes can be used, at temps. up to 450°F., in presence of moisture, deteriorating chemicals and gases, etc.
BRISCOE MFG. CO.

Bristalin®. A palatable raspberry-flavored cough syrup for the relief of coughs of allergic or non-allergic origin. Each oz. contains 0.075 g. BRISTAMIN® dihydrogen citrate, 0.06 cc. fluid extract of ipecac; 0.347 g. ammonium chloride; 0.322 g. sodium citrate; 0.0033 g. menthol. BRISTOL LABORATORIES INC.

Bristamin® APC Tablets. A medicinal for the relief of muscular aches and pains, coryza, headache, and fever of the common cold. Each tablet contains 25 mg. BRISTAMIN®, 210 mg. acetylsalicylic acid, 150 mg. phenacetin, and 30 mg. caffeine.
BRISTOL LABORATORIES INC.

Bristamin® Tablets. The dihydrogen citrate salt of phenyltoloxamine, in the form of 50 mg. tablets. *Use:* As an antihistaminic medicinal for relief from allergies due to dust, pollen, drugs, foods, bacteria, and molds.
BRISTOL LABORATORIES INC.

Bristapen® 200. Sugar-coated tablets, each of which contains 200 mg. (200,000 units) procain PENICILLIN G, 25 mg. BRISTAMIN® dihydrogen citrate, 150 mg. acetylsalicylic acid, 120 mg. phenacetin, and 30 mg. caffeine. *Use:* As a medicine for control of the symptoms of the common cold, and prevention and treatment of secondary infections of the upper respiratory tract. BRISTOL LABORATORIES INC.

Britone Red[NR]. The resinated variety of GRAPHIC RED[NR]. SHERWIN-WILLIAMS CO.

Bromex[NR]. A soil fumigant for the control of most nematodes and soil insects. It can also be used for killing many fungi and most weed seeds when used with gas-tight covers such as LARVACOVERS. It is a solution of methyl bromide (26% by wt.). For soil application, it is injected 5 to 8 in. beneath the soil surface with a FUMIGUN or similar injector.
LARVACIDE PRODUCTS, INC.

Brominol®. A brominated olive oil used as a weighting agent to stabilize the flavoring oils and cloud in citrus flavored emulsions.
ABBOTT LABORATORIES

Bromvegol®. The trademark for food-processing products, in particular Oil Bromated Apricot Kernal.
S. B. PENICK & CO.

Bronco®. (*HBMTN* p. 93). Now a registered trademark.
METALS & CONTROLS CORP., GENERAL PLATE DIV.

Bronze-Arc C®. A phosphor bronze, all-position welding electrode for making high-strength, porosity-free welds in bronze, brass, and copper, and for joining dissimilar metals. Tensile strength, 50,000–65,000 lb./sq.in.; yield strength, 30,000–37,000 lb./sq.in.; hardness, Rockwell B, 72–78.
ALLOY RODS CO.

Bronze-Arc Mn®. A manganese bronze electrode for the welding of manganese bronze. Tensile strength of weld deposit, 65,000 lb./sq.in.; elongation (% in 2″), 41.0%.
ALLOY RODS CO.

Broomcorn△. A plant of the sorghum family, *Holcus sorghum*, grown in the Southwest, in Illinois and Kansas, and in Argentina and Hungary. The fibers of the plant are yellow in color, and when dry are coarse and hard. Used for making brushes and brooms, and for the stems of artificial flowers.

Brown Label® No-Buff®. A water-emulsion floor finish containing waxes, resins and emulsifiers for use in office buildings, etc., where floors are subjected to heavy traffic. Although self-polishing, it possesses buffing characteristics which aid in maintenance and eliminate frequent rewaxing. Can be used on all resilient type flooring—asphalt, vinyl, rubber, etc.,— and on properly sealed wood floors.
S. C. JOHNSON & SON

Bruisewort△. Same as SAPONARIA△.

Brulin Bright[NB]. A highly slip resistant floor finish. Contains no wax, but is used like a wax. Produces a very hard finish, eliminating the need for polishing. Approved by Underwriters Laboratories and Rubber Manufacturers Assoc.
BRULIN & CO.

Brulinsolv[NB]. A grease- and oil-emulsifying concentrate for cleaning engines, aircraft exteriors, and floors. Meets government specifications. Non-toxic and non-irritating to the skin.
BRULIN & CO.

Brunswick Clay[NB]. (*HBMTN* p. 94). No longer available.
UNITED CLAY MINES CORP.

Bry-Cad. A bright cadmium plating process that is operated at a high cathode efficiency and over a wide current density range with very little "gassing" and no spray. Complicated parts containing deep recesses or of intricate shape can be plated uniformly bright with this process. The plating solution used with the process is prepared by dissolving standard BRY-CAD SALT #153 in water and then adding a proper quantity of liquid UDYLITE BRIGHTENER #153. The quantities used depend on the type of operation: hand-operated tanks, semi-automatic or full-automatic machines, barrel plating, etc.
UDYLITE CORP.

Brytene®. A non-toxic, non-flammable protective wax coating for fruits and vegetables. It improves the appearance, retards shrinkage, and preserves the quality.
FRANKLIN RESEARCH CO.

B.S.P. Tablets[NB]. Brown, sugar-coated medicinal tablets, each of which contains 60 mg. bile salts comp., 60 mg. papain, 15 mg. cascara sagrada ext., 30 mg. phenolphthalein, 1.5 mg. oleoresin capsicum.
AMERICAN PHARMACEUTICAL CO.

BSZ-300® Process. (*Supp.* I p. 33). No longer available.
HANSON-VAN WINKLE-MUNNING CO.

B-Tex[NB]. A polyethoxy alkylarylsulfonate designed as a penetrant and wetting agent for the bleaching of textiles with peroxide. It contains a water-soluble, fluorescent whitening agent which exhausts on the fiber during the bleaching operation, producing a pure bluish white.
W. F. FANCOURT CO.

Buck Buffer®. (*Supp.* I p. 33). Now a registered trademark.
SIGMA CHEMICAL CO.

Buckram△. A coarse, plain-woven, open fabric made of COTTON or LINEN. It is heavily sized with gums or water-resistant resins. Used as a stiffening material, for bookbindings, shoe inner soles, and interlinings for leather goods.

Buderma Ointment®. (*HBMTN* p. 95). No longer available.
BUCKMAN LABORATORIES, INC.

Budget[NB]. (Trademark registration pending). A felt-base wall-covering material.
ARMSTRONG CORK CO.

Buffalo®. The trademark for a series of acid black dyes used for dyeing wool.
NATIONAL ANILINE DIV., ALLIED CHEMICAL & DYE CORP.

Buffem®. An abrasive paper coated with a natural flint quartz abrasive. Generally used for buffing leather.
BEHR-MANNING CO.

Bufrite®. An amorphous alumina, in powder form, used for buffing operations. Available in 3 grades: hard, medium, and soft, designed as R-31, R-32, and R-33, respectively.
GENERAL ABRASIVE CO.

Bull Dog. See BOSTON BULL DOG.

Bull Dog Acid Discharge. See BOSTON BULL DOG ACID DISCHARGE.

Bull Dog Acid Suction. See BOSTON BULL DOG ACID SUCTION.

Bull Dog Cord. See BOSTON BULL DOG CORD.

Bull Dog Friction Tape. A black tape for electrical repairs, and for wrapping bat handles, hockey sticks, tennis racquets, etc.
BOSTON WOVEN HOSE & RUBBER CO.

Bull Dog Gold Edge. See BOSTON BULL DOG GOLD EDGE.

Bull Dog Neoprene. See BOSTON BULL DOG NEOPRENE.

Bull Dog Plastic Electrical Tape. A thin, highly-adhesive tape that is resistant to abrasion, weather, water, oils, and corrosive chemicals. Dielectric strength, 7000 volts.
BOSTON WOVEN HOSE & RUBBER CO.

Bull Dog Rotocord. *See* Boston Bull Dog Rotocord.

Bull Dog Splicing Compound. A splicing tape that self-vulcanizes into a solid, watertight joint. It is waterproof and has high electrical resistance.
Boston Woven Hose & Rubber Co.

Bull Frog® Saf-T-Klenz. A cleaner for swimming pools, shower rooms, wash rooms, and steam rooms. It removes unsightly discolorations, reduces the hazard of slippery floors, destroys the cause of many obnoxious odors, and minimizes the conditions that breed and spread infectious germs. It is a powdered material, containing no soap or caustic, that is sprinkled on the surface and allowed to remain for several minutes before it is rubbed over the surface and finally rinsed away. It can be used on copper, brass, or bronze, but is not recommended for painted surfaces or enameled metal-base fixtures.
Berman Chemical Co.

Bullseye®. Smokeless powder used for shotguns, rifles, and small arms. Hercules Powder Co.

Bumintest®. A diagnostic composition used for testing the presence of albumin in urine. Ames Co.

Bunting△. A plain-woven, lightweight, worsted fabric used for making flags, for box linings, and for other industrial uses.

Bunting®. (*HBMTN* p. 96). The name Bunting should have been listed as a registered trade name of the Bunting Brass & Bronze Co. In addition to the line of copper-, tin-, and lead-base bearing alloys listed, the name Bunting is applied to bushings, bearings, bars, and special parts of cast bronze and powdered metals. Bunting Brass & Bronze Co.

Buramine®. Synthetic organic chemicals which are alkylated acid amides and substances derived therefrom. Pennsylvania Chemical Co.

Burlap△. A coarse, heavy cloth made of plain-woven Jute, or Jute-like fibers, and used as a wrapping material for bulky articles, for commercial bags, for upholstery linings, as a backing fabric for linoleum, etc.

Burnek 452ᴺᴱ. A burnishing compound for steel, cast iron, wrought iron and other ferrous alloys. It is readily soluble; non-foaming; free-rinsing; and minimizes rust development. It is not designed for use on aluminum, zinc, or similar light metals.
Wyandotte Chemicals Corp., J. B. Ford Div.

Burnishing Compound No. 321ᴺᴱ. A soap-type compound for burnishing non-ferrous metals.
Wyandotte Chemicals Corp., J. B. Ford Div.

Burnok®. A line of thixotropic paint and enamel vehicles that make possible non-drip jelled paints. Available in the following types and grades:

Burnok No.	Type	Type of oil
3540	Medium oil alkyd—regular	Soya
3741	Medium oil alkyd—low odor	Soya
3840	Medium oil alkyd—odorless	Soya
3929	Pure long oil alkyd	Soya-castor
4040	Long oil alkyd—regular	Soya
4041	Long oil alkyd—odorless	Soya
4042	Long oil alkyd—low odor	Soya
5040	Bodied oil	Modified soya
5041	Bodied oil	Pure linseed

T. F. Washburn Co.

Burns Valve®. A valve for use in conjunction with an automatic inhalational apparatus, which cycles, permitting positive pressure buildup to a determined point, following which the pressure is cut off and exhalation is accomplished by the natural recoil of the patient's chest and diaphragm. It provides intermittent positive pressure.
Mine Safety Appliances Co.

Bursine△. *Same as* Choline△.

Burton Clayᴺᴱ. (*Supp.* I p. 33). No longer available. United Clay Mines Corp.

Burtonite® #7. A cold-water-soluble gum of high viscosity, prepared from guar seeds. Used as a protective colloid, and thickening, suspending, and film-forming agent. A white, free-flowing powder; finer than 175-mesh particle size; moisture content, approx. 9%. Its water solutions are tasteless, odorless, and virtually neutral as to pH. It is a nonionic non-polyuronide; and is compatible with other water-soluble gums, animal gelatin, resins, and plasticizers. Used in the pharmaceutical, food-processing, cosmetic, and chemical-processing industries for the preparation of suspensions and emulsions; as a binder for tablets; as a collector and settling agent in ore flotation; as an additive in drilling-mud compounds, aqueous paints, etc. Burtonite Co.

Burtonite® V-31-E. An edible colloid, in powder form, prepared from Irish Moss. *Use:* As a stabilizer for ice cream mixes. Burtonite Co.

Busan®. (*HBMTN* p. 97). No longer available.
Buckman Laboratories, Inc.

Butesin®. An anesthetic ointment for topical application. Contains butamben and nitromersal.
Abbott Laboratories

Butyn®. A local anesthetic, butacaine sulfate, in powder, solution and tablet forms. Also available with nitromersol in ointment form. It is a crystalline, colorless, odorless powder, very soluble in water, warm alcohol and acetone. Used in place of cocaine for surface anesthesia of mucous membranes and the dye.
Abbott Laboratories

BV. A line of coating materials including:
BV 14. A vehicle for floor paints and stain varnishes.
BV 40. A pure drying alkyd for flats, primers, sealers, semi-gloss paints and undercoats.
BV 155. An all-purpose aluminum vehicle for ready-mixed interior and exterior aluminum paints.
BV 666. A lime-treated oil for one-coat flats, sealers, kalsicoaters, etc.

BV 965-B. A pure phenolic spar varnish for exterior applications and for architectural and marine uses.

BV 1237. A high-grade floor vehicle for floor, porch and deck enamels for wood and concrete, and dado and machinery enamels.

BV 2586. A quick-drying aluminum vehicle for all-purpose, ready-mixed interior aluminum paints; and baking and air-drying industrial paints.

BV 3022-C. An oleo-resinous pigmented flat varnish for furniture, stained woodwork, etc.

BV 4608. A chlorinated rubber vehicle for alkali- and acid-resisting paints for use on fresh or cured concrete surfaces.

BV 4901 WRINKLE VEHICLE. A modified phenolic, pure tung oil liquid for mfg. of wrinkled finishes for typewriters, sewing machines, etc.

BV 6375-A RUBBER BASE FLOOR SEALER. A rapidly drying floor sealer that is unaffected by alkalis, acids, and alcohols. Used as a sealer for new concrete floors to keep them from dusting and as a base for subsequent coatings; and for wood and concrete floors of laboratories and plants where chemical spillage may occur.

BV 6400 ENAMEL VEHICLE. A high gloss liquid possessing good flow and drying properties, for use in one-coat enamels, interior gloss paints, semi-gloss paints, etc.

BV 6441 PENETRATING FLOOR SEALER. An oleo-resinous type floor finish for offices, stores, rooms, auditoriums, etc. It enters the pores of the wood and seals the surface against marring.

BV 6442 QUICK DRYING GYM SEALER. A high-gloss, non-slippery, fast-drying modified-phenolic sealer for gymnasiums, dance floors, recreation floors, etc. It is resistant to repeated washings with soap and water; and is not affected by alkalis and acids.

BV 6522 ALKYD FLOOR SEALER. A pale alkyd-type finish for terrazzo, wood, linoleum and other floors where light color and color retention are important.

BV 6550 GYM SEALER. A waterproof finish having full gloss and a hard surface which is resistant to rubber heel scuff marks. It will not crack or powder-up; and is unaffected by alkalis, acids, and alcohol.

BV 6564 PENETRATING FLOOR SEALER. An oleo-resinous type floor finish for offices, stores, rooms, auditoriums, etc. It enters into the pores of the wood, sealing the surface against marring.

BV 6692 AUTOMOTIVE VEHICLE. A pure phenolic alkyd liquid for automotive enamels and industrial finishes for machinery, motors, tanks, etc.

BV 9400 ENAMEL VEHICLE. A quick-drying, master painters' alkyd vehicle for enamels that are free working, and have excellent gloss and color retention. Used particularly for tile-like interior gloss and semi-gloss white enamels.

New BV 3400 ENAMEL VEHICLE. An oleo-resinous enamel liquid having good brushing and flow properties, for economical one-coat gloss enamels, wall paints, semi-gloss paints, etc.

TTV 121-C. A long oil spar varnish, suitable for outdoor finishes.

BASIC VARNISH AND RESEARCH CORP.

"B.V.M." Wax. See WHITE "B.V.M." WAX.

BX-4M Insulation[NE]. A lightweight, non-combustible, moisture-resistant, blended mineral wool, felted into a semi-rigid blanket form of insulation and designed to meet weight specifications for various service requirements as follows:

NAVY GRADE. Conforms to Navy Specification 32-F-4 for insulation; density, approx. 3 lb./cu.ft. Furnished in 15", 20" and 30" widths, and in lengths of 24" to 60". Thicknesses for NAVY GRADE are ½", 1", 1½" and 2", or plied to greater thicknesses. For overall noise quieting, BX-4M is supplied with flameproof muslin facings.

COMMERCIAL GRADE. Conforms to U. S. Maritime Commission Specification 32-MC-1 for general structural insulation. Density, approx. 3.5 lb./cu.ft.; and with a density of about 6 lb./cu.ft. for Class A-60, A-30, and A-15 bulkhead or deck fire protection. (See also BX-18 BLOCK[NE]).

JOHNS-MANVILLE SALES CORP.

BX-18 Block[NE]. A marine insulating material of the same general composition as BX-4M, but formed into a rigid block insulation for use where some compressive strength or rigidity is desired, such as floors in refrigerated spaces, and the insulation of rectangular air ducts. Weighs 18 lb./cu.ft. Supplied in standard size, 24" x 36", in thicknesses of ½", 1", 1½" and 2" in solid pieces, or plied to greater thicknesses. Also available on special order in cut sizes, and with a factory-applied vapor barrier. Meets U. S. Maritime Commission Specification 32-MC-2.

JOHNS-MANVILLE SALES CORP.

C

C (in diamond)®. The trademark for a line of reinforcing bars, structural shapes, and tie plates.

UNITED STATES STEEL CORP.

C-4[NE]. (HBMTN p. 101). No longer available.

DELAWARE TOOL STEEL CORP.

Cabflex®. A line of plasticizers for vinyl plastics, including CABFLEX® Di-OP (di-iso-octyl phthalate), CABFLEX® DOP (di-2-ethylhexyl phthalate), CABFLEX® ODP (iso-octyl decyl phthalate), CABFLEX® DDP (di-decyl phthalate), CABFLEX® Di-BA (di-iso-butyl adipate), CABFLEX® Di-OA (di-iso-octyl adipate), CABFLEX® DOA (di-2-ethylhexyl adipate), CABFLEX® ODA (iso-octyl decyl adipate), CABFLEX® DDA (di-decyl adipate), CABFLEX Di-OZ (di-iso-octyl azelate), CABFLEX® TCP (tricresyl phosphate), CABFLEX® HS-10 (alkyl aryl phthalate).

GODFREY L. CABOT, INC.

Cab-o-sil®. A colloidal silica prepared in a hot gaseous environment by a vapor-phase hydrolysis of a silicon compound instead of by the usual aqueous precipitation process. Its outstanding properties are high chemical purity, low water content, enormous external surface area, and high degree of particle separation. CAB-O-SIL® functions in extremely small quantities as a reinforcing agent in rubber and plastics, a suspending and flatting agent in paints, as a thixotropic agent in various resins, as an emulsion stabilizer, and as a thickening and gelling agent.

GODFREY L. CABOT, INC.

CAC (High Capacity). Same as CLACK ACTIVATED CARBON.

Cactus[NE]. (HBMTN p. 102). No longer available.

BETHLEHEM STEEL CO.

Cadco®. The trademark for an extensive line of plastics, including cast acrylic rods and tubes, polyethylene and polystyrene sheets, rods and tubes, methacrylate round rods and tubes, acetate sheets and rolls, etc. CADILLAC PLASTIC CO.

Cad-Sol[NE]. A concentrated solution of cadmium cyanide used in preparing cadmium plating baths.
R. O. HULL & CO.

Cadux® Brightener. (*HBMTN* p. 102). No longer available. HANSON-VAN WINKLE-MUNNING CO.

Cadux® HS Process. (*Supp.* I p. 35). No longer available. HANSON-VAN WINKLE-MUNNING CO.

Cadux® Salts. (*HBMTN* p. 102). No longer available. HANSON-VAN WINKLE-MUNNING CO.

Cajeput Oil△. A greenish essential oil distilled from the leaves of the tree *Melaleuca leucadendron*, which grows chiefly in the East Indies. It has a camphor-like odor, and is used in medicine as an antiseptic and counter-irritant, and in perfumes.

Caladex®. A line of specialty corn starches for the paper industry, developed for calender sizing. Available in four grades. A. E. STALEY MFG. CO.

Cal-Bis-Ma®. An antacid which provides rapid, symptomatic relief of gastric hyperacidity. One level teaspoonful contains 585 mg. sodium bicarbonate, 325 mg. calcium carbonate, 195 mg. magnesium carbonate, 146.2 mg. magnesium trisilicate, 16.2 mg. bismuth subcarbonate. WARNER-CHILCOTT LABORATORIES

Calcidrine®. A non-narcotic sedative expectorant containing calcium iodide and ephedrine compound with dihydrocodeinone. Available in form of troches and as a syrup. ABBOTT LABORATORIES

Calcilact®. (*HBMTN* p. 103). No longer available.
ABBOTT LABORATORIES

Calci-Phade V-P 724. A nutritional supplement containing calcium, inositol, phosphorus, and magnesium in organic form. VITAMIN PRODUCTS CO.

Calciplex V-P 725. A nutritional supplement containing the calcium-magnesium salt of inositol phosphoric acid and calcium glycerophosphate with carbamide. VITAMIN PRODUCTS CO.

Calcisalin®. A vitamin-mineral preparation, for prenatal supplementation, in the form of tablets containing calcium lactate, ferrous sulfate exsiccated, VITAMIN A acetate (crystalline), VITAMIN D (irradiated ergosterol), ascorbic acid (as sodium ascorbate), THIAMINE mononitrate, RIBOFLAVIN, niacinamide, calcium pantothenate, pyridoxine hydrochloride, VITAMIN B$_{12}$ crystalline, U.S.P., folic acid, and aluminum hydroxide dried gel, U.S.P. WARNER-CHILCOTT LABORATORIES

Calcium Cyanamid 6-16[NE]. (*HBMTN* p. 103). No longer available. AMERICAN CYANAMID CO.

Calcofluor® Dyes. The trademark for a group of direct dyeing dyes which possess fluorescent properties. Used for dyeing COTTON, LINEN, VISCOSE, ACETATE, NYLON, WOOL and certain synthetics. Also used in soaps as a brightener for textiles.
AMERICAN CYANAMID CO.

Cal-Cofron[NE]. A veterinary feed supplement composed of vitamins and minerals. ABBOTT LABORATORIES

Calco Lake® Dyes. The trademark for a line of water-soluble dyes which, upon precipitation by a metallic salt, are converted into insoluble color lakes. Lakes made from these colors are used extensively by the printing-ink trade. AMERICAN CYANAMID CO.

Calcoloid Dyes[NE]. A line of dispersed vat dyes with controlled particle size for COTTON, VISCOSE, SILK, LINEN, paper, WOOL, and textile printing.
AMERICAN CYANAMID CO.

Calcosol® Dyes. The trademark for a line of vat dyestuffs used in the dyeing and printing of COTTON and RAYON. Vat colors as a class are distinguished by superior fastness to alkali, laundering, soaping, acid, light, bleaching, and other common color-destroying agencies. Marketed in paste or powder form.
AMERICAN CYANAMID CO.

Calcosyn® Dyes. The trademark for a line of direct dyes for the dyeing of certain synthetic fibers, such as cellulose acetates and NYLON.
AMERICAN CYANAMID CO.

Calcozoic® Dyes. The trademark for a line of stabilized azoic dyes developed for the printing of COTTON, LINEN, and VISCOSE fabrics.
AMERICAN CYANAMID CO.

Calen-Acid®. A water-miscible, nonionic, textile finishing agent that can be used as an additive to resins, gums, or other synthetic stiffening agents to produce high-luster calendered finishes. It is an organic silicone-wax emulsion of fine cream consistency, soluble in alcohols and glycols. Used for fine textured WOOL and synthetic blended fibers.
TEXTILE ADJUNCTS CORP.

Calfast®. (*Supp.* I p. 35). No longer available.
GENERAL CHEMICAL DIV., ALLIED CHEMICAL & DYE CORP.

Calgran®. (*HBMTN* p. 105). Now a registered trademark. FOOTE MINERAL CO.

Caligrape[NE]. An imitation California type grape flavor, 1 oz. of which will flavor 4 gal. of syrup.
FLORASYNTH LABORATORIES, INC.

Calmasene T[NE]. A sequestering agent of the polyamino carboxylic acid type used as a chelating agent for hard water salts, ferrous iron, and other metal ions.
BELLE CHEMICAL CO.

Calpan Free-Flo[NE]. A calcium pantothenate mix for incorporating into feedstuffs. ABBOTT LABORATORIES

Calsalt®. A specially-formulated mixture of salt for the control of ice, principally on streets and roads.
COLUMBIA-SOUTHERN CHEMICAL CORP.

Calsoma®. (*HBMTN* p. 106). No longer available.
ABBOTT LABORATORIES

Calstar[NE]. Calcium stearate. Ca(C$_{17}$H$_{35}$COO)$_2$; mol.wt. 607. A fine white powder; insoluble in water and all common solvents; sp.gr. 1.04–1.07; refractive index, 1.52–1.53. *Uses:* As a lubricant and supplementary stabilizer for clear, vinyl products. It is useful in calendered products and extrusions, and also as a mold release agent for plastisols and injection molded articles. In a few products, such as some clear phonograph records, CALSTAR is used as the sole stabilizer. More often, however, an additional stabilizer is desirable. NATIONAL LEAD CO.

Caltemp®. (*Supp.* I p. 35). Now a registered trademark and mfg'd by FIBREBOARD PAPER PRODUCTS CORP., PABCO INDUSTRIAL INSULATIONS DIV., successor to PABCO PRODUCTS INC.

Cambric△. A plain-woven, strong COTTON fabric of fine weave and hard-twist yarn. Used in making varnished electrical insulation and cable windings.

Camoform®. Tablets, each containing 250 mg. CAMOFORM hydrochloride (biallylamicol hydrochloride, Parke-Davis), for treatment of amebiasis.
PARKE, DAVIS & CO.

Camphacidol[NE]. (*HBMTN* p. 106). No longer available. ABBOTT LABORATORIES

Camphor△. A white resin material obtained by steam distillation of the trunks, roots, and large branches of the tree *Cinnamomum camphora* that occurs naturally in China and southern Japan, and is grown in Florida. Chemically it is $C_{10}H_{16}O$ (mol.wt. 152.24), and has a sp.gr. of 0.986–0.996 and melts at 175°C. Soluble in water and in alcohol. Much of the CAMPHOR of commerce is now produced synthetically. *Uses:* In plastics, pharmaceuticals, disinfectants, explosives, chemical intermediate, etc.

Canada Balsam△. *Also known as* CANADA TURPENTINE△. A yellowish, viscous, oleoresinous liquid with a pleasant odor and bitter taste. Obtained from the buds of the balsam fir *Abies balsamea,* found in the northeastern section of the U. S. and in Canada. Sp.gr. 0.983–0.997. Used as a solvent in paints and polishes; in leather dressings; adhesives; and perfumes.

Canada Turpentine△. *Same as* CANADA BALSAM△.

Canaga Oil△. *Same as* YLANG-YLANG OIL△.

Canaigre△. A tanning material extracted from the roots of the low-growing plant *Rumex hymenosepalus* of northern Mexico and the arid areas of southwest U. S. Produces a firm, orange-colored leather.

Canary Seed△. The seeds of the canary grass, *Phalaris canariensis,* which is native to the Canary Islands but is now also grown extensively in Argentina, Turkey and Morocco. In international trade it is referred to by the Spanish name, ALPISTE. CANARY SEED is an important bird food because it is rich in carbohydrates and contains phosphates, iron and other minerals. However, it is low in protein and, therefore, it is generally used as part of a mixture containing the other essential ingredients of a balanced food.

Candelilla Wax△. A yellowish, amorphous wax extracted from the stems of the shrubs *Pedilanthus pavonis* and *Euphorbia antisyphilitica* which grow in the semi-arid regions of Texas and Mexico. Stems yield from 3.5 to 5% wax composed of long-chain hydrocarbons with small amounts of esters. Sp.gr. 0.983; m.p. 67–70°C.; iodine no. 37; saponification no. 45–65; soluble in turpentine. Used in varnishes, furniture and shoe polishes, leather finishes; as a substitute for CARNAUBA wax; etc.

Canrite®. A fast-acting acid-type, can washing compound for removing milkstone and other mineral deposits from dairy equipment. Can also be used to remove inorganic materials from metal surfaces.
DIVERSEY CORP.

Caparsolate®. Arsenamide sodium for veterinary use.
ABBOTT LABORATORIES

Capella Oil. See TEXACO® CAPELLA OIL.

Capitol®. The trademark for a line of: (1) carbon paper; and (2) inked ribbons. INTERCHEMICAL CORP., AULT & WIBORG CARBON & RIBBON DIV.

Caprolan®, Caprolan® Deep-Dye Nylon *and* **Caprolan® Tensile-Tough Nylon.** (*Supp.* I p. 36). The name CAPROLAN® is now a registered trademark.
NATIONAL ANILINE DIV.,
ALLIED CHEMICAL & DYE CORP.

Carageen△. *Same as* IRISH MOSS△.

Caramellone®. An imitation caramel and butterscotch flavor for use in confections and in imitation vanilla flavors. FLORASYNTH LABORATORIES, INC.

Carbicon®. An especially treated silicon carbide abrasive used in both flexible and inflexible forms.
BEHR-MANNING CO.

Carbo-Fluid "H"[NE]. A fluid used for creating a carburizing atmosphere in gas-carburizing furnaces for case hardening of steel. PARK CHEMICAL CO.

Carbogen®. A mixture of oxygen and carbon dioxide. *Uses:* For treating asphyxia from carbon monoxide, alcoholic intoxication, deetherization, morphine narcosis; for prevention of respiratory failure; and for aiding in resuscitation after respiratory failure due to any cause. MINE SAFETY APPLIANCES CO.

Carbomastic Series. A line of epoxy-tar coatings that are resistant to water, salts, acids, alkalis, and solvents. A single application by spray deposits a film 4 to 10 mils thick. *Uses:* For lining pipes and tanks carrying chemicals, and for protection of equipment in petroleum refineries and other plants.
CARBOLINE CO.

Carbose 53[NE]. (*Supp.* I p. 37). No longer available.
WYANDOTTE CHEMICALS CORP.,
J. B. FORD DIV.

Carbose 53[NE]. An additive for use in laundry cleaning as an aid in soil suspension and rinsing.
WYANDOTTE CHEMICALS CORP.,
J. B. FORD DIV.

Car-Care. See LECTON® CAR-CARE.

Carclad[NE]. A chemical resistant finish for transportation equipment such as hopper cars, tank cars, coal cars, freight cars, etc. SHERWIN-WILLIAMS CO.

Cardinal®. A line of felt products similar to OZITE®. All-hair felts are marketed under the name OZITE® while felts composed of hair and jute fibers are usually marketed under the name CARDINAL®. These products include insulation for ice cream shippers, milk cans, etc.; insulation for cold lines, ducts, and equipment; padding for furniture, sports equipment, bicycle and tractor seats; protective padding for equipment during shipment; and GYM MAT FELT, for

use under pads in gymnasiums. The CARDINAL® products are available in the same sizes as the corresponding OZITE® products.
AMERICAN HAIR & FELT CO.

Cardoxide®. A chemical mixture used for removing carbon dioxide from air or other gases.
MINE SAFETY APPLIANCES CO.

Carilloy®. See U.S.S. CARILLOY®.

Carmethose®. Sodium carboxymethylcellulose used medically for the prolonged control of gastric hyperacidity. It relieves pain and facilitates healing by forming a demulcent protective coating over mucosa and peptic ulcer craters. Available as tablets, each containing 225 mg. sodium carboxymethylcellulose and 75 mg. magnesium oxide; and as a peppermint-flavored 5% solution of sodium carboxymethylcellulose.
CIBA PHARMACEUTICAL PRODUCTS INC.

Carmethose®-Trasentine®. A combination antacid and antispasmodic that forms a protective anesthetic coating over mucosa, reduces acidity, and inhibits spasm. Available as tablets, each of which contains 225 mg. sodium carboxymethylcellulose, 75 mg. magnesium oxide, and 25 mg. TRANSENTINE®.
CIBA PHARMACEUTICAL PRODUCTS INC.

Carmine Red△. See COCHINEAL△.

Carnauba Wax△. *Also known as* BRAZIL WAX and CEARA WAX. A hard, high-melting, lustrous wax composed principally of ceryl palmitate, $C_{25}H_{51}$-$COOC_{30}H_{61}$ (mol.wt. 817.51). Obtained from the fan-like leaves of the palm tree *Copernica cerifera*, which grows in the arid region of northeastern Brazil. The wax forms a protective coating on the leaves. When the leaves are dried, the wax becomes flaky and is readily beaten off and melted into cakes or lumps for shipment. Sp.gr. 0.995; m.p. approx. 85°C.; soluble in alcohol and in alkalis. Several grades of CARNAUBA WAX are available on the market, including: (1) FLORA WAX, a high-quality, clear yellow grade; (2) OLHO WAX, a whitish gray material obtained from young yellow leaves; (3) PALHA WAX, obtained from older green leaves, has a grayish-yellow hue, and (4) CHALKY WAX, which is made by adding water to the PALHA WAX during melting. *Uses:* Principally in the mfg. of floor waxes and carbon paper. In liquid floor waxes, it imparts self-polishing properties, and in carbon paper it makes the paper non-smearing and non-greasy. It is also used in shoe polishes, leather finishes, phonograph records, etc.

Carnauba Wax #352[NE]. (*HBMTN* p. 112). No longer being mfg'd by INNIS SPEIDEN & Co.

Carnegie®. The trademark for a line of steel rails, and steel joint bars.
UNITED STATES STEEL CORP., CARNEGIE-ILLINOIS STEEL CORP.

Carnu®. See DEEP GLOSS® CARNU®.

Caroa△. The fiber from the leaves of the plant *Neoglaziovia variegata* of northeastern Brazil. It has nearly twice the strength of JUTE and is lighter in weight and lighter in color. However, it is much harder than JUTE and therefore it cannot be used by itself for BURLAP. For this purpose and for rope, it is mixed with softer fibers; and in mixtures with COTTON, it is used for heavy fabrics and suitings.

Carpetone®. A felt-base floor-covering material.
ARMSTRONG CORK CO.

Car-Plate®. A liquid product consisting of solvent and waxes for use on all automobile finishes. After drying, the excess material is easily wiped off, eliminating the vigorous buffing normally required. It produces a clear finish having excellent water resistance, gloss and durability. It can also be used on painted metal surfaces such as filing cabinets, etc.
S. C. JOHNSON & SON

Cart-N-Seel[NE]. A carton sealing glue.
STEIN, HALL & CO.

Cartun[NE]. (*HBMTN* p. 116). No longer available.
DELAWARE TOOL STEEL CORP.

Carum®. A line of special, chemical-resistant greases that do not dissolve or react in the presence of many active industrial materials. These greases are used for lubricating pumps, glands, valves, packings, stuffing boxes, etc. The following types are available:
CARUM 35 is a water-soluble, stiff grease that is highly resistant to hydrocarbon solvents, including gasoline, kerosene, petroleum solvents, natural gas, etc. Can be used at temps. up to 150°F.
CARUM 60 is a white grease that is not affected by exposure to mild acids, mild alkalis, low-molecular-weight alcohols, water, beer, carbonated beverages, etc. It is not hydrocarbon resistant. Can be used at temps. up to 175°F.
CARUM 200 is a grease formulated especially for the lubrication of equipment handling concentrated or dilute acids, such as sulfuric, hydrochloric, mixed and phosphoric.
CARUM 325 is a black grease developed especially for the lubrication of gland bearings on pumping equipment. Insoluble in all but highly aromatic petroleum products.
ESSO STANDARD OIL CO.

Cascade Impactor[NE]. A device which employs the principle of impaction and sampling of aerosols composed of liquid drops, thus permitting the discriminatory collection of air-borne dust by particle size. *Use:* To collect air-borne contaminants for counting or measurement.
MINE SAFETY APPLIANCES CO.

Casein△. A protein precipitated from skim milk. It is a white to yellow granular material obtained by reacting the milk with dilute acid; by coagulation with rennet, an extract of an enzyme derived from the stomachs of calves and lambs; or by innoculating the milk with the whey from a previous batch. Cow's milk contains about 3% CASEIN. It is insoluble in water and in alcohol, but is attacked by alkalis. Most of the production of CASEIN in this country is by the acid precipitation process. *Uses:* In the mfg. of plastics, adhesives, paper and textile sizes, washable interior paints, leather dressings; and as a diabetic food.

Caspro®. The trademark for a line of building products including:
CASPRO GLO-WHITE. A hard, durable, white finish plaster.
CASPRO VERMICULITE. Lightweight thermal insulation.
CASPRO QUICK-SET. A plastic cement for filling and leveling interior concrete surfaces prior to painting. It is a dry powder which is mixed with

water to soft plaster consistency, and applied by trowel or knife.

CASPRO BOND #28. A plaster bond for use on concrete.

CASPRO SILICONE WATER REPELLENT. A water repellent for brickwork, mortar joints, cinder blocks, asbestos shingles, concrete, artificial stone, stucco, unglazed tile, etc. Available in two grades: SS-3 (3% silicone) and SS-5 (5% silicone).

CASPRO PLASTIC COATING. A strong, lightweight, boiler and pipe covering cement composed of expanded vermiculite, mineral fiber, and a highly refractory and plastic binder.

CALIFORNIA STUCCO PRODUCTS OF N. E., INC.

Castle®. A carpet cushion made from a blend of cattle hair and vegetable fiber. It is sterilized, and permanently mothproofed.

AMERICAN HAIR & FELT CO.

Castor Oil△. A light-yellow to brownish, viscous oil obtained from the seed beans of the castor plant, *Ricinus communis*, grown principally in Brazil but also in India, Russia, Argentina, Haiti, Cuba, Japan, and China. The beans contain from 35 to 55% oil which is recovered by solvent extraction or by being expressed from the beans. The highest quality oil is used for medicinal purposes. The lower grades are used in the mfg. of soap, as a motor lubricant and hydraulic brake-cylinder oil, for treating leather and textiles, etc. Dehydrated CASTOR OIL, made by heating the oil in vacuum in the presence of a dehydrating catalyst such as alumina, FULLERS EARTH, silica gel, phosphoric acid or sulfuric acid, is an important drying oil used in the mfg. of paints and varnishes. Sulfonated castor oil, known as TURKEY RED OIL, is used in the dyeing of COTTON fabrics, particularly with alizarin, and in soaps and cutting compounds. Hydrogenated CASTOR OIL is a hard, non-greasy, white solid that melts at about 82°C. It is used as an extender for waxes in coating compositions, and as a hard grease for making resistant lithium-type lubricating greases.

Catalina®. The trademark for a line of prefabricated homes. UNITED STATES STEEL HOMES, INC.

Catalyn V-P 710. A vitamin concentrate containing VITAMINS A, B, C, D, E, F, and G.

VITAMIN PRODUCTS CO.

Catamine SF[NR]. A cationic-type textile softener that is soluble in cold water. Used on COTTON, NYLON, WOOL and DACRON. LAUREL SOAP MFG. CO.

Cataplex. The name for a line of vitamin tablets: VITAMINS A, A, and C, A and F, B, C, D, E, F, G.

VITAMIN PRODUCTS CO.

Cataplex E₂ V-P 732. A phospholipid synergist of *alpha*-tocopherol from beef chromatin. For experimental use as an adjuvant in VITAMIN E deficient states. VITAMIN PRODUCTS CO.

Catechin△. See GAMBIER△.

Catechu△. An abstract obtained from the heartwood and from the seed pods of the tree *Acacia catechu* of southern Asia. It is available either as a water solution containing about 25% tannin, or as a brownish, brittle solid containing about 50% tannin. *Uses:* In tanning leather, as a dyestuff, and in medicine as an astringent.

Catechutannic Acid△. See GAMBIER△.

Catgut△. String made from the intestines of sheep. After cleaning and soaking in an alkali solution, the intestines are split, drawn through openings in a plate, cured and graded. CATGUT is used for violin strings, tennis racket cords, surgical sutures, etc.

Cathaloy®. A line of high nickel alloys for cathodes of electron tubes. They are of two general types: "A" (active) and "P" (passive).

CATHALOY A-30 contains 0.07–0.13% aluminum as the reducing agent for the oxide coating. It has long life, rapid activation, no interface impedance, no inter-electrode leakage caused by sublimed films, and high emission value.

CATHALOY A-31 is a magnesium alloy activated with tungsten (4%). It has high hot yield strength (approx. 5,000 lb./sq.in.) and maintains good emission characteristics over long periods of time. Recommended for electron tubes subjected to shock and vibration.

CATHALOY A-32 contains both aluminum (0.07–0.13%) and tungsten (2.0–2.5%). It is a high-strength alloy particularly recommended where resistance to shock and vibration are important.

CATHALOY P-50. A passive grade of nickel (99.50%) for power output tubes requiring low grid emission and for tubes which need a seamless passive cathode. Hot yield strength, approx. 2,500 lb./sq.in. SUPERIOR TUBE CO.

Cathomycin®. Crystalline monosodium novobiocin. An antibiotic obtained by fermentation from the microorganism Streptomyces spheroides. *Use:* For the treatment of cellulitis, recurrent and persistant carbuncles, various skin abscesses, postoperative wound infections, varicose ulcer, felons and paronychiae, and staphylococcic septicemia and enteritis.

MERCK SHARP & DOHME

Cati-Coat. See KEM CATI-COAT[NR].

Catiosan[NR]. (*HBMTN* p. 118). No longer available.

ONYX OIL & CHEMICAL CO.

Cat Roll Grease[NR]. A dark green, stringy grease designed to stand up under the severe duty of track roll and other tractor bearings. It is resistant to heat and moisture; adheres well to metal surfaces; and has a m.p. higher than 220°F. Available in light and medium grades. KEYSTONE LUBRICATING CO.

Caustic Gum[NR]. A light tan powder, of low solubility, which readily swells in concentrated caustic solutions. Used in textile printing to produce crinkle or seersucker effects on COTTON fabrics.

STEIN, HALL & CO.

CCA△. *Also known as* STRUX△. Cellular cellulose acetate. An expanded cellulose acetate. It is a unicellular product made by a continuous extrusion process in which the cellulose acetate is converted to a rigid foam by the flash vaporization of the volatile solvent. The density of this foam ranges from 6 to 7 lb./cu. ft. depending on the feed composition and the operating condition of the extruder. Conventional sizes are: 1" x 4", ¾" x 6", ½" x 8", 1½" x 3½" and 1¼" x 4" in boards; and 2¼", 2⅜" and 2½" diameter rods; other dimensions and shapes are available to specifications. This plastic material is characterized by excellent stability, high strength, high thermal resistance; it is easily machined to extremely close tolerances by ordinary woodworking tools. Cellular cellulose acetate is used extensively in the production of laminates using glass cloth, glass mat, metal, or wood in combination with polyester and epoxy resins; as a reinforcement for aircraft control services, random housings, and filler blocks under fuel cells; as a buoyant material for life floats, buoys, and other flotation devices; in the mfg. of X-ray and electronic equipment; for ribs, posts, and framing members in shelters, housing units, trailer bodies, etc.; in gun plugs for jet fighters.

CCH®. A high-test calcium hypochlorite for use in bleaching paper pulp and in the treatment of natural gasoline. OLIN MATHIESON CHEMICAL CORP.

CD Cement 2. A non-flammable, acrylic monomer-base adhesive for acrylic plastics. Produces optically clear parts. Used with a catalyst to obtain rapid setting time. Applied by dip, medicine dropper, hypodermic syringe, brush, or similar methods. DEVCON CORP.

CD Cement 18. A high strength solvent-adhesive formulation developed specifically for the cold assembly of cellulose nitrate articles. The joint produced is fully as strong as the plastic itself. The edges to be cemented are simply dipped in the cement for a few seconds or lightly painted with a brush and assembled. Pieces can be handled almost immediately after assembly. DEVCON CORP.

CD Cement 24. A cement for the belting trade, designed for the cementing of cellulose nitrate innerlayer to leather. The sheet of cellulose nitrate is immersed in the cement for a few seconds and immediately placed between pieces of leather. The composite is bonded by hydraulic pressure without heat. The bond produced is very strong and will withstand severe use. DEVCON CORP.

CD Cement 26. A bodied cement of exceptional strength for bonding cellulose nitrate to itself and to many other substances including wood, fabric, and others. Particularly recommended for use on rough or poorly mated surfaces. It is also used as a protective coating in many industries. DEVCON CORP.

CD Cement 32. A quick-setting, strong adhesive for cellulose and cellulose nitrate. Produces a transparent bond of excellent appearance. The joint is fully as strong as the plastic itself and can be handled almost immediately after use. The edges to be cemented are dipped in the cement for a few seconds or lightly painted with a brush. Ideally suited for a "felt pad" or soak method in which a felt pad is placed in a shallow pan and kept moistened by the liquid. The article is simply touched to the pad and quickly assembled. Widely used for mfg. of toys, athletic equipment, boxes, dispensers, and many other items. DEVCON CORP.

CD Cement 33. A bodied adhesive for use on rough or poorly mated cellulose acetate surfaces or for bonding cloth, cork, and other substances to cellulose acetate. DEVCON CORP.

CD Cement 94. A non-flammable, acrylic monomer-base general-purpose adhesive for acrylic plastics. Used where an extremely strong bond is desired. It is fast-setting, and products can be handled shortly after cementing. The bond is slightly plasticized to impart high impact strength. DEVCON CORP.

CD Cement 114. *Same as* CD CEMENT 94, but with a lower percentage of acrylic monomer. DEVCON CORP.

CD Cement 125. A fast-setting cement for PLEXIGLAS, LUCITE, and other acrylics. Produces medium to high strength bond. Widely used where quick assembly is essential. Ideally suited for "felt pad" method of application. DEVCON CORP.

CD Cement 200. An adhesive for bonding STYROFOAM and similar foamed plastics to themselves and to wood, fabrics, and many other substances. Also used for bonding mirrors to wallboard; cloth and leather to instrument cases; and for a great many other uses. Very high solids; is extremely tough; will not damage thin honeycomb structure or cause shrinkage which results in distorted and weak bond; fast-setting and does not require heat, pressure or any special surface preparation. It dries to a tough, durable, non-tacky film. DEVCON CORP.

CD Cement 201. A mixture of several solvents and penetrants developed specifically for bonding vinyl film to itself. Although quick acting, this product produces a minimum of curl on thin film and still produces a high-strength bond. Widely used by film converters. If desired, scrap or cuttings can be dissolved in this mixture to produce a bodied cement. The strength of the bond can sometimes be increased in this way, especially if the vinyl film is not a standard product or is heavily plasticized. DEVCON CORP.

CD Cement 202. A bodied adhesive for bonding vinyl to vinyl. Of great value for use on rough or poorly-mated surfaces and where a quick initial bond is desired. The solvent mixture is similar to that of CD CEMENT 201, but 202 also contains resins, plasticizers and other ingredients. It has quick penetrating power together with a high film strength. Used for manufacturing bags, curtains, and many other articles. DEVCON CORP.

CD Cement 203. An extremely versatile, very high-strength adhesive for bonding vinyl film, tapes, and molded articles to metal, glass, ceramics, paper, cloth, cork, and many other surfaces. Consists of resins, plasticizers, tackifiers, and other materials. It produces a quick initial bond, and is fast-setting. DEVCON CORP.

CD Cement 204. A slightly viscous adhesive for bonding vinyls and some other plastics to wood, wallboard, paper, and many other porous and non-porous surfaces. It produces a quick initial bond, and is easily applied by brush or machine. DEVCON CORP.

CD Cement 300[NB]. (*Supp.* I p. 39). Now a product of DEVCON CORP., formerly known as CHEMICAL DEVELOPMENT CORP.

CD CEMENT 400. An extremely strong adhesive for bonding polyester plastic to itself and to aluminum, steel, and many other surfaces. It is a thermosetting material that sets without heat or pressure. DEVCON CORP.

CD Cement 1508. A very strong adhesive for polystyrene. It is a very high-tensile and -impact strength cement for general-purpose applications where a clear joint is desirable. It is a bodied cement with a fast setting time, and is particularly recommended for use on rough or poorly mated surfaces. Products can be handled and packed shortly after application. Also used for bonding polystyrene to acrylic plastics, felt insulation, cotton duck, cork, and many other substances. Easily applied by brushing, dipping, or mechanical means.
Devcon Corp.

CD Cement 1509. A solvent-type mixture for cementing polystyrene parts. It produces high tensile and medium-to-high impact strength joints; is fast setting; and non-flammable. Ideally suited for "felt pad" or soak method of application. Devcon Corp.

CD Cement 1516. A bodied or semi-viscous adhesive similar to CD Cement 1508 but faster drying. Has exceptionally high strength. Applied by dipping, brushing, or mechanical methods. Used for industrial products including batteries, electrical assemblies, and many others. Devcon Corp.

CD Cement PS-7. A semi-viscous adhesive for acrylic plastics that can be applied by brush. Will not run or sag and, therefore, can be used on a vertical surface. Dipping is not required. Very fast setting. 100% solids. Does not contain solvents, and there is, therefore, little or no tendency to craze the plastic. Can be used for laminating large blocks. Very high bond strength. Devcon Corp.

CD Cleaner 27. A solvent solution for removing masking tape gums and dirt from cast acrylic sheeting.
Devcon Corp.

CD Dip Polish 231. A polish for producing a mirror finish on cellulose nitrate articles and sheet stock. Objects are simply dipped into the solution and allowed to air dry; no hand polish is required. The treatment removes scratches and eliminates the necessity for press-polishing. Devcon Corp.

CD Lubricant 105. A thin liquid designed specifically to lubricate and facilitate the handling of Nylon mono-filaments used for the mfg. of brushes and similar products. Very fast drying; highly effective. Applied to bristles by machine, drip cup, or spraying.
Devcon Corp.

CD Mold Release A. A non-corrosive, non-staining, effective, long-lasting silicone-type release agent developed specifically for plastic molding and forming. Easily applied by spray or other means. Increases life of molds and reduces rejects; does not carbonize or decompose under normal working temps.; and quickly penetrates every recess. Devcon Corp.

CD Mold Release B[NR]. (*Supp.* I p. 39). Now a product of Devcon Corp., formerly known as Chemical Development Corp.

CD Mold Release B-2[NR]. (*Supp.* I p. 39). Now a product of Devcon Corp., formerly known as Chemical Development Corp.

CD Spray Mask A. A plastic putty for making inexpensive rigid spray masks and stencils for protecting surfaces during spray-painting, cementing, and vacuum coating. Also used for making jigs and fixtures for holding parts during cementing and machining, and low-pressure molds and forming dies, models, and many other products. It can be applied with a putty knife to a vertical surface and will not run or sag; a thick or thin layer can be built up as desired. Hardens to an extremely strong and tough mass 2 hr. after the addition of a hardening agent; no heat or pressure is required. Makes a precision reproduction of the model with little or no shrinkage. Practically unaffected by most solvents, oils, and water. Long shelf life. Devcon Corp.

CD Strip 100[NR]. (*Supp.* I p. 39). Now a product of Devcon Corp., formerly known as Chemical Development Corp.

CD Strip A. A bright red, non-flammable, fast-setting, strippable coating for the protection of Lucite, Plexiglas and other acrylics during cementing, painting, silk screening, machining, shipping, and final assembly. Easily applied by dipping, brushing, or other methods. It is impervious to the attack of cements used for bonding acrylics and, therefore, eliminates crazing and weakening of the plastic at the joint line. Excess cement and coating are quickly peeled off in one piece when desired. Used in place of masking tape. Devcon Corp.

CD Strip B. A tough, non-flammable, water-resistant, strippable coating designed specifically for the protection of acrylic canopies on aircraft during assembly and storage. It is a relatively low cost emulsion or dispersion. Can be applied by spraying or brushing. Devcon Corp.

Cedar Breeze®. Chemically treated paper for the control of moths, moth larvae, and carpet beetles.
Daubert Chemical Co.

Ceilcrete®. A corrosion-resistant surfacing material designed especially for the protection of concrete against the attack of corrosive chemicals. It consists of a mixture of inert fillers and pigments with a 100% synthetic resin binder which cures to a dense, extremely hard, non-porous coating that adheres to concrete with an inseparable bond. It also adheres fairly well to wood and steel of sufficient thickness to avoid flexing. Supplied as a three-component unit consisting of a liquid and a powder, which are mixed immediately before use, and a solvent-type liquid for smoothing the trowelled surface. Available in two grades: Ceilcrete® "B" Black, which has the highest corrosion-resistant properties, and Ceilcrete® "S," which is available in colors, and because of the character of these pigments does not resist corrosion as well as the "B" grade. *Uses:* For surface-coating floors and walls that are subject to corrosive conditions; for lining concrete pipe, tanks, and trenches; etc.
Ceilcote Co.

Ceilinite[NR]. A fire-protecting felt made from Asbestos Roll Fire-Felt® reinforced on one side only with asbestos cloth. Serviceable for temps. up to 1,000°F. Furnished in rolls 36" wide, in ⅛" and ¼" thicknesses, 100 sq.ft. to the roll. Used as an interlining in steel cars; in fireproofing electrical apparatus, such as switch boxes; and for similar services demanding a strong, flexible, fireproof felt.
Johns-Manville Sales Corp.

Ceil-Por®. A translucent, amber-colored, resinous liquid coating material that forms a high gloss, tough, strong elastic film on any surface—wood, metal, concrete, brick, rubber, linoleum, canvas, etc. It is resistant to practically all chemicals, alcohol, gasoline, oil, brine, etc. *Uses:* For coating floors, stacks, fume ducts, pits, etc.; for lining steel bonderizing tanks; as an electrical-insulating coating. CEILCOTE CO.

Celacloud[NE]. A fibrous filling material for use in upholstery, pillows, mattresses, etc.
CELANESE CORP. OF AMERICA

Celafaille®. The trademark for a line of fabrics made wholly or partially of cellulose derivatives.
CELANESE CORP. OF AMERICA

Celallure®. The trademark for a line of fabrics made wholly or partially of cellulose derivatives.
CELANESE CORP. OF AMERICA

Celaloom®. The trademark for a line of fabrics made wholly or partially of cellulose derivatives.
CELANESE CORP. OF AMERICA

Celaspun®. The trademark for: (1) a line of fabrics made wholly or partially of cellulose derivatives; and (2) a line of yarns. CELANESE CORP. OF AMERICA

Celatow®. A tow of filaments made wholly or partially of cellulose derivatives.
CELANESE CORP. OF AMERICA

Celbrook®. The trademark for a line of fabrics made wholly or partially of cellulose derivatives.
CELANESE CORP. OF AMERICA

Celcure®. (*HBMTN* p. 119). Now mfg'd by AMERICAN CELCURE WOOD PRESERVING CORP., formerly CELCURE SOUTHERN CORP.

Cel-Fibe[NE]. A cellulose wadding material for packaging and cushioning applications. Available in a variety of types: bleached, unbleached, moisture-resistant, moisture-absorbent, etc. *Uses:* As a quilting material for garment bags, toys, automobile doors, etc.; as a filter media for purification of air, etc.; as a furniture padding; as a border felt and edging for mattresses; as a cushioning material in packaging, wrapping, etc. PERSONAL PRODUCTS CORP.

Celite®. The trademark for a line of diatomaceous silica products used as filter aids, mineral fillers, and insulations. These materials are produced from an unusual mineral deposit found in southern California, in the White Hills of Lompoc, and consisting of the skeletal remains of very small organisms called diatoms. The mined mineral is crushed, blended, dried, calcined, and flux-calcined to the desired products. The average analysis, on a dry basis, of the uncalcined CELITE is as follows: 89.% SiO_2, 3.7% Al_2O_3, 1.5% Fe_2O_3, 0.1% TiO_2, 0.4% CaO, 0.7% MgO, 0.8% alkalis (as Na_2O), and 3.7% ignition loss (combined H_2O, CO_2 and organics). Sp.gr. 2.0–2.3; particle size, 1–100 micron; bulk density, 8–10 lb./cu.ft. (loose) and 15–28 lb./cu.ft. (wet); hardness (Moh's scale), 4.5–6.5; particle charge, negative. CELITE is inert to most chemical reactants, and is resistant to extremely high-temps., with a softening point of about 2,600°F. JOHNS-MANVILLE SALES CORP.

Celite® **Filter-Aids.** A line of filter aids milled from exceptionally pure diatomaceous silica (CELLITE®), the individual particles being microscopic in size. These filter aids are finely-divided, light in weight, inert, and do not affect the chemical or physical characteristics of the filtrate. In practice, a small quantity of the properly selected CELITE FILTER-AID is added to the liquid to be filtered. This quantity varies from 0.1 to 0.5% of the weight of the liquid, depending upon the nature and amount of suspended matter present. The addition of the filter aid assures the formation of an open, porous cake on the cloth. This cake traps suspended matter, greatly increases the flow rate, reduces operating costs, and increases the clarity of the filtrate. These filter aids can be used with all types of pressure filters. CELITE FILTER-AIDS are available in a number of standard grades designed to provide maximum rates of flow of filtrate for various materials to be filtered.
JOHNS-MANVILLE SALES CORP.

Celite® **Mineral Fillers.** A line of CELLITE® materials available in calcined, uncalcined and a number of special grades for a variety of industrial applications. These fillers are characterized by their low bulk density (8–10 lb./cu.ft.), high liquid absorptive capacity, and relative inertness. Some industrial applications for these fillers are as follows: in adhesives to increase viscosity and to improve the spreading property; as an additive in liquid and solid asphalt-bound products to increase the melting point, improve the penetration, brittleness, toughness, and leveling; as a catalyst carrier where silica is the proper support; as a bulking agent in cleansers, cleaners and detergents; as a filler in dynamites; in fertilizers to improve the free-flowing properties; in textile coating formulations; as an adsorbent in gas purification; as an inert extender in paints, enamels, varnishes, and lacquers; as a filler in molded plastics; as a mold lubricant; as a polishing agent for plastic lenses; as an ingredient of metal and glass polishes; etc. JOHNS-MANVILLE SALES CORP.

Cellamite®. An insulation material, in sheets and blocks, especially useful for ovens and dryers and air-conditioning equipment where humid conditions are encountered. Mfg'd in the same manner as ASBESTOCEL® sheets and blocks, CELLAMITE® may be used in place of ASBESTOCEL® for greater strength and higher temps. (up to 700°F.). Density, about 16 lb./cu.ft.; compressive strength, about 85 lb./sq.in. Furnished 36″ wide, 36″ and 72″ long, and in thicknesses of ½″, 1″, 1½″, 2″, 2½″ and 3″.
JOHNS-MANVILLE SALES CORP.

Cellit®. A group of specially selected acid dyes for ACETATE. They display very good light fastness on ACETATE but only moderate wash fastness.
GENERAL DYESTUFF CO.

Cellitazol®. A group of disperse dyes for use on ACETATE and NYLON. They yield navy and black shades, of very good wash fastness and fairly good to very good light fastness, by diazotization on the fiber and coupling with betaoxynaphthoic acid.
GENERAL DYESTUFF CO.

Celliton®. A group of disperse dyes for general use in dyeing and printing ACETATE, NYLON, and other synthetic fibers. GENERAL DYESTUFF CO.

Cellothyl®. (*HBMT'N* p. 120). Now a product of WARNER-CHILCOTT LABORATORIES, successor to THE MALTINE CO.

Cell-Tite®. (*HBMTN* p. 121). Now a product of B. F. GOODRICH SPONGE PRODUCTS DIV., B. F. GOODRICH Co., successor to SPONGE RUBBER PRODUCTS Co.

Cellu-Brite[NE]. An optical bleaching agent with cellulose substantivity and excellent light fastness. It is a yellow powder containing 65% active ingredients. Solubility: 0.03% in detergent solutions, and 0.001% in hot water; substantive to COTTON, LINEN, VISCOSE RAYON and othe cellulosic fibers. *Uses:* In soaps and detergents to give increased brightness and whiteness to COTTON, LINEN, etc.; in the dyeing, scouring and rinsing of COTTON, LINEN and VISCOSE RAYON fabrics; in mfg. of high-grade, uncoated papers and papers with extremely thin machine coatings; etc.
CARLISLE CHEMICAL WORKS, INC.

Cellunier®-F. A chemical cellulose for the mfg. of CELLOPHANE film and staple fiber. Composition: 91.0% alpha cellulose, 5.2% beta cellulose, 3.8% gamma cellulose. Ash content, 0.16%.
RAYONIER, INC.

Cellu-Pel®. A straight water repellent used to prevent checking, warping and dimensional change of wood. CELLU-SAN DIV., DARWORTH, INC.

Celluphos®. The trademark for organo-phosphates, namely, tributyl phosphate and tripropyl phosphate. *Uses:* As plasticizers, and for general use in the industrial arts. CELANESE CORP. OF AMERICA

Cellu-Quin®. An economical-grade wood preservative, containing water repellents and fungicides, for general use under normal conditions. CELLU-SAN DIV., DARWORTH INC.

Cellu-San®. A water repellent wood preservative containing both fungicides and water repellents. Odorless, tasteless, non-toxic, designed explicitly for the food-handling industry and for use in the preservation of field boxes, hampers, and other wooden food-handling equipment. CELLU-SAN DIV., DARWORTH, INC.

Cel-O-Glass®. (*HBMTN* p. 121). This trademark has been assigned by E. I. DUPONT DE NEMOURS & Co. to the ARVEY CORP.

Celo-Lok[NE]. Wind-resistant, locking, asphalt strip shingles. CELOTEX CORP.

Celopad®. A fiber insulation board for use in packaging. It has cushioning properties; and is water- and grease-resistant, and non-corrosive.
CELOTEX CORP.

Celopak®. A cushioning type of fiber insulation board for use in packaging. It is water- and grease-resistant, and non-corrosive. CELOTEX CORP.

Celo-Roof®. A laminated fiberboard prepared especially for insulating roofs. CELOTEX CORP.

Celo-Siding®. A building board for exterior use. It has a fiberboard core, and is asphalt-coated and granule-surfaced. CELOTEX CORP.

Celotex®. (1) A house mark or general trademark used alone or in connection with other trademarks of the CELOTEX CORP.; (2) fiber insulation board products as building board, sheathing, roof insulation, and as tile and plant interior finish products. Also gypsum board and plaster products, hardboard products, roofing and insulating sidings, mineral wool products, composite structural panels, and acoustical or sound-absorbing products CELOTEX CORP.

Celsheer®. The trademark for a line of fabrics made wholly or partially of cellulose derivatives.
CELANESE CORP. OF AMERICA

Cel-U-Bee Tablets[NE]. A bulk-producing tablet with VITAMIN B_1 for the relief of constipation caused by lack of bulk in the diet, and for the regulation of bowel movements. Each tablet contains 0.5 g. sodium carboxymethylcellulose, and 1 mg. thiamine hydrochloride (B_1). AMERICAN PHARMACEUTICAL Co.

Cemcoat® Filler and Dustproofer. (*HBMTN* p. 122). The name CEMCOAT® is now a registered trademark. L. SONNEBORN SONS, INC.

Cemco Floor Enamel[NE]. (*Supp.* I p. 41). No longer available. HALLEMITE MFG. CO.

Cement 2. *See* CD CEMENT 2.

Cement 18. *See* CD CEMENT 18.

Cement 24. *See* CD CEMENT 24.

Cement 26. *See* CD CEMENT 26.

Cement 32. *See* CD CEMENT 32.

Cement 33. *See* CD CEMENT 33.

Cement 94. *See* CD CEMENT 94.

Cement 114. *See* CD CEMENT 114.

Cement 125. *See* CD CEMENT 125.

Cement 200. *See* CD CEMENT 200.

Cement 201. *See* CD CEMENT 201.

Cement 202. *See* CD CEMENT 202.

Cement 203. *See* CD CEMENT 203.

Cement 204. *See* CD CEMENT 204.

Cement 300. *See* CD CEMENT 300.

Cement 1508. *See* CD CEMENT 1508.

Cement 1509. *See* CD CEMENT 1509.

Cement 1516. *See* CD CEMENT 1516.

Cement PS-7. *See* CD CEMENT PS-7.

Cementseal Exterior. (*HBMTN* p. 122). No longer available. ACORN REFINING Co.

Cementseal Interior. (*HBMTN* p. 122). No longer available. ACORN REFINING Co.

Centrine®. An antispasmodic-anticholinergic medicinal in the form of tablets and solution, and as CENTRINE TABLETS WITH PHENOBARBITAL. CENTRINE is the brand name for aminopentamide (alpha, alpha-diphenyl, gamma-dimethylaminovaleramide). *Uses:* In the adjunctive management of peptic ulcer, pylorospasm, chronic hypertrophic gastritis associated with gastric hyperacidity and hypermotility; for nausea and vomiting of pregnancy, biliary colic, ureteral colic, hyperhiderosis, and enuresis.
BRISTOL LABORATORIES INC.

Ceraloid 356[NE]. A textile-waxing compound. A wax containing antistatic agents of low unsaponifiable content; easily emulsified and scourable. CERALOID 356 and its modification 356WD (water-dispersible) are employed in the after-waxing of NYLON, DACRON, and sized and unsized warp yarn to improve the weaving properties. COLLOIDS, INC.

Ceraloid 365WD[NE]. A water-dispersible wax used as a hot-melt in slashing of synthetic textile fibers. It may be added to size formulations to improve abrasion resistance, to lubricate the fibers and to impart antistatic qualities. Readily removable. COLLOIDS, INC.

Ceraloid X4977D2[NE]. A non-yellowing, polystyrene-type textile softener and lubricant. It improves the binding properties of starches and the sewing qualities of threads. Added prior to brushing or calendering, it promotes excellent luster. It is used as a CARNAUBA wax replacement. COLLOIDS, INC.

Ceramol[NE]. An emulsifier consisting of a carefully balanced blend of cetyl and stearyl alcohols and higher alcohol sulfates. CERAMOL has a wide range of applications because the sulfated alcohols of this mixture and the unreacted alcohols are water-in-oil emulsifiers. ACETO CHEMICAL CO.

Cercon "A" Wax. (*HBMTN* p. 123). No longer available. Company no longer active. HARRY R. LEWIS CO.

Ceres®. A group of pigments prepared to disperse in and to color waxes. GENERAL DYESTUFF CO.

Cerodyn V-P 723. A nutritional supplement containing concentrates from alfalfa, carrot, beef and fish liver lipoids, yeast, wheat germ, rice and peanut bran, liver, mushroom, green peas, fresh veal bone flour, milk solids, malted barley and oat flour, raw sugar. VITAMIN PRODUCTS CO.

Cerol V-P 719. A VITAMIN E preparation, consisting of cold-processed wheat germ oil, in the form of perles. VITAMIN PRODUCTS CO.

Certified Styrroid®. A dispersion of a synthetic copolymer resin latex for admixture with Portland cement and sand to make a floor-surfacing mix, known as CERTIFIED STYRROIDITE®. The floor surface prepared with STYRROIDITE is resilient, quiet, dust free, highly resistant to slipping and skidding, and of attractive gray color. It is not oil and grease proof, or acid and alkali proof, although its resistance to oils and chemicals is greater than that of ordinary concrete. UNITED LABORATORIES, INC.

Certified Styrroidite®. A floor-surfacing material made by mixing CERTIFIED STYRROID® with Portland cement and sand. UNITED LABORATORIES, INC.

Cetaceum△. *Same as* SPERMACETTI△.

Cetosols®. (*HBMTN* p. 125). The name CETOSOL® is now a registered trademark. STEIN, HALL & CO.

Cevadilla△. *Same as* SABADILLA△.

Cevadilline△. *See* SABADILLA△.

Cevadine△. *See* SABADILLA△.

Cevicetyl®. The trademark for a medicinal preparation in tablet form, used in the treatment of the common cold and certain arthritic conditions. CHICAGO PHARMACAL CO.

Cezit®. (*HBMTN* p. 125). Now a registered trademark. SERVICE INDUSTRIES

CF-10. A nonionic, low-foaming, surface-active agent. Its low-foaming property even at high concentrations and vigorous agitation makes it particularly useful in formulations for mechanical dishwashing, automatic home laundering, and cleaning of metal and dairy equipment. ROHM & HAAS CO.

Chain Life. *See* NU AERO® CHAIN LIFE.

Chalcedony△. *See* FLINT△.

Chalky Wax△. *See* CARNAUBA WAX△.

Champion®. The trademark for a line of dynamite. HERCULES POWDER CO.

Champion®. The trademark for a line of prefabricated homes. UNITED STATES STEEL HOMES, INC.

Channel-Duct®. *See* GLASTIC® CHANNEL-DUCT®.

Channel-Lap®. (*Supp*. I p. 42). Should have been listed as a registered trademark. CELOTEX CORP.

Chase Wexford[NE]. (*HBMTN* p. 126). No longer available. GOODALL FABRICS, INC.

Checkit®. (*HBMTN* p. 127). Should have been listed as CHEKIT®. FRANKLIN RESEARCH CO.

Checklac[NE]. Cellulose-base lacquers that simulate the antique checking of china or porcelain. MAAS & WALDSTEIN CO.

Chekit®. Incorrectly listed as CHECKIT® (*HBMTN* p. 127). FRANKLIN RESEARCH CO.

Chem-Bond. A rust-inhibiting metal-conditioning paint base. It removes grease, mill-seale, corrosion and oxidation products; retards corrosion and rusting; and forms a phosphate coating for better adhesion of paint, enamel, and electroplated finishes. BELL-RAY CHEMICAL CORP.

Chemcore. The trade name for a series of quick-baking foundry core oils. CHEMICAL OIL & RESIN CO.

Chemfast[NE]. A line of protective coatings, with excellent chemical resistance, based on DEVRAN® (an epoxy resin). These amine-cured type coatings can be air dried or force dried. (Registration applied for.) TRUSCON LABORATORIES

Chemgard[NE]. A line of plastic protective clothing. *Use:* For protection against hazards from chemical spray or splashes. MINE SAFETY APPLIANCES CO.

Chemical "V"®. (*HBMTN* p. 129). Now a registered trademark. OIL BASE, INC.

Chemical "X"®. (*HBMTN* p. 129). Now a registered trademark. OIL BASE, INC.

Chemklos[NE]. A line of work clothes; namely, shirts, trousers, one-piece coveralls, and laboratory smocks. *Use:* For wear on jobs where acids or caustics are encountered. MINE SAFETY APPLIANCES CO.

Chemlin. The trade name for a series of chemically modified vegetable drying oils.
CHEMICAL OIL & RESIN CO.

Chemlon®. *See* "JOHN CRANE" CHEMLON®.

Chem-o-sol®. A series of plastisol formulations that are converted from liquids to solids without loss of weight or shrinkage, by heating to temps. as low as 350°F. They are dispersions of high-molecular-weight vinyl chloride polymer or copolymer resins in liquid plasticizers. *Uses:* For forming hollow or solid objects by casting; for coating paper, fabric, glass yarn, etc., and for coating metal objects such as electroplating racks, dish drainers, automobile seat springs, etc.
CHEMICAL PRODUCTS CORP.

ChemoTec®. A line of organic bonding agents for bonding metals to metals, non-metals to non-metals, and metals to non-metals such as glass, graphite, asbestos, ceramics, etc., at low heat or no heat and without pressure; and for making castings and coatings with excellent dielectric properties and resistance to moisture and most chemicals. Available in 4 types: rod, powder, paste, liquid. CHEMOTEC® is made from ARALDITE® [Registered trademark of CIBA CO., INC.] and is a thermosetting product which hardens by applications of heat or by the use of a catalyst.
POLYMER INDUSTRIES INC.

Chemox®. An oxygen-breathing apparatus. *Use:* To provide complete respiratory protection against any concentration of toxic gases and any condition of oxygen deficiency. U. S. Bureau of Mines approved.
MINE SAFETY APPLIANCES CO.

Chempoint®. A grouting material.
ARMSTRONG CORK CO.

Chempol® EP-1. A short oil type epoxy resin ester designed primarily for use with urea or melamine in baking applications. It can also be used without the amines in air-dry applications. It makes a superior primer, especially for appliances, such as washing machines, where severe soap and detergent resistance is required. It also develops extreme adhesion and hardness while maintaining very good flexibility. *Uses:* For clear overprint varnishes, metal decorating enamels, primers for refrigerator and washing machines, tube enamels.
FREEMAN CHEMICAL CORP.

Chempol® EP-2. An oxidizing oil ester of an epoxy resin. It has good color and color retention. The slow evaporating solvent present makes it an excellent roller coat vehicle possessing exceptional adhesion, hardness and flexibility. It can be used in air-drying and baking applications, and is compatible with amine modifications. *Uses:* For air-dried implement and cabinet enamels, baked white enamels with 10–20% amine modification, metal-decorating finishes, roller-coat applications.
FREEMAN CHEMICAL CORP.

Chempol® EP-3. An epoxy resin ester formulated to give a faster dry than CHEMPOL EP-1 or EP-2. Its drying is equal to that of the styrenated alkyds. With this rapid dry feature, EP-3 also possesses the increased chemical resistance, flexibility, hardness and adhesion which is inherent in epoxy resins as compared to alkyds. Being modified, however, some sacrifice is made in these features as compared with CHEMPOL EP-1 and EP-2. *Uses:* For clear varnishes, forced-dry wood finishes, shell-casing enamels, very fast air dry primers and enamels.
FREEMAN CHEMICAL CORP.

Chempol® M-2410. A short modified alkyd containing rosin and phenolic resin combined with linseed and tung oil. It has excellent durability, and chemical and gasoline resistance. *Uses:* For drum enamels, garden equipment enamels, machinery enamels, non-lifting primers under lacquer, toy enamels.
FREEMAN CHEMICAL CORP.

Chempol® M-2803. A slightly modified medium oil alkyd. The slight rosin modification imparts excellent gloss with very good gloss retention. *Uses:* For baked automotive primers, dip- and flow-coat application, farm machinery and implement enamels, wood furnitures finishes, general industrial enamels.
FREEMAN CHEMICAL CORP.

Chempol® M-3009. A short modified alkyd designed for fast set and dry. Its unusual compatibility characteristics allow this alkyd to be blended with pure alkyds and certain CHEMPOL styrenated alkyds to produce enamels of varying degrees of flexibility and dry. *Uses:* For casting sealers, drum enamels, engine enamels, implement enamels, machinery enamels, toy enamels; and as a hardener for pure alkyds.
FREEMAN CHEMICAL CORP.

Chempol® M-3423. A non-rosin, short modified alkyd having exceptionally high viscosity at low solids. Being free of rosin and rosin derivatives, it can be used in fast air-dry applications where rosin-type resins cannot be employed. *Uses:* For drum enamels, freight car finishes, metal primers, toy enamels, traffic paints.
FREEMAN CHEMICAL CORP.

Chempol® M-4000. An alkyd wrinkle vehicle designed to give maximum color retention in light-colored wrinkle enamels. Wrinkling characteristics under adverse conditions are good. In combination with melamine and/or urea, hard, durable finishes can be produced. Wrinkle finishes produced with this resin have higher gloss than those produced with oleoresinous types, such as CHEMPOL O-2518.
FREEMAN CHEMICAL CORP.

Chempol® M-4501. A slightly rosin-modified alkyd which meets most automobile company specifications for chassis and frame blacks. Enamels formulated with this resin have excellent adhesion and flexibility with very fast set and dry time. *Uses:* For casting sealers, drum enamels, frame and chassis blacks, industrial air-dry and black enamels, implement enamels, porch and deck furniture enamels, toy enamels, metal primers.
FREEMAN CHEMICAL CORP.

Chempol® O-2211. A high-quality, tung-linseed varnish based on a maleic penta ester gum resin. This varnish is principally intended for use as a clear on floors and trim, and for similar applications. In pigmented films, it must be used with non-reactive type pigments. *Uses:* For wood cabinet finishes, exterior spar varnishes, floor varnishes, and trim enamels.
FREEMAN CHEMICAL CORP.

Chempol® O-2321. An excellent linseed oil-maleic penta varnish that finds its principal use as an all-purpose mixing varnish. Aluminum paints made with this vehicle have excellent leafing characteristics over long periods of storage. *Uses:* For aluminum paints;

bronzing liquids; spar varnishes; and as a mixing and grinding vehicle.   FREEMAN CHEMICAL CORP.

Chempol® O-2512. A tung oil-phenolic varnish, 25-gal. oil length. It is very fast drying, and has exceptional exterior durability. It also has exceptional resistance to alkalis and other chemicals. Its color retention is similar to that of other phenolic varnishes. *Uses:* For varnishes, four-hour enamels, floor enamels, marine spar varnishes, porch and deck enamels, wood radio and television cabinets.   FREEMAN CHEMICAL CORP.

Chempol® O-2518. A tung oil, wrinkle varnish that produces an extremely uniform wrinkle pattern. It can be used with proper drier adjustment as an air-dry or bake vehicle without wrinkle.
FREEMAN CHEMICAL CORP.

Chempol® O-3222. A varnish-type vehicle designed for hammer-effect baking enamels. In combination with melamine, hard, marproof and trouble-free finishes can be obtained. Increased hardness can also be obtained by adding approx. 10% AMBEROL 801 or a similar type resin. Its stability can be extended by the addition of 0.1% diethylamine triamine, based on the weight of solids.   FREEMAN CHEMICAL CORP.

Chempol® O-3316. A high-quality spar varnish that has exceptional exterior durability in clear or pigmented enamels. It also has excellent can stability and anti-skinning characteristics. In combination with long oil alkyds, high quality spar varnishes can be produced at very reasonable cost. *Uses:* For engine primers, marine enamels, wood radio and television cabinets, station wagon finishes, spar varnishes.   FREEMAN CHEMICAL CORP.

Chempol® P-2400. A long-oil, pure alkyd designed for use where color is not a factor and a low cost vehicle is required. It possesses excellent flexibility and gloss. While it takes a little longer to dry than other CHEMPOL long-oil alkyds, this difference can usually be minimized with increased cobalt drier. It has excellent exterior durability. *Uses:* In the mfg. of architectural enamels, machinery enamels, porch furniture enamels, structural enamels, and trim and trellis enamels.   FREEMAN CHEMICAL CORP.

Chempol® P-2405. A long-oil alkyd that has very rapid set and dry-through time without loss of wet edge. It is outstanding in brushability, flow and non-sag, and in color retention. *Uses:* In the mfg. of white and non-yellowing architectural enamels, white hospital maintenance enamels, marine finishes, clear overprint varnishes, and railway finishing enamels.   FREEMAN CHEMICAL CORP.

Chempol® P-2420. A long-oil alkyd possessing good brushability and a long wet edge for uniform lapping. Its color retention is good and its exterior durability is excellent. The drying properties and general performance rank it with the best alkyds. *Uses:* In the mfg. of architectural enamels, bulletin enamels, enamel undercoaters, maintenance enamels, marine finishes, mill whites, porch furniture enamels, structural enamels, and trim and trellis enamels.
FREEMAN CHEMICAL CORP.

Chempol® P-2426. A high-grade, long-oil, soya alkyd vehicle carefully formulated to provide the desirable properties of ease of application, high gloss, and excellent gloss retention, hardness, durability and color. It meets the requirements of Federal specification TT-R-266, Type 1, Class A. *Uses:* For architectural white enamels, bulletin enamels, hospital maintenance enamels, marine finishes, mill whites, wood porch furniture enamels, railway finishes, trim and trellis enamels, undercoaters.
FREEMAN CHEMICAL CORP.

Chempol® P-2901. An odorless flat wall vehicle characterized by its outstanding ease of application, non-penetration and non-setting. Its color retention is excellent. Its long wet edge gives excellent lapping properties. *Uses:* For enamels, flat wall paints, semi-gloss finishes.   FREEMAN CHEMICAL CORP.

Chempol® P-2907. An odorless flat and semi-gloss paint vehicle characterized by its excellent flow, brushing and working properties, and outstanding dilution characteristics with low solvency thinners. *Uses:* In flat wall paints, flat enamels, egg shell enamels, semi-gloss enamels.   FREEMAN CHEMICAL CORP.

Chempol® P-3002. A medium oil alkyd designed for low cost industrial finishes either air dry or bake. It has sufficient phthalic ester to possess greater hardness than is available in long oil alkyds. It has excellent hardness and flexibility, and excellent exterior durability. *Uses:* For automotive chassis blacks, engine finishes, freight car finishes, general utility enamels, interior low-cost brushing enamels, air-dry metal primers, undercoaters.   FREEMAN CHEMICAL CORP.

Chempol® P-3004. A flat wall paint vehicle characterized by its excellent non-penetration, brushability, hold out and flow. Its long wet edge gives it excellent lapping properties. *Uses:* For flat enamels, flat wall paints, semi-gloss finishes.
FREEMAN CHEMICAL CORP.

Chempol® P-3034. A medium-oil alkyd that is especially useful as an air-dry or baking vehicle. Its acid value has deliberately been made high to facilitate good grinding. This resin is especially useful in industrial and trade sales enamels where max. initial color and color retention are required. Recommended for industrial enamels and primers for air-dry and bake applications. *Uses:* For architectural enamels, automotive refinishing enamels, bicycle enamels, bulletin enamels, engine finishes, farm implement enamels, metal primers, wood porch furniture enamels, railway equipment enamels, trim and trellis enamels, semi-gloss enamels.   FREEMAN CHEMICAL CORP.

Chempol® P-3303. A medium-oil oxidizing alkyd possessing excellent properties of weathering, durability, and gloss retention; and having excellent through-dry. Its high reduction properties with petroleum solvents allows formulation of low-cost finishes, and its excellent color and gloss retention makes it especially useful for interior enamels. It is compatible with urea and melamine resins. *Uses:* For non-yellowing interior white enamels, porch and deck enamels, semi-gloss enamels, general utility enamels, maintenance enamels.   FREEMAN CHEMICAL CORP.

Chempol® P-3400. A low-cost, medium-oil soya type alkyd with relatively good color and excellent color and gloss retention. It is useful both in air dry and bake. Due to the dark initial color, its use is limited to other than whites. When baked with compatible ureas, it develops hard marproof films. *Uses:*

For automotive primers, engine finishes, farm implement finishes, freight car finishes, general utility enamels, machinery enamels, metal primers, porch and deck enamels, porch furniture enamels, semi-gloss enamels, toy enamels.   FREEMAN CHEMICAL CORP.

Chempol® P-3401. A low-cost, medium-oil alkyd characterized by its excellent exterior durability, water resistance, and pigment compatibility. *Uses:* For automotive primers, engine finishes, farm implement finishes, freight-car finishes, general utility enamels, machinery enamels, metal primers, porch furniture enamels, porch and deck enamels, semi-gloss enamels, store-front enamels, toy enamels.
  FREEMAN CHEMICAL CORP.

Chempol® P-3427. A medium-oil alkyd which produces enamels of great film toughness and durability for outside exposure. It possesses rapid dry and also positive dry under adverse conditions or with difficult pigments such as black or red. Its color restricts its use to tinted or deep color enamels. *Uses:* For automotive chassis enamels, automotive primers, bicycle enamels, bus and trailer enamels, farm implement enamels, machinery enamels, metal primers, metal sign enamels, porch and deck enamels, railway finishing enamels, store front finishes.
  FREEMAN CHEMICAL CORP.

Chempol® P-3504. A non-drying, medium-oil alkyd resin that is an excellent plasticizer for nitrocellulose lacquers, urea or melamine resin enamels, polyvinyl chloride and chlorinated rubber coatings. It imparts a high degree of toughness, flexibility and weather resistance while at the same time improving adhesion and gloss. It can be used with urea or melamine to form a baking resin.   FREEMAN CHEMICAL CORP.

Chempol® P-3511. A low viscosity, medium-oil alkyd especially useful in trade sales enamels because of its excellent flow, leveling and non-sag properties. This resin is especially useful where enamels of high solids and low viscosity are required. *Uses:* For architectural brushing enamels, metal primers, porch and deck enamels, store front enamels, wood venetian blinds.   FREEMAN CHEMICAL CORP.

Chempol® P-3514. A high-quality, medium-oil alkyd that combines fast set and dry with top performance in either dip or spray applications. It has superior hardness, toughness, high gloss and color retention. *Uses:* For automobile refinishing enamels, bicycle enamels, bus and trailer enamels, farm implement enamels, wood furniture finishes, machinery enamels, metal primers, metal sign finishes, porch furniture finishes, railway finishes, traffic paints.
  FREEMAN CHEMICAL CORP.

Chempol® P-3600. A very high quality, medium-oil-length alkyd especially designed for max. compatibility with other resins including chlorinated rubber (PARLON) and vinyl resin (VINYLITE VAGH). It is useful alone for fast set and dry with early hardness development without brittleness on aging. With varying amounts of chlorinated rubber, very fast drying finishes can be formulated which exhibit excellent gasoline resistance and resistance to chemical attack. Used with vinyl resins, similar desirable results can be achieved. *Uses:* For implement enamels, outdoor metal sign enamels, engine enamels, machinery enamels.   FREEMAN CHEMICAL CORP.

Chempol® P-3620. A medium-oil alkyd vehicle possessing excellent speed of set and dry even under adverse conditions of weather and moisture. It dries rapidly and with high gloss even when formulated with such poor drying pigments as reds and blacks. It makes a top quality maintenance enamel for brush and spray application for either inside or exterior use. *Uses:* For automotive chassis enamels, automotive refinishing enamels, bus and trailer enamels, brushing enamels, general utility enamels, machinery enamels, metal primers, exterior metal sign enamels, air-dry porch furniture enamels; and spray, dip, and flow-coat industrial enamels.
  FREEMAN CHEMICAL CORP.

Chempol® P-4000. A low-cost baking alkyd for use where a dark vehicle is not a deterrent. Its color retention under baking conditions is good; it will tolerate substantial amounts of low solvency thinners such as mineral spirits and VM&P naphtha; and it can be used with urea or melamine resins. This combination of properties makes it especially useful for many baking applications where low cost is a primary consideration. It has excellent flexibility and adhesion. Its high resistance to salt spray makes its use desirable where coatings must meet such a test. *Uses:* For automotive baking enamels; bicycle enamels, metal cabinet enamels, bake-type furniture finishes, metal porch furniture finishes, radio and television cabinet finishes.   FREEMAN CHEMICAL CORP.

Chempol® P-4006. A high-quality, low cost, white baking alkyd enamel. It can be used as a base resin for all baking-type finishes since it has excellent resin and amine compatibility. It has a relatively fast cure and excellent adhesion and flexibility. It also makes excellent baking primers. *Uses:* For white, non-yellowing baking enamels, metal finishes, bake primers.   FREEMAN CHEMICAL CORP.

Chempol® P-4010. A medium-short alkyd that has been carefully compounded with a higher than usual phthalic ester content and properly modified with linseed oil. The result is a resin of very rapid set and dry-through combined with a high resistance to solvent lifting. It is an excellent leveling and flowing resin. The fast set is comparable to that of the rosin-modified types but without the subsequent tendency toward brittleness. This resin is also useful for baking under adverse conditions, such as at low temp. It may be used with urea or melamine. *Uses:* For automotive refinishing enamels, bicycle enamels, bus and trailer enamels, four-hour enamels, railway finishes, and spray, dip, and roller-coat enamels.
  FREEMAN CHEMICAL CORP.

Chempol® P-4101. A relatively fast curing, white baking alkyd. Its excellent adhesion and flexibility make it a very desirable resin for use in any metal-forming operation. When used with driers in lacquer formulations it prevents the danger of "lifting" when later coats are applied. *Uses:* For appliance whites, automotive enamels, fluorescent light fixture enamels, heat-resistant baking enamels, hospital equipment, finishes, bake-type metal finishes; and as a lacquer plasticizer.   FREEMAN CHEMICAL CORP.

Chempol® P-4151. An extremely fast curing, baking alkyd with properties similar to CHEMPOL® P-4101. It produces a harder film than P-4101 although its color retention is not quite as good. It possesses

excellent spray ability. *Uses:* For automotive enamels, furniture finishes, gasoline pump enamels, range enamels, refrigerator enamels, white baking enamels.
FREEMAN CHEMICAL CORP.

Chempol® P-4154. A short-oil, non-oxidizing alkyd resin with a very pale original color and designed to have excellent color and gloss retention under prolonged overbakes of 200°F. It is amine compatible and can be used as a lacquer plasticizer in very pale lacquers. *Uses:* For washing machine enamels, drying machine enamels, automotive enamels, special non-yellowing enamels; and as a lacquer plasticizer.
FREEMAN CHEMICAL CORP.

Chempol® P-4300. A baking alkyd possessing the important advantages of excellent flexibility, adhesion and color retention together with good hardness. It is especially recommended where high adhesion and flexibility are required. It also possesses excellent salt-spray and humidity resistance, and high soap and detergent resistance. *Uses:* For clear catalyzed finishes, die-casting finishes, heat-resistant enamels, metal-decorating finishes, molded phenolic cabinet finishes, metal radio and television cabinet finishes, range enamels, refrigerator enamels, roller-coat enamels, washing machine enamels; and as a lacquer plasticizer.
FREEMAN CHEMICAL CORP.

Chempol® P-4321. A non-oxidizing pure phthalic resin that produces extremely good white baking enamels. It has a very pale color and good color retention at high baking temps. and on overbakes. Its excellent alkali resistance allows frequent washings without loss of gloss. This resin also has excellent color retention in and stability with nitrocellulose lacquers. *Uses:* For heat-resistant enamels, detergent-resistant enamels, range enamels, refrigerator enamels, venetian blind enamels, washing machine enamels; and as a lacquer plasticizer.
FREEMAN CHEMICAL CORP.

Chempol® P-4400. A specially developed, high-heat-resistant, non-oxidizing alkyd resin with outstanding color and gloss retention on overbakes. It should always be used over a non-yellowing primer. *Use:* For range and stove enamels and other high-heat-resistant enamels.
FREEMAN CHEMICAL CORP.

Chempol® P-4723. A baking alkyd designed for high-quality white baking enamels. It has an extremely pale color and outstanding color retention, even at high baking temps. Its excellent alkali resistance allows frequent washing without loss of its high gloss. It is extremely stable when used as a plasticizer in nitrocellulose lacquers, and is particularly useful for extremely clear lacquers requiring max. durability. *Uses:* For heat-resistant enamels, bake-type hospital equipment enamels, molded phenolic cabinet finishes, range enamels, refrigerator enamels, venetian blind finishes, washing machine finishes; and as a lacquer plasticizer.
FREEMAN CHEMICAL CORP.

Chempol® S-2200. A specially-formulated styrenated alkyd designed for max. gloss and flexibility. *Uses:* In formulating fast air-dry enamels, and high-gloss hammer finishes.
FREEMAN CHEMICAL CORP.

Chempol® S-2401. An aromatic, soluble, styrenated alkyd suitable for rapid air-dry and baking industrial finishes, and hammer finishes. Enamels formulated with S-2401 cure very rapidly over a wide range of temps. to hard tough films. These enamels have excellent water resistance, gloss, color, durability and chemical resistance.
FREEMAN CHEMICAL CORP.

Chempol® S-2403. A soya-castor, vinyl toluene-modified alkyd resin characterized by its excellent color and color retention, and rapid set and dry. *Uses:* For fast air-dry and baking enamels, fiberboard finishes, hammer finishes, implement enamels, shell-casing enamels.
FREEMAN CHEMICAL CORP.

Chempol® S-2407. An oil, vinyl toluene-modified alkyd. It is very stable in a dip tank. *Use:* For fast-drying industrial enamels.
FREEMAN CHEMICAL CORP.

Chempol® S-2600. A vinyl toluene alkyd that tolerates innite dilution with mineral spirits, grinds excellently on a roller mill, and is compatible with a wide range of alkyds. In combination with a medium pure alkyd it dries in less than 30 min. *Uses:* For industrial air-dry enamels, and brush enamels.
FREEMAN CHEMICAL CORP.

Chempruf[NR]. A protective suit of butyl-FAIRPRENE fabric. *Use:* For protection against toxic concentrations of chemicals. It offers complete body protection.
MINE SAFETY APPLIANCES CO.

Chemrez. The trade name for a series of alkyd resins and hard gums for use in the protective coatings industry.
CHEMICAL OIL & RESIN CO.

Chemtred[NR]. A rubber-base enamel for unpainted concrete floors below-grade, and for above-grade floors subject to acid, alkali, oil or water conditions.
HALLEMITE MFG. CO.

Chemvar. The trade name for a series of oleoresinous varnishes for the protective coatings industry.
CHEMICAL OIL & RESIN CO.

Cherry Coposil®. Incorrectly listed as CHERRY COPSIL® (*Supp.* I p. 43).
CALIFORNIA SPRAY-CHEMICAL CORP.

Cherry Copsil®. (*Supp.* I p. 43). Should have been listed as CHERRY COPOSIL®.
CALIFORNIA SPRAY-CHEMICAL CORP.

Chia-seed Oil△. A clear, amber-colored oil extracted from the seeds of the plant *Salvia hispanica* of Mexico. The seeds yield about 30% oil which contains about 39% linolenic acid, 45% linoleic acid, 5% palmitic acid, 2.7% stearic acid together with some arachidic, oleic and myristic acids. Sp.gr. 0.936; iodine no. 72; acid no. 1.4. It is used principally as a drying oil for paints and varnishes.

Chicle△. The coagulated latex obtained from incisions in the trunk of the evergreen tree *Achras zapota* and some other species of southern Mexico, Guatemala, and Honduras. Crude CHICLE has a reddish-brown color. The purified and neutralized gum is a white to pink amorphous powder that is insoluble in water. Used chiefly as a chewing gum base.

Chifonese®. The trademark for a line of fabrics made wholly or partially of cellulose derivatives.
CELANESE CORP. OF AMERICA

Chi-lon®. A nylon cloth material coated both sides with Paracril® (*HBMTN* p. 421), weighing 43 oz. per sq.yd., used as a diaphragm material for the flexible membrane in Vaporspheres®, Vaportanks and Hortondome Roofs. The diaphragm inflates with vaporization from stored liquids during filling and breathing.
Chicago Bridge & Iron Co.

China Bark△. *Same as* Quillaja△.

China Clay△. *Same as* Kaolin△.

China Wood Oil△. *Same as* Tung Oil△.

Chippewa®Can.. *See* Atlas Chippewa®Can..

Chlo-Dur. *See* Tuf-On Selenium Rectifier Coatings.

Chloral[NR]. A chlorinated ether solvent used in textile processing to remove waxes, coning oils, etc. from all natural yarns, including Wool, and all types of Rayon. It acts as a buffer against alkalinity and can be used directly in the peroxide bath where bleaching and scouring are carried out in the same bath. It is a non-toxic, amber-colored liquid that dissolves readily in warm water. It has a pH of 6.5 in a 1% solution.
Mac Chemical Co.

Chlorax® "40". A weed killer containing 40% sodium chlorate and 58% sodium metaborate. It is in powder form, for dry or spray application. *Use:* For the control of shallow and deep-rooted weeds and grasses. It inhibits regrowth.
Chipman Chemical Co.

Chlorazene®. (*HBMTN* p. 130). No longer available.
Abbott Laboratories

Chlor-Bor®. A chlorate-borate herbicide.
Pennsylvania Salt Mfg. Co.

Chlorea®. A weed and grass killer for use along fence lines, in driveways and playgrounds, parking areas, railroad rights-of-way, etc. It is safe to use around buildings and other structures since it does not create a fire or poison hazard. Applied in dry form or as a water-mixed spray. It contains 40% sodium chlorate, 57% sodium metaborate, and 1% 3(p-chlorophenyl)-1,1-dimethylurea.
Chipman Chemical Co.

Chlorextol®. A nonflammable transformer insulating fluid. It is a synthetic non-sludging liquid of high dielectric strength used in place of oil as a cooling and insulating medium in transformers.
Allis-Chalmers Mfg. Co.

Chlorinated Rubber△. A material produced by reacting rubber with chlorine. The rubber is chlorinated in solution, generally with carbon tetrachloride or a mixture of hexachloroethane and carbon tetrachloride as the solvent. The reaction is carried out at a temp. of 80°–100°C.; when about 65% chlorine has been absorbed, further addition is cut off and heating continued until no more hydrogen chloride is evolved. Sp.gr. 1.64; bulking value, 0.0735 gal. per lb.; soluble in hydrocarbons, carbon tetrachloride, and in esters; insoluble in water. *Uses:* In the mfg. of paints and other finishes, inks, paper coatings, textile finishes and adhesives.

Chlorogiene®. A medicinal preparation, in powder form, which combines the soluble chlorophyllins with lactose in an acid complex. For use in routine vaginal hygiene and for the elimination of leukorrhea, pruritus, and odor.
Purdue Frederick Co.

Chloro-IPC△. *Same as* CIPC△.

Chlorophenesin®. (*Supp.* I p. 44). Now a registered trademark.
Chemo Puro Mfg. Corp.

Chlorophyll△. The green-coloring matter of plants, the presence of which is necessary for photosynthesis to take place. Obtained by solvent extraction from the leaves of various plants. Produced commercially as a crystalline powder that has a m.p. of 183°C., and is soluble in alcohol. It is used as a coloring material for foods, in soaps, dentifrices, chewing gum, etc., and in household air-purifying agents because of its ability to combine with carbon dioxide of the air to form formaldehyde which reacts with the impurities in the air.

Chlorostrep® Kapseals®. A medicinal consisting of a combination of 125 mg. Chloromycetin (chloramphenicol, Parke-Davis) and 125 mg. dihydrostreptomycin (as the sulfate) per Kapseal.
Parke, Davis & Co.

Chlorothene®. A chlorohydrocarbon solvent containing methylchloroform, used mainly for cold cleaning of metals.
Dow Chemical Co.

Chlor-Tergent®. A chlorinated detergent that cleans, sanitizes and deodorizes in a single operation. It is a powder which is mixed with water prior to use. It is sudsless and therefore does not form any foam or air pockets in cleaning equipment.
Oakite Products, Inc.

Chobeline®. (*HBMTN* p. 131). No longer available.
Reed & Carnrick

Chocolatone®. An imitation powdered chocolate flavor for use as a fortifier and extender for cocoa.
Florasynth Laboratories, Inc.

Choledyl®. A stable and readily water-soluble theophylline salt of choline. *Use:* In medicine for the treatment of congestive heart failure, angina pectoris, premenstrual tension, and bronchial asthma.
Nepera Chemical Co.

Choline△. *Also known as* Sincaline△, Bilineurine△, Amanitine△, Gossypine△, Vidine△, Bursine△, Luridine△, *and* Fagine△. (β-hydroxyethyl) trimethylammonium hydroxide. $C_5H_{15}NO_2$; mol.wt. 121.18. It is found in many plants, such as hops, belladonna, strophantus, etc.; in animal organs such as the bile and brain; and in the yolk of eggs. It is the basic constituent of Lecithin. Prepared synthetically from trimethylamine and ethylene chlorohydrin or ethylene oxide. A strongly alkaline, viscid liquid that absorbs carbon dioxide from the air; very soluble in water and in alcohol; insoluble in ether. The chloride of choline is used in medicine in the treatment of liver disorders, hypertension, ileus and tachycardia. It is also used as a feed supplement, especially for poultry.

Cholmodin®. A laxative composition containing deoxycholic acid and extract of aloe.
Ames Co.

Chondrus△. *Same as* Irish Moss△.

Chromar. A line of welding wire, in sizes of ⁵⁄₆₄" to ¼", for submerged arc welding of stainless steel. Available in 17 grades, corresponding to the following types: 308, 308L, 309, 309Cb, 310, 312, 316, 316L, 330, 347, 349, 410, 420, 430, 446, 502, and 521. ARCOS CORP.

Chroma-Tone[NE]. An asbestos-cement siding shingle with a rustic, wild-grain texture. Available in the following pastel colors: Driftwood Gray, Sandalwood Tan, and Elmwood Green. NATIONAL GYPSUM CO.

Chromel® Alloy 502. (*HBMTN* p. 132). Now known as HOSKINS® ALLOY 502. HOSKINS MFG. CO.

Chromewear®. A tool steel (U. S. Patent No. 2,174,286) especially developed to offer the highest possible wear resistance. High carbon (2.30%) and vanadium (4.75%) give this steel high resistance to abrasion with chromium (5.25%) adding to the depth of hardness. Ideal for brick mold liners, side and end plates, extrusion dies and other parts requiring extreme wear resistance. Because of this latter quality, CHROMEWEAR should be confined to applications where machining and grinding requirements are relatively simple. It can be heat treated to a very high hardness, and is tough enough for most tool applications. VANADIUM-ALLOYS STEEL CO.

Chromicoat®. A brown-colored powder containing chromium compounds. Used as a pre-paint conversion coating for aluminum, and aluminum and zinc die castings. OAKITE PRODUCTS, INC.

Chromindigen®. A line of mordant acid dyestuffs for dyeing navy shades on WOOL. They have excellent fastness properties. GENERAL DYESTUFF CO.

Chromogard. See ENSIGN 345 CHROMOGARD[NE].

Chromogene®. A line of mordant acid dyestuffs for dyeing black or gray shades on WOOL. They have excellent fastness properties. GENERAL DYESTUFF CO.

Chromoglaucine®. A line of mordant acid dyestuffs for dyeing WOOL and printing COTTON, by chrome methods. GENERAL DYESTUFF CO.

Chromotex®. (*HBMTN* p. 133). Formerly mfg'd by OLIN MATHIESON CHEMICAL CORP., now a product of ENDRISS CHEMICALS.

Chromoveil[NE]. A decorating process whereby fine lines of color are applied in a varied tracery on ceramic ware. CHROMOVEIL colors are available for use on pottery either for overglaze or underglaze work as well as on porcelain enamel or glassware. The colors are normally prepared in a special tacky medium and shipped in that form. It is applied with a special gun equipped with a veiling head and pressure regulator. A light coat can be applied to simulate the veins of marble or a greater amount can be applied to obtain a lace effect. PEMCO CORP.

Chrysotile[△]. See ASBESTOS[△].

CI-104[NE]. (*Supp.* I p. 44). No longer available. JOHN B. MOORE CORP.

Cibalan® Salt H. A dyeing assistant for use in the dyeing of NYLON and in the dyeing and bleaching of leather. CIBA CO.

Cibalan® Salt N. A non-ionic, neutral, dyeing assistant for use in the dyeing of WOOL, SILK, and NYLON. A clear, yellowish solution, readily soluble in cold water. It increases penetration, promotes level dyeing, and improves the appearance of the dyed material. CIBA CO.

Cibalan® Salt S. A dyeing assistant for use in the dyeing of WOOL and polyamide fibers. CIBA CO.

Cibalgine®. An analgesic, antipyretic and sedative used in the treatment of nervous irritability caused by a combination of anxiety and pain. Available in form of yellow tablets, each containing ½ gr. DIAL® and 3½ gr. aminopyrine; and as 2 ml. ampuls, each ml. of which contains 2½ gr. DIAL® and 3½ gr. aminopyrine. CIBA PHARMACEUTICAL PRODUCTS INC.

Cimcut® Base Additive. (*Supp.* I p. 445). No longer available. CINCINNATI MILLING PRODUCTS DIV.

Cinchona[△]. The bark of a number of species of evergreen trees of the genus *Cinchona*, which is native to the Andes from Mexico to Peru. These trees, however, are now grown in many tropical countries, chiefly as a source of quinine. The hard, thick grayish bark is dried and powdered, and the alkaloids recovered by solvent extraction.

Cinerin. See PYRETHRUM[△].

Cinnamon[△]. The highly aromatic, thin, yellowish-brown bark of the tropical evergreen laurel tree *Cinnamomum Zeylanicum*, of Ceylon, China, and the East Indies. It is used as a spice, and as a flavor in confectionary, perfumery, and medicine.

CIPC[△]. *Also known as* CHLORO-IPC. Isopropyl chlorocarbonilate. $C_{10}H_{16}ClNO_2$; mol.wt. 217.70. A liquid weed killer. It is moderately soluble in petroleum oils (10% in kerosene); miscible with lower alcohols, aromatic hydrocarbons, and most organic solvents. Its selective growth activity makes it suitable for inhibition of sprouting of potato tubers, and for pre-emergence weed control, especially on soya beans.

Circo® Heat Transfer Oils. Naphthenic-base oils for use as heat-transfer media in closed circulating systems equipped with expansion tanks. They have high thermal stability and exceptional resistance to sludging. Under the conditions of recommended service, they do not form hard carbon, which acts as an insulator at the very points where high heat transfer is desired, and they will not crack into light compounds and thus create a fire hazard. Important properties of the two grades of CIRCO® HEAT-TRANSFER OILS are as follows: viscosity at 210°F., SUS, 80–90 for CIRCO XX HEAVY and 150–175 CIRCO XXX HEAVY; sp.gr., API, 17.0–20.0 for CIRCO XX and 16.5–19.0 for CIRCO XXX; fire point, °F., 430 for CIRCO XX and 510 for CIRCO XXX; max. working temp. °F., 450 for CIRO XX and 600 for CIRCO XXX. SUN OIL CO.

Circo® Hydraulic Oils. A line of moderately refined, vacuum distillates from selected crudes. Especially useful as lubricants under conditions where: (1) operating temps. are below 120°F., (2) leakage is above normal, (3) FULLER'S EARTH filters are used, and (4) excessive contamination is present. SUN OIL CO.

Circo® Light Process Aid. A general-purpose, naphthenic-type softener for neoprene and natural rubber.

Used in the mfg. of nonstaining reclaims and butyl inner tubes. Sp.gr. 0.9242; viscosity, 4.2 centistokes at 210°F. SUN OIL CO.

Circo® Lubricating Oils. A line of straight mineral oils designed for the general lubrication of industrial machinery. Especially suitable for once-through applications, regardless of operating temps. SUN OIL CO.

Circomar® -5AA. A dark, free-flowing, liquid softener of the asphalt-flux type for natural rubber, GR-S polymers, or blends of GR-S with natural rubber. It is easy to handle at room temp. Used in the mfg. of tires. SUN OIL CO.

Circomar® -25. A dark, heavy, viscous, liquid softener of the asphalt-flux type for natural rubber, GR-S polymers, or blends of the latter with natural rubber. Used in the mfg. of tires. SUN OIL CO.

Circomar® -110. A rubber process aid. It is a very low cost, soft asphaltum specially developed for use in the mfg. of tires. SUN OIL CO.

Circosol® -2XH. A heavy, clear, transparent, viscous liquid having a pale green color. Composed of hydrocarbons of comparatively high molecular weight, derived entirely from selected crudes. Its composition may be regarded as relatively naphthenic. Sp.gr. 0.9465; viscosity, SUS at 210°F., 85; aniline point, 175°F.; aromatics (% by wt.), 48. *Uses:* As a process aid in the mfg. of commercial rubber goods involving the use of natural rubber, reclaims, and particularly GR-S polymers; it is also used to a great extent in the mfg. of oil-extended cold GR-S polymers. SUN OIL CO.

Citrex Syrup®. A children's cough syrup containing sodium citrate, ammonium chloride, syrup ipecac, extract cascara, chloroform, and flavoring.
ABBOTT LABORATORIES

Citrisan[NR]. A citrus bioflavonoid compound in tablet form. Each tan tablet contains 5 g. salicylamide, 8.5 mg. ascorbic acid (VITAMIN C), and 5.0 mg. lemon bioflavonoid complex. *Uses:* For the prevention and treatment of the common cold and respiratory infections; for the prevention of capillary fragility by control of the capillary syndrome induced by viruses and bacteria; and for the treatment of rheumatoid arthritis, rheumatic fever; and symptomatic hemorrhage. CHICAGO PHARMACAL CO.

Citroflex® 2. Triethyl citrate. $CH_2(CO_2C_2H_5)$ COH-$(CO_2C_2H_5)$ $CH_2CO_2C_2H_5$. Mol.wt. 276.3; b.p. (1 mm. Hg) 127°C.; sp.gr. (25°/25°C.), 1.136. A plasticizer for resins and plastics, particularly in food-packaging applications. Compatible with cellulose acetate, cellulose acetate-butyrate, cellulose nitrate, chlorinated rubber, ethyl cellulose, polyvinyl acetate, polyvinyl butyral, polyvinyl chloride, polyvinyl chloride-acetate, polyvinylidene chloride. Accepted by U. S. Food and Drug Administration for use as a component of plastic wrappers for packaging foodstuffs.
CHAS. PFIZER & Co.

Citroflex® 4. Tributyl citrate. $CH_2(CO_2C_4H_9)$ CO-H$(CO_2C_4H_9)CH_2CO_2C_4H_9$; mol.wt. 360.4; b.p. (1 mm. Hg) 170°C.; sp.gr. (25°/25°C.), 1.042. A plasticizer for resins and plastics. Compatible with cellulose nitrate, chlorinated rubber, ethyl cellulose, polyvinyl acetate, polyvinyl butyral, polyvinyl chloride, polyvinyl chloride-acetate, polyvinylidene chloride. An internal plasticizer for polyurethane resins.
CHAS. PFIZER & Co.

Citroflex® A-2. Acetyl triethyl citrate. CH_2-$(CO_2C_2H_5)C(O_2CCH_3)(CO_2C_2H_5)CH_2CO_2C_2H_5$; mol. wt. 318.3; b.p. (1 mm. Hg) 132°C.; sp.gr. (25°/25°C.), 1.135. A plasticizer for resins and plastics, particularly in food-packaging applications. Compatible with cellulose acetate, cellulose acetate-butyrate, cellulose nitrate, chlorinated rubber, ethyl cellulose, polyvinyl chloride, polyvinyl chloride-acetate, polyvinylidene chloride. Accepted by U. S. Food and Drug Administration and by Meat Inspection Branch, U. S. Dept. of Agriculture for use as a component of plastic wrappers for packaging foodstuffs.
CHAS. PFIZER & Co.

Citrosynth Oils[NR]. Three flavoring oils—lemon, lime, and orange—each consisting of a mixture of the natural fruit oil and other natural oils.
FLORASYNTH LABORATORIES, INC.

Clack Activated Carbon (High Capacity). *Also known as* CAC (HIGH CAPACITY). A black, granular filter carbon used for the removal of taste, odor, and color from water supplies. It is distinguished by its rugged grain structure and high density. The internal structure of the CAC (HIGH CAPACITY) grain consists of a balanced proportion of large to small diameter pores. These pores efficiently adsorb and retain the taste, odor, and color components contained in water. It is very effective for the removal of free chlorine and orthochlorophenol, which results from the chlorination of waters containing phenols from industrial wastes. *Uses:* In domestic and industrial pressure-type filter installations.
CLACK WATER TREATMENT, INC.

Clad®. A self-polishing floor wax made from a blend of Carnauba and synthetic waxes. It is waterproof, slip resistant, and resistant to marring and scuffing.
J. I. HOLCOMB MFG. CO.

Clairanese®. The trademark for a line of fabrics made wholly or partially of cellulose derivatives.
CELANESE CORP. OF AMERICA

Clar-Apel® Cellulose Film. (*HBMTN* p. 135). No longer available. E. I. DU PONT DE NEMOURS & Co.

Clarapent® Neutrascour. A neutral scouring agent for raw wool, requiring the use of no additives or builders such as alkalis or salts. It permits the scouring cycle to be operated at lower temps., thus producing cleaner, whiter stock, less fiber damage and longer staple. ATLAS COLOR & CHEMICAL CO.

Claremont "PE" Series. A complete range of granular color concentrates for coloring polyethylene manufactured by conventional calendering, extrusion, or injection molding processes. Simple tumbling of the required amount of color granules with the polyethylene is sufficient to insure uniform and speck-free color distribution in the end product.
CLAREMONT PIGMENT DISPERSION CORP.

Claremont "RP" Series. A line of inks in a full color range, including metallics, for rotogravure printing on treated polyethylene film.
CLAREMONT PIGMENT DISPERSION CORP.

Claremont "UR" Series. A line of color paste concentrates for pigmenting urethane foams. The colors are dispersed in a polyester to form smooth, free-flowing pastes, which can be added at any point prior to the foaming stage.
CLAREMONT PIGMENT DISPERSION CORP.

Claremont "VC" Series. A line of ink concentrates in white, black, various colors, and metallics, for printing on vinyl film and sheeting.
CLAREMONT PIGMENT DISPERSION CORP.

Clarite[NE]. A barium-cadmium organic complex stabilizer for vinyl resins. It combines excellent heat stability with good light stability and clarity. Supplied as a two-component system. CLARITE A, soft white powder and CLARITE B, a clear, straw-colored liquid. CLARITE A is used at a level of from 1.25% to 2%, based on the resin, depending upon the particular combination of stability, clarity and lubricity desired. Generally 1% of CLARITE B is sufficient with this level of CLARITE A. *Uses:* As a heat and light stabilizer for extruded and molded clears and vinyl flooring.
NATIONAL LEAD CO.

Claro®. The trademark for a line of electrical resistors and controls. (Registration No. 613,521; Class 21; Oct. 4, 1955.)
CLAROSTAT MFG. CO.

Clarofin R-40[NE]. A cation-active, substantive, textile-finishing agent. It is a synthetic amino condensate that produces a permanent softness and hand to COTTON, RAYON, ACETATE, WOOL and NYLON. Soluble in hot water; pH (1% solution), 5; does not stain whites.
MAC CHEMICAL CO.

Clarostat®. The trademark for ballast resistors, adjustable resistors, metal tube resistors, power resistors, fixed resistors, resistor potentiometers, rheostats, volume controls, attenuators, electrical resistance heating elements, voltage dividers, ballast tubes, line ballasts, voltage regulators, shunts, fuses, chokes, switches, ion traps, synchronous motors, and parts thereof.
CLAROSTAT MFG. CO.

Clarostat (in Symbol)®. The trademark for ballast resistors, adjustable resistors, metal tube resistors, power resistors, fixed resistors, resistor potentiometers, rheostats, volume controls, attenuators, electrical resistance heating elements, voltage dividers, ballast tubes, line ballasts, voltage regulators, shunts, fuses, chokes, switches, ion traps or beam benders for cathode ray tubes, synchronous motors, and parts thereof.
CLAROSTAT MFG. CO.

Clay Deflocculants No. 2 and 5[NE]. Liquid dispersing agents for ceramic bodies.
R. T. VANDERBILT CO.

Cleaneasy®. Round, hospital style nursing bottles, graduated in both oz. and cc. Available in 4 oz. and 8 oz. sizes.
ARMSTRONG CORK CO.

Cleaner 27. *See* CD CLEANER 27.

Clearfresh[NE]. Colorless wax emulsions for potatoes, formulated to reduce shrinkage through control of moisture loss and to minimize sprouting. They form a clear, wax coating that protects potatoes through shipping and marketing. For use on all varieties of potatoes.
S. C. JOHNSON & SON

Clearkote[NE]. A new type of wood floor finish. Produces a film of outstanding toughness and unusually light color. Approved by Maple Flooring Assoc.
BRULIN & CO.

Cleartone[NE]. A mechanical diaphragm type of communicating device which, when used in conjunction with gas-mask facepieces, permits voice communication from the wearer to surrounding persons.
MINE SAFETY APPLIANCES CO.

Clear-Vue[NE]. The trade name for a dust respirator.
MINE SAFETY APPLIANCES CO.

Climatic Paints[NE]. The trademark for a line of consumer paints.
GLIDDEN CO.

C Line®. The trademark for a line of electrical resistors. (Registration No. 613,501; Class 21; Oct. 4, 1955).
CLAROSTAT MFG. CO.

Cling®. An oil-less treatment for yarn sweepers and dusters to increase the pick-up power.
J. I. HOLCOMB MFG. CO.

Clinistix®. An enzymatic diagnostic composition for detecting the presence of glucose in urine.
AMES CO.

Clinitest®. A diagnostic composition for detecting the amount of sugar in urine.
AMES CO.

Clipper Seal Packing[NE]. A precision-molded, oil-seal packing consisting of a one-piece molded body (the seal) and a garter spring for adjusting the lip pressure. The tough, dense heel and the soft, flexible lip are concentrically molded into a single unit. No metal case is required. Besides providing an effective lubricant-retaining, dirt-excluding seal of wide adaptability and long-wearing qualities, this construction simplifies installation and assures quick, easy removal without damage to the seal. The outer heel is resilient enough to conform to cavities that are slightly out-of-round and the garter spring helps the lip maintain contact even when bearing wear has caused slight eccentricity or shaft run-out. Available in several different styles.
JOHNS-MANVILLE SALES CORP.

Clor®. A disinfectant, cleaning, and bleaching agent.
PENNSYLVANIA SALT MFG. CO.

Clorital®. A disinfectant.
PENNSYLVANIA SALT CO.

Cloudinol. *See* ENTRAPPED® POWDERED CLOUDINOL, FLAVORS.

Cloudinol N[NE]. A clouding medium for citrus and other beverages.
FLORASYNTH LABORATORIES, INC.

Clove Oil△. *See* CLOVES△.

Cloves△. The dried flower buds of the evergreen tree *Caryophillus aromaticus*, which is grown chiefly in Zanzibar, but also in Madagascar, East Africa, and the East Indies. The buds are used principally as a highly aromatic spice. The buds are also used to obtain a pungent, yellowish oil known as CLOVE OIL, which contains about 85% eugenol and some clovene and other terpene compounds. CLOVE OIL is used as a flavoring material in tooth paste, in the production of artificial vanilla, and as a medicinal antiseptic.

Cly-Q-Pak®. A disposable set for administration of parenteral fluids.
ABBOTT LABORATORIES

C. M. 118. *See* Pax® C. M. 118.

Coalkote. (*HBMTN* p. 137). No longer available.
SUN OIL CO.

Cobenzil®. A sedative expectorant. Contains codeine phosphate, sodium citrate, ammonium chloride, ipecac syrup, menthol and aromatics in a benzoinated cough syrup. ABBOTT LABORATORIES

Cocell[NE]. Clear finishes and pigmented enamels of cellulose base for use on metal.
MAAS & WALDSTEIN CO.

Cochineal△. A dyestuff material obtained from the female species of the *Coccus cacti*, an insect that feeds on species of cactus of Mexico. These dark, reddish brown insects are wingless; at the egg-laying season they are brushed off the plants, boiled, and then dried. COCHINEAL contains from 10 to 20% pure coloring matter, carminic acid, mostly in the eggs. CARMINE RED, $C_{11}H_{12}O_7$, is obtained by boiling the COCHINEAL with mineral acid. It produces brilliant red lakes of various hues with different metals. Before the development of coal-tar dyes, COCHINEAL was the most important coloring material available.

Cochise®. The trademark for a patented medicinal used in the treatment of eczema. It is available in two forms: (1) a liquid, for application in the morning, which is compounded of tincture of benzoin, glycerine, and bichloride of mercury; and (2) an ointment, for application at night, which is compounded of petroleum jelly, white wax, and yellow oxide of mercury. CHATHAM PHARMACAL

Cocobola△. *Also known as* HONDURAS ROSEWOOD△. The wood of the hardwood tree *Dalbergia retusa*, of Central America, chiefly Panama and Costa Rica. It is a heavy, extremely hard wood having orange and red bands with dark streaks. The wood takes an extremely fine polish. *Uses:* For canes, turnery, inlaying, scientific instrument cases, knife handles, etc.

Coconut Oil△. *Also known as* COPRA OIL△. The oil obtained from the thick kernel or meat that adheres to the inside of the shell of the large nuts of the palm tree, *Cocus nucifera*, that grow along the coasts of tropical countries. Sp.gr. 0.926; m.p. 27–32°C.; saponification no. 251–263; iodine no. 8–9.6; contains 45–48% lauric acid, 17–20% myristic acid, 5–7% palmitic acid, up to 5% stearic acid, and some oleic, caprylic and caproic acids. The dried meat, called COPRA, contains 60–65% oil, which is recovered by pressing. The principal producing areas of COCONUT OIL and COPRA are the East Indies, southern Asia, the Philippines and the South Sea Islands. *Uses:* As a food oil; in mfg. of soap; as a source of lauric acid; etc.

Coco-Ster Compound. *See* TROY COCO-STER COMPOUND.

Co-Deltra[NE]. Medicinal tablets, each of which contains 2.5 mg. DELTRA® (prednisone, Merck), 50.0 mg. magnesium trisilicate U.S.P., and 0.3 g. dried aluminum hydroxide gel U.S.P. Used for the treatment of patients receiving adrenocortical steroids who need antacid therapy to modify the hyperacidity which is frequently associated with adrenocortical steroid therapy. MERCK SHARP & DOHME

Coelestol®. A line of level-dyeing acid blues, of good light fastness, used for dyeing WOOL.
GENERAL DYESTUFF CO.

Coflex®. A line of stretchable, plastic-coated, upholstery fabrics. INTERCHEMICAL CORP., COTAN DIV.

Cohyde®. A line of plastic-coated fabrics for a wide variety of purposes. INTERCHEMICAL CORP., COTAN DIV.

Co-Hydeltra[NE]. Medicinal tablets, each of which contains 2.5 mg. HYDELTRA® (prednisolone, Merck), 50.0 mg. magnesium trisilicate U.S.P., and 0.3 g. dried aluminum hydroxide gel U.S.P. Used for the treatment of patients receiving adrenocortical steroids who need antacid therapy to modify the hyperacidity which is frequently associated with adrenocortical steroid therapy. MERCK SHARP & DOHME

Coir△. A fiber obtained from the outer husks of the coconut. The fiber is retted from the husks, hammered with wooden mallets, and then combed and bleached. The long, coarse fibers are used for making brushes; the fine, curley fibers are spun into COIR yarn, which is easily dyed and used for making mats, cordage, and coarse cloths. In the West Indies, COIR fiber is mixed with SISAL and JUTE to make a coffee-bag cloth; in the Pacific islands, it is used with cement to make a hard-setting, light-weight board for siding; in India, it is used to make a fiberboard by bonding it with shellac and then pressing and baking the sheets.

Colac. A pasteurized, homogenized, concentrated ice cream mix made from cream, whole milk, sugar, egg yolk, gelatin, celluose glycolate, algin, and vanillin.
M & R DIETETIC LABORATORIES, INC.

Colfoam®. A thermal insulation made from a frothed resinous composition. It contains 99% trapped air by volume. Thermal conductivity, 0.18–0.21 B.t.u.-inch/hr. × sq.ft. × °F.; density, 0.8 lb./cu.ft. It is resistant to moisture and corrosion; will not support combustion; is not affected by low temps.; and will withstand a sustained temp. of 120°F. without deterioration, and 300°F. with a max. shrinkage of 15% by volume. It is also one of the most efficient materials for soundproofing: Q factor, 130. COLTON CHEMICAL CO.

Colfoam® Microballoon® Spheres. Hollow unicellular spheres, from 2 to 6 microns in diam., made from urea-formaldehyde plastic. Compressive strength 30–50 lb./sq.in.; bulk density, 3.7 lb./cu.ft.; color, white; decomposition temp., 350°F. *Uses:* As a floating cover on oil in storage tanks to reduce loss due to "breathing"; as a lightweight filler for various plastic compositions—polyester, epoxy, polyethylene, etc.—plastisols, organisols, plaster and concrete; as an opacifier for wax coatings for paper; as a porosity modifier for ceramics and in powder metallurgy; and as an additive to seismographic explosives to aerate the gel and overcome desensitization resulting from tight packing. COLFOAM® is a registered trademark of COLTON CHEMICAL CO.; MICROBALLOON® is a registered trademark of STANDARD OIL CO. OF OHIO.
COLTON CHEMICAL CO.

College®. The trademark for a line of inked ribbons.
INTERCHEMICAL CORP., AULT & WIBORG CARBON & RIBBON DIV.

Colliery King. *See* BOSTON COLLIERY KING.

Colloresin. (*HBMTN* p. 139). No longer available; Company liquidated as of Oct. 1, 1955.
GENERAL DRUG CO.

Colonial No. 6 Non-Shrinkable®. Incorrectly listed as NON-SHRINKABLE® (*HBMTN* p. 401).
VANADIUM-ALLOYS STEEL CO.

Colony[NE]. A stone-patterned insulating siding for building construction. CELOTEX CORP.

Colophony[△]. Same as ROSIN[△].

Colored Metalsium[NE]. A metallic hardener for heavy-duty floors. It is made from gray cast iron ground to give slightly elongated particles with jagged edges, and lime-resistant mineral colors—tile red, brick red, brown, battleship gray, and green. It is the same as METALSIUM® (*HBMTN* p. 360) with color added. CERESIT WATERPROOFING CORP.

Colorex®. (*HBMTN* p. 140). No longer available.
STAUFFER CHEMICAL CO.

Color Fix® No. 128 *and* No. 384. (*Supp.* I p. 487). Should have been listed as registered trademark.
THOMPSON CHEMICALS CORP.

Colorfresh®. Wax emulsions formulated to reduce shrinkage of potatoes through control of moisture loss and to minimize sprouting. Available with coloring material for red potatoes that complies with federal regulations concerning food coloring. For use on russet, red and sweet potatoes.
S. C. JOHNSON & SON

Colorimetric[NE]. A line of instruments to indicate the presence and percentage of an atmospheric contaminant. They employ a chemical which changes color proportional to the concentration of the contaminant in the air sample.
MINE SAFETY APPLIANCES CO.

Color-Vu. *See* CRAFTINT COLOR-VU PAPERS.

Colpotab®. A trichomonacide containing tyrothrycin, chlorophyll, and phenyl mercuric acetate. Used topically for the treatment of trichomonas vaginalis and other vaginal infections. PURDUE FREDERICK CO.

Columbia® Calcium Chloride. Formerly known as 3-C CALCIUM CHLORIDE® (*HBMTN* p. 636).
COLUMBIA-SOUTHERN CHEMICAL CORP.

Columbia-Southern®. The registered trade name of the COLUMBIA-SOUTHERN CHEMICAL CORP., a subsidiary of PITTSBURGH PLATE GLASS CO.

Colza Oil[△]. Same as RAPESEED OIL[△].

Combat®. A line of felt products made of all jute fiber. Many of the products sold under the name COMBAT® are similar to products sold under the names of OZITE® and CARDINAL®. The OZITE® products are all hair, and the CARDINAL® products are blends of hair and jute fiber. AMERICAN HAIR & FELT CO.

Combuthal®. An intravenous anesthetic for veterinary use. ABBOTT LABORATORIES

Comfo®. The trademark for a line of respirators. *Use:* For protection against all dusts and light concentrations of organic vapors and **acid gases**.
MINE SAFETY APPLIANCES CO.

Comfo Cap. *See* MSA COMFO CAP®.

Commando Drill Rod®[Can.]. A drill rod made from high quality, water hardening tool steel. The standard stock is made from ATLAS®[Can.] X-10; if the rod is to be used for cutting tools such as taps, reamers, twist drills, etc., it is made from ATLAS®[Can.] X-12. Supplied in 3-ft. lengths. ATLAS STEELS LTD.

Commerce®. Registered trade name for petrochemicals and petrochemical derivatives mfg'd by the COMMERCE CHEMICAL CORP.

Commerce®. Registered trade name for a line of petroleum products mfg'd by the COMMERCE OIL CORP. Included in the line are: (1) motor and diesel engine oils; (2) Pennsylvania motor oil; (3) aviation oils; (4) marine oils; (5) industrial oils; (6) grease and gear lubricants; (7) U.S.P. and technical white oils; (8) U.S.P. filtered and technical petrolatums; (9) fully refined, semi-refined, and crude scale waxes.
COMMERCE OIL CORP.

Com-Plus®. A line of additives for petroleum products. COMMERCE CHEMICAL CORP.

Compocillin-V[NE]. A penicillin preparation, PENICILLIN V, for oral administration.
ABBOTT LABORATORIES

Composition No. 97, No. 98, *and* No. 99. (*HBMTN* p. 142 *and* 143). Should have been listed as OAKITE® COMPOSITION No. 97, No. 98, *and* No. 99.
OAKITE PRODUCTS, INC.

Compound III. *See* TROY COMPOUND III.

Compound 118[△]. Same as ALDRIN[△].

Compreg[NE]. (*Supp.* I p. 49). No longer available from FARLEY & LOETSCHER MFG. CO.

Compressive Shrinking Oil S-261-C[NE]. Incorrectly listed as SANFORIZING OIL S-261-C[NE] (*Supp.* I p. 209).
JACQUES WOLF & CO.

Conax®. A line of thermocouples, thermocouple assemblies, thermocouple protection tubes, and pressure sealing thermocouple glands. The latter permit operation from −300°F. to +1,850°F., and from full vacuum to 20,000 lb./sq.in. CONAX CORP.

Concordal[NE]. An imitation flavoring oil for the mfg. of Concord grape flavors.
FLORASYNTH LABORATORIES, INC.

Concord Yellow Jack. *See* BOSTON CONCORD YELLOW JACK.

Concretite®. A specially formulated, colorless liquid concentrate which is added to the gauging water used in concrete mixes to produce concrete of greater density, hardness, and high early compressive strength. It permits speedy removal of forms; provides greater strength for heavy-duty floors; allows a comparatively light 2-inch topping to be placed over old floors instead of replacing with a thicker slab of ordinary concrete; the high early compressive strength of the concrete permits the use of floors within 24 hr. after they have been laid; and the increased density makes the concrete resistant to the damaging effects of acids, grease and oil, and retards the penetration of rain and moisture; and its bonding qualities permit effective patching or plaster coating of spalled interior or exterior walls. STONHARD CO.

Condensed Oil No. 50[NE]. A lubricating oil for electric motors, air compressors, generators, blowers, fans, line shafting and other machinery. Suitable for temps. up to 225°F. Made from paraffin-base petroleum oils with high flash and fire points, and selected grease-film materials. KEYSTONE LUBRICATING CO.

Congo Copal△. *See* COPAL△.

Conoco H-300[NE]. Secondary plasticizer for vinyl resins. It is a slightly off water-white, oily liquid with a mild pleasant odor. Sp.gr. (100°F.), 0.965; mol.wt. 300; bromine no. 0.40; aniline point, 30°C.; viscosity (100°F.), 19.9 centipoises; flash point (C.O.C.), 335°F.; freezing point, below —40°F.; distillation range, 600–740°F. CONTINENTAL OIL CO.

Conq-R-Dust[NE]. A concrete sealer, composed of synthetic resins and waxes, which eliminates the dusting of concrete floors. Neutralizing of concrete is not necessary prior to application. It resists moisture, alkali and acids; and floors can be painted or tiled without removing sealer. Can also be used on slate and other stone-type floors. S. C. JOHNSON & SON

Conseco®. Trademark for paper products, including covers, paper napkins, and paper towels in dispensing containers and sold as a unit. The name CONSECO® is also used for seat covers in roll form; the name PROCO® is used for covers in folded form.
CONSOLIDATED COVER CO.

Conserv Wax. (*HBMTN* p. 144). No longer available. The HARRY B. LEWIS CO. is no longer active. It has been supplanted by the COMMERCE OIL CORP. and the COMMERCE CHEMICAL CORP.

Consol®. An antitussive-expectorant for controlling coughs. Supplied as a pleasant-tasting, thixotropic suspension, each 5 cc. (teaspoonful) of which contains 5 mg. Narcotine, 50 mg. terpin hydrate and 3 mg. DECAPRYN® (doxylamine) succinate. Rx.
WM. S. MERRELL CO.

Consolets®. A cherry-flavored throat troche for cough control. Each CONSOLET® contains the same medicaments present in each 5 cc. of CONSOL® thixotropic suspension. WM. S. MERRELL CO.

Consoweld®. (*HBMTN* p. 144). Now a product of CONSOWELD CORP., successor to CONSOLIDATED WATER POWER & PAPER CO.

Contact Wax[NE]. A protective floor finish for use on electrically conductive floors. It seals out dirt, powder, etc., which adversely affect floor conductivity.
BRULIN & CO.

Continental Clay[NE]. A kaolin clay. *Use:* As a carrier for insecticidal and fungicidal dusts and wettable concentrates. R. T. VANDERBILT CO.

Continex® **CF.** An oil-type furnace black. Used in natural and synthetic rubber, all types of rubber products, belts, hose, special tire treads, and special heels where electrical conductivity is required.
WITCO CHEMICAL CO.

Continex® **FEF.** A fast-extruding, oil-type furnace black. Used in natural and synthetic rubber where smooth extrusion is required. For mechanical goods, cable jackets and inner tubes. WITCO CHEMICAL CO.

Continex® **HAF.** A high-abrasion, oil-type furnace black. Used in natural and synthetic rubber, especially cold GR-S for tire treads, and solid tires and industrial tires where max. abrasion resistance is required. WITCO CHEMICAL CO.

Continex® **ISAF.** An intermediate, super-abrasion, oil-type furnace black. Used in natural and synthetic rubber for tire treads, tank blacks, and solid industrial tires where max. abrasion resistance, cracking resistance of tire treads, and cut resistance are required.
WITCO CHEMICAL CO.

Continex® **SRF-NS.** A semi-reinforcing, non-staining, natural gas-type furnace black. Used in natural and synthetic rubber. Recommended for black trim on white footwear, automotive window channel, and all types of molded and extruded mechanical goods that come in contact with white and colored lacquers.
WITCO CHEMICAL CO.

Contractors®. The trademark for a line of dynamite.
HERCULES POWDER CO.

Convalets®. Stress formula vitamins in tablet form.
ABBOTT LABORATORIES

Coolband®. The trademark for a line of sweatbands used to prevent perspiration from entering the eyes from the forehead. MINE SAFETY APPLIANCES CO.

Cool Cap[NE]. A protective cap designed to provide adequate ventilation to the wearer. *Use:* By miners, for head protection. MINE SAFETY APPLIANCES CO.

Cooler®. The trademark for a line of cement-coated nails. UNITED STATES STEEL CORP.

Copal△. A term used to designate several different types of fossil and other hard resins found in nearly all tropical countries, and used in the mfg. of varnishes, lacquers, adhesives, and coatings. They vary in color from white through yellow, red, brown, to brownish-black, and have a sp.gr. of 1.04–1.13. Commercial COPALS are generally classified into the following 5 groups: East African, West African, Manila, East Indian, and South American. All COPALS are soluble in alcohol, linseed oil, and in turpentine; however, they are distinguished from other types of resins by their solubility in chloral hydrate. The hardest and the highest quality COPALS come from Africa; ZANZIBAR COPAL, one of the hardest of the varnish resins, is obtained from the tree *Trachylobium verrucosum*. It has a m.p. of 240°–360°C. CONGO COPAL, from Guinea, has a m.p. of 180°–200°C. In the East Indies, COPAL resin is obtained from the tree *Agathis alba;* in Malaya, the COPAL is known as WHITE DAMMAR and is obtained from the tree *Dammara orientalis;* in the Philippines, the COPAL is known as MANILA COPAL, and is obtained from the *Almacido* tree. The semi-hard and soft copals are obtained directly from the trees by tapping. In the United States, fossil COPALS of high quality are obtained by separation from low-grade coals in Utah.

Copar®. (*HBMTN* p. 146). No longer available.
GENERAL CHEMICAL DIV.,
ALLIED CHEMICAL & DYE CORP.

Copel®. (*HBMTN* p. 146). Now a registered trademark. HOSKINS MFG. CO.

Copofilm®. (*HBMTN* p. 146). No longer available.
TENNESSEE CORP.

Copoloid[NE]. (*HBMTN* p. 146). No longer available.
MILLER CHEMICAL & FERTILIZER CORP.

Coposil. See CHERRY COPOSIL®.

Copperbrite #48. See LONCO COPPERBRITE #48.

Copper-Hard. See HEWITT COPPER-HARD[NE].

Copra[△]. The dried meat of the coconut, from which coconut oil is obtained.

Copra Oil[△]. *Same as* COCONUT OIL[△].

Cop-R-Nap®. (*HBMTN* p. 147). New a registered trademark.
OSMOSE WOOD PRESERVING CO. OF AMERICA

Coprote® Dust. (*HBMTN* p. 147 and *Supp.* I p. 50). No longer available. GENERAL CHEMICAL DIV.,
ALLIED CHEMICAL & DYE CORP.

CopWeld. See EUTEC-COPWELD®.

Corac[NE]. Rack enamels and stop-off coatings of lacquer or synthetic resin base that resist plating.
MAAS & WALDSTEIN CO.

Coral[△]. A shiny, hard, calcareous material composed of the skeletons of *Corallium nobile* and other species of aquatic protozoa. The structures are built up by these creatures into forms resembling leafless trees or shrubs, fans, mushrooms or cups. Red and pink CORALS come from the Indian Ocean, and off the coast of northeastern Africa; black CORAL is found in southeastern Asia. The red and black varieties are very hard and take a high polish; the pink variety is much softer. The colored corals are used in making jewelry, buckles, beads, novelties, etc.

Coramine®. A 25% aqueous solution of nikethamide, used as a circulatory, central nervous system, and respiratory stimulant.
CIBA PHARMACEUTICAL PRODUCTS INC.

Cordfil®. (*HBMTN* p. 148). No longer available.
RAYON PROCESSING CO. OF R. I.

Cordopreg®. A line of dry-process molding materials consisting of reinforcing fabrics impregnated with synthetic resins. The reinforcing materials are glass fibers and cloths, and ORLON and other synthetic cloths. The resins are stabilized polyesters, fire-resistant polyesters, modified diallyl phthalates, and epoxies. All formulations contain the catalyst necessary for cure by the application of heat without pressure. However, for best development of properties, some pressure is recommended. Pressure can vary from 12 to 14 lb./sq.in. in vacuum bag molding to high pressure in compression molding.
CORDO MOLDING PRODUCTS, INC.

Cordurol®. (*HBMTN* p. 148). Now a registered trademark. L. SONNEBORN SONS, INC.

Coresite Cement[NE]. An especially compounded hydraulic-type mortar, resistant to attack by acids, alkalis, and salt solutions at pH from 3 to 14; and unaffected by organic solvents. It hardens at temps. as low as 40°F.; and is resistant to vitrification at temps. as high as 1,800°F. *Use:* For bonding bricks for chemical applications. MAURICE A. KNIGHT

Corex[NE]. The trade name for a stainless steel designed for sulphuric acid service.
UNITED STATES STEEL CORP.

Corfoam. A foaming-type phenolic resin designed to produce light weight structural cores, especially for stretch dies, models and laminated fixtures.
REZOLIN, INC.

Corhart® ZAC® Electrocast®. Incorrectly listed as ZAC® ELECTROCAST® (*HBMTN* p. 631).
CORHART REFRACTORIES CO.

Cork[△]. The thick, spongy bark of a species of the oak tree, *Quercus suber,* grown in Spain, Portugal, Italy, Algeria, Morocco, Tunisia, and to a limited extent in the United States. It is characterized by its peculiar cellular structure, with more than 50% of its volume in air cells. Due to its lack of capillarity, cork does not absorb moisture. Its very low sp.gr. of 0.15–0.20 makes it one of the lightest materials of commerce; it also has a very low thermal conductivity. When dried, cork is light, porous, easily compressed, and very elastic. *Uses:* For bottle stoppers, insulation, vibration pads, floats, gaskets, oil retainers, roll coverings, etc.

Corker®. The trademark for a line of cement-coated nails. UNITED STATES STEEL CORP.

Corlex®. A high-pressure plastic laminate for counter, sink, and bar tops; wall surfaces; etc. It is decorative, easy-to-clean, extremely durable and resistant to heat, stains, and scratches. It is not harmed by soapy water, cleaning detergents, and other forms of household detergents. For adhering it to surfaces, ARMSTRONG No. S-1200 CORLEX CEMENT is recommended. ARMSTRONG CORK CO.

Corlok[NE]. A self-hardening silicate cement containing no sodium or fluoride.
PENNSYLVANIA SALT MFG. CO.

Corn Steep Liquor[△]. A concentrated product produced by steeping corn kernels in slightly acidic water. It contains nitrogenous and other organic and inorganic substances in soluble form. Typical properties: solids, 50–52%; protein, 22–24%; reducing sugars (as dextrose), 5.5–7.5%; lactic acid, 7.5–11.5%; ash, 8.0–9.5%; pH, 3.7–3.9. *Uses:* As a valuable protein supplement to animal feeds, and as a nutrient in microbiological processes, particularly in the production of antibiotics, yeasts, etc.

Corobond®. A synthetic-resin bonding cement for brick and tile. Characterized by its excellent workability and chemical and thermal resistance. It hardens to an extremely dense material which provides high mechanical strength to the bond. Supplied as a two-component unit, a powder and a liquid, which are mixed just before use. It is used in the construction of acid pickling and neutralizing tanks, plating-room floors, drains, sewers, linings for chemical process tanks, etc. CEILCOTE CO.

Corogard®. A group of sprayable, air-drying coatings for protecting metals. These coatings are used under severe service conditions when corrosion or corrosion plus abrasion are problems. Proper combinations of COROGARD coatings form protective coating systems to meet many types of service.
MINNESOTA MINING & MFG. CO.

Coronado®. The trademark for a line of prefabricated homes. UNITED STATES STEEL HOMES, INC.

Coronized®. Glass fabrics treated so as to be softer and capable of better draping.
OWENS-CORNING FIBERGLAS CORP.

Corosex®. A specially processed, hard, bead-like magnesia adapted for use in gravity and pressure filters to neutralize acidity in water supplies and to increase the pH value. By neutralizing the free carbon dioxide in water, CORROSEX corrects red water conditions and renders the water non-corrosive and stable. It is also useful in iron and manganese removal where a pH increase is desired.
CLACK WATER TREATMENT, INC.

Corotop®. A roofing material in the form of mats of glass fibers bonded together with a resinous binding material. OWENS-CORNING FIBERGLAS CORP.

Corrucote®. A plastic lacquer for use as a coating on translucent plastic panels. The surface and light transmission of panels which have dulled and weathered over extended years of service may be rejuvenated by application of clear CORRUCOTE. In addition to the clear lacquer, CORRUCOTE is also mfg'd in six colors, to be used when light transmission reduction is desired. These colors are green, blue, coral, yellow, and white.
L-O-F GLASS FIBERS CO., CORRULUX DIV.

Corrugating Starch #1[NB]. A specialty corn starch for the paper board corrugating industry. Extensively used as a carrier because of its resistance to viscosity breakdown. A. E. STALEY MFG. CO.

Corrugating Starch #5[NB]. A specialty corn starch for the paper board corrugating industry. It is a secondary starch of superior water-holding properties.
A. E. STALEY MFG. CO.

Corrumastic®. A water-clear plastic compound for application between laps of translucent panels for weather-sealing purposes. L-O-F GLASS FIBERS CO., CORRULUX DIV.

Cor-Ten®. See U.S.S.® COR-TEN®.

Corundum[△]. A very hard, crystalline mineral used as an abrasive. Consists of natural aluminum oxide, Al_2O_3, together with varying quantities of impurities. Found in Burma, India, South Africa and the Near East, and in Georgia and the Carolinas in the United States. However, most of the production comes from the United States. When pure, the mineral is colorless, but it usually contains metallic oxides, and the color of the commercial grades are white, gray, pink, yellow, brown, red, and blue. CORUNDUM has a hardness of about 8.8 on the Moh scale, a sp.gr. of about 4, and a m.p. of about 1,950°C. It also has a high refractive index. The finest quality, clear, colored crystals are used as gem stones; other grades are used as an abrasive. CORUNDUM is also mfg'd artificially in an electric furnace.

Coryban®. A medicinal, in capsule form, for relief of the common cold. Each capsule contains 230 mg. salicylamide, 120 mg. acetophenetidin, 30 mg. caffeine, 10 mg. prophenpyridamine maleate, 20 mg. ascorbic acid, and 20 mg. purified hesperidin.
J. B. ROERIG & CO.

Cosmic® Black. A bone black pigment for use in the mfg. of paint, varnish, lacquer, plastics, ink, paper, etc. It is an air-floated, uniform product ($99^{1}/_{2}\%$ through a 325-mesh screen) that is available in 27 grades for specific applications. Characterized by high stability and tinting strength, low oil absorption, and extreme jetness.
AMERICAN AGRICULTURAL CHEMICAL CO.

Cotton[△]. The fiber of the blossom of several species of plants of the genus *Gossypium* of the mallow family. It is a tropical plant that is grown in many parts of the world. In the United States, the plant grows well in a belt across the southeastern section and as far north as Virginia. The fiber contains from 88 to 96% cellulose on a dry basis, together with some protein, pectin, sugars, and from 0.4 to 0.8% wax. COTTON has a wide variety of uses for making fabrics, cordage, padding, and as a source of cellulose for making plastics, RAYON and explosives. ABSORBENT COTTON is made by thoroughly cleaning the cotton fibers and removing the natural wax with a solvent, such as ether. COTTON batting is raw cotton carded into matted sheets and made up into rolls for padding purposes.

Cottonseed Oil[△]. The oil expressed from the seed of the cotton plant, *Gossypium*. When the seeds are crushed whole, the oil is dark and requires careful refining. Generally, the seeds are first hulled before crushing, and the resulting oil is practically colorless and odorless. Sp.gr. 0.915–0.921; saponification no. 192–200; iodine no. 110. The seeds from Upland COTTON yield about 25% oil containing about 40% linoleic acid, 30% oleic acid, and 20% palmitic acid. COTTONSEED OIL is used principally as a food oil in salad oils, margarine, cooking fats; and for packing sardines. It also finds wide industrial use in lubricants, cutting oils, soaps, quenching oils, paints, etc.

Coupler 2, 3, 6®. Incorrectly listed as 2,3,6® (*Supp.* I p. 269). NATIONAL ANILINE DIV.
ALLIED CHEMICAL & DYE CORP.

Coverlac®. A strippable plastic coating designed especially for protecting metal surfaces during factory operations. It sprays on easily to form a tough, elastic, clear film that is capable of withstanding scratches, dirt, grease and other handling and manufacturing hazards. Available in transparent orange, clear, or in specified colors, and in formulations for specific applications, including:
COVERLAC SC 240, for protection of porcelain and enamel.
COVERLAC SC 242, for use as a high-temp. masking compound.
COVERLAC SC 236, for long term storage protection of metal. Meets specification MIL-S-8141 for outdoor storage of aircraft and parts.
COVERLAC 224 B, for protection of outdoor architectural metals. SPRAYLAT CORP.

Covicone®. A protective cream for contact dermatoses. It is a special plasticized combination of silicone (dimethylpolysiloxane), nitrocellulose and castor oil in a vanishing cream base. ABBOTT LABORATORIES

C. P. Grease[NB]. A line of black, waterproof greases for use in plain and anti-friction bearings on mining, contractors', and similar equipment subject to surface water and dirt. M.p. above 200°F. Available in various consistencies.   KEYSTONE LUBRICATING CO.

Crackerjack®. The trademark for a line of fertilizers. INTERNATIONAL MINERALS & CHEMICAL CORP.

Craftint "66" Drawing Inks[NB]. A line of free-flowing and permanent inks for pen or brush applications. Available in jet black and 17 translucent colors.   CRAFTINT MFG. CO.

Craftint Color-Vu Papers[NB]. Matte-finish papers in 24 basic hues, with 4 tints and 3 shades of each hue, and 8 grays and black. They are stainproof and have washable surfaces. Used by artists, designers, decorators, advertising and display men, etc.   CRAFTINT MFG. CO.

Craftint Doubletone[NB]. A drawing paper with two hidden screens which yield four different tones: solid black, white, and two shades of gray. With this paper, an artist can create a combination highlighted halftone effect in his original copy. Available in 17 patterns, which are made visible with DEVELOPERS No. 21 and No. 22.   CRAFTINT MFG. CO.

Craftint Foilcraft[NB]. A line of laminated and varnished foil papers in brilliant metallic colors. *Use:* For gift wrappings, window displays, decorations, greeting cards, book covers, shelf paper, etc.   CRAFTINT MFG. CO.

Craftint Singletone[NB]. A chemically treated drawing paper with a single hidden tone. It is used where straight shading effects are desired. Available in 59 patterns, which are made visible with DEVELOPER No. 6.   CRAFTINT MFG. CO.

Craftint Super White "37"[NB]. An intense white artist's paint that covers India ink and grease pencil layouts in a single stroke. It does not turn yellow or discolor with age.   CRAFTINT MFG. CO.

Crandon[NB]. A line of coated papers.   KIMBERLY-CLARK CORP.

Crater. *See* TEXACO® CRATER.

Crater X Fluid. *See* TEXACO® CRATER X FLUID.

"Cravenette"®. The trademark for chemical compositions for processing fabrics and garments made of wool, cotton, and synthetic fibers and blends thereof to make them water repellent.   CRAVENETTE CO., U.S.A.

Craxement[NB]. Incorrectly listed as CRAXMENT[NB] (*HBMTN* p. 151).   CERESIT WATERPROOFING CORP.

Craxment[NB]. (*HBMTN* p. 1515). Should have been listed as CRAXEMENT[NB].   CERESIT WATERPROOFING CORP.

Cream Softener[NB]. (*HBMTN* p. 151). No longer available.   AMERICAN CYANAMID CO.

Crepenese®. The trademark for a line of fabrics made wholly or partially of cellulose derivatives.   CELANESE CORP. OF AMERICA

Creslan®. An acrylic fiber, in staple and tow form, both bright and semi-dull.   AMERICAN CYANAMID CO.

Crest®. The trademark for a line of: (1) accounting, teletype and adding machine rolls; (2) carbon paper; and (3) inked ribbons.   INTERCHEMICAL CORP., AULT & WIBORG CARBON & RIBBON DIV.

Crestone®. A striated mineral-wool acoustical material. The ridges and valleys of the surface form strong directional lines of high light and shadow which create a pleasing effect. It is coated with two coats of white latex paint. Light reflection coefficient 70%; sound-absorption coefficient, for ⅝" thickness when mechanically supported, 0.38 at 125 cycles and 0.55 at 500 cycles. When cemented to plaster, the corresponding sound-absorption coefficients are 0.16 and 0.69, respectively.   ARMSTRONG CORK CO.

Crocus Cloth△. A fabric coated with red iron oxide and used as a fine abrasive for polishing metals.

Crown®. The trademark for a line of spring wire, music wire or piano wire.   UNITED STATES STEEL CORP.

Crown (in design)®. The trademark for a line of container caps provided with fluted skirts, screw and lug caps, home canning caps, sanitary metal caps for milk, fruit juices, etc.   CROWN CORK & SEAL CO.

Crown Brand®. The trademark for an insect powder.   S. B. PENICK & CO.

Cryogel®. (*HBMTN* p. 155). Now a registered trademark.   MALLINCKRODT CHEMICAL WORKS

Cryptostegia Rubber△. A natural rubber obtained from the leaves of two species of perennial vines native to Madagascar, *Cryptostegia grandiflora* and *C. Madagascariensis.* The former was grown in India, and the rubber obtained from it was known as PALAY RUBBER△. The plant was brought to Mexico and Florida as an ornamental and now grows extensively in Mexico and the West Indies. The max. rubber content, about 2–3% of the dry weight of the leaf, it obtained from leaves taht are about 3½ months old. The leaves also contain about 8% resin, which must be removed from the rubber to prevent the product from being tacky and soft.

CrysCoat®. The trademark for a group of materials used to apply zinc or iron phosphate coatings to ferrous and non-ferrous metals by tank or spray methods. Group includes: CRYSCOAT HC, CRYSCOAT LT, CRYSCOAT SW, CRYSCOAT No. 47, CRYSCOAT No. 87, CRYSCOAT No. 89, CRYSCOAT No. 89M, and CRYSCOAT FH RINSE.   OAKITE PRODUCTS, INC.

Crystallose®. (*HBMTN* p. 155). No longer available.   HEYDEN CHEMICAL CO.

Crystle®. (*HBMTN* p. 155). No longer available.   MARBLETTE CORP.

Crystolux[NB]. The trade name for a white enamel.   BURGESS, FOBES CO.

CS-137[NB]. A barium-sodium organic complex in the form of a 70% solids paste in di-2-ethylhexyl phthalate (DOP). Sp.gr. 2.10. It is an excellent anti-oxidant stabilizer for clear vinyl products. It provides excellent light and outdoor weathering stability; used at normal concentrations in thin films, it gives as much as 2–3 years of outdoor stability without significant breakdown. When used alone, however, it does not have the high heat stability characteristics of CLARITE or PROVINITE. Therefore, its principal use is in vinyl organosols and solution coatings over cloth

or metal. It is also useful in plastisol and thin calendered films requiring good weathering resistance.
NATIONAL LEAD CO.

C.S.A. Tablets, Improved[NR]. Red, specially coated, analgesic tablets used in medicine to relieve and control minor muscular aches and pains, simple headache, simple neuralgia, minor menstrual pains, and minor pain associated with simple head colds. Contains salicylamide, glutamic acid, and para-aminobenzoic acid. AMERICAN PHARMACEUTICAL CO.

Cuba Wood△. Same as FUSTIC△.

Cube. See LONCHOCARPUS△.

Cumberland Clay®. (*HBMTN* p. 156). No longer available. UNITED CLAY MINES CORP.

Cumopyran®. A synthetic anticoagulant for blood. Chemically it is cyclocumarol. Available in tablet form. ABBOTT LABORATORIES

Cumpac®. A rod and plunger packing material that combines low friction contact with the rod and effective sealing action against the entire stuffing box area. Furnished in sets, molded to size, and in fabric construction, formed to size and shape, lubricated and graphited. *Uses:* For elevator worm-gear shafts, hydraulic valve rods, reciprocating and rotating rods, and plungers and shafts.
JOHNS-MANVILLE SALES CORP.

Cupferron△. The ammonium salt of N-nitrosophenylhydroxylamine. $C_6H_9N_3O_2$; mol.wt. 155.16; m.p. 159–162 C.; freely soluble in water or alcohol. *Uses:* As a reagent for precipitating or extracting iron, titanium, molybdenum, vanadium, etc. from acid solutions; in the colorometric estimation of aluminum; in uranium assay.

Cuplopax®. A refractory material. It is a compound consisting of silica gravel, silica sand, and a fireclay mixture. INTERNATIONAL MINERALS & CHEMICAL CORP.

Cupolinor®. The trademark for machines in which air is dispersed throughout fire clay, ganister, dolomite and other refractory materials, and thereby pneumatically conveying and applying these refractory materials. INTERNATIONAL MINERALS & CHEMICAL CORP.

Cuprinol® Sav-it®. (*HBMTN* p. 157). The name SAV-IT® should have been listed as a registered trademark. CUPRINOL DIV., DARWORTH, INC.

Cuprochrome[NR]. A copper-chromium alloy for grid side rods and support wires in electronic tubes.
WILBUR B. DRIVER CO.

Cuprodie. A nickel-chromium-molybdenum-copper die block and hot-work die steel. Furnished in three different hardness ranges from 477 to 341 Brinell. Furnished heat-treated only. A. FINKL & SONS CO.

Cure-Set Adhesive[NR]. (*Supp.* I p. 54). Now a product of THE BORDEN CO., CHEMICAL DIV., successor to PIONEER LATEX & CHEMICAL CO.

Curex® Flea Duster. A duster equipped with removable rubber bulb for easy refilling, and filled with 1½ oz. of dust containing 3% ROTENONE and CUBE RESINS. Also packed in refill containers. *Use:* For the control of fleas, sticktites and lice on dogs and cats. LETHELIN PRODUCTS CO.

Cutrilin®. (*HBMTN* p. 157). No longer available.
AMERICAN CYANAMID CO.

Cuttle Bone△. Also known as CUTTLEFISH BONE△. A calcareous powder made from the internal shell of a Mediterranean Marine mollusk of the genus *Sepia*. Used as a fine polishing material for jewelry and in tooth powders.

Cuttlefish Bone△. Same as CUTTLE BONE△.

C-V Rings. See "JOHN CRANE" CHEMLON®.

CWAB[NR]. A thick, heavy grease used as a glass-mold parting compound. R. T. VANDERBILT CO.

Cyacor[NR]. (*HBMTN* p. 158). No longer available.
AMERICAN CYANAMID CO.

Cyamite®. The trademark for an ammonia nitrate blasting agent which is not sensitive to the shock of an electric blasting cap, rifle slug or primacord. The bore hole must be primed with regular dynamite to shoot. AMERICAN CYANAMID CO.

Cyamon®. The trademark for an ammonium nitrate blasting agent which is designed for safe handling in the field. It is not sensitive to a blasting cap, rifle slug, primacord, flame or impact of heavy steel weights. AMERICAN CYANAMID CO.

Cyamon® Primers. The trademark for a special primer that is sensitive to an electric blasting cap and primacord. Used to detonate CYAMON blasting agents.
AMERICAN CYANAMID CO.

Cyan[NR]. The trademark designated for a line of both blue and green phthalocyanine pigments which possess excellent fastness to light, exceptional resistance to acids, alkalis, organic solvents, fats, oils, etc. and high strength and brightness of hue. *Uses:* In paint, lacquer, enamel, printing ink, plastic, rubber, floor tile, leather, etc. AMERICAN CYANAMID CO.

Cyana®. The trademark used in connection with textile finishes obtained by applying AEROTEX RESINS and other products of the TEXTILE RESIN DEPT., AMERICAN CYANAMID CO.

Cyanamer® 370, Acrylic Polymer. A sodium salt of a water-soluble acrylic polymer. It is a light, cream-colored, free-flowing solid; slightly hygroscopic; stable to light and heat; can be dissolved in water, and has a high calcium salt tolerance (5,000 p.p.m.); may be used in the entire pH range above 4; below pH 4, it will coagulate. *Uses:* As a thickener and stabilizer for natural and synthetic latices; in water-soluble adhesives; as a dispersing agent, flocculating agent, binding agent in ceramics, and film former. AMERICAN CYANAMID CO.

Cyana® Permel® Finish. A durable water-repellent finish for textile fabrics. AMERICAN CYANAMID CO.

Cyana® Permel Plus® Finish. A combination of PERMEL RESIN B and other resins which gives water, spot, and wrinkle resistance to synthetic and COTTON fabrics. It also markedly improves the wear properties of the resin-treated fabrics.
AMERICAN CYANAMID CO.

Cyana® Purifying Finish. A durable finish designed to reduce body odor development on textiles.
AMERICAN CYANAMID CO.

Cyana® Shrinkage Control Finish. A durable resin finish designed to reduce shrinkage of Cotton knit goods. American Cyanamid Co.

Cyana® Silicone Finish. A durable water-repellent finish for Rayon and synthetic fabrics.
American Cyanamid Co.

Cyana® Silicone Plus Finish. A combination of Aerotex Water Repellent S and other thermosetting resins designed to provide water repellency plus durable wrinkle recovery on a variety of natural fabrics, synthetics and blends. Improvement in abrasion resistance and tear strength is also obtained.
American Cyanamid Co.

Cyana® Superset® Finish. A durable finish for Cottons. It produces excellent wrinkle recovery.
American Cyanamid Co.

Cyanatex®. The trademark for a textile softener or finishing agent. American Cyanamid Co.

Cyanatex® 3119 Softener. A soft white paste recommended as a versatile textile finishing aid. It is compatible with all types of finishing materials and is very resistant to discoloration.
American Cyanamid Co.

Cyanatex® Anti-foam. A combination of tallow and other fats with foam-eliminating oils. Used to prevent or reduce foam formation in the production of paper, textiles, water-dispersible paints, etc. Available in two grades: Cyanatex® Anti-Foam Regular, and Cyanatex® Anti-Foam H.
American Cyanamid Co.

Cyanatex® Cream Softener. A sulfonated tallow softener for finishing hosiery, knitted fabrics, Voiles, Crepes, Organdies, shirtings, sheetings, Silk piece goods, Cotton, Rayon, etc. It emulsifies readily in water, forming a permanent white emulsion. Available in three grades: 25%, 50% and 75%.
American Cyanamid Co.

Cyanatex® Dyeing Assistant EM. A milky-white liquid emulsion recommended as a carrier in the dyeing of Dacron® (trademark of du Pont Co. HBMTN p. 159), Arnel® and Acetate. It is relatively non-toxic, requires no extensive preparation or removal, produces good color value at low temps., and does not affect light fastness.
American Cyanamid Co.

Cyanatex® SB 100 Softener. A synthetic anionic textile softener in the form of a cream-colored paste. It is recommended for the finishing of natural and synthetic fabrics to provide softness, lubricity and freedom from discoloration or rancidity in storage.
American Cyanamid Co.

Cyanex®. The trademark for an ammonia-type dynamite designed for greater penetration of the mass and less pulverization than is produced with most other types of dynamite.
American Cyanamid Co.

Cyclocel®. (*HBMTN* p. 158). Now mfg'd by Minerals & Chemicals Corp. of America, successor to Attapulgus Clay Co.

Cyclone®. The trademark for a line of chain-link fencing, lawn fenching, picket fencing, trellises, fence posts and gates, wire screen cloth, wire mesh partitions, hardware cloth and window guards; wire baskets, flexible steel mats and conveyor belting.
United States Steel Corp., American Steel & Wire Div., Cyclone Fence Dept.

Cyclops. See Boston Cyclops.

Cycoil®. Mechanical, viscous-type dust arrestors or collectors of the oil-bath type for use with internal-combustion engines and gas pipe lines.
American Air Filter Co.

Cyfor® Fortified Rosin Sizes. The trademark for a series of dry and liquid fortified rosin sizes for the paper industry. American Cyanamid Co.

Cykel 70. (*Supp.* I p. 55). No longer available.
Spencer Kellogg & Sons

Cykelsoy®. (*HBMTN* p. 159). No longer available.
Spencer Kellogg & Sons

Cylectric[NE]. See Petreco® Electropherre[NE] Desalting Process.

Cymac®. The trademark for a line of methylstyrene thermoplastic molding compounds.
American Cyanamid Co.

Cymel®. A line of thermosetting melamine-formaldehyde resins available as molding compounds, laminating resins, resin adhesives, and as solutions in organic solvents. When compounded with suitable fillers, Cymel forms odorless, tasteless, and chemically inert molding compounds.

Cymel laminating resins are designed to produce laminates composed of layers of glass cloth, asbestos, canvas or paper. Laminates may be obtained in highly colored translucent or opaque shades, and provide a hard, durable surface. They are non-flammable, have very high arc and track resistance, and are impervious to most of the common solvents. They are produced by the conventional high-pressure laminating technique, although formulations are available which permit the use of low or intermediate pressures. These laminates are used for table tops, translucent signs, electrical control panels, insulators, name plates, graphic stock, and wall panels. Cymel coating resins are available as solutions in mixtures of xylol and butanol and other special solvents. They are used in combination with the Rezyl and Cycopol resins in fast-baking finishes for metal objects. In comparison to Beetle coating resins, Cymel coating resins bake faster and have improved color retention, heat and light stability, chemical resistance, and exterior durability.

The following molding compounds are available:

Cymel designation	Filler	Description and uses
1077 and 1079	Alpha-celluose	Superior to urea-formaldehyde compounds in resistance to water, food staining, abrasion, acids, alkalies, and heat; sp.gr. 1.5; tensile strength 7,000–8,000 lb./sq.in.; particularly useful for buttons, tableware, lighting fixtures, and reflectors; available in many opaque and translucent colors for compression or transfer molding

Cymel designation	Filler	Description and uses
1502	Cellulose	Made for industrial and electrical uses; notable for its arc resistance, dielectric strength, low sp.gr. (1.53), and its ease of molding by compression or transfer methods; it has a low water absorption, will not support combustion, and has a durable surface; recommended for automotive, truck or tractor ignition parts, circuit breakers, switch plugs, and similar uses; supplied in granular form.
3020	Chopped cotton fabric	Supplied in form of loose particles in a limited range of bright colors for compression or transfer molding; an excellent material for applications requiring resistance to shock; has high flexural strength, arc resistance, and heat and fire resistance, and low water absorption; typical applications are food trays, circuit breakers, insulation on electric motors, tableware, etc.

Properties of the standard CYMEL resin solutions are as follows:

Cymel resin designation	Solids, % by weight	Butanol-xylol, %	Petroleum aromatic solvent, %	Viscosity (Gardner-Holdt)	Acid no. solids	Approx. wt., lb./gal.
Cymel 245-8 (unmodified)	50	50	—	L-O	1 (max.)	8.3
Cymel 248-8 (unmodified)	55	45	—	N-Q	1 (max.)	8.4
Cymel 247-10	60	40	—	T-W	1 (max.)	8.4
Cymel 243-3	60	—	40	V-Y		8.5

AMERICAN CYANAMID CO.

Cynol® Rewetting, Softening & Defoaming Agents. The trademark for a series of rewetting, softening and defoaming agents used in the mfg. of paper. Available in liquid form. AMERICAN CYANAMID CO.

Cypan®. A drilling mud conditioner designed for use in drilling fluids to control the water loss from the system. It is a high-molecular weight acrylic-type polymer supplied as free-flowing flakes. Its performance properties are excellent at a temp. of 350°F., and in highly contaminated systems.
AMERICAN CYANAMID CO.

Cypel® Resin. An anionic resin emulsion applied as a surface coating to paper or paperboard to impart grease resistance, improve printing qualities, gloss, and heat-sealing properties. AMERICAN CYANAMID CO.

Cyper®. Blue-black and black basic dyestuffs for dyeing leather and for coloring suede dressings.
GENERAL DYESTUFF CO.

Cyron® Chemical Size. The trademark for a synthetic sizing material for the paper industry. CYRON permits sizing of alkaline as well as acid paper, and may be added either to the pulp or as a coating.
AMERICAN CYANAMID CO.

Cyzac®. The trademark for a group of thermosetting resinous compositions for board surfacing and protective finishes. AMERICAN CYANAMID CO.

D

D-6[NR]. A free-flowing powder consisting of milk solids, polyoxyethylene sorbitan monostearate and sugar. Its principle use is as a whipping agent and emulsifier in dry cake mixes.
H. T. VANDERBILT CO.

D-7[NR]. A free-flowing powder consisting of milk solids, sorbitan monosterate, polyoxyethylene sorbitan monostearate and sugar. Its principle use is as a whipping agent and emulsifier in dry cake mixes.
H. T. VANDERBILT CO.

D-25 Cylinder Oil[NR]. A 6% compound oil for use in the presence of fairly wet steam at pressures of 50–100 lb./sq. in. KEYSTONE LUBRICATING CO.

D-50 Cylinder Oil[NR]. A 6% compound oil for use at pressures up to 100 lb./sq. in. where there is little or no control or conservation of oil and where the steam is wet. KEYSTONE LUBRICATING CO.

Daintex®. (*HBMTN* p. 161). No longer available.
HERCULES POWDER CO.

Daisy. A washing powder for cleaning and sanitizing dishes, glasses, silver and utensils.
TROY INDUSTRIAL PRODUCTS,
DIV. OF GLOBE SANITARY SUPPLY CO.

Dalmation Insect Powder△. Same as PYRETHRUM△.

Dalmation Powder△. Same as PYRETHRUM△.

Damascus. See BOSTON DAMASCUS.

Dambose△. Same as INOSITOL△.

Dammar△ The resin from various species of trees of the genus *Shorea, Blanocarpus,* and *Hopea*. DAMMAR is classified according to color and size, the best grades being colorless and in large lumps. The pale-colored, high-quality grade from Batavia and Sumatra are obtained from species of *Hopea*. The Malayan black DAMMAR, known as DAMMAR HITAM, is from the species *Blancocarpus*. DAMMAR is obtained by tapping the trees and collecting the solidified gums after several months. Sp.gr. about 1.04–1.12; m.p. from 100° to 120°C. Used in making spirit varnishes, lacquers, adhesives, coatings, etc.

Dandelion Rubber△. The gum latex extracted from the roots of the Russian dandelion. When separated from its resin content, this rubber has practically the same properties as the rubber obtained from the Hevia tree. The roots contain up to 10% rubber after the plant has passed the first-year flowering period. The normal yield is about 6% rubber.

Dari-Kleen®. A sanitizing cleaner used primarily for milkstone removal.
PENNSYLVANIA SALT MFG. CO.

Darthronol. A vitamin preparation particularly for the treatment of arthritis. Each tablet contains 50,000 U.S.P. units VITAMIN D, 5,000 U.S.P. units VITAMIN A, 75 mg. VITAMIN C, 3 mg. VITAMIN B₁, 2 mg. VITAMIN B₂, 0.3 mg. VITAMIN B₆, 16 mg. NIACINAMIDE, 1 mg. calcium pantothenate, and 4 mg. mixed tocopherols. J. B. ROERIG & CO.

Davac®. A line of adhesive label papers that do not curl or wave. They have smooth surfaces that print well; and they feed, deliver, jog, perforate, and die-cut like ungummed papers. NASHUA CORP.

Dayalets®. A multivitamin preparation in tablet form. ABBOTT LABORATORIES

DCM. (Trademark registration pending). A free-flowing, alkaline powder with high lime-sequestering properties. Used for machine dishwashing.
OAKITE PRODUCTS, INC.

DCPM△. Also known as OXYTHANE. Di-p-chlorodiphenoxymethane. $C_{13}H_{10}Cl_2O_2$; mol.wt. 269.14. A colorless solid made by treating an alcohol dispersion of equimolecular amounts of sodium and p-chlorophenol with dichloromethane. M.p. 65°C.; practically insoluble in water and petroleum oils; slightly soluble in alcohol; readily soluble in ether and in acetone. It is highly toxic to phytophagous mites and to their summer eggs. Used as a persistent contact acaricide; effective for some seven days in the greenhouse.

DDD△. Also known as TDE△. 2,2-Bis (p-chlorophenyl)-1,1-dichloroethane. $C_{14}H_{10}Cl_4$; mol.wt. 320.05. An insecticidal material that is from $1/5$ to $1/10$ as toxic as DDT to mammals. Prepared commercially by the chlorination of ethyl alcohol below 35°C. until the lower layer has a density of 1.29, and this is condensed with chlorobenzene. The technical product contains 7–8% of the o,p'-isomer, but is mostly the p,p-isomer, with a m.p. of 110°C. DDD has solubilities similar to those of DDT; it is slightly less irritating to the skin; and is, in general, somewhat less effective for most insects than DDT but is superior for the control of mosquito larvae, red-banded and fruit-tree leaf rollers, and tomato and tobacco hornworms.

D-D® Soil Fumigant. A mixture of dichloropropane and dichloropropene used to kill nematodes in soils in which tobacco, citrus fruits, pineapples, vegetables, and COTTON are grown. SHELL CHEMICAL CORP.

Dead Easy®. The trademark for an insecticide.
S. B. PENICK & CO.

Dearborn Red[NE]. A series of inexpensive red color pigments recommended for good exterior durability. Available in light red and dark red shades.
SHERWIN-WILLIAMS CO.

Decaboard. A rigid-type, decorative-surfaced, laminated-plastic hardboard panel for headboards of beds, coffee tables, display panels, etc. DECAR PLASTIC CORP.

Decaflex. A low-caliper grade DECARLITE that can be bent at room temp. DECAR PLASTIC CORP.

Decaform. A post-forming grade of DECARLITE. It can be formed by heat and pressure to conform to the job requirements. DECAR PLASTIC CORP.

Decarlite. A decorative plastic sheet laminate available in many designs and colors and various wood grains. *Use:* For tables, school desks, counters, bars, etc. DECAR PLASTIC CORP.

Decholin®. A hydrocholeretic agent containing dehydrocholic acid. AMES CO.

Deco[NE]. The trade name for a white primer and sealer for wood. BURGESS, FORBES CO.

Decolon® RU. A substantive, alkali-stable textile softener, compatible with anionic and nonionic finishes. It offers great resistance to washing, dry-cleaning, discoloration and odor development; does not affect the shrinkage; has no adverse effect on gas fading of acetate colors; has little tendency to adversely affect light fastness or to discolor white goods; has negligible tendency to scorch under a hot iron; and produces superior smoothness of hand.
DEPAUL CHEMICAL CO.

Decoray®. A linoleum flooring material, 0.070" thick, for light residential service. ARMSTRONG CORK CO.

Decra-Brite[NE]. A decorative glass fiber blanket, especially useful for making decorations to be used around the home—on fireplace mantles, under Christmas trees, etc. L. O. F. GLASS FIBERS CO.

Decto-Stick®. A furniture-repair kit consisting of 4 colored sticks of a waxy material and a scraper for rubbing the product into dents, nicks, gouges, etc., of natural finished or stained woodwork, radios, furniture, leather, and other articles. Colors can be blended while rubbing-in; no heat or premixing is required. DECTO PRODUCTS CO.

Ded-N-Dun®. (*HBMTN* p. 164). Now a registered trademark. ATHELSTAN PRODUCTS CO.

Deenax®. (*Supp.* I p. 58). This product is marketed by the ENJAY CO., INC., an affiliate of the ESSO STANDARD OIL CO.

Deep Gloss® Carnu®. A liquid, one-step auto polish composed of cleaning agents and gloss-producing chemicals suspended in water. It cleans and polishes in one operation and intensifies colors, which makes them darker and richer in tone. Can be used on either lacquer or enamel, and is excellent for all but exceptionally heavily-weathered finishes.
S. C. JOHNSON & SON

Deepset[NE] **Salt L.** A chemical used in the aftertreatment of polyamide fibers and fabrics which have been colored with anionic dyes.
NATIONAL ANILINE DIV.,
ALLIED CHEMICAL & DYE CORP.

Dee-T-Cide®. The trademark for agricultural chemicals having insecticidal properties.
PENNSYLVANIA SALT MFG. CO.

Dee-Zol. A diesel fuel additive which softens and removes carbon deposits from injectors, valves, and piston rings, and prevents further carbonization; lubricates the parts which come in contact with the fuel; and absorbs moisture in fuel tanks, lines, and carburetors. BELL LABORATORY, INC.

Defoamer F-947[NE]. A 100%-active defoaming agent in the form of a soft wax, which is easily dispersible in hot water to give a nonionic emulsion. Suitable for all textile operations where foam is undesirable. PIONEER CHEMICAL WORKS, INC.

Defoamer H-450[NE]. A patented, nonionic, self-emulsifying wax, which disperses readily in hot water (above 60°C.) to form a smooth, milky liquid. Recommended for removing undesirable foam and froth in textile and paper processing. PIONEER CHEMICAL WORKS, INC.

De-Fol-Ate®. A magnesium chlorate-chloride defoliant. PENNSYLVANIA SALT MFG. CO.

Degalol®. A fat emulsifier and biliary replacement agent containing deoxycholic acid. AMES CO.

Degras△. A brownish, waxy fat obtained from the wool of sheep. It has a faint, disagreeable odor, and contains lanoceric acid, $C_{30}H_{60}O_4$, lanopalmic acid, $C_{15}H_{30}O_3$, and lanosterol. In its crude form, DEGRAS is also known as WOOL GREASE; when purified and hydrated, it is known as LANOLIN. DEGRAS is used in the mfg. of leather dressings, as a rubber softener, in lubricating greases, in slushing oils, and for preparing LANOLIN.

Deguelia Root△. *Same as* DERRIS ROOT△.

Dehydrol®. A dehydrated castor oil for use as a drying oil in the mfg. of alkyd resins and varnishes and in paints, enamels, etc. It has excellent color retention, good drying, good water resistance, and good durability. SHERWIN-WILLIAMS CO.

Dektomat®. A photographic developer designed especially for the continuous processing of sensitized paper. EASTMAN KODAK CO.

Delectrol 379[NE]. A 100%-active, readily emulsifiable, non-yellowing, non-ionic, anti-static oil used for coning, throwing, finishing and after-oiling of sized synthetic yarns, worsted, etc. It may be added to worsted or woolen oils to reduce static or excessive drag in yarns. COLLOIDS, INC.

Delpac[NE]. A rubber antioxidant. Chemically it is di-tert butyl para cresol. HERCULES POWDER CO.

Delrad®. An algicide. HERCULES POWDER CO.

Delsey®. A registered trademark for a line of creped wadding and other paper products. KIMBERLY-CLARK CORP.

Delsteel® Alloy. (*HBMTN* p. 166). The name DELSTEEL® is now a registered trademark. DELAWARE TOOL STEEL CORP.

Deltacortone[NE]. (*Supp.* I p. 59). No longer available. SHARP & DOHME DIV., MERCK & CO.

Delvinal®. A brand of vinbarbital for use in veterinary medicine. It is 5-ethyl-5-(1-methyl-1-butenyl) barbiturate. *Use:* For sedation and anesthesia in dogs. MERCK SHARP & DOHME

Demal 14[NE]. (*HBMTN* p. 167). No longer available. EMULSOL CHEMICAL CORP.

Demerara Greenheart△. *Same as* GREENHEART△.

Denflex Plastisol Primers[NE]. Coating compositions specifically designed to bond vinyl plastisols to a wide variety of surfaces such as steel, aluminum, copper, brass, galvanized metal, glass, ceramics, and NYLON. For best results it is advisable to use the recommended DENFLEX PLASTISOLS as topcoats. The primer is applied by dipping, spraying, brushing, or roller coating. It is usually baked briefly at 250°F. or higher, and then the plastisol is applied. The plastisol is cured at 350°F. DENNIS CHEMICAL CO.

Densitol®. A brominated vegetable oil used as a stabilizing agent for liquid foods or beverages. ABBOTT LABORATORIES

Dentabest®. (*Supp.* I p. 59). No longer available. E. I. DU PONT DE NEMOURS & CO.

Deo-Base®. (*HBMTN* p. 167). Now a registered trademark. L. SONNEBORN SONS, INC.

Deodall®. A trademark for a multi-purpose masking agent for use in varnishes, lacquers, cleaners, polishes, oils and other products. SINDAR CORP.

Deodorite®. Activated charcoal for the purification and recovery of air. BARNEBEY-CHENEY CO.

Deoleated®. The trademark for an almond meal. S. B. PENICK & CO.

Deoterge®. (Registration No. 627,990; Class 52; May 29, 1956). *See* AIRKEM DEOTERGE®.

Depancol®. (*HBMTN* p. 167). Now a product of WARNER-CHILCOTT Laboratories, successor to THE MALTINE CO.

Depco® Bleach Assist. A completely water soluble, nontoxic, and substantive stabilizer for use with sodium chlorite bleaching. It protects against corrosion, diminishes offensive odor, and controls the development of chlorine dioxide, thus reducing loss of bleaching agent and producing better whites. *Use:* In the bleaching of DACRON, ORLON, NYLON, and COTTON yarns. DE PAUL CHEMICAL CO.

Depco® Fix N. A cold-water-soluble, cationic resin fixative for direct dyes used on COTTON and RAYON. It prevents migration of color and staining, and causes little change in shade and light fastness when used in aftertreatment. DE PAUL CHEMICAL CO.

Depcogel® 3X. An anionic detergent and wetting agent for use on all natural and synthetic fibers. It has excellent resistance to hard water, and excellent stability to acids and alkalis. DE PAUL CHEMICAL CO.

Depcolin®. A buffering agent for use in textile dyeing. It provides sufficient acidity for rapid oxidation of aniline to aniline black. It prevents fiber damage, and reduces steaming time to a minimum. DE PAUL CHEMICAL CO.

Depcoset® RI. A resinous textile finishing agent that provides durable stability and crease resistance. It can be used for embossing and glazing on all types of durable mechanical finishes. DE PAUL CHEMICAL CO.

Deracloud®. The trademark for a line of agricultural and animal insecticides. S. B. PENICK & CO.

Deramist®. The trademark for a line of agricultural and animal insecticides. S. B. PENICK & CO.

Derrilox®. The trademark for: (1) a flea and lice powder; and (2) an animal shampoo.
S. B. PENICK & CO.

Derrin△. *Same as* ROTENONE△.

Derris Root△. *Also known as* TUBA ROOT, DEGUELIA ROOT, and AKER-TUBA. The roots of plants belonging to the genus *Derris,* of which more than 80 have been described. The insecticidal properties of DERRIS ROOT, long used by natives as fish poisons, were known to the Chinese. The dried roots of the leguminous shrub, *Derris ellipitica* are cultivated in Malaya, Indonesia, and the Belgian Congo. The chief insecticidal compound in DERRIS ROOT is ROTENONE (usually present in amounts from 5–6%) accompanied by small amounts of related compounds. Used as an insecticide, and as a source of ROTENONE and rotenoid compounds.

Desbutal®. An antidepressant and sedative consisting of methamphetamine hydrochloride and pentobarbital sodium. Available in form of capsules.
ABBOTT LABORATORIES

Descotone®. (*Supp.* I p. 59). No longer available.
SHARP & DOHME DIV., MERCK & CO.

Desmer O-112®. (*Supp.* I p. 60). Now a registered trademark. JACQUES WOLF & CO.

Desoxets®. An appetite depressant in tablet form. Contains methamphetamine hydrochloride and multiple vitamins. ABBOTT LABORATORIES

Deterge. A deflocculant for water-wash paint-spray booths. It consists of a complex mixture of alkaline salts, foam depressants, and surface-active agents.
NATIONAL RESEARCH & CHEMICAL CO.

Detergent D^{NR}. (*HBMTN* p. 168). No longer available. CIBA CO.

Detergol®. A heavy, liquid, alcoholic-potash soap used in the formulation of wetting, leveling and textile desizing agents, and as a wetting agent for leather.
ULTRA CHEMICAL WORKS

Dethdiet®. A RED SQUILL rat poison in powdered form, standardized to a potency of 500 mg./kg.
S. B. PENICK & CO.

Deva-Metal^{NR}. A homogeneous, solid-powder metallurgy product formed from a combination of primary or alloy metal powders with graphite (up to 30%). It is limited in size and shape only by availability of dies and pressure of presses. Can be machined, soldered, brazed, or pressfit into housings. Can be used over a temp. range of —300°F. to +1,250°F. upon selection of proper metal bond. Available in bronze, brass, iron, nickel, etc. *Uses:* As a self-lubricating metal in specific applications such as bearings, seals, packings, piston rings, and slide plates where existing materials do not meet service requirements.
DEVA-METAL CORP.

Devcon®. (*Supp.* I p. 60). Now a product of DEVCON CORP., formerly known as CHEMICAL DEVELOPMENT CORP.

Developer No. 6. *See* CRAFTINT SINGLETONE.

Developers No. 21 *and* **No. 22.** *See* CRAFTINT DOUBLETONE.

Devil®. A rubbermaker's grade of ground crude sulfur. OLIN MATHIESON CHEMICAL CORP.

Devran®. A line of epoxy resin polymers for use in protective coatings. Paints made with DEVRAN are fast-drying, long-wearing, and resistant to most oils, acids, alkalis and cleaning compounds.
TRUSCON LABORATORIES

Dexcel®. A line of industrial adhesives, and wall- and floor-tile cements.
DACAR CHEMICAL PRODUCTS CO.

Dextrinase®. A diastatic enzyme with high saccharogenic activity, used in food products such as high dextrose equivalent corn syrups.
TAKAMINE LABORATORIES

Dextrotest®. A diagnostic composition for the estimation of blood sugar. AMES CO.

DFDT△. An insecticidal material developed in Germany during World War II and known as GIX. Chemically, it is 2,2-bis-(*p*-fluorphenyl)-1,1,1-trichloroethane. The technical material is a viscous, colorless liquid prepared by condensing fluorobenzene with chloral in the presence of sulfuric acid, and contains up to about 10% of the *o,p'*-isomer (b.p. 135–136°C. at 9 mm. Hg), but chiefly the *p,p'*-isomer (m.p. 45°C.). Has a much shorter residual activity than DDT, acts more quickly, and is somewhat less toxic to mammals. The *p,p'*-isomer has the following solubilities in grams per hundred ml. of solvent at 27°C.: carbon tetrachloride, 650; cyclohexanone, 850; dibutylphthalate, 260; refined kerosene, 140; mineral oil, 83; xylene, 670.

Diace^{NR}. (Trademark registration applied for). A medicinal: diacetyldihydroxyphenylisatin.
BLAIR LABORATORIES, INC.

Dial®. A barbiturate of moderately prolonged effect. It is a fine white powder, soluble in alcohol and ether, and slightly soluble in water. Shorter acting than phenobarbital, but longer acting than pentobarbital and hexobarbital. Supplied in the form of ½ gr. tablets. CIBA PHARMACEUTICAL PRODUCTS INC.

Diamond®. The trademark for a galvanized woven wire fence with a 2" diamond mesh.
UNITED STATES STEEL CORP.

Diamond® Floor Finish. A glossy, durable, non-slippery mopping varnish. HILLYARD CHEMICAL CO.

Dianil®. A line of direct dyes, of commercial fastness properties, for dyeing COTTON, RAYON, and other cellulosic fibers. GENERAL DYESTUFF CO.

Diasone®. Sulfoxone sodium tablets used in the treatment of leprosy. ABBOTT LABORATORIES

Diatomaceous Earth△. A group of compact, granular or amorphous minerals formed of fossil diatoms in extensive beds. In the United States, it is mined principally in Oregon, California, Washington, Idaho, and Nevada. The mined material is crushed and calcined. When pure it is practically white, but the presence of impurities imparts a gray, brown or greenish color. It has a density of about 12–17 lb.

per cu.ft. *Uses:* As an abrasive, filter aid, filler in paints and molded plastics; in metal polishes and soaps; for making insulating blocks and boards. Diatomite block has a porosity of 90% of its volume and makes an excellent filter. Finely powdered, uncalcined, amorphous DIATOMACEOUS earth is used in paper finishes, in Portland cement mixtures, and as a flatting agent in paints. Insulating brick cut from diatomite is capable of withstanding temps. as high as 1,600°F.

Diatussin®. An antitussive containing extracts of Thyme and Drosera in aqueous alcoholic menstruum.
AMES CO.

Diazanil®. A line of direct dyes for COTTON and RAYON. They are considerably improved in wet fastness by diazotization on the fiber and coupling with a developer. GENERAL DYESTUFF CO.

Diazo®. (*HBMTN* p. 171). No longer available.
GENERAL DYESTUFF CO.

Diazyme®. Enzyme substances primarily for use in degumming silks and fibrous materials, and for desizing and destarching. TAKAMINE LABORATORIES

Dibistine®. A combination of the two antihistamine drugs, PYRIBENZAMINE® and ANTISTINE®, used in the relief of discomfort from hay fever and other forms of allergic rhinitis, atopic dermatitis, drug reactions, etc.
CIBA PHARMACEUTICAL PRODUCTS INC.

Dicaldimin®. A calcium, phosphorus, iron and vitamin preparation in capsule form. Used as a dietary supplement especially during pregnancy.
ABBOTT LABORATORIES

Dicalets®. A multivitamin and mineral preparation in tablet form. Used in supplementing the diet of expectant and nursing mothers. ABBOTT LABORATORIES

Dicalite® 7. A filteraid produced from diatomaceous earth, especially for the filtration of dry-cleaning solvents. It contains an additive which renders the solvent conductive and prevents problems due to the accumulation of static from the friction of the garments in the dry-cleaning washer.
GREAT LAKES CARBON CORP.

Dicalite® Speedflow, Speedex, Speedplus, Superaid, *and* 4200. A line of diatomaceous filteraids used in the filtration of many liquids. These names designate different grades which vary almost entirely in their "speed" or capacity, in gallons of through-put per hr. These materials are all finely powdered, averaging from 17 to 19 lb. per cu.ft. in cake density. They are composed of chemically inert amorphous silica, and are so processed that they cannot affect the flavor or taste of any liquid during filtration.
GREAT LAKES CARBON CORP.

Dico®. A hand cleaning compound for bake pans and cooking utensils. DIVERSEY CORP.

Dicoloid®. A granular, acidic-type milkstone remover. It contains highly refined abrasive chemicals that provide scouring action in addition to milkstone removal. Harmless to tinned copper, tinned iron, stainless steel, MONEL, nickel and glass-lined surfaces.
DIVERSEY CORP.

Dictator Special. *See* PAX® DICTATOR SPECIAL.

Di-Cup[NE]. Dicumyl peroxide used as a catalyst for vinyl polymerization and as a curing and vulcanizing agent for plastics and rubber. HERCULES POWDER CO.

Dieldrin[△]. 1,2,3,4,10,10-Hexachloro-6,7, epoxy-1,4,4a,-5,6,7,8,8a-octahydro-1,4-*endo*, exo-5,8-dimethanonaphthalene. $C_{12}H_8Cl_6O$; mol.wt. 380.94. An insecticidal material of high contact and stomach toxicity to most insects; highly persistent and effective in the control of many crop pests. Technical DIELDRIN is an almost odorless, light tan, flaky solid containing about 76% of the above compound and 13% of other insecticidally active compounds, and melting at about 150°C. Insoluble in water; slightly soluble in mineral oils; moderately soluble in acetone; soluble in aromatic solvents. Available as wettable powders, emulsifiable concentrates, and dusts.

Diesel Gumout®. A liquid fuel-oil additive designed to dissolve sludge and gum. It is added in the ratio of 1 pt. of additive to each 50 to 100 gal. of fuel oil.
PENNSYLVANIA REFINING CO.

Digifortis®. A medicinal in ampoules for injectable use and in KAPSEALS and tablets for oral use in the management of certain heart conditions.
PARKE, DAVIS & CO.

Digipoten[NE]. (*HBMTN* p. 172). No longer available. ABBOTT LABORATORIES

Di-Hard®. The trademark for a line of pump liners and barrels, plunger pumps, and water tubes for swivels. UNITED STATES STEEL CORP.,
OIL WELL SUPPLY DIV.

Dihydro Vanillion C®. An imitation vanilla flavor that imparts an aroma and taste similar to that of Mexican beans. FLORASYNTH LABORATORIES, INC.

Di-Lok®. *See* U.S.S.® DI-LOK®.

Dimethoxy-DDT[△]. *Same as* METHOXYCHLOR[△].

Dimite[△]. *Also known* as DMC[△]. An acaricide effective against European red mite, Schoenii mite, Two-Spotted mite, and red spiders on orchard fruits. Also effective against red spiders on greenhouse roses, Cyclamen mite on delphinium, and Spruce mite on conifers. Consists of 25% *p, p'* dichlorodiphenyl methyl carbinol. Water-mixable and compatible with most commonly used insecticides and fungicides except those of an acid nature. Generally used at a conc. of 1 pint in 100 gal. water. It is non-toxic to humans.

Dinoseb[△]. Dinitrobutylphenol. 2-(1-Methyl-n-propyl)-4:6-dinitrophenol. $C_{10}H_{12}O_5N_2$; mol.wt. 240.22. A potent stomach and contact insecticide, but it is limited by phytotoxicity to dormant or delayed dormant use on fruit trees. It is also a potent weedkiller that exhibits some selective action. The pure compound has a m.p. of 42°C.; it is practically insoluble in water but soluble in petroleum oils and most organic solvents. Commercially available as an oil solution for preparing emulsions, as water-soluble salts for use in water solution, and as an aqueous solution of its triethanolamine salt.

Diokem®. *See* NEW DIOKEM®.

Dipac[NE]. A delayed-action sulfonamide rubber accelerator. PENNSYLVANIA SALT MFG. CO.

Dipak®. A completely-soluble, strong alkaline, heavy-duty cleaner designed for cleaning of heavily-contaminated porous surfaces and for the removal of cooked-on fat deposits from equipment, floors, etc. It rinses freely and does not effect iron, copper, stainless steel, nickel or MONEL. Applied by soaking or brushing with long-handled bristle brush.
DIVERSEY CORP.

Di-Paralene®. A synthetic, long-acting, antihistamine drug of low toxicity, in tablet form. Chemically, it is chlorcyclizine hydrochloride.
ABBOTT LABORATORIES

Dipentene®. A narrow-boiling-range terpene hydrocarbon solvent which can be used in place of turpentine as in the formulation of protective coatings.
HERCULES POWDER CO.

Dip-Pak®. A line of strippable coatings used for the temporary protection of tools, gears and machined parts during processing, storage and shipping. They are solid materials supplied as plastic briquettes which are melted prior to use. The parts to be coated are dipped into the molten plastic, withdrawn and allowed to cool.
FIDELITY CHEMICAL PRODUCTS CORP.

Dip Polish 231. See CD DIP POLISH 231.

Dippo Silver Cleaner[NR]. (*Supp.* I p. 62). No longer available.
ULTRA CHEMICAL WORKS

Dippo Suds®. An alkyl aryl sulfonate. It is an anionic detergent in bead form.
ULTRA CHEMICAL WORKS

Di-Sanite. See OAKITE® DI-SANITE.

Dishine. A free-rinsing, powder synthetic detergent for dishwashing.
J. I. HOLCOMB MFG. CO.

Dispersal 995[NR]. A nonionic, emulsifying, degreasing and scouring agent available as a concentrated, clear, viscous liquid. It is stable to acids and alkalis; and compatible with all of the usual chemicals used in textile processing.
COLLOIDS, INC.

Dispersal 1278[NR]. A concentrated polyglycol ester used as a dispersing agent, wetting agent or lubricant in acid textile-processing operations such as crabbing; in synthetic or WOOL dyeing; or as an emulsifier and WOOL-protective agent in acid scouring.
COLLOIDS, INC.

Dispersing Agent N.F.L.[NR]. A surface-active agent used in textile processing to improve level dyeing with fast direct colors, acetates and acid dyes. The addition of as little as ½ to 1% of this agent to any dye bath prior to adding the dyestuff improves the penetration of the dye as well as insuring improved level dyeing.
MAC CHEMICAL CO.

Disperso®. Wettable grades of metallic stearates, including zinc stearate, calcium stearate and aluminum stearate. These grades are more readily suspended in water than standard metallic stearates, and are used in processes requiring dispersion of stearate in water.
WITCO CHEMICAL CO.

Dispersol[NR]. A dispersing agent for promoting the suspension of finely divided particles in aqueous systems. Suitable for use with clays, pigments, resins, etc. It is a clear yellow, viscous, alkaline solution containing approx. 50% solids. The volatile portion consists of water and alcohol-type solvents. pH, approx. 9. *Uses:* In mfg. of emulsion paints, leather finishes, wax and resin emulsions, dye dispersions, etc.
ABCO CHEMICAL CO.

Dissolving Salt B. A dissolving and fixing auxiliary principally for textile printing. It accelerates the migration of the dyestuff through the outer surface of the particles of the thickening and prevents the adsorption of the leuco substances by the starch thickening. Therefore, it increases the color value and gives more level prints with a wide range of vat dyestuffs. It also improves the solubility of some of the soluble vat dyestuffs.
NOVA CHEMICAL CORP.

Dithac-W®. A vulcanization accelerator.
PENNSYLVANIA SALT MFG. CO.

Ditran®. A general-purpose cleaner for use on reactive metals such as aluminum and zinc.
DIVERSEY CORP.

Diversey No. 16[NR]. A liquid paint stripper and emulsion cleaner possessing excellent wetting and emulsifying properties. It can be used as a: (1) safe, non-toxic solvent for removing oily and greasy solid particle contamination, such as polishing and buffing compounds, drawing compounds, smut and dirt; (2) water emulsion for general cleaning of ferrous parts in automatic machines where temporary rustproofing is required; (3) light-duty rustproofing compound, especially for neutralizing and removing fingerprints and smudges; and (4) paint stripper.
DIVERSEY CORP.

Diversey No. 519[NR]. A spray cleaner for ferrous and non-ferrous metals, including aluminum, steel, copper, brass and zinc. It is free-draining and free rinsing; and has rapid wetting action.
DIVERSEY CORP.

Diversey No. 808[NR]. An inhibited, heavy-duty, non-etching alkaline cleaner for aluminum. It rinses freely in clear, warm water or cold flowing water, and it effectively removes grease, oil, etc.
DIVERSEY CORP.

Diversol® CX. A pink-colored bactericide, disinfectant and deodorizer containing alkaline sodium phosphate and sodium hypochlorite. Especially useful for use in food-processing plants.
DIVERSEY CORP.

Divi-divi[△]. The dried seed pods of the tree *Caesalpinia coriaria*, produced chiefly in Colombia, Dominican Republic, and Venezuela. The pods are about 3 in. long and contain up to 45% pyragallol tannin. Used chiefly in blends with other tannins in the tanning of leather; it increases the acidity of the tannin; imparts a light color to the leather; and plumps and softens the leather.

Divo®. A wetting agent-type dairy cleaner. Used for cleaning separators, milking machines, milk pails, utensils, etc. around the farm or home.
DIVERSEY CORP.

Divobond®. An agent that permits the spray cleaning and simultaneous phosphatizing of metals to provide improved adhesion of organic finishes. From 1 to 3 oz. of DIVOBOND are used per gal. of water at 160°–180°F. It does not form any sludge or scale.
DIVERSEY CORP.

Divobond® ST. A free-flowing granular material that is used to impart an amorphous iron phosphate coating to steel in an immersion operation. The thin, tight phosphate coat will prevent corrosion and promote adherence of all organic finishes. DIVERSEY CORP.

Divobrite®. A caustic-base, bottle-washing compound, designed especially for use in hard water areas. Readily soluble in warm or cold water. Can also be used for circulation and soak cleaning of evaporators, vacuum pans, juice pasteurizers, etc. DIVERSEY CORP.

Divo-Dip®. A non-toxic stain remover for china and plastic dinnerware. DIVERSEY CORP.

Divolume®. An alkaline cleaner for use on aluminum surfaces only. Removes carbonized oils, greases and similar contaminations. Will not damage aluminum, anodized aluminum or most aluminum alloy equipment, in any concentration or at any temp., regardless of length of contact. DIVERSEY CORP.

Dixie®. An all-vegetable, fully hydrogenated shortening for use in baking, frying and pastry making.
ANDERSON, CLAYTON & CO. FOODS DIV.

DM-30[NE]. A free-flowing powder consisting of milk solids, and mono- and diglycerides of fat-forming fatty acids. Its principle use is as an emulsifier and softener in dry-sweet-yeast-raised bakery product mixes.
R. T. VANDERBILT CO.

DMC[△]. Same as DIMITE[△].

DMDT[△]. Same as METHOXYCHLOR[△].

DNC[△]. Also known as DNOC[△]. Dinitrocresol. 2-Methyl-4,6-dinitrophenol. $C_7H_6N_2O_5$, mol.wt. 198.14. Yellow, odorless crystals; m.p. 85.8°C.; mfg'd by sulfonation of o-cresol, followed by controlled nitration; almost insoluble in water; soluble in most organic solvents and in acetic acid. It is poisonous to man, especially by ingestion. Strongly phytotoxic and, therefore, used as a weed killer. It is a potent stomach poison and contact insecticide that is toxic to the eggs of certain insects. Its insecticidal uses are limited by its phytotoxicity to dormant sprays, baits, and on waste land areas to control such insects as locusts. Generally marketed with a moisture content of up to 10% to reduce explosive hazards, and as the sodium or amine salts. Ammonium sulfate is sometimes added as an "activator" to the sodium salt.

DNOC[△]. Same as DNC[△].

DoAll®. Trade name for products of the DOALL CO. Among the products are:
DOALL No. 120. A light viscosity, mineral-oil-base cutting fluid for machining aluminum, copper, bronze, and most other non-ferrous alloys.
DOALL No. 470. An all-purpose, water-soluble oil for general shop use. It is a heavy-duty cutting oil with extreme-pressure properties and excellent anti-weld characteristics. Used for the sawing of stainless steel, high alloys, and titanium.
DOALL HI-DUTY WAY LUBRICANT. A lubricant for the ways of machine tools.
(See also KLEEN-FLUSH, KLEEN-KOOL, POWER CUT®, and SAW EEZ.) DOALL CO.

Doh-Tone®. Chemical compounds used in the milling and baking industries for improving the strength and color of flour. PENNSYLVANIA SALT MFG. CO.

Dolfinite®. A line of marine products including paints, enamels, varnishes, sealers; joint, bedding, planking, caulking, seam, and antisweat insulation compounds; cements; etc.
DOLPHIN PAINT & VARNISH CO.

Donopak®. The trademark for a disposable set for collection of blood by vacuum or by gravity.
ABBOTT LABORATORIES

Donopak-Ette®. The trademark for a disposable set for collection of blood by vacuum.
ABBOTT LABORATORIES

Donovo. A prophylactic hand cream containing 15% hydrous lanolin and USP menthol in a hydrophilic cream base. CHASE CHEMICAL CO.

Door-Ease® Dripless Oil. A general-purpose lubricating oil containing a corrosion inhibitor. *Uses:* For loosening rusty or tight bolts, nuts, etc.; for lubricating hinges, door handles, generators, starters, brake fittings, etc. AMERICAN GREASE STICK CO.

Door-Ease® Stainless Stick Lubricant. A stick lubricant that can be used on metal, wood, rubber, plastic, glass, and other surfaces. It prevents squeaks, wear, and rusting. It is stainless, and easy to apply. Can be used to lubricate car door fittings, hood lacings and rubber parts such as seals on car doors, rubber bumpers and alignment pads, etc.
AMERICAN GREASE STICK CO.

Doriden®. An oral, non-barbiturate hypnotic and sedative especially useful for preoperative sedation, for elderly patients, for neuropsychiatric patients, and for patients suffering from severe chronic disease.
CIBA PHARMACEUTICAL PRODUCTS INC.

Dorisyl[NE]. A proprietary synthetic aromatic chemical. A practically colorless liquid with a rose-lily bouquet coupled with top notes of methyl ionone and orris. DOW CHEMICAL CO.

Dorlone[NE]. A soil fumigant containing 75.2% mixed dichloropropenes, 18.7% ethylene dibromide, and 6.1% inerts, for use in controlling plant parasitic nematodes. DOW CHEMICAL CO.

Dormasol®. (*Supp.* I p. 63). No longer available.
GENERAL CHEMICAL DIV.,
ALLIED CHEMICAL & DYE CORP.

Dormatone®. (*HBMTN* p. 177). No longer available. AMERICAN CHEMICAL PAINT CO.

Dornavac®. Pancreatic dornase. A veterinary medicinal. It is the enzyme desoxyribonuclease, extracted from beef pancreas and lyophilized for increased stability. *Use:* For local application to liquify thick, purulent debris in rhinotracheitis (red nose), pneumonia, mastitis, abscesses, wounds, chronic navel infections, sinusitis, fistulous withers, and alveolar periostitis. MERCK SHARP & DOHME

Double Brand. (*HBMTN* p. 178). No longer available. A. MILNE & CO.

Doubletone. See CRAFTINT DOUBLETONE.

Double XX®. A line of resinoid-bonded abrasive cut-off wheels reinforced with a layer of glass fiber mesh on each side. The abrasives used are ELECTROLON® (silicon carbide), for cutting non-metals, includ-

ing all building materials, and BOROLON® (aluminum oxide), for cutting all metals, including steel.
SIMONDS ABRASIVE CO.

Dowfax[NR]. The trade name for a series of surface-active agents. DOW CHEMICAL CO.

Dowlube®. A liquid lubricating composition especially useful for adding to the fuel of two-cycle engines. DOW CHEMICAL CO.

Dowpac[NR]. A polystyrene tower-packing media.
DOW CHEMICAL CO.

Dowpon[NR]. Weed killing composition containing DALAPHON (α,α-dichloropropionic acid) for farm use.
DOW CHEMICAL CO.

Dow-Tri[NR]. A metal-degreasing fluid containing trichloroethylene. DOW CHEMICAL CO.

Doxol[NR]. Dioctyl sodium sulfosuccinate, Blair, in effective doses of 100 mg. per table. Used for the treatment and prevention of constipation.
BLAIR LABORATORIES, INC.

DPi®. The trademark for a line of VITAMIN A, VITAMIN E, distilled monoglycerides, distilled acetylated monoglycerides, food emulsifiers, feed supplements, organic chemicals.
DISTILLATION PRODUCTS INDUSTRIES,
DIV. OF EASTMAN KODAK CO.

Draft/Stop®. Forced-draft heating, cooling, and ventilating units of the cabinet type.
AMERICAN AIR FILTER CO.

Dragon's Blood△. A resinous secretion obtained from the fruits of *Daemonorops propinquus* Becc., *D. draco* Blume, and other species of *Daemonorops*, *Palmae*, grown in Sumatra, Borneo and India. The resin from this secretion is odorless and practically tasteless; it has a vitreous fracture; and when powdered has a bright crimson color. Melts at about 120°C. with sublimation of some benzoic acid; insoluble in water; soluble in alcohol. Used for coloring lacquers and varnishes, and occasionally plasters; in photoengraving on zinc, it is used to protect metal parts that are not to be etched.

Drapetex 35[NR]. A cationic textile softener characterized by high and rapid solubility and unusual stability to acids, mild alkalies, and salts. It produces a full and lofty hand on cellulosic and synthetic fabrics and shows low yellowing at high temps. It is used as a softener in resin finishes, where high acid-stability and good solubility are required. It also produces good antistatic properties on synthetic fabrics.
HART PRODUCTS CORP.

Drapex 4.4®. An epoxy plasticizer for heat and light stabilization of vinyl compounds. It also provides excellent low-temp. flexibility. Sp.gr. (25/25°C.), 0.920; viscosity, (Brookfield @ 25°C.), 40 centipoises; freezing point, -22°C.; color (Gardner), 5–6.
ARGUS CHEMICAL CORP.

Drawax 930 and 931[NR]. Similar to DRAWAX 936 but in less soluble form. Used in the rubber, plastic, and metal trades as a lubricant and mold-release agent. COLLOIDS, INC.

Drawax 936[NR]. A synthetic wax of high lubricity, high m.p., and excellent adhesion to yarns or fabrics. It is non-yellowing and has excellent stability even at high temps.; is compatible with starch, all types of resin formulations, glues, caseins, and all types of textile finishes. Used where lubricity is required and softness is not critical. Especially suitable for improving the sewing of resin-treated goods with minimum of needle breakage. COLLOIDS, INC.

Draw-Bright 600[NR]. A salt for tempering steel parts. It produces clean, bright surfaces, and removes rust and scale. Steel parts show no discoloration after tempering in DRAW-BRIGHT and water quenching. It is not recommended for tempering high-speed steels since it contains a small amount of cyanide. M.p. 500°F.; working range, 600–1,200°F.; weight, 100 lb./cu.ft. PARK CHEMICAL CO.

Draw-Bright 750[NR]. A tempering salt similar to DRAW-BRIGHT 600 except that it has a higher m.p.—650°F.—and a narrower working range—700 to 1,200°F. PARK CHEMICAL CO.

Drawcote®. An industrial lubricating and cooling composition for forming a dry, homogenous, self-adherent lubricating and cooling film on metal stock. The film lubricates the metal during subsequent die-forming and other shaping operations.
PENNSYLVANIA SALT MFG. CO.

Draw-Kleen®. (*HBMTN* p. 182). Should have been listed as a registered trademark. CRAFTINT MFG. CO.

Drawlene®. A lubricating material which is added to varnishes and coatings used for metal decorating.
INTERCHEMICAL CORP., FINISHES DIV.

Drex. See SUPER DREX®.

Drex "8"®. (*HBMTN* p. 183 and *Supp.* I p. 63). No longer available. NOPCO CHEMICAL CO.

Dri-Bake®. Silicone resins and other silicone products used to coat the surfaces of cooking and baking utensils in order to facilitate the release of goods baked in such utensils. GENERAL ELECTRIC CO.

Dri-Clor®. A laundry bleaching agent.
PENNSYLVANIA SALT MFG. CO.

Drildust[NR]. A dust-collecting device used in conjunction with mine roof bolt drills.
MINE SAFETY APPLIANCES CO.

Drillalloy[NR]. (*HBMTN* p. 184). No longer available. DELAWARE TOOL STEEL CORP.

Drillyfe[NR]. (*HBMTN* p. 184). No longer available.
BEE CHEMICAL CO.

Driocel®. (*HBMTN* p. 184). Now mfg'd by MINERALS & CHEMICALS CORP. OF AMERICA, successor to ATTAPULGUS CLAY CO.

Driocel S®. A desiccant. An activated bauxite used specifically to overcome souring of light hydrocarbon liquids, such as low-pressure-gas products, in the final drying step. Produces a sweet, dried product; exhibits long service life; does not increase heavy ends by polymerization. Other suggested uses include drying of chlorinated and fluorinated hydrocarbons.
MINERALS & CHEMICALS CORP. OF AMERICA

Drugology®. The trademark of a publication of botanical drugs. S. B. PENICK & CO.

Drycid®. An inhibited, acidic descaler and deruster in powder form. Used to remove water scale, iron sulfide, rust and other metal oxides. Excellent for descaling and derusting operations in recirculating systems which contain parts fabricated with dissimilar metals. OAKITE PRODUCTS, INC.

Drycol®. A line of coloring pigments for thermoplastic materials. Available in a number of different colors. GERING PRODUCTS INC.

Dry-Developer[NE]. A photographic developing apparatus for any ammonia-developing material exposed to ultraviolet light in a vacuum frame, blue print machine, diazo-moist printer or similar types of reproduction equipment. It accommodates material up to 24″ wide, and operates at a constant speed of 6 ft./min. TECNIFAX CORP.

Dryette®. The trademark for chemical compositions for processing fabrics and garments made of wool, cotton, and synthetic fibers and blends thereof to make them water repellent. CRAVENETTE CO., U.S.A.

Dry Exsize-T®. A highly concentrated EXSIZE-T® in dry powdered form. PABST BREWING CO., INDUSTRIAL PRODUCTS DIV.

Drygalv[NE]. A cold galvanizing compound for depositing a film of approx. 95% zinc on iron and steel. It is applied like a paint, and forms a film comparable to that obtained by hot-dip application. The film withstands the salt spray test for 1,000 hr. AMERICAN SOLDER & FLUX CO.

DS-207®. Dibasic lead stearate. $2PbO \cdot Pb \cdot (C_{17}H_{35}COO)_2$; mol.wt. 1,221. A soft, white unctuous powder; sp.gr. 2.02; refractive index, 1.60; insoluble in all common solvents. *Use:* As a stabilizer and lubricant for vinyl resins. NATIONAL LEAD CO.

D & S Core & Mold Wash[NE]. A plastic-type, core and mold wash base that is suitable for suspending refractory materials in foundry core and mold washes. It is particularly suitable where zircon refractories are used because of its silica-free nature. To prepare a suitable zircon core and mold wash, the following formulation can be used: 17 lb. D & S CORE & MOLD WASH, 32 lb. zircon flour of 200 mesh, 33 lb. zircon salt, and 18 lb. water. M. A. BELL CO.

DSX-11®. A room deodorant. J. I. HOLCOMB MFG. CO.

D-Tac. (*HBMTN* p. 185). Should have been listed as POLYMEL® D-TAC. POLYMEL CORP.

Dual Dye®. A dyestuff for lubricating oil. NOPCO CHEMICAL CO.

Duflex[NE]. Flexible finishes of lacquer or synthetic resin base. MAAS & WALDSTEIN CO.

Dulcet®. The trademark for a line of sugar tablets. ABBOTT LABORATORIES

Du-Lite® Oxiblak®. The trademark for steel oxidizing salts. DU-LITE CHEMICAL CORP.

Dum Dum Calk. See ARCO NON-SHRINKING DUM DUM CALK[NE].

Dumore®. A general-purpose cleaner for farm applications. Designed for use with soft to moderately hard water. DIVERSEY CORP.

Duo-Dustin®. A registered trademark for a line of chemically treated paper sheets for dusting and polishing. KIMBERLY-CLARK CORP.

Duomat®. A non-carbonate type of photographic developer for use in continuous paper processing equipment. EASTMAN KODAK CO.

Duomatic®. A registered trademark covering a type of control assembly for semi-automatic water softeners. It is unique in that it has only two controls—a two-position, three-way, manually controlled valve, and a two-position, three-way timing mechanism. CLACK WATER TREATMENT, INC.

Duo-Tex®. An intumescing, fire-resisting paint. CELOTEX CORP.

Duozine®. A sulfonamide preparation for oral administration. Consists of a combination of sulfadiazine and sulfamerazine (dia-mer-sulfonamides) in sugar tablets, standard tablets and suspension forms. ABBOTT LABORATORIES

Durabutton®. Resilient wear inserts employed in foundry mold apparatus such as core boxes, flasks, and the like. INTERNATIONAL MINERALS & CHEMICAL CORP.

Dur-Ace[NE]. A thermoplastic resin-rubber copolymer characterized by its good resistance to most inorganic chemicals and some organics, extremely good impact resistance, and good mechanical and electrical properties. It is softened by ketones, esters and chlorinated hydrocarbons. Sp.gr. 1.05–1.12; tensile strength, 4,200–5,000 lb./sq.in.; heat distortion temp. 145°–175°F. Available in a number of different colors, and in the form of tubing, pipe and fittings, rod and sheets. AMERICAN HARD RUBBER CO.

Duracel®. The trademark for a line of cellulose acetate coating compositions or lacquers. MAAS & WALDSTEIN CO.

Dura Cement®. An adhesive cement for foundry apparatus. *Use:* For cementing rubber and plastics to iron. INTERNATIONAL MINERALS & CHEMICAL CORP.

Duracoat®. (*Supp.* I p. 65). Now a registered trademark. HEATBATH CORP.

Duralene®. A line of finishes for leather. They are sold principally to leather tanners. B. B. CHEMICAL CO.

Duramat®. A glass fiber-reinforced outer pipe wrap designed specifically for pipeline construction. Applied over the reinforced enamel, it provides a tough skin, protecting the enamel from mechanical damage during handling, lowering-in, and back-filling. It is composed of a balanced combination of bitumens reinforced with chemical-type glass fiber mat and parallel strands of VITRON glass yarns. L.O.F. GLASS FIBERS CO.

Duramesh[NE]. An open-mesh fabric woven from inorganic glass fiber yarn and coated with a balanced combination of bituminous and synthetic resins.

Used principally for wrapping field joints, valves, and fittings. It is applied easily by hand or machine.
L.O.F. Glass Fibers Co.

Duran®. (*HBMTN* p. 190). Should have been listed as Masland Duran®.
Masland Duraleather Co.

Duranap®. An imitation suede fabric made by covering cloth with a cement coating and then applying a loose flock to the cement so as to bond the flock in place.
B. B. Chemical Co.

Durapak®. The trademark for a parchmentized kraft paper.
Paterson Parchment Paper Co.

Duraplastic®. An air-entraining portland cement. It is a true portland cement in which an air-entraining agent has been interground during mfg. It makes a very durable concrete for concrete paving, structural and mass concrete, stucco and manufactured concrete products.
Universal Atlas Cement Co.

Duraprem[NR]. A line of printing inks for plastics. They are based on various synthetic resins.
Maas & Waldstein Co.

Durarod®. A resilient seal for foundry core boxes and sand-charging apparatus.
International Minerals & Chemical Corp.

Durasol®. (*HBMTN* p. 191). Should have been listed as Masland Durasol®.
Masland Duraleather Co.

Durastrip®. A resilient sheet used in foundry mold apparatus such as core boxes, flasks, and the like.
International Minerals & Chemical Corp.

Duratube®. A resilient blow tube for foundry mold apparatus, such as blow plates, core boxes, flasks, and the like.
International Minerals & Chemical Corp.

Dura-wood®. The trademark for a wood preservative.
Cuprinol Div., Darworth Inc.

Durex®. A line of self-lubricating bearings and structural parts made of metal powders.
Moraine Products Div. of General Motors Corp.

Durez®. A line of phenol-formaldehyde molding compounds and resins. The molding compounds are used for the mfg. of chemical equipment, pump impellers, electrical apparatus, handles, knobs, photographic equipment, industrial equipment, etc. Straight phenol-formaldehyde, modified phenol-formaldehyde, terpene phenolic and furfuryl alcohol resins are supplied in various forms for use in brake linings, grinding wheels, laminates, rubber compounds and cements, varnishes, wax emulsions and many other products.

Durez Molding Compounds. These materials are supplied in three forms: powder or granular, nodular or rice-like, and fluff or macerated fabric. They are made with various types of fillers, both organic and inorganic. Description and properties of a number of Durez Molding Compounds are as follows:

Durez No.	Type	Description	Type of filler	Sp. gr.	Flexural strength, lb./sq.in.
55	Heat resisting	A material having good impact resistance combined with excellent heat resistance.	Mineral	1.66	9,000
75	Special property	A compound designed to have high finish and good chemical resistance.	—	1.38	10,000
77	Special property	A compound of low gravity and high chemical resistance. It can be machined, sanded, and buffed.	—	1.25	9,000
260	General purpose	A material combining good physical and electrical properties with excellent machining characteristics.	Wood flour	1.38	9,000
265	General purpose	An exceptionally fast-curing material for use on a wide variety of molded articles consistent with the characteristics of a fast-curing molding compound.	Wood flour	1.38	9,000
791	General purpose	An extremely versatile material characterized by a fast cure and a long flow. Designed to meet the requirements of MIL-P-10420, Class 2.	Wood flour	1.37	11,000
792	General purpose	A material characterized by rigid set and low shrinkage. It has excellent electrical insulation resistance properties combined with an above-average heat resistance.	Wood flour	1.40	11,000
1308	Heat resisting	A low gravity material designed for medium heat-resisting applications.	Organic and mineral	1.59	9,000
1544	Impact	A compound of very high impact resistance and excellent lustrous finish. It is designed to meet the requirements of MIL-M-14E, Type CFG.	Cotton flock	1.36	11,000
1905	Impact	A medium-impact material in nodular form to facilitate preforming in automatic machines.	Rag	1.46	9,000
1910	Impact	Similar to 1905 but contains graphite; designed for anti-friction parts.	Cotton	1.45	8,500
2260	General purpose	A high-quality, general-purpose material closely controlled in mfg.	Wood flour	1.37	10,500

Durez No.	Type	Description	Type of filler	Sp. gr.	Flexural strength, lb./sq.in.
2271	Electrical	A compound possessing high dielectric strength at elevated temp.	Organic	1.36	11,000
3949	Non-bleeding	A material characterized by fast cure and minimum odor.	Organic	1.42	9,000
3971	Non-bleeding	A compound possessing good finish, long flow, and rigid set.	Organic	1.36	10,000
11540	General purpose	A high-quality compound having closely controlled properties.	Wood flour	1.37	12,000
11864	Heat resisting	A mineral-filled phenolic molding compound with excellent heat resistance, fast cure and good moisture resistance designed to meet MIL-M-14E, Type MFH, and MIL-P-10420, Class 8.	Mineral	1.88	9,000
12708	Electrical	A soft-setting compound designed for high arc resistance. It does not crack around inserts.	Mineral	1.84	9,000
13124	Impact	A high impact material providing an unusually good molded finish, and suitable for use in automatic equipment.	Cotton flock	1.38	10,000
13856	Chemical resistant	A one-step material especially suited for molded parts in contact with water, such as washing machine agitators, pumps and valves. Particularly where parts are dry on one side and wet on the other.	Organic	1.41	9,500
14482	Impact	A high-impact material designed to meet the requirements of MIL-M-14E, Type CFI 20.	Fabric	1.38	10,000
14893	Heat resisting	A material possessing good versatility and extremely fast cure. Can be exposed to 450° F. for relatively long periods of time without serious impairment of physical properties. It is designed to meet the military specifications MIL-M-14E, Type MFH.	Mineral	1.54	8,000
15528	General purpose	An ammonia-free compound designed to eliminate corrosion of electrical contacts and inserts. It meets the requirements of MIL-P-14E Type CFG.	Wood flour	1.38	10,000
16221	Impact	A glass fiber-filled material of high strength and excellent dimensional stability.	Glass fibers	1.90	25,000
16274	Electrical	A compound possessing excellent electrical properties combined with good dimensional stability and resistance to water. It is designed to meet the requirements of military specification MIL-M-14E, Type MFE.	Mineral	1.75	9,500
18001	Electrical	A material possessing excellent dimensional stability and arc resistance together with improved impact resistance. Supplied in the form of small nodules, it is dust-free and suitable for use in automatic equipment.	Mineral	1.66	9,500

Durez Diallylphthalates. Durez now manufactures two thermosetting diallylphthalate materials. Durez 16694 is an Orlon-filled molding compound recommended for electrical applications where exposure to high humidity for long periods is encountered. It has high impact and excellent dimensional stability characteristics. It can be molded around large inserts without cracking. Durez 17877 is a mineral-filled diallylphthalate compound with excellent electrical properties and good dimensional stability.

Durez Resins. These are grouped into two general classifications: (1) Industrial Resins, and (2) Protective Coating Resins. They are supplied in lump, powder, and liquid resin forms, and in the form of solutions. The solutions are generally made with denatured alcohol, acetone, or a combination of alcohol and other solvents, and contain from 50 to 70% solids.

Durez Industrial Resins. These are phenol-formaldehyde thermosetting resins and furfuryl alcohol resins. They are used as binders for a wide variety of fillers to develop such desirable properties as water and chemical resistance, heat resistance, high strength both at room temp. and elevated temp., good electrical properties, abrasive resistance, and, with different modifiers, a range of hardness and toughness. Their availability in so many different forms and the wide range of properties make them extremely versatile for use in many applications. A few of the major applications include bonding of sand for shell molds and cores, modification of rubber compounds and rubber-base solvent cements, bonding of asbestos fiber for automotive brake linings and clutch facings, bonding wood particles into boards and molded shapes, bonding glass and other fibers into insulation batts, and the impregnation of paper and fabric for laminating and other uses. The furfuryl alcohol resins when used with acid accelerations serve as binders for inert fillers in corrosion-resistant mortars.

Durez Protective Coating Resins. These resins are used in two major types of products: oleoresinous varnishes and wax emulsion floor finishes. The resins available for use in oleoresinous coating formulations may be classed as 100% phenolics and terpene phenolics. The 100% phenolics are used in the mfg. of weather- and salt-spray resistant spar varnishes, boat and bridge paints, and anti-corrosive finishes. The terpene phenolics are much harder and higher melting than the 100% phenolics and are especially suitable for floor varnishes and floor paints. The terpene phenolics also are used in heat-set type printing inks.

In the wax emulsion floor finishes, both the terpene phenolics and the non-phenolics are used: The terpene phenolics contribute water resistance, hardness, improved gloss and slip resistance to wax emulsions. The non-phenolic resins are used as replacements for shellac in emulsion polishes and impart improved leveling or "lay-down" properties, water resistance and extra hardness.
Durez Plastics Div., Hooker Electrochemical Co.

Durheat[NE]. The trade name for a line of lacquers, enamels and varnishes that are resistant to heat.
Maas & Waldstein Co.

Durocrete. A concrete floor-patching material for filling holes and ruts in floors where water, oil and grease or heavy trucking conditions are serious.
Klee Waterproofing Corp.

Durodi. A nickel-chromium-molybdenum-silicon die block and hot-work die steel furnished in both heat-treated and annealed conditions.
A. Finkel & Sons Co.

Duromit. A product, available in 12 colors, for coloring and hardening concrete floors in factories, showrooms, schools, patios, walks, and terraces.
Klee Waterproofing Corp.

Duron #90[NE]. An epoxy-based resin cement with excellent adhesion to metals, wood, glass, brick, tile, etc. It is resistant to most acids, alkalis, and solvents. *Use:* In the construction and repair of chemical equipment.
Electro-Chemical Engineering & Mfg. Co.

Durpon®. A series of drawing compounds for tubes, rods, wires and the like.
Nopco Chemical Co.

Dursign[NE]. A sign-masking paste for blocking out letters and designs in sign making.
Maas & Waldstein Co.

Dus-Cop®. (*Supp.* I p. 67). No longer available.
General Chemical Div., Allied Chemical & Dye Corp.

Dustchek®. (*Supp.* I p. 67). Now a registered trademark.
Franklin Research Co.

Dustnox[NE]. An oilless dressing for dust mops used for damp mopping. It aids in the removal of dust and surface soil.
U. S. Sanitary Specialties Corp.

Dust-Stop®. Air filters and air filter media of the adhesive impingement type.
Owens-Corning Fiberglas Corp.

Dust-Vue Microprojector[NE]. A projection device used in conjunction with a microscope for magnification and projection onto a screen of dust particles; thus permitting easy counting and particle size determination.
Mine Safety Appliances Co.

"Dutch Boy" Nalplex®. The trademark for a water-emulsion type, odorless, flat, interior finish coat paint made with acrylic latex, titanium and other pigments. Available in white, off white, and 18 colors. It has a spreading rate of approx. 500 sq.ft. per gal., and it dries in 1 to 2 hr., and can be recoated in 4 hr. It can be applied directly to painted, unpainted or wall-papered surfaces of plaster, wallboard, etc.; and no primer is required on other than a bare iron or steel surface. *Use:* On all interior walls and ceilings.
National Lead Co.

Duval®. The trademark for a line of essential oils, perfume specialties, and perfume bases for cosmetic and industrial applications. Mfg'd by the Compagnie Duval Div. of the S. B. Penick & Co.

Dux® **Primer.** (*HBMTN* p. 195). No longer available.
E. I. du Pont de Nemours & Co.

Dux® **Putties.** (*HBMTN* p. 195). No longer available.
E. I. du Pont de Nemours & Co.

Dyal®. A line of drying and non-drying synthetic resins of the alkyd type. Used in paints, enamels, lacquers, and printing inks; and as plasticizers in rubber, plastics, and lacquers. Available in several types: pure, oil-modified, and resin-modified.
Sherwin-Williams Co.

Dyeset®. A laundry sour.
Pennsylvania Salt Mfg. Co.

Dyform. A hot-melt casting plastic used for high-impact, metal-forming tools. Available in 2 grades: Dyform 720, a metallic-green material for making punches in connection with metal die cavities; and Dyform 721, a metallic-gray material for drop hammer rings or other applications where a softer material is required.
Rezolin, Inc.

Dymal®. A line of synthetic resins based on maleic anhydride. They are similar to the Dyal® resins and are used for the same purpose.
Sherwin-Williams Co.

Dymerex®. A resin composed of the dimer of abietic acid with an acid number of 148, a drop melting point of 150°C., and USDA color of I-K. *Uses:* In paints, varnishes, resins, adhesives, floor coverings, etc.
Hercules Powder Co.

Dynahue®. A detergent composition primarily adapted for laundry use.
Pennsylvania Salt Mfg. Co.

Dynaprene®. A line of flexible, insulated, electric cable, jacketed with an oil-resisting neoprene sheathing. Characterized by high flex resistance and excellent impact resistance. Designed to withstand the rough operating conditions encountered in the mining industry. WHITNEY BLAKE CO.

Dynavis® Oils. A line of low-pour-point, high-viscosity-index, inhibited lubricating oils designed for use in internal-combustion engines operating at moderate loads and speeds. SUN OIL CO.

Dyphene®. A line of pure-phenolic synthetic resins used in paints, enamels, etc. SHERWIN-WILLIAMS CO.

Dyphenite®. A line of modified-phenolic synthetic resins used in paints, enamels, etc.
SHERWIN-WILLIAMS CO.

Dyphos®. Dibasic lead phosphite. $2PbO \cdot PbHPO_3 \cdot \frac{1}{2}H_2O$; mol.wt. 743. Fine, acicular white crystals; sp.gr. 6.94; refractive index, 2.25; insoluble in all common solvents. *Use:* As an anti-oxidant heat and light stabilizer for vinyls, especially with paste resins.
NATIONAL LEAD CO.

Dypol[NE]. A line of polyester resins used in making reinforced plastic products. SHERWIN-WILLIAMS CO.

Dysco[NE]. (*HBMTN* p. 196). No longer available.
ABBOTT LABORATORIES

Dythal®. Dibasic lead phthalate. $(C_6H_4)(COOPbO)_2$-Pb; mol.wt. 818. Fluffy, yellow-white, crystalline powder; sp.gr. 4.6; refractive index, 1.99; insoluble in all common solvents. *Use:* As a general-purpose, light and heat stabilizer for vinyl resins.
NATIONAL LEAD CO.

E

Eagle®. The trademark for a line of steel sheets and black sheets. UNITED STATES STEEL CORP.

Ear Defenders[NE]. Plugs for use in the ears as protection against potentially damaging noises.
MINE SAFETY APPLIANCES CO.

Earsaver[NE]. A cap equipped with noise-eliminating ear cushions, for protection against exposure to high level noises. MINE SAFETY APPLIANCES CO.

Earth Wax△. Same as OZOKERITE△.

Eastofix®. The trademark for a line of wash fast dyes for acetate. EASTMAN CHEMICAL PRODUCTS, INC.

Easy-Care. *See* LECTON® EASY-CARE.

Eau Grison△. Same as LIME SULFUR△.

Ebonol® "C" and "C" Special. Patented mixtures of alkalis and strong oxidizing agents for blackening and coloring copper and copper alloys containing 65–100% copper. EBONOL "C" SPECIAL has a much greater blackening ability than EBONOL "C," blackening over twice the area per pound, and giving a more adherent finish. EBONOL® is registered trademark No. 408,618.
ENTHONE, INC.

Ebony△. The wood of various species of trees of the ebony family, *Ebenaceae,* although the name is also applied to some woods of the genus *Dalbergia,* family Leguminosae. BLACK EBONY, from the tree *Diospyros dendo* of West Africa, and EBONY, from the tree *D. melanoxylos,* of India, are the true ebonies. This hard, black wood is valuable for parts subject to great wear, for ornamental inlaying, piano keys, and turnery.

E. C.®. A smokeless shot gun and rifle powder.
HERCULES POWDER CO.

Ecco-847[NE]. A textile softener consisting of a light-colored sulfonated tallow. It gives clear solutions at 5% conc.; and has excellent heat resistance (does not yellow for 60 sec. at 400°F.).
EASTERN COLOR & CHEMICAL CO.

Eccoclean RPW[NE]. A 100%-active self-emulsifiable roller and screen cleaner for use in the textile industry. It can be used as is or in water dilution to form stable emulsions. *Uses:* For cleaning silk screens, rollers and blankets. EASTERN COLOR & CHEMICAL CO.

Ecco Defoamer PD[NE]. A stable thin paste containing a synergistic combination of silicone and other defoamers. Easily dispersible in water at any temp. *Use:* In all textile operations, and particularly for the defoaming of latex emulsions during padding or printing. EASTERN COLOR & CHEMICAL CO.

Ecco Defoamer PL[NE]. A water-thin, practically odorless emulsion, easily dispersible in water during use. *Use:* In all textile operations, particularly for those in which an odorless defoamer is required.
EASTERN COLOR & CHEMICAL CO.

Eccopel[NE]. A renewable, single-package, wax-emulsion textile water repellent. The emulsions are stable during storage and during use. Spray ratings of 100% can be obtained at conc. of 5–10% on COTTON, WOOL, and RAYON. *Use:* Particularly where stability to beating and low foam is desired.
EASTERN COLOR & CHEMICAL CO.

Eccosyn[NE]. A fulling agent for wool. It is compatible with alkalis normally used in processing, and will not salt out on addition of alkalis or alkali carbonates; and it possesses good detergent and emulsifying properties.
EASTERN COLOR & CHEMICAL CO.

Ecco-W-88[NE]. A low cost but highly efficient liquid wetting agent for use in general textile applications.
EASTERN COLOR & CHEMICAL CO.

Eccowax UL-100[NE]. A water-dispersible textile-finishing agent available in cationic and nonionic forms and in any desired conc. It is a 100%-active base that yields a non-yellowing soft hand on COTTON or RAYON. For use particularly on high-speed, high-temp. padders and driers.
EASTERN COLOR & CHEMICAL CO.

Eccowet LF[NE]. A low-foaming wetting agent, stable in both acid and alkaline dyeing and finishing baths. *Use:* For WOOL dyeing or other operations in which foaming is a troublesome factor.
EASTERN COLOR & CHEMICAL CO.

Eclipse®. A line of thin-boiling corn starches which have been modified by acid hydrolysis. They are available over a wide range of viscosities. *Uses:* As briquetting binders in various applications, and in the mfg. of adhesives which set to a definite gel. In the textile industry, they are used in warp sizing and in finishing. The paper industry uses them for tub and press sizing, calender sizing, laminating and combining, and in bag pasting operations. They are also used in various food products, particularly in starch jelly candies. A. E. STALEY MFG. CO.

Ecomul[NR]. Emulsion-type undercoats and finishes based on polyvinyl acetate and other synthetic resins.
MAAS & WALDSTEIN CO.

Econoflex. A light, translucent, flexible high-test hide glue. It has strong immediate tack that remains workable for a long period. *Use:* In paper box mfg. for both tight- and loose-wrap operations on automatic and semi-automatic machines.
SWIFT & CO., GENERAL ADHESIVE PRODUCTS DEPT.

Economagic®. A low-cost, low-weight oil-base mud. When mixed with low-gravity (16°–30° API) asphaltic-type crude oil it may be used in average-temp., shallow holes and for workovers in depleted oil sands. It deposits a paper-thin mud cake and gives max. protection to the producing formations. It is a white powder, mixed in the ratio of 10 lb. per barrel of crude oil to produce an excellent lightweight mud.
OIL BASE, INC.

"Economy 250". See ASBESTONE® "ECONOMY 250".

Econo-Pine. See TROY ECONO-PINE.

EC and ECT Stabilizers[NR]. Dry, white powders designed as cutting agents for starches in warp sizing.
STEIN, HALL & CO.

E-D-E®. (*Supp.* I p. 69). No longer available.
GENERAL CHEMICAL DIV.,
ALLIED CHEMICAL & DYE CORP.

Edg-R-Discs[NR]. A silicon carbide abrasive paper, and paper-and-cloth combination discs used for floor sanding.
BEHR-MANNING CO.

Edsoy®. A completely refined, deodorized, soybean oil. The max. specifications are: free fatty acids, 0.05%; color, 2020Y-2.0 R; flavor, bland; cold test, clear and brilliant. Physical and chemical data: iodine value, 128–135; peroxide value, 0.0–0.5%; saponification no. 186–191; viscosity (Saybolt-Universal, 100°F.) 163–167 sec. *Uses:* In the mfg. of sulfonated oil because of its excellent color and color-retention properties; as a foam arrester in the preparation of yeast, sugar, antibiotics, etc.; and as an effective plasticizer in various applications such as in yeast cake. In the food industry, it is used in the preparation of mayonnaises and salad dressings; in the packing of fish products; and as a shortening and pan grease ingredient in the baking industry.
A. E. STALEY MFG. CO.

Eff-Plus V-P 731. A VITAMIN F_2 complex in capsule form.
VITAMIN PRODUCTS CO.

Eflex V-P 720. A VITAMIN F preparation in the form of perles. Contains essential unsaturated fatty acids (arachidonic, linoleic, linolenic) from flax, beef lipoids, with soybean lecithin. VITAMIN PRODUCTS CO.

Eiderdown®. The trademark for bar and powdered soaps.
S. B. PENICK & CO

EKC®. (*HBMTN* p. 199). Products under this trademark are now distributed by the DISTILLATION PRODUCTS INDUSTRIES, DIV. OF EASTMAN KODAK CO.

Ektachrome®. Photographic processing chemicals, namely, developers, hardener, bleach, clearing and fixing bath, and stabilizer.
EASTMAN KODAK CO.

Ektagraph®. Photographic processing chemicals, namely, activator, stop bath, and stripping solvent.
EASTMAN KODAK CO.

Ektonol®. A non-carbonate type of photographic developer for processing warm-tone papers.
EASTMAN KODAK CO.

Eldec® Kapseals®. A physiologic nutritional supplement of minerals, vitamins, digestive enzymes, protein factors, and sex hormones.
PARKE, DAVIS & CO.

Eldoplast 45®. A high-mol.wt. (mol.wt. 430) mixed-ester-type plasticizer for vinyl chloride-vinyl acetate copolymers, vinyl butyral resins, and ethyl cellulose resins. It combines excellent low-temp. performance with low volatility. Color (Lovebond 5¼"), 10.8Y, 2.6R (max.); boiling range (2.5 mm. Hg), 180–247°C.; settling point, −10°C. (approx.); sp.gr. (25/25°C.), 0.965; viscosity (25°C.), 16.5 cps.; acid no. 0.94 (max.); flash point, 185° C.; fire point, 216°C.; soluble in common organic solvents; insoluble in water.
FOREMOST FOOD AND CHEMICAL CO.,
EL DORADO DIV.

Electro-AIRMAT®. Electrical ventilating air cleaners or precipitators of the stationary dry cell type, having a sheet-like dielectric filter medium.
AMERICAN AIR FILTER CO.

Electrobestos[NR]. A greyish-white material which is widely used for arc or flame barriers and for parts of small ovens, muffles, or other apparatus exposed to heat. It is composed of asbestos fiber and high-temp. clays molded to shape in a cold plastic mass, impregnated with a liquid binder and heat treated. It is used in equipment subject to steady or intermittent heat up to 1,200°F., including muffle furnace trays, arc deflectors, electric power panels, small furnaces and ovens, soldering cups, etc.
JOHNS-MANVILLE SALES CORP.

Electrofining[NR]. See PETRECO® ELECTROFINING[NR].

Electro-KLEAN®. Electrical ventilating air cleaners or precipitators of the domestic household type.
AMERICAN AIR FILTER CO.

Electro-MATIC®. Electrical ventilating air cleaners or precipitators of the automatic self-cleaning type.
AMERICAN AIR FILTER CO.

Electro-PL®. Electrical ventilating air cleaners or precipitators of the stationary non-ionizing dry cell type, having a removable, air-porous, sheet-like dielectric filter medium.
AMERICAN AIR FILTER CO.

Electrosphere[NR]. See PETRECO® ELECTROSPHERE[NR] DESALTING PROCESS.

Elemi△. A soft, sticky, opaque resin with a pleasant odor, obtained from the Pili tree *canarium luzonicum*, of the Philippines. Contains dipentene and a related terpinene oil, phellandrene. The Pili trees are hacked or stripped, and the resin collects on the bark; each tree yields about 5 lb. of the resin per year. ELEMI is used in lacquers and in lithographic inks to provide body and elasticity; in medicine, it is used in making ointments.

Elftex®. A line of furnace carbon blacks used in the mfg. of inks and paints.
GODFREY L. CABOT, INC.

Elixirin®. The trademark for a line of wet ink varnishes for metal decorating.
INTERCHEMICAL CORP., FINISHES DIV.

Elkosin®. A sulfonamide characterized by its high solubility, low acetylation, and high therapeutic blood levels. Provides effective antibacterial action in a number of systemic and urinary tract infections. Available for oral administration in scored tablets of 0.5 g., and as a strawberry-flavored suspension in syrup containing 0.25 g. per 4-ml. teaspoonful.
CIBA PHARMACEUTICAL PRODUCTS INC.

El Rey®. A line of asphalt shingles.
CELOTEX CORP.

El-tex[NE]. A cement composed of hydraulic cement, synthetic resins, and graded aggregate. It will adhere to old concrete and may be feather-edged. It is used as a topping for concrete floors or to repair cracked or worn concrete.
ELECTRO-CHEMICAL ENGINEERING & MFG. CO.

Emargol®. An edible, 50% aqueous paste of mono- and di-glycerides and their sodium sulfoacetates. It is used in the bakery industry as an emulsifier and anti-spattering agent. EMULSOL CHEMICAL CORP.

Emboset BM®. A methylated urea formaldehyde resin in liquid form. It has outstanding storage stability and bath stability. Recommended for application to cellulosic fabrics where outstanding crease recovery and shrinkage control are required. It is also an excellent resin for embossing and other mechanical finishes. The performance pattern of EMBOSET BM is similar to that obtained with ethylene urea resins with the exception that EMBOSET BM will retain chlorine. It is recommended for any resin finishing application where high crease recovery values and extreme durability are required, and where chlorine resistance is not an important factor.
METRO-ATLANTIC INC.

Emboset NR®. A highly concentrated thermosetting resin solution, which was developed primarily for the finishing of nylon sheers, taffetas, and similar fabrics, where a durable, crisp, resilient hand is desired. It is also effective when used on rayon acetate blends, acetate and silk, where added body and stiffness are required in the finished fabric. It has excellent storage stability and solutions of the product containing the recommended amounts of catalyst have unusually long bath life. It is applied and cured by the same general methods normally used with urea or melamine formaldehyde resins. METRO-ATLANTIC INC.

Emboset Z®. A fiber-reactant ethylene urea resin, which produces outstanding crease recovery and shrinkage control in cellulosic fabrics, with a minimum of chlorine retention. The effects produced with this resin show outstanding resistance to laundering and dry cleaning. Recommended for minimum-care finishes on cotton and crease- and shrink-resistant finishes on rayons, and for mechanical finishing of all cellulosic fibers. The hand obtained with EMBOSET Z is soft and resilient. METRO-ATLANTIC INC.

Emcol 4155[NE]. A high foaming, anion-active, fatty amide sulfonate detergent in a spray-dried powdered form. It is used in formulating liquid bubble baths, dish detergents, shampoos, textile detergents, etc.
EMULSOL CHEMICAL CORP.

Emcol 4400A[NE]. A synthetic detergent.
EMULSOL CHEMICAL CORP.

Emcol 5120[NE]. A fatty alkanolamine condensate product possessing good foaming and detergent properties. *Uses:* In the formulation of automobile polishes, waterless hand cleaners, etc.
EMULSOL CHEMICAL CORP.

Emcol 5130[NE]. A fatty alkanolamine condensate product possessing good emulsifying, detergent, and foam-building properties. *Uses:* In formulating automobile polishes, laundry detergents, liquid soaps, shampoos, etc. EMULSOL CHEMICAL CORP.

Emcol 5137[NE]. A fatty alkanolamine condensate product possessing good emulsifying and detergent properties. It is used in formulating heavy-duty liquid cleaners, waterless hand cleaners, white sidewall tire cleaners, etc. EMULSOL CHEMICAL CORP.

Emcol 5138[NE]. A fatty alkanolamine condensate product possessing good emulsifying and detergent properties. It is used in formulating automobile polishes, coolant oils, rug cleaners, and waterless hand cleaners; in pigment grinding; and as an oil-in-water emulsifier. EMULSOL CHEMICAL CORP.

Emcol 6020[NE]. An oil-soluble detergent and emulsifying agent. It is an amine dodecyl benzene sulfonate. EMULSOL CHEMICAL CORP.

Emcol E607-L[NE]. (*HBMTN* p. 207). No longer available EMULSOL CHEMICAL CORP.

Emcol H-31A[NE]. A POLYETHYLENE GLYCOL 400 OLEATE used as an emulsifier for mineral oil; as a wetting agent; and as a viscosity stabilizer for vinyl plastisols. EMULSOL CHEMICAL CORP.

Emcol H-35A[NE]. An emulsifier for fats and oils, consisting of a POLYETHYLENE GLYCOL 400 STEARATE.
EMULSOL CHEMICAL CORP.

Emcol H-52[NE]. A blend of anionic and non-ionic surface-active agents used as an emulsifier for aliphatic hydrocarbons, including, kerosene, fuel oil, etc.
EMULSOL CHEMICAL CORP.

Emcol H-83T[NE]. A blend of anionic and non-ionic emulsifiers designed for use in preparing emulsifiable concentrates of TOXAPHENE or CHLORDANE.
EMULSOL CHEMICAL CORP.

Emcol H-85T[NE]. A blend of anionic and non-ionic emulsifiers used in preparing emulsifiable concentrates in xylene of various insecticides including DDT, DIELDRIN, ENDRIN, HEPTACHLOR, CHLORDANE, METHOXYCHLOR, etc. EMULSOL CHEMICAL CORP.

Emcol H-300X[NE] *and* **Emcol H-500X**[NE]. Blends of anionic and non-ionic emulsifiers designed for preparing emulsifiable concentrates of herbicides.
EMULSOL CHEMICAL CORP.

Emcol H-A *and* **Emcol H-B**[NE]. Anion-active emulsifying agents specifically designed for application in liquid fertilizer-liquid pesticide mixtures. They are free-flowing amber liquids with a mild odor and a sp. gr. of 1.01. Blends of these two agents can be used to formulate emulsifiable concentrates of a wide variety of toxicants. When combined with liquid fertilizers, emulsifiable pesticide concentrates formu-

lated with EMCOLS H-A and H-B readily form emulsions with a minimum of agitation.
EMULSOL CHEMICAL CORP.

Emcol K-8300[NR]. An anion-active fatty amide derivative supplied as an aqueous concentrate. It is an amber-colored liquid; total solids, 39–40%; active ingredients, 33–35%; wt. per gal. 9.17 lb.; stable in concentrated or dilute solutions at pH of 4 to 7; moderately soluble in solutions of electrolytes, aqueous solutions of ethanol, ethylene glycol, acetone, etc.; insoluble in fats, oils, hydrocarbons and chlorinated hydrocarbons. *Uses:* As an emulsifier in the preparation of "cold" rubber latices; as a stabilizer for natural and synthetic latices or latex formulations, including "foam" rubber, adhesives, etc.
EMULSOL CHEMICAL CORP.

Emcol MS-16[NR]. (*HBMTN* p. 208). No longer available. EMULSOL CHEMICAL CORP.

Emcol P10-59[NR]. An oil-soluble detergent and emulsifying agent. It is an amine dodecyl benzene sulfonate. EMULSOL CHEMICAL CORP.

Emerald Green△. Same as PARIS GREEN△.

Emeraldol®. A line of level-dyeing acid dyes, of good light fastness, for dyeing bluish greens on WOOL.
GENERAL DYESTUFF CO.

Emerel®. An all-purpose cleaner which consists of a concentrated blend of neutral soaps and detergents. Designed to remove imbedded dirt, hold soil in suspension, and prevent the development of hard water deposits. It is very effective on terrazzo floors and can be used for floors, woodwork, and all resilient-type flooring. S. C. JOHNSON & SON

Emeri-Bond[NR]. An agent for bonding EMERI-CRETE FLOORING® (*HBMTN* p. 208) to new or/old concrete floors. It is a two-package system: powder and paste, which are mixed in the ratio of 40 lb. powder to 1 gal. paste. This mix will cover approx. 100 sq. ft. with a layer 1/16" thick WALTER MAGUIRE CO.

Emeri-Brick[NR]. A heavy-duty, high-heat-resistant brick for flooring. It is very resistant to heat and thermal shock. WALTER MAGUIRE CO.

Emeritex[NR]. An aggregate hardener for heavy-duty concrete floors. It is a mineral emery produced from American ore, crushed, and graded into a mixture of sharp, irregular particles. Aluminum oxide content, 45% and over; ferric oxide content, 25% and over. Because of its extreme hardness, EMERITEX is much more wear-resistant than stone, gravel, trap rock, and other materials used in the construction of heavy-duty floors. It also has non-slip properties which improve with use, and it is resistant to food acids, and washing solutions encountered in food-processing plants, breweries, canning plants, etc.
AQUABAR CO.

Emeri-Topcrete®. A surface hardener for concrete floors. It is a mixture of CORTLAND EMERY AGGREGATE[NR] (*HBMTN* p. 149) and cement. EMERI-TOPCRETE (4 parts) is mixed with Portland cement or high-early-strength cement (1 part) and then mixed with water and applied to concrete floors to provide a non-slip, non-porous, non-dusting, moisture-resistant, hard and tough surface, WALTER MAGUIRE CO.

Emerox® **1110 Azelaic Acid.** Formerly known as EMEROX® 9110 AZELAIC ACID (*Supp.* I p. 73).
EMERY INDUSTRIES, INC.

Emerox® **9110 Azelaic Acid.** (*Supp.* I p. 73). Now known as EMEROX® 1110 AZELAIC ACID.
EMERY INDUSTRIES, INC.

Emersoft® **7000.** A non-ionic textile finishing agent for improving the softness of COTTONS, and for imparting luster, resistance to water spotting, better sewability, and resistance to yellowing. It is a non-corrosive, 95%-active, light-colored paste which readily disperses in warm water (140°F.). The dispersions are stable for long periods over a wide pH range (3.5-12). EMERSOFT 7000 is compatible with starches, weighting materials, and wetting and re-wetting agents. EMERY INDUSTRIES, INC.

Emersol® **300 Series.** (*HBMTN* p. 209). No longer available. EMERY INDUSTRIES, INC.

Emery△. A fine-grained, impure variety of CORUNDUM, containing 55–75% Al_2O_3 together with other minerals, usually MAGNETITE. Occurs as a dark brown, granular, massive material with a sp. gr. of 3.7–4.3 and a hardness of about 8. Used as an abrasive in powder form, and in blocks and wheels for grinding operations. Produced principally in Greece and Turkey, although some EMERY is mined at Peekskill, N. Y.

E.M.E. Syrup[NR]. (*HBMTN* p. 209). No longer available. ABBOTT LABORATORIES

Emkabase. An emulsifier for mineral oils. One part will mix cold with many times its own volume of mineral oil to form a bright oil. The emulsion, which is very stable, is used as a textile lubricant and softener. EMKAY CHEMICAL CO.

Emkacide GFI-40. A durable type gas-fading inhibitor for ACETATE colors. Used in the dye bath.
EMKAY CHEMICAL CO.

Emkacide MP. A combination mildew preventative and deodorant. It is recommended for use in the final rinse on textiles which must lay wet between dyeing and finishing, particularly in hot weather.
EMKAY CHEMICAL CO.

Emka Defoam Concentrate. An extremely efficient defoaming agent. A few drops will eliminate troublesome foam. Used particularly in the textile industry.
EMKAY CHEMICAL CO.

Emka Finish A. A modified gum arabic-base weighter textile finish. EMKAY CHEMICAL CO.

Emka Finishing Oil. A sulfonated oil-type softener. It shows excellent resistance to yellowing and development of rancidity. EMKAY CHEMICAL CO.

Emkafix R. A fixative for direct colors. It improves resistance to bleeding in warm water; improves fastness to perspiration and hot wet-pressing, and fastness to washing; and prevents migration of color. Applied on jigs, boxes, or padders in conc. of 2–4%.
EMKAY CHEMICAL CO.

Emkafol D. A textile wetting and rewetting agent with leveling properties. It is a dyeing assistant for use in COTTON-RAYON combinations and also for use in conjunction with enzymes for the more effective removal of starch sizings. EMKAY CHEMICAL CO.

Emkafume S. A non-durable type gas-fading inhibitor for ACETATE colors. It is used as a topping-off inhibitor in finishing. Applied in the quench after the use of a durable type of inhibitor in dyeing. It gives protection to meet the most rigid of gas-fading tests. EMKAY CHEMICAL CO.

Emkagen 49. A blend of an amine condensate and an alkyl aryl sulfonate, for use as a print wash to remove gums in the textile industry. It is a neutral detergent, effective and soluble at all temps.
EMKAY CHEMICAL CO.

Emkagen Concentrate. A synthetic detergent, an amide amine condensate in liquid form, having 100% active ingredients. It is readily soluble in cold water and may be diluted to any concentration. Solutions will not separate, jell, or settle out on standing. It possesses excellent detergency, wetting-out, and emulsifying properties. EMKAY CHEMICAL CO.

Emkagen RS. A dyeing assistant and textile scouring agent composed of highly active blends of chelating agents and detergents. It is very effective in the presence of metallic contaminents and under hard water conditions. EMKAY CHEMICAL CO.

Emka Konetex. An emulsifiable oil used for coning RAYON, NYLON, and other synthetic yarns. It may be used either as is or in water emulsion.
EMKAY CHEMICAL CO.

Emkalane MF. A fluid paste product for use as a leveling agent in WOOL and worsted dyeing, both in the raw stock or piece. Particularly helpful in dyeing tippy WOOL. It is compatible with all ingredients used in WOOL dyeing. EMKAY CHEMICAL CO.

Emkalite. A blend of synthetic detergents and mild alkalies, in powder form, for use in the textile industry.
EMKAY CHEMICAL CO.

Emkalite MS. A free-flowing white powder, readily soluble in warm water, composed of detergents, alkalis, and active bleaching agents. Particularly helpful for the removal of moats in the scouring of COTTON fabrics. EMKAY CHEMICAL CO.

Emkalon AX. A substantive anionic softener, in paste form, easily dissolved in warm water. It is compatible with gums, weighters, gas-fading inhibitors, and similar materials used in textile-finishing baths. EMKAY CHEMICAL CO.

Emkalon BT. A softener finish for COTTON piece goods. When used in conjunction with starch, it embodies the desirable features of an anionic substantive softener as to permanency to washing, while, at the same time, adding smoothness and luster. Withstands high heat without yellowing.
EMKAY CHEMICAL CO.

Emkalon C-50. A cationic textile softener in liquid form, readily soluble in water. It causes minimum color bleeding in finishing. EMKAY CHEMICAL CO.

Emkalon CX. A cationic softener in paste form, readily soluble in warm water. For use on RAYON, ACETATE and COTTON to produce a soft, drapey hand, resistant to washing. It shows excellent non-yellowing tendencies on whites. EMKAY CHEMICAL CO.

Emkalon H-460. A substantive anionic softener in paste form, soluble in water. It has excellent stability in acids, alkalis, or neutral baths; it is compatible with thermosetting-type resins of the urea-formaldehyde or melamine types; and it has outstanding resistance to yellowing under high heat.
EMKAY CHEMICAL CO.

Emkalon N Base. A 100%-active substantive textile softener useful as an economical starting point for the preparation of both anionic and cationic softeners.
EMKAY CHEMICAL CO.

Emkalon OS. A cationic softener for ORLON® and ORLON®-wool mixtures. It produces a velvety, desirable hand. EMKAY CHEMICAL CO.

Emkanet B. A stiff resin finish for veils and nets.
EMKAY CHEMICAL CO.

Emkanol MA. A concentrated, cresylic-base penetrating and wetting agent compounded to give max. penetration and wetting action in caustic liquors of mercerizing strength. EMKAY CHEMICAL CO.

Emka Non-Snag BD. A readily soluble thermoplastic-type resin for finishing NYLON hosiery. It produces a snag resistant, dull finish, permanent to washing. EMKAY CHEMICAL CO.

Emkanyl 85. A specially prepared nonionic leveling agent for use in the dyeing of NYLON hosiery. It gives very good union between leg and welt.
EMKAY CHEMICAL CO.

Emkapel C. A one-piece, wax-type textile water repellent of the semi-durable type. It is a free-flowing, thin liquid in both cold and warm weather. Easy to apply. Gives a good spray rating.
EMKAY CHEMICAL CO.

Emkapene RW. A clear, soluble mixture, composed of sulfonated oils blended with pine oil. It is an excellent leveling agent and dye assistant, particularly in the dyeing of RAYON knit goods.
EMKAY CHEMICAL CO.

Emka Permadul DS-2. A permanent dulling agent for NYLON piece goods and hosiery. Compatible with cationic finishes. EMKAY CHEMICAL CO.

Emka Permadul O. An homogenized dispersion of titanium dioxide so treated that when applied to RAYON and ACETATE fabrics in the quetsch, it produces a permanent dulling effect.
EMKAY CHEMICAL CO.

Emkapon K. A paste detergent composed of sulfated fatty amides. It has excellent scouring, emulsifying, wetting and leveling properties. Used in the textile industry. EMKAY CHEMICAL CO.

Emkapruf AFP. A highly concentrated, flame-resistant textile finish which will not discolor or change shades on drying under high heat.
EMKAY CHEMICAL CO.

Emkapruf FL. A flame-retardant textile finish in liquid form. A proportion of 1 to 2 lb. per gal. will give no dusting on drying. EMKAY CHEMICAL CO.

Emka Ribbon Finish. A clear, soluble, alkyd resin textile finish which requires no curing. Used on ACETATE, it gives a stiff, papery, lustrous finish.
EMKAY CHEMICAL CO.

Emkaron. A bleaching and dyeing assistant for ORLON. It produces a better white, and helps prepare the fabric for the dyeing process.
EMKAY CHEMICAL CO.

Emkasize CT Concentrate. A combination starch lubricant and binder for use in the textile industry.
EMKAY CHEMICAL CO.

Emkastat K. A textile auxiliary designed to meet the problems of static present in the processing of synthetics. It is easy to apply, and only small amounts are usually required. EMKAY CHEMICAL CO.

Emka Supertex. A penetrant and leveler for use in the dyeing of NYLON hosiery.
EMKAY CHEMICAL CO.

Emkatan K. A synthetic anionic softener and lubricant. It is used as a finish for COTTON and RAYON knit goods, and as a lubricant on dyed skeins to improve winding and to eliminate chafing and abrasions in winding. It is also a good anti-static on NYLON. EMKAY CHEMICAL CO.

Emkatard. A dispersing agent for vat dyestuffs. It has exceptionally good leveling qualities, is perfectly stable in hydrosulfite and caustic, and is non-foaming.
EMKAY CHEMICAL CO.

Emkaterge A *and* B. Detergents for the preparation of baths for the removal of graphite from NYLON lace and combinations of NYLON with other fibers.
EMKAY CHEMICAL CO.

Emkaterge NA-2. A high-strength, heavy liquid which, when cut with three parts of water, makes a ready-for-use, liquid, graphite remover compound for use on NYLON lace. EMKAY CHEMICAL CO.

Emkatex 49-P. An amber-colored gel containing synthetic penetrants with terpenes. It is an excellent scouring assistant and a unique dyeing assistant and leveling agent for RAYON, ACETATE, NYLON, and SILK. It foams nicely even in an acid bath. and is not affected by hard water. EMKAY CHEMICAL CO.

Emkatex A-1. A bright oil, containing emulsified solvents and terpenes, used as a cleaner for oil and grease soils in the textile industry.
EMKAY CHEMICAL CO.

Emkatex F-2. A blend of synthetic detergents and solvents used in the textile industry for the effective removal of loom grease and dirt.
EMKAY CHEMICAL CO.

Emkatex N-25. A non-ionic dispersing agent used as a retardant in vat dyeing and printing. It is a good stripping assistant for vat and naphthol colors when used with hydrosulfite and caustic soda. It is highly resistant to the action of salts present in hard water. It is a good dye dispersant and anti-static agent. EMKAY CHEMICAL CO.

Emkatex NE. A clear, amber-colored oil, readily soluble in water, composed of synthetic detergents and special emulsifying and dispersing agents. Used as a dispersing and leveling agent in the dyeing of RAYON, ACETATE and NYLON fabrics. It is free rinsing, and will not leave any odors if left in the material.
EMKAY CHEMICAL CO.

Emkawate. A concentrated textile weighter finish containing 80% active matter. It is a blend of selected plasticizers with a gum resin binder. It imparts a full soft hand. It is compatible with gums and glues, and is used with them if a full firm hand is desired. It is an excellent spun RAYON finish.
EMKAY CHEMICAL CO.

Emkawate OB. A gum resin finish, soluble in warm water, used for imparting weight, body and firmness to synthetic fabrics. It is compatible with most anionic, cationic and resin finishes.
EMKAY CHEMICAL CO.

Emkazyme. A standardized mixture of amylolytic enzymes and catalysts for use in the textile industry.
EMKAY CHEMICAL CO.

Emolein® 2957 *and* 2958. Lubricant esters. No 2957 is di-iso-octyl azelate; No. 2958 is di-2-ethylhexyl azelate. They are characterized by low pour points, high flash and fire points, and excellent viscosity-temp. relationships. They are used as lubricants for aircraft, gas turbines, instruments and other equipment where very high or very low temps. are encountered or where the equipment must operate over a wide temp. range ($-100°$ to $+400°F$.). Typical properties of these esters are:

Property	Emolein 2957	Emolein 2958
Viscosity, centistokes		
at 210°F.	3.34	2.96
at −65°F.	7,000	6,400
Neutralization no.	0.3	0.3
Hydroxyl no.	2.0 (max.)	2.0 (max.)
Flash point, °F.	425	520
Fire point, °F.	450 (min.)	450 (min.)
Pour point, °F.	−85	−100
Sp.gr. (25°C.)	0.9123	0.9124
Specific heat, B.t.u./lb. x °F. (at 75°F.)	0.52	0.52

EMERY INDUSTRIES, INC.

Empire®. A line of rawhide mallets in weights from 2 to 44 oz.; and plastic mallets, in weights from 4 to 18 oz. GREENE, TWEED & CO.

Empire[NR]. (*Supp.* I p. 73). No longer available.
HANSON-VAN WINKLE-MUNNING CO.

Emulsacera[NR]. A wax for use in the preparation of water-emulsion floor polishes for linoleum, asphalt-base floor tile, vinyl tile, etc.
INTERNATIONAL WAX REFINING CO.

Emulsarin®. The trademark for an emulsifier.
S. B. PENICK & CO.

Emulsaromes[NR]. A line of flavoring materials for the mfg. of syrups, ice creams and baked foods. They are colloidal suspensions.
FLORASYNTH LABORATORIES, INC.

Emulsept®. (*HBMTN* p. 209). No longer available.
EMULSOL CHEMICAL CORP.

Emulsion 63[NR]. (*HBMTN* p. 210). No longer available. ADVANCE SOLVENTS & CHEMICAL CORP.

Emulsoblack®. (*HBMTN* p. 210). No longer available. WITCO CHEMICAL CO.

Emultex®. A line of special water-dispersible lecithin concentrates, derived from natural soybean phosphatides. They are clear, amber-colored substances containing less than 1% moisture and less than 6% free fatty acids. Insoluble constituents are, in benzene, 0.08% (max.); and, in acetone, approx. 60%. *Uses:* In textile warp-sizing compounds, liquid soaps, leather tanning and other nonfood applications; as an additive for certain petroleum products; and in latex-emulsion and protein-type paints where they contribute to the stability. A. E. STALEY MFG. CO.

Enbond "Z" Process[NE]. A process for preparing zinc-base die castings for plating with copper, nickel, or chromium. It consists of ENBOND CLEANER Z-21, a high detergency anodic cleaner, and ENBOND ACTIVATOR Z-73. The cleaner is a non-dusting, inhibited alkali mixture. It is used in concentrations of 6 to 8 oz./gal., at 6 volts, and at temps. of 160–180°F. After the castings are cleaned, they are treated with a 4 oz./gal. solution of the activator for 5–10 sec. at room temp. ENTHONE, INC.

Endrin[△]. The *endo-endo* isomer of DIELDRIN. Chemically, it is 1,2,3,4,10,10-hexachloro-6,7-epoxy-1,4,4a,5,6,7,8,8a - octahydro - 1,4 - *endo-endo* - 5,8 - dimethanonaphthalene. $C_{12}H_8Cl_6O$; mol.wt. 380.94. A white, crystalline solid, melting with decomposition at temps. about 200°C.; insoluble in water; soluble in common organic solvents, but more soluble in aromatic than in paraffinic hydrocarbons; compatible with all commonly-used pest-control materials. Recommended for the control of cotton pests, except pink bollworm; shows promise of being effective against lepidoterous, hemipterous, and homopterous pests of crop plants. Available as an emulsifiable concentrate, wettable powder, and as a dust.

Enduron[NE]. An allyl base copolymer based on C.R. 39® (*HBMTN* p. 151). Available as cast plastic sheets, special shapes such as circles, square, etc., and as lenses for safety and ophthalmic purposes.
PIONEER SCIENTIFIC CORP.

Energetic®. (*HBMTN* p. 213). Now a registered trademark. ARMOUR AND CO.

Ensign 345 Chromogard[NE]. A removable, rust- and corrosion-resistant protective coating for automotive chrome and stainless steel. It is a transparent amber coating that is highly resistant to water, salt, abrasion, and temp. changes. It can be applied to warm or cold, damp or dry metal by brush, spray, or cloth; and it can be removed readily with any organic solvent, including kerosene. One application will give one full winter's service. ENSIGN PRODUCTS CO.

Ensign 714 Epcovar[NE]. A marine spar varnish-type protective coating. ENSIGN PRODUCTS CO.

Ensign 803 Epcostrip[NE]. Incorrectly listed as ENSIGN 803 EPOSTRIP.[NE] (*Supp.* I p. 75).
ENSIGN PRODUCTS CO.

Enterab®. The trademark for an improved line of enteric-coated medicinal products.
ABBOTT LABORATORIES

Enterosulfon®. An intestinal antiseptic used in pre-operative routine in surgery, and in the treatment of ulcerative colitis, bacillary dysentery, and acute enteritis. Supplied in the form of tablets, each of which contains 0.05 g. phthalysulfacetamide.
CONSOLIDATED MIDLAND CORP.

Entero-Vioform® Tablets. A medicinal for the treatment of simple infectious diarrhea and amebic dysentery. A stable, practically odorless and tasteless compound with a powerful antiseptic action against most organisms which cause the diarrhea and dysentery. CIBA PHARMACEUTICAL PRODUCTS INC.

Enthobrite CU-55[NE]. A product which is added to water for treatment of copper and copper-base alloys to inhibit tarnishing and corrosive attack. It forms an invisible coating which protects the surface against finger marking and high-humidity atmospheres at temps. up to 200°F. ENTHONE, INC.

Enthone Black Wax Emulsion No. 19[NE]. A wax dispersion that is the same as ENTHONE CLEAR WAX EMULSION No. 18 except that it is pigmented black. It has excellent hiding power, and can be used to produce black surfaces on light surfaces, such as steel, zinc, and aluminum. ENTHONE, INC.

Enthone Cleaner 99[NE]. A highly alkaline detergent for fast, thorough electrolytic cleaning of steel. Recommended concentrations: 8 oz./gal. for general cleaning; 12–16 oz./gal. for anodic smut removal.
ENTHONE, INC.

Enthone Clear Wax Emulsion No. 18[NE]. A wax dispersion used for finishing blackened metal surfaces, tin plate, aluminum, and steel. It leaves a hard, medium-gloss, ductile, corrosion-resistant coating. Particularly valuable for protecting etched aluminum against finger marking. Applied by dipping, brushing, wiping, or spraying. ENTHONE, INC.

Enthone Compound B-102[NE]. A mild, highly active barrel finishing burnishing material suitable for use on most metals, including brass, bronze, steel, zinc-base die-castings, aluminum, nickel and chromium plate.
ENTHONE, INC.

Enthone Enamel Stripper "P"[NE]. A non-volatile stripper for synthetic enamels such as alkyd and urea-resin types. It is non-tarnishing, nonflammable, fast acting and free rinsing. For use, it is diluted with water heated to 150–180°F. It will not attack aluminum, copper, brass, silver, zinc, cadmium, or steel.
ENTHONE, INC.

Enthone Stripper S-300[NE]. A powerful emulsion-type stripper for synthetic enamels, including alkyd, melamine, and urea-formaldehyde types. Safe for use with most metals, including steel, copper, and brass. With active metals such as aluminum, magnesium, and zinc there may be slight attack. Can be used at room temp. or at 140–150°F.
ENTHONE, INC.

Enthowax Q-524[NE]. A lubricating wax emulsion in concentrated form. It is diluted with up to 20 parts water and applied by dip, spray or brush to metal surfaces to form a lubricating, corrosion-resistant coating. ENTHONE, INC.

Entrapped® Plantarome® Foam Producer. A foaming agent for root beer and other beverages where foam is desired. Mfg'd from cactus and other vegetable extractions. FLORASYNTH LABORATORIES, INC.

Entrapped® Powdered Clouding Flavors. Flavors in orange, lemon, lime, and lemon-lime which are used for making imitation beverages that simulate the natural fruit juices in flavor and appearance.
FLORASYNTH LABORATORIES, INC.

Entrapped® Powdered Cloudinol. A product for adding cloudiness to imitation fruit beverages to simulate fresh fruit juice in appearance.
FLORASYNTH LABORATORIES, INC.

Entrapped® Powdered Flavors. A line of non-hygroscopic, instantly dispersable flavors for use in beverages, gelatin desserts, cake mixes, pharmaceuticals. FLORASYNTH LABORATORIES, INC.

Epcovar. *See* ENSIGN 714 EPCOVAR[NE].

Ephetal®. (*HBMTN* p. 215). No longer available.
ABBOTT LABORATORIES

Ephynal® Acetate. A stable, potent VITAMIN-E compound for the treatment of menopausal complaints, habitual and threatened abortion, placental detachment, peripheral vascular disorders, and fibrositis. It is the acetic acid ester of pure alpha-tocopherol in tablet and capsule forms.
HOFFMANN-LA ROCHE INC.

Ep.Kote®. (*Supp.* I p. 76). No longer available.
FURANE PLASTICS, INC.

Epolene® E. An emulsifiable polyethylene wax. It has a softening point of 102°C., sp.gr. of 0.935, mol.wt. of approx. 2,500, viscosity at 250°F. of 1,500–1,900 cps., and saponification no. of 24–25. *Uses:* In self-polishing floor waxes; for paper coating; and in leather finishes. EASTMAN CHEMICAL PRODUCTS, INC.

Epolene® N. A polyethylene wax. It is a low-molecular-weight polyethylene which cannot be emulsified. It has a softening point of 106°C., sp.gr. of 0.925, mol.wt. of approx. 2,500, and viscosity at 250°F. of 2,200–2,700 cps. *Uses:* For paraffin upgrading; in polish preparation; for paper coating; in printing inks and rubber compounding.
EASTMAN CHEMICAL PRODUCTS, INC.

Epon Curing Agent®. The registered trademark for curing agents D, T, U, Z, and BF3-400. By the addition of these amine curing agents, EPON® resins harden to form clear tough polymers with high physical strength, excellent chemical resistance, and good electrical properties. Application of the resins to such products as tools and dies, printed circuits, and aircraft structures is increasing rapidly.
SHELL CHEMICAL CORP.

Eposet®. A potting compound, based on epoxy resins, used for setting bristles in brushes.
H. V. HARDMAN CO.

Epoxidol®. An epoxy type, light-colored, polymeric plasticizer, offering outstanding booster action to heat stabilizers, coupled with low volatility and a high degree of resistance to soaps and detergents.
REICHHOLD CHEMICALS, INC.

Epoxin®. A line of colored baking enamels based on epoxy resins and characterized by excellent resistance to acids, alkalis, chemicals, salt spray, humidity, and water immersion. When properly baked, they yield very hard, marproof, highly resistant films with excellent toughness, flexibility, and adhesion. Enamels identical to EPOXIN, but in black, are sold under the name NIPOXIN®. INTERCHEMICAL CORP., FINISHES DIV.

Epoxy Resins[△]. Synthetic resins produced by reacting epichlorohydrin with bisphenol-A. The condensation is carried out in a caustic media. By varying the proportions of the reacting materials it is possible to obtain polymers of varying molecular weights—from about 400 to 8,000—ranging from amber liquids to clear hard solids with m.p. up to 150°C. EPOXY RESINS are now widely used in plastic tooling and electrical potting and encapsulation, for the mfg. of high-strength laminates, coatings, adhesives, casting compositions, etc.

Eramide®. A bacitracin ointment containing chlorcyclizine hydrochloride and sulfacetamide, and designed for veterinary use. ABBOTT LABORATORIES

Erganil®. A group of metalized acid dyestuffs of very good fastness properties. Especially recommended for dyeing high-grade leathers.
GENERAL DYESTUFF CO.

Ergotole®. (*Supp.* I p. 77). No longer available.
SHARP & DOHME DIV., MERCK & CO.

Erusto® Dry Spotter. (*HBMTN* p. 216). No longer available. PENNSYLVANIA SALT CO.

Erustohue®. A preparation for use in laundries for souring and bluing in one operation.
PENNSYLVANIA SALT MFG. CO.

Erusto-Max®. A laundry sour.
PENNSYLVANIA SALT MFG. CO.

Erustomoth®. The trademark for an insecticide.
PENNSYLVANIA SALT MFG. CO.

Erusto® Pre-Spotter. (*HBMTN* p. 216). No longer available. PENNSYLVANIA SALT CO.

Erusto-Ray[NE]. A laundry sour.
PENNSYLVANIA SALT MFG. CO.

Erustosol®. A laundry souring compound.
PENNSYLVANIA SALT MFG. CO.

Erysipogen[NE]. A medicinal for the control of erysipelas in swine and turkeys. It is Erysipelas Bacterin prepared from a whole culture of *Erysipelothrix rhusiopathiae*, chemically killed, adsorbed on aluminum hydroxide, and concentrated.
MERCK SHARP & DOHME

Erythrocin®. An antibiotic, erythromycin stearate, particularly effective against gram-positive organisms.
ABBOTT LABORATORIES

Erythromid[NE]. An antibiotic in tablet form. Consists of erythromycin stearate and triple sulfas.
ABBOTT LABORATORIES

Erythrotil®. An erythromycin-streptomycin ointment for veterinary use. ABBOTT LABORATORIES

Essex®. (*Supp.* I p. 78). No longer available.
HANSON-VAN WINKLE-MUNNING CO.

Esso-Mar EP56. A high-quality marine steam-turbine oil containing a special load-carrying additive designed to minimize gear-tooth wear in turbine reduction units. Characterized by its excellent oxidation stability and rust prevention, anti-foaming and demulsibility properties. Meets U. S. Navy Specification MIL-L-17331A as a 2190-TEP extreme-pressure oil.
ESSO STANDARD OIL CO.

Esso-Mar EP65. A marine steam turbine oil similar to ESSO-MAR EP56 except that it has a higher viscosity.
ESSO STANDARD OIL CO.

Estacod®. (*HBMTN* p. 217). No longer available.
NOPCO CHEMICAL CO.

Estate®. (Trademark registration pending). A vinyl-plastic flooring material.
ARMSTRONG CORK CO.

Estor HD®. A heavy-duty lubricating oil for certain types of diesel engines including many of the larger stationary engines, especially those that operate at intermediate speeds. Available in 5 viscosity grades: 10, 20, 30, 40 and 50. All grades are fully detergent, have high oxidation stability properties, and prevent the formation of rust.
ESSO STANDARD OIL CO.

Est-R-Lux. A line of alkyd-base interior, odorless enamels. They have excellent leveling and hiding properties, and good color retention.
ACORN REFINING CO.

Estrobond®. (*Supp.* I p. 78). Now a registered trademark, and product sold through EASTMAN CHEMICAL PRODUCTS, INC.

Estron®. Cellulose acetate yarn and staple fiber.
EASTMAN CHEMICAL PRODUCTS, INC.

Estynox®. (*Supp.* I p. 78). Now a registered trademark.
BAKER CASTOR OIL CO.

Etchalume® **14.** Incorrectly listed as ETCHLUME® 14 (*Supp.* I p. 79).
ENTHONE, INC.

Etchlume® **14.** (*Supp.* I p. 79). Should have been listed as ETCHALUME® 14.
ENTHONE, INC.

Eternit®. (*HBMTN* p. 217). No longer available.
RUBEROID CO.

Ethacreo®. (*Supp.* I p. 79). No longer available.
SHARP & DOHME DIV., MERCK & CO.

Ethan Allen®. The trademark for a line of colonial and American provincial furniture.
T. BAUMRITTER CO.

Ethylac® **#650.** 2-Benzothiazyl-N,N-diethylthiocarbamyl sulfide. ; mol. wt. 282.4. A free-flowing, light yellow to tan powder; sp.gr. 1.27; m.p. 69°C. (min.). *Uses:* As a rubber vulcanization accelerator, and lubricating oil additive.
PENNSYLVANIA SALT MFG. CO.

Ethylex®. A line of hydroxy ethyl ether derivatives of corn starch having properties quite different from corn starch. These gums possess good viscosity stability, reduced gelling tendency, and excellent flow characteristics. Films of ETHYLEX gums are clearer, more flexible, and more readily redispersed in water. They are produced in two grades based on the degree of ether substitution. Each grade is offered in a wide range of viscosities. ETHYLEX is also the trade name for a line of finishing gums developed especially for the textile industry. *Uses:* In a wide variety of applications throughout the paper and textile industries, and as thickening or stabilizing agents for water-base resin-emulsion paints.
A. E. STALEY MFG. CO.

Eticyclol®. An oral estrogen of high potency. Ethinyl estradiol. Derived from alpha-estradiol, a hormone of graafian follicle, and available in compressed tablets and as LINGUETS®. Indicated in all conditions associated with estrogenic deficiency: menopausal syndrome, primary amenorrhea, hypogenitalism, functional uterine bleeding, etc.
CIBA PHARMACEUTICAL PRODUCTS INC.

Eukesol®. A group of pigments especially selected and prepared for finishing leather, which is usually first dyed with aniline colors.
GENERAL DYESTUFF CO.

Eureka Core Paste®. A red powdered core paste which, when mixed with water, makes a smooth paste possessing excellent green and dry strength. It air dries rapidly but it can be oven dried where speed is necessary. Joints made with this paste are stronger than the core itself.
M. A. BELL CO.

Eutec-CopWeld®. A brazing alloy, in paste form, for joining copper, brass, and bronze. Bonding temp. 1,350°F.
EUTECTIC WELDING ALLOYS CORP.

Eutectic Low Temperature Welding Alloys®. A line of torch- and arc-welding rods that require less heat (or amperage) than conventional rods. The lower heat input minimizes distortion, warping, stress, and embrittlement.
EUTECTIC WELDING ALLOYS CORP.

Euvon ASN. A wetting agent, protective colloid and solvent for NAPHTHOL AS dyeings. It is a dark brown liquid readily soluble in water, of weakly alkaline reaction. It prevents the precipitation of calcium or magnesium compounds in coarse form or their deposit on textiles. Because of its protective colloidal properties, it prevents any flocculation of naphthol formed by hydrolysis.
NOVA CHEMICAL CORP.

Evenized®. Cascara bark U.S.P. Crude bark, broken into small chip size, free from stones, metal, dirt, and other extraneous matter, and packed in burlap bags.
S. B. PENICK & CO.

Everlube 1329. A corrosion- and abrasion-resistant plastic coating for aluminum, magnesium, steel, titanium and other metals. It can be applied over anodizing, phosphate treatment, or cadmium plating, but not over zinc chromate primer. It is mixed with a catalyst before application by brush or spray and cured by air drying for 7 days at room temp. or by baking for 10 min. at 250°F.
EVERLUBE CORP. OF AMERICA

Everyday®. A line of pre-packaged letterpress printing inks.
INTERCHEMICAL CORP., PRINTING INK DIV.

Excellay®. The trademark for pre-formed wire rope.
UNITED STATES STEEL CORP.

Excelon®. A vinyl-asbestos flooring material, available as tiles in a variety of colors and designs.
ARMSTRONG CORK CO.

Excelsior®. The trademark for a line of carbon blacks used in the mfg. of paint. Characterized by their high hiding power and high tinting strength. Available as: (1) EXCELSIOR STANDARD, a powdered form of impingement carbon black, and used as an all-purpose paint black; and (2) EXCELSIOR BEADS, a dustless, free-flowing form of regular color impingement black that is especially useful for ball-mill grinding.
COLUMBIAN CARBON CO.

Excelsior Oil A[NR]. (*HBMTN* p. 222). No longer available.
GENERAL DYESTUFF CO.

Exlon[NR]. An automotive finish that combines the drying speed of lacquer and the gloss of enamels. It can be applied in 15 to 20 min. to the average car; no drying time needed between coats. Dries in about 60 min. Available in all the popular colors of present-day automobiles. (Registration applied for.)
SHERWIN-WILLIAMS CO.

Exol-K145®. A textile bleaching assistant for use with hydrogen peroxide. It accelerates the bleaching operation and produces clearer and brighter whites and more uniformly absorbent fabrics.
SOLUOL CHEMICAL CO.

Exon®. The trademark for a complete series of polymers and copolymers of vinyl chloride, produced in a range of molecular weights by both emulsion and suspension polymerization methods. Included in this line of resins are the following:

EXON 402-A, a polyvinyl chloride resin specifically designed for unplasticized rigid applications. This resin, when compounded with efficient stabilizers and lubricants, may be processed by standard calendering, laminating, molding, and extrusion techniques into a thermoplastic construction material. It is non-flammable, highly resistant to corrosion, and possesses excellent electrical and physical properties. It finds use in the mfg. of fume hoods and ducts, storage tanks, chemical piping, plating tanks, etc.

EXON 450, a powdered, vinyl chloride copolymer resin of intermediate molecular weight which may be used in solution resin work. It is soluble in ketones, will tolerate aromatic hydrocarbons, and is compatible with vinyl plasticizers, pigments and stabilizers. Solutions of this resin may be made by sifting the resin into the required solvents under continuous agitation to prevent agglomeration of the particles. Coatings based on EXON 450 may be applied by brushing, spraying, coating and dipping methods. It is used in compounding printing inks, strippable coatings, and protective liners and coatings for paper, cloth, metal and other substrates.

EXON 461, a fluorine-containing polymer with excellent heat, light, and chemical resistance. It has good solubility in conventional paint and lacquer solvents, allowing it to be used as an air-drying coating. Supplied as a white, granular powder which can be dissolved directly in ketones, ethers, esters, and aromatic and chlorinated hydrocarbons. Solutions ranging up to 40% total solids can be prepared by adding the resin slowly to the solvent at room temp. with mild agitation. The solutions may be spread, brushed, roller coated, or in the high viscosity ranges, knife or bar coated. Films dry to transparent, glossy surface.

EXON 468, a powdered, medium-low molecular weight vinyl chloride copolymer that is compatible with the conventional vinyl plasticizers, stabilizers and pigments. It can be used as a soft compounding resin to lower the processing temps. of higher molecular weight resins. It is especially suitable for use in highly-filled vinyl-asbestos tile because of its low-temp. processing characteristics. The high bulking density (0.6 g./cc.) of EXON 468 permits an increase in Banbury capacity of up to 10% over other resins. As a solution resin it can be used in the mfg. of vinyl printing inks and coatings for special applications.

EXON 470, an extremely versatile, vinyl chloride polymer resin that is highly soluble in ketones, has high tolerance for aromatic hydrocarbons, and is compatible with alkyd-type resins. It is easily dissolved by sifting the resin into the solvent with continuous agitation to prevent agglomeration of the particles. The excellent solubility of this resin permits the incorporation of exceedingly high proportions of aromatic-type solvents: as much as 90% aromatic solvent has been found practical for some applications. The resin solution can be applied by brushing, spraying, knife coating, roller coating, dipping, etc. Coatings based on this resin have good adhesion to metals, alkyd surfaces and vinyl surfaces; good chemical, water, and abrasion resistance; they are stable to heat and light; and have good transparency and clarity.

EXON 471, a vinyl chloride copolymer resin especially designed for solution coating work. It has high solubility in ketones and good tolerance for aromatic diluents. It is easily dissolved by sifting the resin into the solvent with agitation. Numerous solvent systems are possible, permitting this resin to be used in a wide variety of applications. Common lacquer techniques can be used to apply the coatings. The coatings are transparent, colorless and glossy; stable to heat; resistant to grease, chemicals, ultra-violet light, and weather; adhere well to vinyl, paper, cloth and wash primers; and are non-adherent (strippable) to metals.

EXON 480, a powdered, medium-low molecular weight vinyl chloride copolymer characterized by good heat and light stability for a resin of its high thermoplasticity. It is compatible with the conventional vinyl plasticizers, stabilizers, and pigments. It can be used as a soft compounding resin to lower the processing temps. of higher molecular weight resins. It can be used to produce vinyl phonograph records with high tonal quality and resistance to breakage. As a solution resin, it can be used in the mfg. of vinyl printing inks, and coatings for special applications.

EXON 481, a powdered, vinyl chloride copolymer of high molecular weight, developed primarily for solution applications. It is soluble in ketones and will tolerate moderate proportions of aromatic-type solvents when ketones are also present. Its good compatibility with plasticizers, stabilizers, and pigments permits considerable latitude in formulating printing inks, strippable coatings, protective coatings, and decorative coatings. These coatings have high tensile strength, and may be applied by the usual lacquer techniques.

Exon 485, a powdered vinyl chloride copolymer of medium molecular weight, developed for solution coating applications where good clarity, gloss, tensile strength, and abrasion resistance are required. The resin is soluble in ketones and it will tolerate large proportions of aromatic diluents. Solutions based on this resin can be applied by common lacquer techniques.

Exon 500, a powdered, high molecular weight polyvinyl chloride resin having excellent electrical properties, color, heat and light stability, physical toughness, and chemical inertness. A wide variety of electrical products may be produced with this resin by varying the amounts and types of plasticizers, stabilizers, fillers, color pigments, lubricants and extenders.

Exon 654, a high molecular weight polyvinyl chloride, stir-in type plastisol resin. It is a very fine white powder having a particle size of about one micron, which makes it ideally suited for dispersion. Fluid dispersions of this resin, in any of the numerous plasticizers, can be made by simple stirring.

Exon 700 XR-59, a latex containing a vinyl chloride polymer resin. It is a white liquid with a total solids content of 52–55% and a pH of 7–7.5; average particle size, 1 micron; sp.gr. of latex, 1.16–1.17; Brookfield viscosity at 25°C., 10–14 centipoises. This latex possesses excellent mechanical stability, and it is adaptable to film forming and impregnating applications. Films cast from this latex exhibit good heat and light stability. It is compatible with conventional vinyl plasticizers, stabilizers, and pigments.

Exon 905, a high molecular weight polyvinyl chloride resin characterized by its excellent physical properties, heat and light stability, and smooth processability. It is used for the mfg. of all types of calendered film and sheeting, injection-molded sections, and in the extrusion of gasketing, belting, and clear garden hose.

Exon 915, an intermeidate molecular weight polyvinyl chloride resin characterized by its ease of processing, good blending characteristics, and fast fusion rate. It is used for the same applications as Exon 905.

Exon 925, the lowest molecular weight resin in the series of Exon 905, 915 and 925. It is a fast-fusing, polyvinyl chloride resin. When processing temp. or compounding limitations restrict the use of Exon 915, then Exon 925 can be used with very little sacrifice in physical properties.

Exon 4012, a filled, unmodified, polyvinyl chloride compound formulated specifically for injection molding. Characterized by its excellent chemical resistance. Sp.gr. 1.44; tensile strength, 6,600–6,900 lb./sq.in.

Exon 4203, an unfilled and unmodified polyvinyl chloride compound formulated specifically for injection molding. It is particularly useful for applications requiring the highest possible chemical resistance. Sp.gr. 1.40; tensile strength, 7,300–7,500 lb./sq.in.   Firestone Plastics Co.

Ex-O-Wax®. (*HBMTN* p. 222). No longer available.   Nopco Chemical Co.

Expello®. A chemical for cleaning drains and sinks.   Pennsylvania Salt Mfg. Co.

Explosimeter®. A type of combustible gas detector. *Use:* For protection against the possibility of explosion due to combustible gases in the air.
     Mine Safety Appliances Co.

Expray 541[NE]. An alkaline spray wash cleaner for zinc die castings. It contains alkaline ingredients, phosphates, and synthetic detergents. *Use:* For removing buffing compounds, solvents, etc.
     Wyandotte Chemicals Corp., J. B. Ford Div.

Exsize-T®. A standardized desizing solution containing amylolytic enzymes. *Use:* In the textile industry for removal of starch-base sizes from cloth. (*See also* Dry Exsize-T® *and* Super Exsize-T®.)
     Pabst Brewing Co., Industrial Products Div.

Exsol[NE]. A soil, grease, and graphite remover for Cotton, Rayon, Woolens and the newer synthetic textiles. It is a blend of polyethylene-propylene ethers coupled with mutual solvents.
     W. F. Fancourt Co.

Extelite®. An extender composition for use especially with phenol-formaldehyde, synthetic-resin, aqueous, adhesive solutions used in the mfg. of plywood.
     Agrashell, Inc.

Extender 600[NE]. (*HBMTN* p. 222). No longer available.   Harwick Standard Chemical Co.

Exzyme®. A proteolytic product. *Use:* In the drycleaning industry for digesting proteinaceous stains.
     Pabst Brewing Co., Industrial Products Div.

Eye Comfort®. A paint system for the interior of homes, factories, offices and public buildings. The colors are selected to produce an environment for max. visual comfort, thus enabling individuals to work and study better, and to provide them with more cheerful recreation areas.
     Truscon Laboratories

E-Z Code. A line of self-adhering, pre-printed, wire and cable identification markers.
     Western Lithograph Co., Westline Products Div.

Eze Cleaner. See Parko® Eze Cleaner.

Eze-Wax. See Parko® Eze-Wax.

Ezytite®. Metal closures for tanks, drums, carboys, and similar receptacles.   Pennsylvania Salt Mfg. Co.

F

F (in shield)®. The trademark for ferrous metal castings.   United States Steel Corp.

F-1402 Wall Tile Cement. See Armstrong F-1402 Wall Tile Cement[NE].

Fabripel®. A zirconium acetate water repellent for all types of fabrics including Acetates, mixtures, Nylon, and other synthetics. Applied by a one-bath process, it provides durable water repellency, and excellent hand and finish. It is an extremely stable emulsion and does not require the addition of protective colloids to insure stability.
     Fabric Chemicals Co.

Factolac®. The trademark for an emulsifier.
S. B. PENICK & CO.

Fagine△. Same as CHOLINE△.

Fairtex^NB. An alkaline pressure gun and soak tank cleaner. WYANDOTTE CHEMICALS CORP., J. B. FORD DIV.

Fanal®. A line of phosphotungsto and/or molybdate toners and lakes of basic dyes used in formulating lithographic printing inks and coatings.
GENERAL DYESTUFF CO.

Fancoseal^NB. An emulsion, containing lanolin in conjunction with vegetable waxes, used for softening and lubricating NYLON hosiery. It is compatible with other conventional hosiery finishes; and gives excellent boarding properties. W. F. FANCOURT CO.

Fancosol^NB. A nonfoaming polyethoxy alkyl nonionic penetrant, wetting agent and detergent. *Use:* As a penetrant and dyeing assistant for package, vat, or skein dyeing, to give greater uniformity of shade. It is particularly useful where foam is a problem.
W. F. FANCOURT CO.

Fancosol P^NB. An amphoteric quaternary ammonium compound used as a dye assistant for all acetate, acid, or basic dyestuffs. When used in small amounts it is an excellent dye assistant, and when used in larger amounts it reduces the shade of overdyed ACETATE and NYLON fabrics from 10 to 50%.
W. F. FANCOURT CO.

Farlwood^NB. (*HBMTN* p. 225). No longer available. FARLEY & LOETSCHER MFG. CO.

Fastdry Core Paste^NB. A ready-to-use, semi-liquid core paste that can be dispensed with a common barrel pump or a 2″ molasses gate. The elimination of hand mixing and the fast-drying qualities of this core paste make possible extremely fast core pasting operations. M. A. BELL CO.

Fast-Kill. A household insecticide in an aerosol bomb dispenser. Contains chlordane "1068" and piperonyl butoxide. *Use:* For killing ants, crickets, spiders, scorpions, carpet beetles, silverfish, and roaches.
CLAIRE MFG. CO.

Fastusol®. A line of direct dyes, of good (5) or better light fastness, for dyeing COTTON, RAYON, LINEN, SILK, and paper. GENERAL DYESTUFF CO.

Fast Yellow. See R-B-H FAST YELLOW^NB.

Favorite®. A line of reversible ratchet socket wrenches for U.S. Std. nuts from ¼″ to 1¼″, and with handle lengths from 15″ to 27″.
GREENE, TWEED & CO.

F & B. The trade name for a line of fertilizers, animal repellents, weed killers, drainpipe and cesspool cleaners, and other products of FAESY & BESTHOFF, INC.

F & B Starter Grower 15-30-15. An all-soluble plant food for vegetables, fruits, shrubs, house plants, and seedling transplants. Used in the proportion of 3 lb. to 100 gal. of water per acre.
FAESY & BESTHOFF, INC.

FCC® No. 1. A chromium-nickel steel that can be hardened all over, or selected areas can be flame hardened. Used for machine parts subject to heavy stress, and short run hot forming on slow-moving equipment. Type: SAE 3150. Percentage composition: 0.50 C, 0.55 Mn, 0.35 Si, 0.65 Cr, 1.65 Ni.
ALLEGHENY LUDLUM STEEL CORP.,
FORGING & CASTING DIV.

FCC® 5X1 Special. A tool and die steel which, when heat treated, is extremely resistant to heat checking and abrasion and has high compressive strength. AISI Type H-21. Percentage composition: 0.33 C, 0.30 Mn, 0.30 Si, 2.75 Cr, 1.75 Ni, 0.25 Mo, 9.75 W, 0.30 V, balance Fe.
ALLEGHENY LUDLUM STEEL CORP.,
FORGING & CASTING DIV.

FCC® 5X1-V. A general-purpose, cast-to-shape, tool and die steel for hot forming operations, tools, dies, cams, and machinery parts. AISI Type H-13. Percentage analysis: 0.40 C, 0.35 Mn, 1.00 Si, 5.00 Cr, 1.25 Mo, 1.00 V, balance Fe.
ALLEGHENY LUDLUM STEEL CORP.,
FORGING & CASTING DIV.

FCC® ALX. A tool alloy available as cast bits. Percentage composition: 2.00 C, 0.50 Mn, 0.40 Si, 33.00 Cr, 0.70 Mo, 16.50 W, 42.00 Co; plus boron.
ALLEGHENY LUDLUM STEEL CORP.,
FORGING & CASTING DIV.

FCC® CTS. An SAE 1095 steel used for inserts and other parts of dies that are not hardened. Percentage composition: 0.90 C, 0.35 Mn, 0.30 Si, balance iron.
ALLEGHENY LUDLUM STEEL CORP.,
FORGING & CASTING DIV.

FCC® CV. An SAE 6135 steel for machinery parts. Percentage composition: 0.35 C, 0.70 Mn, 0.30 Si, 1.00 Cr, 0.20 V, balance iron.
ALLEGHENY LUDLUM STEEL CORP.,
FORGING & CASTING DIV.

FCC® EZ. An oil-hardening die steel used in the form of bushings, chuck jaws, cold forming or bending dies, ring gages, and similar tools. SAE Type O-6. Percentage composition: 1.40 C, 1.00 Mn, 1.40 Si, 0.25 Cr, 0.25 Mo, balance Fe.
ALLEGHENY LUDLUM STEEL CORP.,
FORGING & CASTING DIV.

FCC® Fernite® 24. A special tool steel for certain exacting hot work applications such as draw bench dies for tube sizing, hot tube reducing rings, etc. Percentage composition: 2.30 C, 24.00 Cr, 5.25 W, balance iron. ALLEGHENY LUDLUM STEEL CORP.,
FORGING & CASTING DIV.

FCC® Flamhard. A flame-hardening die steel used for all types of dies where working edges can be selectively hardened against abrasion and wear by the torch-hardening process. Type: SAE 4150. Percentage composition: 0.50 C, 1.15 Mn, 0.50 Si, 1.20 Cr, 0.40 Mo, 0.12 V, balance iron.
ALLEGHENY LUDLUM STEEL CORP.,
FORGING & CASTING DIV.

FCC® Nitri-Cast-Iron. An alloy for nitriding, developed expressly to cope with the severe service demanded in cylinders of internal-combustion engines, pumps, machinery bushings, etc. Percentage composition: 2.70 C, 0.60 Mn, 2.65 Si, 1.00 Cr, 0.23 Mo, 0.98 Al, balance iron.
ALLEGHENY LUDLUM STEEL CORP.,
FORGING & CASTING DIV.

FCC® Roloy. An air-hardening, cast-to-shape tool steel used for welded tube-mill and cold-forming rolls. AISI Type D-2 (Mo). Percentage composition: 1.50 C, 0.40 Mn, 0.40 Si, 12.00 Cr, 0.25 Ni, 0.90 Mo, 0.50 V, 0.75 Co, balance iron.
ALLEGHENY LUDLUM STEEL CORP., FORGING & CASTING DIV.

FCC® Roloy No. 2. An air-hardening, non-deforming die steel used for blanking and forming punches and dies and small size tube-forming or -rolling dies. AISI Type A2. Percentage composition: 1.00 C, 0.35 Mn, 0.35 Si, 5.00 Cr, 1.15 Mo, 0.50 V, balance iron.
ALLEGHENY LUDLUM STEEL CORP., FORGING & CASTING DIV.

Fel[NE]. A concentrated lanolin emulsion, dispersible in water and compatible with all conventional hosiery finishes. Used on NYLON hose to produce a soft, pliable hand; to aid the exhaustion of other hosiery finishes; and with delustering agents for uniform, even dulling along with sheerness. W. F. FANCOURT CO.

Felanol Powder[NE]. A mildly alkaline, powder-type textile detergent of the sulfated amide-type and containing complex phosphates. E. C. FEELEY CO.

Felcobase Sal[NE]. An emulsifier developed especially for emulsifying methyl salicylate when used in textile dyebaths. E. C. FEELEY CO.

Felcofix[NE]. An efficient aftertreatment for direct, developed, sulfur, and other dyes to improve fastness to washing. It is mildly cationic and has little effect on shade and fastness in most cases. Normally used without copper but can be used with copper or formaldehyde where these agents are helpful.
E. C. FEELEY CO.

Felcofix CM[NE]. A temporary color fixing agent for use on direct, developed, and similar dyes. Usually applied in the last rinse bath, prior to drying or subsequent processing, to reduce or prevent bleeding of colors during wet handling. E. C. FEELEY CO.

Felcofix O[NE]. An efficient aftertreatment for direct, developed, and sulfur dyes to improve wash fastness. It is mildly cationic and has little effect on shade and brightness. Particularly useful where odor is a problem since it leaves no residual odor. E. C. FEELEY CO.

Felcolan GL[NE]. A highly efficient textile softener and lubricant especially designed for use on NYLON and HELANCA hosiery. It is slightly cationic in nature, and contains lanolin in dispersible form. It improves knitting quality of HELANCA yarn. E. C. FEELEY CO.

Felcolloid W[NE]. A protective colloid used in processing WOOL and SILK. It hinders the action of sulfides and alkalis, and also protects WOOL during chrome dyeing, leaving the fibers fuller and softer.
E. C. FEELEY CO.

Felcolube 121[NE]. A highly-efficient textile softener for piece goods and package machine work. It provides high lubrication and efficient knitting characteristics. Consists of a blend of anionic softeners and mineral oil. Disperses easily and completely in hot or cold water and does not separate in the bath on long standing. E. C. FEELEY CO.

Felcolube 146[NE]. A high lubricity-type textile softener containing anionic esters and sulfonated fatty oils. Maintains good dispersion in the bath with no separation or scum formation. Suitable for piece goods and package application on yarn.
E. C. FEELEY CO.

Felcolube K[NE]. A fatty ester-type napping lubricant for woolens. With this material, fewer passes are needed to yield a smooth, even and clean nap. Does not wash off readily, and retains a desirable "hand" through to the finished piece, reducing or eliminating further finishes. Has excellent resistance to yellowing from heat and storage. E. C. FEELEY CO.

Felcomine SX[NE]. A low-foaming combination of anionic and non-ionic wetting agents, especially useful in textile processing. E. C. FEELEY CO.

Felcomine VAB[NE]. A dyeing assistant that combines high wetting and leveling efficiency with desirable low foaming properties. It is useful in most types of dyeing, especially where foam build up interferes with proper processing. It is anionic in character and instantly soluble in water at any temp.
E. C. FEELEY CO.

Felco Retarder V[NE]. A complex lignin material used as a leveling agent in vat dyeing. E. C. FEELEY CO.

Felcotex[NE]. An efficient textile conditioner and hygroscopic agent for application to yarns and piece goods to improve hand and moisture regain properties. Has no effect on shade or fastness. It is highly compatible with other types of finishing agents.
E. C. FEELEY CO.

Felcowhite 174[NE]. A highly-efficient fluorescent finish designed to improve the whiteness of WOOL, ACETATE and NYLON. It is a stable liquid that dissolves readily in the bath. E. C. FEELEY CO.

Felcowhite 180[NE]. A highly efficient fluorescent finish designed to improve the whiteness of COTTON and RAYON. It is a stable liquid that dissolves readily in the bath. E. C. FEELEY CO.

Fel-Pro No. 131[NE]. (*HBMTN* p. 228). No longer available. FELT PRODUCTS MFG. CO.

Felsyn 61[NE]. A water-dispersible dyeing assistant of the phenolic type for use in DACRON dyeing. It has the advantage over para-phenyl phenol in that it is not necessary to predissolve it with caustic soda or to acidify between the pretreatment and the dyeing. May be diluted with water and added directly to the dyebath. Leaves the goods with a good soft hand. E. C. FEELEY CO.

Felsyn 187[NE]. A highly efficient type of assistant or "carrier" for dyeing DACRON. A fine-particle-size emulsion of the active agent is developed, and the bath remains stable during long dyeing cycles. Very little settling of the carrier particles takes place on long standing. Those particles that do settle out are readily dispersed on further agitation.
E. C. FEELEY CO.

Felsyn MS[NE]. A DACRON dyeing assistant based on methyl salicylate and compounded with emulsifiers designed to provide a very fine particle size emulsion in the dyebath. E. C. FEELEY CO.

Felt△. A fabric of wool, fur or hair made by matting together the moistened fibers under pressure. Most commercial felts are made of mixtures of fibers, generally containing about 20% wool. *Uses:* For insulation, sound and vibration absorption, paddings and linings, hats, etc.

Feltone[NE]. (*HBMTN* p. 228). No longer available.
TEXTILEATHER CORP.

Femandren® Linguets®. A potent estrogen-androgen used to relieve depression, hot flashes, nervousness, exhaustion, and related symptoms common in menopausal and post-menopausal states; to relieve pain and retard bone rarefaction in osteoporosis; and to improve mood, build tissue, and promote well being in geriatric patients. Consists of a combination of ethinyl estradiol and methyltestosterone.
CIBA PHARMACEUTICAL PRODUCTS INC.

Fend-A®. A protective hand cream. *Use:* To protect the skin against contact dermatitis from dust-borne irritants, grime, dirt, grease, wax, paint, varnish, ink, tar and other adhesive or anhydrous staining compounds.
MINE SAFETY APPLIANCES CO.

Fend-E® A protective hand cream. *Use:* To provide barrier skin protection against cutting oils and cooling compounds of low water content: gasoline, kerosene, naphtha, carbon tetrachloride, and other solvents, vegetable and mineral oils.
MINE SAFETY APPLIANCES CO.

Fend-F®. A protective hand cream. *Use:* To help guard against dermatoses from aluminum, magnesium, zinc, and brass dusts, fruit and vegetable fuzz, chlorinated solvents. It forms an effective barrier against irritations caused by fibrous glass, mineral wool, etc. It is also a utility preparation for skin protection against organic solvents in general.
MINE SAFETY APPLIANCES CO.

Fend-I®. A protective hand cream. *Use:* To provide barrier skin protection against water or water-soluble irritants such as acids and alkalis, cooling and cutting oils of high water content, formaldehyde, wet cement, insecticides and fungicides, coal tar distillates and residues.
MINE SAFETY APPLIANCES CO.

Fend-I Special®. A protective hand cream. *Use:* To afford barrier skin protection against dilute or strong acids and alkalis, cooling lubricants, and cutting oils of high water content, formaldehyde, wet soda ash, wet asphalt, wet cement, various metals and metallic salts, dyes, insecticides and fungicides, coal-tar distillates and residues, organic acids and phenols. It is readily removed with mild soap and warm water.
MINE SAFETY APPLIANCES CO.

Fend-L®. A protective hand cream. *Uses:* As a sunscreen, to protect those who are exposed to the penetrating rays of the sun. It also affords protection against infrared and ultra-violet rays to which welders and cutters are exposed. Protection is also provided to those who work in the open against grime, grease, and dirt.
MINE SAFETY APPLIANCES CO.

Fend-O®. A protective hand cream. *Uses:* To provide barrier skin protection against dry chemicals such as the nitro derivatives: trinitrotoluol, tetryl; and metallic salts such as lead azide, mercury fulminate, tracer charges and primer mix. Additional protection is also provided against irritation caused by dilute acids, alkalis, hydrocarbons, solvents, coal-tar distillates, phenols, wood-preserving compounds, creosote, resins, and metals.
MINE SAFETY APPLIANCES CO.

Fend-PC®. A protective hand cream. *Uses:* To afford protection against dust-borne irritants, grime, dirt and grease. It is of value in reducing perspiration where perspiration is the cause of skin irritation. It also prevents corrosion in the handling of polished metal parts and precision instruments due to excessive perspiration.
MINE SAFETY APPLIANCES CO.

Fend-Silicone[NE]. A protective hand cream. It is particularly effective as a protective barrier against water or irritants dissolved in water, dusts, acids, and alkalis.
MINE SAFETY APPLIANCES CO.

Fend-U®. A protective hand cream. *Uses:* To provide barrier skin protection against cutting oils of low water content; cutting oils with soap and high water content; kerosene and other petroleum distillates; carbon tetrachloride and other degreasers and solvents; benzol and other coal-tar distillates; creosote and other wood preservatives, and wood essences.
MINE SAFETY APPLIANCES CO.

Fend-X®. A protective hand cream. *Uses:* This modern skin conditioner is specifically designed for routine daily use to keep the hands naturally soft and smooth and to help prevent cracking and drying of the skin. It is ideally suited for industrial workers and other persons who are aware of the need for constant good care of their hands. The emollient effect of FEND-X aids the skin after exposure to weather, water, dirt and grime, as well as common household irritants.
MINE SAFETY APPLIANCES CO.

Ferdico Aviation No. 30. (*Supp.* I p. 83). No longer available.
L. W. FERDINAND AND CO.

Fermex®. Enzyme preparations derived from *Aspergillus oryzae*, for use in the baking industry. Furnished in two grades: FERMEX C, which is high in amylolytic and low in proteolytic activity; and FERMEX MT, which is high in both amylolytic and proteolytic activity.
WALLERSTEIN CO.

Fernite® 24. See FCC® FERNITE® 24.

Ferophos[NE]. (*HBMTN* p. 229). No longer available.
ABBOTT LABORATORIES

Ferox®. A treatment for fiberboard to make it resistant to attack by termites and fungi.
CELOTEX CORP.

Feroxolene[NE]. (*HBMTN* p. 229). No longer available.
SERVICE INDUSTRIES

Ferritex[NE]. (*HBMTN* p. 230). No longer available.
TRUSCON LABORATORIES

Ferro-cide[NE]. The trade name for a line of metal paints.
BURGESS, FOBES CO.

Ferro-Desicol® Kapseals®. A medicinal consisting of ferrous sulfate with bile, for the treatment of certain types of anemia.
PARKE, DAVIS & CO.

Ferrolox[NE]. A metal-protective coating material. It forms a dense film that prevents attack by moisture and other rust-producing agents.
HALLEMITE MFG. CO.

Ferronord®. An oral iron-amino acid complex which is unusually well tolerated. The absorption of this medicinal is five times that of ordinary ferrous sulfate.
NORDMARK PHARMACEUTICAL LABORATORIES, INC.

Ferroplus V-P 722. Tablets, each of which contains 10 mg. of iron organically combined as iron phytate, with extracts of alfalfa and beef liver including 1 mg. natural VITAMIN B_{12}.
VITAMIN PRODUCTS CO.

Ferrosol Powder WS *and* **Ferrosol Liquid.** See ORCO FERROSOL POWDER WS *and* ORCO FERROSIL LIQUID.

Ferrostan®. The trademark for a coated tin plate, coated by an electrolytic process.
UNITED STATES STEEL CORP.

Ferrox Yellow®. (*HBMTN* p. 231). No longer available.
WITCO CHEMICAL CO.

Ferti-Liquid® 10-20-10. An all-purpose liquid fertilizer containing a penetrating agent for rapid plant assimilation. Available nitrogen, P_2O_5, and K_2O, are 10, 20, and 10%, respectively. It also contains VITAMIN B (5.00 ppm.) and the following trace elements: manganese (1.25 ppm.), boron (2.00 ppm.), copper (1.00 ppm.), zinc (1.0 ppm.), cobalt (0.02 ppm.), iron (1.00 ppm.), molybdenum (0.02 ppm.), magnesium (0.01 ppm.).
CLOVER CHEMICAL CO.

Fertilis®. The trademark for a line of fertilizers.
INTERNATIONAL MINERALS & CHEMICAL CORP.

Ferti-Lux®. (*Supp.* I p. 84). No longer available.
DORAN CHEMICAL CORP.

Fibercast®. (*Supp.* I, p. 848). This product is manufactured by the FIBERCAST CORP., owner of the trademark. It is distributed by the YOUNGSTOWN STEEL PRODUCTS CO.; the YOUNGSTOWN STEEL PRODUCTS CO. OF CALIFORNIA; and the CONTINENTAL SUPPLY CO.

Fiberfilm. An electrical insulation made from glass microfibers and polytetrafluoroethylene. Films, from 0.8 to 1.7 mils, are available in both porous and nonporous forms, and operate well at 200 to 250°C. Dielectric breakdown of standard films (1.2 mils), 1,750 volts d.c.; dielectric constant at 25° and 1 kc., 2.1. *Uses:* As a dielectric for high-temp., low-loss capacitors of both dry and wet types; and as interlayer insulation in coils, wire, and cable for high temp.
AMERICAN MACHINE & FOUNDRY CO.

Fiberite®. The trademark for a line of high impact, phenolic and melamine molding materials manufactured to comply with all existing military, commercial, and industrial specifications covering impact materials. FIBERITE® materials are reinforced with a large variety of cotton, asbestos, glass, and synthetic fibers, and include all known types of phenolic and melamine resins. The reinforcing fibers are incorporated to give the finished molded parts high impact, wear, shock, heat and chemical resistance as well as excellent electrical properties. Available in a wide range of colors; they can be molded in existing molds at standard temp. and pressures. *Uses:* Automotive timing gears, industrial truck casters, electrical circuit breakers, terminal strips, outdoor theater speakers, welding gun components, housings, handles, grips, gunstocks, oil-well parts, pulleys, sheaves, conveyor buckets, etc.
FIBERITE CORP.

Fibretex. See PERFORATED FIBRETEX[NE].

Fibrex®. A line of fast-cutting, reinforced, resinoid-bonded grinding wheels for use with portable disc sanders and right-angle portable grinders. They are similar to SIMEX® wheels but are recommended for lighter grinding operations where finish is important, and where slight flexibility of the wheel is desired.
SIMONDS ABRASIVE CO.

Fibrocel®. A pipe insulation for hot and cold water, low-pressure steam, and combination wet heating and cooling system pipes. Available in 3 jacket styles:
FIBROCEL C, for steam or hot water at temps. of 60° to 300°F. Furnished with standard or special weight canvas jacket and metal bands.
FIBROCEL G, for steam or hot water at temps. of 60° to 300°F. Furnished with glazed white-plastic-coated paper jacket and metal bands.
FIBROCEL VB, for chilled water or dual service at temps of 35° to 200°F. Furnished with vapor barrier jacket consisting of aluminum foil, faced both sides with creped natural KRAFT paper, adhered with special non-asphaltic waterproofing laminant. Finish may be painted, if desired. Useful for cold pipes subject to sweating.
JOHNS-MANVILLE SALES CORP.

Fibro-Cel®. An insulating filler consisting of a mixture of diatomaceous silica and long fiber asbestos. Suitable for use at temps. up to 1,800°F.; approx. wt. 18 lb./cu.ft. when packed in place. Because it has very little tendency to settle or filter through cracks. FIBRO-CEL is especially suited for use as a filler in gas generator sets, etc.
JOHNS-MANVILLE SALES CORP.

Fibrofil®. An insulating fill consisting of a mixture of diatomaceous silica and asbestos fiber. Max. service temp. 1,800°F.; average packed density, 18 lb./cu.ft.
JOHNS-MANVILLE SALES CORP.

Fibroin[△]. See SILK[△].

Fibrous Filler[NE]. A product used as a filler in paper and paperboard, and composed of extremely fine hydrous calcium silicate particles precipitated on cellulose fiber. It is prepared and used in paper mills under a license agreement with the R. T. VANDERBILT CO., INC.

Fiege Tiger-Claw® The trademark for a line of wire rope fittings.
UNITED STATES STEEL CORP.

Fijoline®. A base for cosmetic lotions, etc.
S. B. PENICK & CO.

Filigree®. The trademark for a line of carbon paper.
INTERCHEMICAL CORP.,
AULT & WIBORG CARBON & RIBBON DIV.

Filmcol® Proprietary Solvent. A modified ethyl alcohol solvent for limited applications where the ethyl acetate and hydrocarbon denaturants present in NEOSOL® proprietary solvent are not compatible with the intended use. The modified formula has been approved by the Alcohol and Tobacco Tax Div. of the Internal Revenue Service, and use of the solvent is permitted by authorized companies in the film, rotogravure, lithograph, photographic, printing ink, and zinc etching industries or others that may from time to time be approved by the Div. To comply with the regulations established by the Alcohol and To-

bacco Tax Div. governing the sale and use of Filmcol Proprietary Solvent, sales and deliveries are limited to authorized users or recognized established jobbers in the specific industries listed above or as may otherwise be approved. Approval to receive and use Filmcol by individual companies, where valid objections against regular proprietary solvents exist must be obtained by the user from the Assistant Regional Commissioner, Alcohol and Tobacco Tax Div., in the area where the user is located.
Shell Chemical Corp.

Filmtab®. The trademark for a line of film-sealed medicinal tablets. Abbott Laboratories

Filmtex®. A decorating material consisting of a cotton backing to which is attached designs in waterproof plastic. The whole sheet is then covered with a protective layer of clear plastic. It is tough and durable, waterproof and wrinkle-proof, and it can be sewn by hand or machine. *Uses:* For wall coverings, window curtains, drapes, upholstery, seat covers, crib sheets, table covers, book covers, etc.
Elm Coated Fabrics Co.

Filon®. Translucent, corrugated and flat, plastic structural panels reinforced with Fiberglas® and nylon. Used for skylights, porch enclosures, shower doors, factory glazing, partitions, fences, greenhouses, and numerous other applications where shatterproof, light-transmitting panels are needed. Available in 5½, 6, and 8 oz./sq.ft.; in widths from 25″ to 40″; in lengths from 4 to 12 ft.; and in clear and various colors. Filon Plastics Corp.

Filter-Cel®. One of a series of Celite® Filter-Aids made of exceptionally pure diatomaceous silica. Filter-Cel is capable of removing slimy or colloidal type material of less than 0.1 micron in size. It is especially useful in the pressure filtration of such materials as milk, sugar, vinegar, precious metals, lard (wet and dry rendered), etc.
Johns-Manville Sales Corp.

Filterdown®. Rolls of fiber glass and cotton wadding used for mechanical, dry-type, ventilating air filters of the foldable frame and stationary pocket types.
American Air Filter Co.

Filter Sand△. A natural sand used as a filter media, especially in water treatment. A good Filter Sand must be of fairly uniform size (grains of 0.35 to 0.65 mm. in diameter), free from clay and organic matter, and chemically pure, containing not more than 2% combined carbonates. Most Filter Sands come from ocean beaches, lake deposits and some sand banks.

Fil-Trolax®. A fluid dry-cleaning soap.
Pennsylvania Salt Mfg. Co.

Finespirit®. A trademark for a spirit hectograph. Interchemical Corp.,
Ault & Wiborg Carbon & Ribbon Div.

Finesse®. An all-vegetable, fully hydrogenated shortening for use in baking, frying and pastry making. Anderson, Clayton & Co. Foods Div.

Finesse®. The trademark for a line of carbon paper. Interchemical Corp.,
Ault & Wiborg Carbon & Ribbon Div.

Finessemaster®. The trademark for a spirit hectograph. Interchemical Corp.,
Ault & Wiborg Carbon & Ribbon Div.

Fine-Tex®. A fine-textured, patterned glass for glazing industrial buildings. It provides medium distribution of light, and is easy to clean.
Mfg'd by Blue Ridge Glass Corp.
Distributed by Libbey-Owens-Ford Glass Co.

Finish 3-164. (*HBMTN* p. 233). Formerly mfg'd by U. S. Finishing Co., now a product of USF-Aspinook Finishing Div., Gera Corp.

Fireclad[NE]. A fire- and weather-resistant jacketing for outdoor insulated pipe lines. It consists of a tough substantial sheet of asphalt-saturated asbestos felt, over which is cemented on one side an unsaturated asbestos sheet. The complete sheet is reinforced with a fabric of tough, flexible glass threads.
Philip Carey Mfg. Co.

Firefite®. The trademark for a line of electrical wire and cable. United States Steel Corp.

Fire-Snuf®. See Resolite Fire-Snuf®.

Firetard Jacket. See Asbestos Firetard Jacket[NE].

Fixateur. (*HBMTN* p. 235). No longer available. Company liquidated as of Oct. 1, 1955.
General Drug Co.

Fixomat®. A photographic fixer especially adapted for continuous paper processing. Eastman Kodak Co.

Fixtohm®. The trademark for a line of electrical resistors. Campbell Industries, Inc.

Flair Shortening[NE]. An all-vegetable, fully-hydrogenated shortening for use in baking, frying and pastry making. Anderson, Clayton & Co. Foods Div.

Flameout. See Boston Flameout.

Flame Retardant Base. A textile fireproofing product. At high temps. it develops gases, which prevent the treated material from coming into contact with air in case of fire. Such textiles are not combustible, but can be made to flame only with difficulty.
Nopco Chemical Corp.

Flamhard. See FCC® Flamhard.

Flash Gloss®. The trademark for coated paper used for printing purposes. (Registration No. 628.273; Class 37; June 5, 1956). Consoweld Corp.

Flavan[NE]. A vanilla-vanillin sugar flavor concentrate. Florasynth Laboratories, Inc.

Flavazine®. A line of medium fastness, level-dyeing acid dyes for Wool. They are also used for the mfg. of lakes, and for surface-coloring paper.
General Dyestuff Co.

Flavophosphine®. A line of brownish-yellow basic dyes for dyeing leather. General Dyestuff Co.

Flavor-Feen®. A veterinary medicinal for removal of stomach worms, hook worms, and nodular worms from cattle; and stomach worms, hook worms, nodular and large mouthed bowel worms from sheep. Available as: (1) a liquid, each fluid oz. of which contains 7.5 g. phenothiazine (flavored) in a palatable,

refined nutrient base; and (2) a flavored powder containing 96% by wt. of phenothiazine NF, and 4% of a flavoring material.
ATOMIC BASIC CHEMICAL CORP.

Flawmaster. A metal putty or "cold solder" used to fill blowholes in machined and raw castings. It is used to eliminate sand pits, small gas holes, shrinkage cracks, deep nicks and scratches, machining flaws and porous areas in precision metal parts. It is supplied as a 3-component kit: a syrupy, epoxy-based compound, a hardener, and a finely pulverized blended powder. The components are mixed to the desired consistency before use. The metal powder is furnished in aluminum, brass, bronze, zinc, iron, and magnesium. It adheres to all metals, both ferrous and non-ferrous, and by proper selection of the metal powder it can be made to match the color of the metal on which it is to be used. The cured FLAWMASTER can be sanded or machined.
CARL H. BIGGS CO.

Flaxoap[NE]. A vegetable oil base for general cleaning purposes.
SHERWIN-WILLIAMS CO.

Fleckel[NE]. An artistic, ready-to-use, clear gloss ceramic glaze containing flecks of color. It is applied over bisque-fired plain or decorated ceramic ware or it can be combined with matte or satin glazes for decorative color variations.
PEMCO CORP.

Fleet Wing®. (*Supp.* I p. 86). No longer available.
PITTSBURGH PLATE GLASS CO.

Flexboard®. An asbestos building board for exterior and interior applications, made of asbestos and cement combined under great pressure, then hydraulically repressed for additional strength and toughness. It is a dense sheet material that is fire-resistant, and rot- and corrosion-proof. It can be nailed and otherwise worked with power or hand tools. Furnished in unpolished sheets of natural gray color. Not recommended for decorative purposes. Sheets are supplied in thicknesses of 1/8", 3/16" and 1/4", in sizes of 4' × 4' and 4' × 8'. A special, waterproof adhesive for applying (spot-cementing) FLEXBOARD® is also available.
JOHNS-MANVILLE SALES CORP.

Flexbond 800. A polyvinyl acetate copolymer emulsion for use as a vehicle in the mfg. of primers, sealers, and interior and exterior paints. Total solids, 51–53%; viscosity (Brookfield at 77°F.), 400–800 centipoises; color, white-milky; pH, 5.0–6.0; wt. per gal., 9.0 lb.
COLTON CHEMICAL CO.

Flexcel[NE]. Paints and flexible finishes of lacquer or synthetic-resin base.
MAAS & WALDSTEIN CO.

Flex-Deck[NE]. The trade name for a line of flat wire conveyor belts.
UNITED STATES STEEL CORP., AMERICAN STEEL & WIRE DIV.

Flexer. See BOSTON FLEXER.

Flex-Grid[NE]. The trade name for a line of wire conveyor belts.
UNITED STATES STEEL CORP., AMERICAN STEEL & WIRE DIV.

Flexible Mold Compound #201. An epoxy resin compound, in liquid form, which, after the addition of a catalyst, sets to the consistency of hard rubber. Used to make molds for casting parts which are the exact duplicate of the original model.
CARL H. BIGGS CO.

Flexichrome®. Photographic chemicals, namely, bleach, dye, print, lacquer, masking lacquer, lacquer thinner, and water colors.
EASTMAN KODAK CO.

Flexigate®. A new type of gating material for foundry use, developed to eliminate costly cutting and fitting operations. May be molded to fit any pattern simply by bending to the desired angle. It eliminates the necessity of cutting gates for each pattern.
M. A. BELL CO.

Flexogem®. A line of special, heat-resistant flexographic inks.
INTERCHEMICAL CORP., PRINTING INK DIV.

Flexohm®. The trademark for a line of flexible electrical resistors. (Registration No. 564,191; Class 21; Sept. 16, 1952.)
CLAROSTAT MFG. CO.

Flexoresin B1[NE]. (*HBMTN* p. 237). No longer available.
GLYCO PRODUCTS CO.

Flexotuf®. A line of flexographic inks for printing on polyethylene.
INTERCHEMICAL CORP., PRINTING INK DIV.

Flint[△]. An opaque variety of chalcedony, or nearly pure amorphous quartz which shows no visible structure. Deposited from colloidal solution; contains from 96–99% silica; various impurities impart dark dull colors; breaks or chips with a convex, undulating surface; sp.gr. 2.6; hardness, 7. Used chiefly as an abrasive, in pottery and glass mfg., and as grinding pebbles. (*See also* POTTERS' FLINT.)

Flint®. (*HBMTN* p. 238). Now a registered trademark.
ARMOUR AND CO.

Flintseal® JFR. A jet-fuel-resistant joint-sealing compound.
FLINTKOTE CO.

Flo®. An all-vegetable, fully hydrogenated shortening for use in baking, frying and pastry making.
ANDERSON, CLAYTON & CO. FOODS DIV.

Flo®. A fluid dry-cleaning soap for use in petroleum systems employing filter and still.
PENNSYLVANIA SALT MFG. CO.

Floatcoat. See TEXACO® FLOATCOAT.

Floats Off®. A liquid synthetic detergent for general floor-cleaning purposes, and for washing walls, windows, store fixtures, etc.
J. I. HOLCOMB MFG. CO.

Flomax 25[NE]. A barium-cadmium organic complex stabilizer for vinyls. It is a clear yellow liquid that is miscible in mixtures of hydrocarbon solvents with ketones, esters, CELLOSOLVE®, etc. Sp.gr. 1.03. It is readily incorporated, and imparts a very high degree of clarity. It is entirely compatible with vinyls, and it shows very little plating tendency. It imparts to the vinyl film a dry and tack-free surface which is ideal for heat sealing and printing. Recommended for plastisols, organosols, and solution coatings because of its ready dispersion, low viscosity, clarity and compatibility.
NATIONAL LEAD CO.

Florasynth®. Trademark for flavoring materials, perfumes, food colors and other products of FLORASYNTH LABORATORIES, INC.

Floravanol "C" #30[NE]. A coumarin replacement. This flavoring material is approx. equivalent on a weight basis to coumarin.
FLORASYNTH LABORATORIES, INC.

Flora Wax△. *See* CARNAUBA WAX△.

Florene®. (*HBMTN* p. 239 and *Supp.* I p. 87). No longer available. SINDAR CORP.

Flor-Sho[NE]. (*Supp.* I p. 88). No longer available.
PENETONE CO.

Flourish®. A slip-resistant floor finish for asphalt, rubber, vinyl, linoleum, cork, terrazzo, wood, and all other floors. It dries to a self-polishing gloss without buffing. U. S. SANITARY SPECIALTIES CORP.

Flouro-Foil[NE]. Aluminum or stainless steel foil coated on one side with a TEFLON dispersion. The foil may be bonded to wood, concrete, or metal to give an inert, non-stick surface. It is used on chutes, rolls, feed hoppers, etc., where adhesion of the product being handled is a problem.
ELECTRO-CHEMICAL ENGINEERING & MFG. CO.

Flowerols[NE]. A line of flower oils for perfumes and toilet waters. FLORASYNTH LABORATORIES, INC.

Fluer-O-Plas K[NE]. (*HBMTN* p. 240). No longer available. KRIEGER COLOR & CHEMICAL CO.

Fluftex®. (*HBMTN* p. 240). Should have been listed as a registered trademark.
AMERICAN MAIZE PRODUCTS CO.

Flushol[NE]. A heavy-duty cleaner for removing stubborn oil, grease, wax and dirt accumulations from concrete, wood and metal surfaces. It is brushed on and then flushed off. HALLEMITE MFG. CO.

Fluxing Stone△. A common name for the limestone or dolomite used in the melting of iron to form a slag of the impurities.

Fly-A-Way Aerosol[NE]. An insecticide, in an aerosol spray container, for control of house flies, barn flies, stable flies, gnats, mosquitoes, roaches and other pests in dairies, on farms, in restaurants, and in poultry and hog houses. Active ingredients: 0.25% pyrethrins, 2.00 piperonyl butoxide (tech.), 9.75% petroleum distillates.
MILLER CHEMICAL & FERTILIZER CORP.

Fly-Away Dairy Spray. An insecticide for the control of horn flies, mosquitoes, gnats, and midges on cattle and other animals. Active ingredients: 0.189% piperonyl butoxide (tech.), 0.023% pyrethrins, 5.852% butyoxypolypropylene glycol, and 93.98% mineral oil. MILLER CHEMICAL & FERTILIZER CORP.

Fly-Away Dairy Spray Concentrate. An insecticide for use on dairy cattle and other animals to control horn flies, mosquitoes, gnats, stable flies, house flies, horse flies, cattle lice, fleas, and ticks. For use on animals, it is diluted with water. For use as a space spray to control stable flies, house flies, mosquitoes, and gnats, it is diluted with water or oil. Active ingredients: 53.29% butoxypolypropylene glycol, 5.38% piperonyl butoxide (tech.), 0.54% pyrethrins, and 25.72% petroleum distillate.
MILLER CHEMICAL & FERTILIZER CORP.

FM-47. *See* BLOOMINGDALE ADHESIVE FM-47 *and* BLOOMINGDALE ADHESIVE FM-47 FILM.

Foamicide 581[NE]. A defoamer that is especially suitable for use with glues, starch, latex or resin formulations. COLLOIDS, INC.

Foamicide 581B[NE]. A non-toxic, non-ionic, concentrated defoamer for the textile industry. It is effective with all types of resins (water solutions or solvent systems) as well as latex, polyvinyl acetates, pigments and printing pastes for sizing, dyeing and finishing operations. Will not interfere with viscosity or adhesion or with dyeing, finishing or printing processes.
COLLOIDS, INC.

Foamicide S[NE]. An antifoaming agent for use in neutral or alkaline solutions. It consists of two liquid organic antifoaming agents adsorbed on a mild alkali carrier. In appearance it is a moist white powder. Alkalinity, 34.7–37.0%. *Use:* To reduce excessive foaming in pressure or hydro bottlewashing machines.
WYANDOTTE CHEMICALS CORP., J. B. FORD DIV.

Foam'n Fabric *and* **Foam-on-Fabric**[NE]. (*Supp.* I p. 89). This product, foam rubber fused to cloth, is now marketed under the RESTFOAM® trademark.
HEWITT-ROBINS INC.

Foilcraft. *See* CRAFTINT FOILCRAFT.

Foiltone[NE]. A line of metal-coated sheet materials. Included in the line are aluminum-coated paper, polyethylene, and MYLAR. The metal is deposited by a high-vacuum process. *Uses:* For decorative purposes and as packaging materials.
NATIONAL RESEARCH CORP.

Folbexii[NE]. (*HBMTN* p. 242). No longer available.
CHICAGO PHARMACAL CO.

Fold-Spray®. A rubber fountain syringe.
ARMSTRONG CORK CO.

Fomout[NE]. Liquid- and paste-type defoamants for control of foam in pulp and paper mill systems and in waste effluents. R. T. VANDERBILT CO.

Fomrez No. 50®. A polyester for the production of flexible urethane foams. WITCO CHEMICAL CO.

Fonate. (*HBMTN* p. 242). No longer available.
BEACON CO.

Fontana[NE]. A line of coated papers.
KIMBERLY-CLARK CORP.

Forestone®. The trademark for a line of acoustical products. SIMPSON LUMBER CO.

Formbond®. (*Supp.* I p. 89). Now a registered trademark. ACME WIRE CO.

Form-Saver[NE]. A coating for preserving and protecting plywood forms. It is a blend of synthetic resins in fast-evaporating solvents. It is free of grease, wax, oil, shellac and varnish. When applied, FORM-SAVER bonds firmly to the wood and seals the surface with a continuous film which is resistant to mechanical abrasion and to water and lime liberated during the hydration of cement. Applied by brush or dip methods. L. SONNEBORN SONS, INC.

Formula 44. A colorless, odorless, non-toxic fungicide used in dilutions of 1¼–1¾ oz. of the concentrate per gal. of water to kill Trichophyton Interdigitale (a fungus causing athlete's foot). It is used in foot baths, and for mopping floors.
J. I. HOLCOMB MFG. CO.

Formula #99®. (*HBMTN* p. 243). Now a registered trademark. ARMOUR AND CO.

Formula 900^NE. (*Formerly known as* FORMULA 91). A cleaner designed to remove build-up of soap scum from resilient and non-resilient floors. It is especially suitable for removing hazardous soap build-up on conductive flooring in hospital operating rooms.
FRANKLIN RESEARCH CO.

Formula 3117^NE. A polyester resin, supplied in low viscosity form, for the impregnation of fabrics, and for casting, sealing, etc. It can be cured at room temp. by the use of a catalyst.
NARMCO RESINS & COATINGS CO.

Formula TL-13 Floor Cleaner. *See* PAX® FORMULA TL-13 FLOOR CLEANER.

Fortecel®. The trademark for a line of yarns.
CELANESE CORP. OF AMERICA

Fortenese®. The trademark for a line of yarns.
CELANESE CORP. OF AMERICA

Forticon®. A multivitamin preparation containing minerals and amino acids in addition to vitamins. Used in the treatment of vitamin, mineral, and protein deficiencies; especially useful during pregnancy and lactation, convalescence, and in general malnutrition. Available in capsule form.
CONSOLIDATED MIDLAND CORP.

Fortiflex®. Synthetic thermoplastic polyolefin resins of excellent dimensional stability and form retention even at high temps. Resistant to acids, alkalis, and many other chemicals. *Uses:* For bottles and containers, pipe and fittings, electrical products, toys, appliances, etc. CELANESE CORP. OF AMERICA

Fortracin®. A brand of bacitracin, used as a bulk feed supplement. S. B. PENICK & CO.

Forvecil®. Penicillin procaine in aqueous suspension, for veterinary use. ABBOTT LABORATORIES

Fosclean®. Chemical substances used in treating metals preparatory to stamping, drawing, extruding, or other forming or deforming operations, or preparatory to painting; or for forming a corrosion-resistant surface on the metal. PENNSYLVANIA SALT MFG. CO.

Fosdraw®. A chemical substance used in treating metals preparatory to stamping, drawing, extruding, and other forming or deforming operations.
PENNSYLVANIA SALT MFG. CO.

Fossil Flour^△. *Same as* INFUSORIAL EARTH^△.

Fostarene®. Polystrene molding plastics. Available in general-purpose grade, and in a high-impact grade. The general-purpose grade has the following properties: sp.gr. 1.05; tensile strength, 4,500 lb./sq.in.; flexural strength, 7,000 lb./sq.in.; deformation under load, 5–7% at 4,000 lb./sq.in. and 50°C.; elongation in tension, 20–30% in 2″; volume resistivity, 10^8+ ohms/cm.; heat distortion temp., 73–75°C. Properties of the high-impact grade are: sp.gr. 1.05; tensile strength, 6,500 lb./sq.in.; flexural strength, 9,500 lb./sq.in.; deformation under load, 0.8% at 4,000 lb./sq.in. and 50°C.; elongation in tension, 1.8% in 2″; volume resistivity, 10^{14} ohm/cm.; heat distortion temp., 82°C.
Mfg.'d by FOSTER GRANT CO.
Sole Distributor, H. MUEHLSTEIN CO.

Four Leaf®. A powdered phosphate rock for use as a fertilizer.
INTERNATIONAL MINERALS & CHEMICAL CORP.

Four Leaf Clover (Design)®. Powdered phosphate rock for use as a fertilizer.
INTERNATIONAL MINERALS & CHEMICAL CORP.

FreeFlow. *See* "JOHN CRANE" CHEMLON®.

Freemax®. *See* U.S.S.® FREEMAX®.

Freezist^NE. A freeze-thaw stable starch, suitable for the frozen-food industry. It is used as a thickener in pie fillings. PAISLEY PRODUCTS INC.

French Chalk^△. *Same as* TALC^△.

French Green^△. *Same as* PARIS GREEN^△.

Fresco Acoustical Tile^NE. An acoustical tile so finished as to have a strippled effect.
OWENS-CORNING FIBERGLAS CORP.

Freshettes®. Perfumed crystal blocks for odor control in locker rooms, lavatories, rest rooms, and closets.
J. I. HOLCOMB MFG. CO.

Fribase®. An all-vegetable, fully hydrogenated shortening for use in baking, frying and pastry making.
ANDERSON, CLAYTON & CO. FOODS DIV.

Frodex® (Corn Syrup Solids). (*HBMTN* p. 245). The name FRODEX should have been listed as a registered trademark. AMERICAN MAIZE PRODUCTS CO.

Fruitex Dust®. (*HBMTN* p. 246). No longer available. NIAGARA CHEMICAL DIV.,
FOOD MACHINERY & CHEMICAL CORP.

Fruit Fix® 133, 200 *and* 800. (*Supp.* I p. 91). The name FRUIT FIX® should have been listed as a registered trademark. THOMPSON CHEMICALS CORP.

Fruitosynth Flavors®. A line of 26 concentrated fruit flavors made from blends of essential oils, aromatics, and fruit and plant extractions.
FLORASYNTH LABORATORIES, INC.

Fry-Base®. An all-vegetable, fully hydrogenated shortening for use in baking, frying and pastry making.
ANDERSON, CLAYTON & CO. FOODS DIV.

FS. A nickel-chromium-molybdenum die block and hot-work die steel furnished annealed only.
A. FINKL & SONS CO.

Fuchsine. *See* AZO FUCHSINE®.

Fuelguard^NE. A sludge inhibitor and dispersant, and corrosion inhibitor for distillate fuel oils. It prevents the formation of soluble gums and insoluble sludge, disperses any small sludge particles that may be present in the oil, prevents the discoloration of the oil, and provides good corrosion protection for tanks and pipelines in the presence of water.
CARLISLE CHEMICAL WORKS, INC.

Fugitints®. A line of water-soluble and oil-soluble dyestuffs and dispersible pigments used for the identification of yarns in spinning. They are especially useful for this purpose because of their economical tinctorial value and because of the ease with which they are subsequently removed in scouring.
GENERAL DYESTUFF CO.

Fuller's Earth△. A soft, opaque clay analyzing about 75% silica, 10–20% alumina, 1–4% lime, 2–4% magnesia and often some iron oxide. Its color varies from a greenish white to a greenish brown. *Uses:* For clarifying and bleaching fats, greases, and mineral and vegetable oils; and as a pigment extender.

Fuller's Herb△. Same as SAPONARIA△.

Full Random[NE]. (Trademark registration pending). An acoustical insulation material.
ARMSTRONG CORK CO.

Fultex A[NE]. A complex fatty amino amphoteric compound for use in the fulling of woolen fabrics. It shortens the time required for fulling, and leaves the WOOL soft. It is not affected by water hardness, and readily rinses from the fabric. W. F. FANCOURT CO.

Fum-Aromas®. The trademark for an incense.
S. B. PENICK & CO.

Fumazone[NE]. A soil fumigant for use in controlling certain nematodes in land to be planted to cotton and to ventura lima beans. Composed of 47.6% 1,2-dibromo-3-chloropropane, and 52.4% inert ingredients.
DOW CHEMICAL CO.

Fume-Saf White®. (*HBMTN* p. 247). No longer available. TRUSCON LABORATORIES

Fumigun[NE]. An injector for applying soil fumigants. (*See* BROMEX.) LARVACIDE PRODUCTS, INC.

Fungidust®. (*Supp.* I p. 92). No longer available.
GENERAL CHEMICAL DIV.,
ALLIED CHEMICAL & DYE CORP.

Fur-Ag®. A furfural residue used as a conditioner in mixed fertilizers.
QUAKER OATS CO., CHEMICALS DEPT.

Furane Resins△. A group of heat- and corrosion-resistant resins based on the use of furane derivatives in the synthesis. The reaction product of furfural and phenol results in a line of molding compounds; furfuryl alcohol can be reacted with dimethylolurea to produce low-shrink wood adhesives; furfuryl alcohol is capable of self-resinfication in the presence of acid catalysts and yields acid-resisting resin cements for brick setting; furfuryl alcohol can be reacted with formaldehyde to produce various coatings and resin cements; and furfuraldehyde is reactive with various ketones, forming coatings and cements. Pure furfuryl alcohol polymers form resins that in the cured state have excellent resistance to acids, alkalis, and solvents, good thermal stability, and retain their strength and corrosion resistance at temps. up to 400°F.

Furethrin△. A new synthetic pyrethroid. *dl*-2-(2-furfuryl)-4-hydroxy-3-methyl-2-cyclopenten-1-one ester of *dl*-cistrans-chrysanthemum monocarboxylic acid. $C_{21}H_{26}O_4$; mol.wt. 342.44. A pale yellow liquid; b.p. 187–188°C. (4 mm. Hg); insoluble in water; soluble in refined kerosene. Tested against houseflies, this insecticidal material and its *d-trans* acid isomer caused rapid knockdown and was as toxic as natural pyrethrins; the *d-trans* acid isomer being about twice as toxic as FURETHRIN.

Furniture-Care. See Lecton® Furniture-Care.

Fustic△. *Also known as* CUBA WOOD△. The wood of the tree *Chlorophora tinctoria*, of tropical America. It is used for cabinet making and as a dyewood. The liquid extract of this wood produces the yellow dyestuff, MORIN, $C_{15}H_{11}O_7$, and the red dye, MORINDONE, $C_{15}H_{11}O_5$.

Fut-Sure®. A special abrasive grain, containing more than 90% crystalline aluminum oxide, for use on stair treads, sidewalks, floors, building entrances, railway stations, ramps, shower floors, swimming pool areas; and around machinery, etc. For cast-metal stair treads FUT-SURE is put into the molten metal; for concrete surfaces, it can be troweled into the surface or mixed in with the finish coat; for composition stair treads, a mixture of FUT-SURE and composition binder is poured into recesses in the surface.
GENERAL ABRASIVE CO.

Fuzohm®. The trademark for a line of electrical resistors. (Registration No. 618,124; Class 21; Dec. 27, 1955.) CLAROSTAT MFG. CO.

FX. A nickel-chromium-molybdenum die block and hot-work die steel furnished heat-treated in four hardness ranges from 477 to 269 Brinell.
A. FINKL & SONS CO.

Fybrol®. (*HBMTN* p. 247). Now a registered trademark. L. SONNEBORN SONS, INC.

G

Galex® Pellets. A stabilized, non-oxidizing rosin in free-flowing pellet form. Packaged in 50 lb. multi-wall bags. *Mfg'd by* G & A LABORATORIES, INC.
Distributed by NATIONAL ROSIN OIL PRODUCTS, INC.

Gallicide®. A water-soluble complex of phenyl mercuric acetate for use as a slimicide in paper mills. Contains 11.9% phenylmercury monoethanolammonium acetate, corresponding to 6% mercury. It is a water-white liquid, completely soluble in water, and stable in storage. GALLOWHUR CHEMICAL CORP.

Gallimycin[NE]. A poultry antibiotic consisting of erythromycin stearate. ABBOTT LABORATORIES

Gallosan®. A slimicide for use in paper mills. It is 3,5-dimethyltetrahydro-1,3,52H-thiadiazine-2-thione; and is a straw-to-tan-colored crystalline solid, with a m.p. of 105–107°C. Soluble in trichloroethylene, ethylene dichloride, acetone, and cyclohexanone; slightly soluble in ethyl alcohol, xylene, and water. GALLOWHUR CHEMICAL CORP.

Gallotox®. A non-volatile seed disinfectant for the control of damping-off, seed rot, seedling blights, and other diseases of wheat, oats, barley, sorghum, flax, and COTTON. Applied in the form of a slurry.
GALLOWHUR CHEMICAL CORP.

Gallotox® 51. A liquid mercural seed disinfectant It is a volatile, completely water-soluble fungicide Active ingredients: 5% phenylmercury acetate and 1% ethylmercury acetate. It protects against damp-

ing-off, seed rot, and certain seedling blights caused by seed-borne and soil-borne organisms. Used on wheat, oats, barley, sorghum, rye, flax, and cotton.
GALLOWHUR CHEMICAL CORP.

Galls[△]. A tanning material obtained from the nutgalls, or gall nuts, from the oaks of Europe and the Near East, and from the SUMAC of China and Japan. They are very high in tannin: 50–70%.

Galustre[NE]. Lacquers and enamels of lacquer and resin base for use of galvanized iron or zinc.
MAAS & WALDSTEIN CO.

Galvaprep®. A chemical preparation for treating and coating galvanized and other zinc surfaces prior to painting. NEILSON CHEMICAL CO.

Galvomag[NE]. A proprietary magnesium alloy composition for use as an anode to prevent corrosion of iron structures such as pipelines and ship hulls which are buried in the ground or covered by water. This type of corrosion prevention is commonly referred to as cathodic protection. DOW CHEMICAL CO.

Gambier[△]. A tanning and dyeing material extracted from the leaves and twigs of the shrubs *Uncaria gambier, U. Dacyoneuro*, and other species of India, Malaysia, and the East Indies. GAMBIER contains CATECHIN, $C_{15}H_{14}O_6$, a yellow astringent dye that is soluble in hot water and alkali solutions, and a reddish tannin material called CATECHUTANNIC ACID. *Uses:* In tanning of leather; in dyeing fabrics; for fixing basic dyes; in boiler compounds; and in pharmaceuticals.

Gammanol®. A series of petroleum sulphonates useful as emulsifiers and wetting agents.
NOPCO CHEMICAL CO.

Gantrex®. A vitamin-mineral-trace element combination used as a metabolic supplement. Supplied as a tonic to facilitate dietary control, etc.
WM. S. MERRELL CO.

Gantricillin® (100). A medicinal in tablet form. Each tablet contains 0.5 g. GANTRISAN® and 100,000 units crystalline VITAMIN G potassium. Useful in the treatment of infections which respond more readily to a combination of two antibacterial agents than to a single one. HOFFMANN-LA ROCHE INC.

Gantricillin® 300. A medicinal consisting of 0.5 g. GANTRISAN® and 300,000 units crystalline PENICILLIN G potassium per tablet. It affords potent action against a wide range of gram-negative and grampositive organisms. HOFFMANN-LA ROCHE INC.

Gantrisin® Cream. A medicinal consisting of 10% GANTRISAN® (3,4-dimethyl-5-sulfanilamido-isoxazole) in a vanishing cream base. Used for the treatment of vaginal and cervical infections.
HOFFMANN-LA ROCHE INC.

Gantrisin® Ear Solution. A medicinal consisting of 4% GANTRISAN® in the form of the diethanolamine salt, 10% urea, and 3% chlorobutanol in a propylene glycol vehicle. Effective against a wide variety of gram-positive and gram-negative microorganisms. Available in ½-oz. vials with an enclosed dropper.
HOFFMANN-LA ROCHE INC.

Gantrisin® Nasal Solution. A sulfonamide medicinal for the treatment of nasal infections and the relief of congestion. Contains 4% GANTRISIN® in the form of the diethanolamine salt, 0.25% NEO-SYNEPHRINE HYDROCHLORIDE, and 1:100,000 phenylmercuric nitrate.
HOFFMANN-LA ROCHE INC.

Gantrisin® Ophthalmic. A medicinal for the treatment of eye infections. It is a sterile, isotonic solution containing 4% GANTRISIN® in the form of its diethanolamine salt. Effective against streptococci, staphylococci, pneumococci, meningococci, gonococci, H. influenzae, E. coli, and B. proteus.
HOFFMANN-LA ROCHE INC.

Garan® Roving. A glass fiber, plastic reinforcement material made with a silicone-type binder. It is treated with a special sizing material known as GARAN® SIZING. This roving bonds strongly and uniformly to polyester and other molding resins. The improved bonding prevents moisture from moving along the glass fibers. L.O.F. GLASS FIBERS CO.

Garden Duster[NE]. A plastic, refillable container filled with PLANT GARD[NE] (*Supp.* I p. 186), a rotenone-copper insecticide for the control of many chewing and sucking insects and fungous diseases on many garden vegetables and flowers. AGKEM, INC.

Garnet[△]. The name for a large group of hard minerals having the general formula $3RO \cdot R_2O_3 \cdot 3SiO_2$ where R is Ca^{++}, Mg^{++}, Fe^{++} or Mn^{++}, and R_2 is Al^{+++}, Cr^{+++} or Fe^{+++}. Hardness varies from about 6 to 7.5 and the sp.gr. from 3.4 to 4.3; m.p. about 1,300°C. GARNETS occur in a wide variety of rocks in many parts of the world. The color of GARNET ranges from red to brown, yellow, green or black. Used chiefly as an abrasive in the form of paper and cloth, and for bearing pivots in watches; the finest quality specimens are used as gem stones.

Gar-Vor® Compound. (*Supp.* I p. 95). No longer available. VORIS LABORATORIES

Gascope®. Combustible gas detection instruments. *Uses:* For detection of combustible gases in minute traces or heavy concentrations, and pin-pointing gas leaks in distribution systems.
MINE SAFETY APPLIANCES CO.

Gearteck[NE]. A gear-tooth lubricant. It is a liquid which is applied by brush or swab onto the teeth of open or semi-enclosed gears or by pouring into gear enclosures. It is highly adhesive, and is not readily thrown from gears operating at high speeds. It sets to a nearly dry load-bearing film.
PENNSYLVANIA REFINING CO.

Gelex®. (*HBMTN* p. 250). Should have been listed as a registered trademark.
AMERICAN MAIZE PRODUCTS CO.

Gelobarin®. (*Supp.* I p. 95). No longer available.
SHARP & DOHME DIV., MERCK & CO.

Gelusil®. A medicinal used for the relief of gastric hyperacidity or for acid control in the management of peptic ulcer. Each teaspoonful or tablet contains 0.5 g. magnesium trisilicate, and 0.25 g. aluminum hydroxide. WARNER-CHILCOTT LABORATORIES

Gemglo®. A high gloss, flexographic ink.
INTERCHEMICAL CORP., PRINTING INK DIV.

Gemonil®. An anticonvulsant in tablet form. Chemically it is metharbital, 5,5-diethyl-1-methyl-barbituric acid. ABBOTT LABORATORIES

Gemtone®. A high finish, letterpress process ink. INTERCHEMICAL CORP., PRINTING INK DIV.

Genacryl®. A line of straight, water-soluble basic dyes of a new type, which give bright, strong shades on acrylic fibers. They are characterized by very good light and wet fastness. GENERAL DYESTUFF CO.

Genalan®. A group of neutral-dyeing, premetalized acid dyestuffs recommended primarily for dyeing very fast shades on WOOL by a short dyeing procedure. They provide better preservation of fiber quality than is commonly obtained with other dyestuffs of equal fastness. They are also useful for dyeing fast shades on leather, polyamide fibers, SILK, and polyester fibers; and for printing all types of textile fibers for which they can be satisfactorily used as a dye. GENERAL DYESTUFF CO.

Gendyco®. Solutions of stabilized diazotized organic bases which can be mixed with alkaline solutions of naphthols of the AS series for printing COTTON and RAYON. Upon steaming in acid vapors or upon the breakdown of acid-forming substances, these components of the print paste couple to form insoluble azo dyes in and on the fiber. GENERAL DYESTUFF CO.

Generalime[NE]. (*HBMTN* p. 251). No longer available. HANSON-VAN WINKLE-MUNNING CO.

Geneva®. The trademark for a line of structural steel shapes. UNITED STATES STEEL CORP.

Gen-Flo®. A rubber latex for water-mix paints. Characterized by very fine controlled particle size. GENERAL TIRE & RUBBER CO.

Genicide® and Genicide®-A. (*HBMTN* p. 252). No longer available. GENERAL CHEMICAL DIV., ALLIED CHEMICAL & DYE CORP.

Genidust®. (*HBMTN* p. 252). No longer available. GENERAL CHEMICAL DIV., ALLIED CHEMICAL & DYE CORP.

Geniphene®. (*HBMTN* p. 252 and *Supp.* I p. 96). No longer available. GENERAL CHEMICAL DIV., ALLIED CHEMICAL & DYE CORP.

Genisul®. (*HBMTN* p. 252 and *Supp.* I p. 96). No longer available. GENERAL CHEMICAL DIV., ALLIED CHEMICAL & DYE CORP.

Gentamine Tablets[NE]. An antineuralgic, analgesic, antipyretic that provides an effective combination of synergistic analgesics for prompt relief from pain in such conditions as rheumatoid arthritis, rheumatic fever, neuritis, bursitis and other painful neuralgic conditions. AMERICAN PHARMACEUTICAL CO.

Genuwood®. A decorative plastic laminate made with genuine veneer. PARKWOOD LAMINATES, INC.

Geranol®. A line of level-dyeing anthraquinone acid dyestuffs for dyeing reddish-violet shades of very good fastness properties on WOOL yarns and piece goods as well as on stock and hat bodies. They are also useful for shading dyeings in a chrome dyebath. GENERAL DYESTUFF CO.

Ger-Flex®. A line of polyvinyl plastic tubing. GERING PRODUCTS INC.

Gerix®. A dietary supplement for adults. It is a wine-flavored appetite stimulant and nutritional supplement which provides balanced amounts of important nutritional elements, including the B-complex factors and iron for use in aiding appetite failures due to inactivity of old age and the languor of convalescence. ABBOTT LABORATORIES

Gerlite®. An extruded acrylic plastic sheet, available either clear or colored, up to 54" wide and 0.125" thick, and in any practical length. GERING PRODUCTS INC.

Germicin[NE]. An antiseptic and germicide for use in skin and mucous membrane antisepsis in surgery, obstetrics and gynecology, urology, ophthalmology, otorhinolaryngology, etc. It is a liquid mixture of high molecular weight alkyldimethylbenzyl ammonium chlorides; freely soluble in water, forming a clear, colorless, almost odorless solution. CONSOLIDATED MIDLAND CORP.

Germocid. A preservative and disinfectant for textiles. It kills certain bacteria and fungoid growths. It has wetting and re-wetting properties; is readily soluble in water, forming clear solutions; is stable against acids, alkalis, hard water, and metal salts; and has a faint, not unpleasant odor. NOVA CHEMICAL CORP.

Ger-Pak®. A line of polyethylene film, sheet, and layflat tubing for packaging and other applications. It is resistant to moisture, fungus growth, oxidation, and many acids, alkalis, and other chemicals; and is tough and strong, odorless and tasteless. The film is available in thicknesses from 1¼ to 6 mils, and up to 20 ft. wide. *Uses:* For packaging fruits and vegetables, other food products, and manufactured articles; for lining drums and other shipping containers; as a vapor barrier in building construction; as a concrete curing membrane; for covering equipment outdoors to protect it against the weather; etc. (*See also* Printable "TS" GER-PAK®.) GERING PRODUCTS INC.

Gerrard®. The trademark for a line of steel strapping and strapping machines and equipment. UNITED STATES STEEL CORP.

Ger-Tube®. A line of polyethylene plastic tubing. GERING PRODUCTS INC.

GFN Inhibitor Base. A completely soluble product used in textile dyeing and finishing to prevent fading of gas-sensitive acetate dyeings. It has no effect on the brightness of the dyed shade. NOVA CHEMICAL CORP.

Giant®. (*HBMTN* p. 255). Now a registered trademark. ARMOUR AND CO.

Gide-Rite®. The trademark for a line of sign posts. UNITED STATES STEEL CORP.

Gilron®. An industrial metal cleaner. It is the same as GILRONCO®. PENNSYLVANIA SALT MFG. CO.

Gilronco®. An industrial cleaner for cleaning metal articles; and particularly for cleaning metal articles in electrolytic baths. PENNSYLVANIA SALT MFG. CO.

Gilronex®. A rustproofing composition for temporarily preventing rusting of metal between different steps of processing.
PENNSYLVANIA SALT MFG. CO.

Gilsonite△. A naturally occurring asphalt. It is a lustrous, black, almost odorless, brittle solid; sp.gr. 1.10; m.p. range, 275–330°F.; soluble in alcohol, turpentine and mineral spirits. Mined in the U. S. in Colorado and Utah. *Uses:* For roofing, paving, in rubber compounds, and in waterproof paints.

Gilsulate®. A mixture of specially selected, sized, and blended gilsonites, used for insulation and corrosion protection of hot underground pipes. Available in 3 types: (A) for temp. range of 220–300°F.; (B) for 300–385°F.; and (C) for 385–520°F. Particle size, less than 1/8"; thermal conductivity of GILSULATE envelope, 0.6 B.t.u.-inch/hr. x sq.ft. x °F.
AMERICAN GILSONITE CO.

Gilt Edge. A line of oak-tanned flat leather belting for power transmission. Available in thicknesses of $^{11}/_{64}$" to $^{34}/_{64}$" and in widths of 8" to 76".
J. E. RHOADS & SONS

Gingelly△. *See* SESAME OIL△.

Gingilli Oil△. *See* SESAME OIL△.

Gix△. Same as DFDT△.

Glade® (Aerosol). A spray-type air freshener which is unique in that it chemically destroys mal-odors instead of reodorizing or causing olfactory paralysis. Available in two scents, Blossom and Evergreen.
S. C. JOHNSON & SON

Glade® (Wick). A pleasantly scented air deodorizer for use in combatting continuing indoor odors such as from newly painted areas, musty closets, basements, etc. The bottle has a stationary wick, and, because of its design, is not easily tipped. It is non-flammable, and available in Evergreen and Blossom scent.
S. C. JOHNSON & SON

Glascast. A process for precision casting of metals through use of glass molds. Designed especially for high-temp. alloys, the process is fast and economical, and gives good surface finish and dimensional control. GLASCAST powder, a 96% silica glass, is mixed with water to produce a casting slip which is poured into a plaster mold. After drying, the glass shell is removed from the plaster and fired. Metal pouring temps. can be as high as 3,200°F.; tolerances of ±0.005" can be obtained. CORNING GLASS WORKS

Glaskote[NE]. A prefabricated plasticized enamel tape reinforced with a glass fabric and wound in rolls for use in weatherproofing and corrosion-proofing work on processed piping and underground transmission lines. TWINSBURG-MILLER CORP.

Glasohm®. The trademark for a line of resistors, fixed resistors, power resistors, ballast resistors, and glass-insulated resistors. (Registration No. 518,370; Class 21; Dec. 6, 1949). CLAROSTAT MFG. CO.

Glastic® Channel-Duct®. Fiberglass-reinforced polyester channel for use by manufacturers of control panels and others who utilize complex wiring layouts. CHANNEL-DUCT® simplfies assembly and expedites layout changes. The channels are flame resistant and resist warping. GLASTIC CORP.

Glaze. A self-polishing floor wax made from a blend of Carnauba and two synthetic waxes. It is waterproof, slip resistant, and resists chipping and flaking.
J. I. HOLCOMB MFG. CO.

Glazetex. (*HBMTN* p. 257). No longer available.
ACORN REFINING CO.

Gleam®. An all-hydrogenated vegetable shortening of the emulsifier type. It is a specialty shortening for cakes and icings.
ANDERSON, CLAYTON & CO. FOODS DIV.

Gleme. A glass cleaner in an aerosol bomb dispenser. It is sprayed on the glass and then wiped off.
CLAIRE MFG. CO.

Glen Eden® Margarine. A margarine made of hydrogenated soybean and cottonseed oils, nonfat dry milk, water, salt, LECITHIN, 0.1% sodium benzoate added as a preservative, artificial coloring, and 15,000 units of VITAMIN A per lb.
ANDERSON, CLAYTON & CO. FOODS DIV.

Glidair[NE]. A line of aviation finishes.
GLIDDEN CO.

Glidden®. The trademark for a galvanized 2-point (round point) barbed wire, with barbs spaced 4" apart. UNITED STATES STEEL CORP.

Gliddencoat®. (*HBMTN* p. 257). Now a registered trademark. GLIDDEN CO.

Gliddol®. Natural soybean lecithins for use in paint, petroleum, chocolate, baking, margarine, plastics.
GLIDDEN CO.

Glidkote®. Wood conversion varnishes for wood furniture and other wood products. GLIDDEN CO.

Globaline. Tetraglycine hydroperiodide. $(NH_2CH_2COOH)_4 \cdot HI_{3.5}$. Typical analysis: active iodine, 42.2%; ash, 0.09%; total nitrogen, 7.48%; loss of iodine (in 7 days at 130°F.), 0.5%. Practically odorless, shiny, metallic-gray crystals. *Use:* As a rapid positive purifier of water, particularly for field use in canteens; and for the purification of water for stock and poultry use. ARAPAHOE CHEMICALS, INC.

Globe Kold Dip Metal Cleaner. A heavy, concentrated immersion-type liquid cleaner for removing oil, grease, and heavy soil from motor blocks, brake drives, etc. TROY INDUSTRIAL PRODUCTS,
DIV. OF GLOBE SANITARY SUPPLY CO.

Glo-Coat®. *See* HARD GLOSS® GLO-COAT®.

Glo-Coater®. A long-handled wax applier with plastic head. The applied pad is made of chenille cloth and can be removed for washing. It can be used with all liquid-type floor finishes. S. C. JOHNSON & SON

Glo-Ray®. The trademark for a line of gloss printing inks. INTERCHEMICAL CORP., PRINTING INK DIV.

Gloria®. The trademark for a line of stencils.
INTERCHEMICAL CORP.,
AULT & WIBORG CARBON & RIBBON DIV.

Gloriamaster®. The trademark for a spirit hectograph. INTERCHEMICAL CORP.,
AULT & WIBORG CARBON & RIBBON DIV.

Gloriaspirit®. The trademark for a spirit hectograph.
INTERCHEMICAL CORP., AULT & WIBORG CARBON & RIBBON DIV.

Glov-Cote. (*HBMTN* p. 258). No longer available.
CHASE CHEMICAL CO.

Glo-White. See CASPRO®.

Glue-Beeds®. An animal glue in the form of small (8-mesh) dust-free pellets. Available in two grades: low viscosity and high viscosity. *Uses:* As a binder for clay and mineral coatings; paper size; oil- and organic solvent-proof saturant; and coagulant in white water recovery systems.
BURTONITE CO.

Glutazyme®. A preparation consisting of monosodium *l*-glutamate, NIACIN, thiamin mononitrate, riboflavin, ascorbic acid, pyridoxine, ferrous sulfate and dicalcium phosphate. Indicated for the treatment of cerebral dysfunction. Enhances cerebral tissue metabolism, enzymatic oxidations, and cerebral vascular flow, which is reduced markedly during the aging process.
PURDUE FREDERICK CO.

Glycinal HD2. A solvent and fixing agent for use in vat color printing of textiles. It is a yellow, hygroscopic liquid with a neutral reaction; soluble in water.
NOVA CHEMICAL CORP.

Glycox® 1300. (*HBMTN* p. 259). No longer available.
GLYCO PRODUCTS CO.

Glycox® 1400. (*HBMTN* p. 259). No longer available.
GLYCO PRODUCTS CO.

Go-Jo® Hand Cleaner. A cream-type hand cleaner, used with or without water, to remove grease, grime, etc. It has a pH of 7.5; contains no harmful caustics or irritating abrasives; does contain lanolin and specially-selected emollients to condition the skin, and germicidal antiseptics to guard against infections.
GOJER, INC.

Go-Jo® Protective Hand Cream. A protective hand cream designed for persons with tender, sore or sensitized skin.
GOJER, INC.

Gold Bond® Holostud. A low-cost, strong, lightweight, non-load bearing partition that is adaptable to almost any type of building. The partition is made of gypsum lath which is clipped to the chords of prefabricated steel. GOLD BOND GYPSOLITE® or GOLD BOND® gypsum cement plaster is applied to the gypsum lath to complete the system. The unit has excellent fire resistance and sound ratings.
NATIONAL GYPSUM CO.

Gold Bond® Sprayolite. A sound-absorbing, decorative, non-combustible acoustical plaster finish. It may be troweled or sprayed on; has high bonding power; dries to form a porous, non-absorbing surface; has a noise reduction coefficient of 0.55.
NATIONAL GYPSUM CO.

Golden Capri^{NR}. A cottonseed salad oil and liquid shortening. (Trademark registration pending).
ANDERSON, CLAYTON & Co. FOODS DIV.

Golden Lavender®. The trademark for cosmetics in the nature of lotions and colognes.
MAX FACTOR & CO.

Golden Mist Margarine^{NR}. A margarine made of hydrogenated soybean and cottonseed oils, nonfat dry milk, water, salt, LECITHIN, 0.1% sodium benzoate added as a preservative, artificial coloring, and 15,000 units of VITAMIN A per lb.
ANDERSON, CLAYTON & CO. FOODS DIV.

Gold Leaf®. A line of rubber sundries, including water bottles, fountain syringes, and combination syringes, for sale by druggists.
ARMSTRONG CORK CO.

Gold'n:Wedge® Margarine. A margarine made of hydrogenated soybean and cottonseed oils, nonfat dry milk, water, salt, lecithin, 0.1% sodium benzoate added as a preservative, artificial coloring, and 15,000 units of vitamin A per pound.
ANDERSON, CLAYTON & CO. FOODS DIV.

Goodallite®. (*HBMTN* p. 260). Now mfg'd by GOODALL-SANFORD, INC., successors to GOODALL FABRICS, INC.

Gossypine[△]. Same as CHOLINE[△].

Grafon^{NR}. A quick-drying colloidal graphite product in an aerosol self-spraying can. *Uses:* For lubrication and protection of metal surfaces. Within a few seconds after application, it forms a dry colloidal graphite film.
GRAFO COLLOIDS CORP.

Grain-Tex®. An insulating siding material with a wood grain design.
MASTIC ASPHALT CORP.

Granette®. A vinyl-plastic floor-covering and counter-top material for residential and institutional uses.
ARMSTRONG CORK CO.

Gran-Form^{NR}. A fertilizer.
PENNSYLVANIA SALT MFG. CO.

Granger. See BOSTON GRANGER.

Granitex^{NR}. A sealer and preservative for concrete floors. It seals the pores, thereby preventing the collection of dirt and dust and the penetration of oil and grease; and holds the surface particles together with a tough, resinous binder.
TRUSCON LABORATORIES

Gransize®. A specialty corn starch offered to the textile industry for various applications in warp sizing and also in the finishing of heavy fabrics.
A. E. STALEY MFG. CO.

Granular Frodex®. A corn syrup solids in granular form—fine, granular, and coarse. Except for particle size, it is the same as regular FRODEX, (*HBMTN* p. 245), which is a powdered product.
AMERICAN MAIZE PRODUCTS CO.

Grapeseed Oil[△]. The oil obtained by pressing or extraction of the seeds of various grapes. The seeds contain 10–15% oil, composed of about 32% oleic acid, 52% linoleic acid, together with small quantities of palmitic, stearic and arachidic acids. The cold-pressed oil is almost colorless, rather sweet, and is similar to olive oil. The hot-pressed oil is dark green and rather bitter. Refined GRAPESEED OIL has a delicate green color and a nutlike taste. *Uses:* As an edible oil; in the mfg. of paint and soap.

Graph-Air®. A graphitic air-hardening tool steel with excellent low-temp. (1,450°–1,525°F.) hardening characteristics, and good machinability, stability, and wearability.
TIMKEN ROLLER BEARING CO.

Graphic Red^{NR}. A series of Lithol Reds especially recommended for printing inks, paints, enamels, rubber, etc., where requirements are not severe and inexpensive pigmentation is essential. They are available in dry form and dispersed in various organic vehicles designed for use in enamels, printing inks and rubber. They are the non-resinated type of Lithol Reds. The resinated grades are sold as BRITONE RED. Available in the following grades:

Trade Name	Chemical Name	Shade
Graphic Maroon	Calcium Lithol Red	Maroon
Graphic Red M	Barium Lithol Red	Medium Red
Graphic Red R	Calcium Lithol Red	Bluish Red
Graphic Red Y	Sodium Lithol Red	Yellowish-Red

SHERWIN-WILLIAMS CO.

Graposynth®. An imitation grape oil, 1 oz. of which will flavor 2 gal. of syrup.
FLORASYNTH LABORATORIES, INC.

Grass Tree Gum△. *Same as* RED ACAROID△.

Gravinol®. A brominated vegetable oil for use as a stabilizing agent in the preparation of non-alcoholic maltless soft drinks. ABBOTT LABORATORIES

Gray's Compound®. A compound of gentian, dandelion, sherry wine, glycerin, phosphoric acid, tr. cardamon compound and sugars. Used as an appetite stimulant. It has a tonic, stomachic, and carminative effect. PURDUE FREDERICK CO.

Grayson® Margarine. A margarine made of hydrogenated soybean and cottonseed oils, nonfat dry milk, water, salt, LECITHIN, 0.1% sodium benzoate added as a preservative, artificial coloring, and 15,000 units of VITAMIN A per lb.
ANDERSON, CLAYTON & CO. FOODS DIV.

Gray Stone®. A finishing plaster for walls.
CELOTEX CORP.

Greasolve. An emulsifying grease solvent, in concentrated form, which is diluted in 8–10 parts kerosene and used for cleaning motors, pumps, machinery, concrete floors, etc. J. I. HOLCOMB MFG. CO.

Greek Ascoloy®. This is a special corrosion- and heat-resisting stainless steel (U. S. Patent No. 2,227,-891) with greatly improved high-temp. properties. This tungsten (3.00%), nickel (2.00%) stainless steel offers strength and creep characteristics excelling those of a straight 12.00% chromium steel. It has a high creep strength, comparable or superior to austenitic stainless steels up to 1,100°F., and has good resistance to softening at 900°F. It can be easily machined, and in the annealed state has fair stamping, punching and drawing qualities. The annealed hardness ranges from Brinell 241 to 277. GREEK ASCOLOY can be heat treated to a hardness of Rockwell "C" 42–46 when oil-quenched from 1,750°F. The tensile properties at room temp. show an ultimate strength of 135,000 lb./sq.in. Because it has good resistance to oxidation, it can, therefore, be used for continuous service at temps. up to 1,000–1,100°F. It is particularly adapted for parts requiring high creep resistance characteristics, such as turbine buckets, jet-engine blades, valve stems for high-pressure steam service, and heat interchangers. VANADIUM-ALLOYS STEEL CO.

Green-Bak[NB]. An abrasive consisting of an aluminum oxide-coated fiber disc. BEHR-MANNING CO.

Green Butter△. *Same as* BORNEO TALLOW△.

Greenheart△. *Also known as* DEMERARA GREENHEART△ *and as* BIBIRU△. The wood of the tree *Octotea rodioei* of British Guiana. It has good resistance to fungi and termites. The heartwood is light olive to nearly black in color, and the sapwood is pale yellow to green. *Uses:* For shipbuilding, dock timbers, planking, and lock gates.

Green Label. *See* AIRKEM® GREEN LABEL.

Greenohm®. The trademark for resistors, fixed resistors, power resistors, ballast resistors, and ceramic-insulated resistors. (Registration No. 518,371; Class 21; Dec. 6, 1949). CLAROSTAT MFG. CO.

Greenohm Jr.®. The trademark for fixed electrical resistors. (Registration No. 567,443; Class 21; Dec. 9, 1952). CLAROSTAT MFG. CO.

Greenwich Lye®. The trademark for a brand of lye.
PENNSYLVANIA SALT MFG. CO.

Griffco®. A line of polyvinyl acetate emulsions.
NOPCO CHEMICAL CO.

Grip[NB]. A skidproofing coating for all types of slippery surfaces. Applied by brush or trowel. It remains non-skid under wet, dry, oily or soapy conditions. HALLEMITE MFG. CO.

Gripclad[NB]. A two-package primer for aluminum, zinc-coated steel, and terneplate. It has excellent chemical resistance and adhesion and dries quickly.
SHERWIN-WILLIAMS CO.

Grip-Dek[NB]. A lightweight, non-slip, mastic floor surfacing material for use on steel, concrete, and wood flooring and decks. It is resistant to oils, grease, mineral acids, alcohols, mild acids, sea water, alkalis, etc.; it bonds securely to the underlying surface; is resistant to shock, vibration, and wear; and resistant to fire. Applied by trowel, brush or spray. Available in 8 colors.
FIBREBOARD PAPER PRODUCTS CORP.

Griplate[NB]. A one-package primer for aluminum, zinc-coated steel, and terneplate. It has excellent chemical resistance and excellent adhesion and dries quickly. SHERWIN-WILLIAMS CO.

Gripotan. A line of oak-tanned flat leather belting for power transmission. Available in thicknesses of $18/64''$ to $34/64''$ and in widths of 12'' to 76''.
J. E. RHOADS & SONS

Griptite[NB]. A bright or galvanized wire fence staple with legs of unequal length. Overall length, 1½''.
UNITED STATES STEEL CORP.

Gritcloth®. A line of sanding fabrics including sheets, discs, and rolls coated with aluminum oxide (grit sizes 100 to 320), and silicon carbide (grit sizes 100 to 600). BAY STATE ABRASIVE PRODUCTS CO.

G-T® Ring. *See* PALMETTO G-T® RING.

Guaiacum Oil△. *Also known as* GUAIACWOOD OIL△. A light gray essential oil distilled from the wood of the guayacan tree of Paraguay. The wood yields from 5 to 6% oil which has a very pleasant odor, and is solid at temps below 45°C. Used in medicine, soaps, and perfumes.

Guaiacwood Oil△. *Same as* GUAIACUM OIL△.

Guayule△. A perennial plant, *Parthenium argentatum*, of the Compositae family, that contains in the dry state up to 22% GUAYULE rubber. The plants are hard, woody shrubs that mature into the highest rubber content in seven years. The plant is uprooted, crushed, and pulverized; and the rubber recovered by flotation. The rubber contains from 20–25% resin which can be removed by solvent extraction with a suitable solvent.

Gum Accroides△. *Same as* ACAROID RESIN△.

Gum Arabic△. *Also known as* ACACIA GUM△. A gum obtained from the small tree *Acacia arabica* and various other species of acacia trees of Africa. The trees are wounded and the sap allowed to run out, forming yellowish, transparent lumps. It is soluble in water, but insoluble in alcohol. The major production of GUM ARABIC comes from the Egyptian Sudan where it is obtained from a wild tree *A. verek*. The gum exported from the Arabian ports on the Red Sea is known as SENNAR GUM. A grade of gum obtained from the tree *A. senegal*, found in the dry regions of French West Africa, is known as GUM SENEGAL. A brittle, low grade of GUM ARABIC, known as GUM TALHA, TALCO GUM, or TALH GUM is obtained from the North African acacia, *A. stenocarpa*. GUM ARABIC is used in the mfg. of adhesives, for thickening inks, as a binder and filler of textiles, for thickening rubber latex, as a suspending medium in medicines, etc.

Gum Kino△. *Same as* KINO RESIN△.

Gum Rosin△. *See* ROSIN△.

Gum Senecal△. *See* GUM ARABIC△.

Gum Talha△. *See* GUM ARABIC△.

Gum Tragacanth△. *Same as* TRAGACANTH△.

Gum Zanzibar△. *Same as* ANIMI GUM△.

Gun Iron. (*HBMTN* p. 264). Should have been listed as HUNT-SPILLER® GUN IRON.
HUNT-SPILLER MFG. CORP.

Gurjun Balsam△. *Also known as* WOOD OIL△. An oleoresin obtained from various species of the tree, *Dipterocarpus,* which is grown in India, Burma, Ceylon and the Malaya Peninsula. It is a clear liquid with a greenish fluorescence; sp.gr. 0.955–0.966; soluble in benzene. Used in lacquers and varnishes designed to withstand elevated temps.

Gutta Percha△. A gum obtained by boiling the sap of various species of trees of the order *Sapotaceae*, chiefly *Palaquium gutta* and *P. oblongifolia,* native to Borneo, New Guinea, and Malaya. It is a grayish white material that is very pliable but not as elastic as rubber. Like rubber, it can be vulcanized with sulfur. It molds easily at 180°F. It is used principally as a covering for electric cables, and for mixing with natural rubber for such products as golf balls, dental fillings, washers, valve seats, adhesives; for impregnating driving belts; etc.

Gym Finish. *See* RED LABEL GYM FINISH^NE.

Gynestrol®. The trademark for estrogenic hormone preparations. S. B. PENICK & CO.

Gyrocoil®. A line of electric blasting caps.
HERCULES POWDER CO.

Gyromet®. *See* MALLORY 1000 GYROMET®.

H

H-300. *See* CONOCO H-300^NE.

Haiari. *See* LONCHOCARPUS△.

Hairinsul®. A thermal insulation made of cattle hair. The name HAIRINSUL® is applied to products sold to the railroad industry.
AMERICAN HAIR & FELT CO.

Halco-Lume^NE. An asbestos-fibred roofing preservative with an aluminum finish. It rejuvenates dried out roofs, waterproofs them, and seals out heat, in one application. HALLEMITE MFG. CO.

Haliver®. The trademark for halibut liver oil that is rich in VITAMINS A and D. ABBOTT LABORATORIES

Hallephane^NE. A pure BAKELITE resin varnish. It is non-whitening; and has excellent resistance to alcohol, alkalis and other paint-destroying chemicals.
HALLEMITE MFG. CO.

Halletone^NE. (*Supp.* I p. 101). No longer available.
HALLEMITE MFG. CO.

Halloy^NE. A high-lead-alloy solder, specially treated to reduce the surface tension of the metal so that it will readily adhere to steel, copper, or brass parts, cover with a reasonably smooth bright surface, and give increased protection against corrosion. It is less expensive than an ordinary solder, yet its resistance to corrosion by atmosphere, hot or cold water, and weak acid is far greater than that of any ordinary solder coating. It has good bonding characteristics; it is very ductile; and one lb. covers approx. 47 sq.ft. of surface. The average thickness of the coating is 0.000015", or about the same as for standard dipped solder coatings. HALLOY should be used at about 725°F., and can be applied after proper cleaning and fluxing with any good 50° Bé. standard soldering flux. Ordinary solders will readily adhere to HALLOY coatings. HEWITT METALS CORP.

Hamicote® D-20. A non-graphitic, die-casting, forging and metal-drawing lubricant. It is a slightly alkaline, clear, amber-colored liquid that disperses readily in water. Completely soluble in Stoddard solvent, kerosene or mineral oils. It will withstand temps. up to 3,000°F. without complete evaporation or vaporization; a uniform, residual metallic film is formed which insures complete release of metals, glassware, etc. Can be used with zinc, aluminum, copper, brass, bronze, steel, magnesium, lead, titanium, stainless steel, glass, etc. in die casting, press forging, drop forging, upset forging, drawing, stamping, extruding, etc. HARRY MILLER CORP.

Hamicote® D-20-500. *Same as* HAMCOTE® D-20 except that its viscosity is much higher. It is a clear, dark red, viscous liquid that is especially useful, because of its higher viscosity, as a lubricant in drop forging and extruding operations where increased adhesiveness is important. HARRY MILLER CORP.

Hamikleer® 1391. A synthetic coolant and rust preventive for use on all ferrous metals. It is a slightly alkaline, odorless, light red, transparent liquid that dissolves readily in water. It is non-gumming, non-flammable, does not turn rancid, contains no oils, and does not foam. Used for such operations as grinding, cutting, broaching, milling, turning, drilling, reaming, etc. HARRY MILLER CORP.

Hammerguild®. An attractive and durable enamel which produces a lustrous metal-like finish, simulating hammered metal, but which is smooth to the touch and can be easily cleaned. Available in air-dry and bake types, in several different colors. Used on metal novelties, auto heaters, radios, air-conditioning equipment, etc. FIDELITY CHEMICAL PRODUCTS CORP.

Hammerlin® Enamels. (*HBMTN* p. 266). The word HAMMERLIN® is now a registered trademark. INTERCHEMICAL CORP., FINISHES DIV.

Hammond's® Horicum. (*Supp.* I p. 101). No longer available. HAMMOND PAINT & CHEMICAL CO.

Hamp Waxes[NB]. (*HBMTN* p. 266). No longer available. WITCO CHEMICAL CO.

Handi-Floats[NB]. See SPONGEX® HANDI-FLOATS.

Handi-Pack®. Polystyrene plastic capsule vials with snap caps. Available in sizes from 2 to 14 drams. ARMSTRONG CORK CO.

Handy Hi-Temp.[NB]. A line of brazing alloys in powder, resin-bonded sheet, cast rod, and fabricated and sintered shapes. Used for high-strength bonding of stainless steel, steel, INCONEL, and copper as well as other metals with melting points above those of the alloys. Available in the following grades:
HI-TEMP 72. For max. wear and highest corrosion resistance. Composition: 72.50% Ni, 5.00% Si, 3.50% B, 16.00% Cr. M.p. 1,820–1,830°F.
HI-TEMP 82. For general-purpose brazing where high corrosion resistance is required. Composition: 82.00% Ni, 4.50% Si, 2.90% B, 7.00% Cr. M.p. 1,790–1,800°F.
HI-TEMP 91. For general-purpose brazing requiring superior penetration. Composition: 91.25% Ni, 4.50% Si, 2.90% B. M.p. 1,790–1,800°F.
HI-TEMP 93. For max. joint toughness. Composition: 93.25% Ni, 3.50% Si, 1.90% B. M.p. 1,900–1,910°F. HANDY & HARMAN

Hansa®. A group of yellow pigment toners of excellent fastness to light, acid, and alkali. They are used for lithographic printing inks, wallpaper coatings, paints, and for other purposes where the benzidine yellows are now sufficiently fast. GENERAL DYESTUFF CO.

Hard Gloss®. See HEAVY-DUTY HARD GLOSS®.

Hard Gloss® Glo-Coat®. A self-polishing type floor finish which imparts a durable, glossy film. It resists scuffing, and can be used on linoleum, asphalt tile, vinyl, rubber, wood, terrazzo, etc. S. C. JOHNSON & SON

Hard Rubber△. A thermosetting plastic material made by adding 25% or more of sulfur to crude or synthetic rubber, and hardening by vulcanization at controlled temps. for a specific time. By varying these processing conditions or by adding softeners, reinforcing fillers, inert fillers and/or pigments, it is possible to produce grades having definite, predetermined properties suitable to the particular use to which the finished article is to be applied. The most commonly used filler is hard rubber dust because it facilitates handling, reduces cure time and reduces shrinkage. A number of other fillers are also used as extenders, including silicates of various kinds, talc, wood pulp, etc. Mica, aluminum, bronze, litharge, graphite, cork and other special materials are also added where special properties are desired. HARD RUBBER parts can be made by the following methods: (1) molding, (2) blown process for hollow parts, (3) pressing process, (4) machining for rods and tubes, (5) stamping from sheet and (6) hand-wrapping. HARD RUBBER is non-flammable, and resistant to most chemicals, acids, and alkalis; it has good electrical insulating properites at low and high voltages and frequencies, high resistance to impact and shock, and excellent thermal insulating properties. *Uses:* For pipe, fittings, and tubing; as a covering for tanks, ducts, stacks, etc.; for commercial parts and equipment; for chemical processing equipment, etc.

Hardy Nickel Iron[NB]. A basic, electric furnace steel designed for machinery parts that require max. toughness and resistance to vibratory stresses and where tensile strengths in excess of 55,000 lb./sq.in. are not required. Typical analysis, %: 0.08 carbon, 0.25 manganese, 0.040 phosphorus (max.), 0.040 sulfur (max.), 0.20 silicon, and 2.00 nickel. ATLAS STEELS LTD.

Harflex® 300. An easy-processing, permanent plasticizer for vinyl resins. Used for such products as refrigerator gaskets, cable jackets, baby pants, sealants, upholstery, and medical tubing. A moderately viscous liquid or semi-solid; color, very pale straw; odor, mild; cloud point (ASTM), 10°C.; refractive index (30°C.), 1.4654; sp.gr. (30/20°C.), 1.089; viscosity (100°F.), 1,150 centistokes; acid value, 2 (max.). Soluble in acetone, butyl acetate, benzene, methylene dichloride; partially soluble in ethyl alcohol, butyl alcohol, hexane; insoluble in water. HARCHEM DIV., WALLACE & TIERNAN, INC.

Harflex® 325. A non-migratory polymeric plasticizer that combines excellent compatibility and good processing characteristics. A clear liquid; color (Gardner-Holdt), 5 (max.); odor, mild; sp.gr. (25/25°C.), 1.100; ester content, 99.0% (min.). Soluble in ketones, benzene, carbon tetrachloride, ethyl acetate, glycerol; partly soluble in alcohols, petroleum ether, gasoline; insoluble in glycols, water; compatible with vinyl chloride polymers and copolymers, polyvinyl acetate, synthetic rubbers, cellulose nitrate, polymethyl methacrylate; partially compatible with cellulose acetate, ethyl cellulose; incompatible with polystyrene. *Use:* In compounding plastisols, organisols, and plastics used for refrigerator and freezer gaskets, food belting, electrical cable insulation, upholstery, floor and wall coverings, etc. HARCHEM DIV., WALLACE & TIERNAN, INC.

Harflex® 500. (*HBMTN* p. 268). Now a product of HARCHEM DIV., WALLACE & TIERNAN, INC., successor to HARDESTY CHEMICAL CO., INC.

Harmon® Colors. A line of organic pigments in various light-fast brilliant colors. They are durable and stable under severe weathering condition. *Uses:* For automotive and other industrial enamels and lacquers; and for rubber, plastic, printing ink, paper and textiles. B. F. GOODRICH CHEMICAL CO.

Harofix CP[NE]. An after-treating agent for direct dyeing on COTTON, RAYON and other cellulosic fibers. It imparts improved water resistance to many direct dyeings, preventing staining in wet handling and a marked reduction of bleeding even in boiling water. It also improves resistance to perspiration and to bleeding during wet pressing, and improves wash fastness. HART PRODUCTS CORP.

Harshaw®. The registered trade name for all products of the HARSHAW CHEMICAL CO.

Hartex PN[NE]. An assistant for use in peroxide kier bleaching. It gives rapid wetting-out, deactivates enzymes not completely removed from the fabric in desizing, and does not decompose the peroxide.
HART PRODUCTS CORP.

Hartofume C[NE]. A gas-fading inhibitor for the protection of dyed acetate fabrics. It is unaffected by washing and dry cleaning. It is a self-emulsifying, clear, dark amber-colored liquid; and is readily exhausted at 100–120°F. HART PRODUCTS CORP.

Harto-Resin PCS[NE]. A 55% polyvinyl emulsion which imparts a durable full hand to textile fabrics without excessive stiffness. HART PRODUCTS CORP.

Hartoset E[NE]. An etherified urea-formaldehyde resin for crease-proofing and shrinkproofing COTTONS and RAYONS for permanent mechanical effects such as embossing, Schreinering, and glazing, for stiffening of synthetic net fabrics, and for stabilization of knitgoods. It has high stabilizing efficiency, good whiteness retention, gives a soft hand, and is especially recommended for the formulation of "wash-wear" and "drip-dry" finishes. It is readily soluble in water, and has unlimited storage stability.
HART PRODUCTS CORP.

Hartuwet C and B[NE]. A two-package water repellent composition for fabrics. C is a slightly alkaline wax emulsion; B is a solution of heavy metal salts, with a pH of 3.5–5.0. The two components are mixed and applied to COTTON, COTTON-RAYON, COTTON-ACETATE and other textiles to provide durable water repellency.
HART PRODUCTS CORP.

Hartuwet S[NE]. A water-dilutable emulsion containing 30% silicone solids. Used to impart, to textiles, a water-repellent finish that is durable to dry cleaning and laundering, stain resistant, and which improves tear and abrasion resistance. HART PRODUCTS CORP.

Haul King. *See* BOSTON HAUL KING.

Hawkskin®. The trademark for a line of fabrics made wholly or partially of cellulose.
CELANESE CORP. OF AMERICA

Hc Hc[NE]. (*HBMTN* p. 271). No longer available.
DELAWARE TOOL STEEL CORP.

Heath and Milligan® **Paints.** The trademark for a line of consumer paints. GLIDDEN CO.

Heat King. *See* BOSTON HEAT KING.

Heat Sheets. Thin, flexible, film-type electric heating elements for temps. up to 600°F. They are made from glass cloth, refined graphite, and inorganic binders. Only a very thin film of the conducting medium is coated on the 0.004" thick glass cloth. Weight, less than 1 oz. per sq.ft. Available in widths of 1" to 52" in any length, and in film resistances from 10 to 10,000 ohms/sq.in. *Uses:* For residential heaters, household appliances, industrial equipment, and military devices. ELECTRICAL COATINGS, INC.

Heavy Duty®. A heavy-duty cleaning compound. It is a concentrated alkaline cleaner that penetrates grease and cooked-on contamination. Instantly soluble; has good emulsification properties. Effective in cleaning cream-style corn equipment, cook kettles, and similar-processing equipment. DIVERSEY CORP.

Heavy-Duty Hard Gloss®. A self-polishing floor finish conposed of synthetic resins. It provides a finish that resists scuffing and marring, does not trap dirt, is slip-retardant, and has excellent water resistance. Can be used on all types of floors.
S. C. JOHNSON & SON

Heavy Solution Nupercaine®. A local anesthetic consisting of a solution of 1:400 NUPER-CAINE® hydrochloride and 5% dextrose. Useful as a spinal anesthetic, particularly by the saddle block method. It is especially valuable in relief of obstetric pain.
CIBA PHARMACEUTICAL PRODUCTS INC.

Heetclad®. (*HBMTN* p. 272). Now a registered trademark. SHERWIN-WILLIAMS CO.

Helix Bonding Agents. A line of thermosetting epoxy adhesives which will cure at room temp. Included in the line are:

BONDING AGENT R-313. A 100%-solids resin compound in liquid form, cured by the addition of a catalyst. Inert to acids, alkalis, corrosive salt solutions, petroleum solvents, lubricating oils, alcohol, and acetone. Used to bond metal to metal, glass to metal, and most plastics to metal. Bond strength, 3,200 lb./sq.in.

BONDING AGENT R-314. Similar to R-313 but with a much longer pot life—over 8 hr. It will cure in 48 hr. at room temp. or in 2 hr. at 150°–180°F.

BONDING AGENT R-318. Similar to R-313 except that it is slightly opaque, slightly thicker, and retains a slight flexibility after it is cured and can, therefore, withstand heavy vibration.

BONDING AGENT R-363. Similar to R-313 except that upon cure it is somewhat more flexible. It adheres to hard, polished surfaces, and is extensively used for sealing glass to metal. Also used for metal to metal seals, and for insulating electrical wiring and connections.

BONDING AGENT R-385. A one-component metal adhesive in heavy paste form. Cure is effected by heating for 1 hr. at 325°F.

BONDING AGENT R-390. Similar to R-313 but in the form of a heavy black paste. Because it is so tacky, no clamps are necessary to hold small parts together.

BONDING AGENT R-823. Similar to R-313 but much thinner. Used where only a thin glue line is necessary, or for vacuum impregnation. Bond strength; 2,500 lb./sq.in. Used to attach small metal parts to metals and other materials; to insulate electrical wiring and connections; to hermetically seal instruments, electrical circuits and components. CARL H. BIGGS CO.

Helix Potting Compounds. A line of 100%-solids, epoxy-based compounds, in liquid form, which will cure at room temp. with negligible shrinkage. Used for encapsulating electrical components which are vulnerable to moisture or fungus. Included in the line are:

POTTING COMPOUND P-415. A low-priced material for use under moderate temp. conditions. Remains flexible after cure. Curing time at room temp., 24 hr. Pot life, 8 hr.

POTTING COMPOUND P-420. Has excellent adherance to metal; retains some flexibility after cure; most suitable for potting in a can. Curing time at room temp., about 2 hr.

POTTING COMPOUND P-430. Similar to R-420 and used for the same purposes. When fully cured it remains rubbery rather than becoming hard as does R-420.

POTTING COMFOUND P-460. Similar to P-420 but recommended for casting, particularly in rubber molds. CARL H. BIGGS CO.

Helizaron. A line of pigment dyestuffs. They are water-resin dispersions of excellent tinctorial strength. Used with HELIZARON BINDERS, they exhibit excellent fastness properties. *Use:* For textile padding and printing. NOVA CHEMICAL CORP.

Hematest®. A diagnostic for the detection of occult blood. AMES CO.

Hemosules®. A vitamin preparation for the treatment of nutritional and secondary anemia. Each capsule contains: 162.0 mg. ferrous sulfate, dried, U.S.P.; 1.0 mg. THIAMINE HYDROCHLORIDE (VITAMIN B₁); 1.0 mg. RIBOFLAVIN (VITAMIN B₂); 15.0 mg. ascorbic acid (VITAMIN C); 4.0 mg. niacinamide, 0.5 mg. pyridoxine hydrochloride (VITAMIN B₆); 0.47 mg. *d*-panthenol (equiv. to 0.5 mg. pantothenic acid); 0.2 mg. folic acid; 1.0 mcg. VITAMIN B₁₂, crystalline; 162.0 mg. liver fraction 2, N.F.
WARNER-CHILCOTT LABORATORIES

Hemp△. The fiber from the stalk of the plant *Cannabis sativa*, grown principally in southern Russia, central Europe, the Mediterranean countries, and Asia. It has also been cultivated in the United States. The fiber, obtained by retting, is considerably longer than that obtained from the flax plant but is much coarser and, therefore, is not suitable for fine fabrics. It is used chiefly for cordage, sacking, packings, and as a filler for plastics.

Henequen△. *See* SISAL△.

Henrox #8. An inhibited acid cleaner for use on metals. J. F. HENRY CHEMICAL CO.

Hepa-Desicol® Kapseals®. A medicinal consisting of bile with methionine, choline, betaine, and inositol, for oral treatment of certain liver disorders.
PARKE, DAVIS & CO.

Hepasol[NE]. (*HBMTN* p. 273). No longer available. ABBOTT LABORATORIES

Hepatone®. (*Supp.* I p. 102). No longer available. SHARP & DOHME DIV., MERCK & CO.

Heptachlor△. 1,4,5,6,7,8,8-Heptachloro-3a,4,7,7a-tetrahydro-4,7-methanoindene. $C_{10}H_5Cl_7$; mol.wt. 375.37. A white, crystalline solid with a camphor odor and a m.p. of 95–96°C. The technical product, however, is a soft waxy solid which melts from 46° to 74°C. and contains about 67% HEPTACHLOR and 33% related compounds, such as α-CHLORDANE; it is practically insoluble in water but soluble in ethyl alcohol and in kerosene. HEPTACHLOR has strong insecticidal properties by ingestion or contact; and some fumigant action. Available as a wettable powder, as an emulsifiable concentrate, and as a dust.

Herco®. A smokeless shotgun powder.
HERCULES POWDER CO.

Hercoal®. A dynamite. HERCULES POWDER CO.

Hercocel®. An ethyl cellulose molding powder.
HERCULES POWDER CO.

Hercoflex®. A series of plasticizers particularly suited for use in plastics and surface coatings.
HERCULES POWDER CO.

Hercogel®. A dynamite. HERCULES POWDER CO.

Hercose® AP *and* **Hercose® C.** (*HBMTN* p 274). No longer available. HERCULES POWDER CO.

Herco Tube®. The trademark for a line of blasting caps. HERCULES POWDER CO.

Hercules®. The house mark of the HERCULES POWDER CO. for various chemicals.

Hercules 2400®. A smokeless powder.
HERCULES POWDER CO.

Hercules Red Dot®. A smokeless powder.
HERCULES POWDER CO.

Herculite®. The trademark for a dynamite.
HERCULES POWDER CO.

Herculoid®. Nitrocellulose for use in pyroxylin plastics. HERCULES POWDER CO.

Heritage®. The trademark for a line of fabrics made wholly or partially of cellulose derivatives.
CELANESE CORP. OF AMERICA

Herman Nelson®. Registered trade name for heating and ventilating equipment mfg'd by the HERMAN NELSON DIV. of the AMERICAN AIR FILTER CO., INC.

Hero[NE]. A white glue, ideal for wood joining, paper and fabric gluing jobs, such as household repairs, library binding and repair, and pasting jobs in the office, home and school. PAISLEY PRODUCTS INC.

Heroult®. The trademark for a line of electric furnaces. UNITED STATES STEEL CORP.

Herpoco®. A fertilizer compound consisting of ammonium nitrate and kieselguhr.
HERCULES POWDER CO.

Herringbone. *See* BOSTON HERRINGBONE.

Herring Oil△. The oil obtained by extraction from several species of fish of the herring family, *Clupeidae*. Sp.gr. 0.920–0.933; iodine no. 130–180; saponification no. 179–194. *Uses:* As a quenching oil in heat treatment of metals; in soaps, printing oils, and lubricants; and for finishing leather.

Hetoxin®. (*HBMTN* p. 275). Now a product of WARNER-CHILCOTT LABORATORIES, successor to THE MALTINE CO.

Hetron®. A line of fire-resistant, thermosetting polyester resins. Cured with peroxide catalysts. Suitable for molding with glass fibers, cellulosic fibers or other reinforcing materials. Supplied with and without styrene or other monomers. Used to produce a variety of parts such as automotive bodies, electrical insulating board, translucent flat and corrugated sheets, electrical moldings, radomes, aircraft structural parts, business machine housings, boats and many others. Description and properties of the various resins are as follows:

Hetron No.	Type	Description	Viscosity, poises	Heat distortion point, °F.
93LS	Light stable	For use in translucent corrugated sheet and other applications requiring weathering resistance and light stability. Excellent fire resistance.	6	176
92	General purpose, rigid	General-purpose rigid resin for applications requiring good structural properties and max. fire resistance. Good chemical resistance. Most fire resistant of the HETRONS.	13–18	220
23	General purpose, rigid	General-purpose rigid resin; high viscosity. Very slightly less fire resistant than HETRON 92.	23–27	216
32A	Semi-rigid	Combines high strength and stiffness with resilience and impact resistance. Excellent resistance to crazing during molding and paint baking. Good fire resistance.	13–18	170
32	Semi-rigid	Similar to 32A but a little more flexible and a little less fire resistant.	11–13	150
31	Semi-rigid	More flexible and less fire resistant than HETRON 32.	9–11	120
42	Flexible	Intended for blending with other resins to increase flexibility. Low degree of fire resistance.	13–18	Below room temp.
73	High heat distortion	Combines high strength and rigidity with high heat distortion point. Excellent fire resistance.	23–27	288
72	High heat distortion, chemically resistant	Combines high strength and stiffness with excellent heat distortion temp. and the best chemical resistance of the HETRONS. Fair degree of fire resistance.	13–18	300
63	High heat distortion	Very high heat distortion point when fully cured. Long curing cycle required. Fair degree of fire resistance.	18–23	Over 400
19	Solid	Unsaturated linear polymer without monomer. Suitable for compounding with styrene or other monomers.	—	—
12	Solid	Unsaturated linear polymer without monomer. Suitable for compounding with styrene or other monomers.	—	—

DUREZ PLASTICS DIV., HOOKER ELECTROCHEMICAL CO.

Hewhold. A fast-setting, resin-emulsion adhesive for wood, in ready-to-use form. It requires no heat for curing; and only moderate clamping pressures.
C. B. HEWITT & BROTHERS, INC.

Hewitex[NE]. An elastic urethane foam, light in weight, durable, easy to fabricate, washable, odorless, non-allergic, non-toxic; chemical resistant. *Uses:* For athletic equipment padding; auto dashboard padding; carpet underlays; cushions; shoe innersoles; mats; mattresses; pillows; upholstery; vibration absorbers; thermal insulation; sound absorbers; and for many other consumer and industrial applications. Formerly marketed under the name RESTHANE[NE] (*Supp.* I p. 201).
HEWITT-ROBINS INC.

Hewitt Copper-Hard[NE]. A BABBITT for bearings of woodworking machinery, automatic screw machines, motor axle bearing, grinders, concrete mixers, stationary gas engines, hoisting and road-making machinery, main bearings of oil engines, etc. It is an extremely ductile alloy for normal speeds and pressures; not for bearings subject to severe shock forces and pounding.
HEWITT METALS CORP.

Hewitt-Detroit Body Solder[NE]. An automobile body solder specially treated for plasticity and adherence. It melts easily, paddles smoothly, and does not sputter.
HEWITT METALS CORP.

Hewitt Mill Bearing-Metal[NE]. An extremely tough, hard, durable BABBITT alloy for general service requirements of steel mills, as in roll-neck bearings, strip mill liners, and other types of heavy-duty, slow-revolving machinery. Brinell hardness, 31.2 at 70°F.; compressive strength, 19,100 lb./sq.in.
HEWITT METALS CORP.

Hewmet[NE]. A bearing BABBITT with a fine grained structure, and more plastic than the average lead-base alloys. It carries a heavy load where bearings are ¼" or more in thickness; not recommended for thin-shelled liners subject to vibration or stress, or bearings subject to unusual pounding. Used for bearings of brick- and clay-working machinery, paper and pulp mills, cotton gins, harvesting machinery, elevators, power presses, lathes, refrigeration machinery, and general machine shop applications. Recommended pouring temp. 625°F. HEWITT METALS CORP.

H-H Inhalator[NE]. A portable inhalator for emergency treatment of respiratory failures. It is used in conjunction with manual artificial respiration.
MINE SAFETY APPLIANCES CO.

Hibase®. An all-vegetable, fully hydrogenated shortening for use in baking, frying and pastry making.
ANDERSON, CLAYTON & CO. FOODS DIV.

Hi-Brin®. The trademark for a subsurface pump barrel processed by the patented nitrocycle process of nitriding steel tubes. UNITED STATES STEEL CORP., OIL WELL SUPPLY DIV.

Hi-C. A high-chloride, nickel-plating bath process characterized by its excellent leveling, very high plating range, fast rate of brightening, low hydrogen embrittlement from chromium plating. Baths using this process can be operated at temps. as high as 190°F. UDYLITE CORP.

Hi-Cyan®. (*HBMTN* p. 276 and *Supp.* I p. 103). No longer available. GENERAL CHEMICAL DIV., ALLIED CHEMICAL & DYE CORP.

Hide-a-Mark®. *See* KRYLON® HIDE-A-MARK®.

Hi-den®. (*HBMTN* p. 276). Now a registered trademark. PARKWOOD LAMINATES, INC.

Hi-Fax[NE]. A high-density ethylene polymer.
HERCULES POWDER CO.

Hifect®. A registered trademark for a book paper.
KIMBERLY-CLARK CORP.

Hi-Gam®. LINDANE formulations used as agricultural insecticides on field crops.
PENNSYLVANIA SALT MFG. CO.

Highlite. (Trademark registration pending). A fine, dense, off-white powder that is acidic but not toxic in nature. Has good scouring action. Contains an antitarnish agent for cleaning copper surfaces. Used in food plants, breweries, laundries, etc., where stainless steel, copper and other metals require cleaning, brightening and stain removal.
OAKITE PRODUCTS, INC.

High Load. *See* BOSTON HIGH LOAD.

Hi-Hard®. The trademark for a line of fluid piston rods designed for oil-field and refinery pumps.
UNITED STATES STEEL CORP., OIL WELL SUPPLY DIV.

Hinj®. (*HBMTN* p. 278). No longer available.
ATLAS POWDER CO.

Hippocrates. *See* OCTAGON (HIPPOCRATES)®.

Hi-Resist Core & Mold Wash[NE]. A finished core and mold wash that is mixed with water prior to use. Contains a synthetic resin binder. Very rapid mixing is accomplished with a hand paddle or mechanical mixer. It has a very high fusion point—above 3,700°F.—and controlled penetration which permits the wash to close the pores between the sand grains to a depth of 5 to 7 grains. M. A. BELL CO.

Hi-Speed®. Crown-type bottle closures. They flow freely in the bottling machine, cause less friction on high-speed lines, and create less dust in the crowning machine. ARMSTRONG CORK CO.

Hitemp®. A smokeless powder.
HERCULES POWDER CO.

Hi-Temp. *See* HANDY HI-TEMP[NE].

Hi-Temp Teflinings[NE]. (*HBMTN* p. 278). No longer available.
ELECTRO CHEMICAL SUPPLY & ENGINEERING CO.

Hi Vel®. A smokeless powder.
HERCULES POWDER CO.

H.M.C.®. A medicinal in the form of hypodermic tablets containing hyascine hydrobromide, morphine hydrobromide and extract cactus.
ABBOTT LABORATORIES

Hob-A-Form[NE]. (*HBMTN* p. 279). No longer available. PENNINSULAR STEEL CO.

Hodi[NE]. A hot-work steel composed of 0.28% carbon, 0.30% manganese, 0.30% silicon, 9.50% tungsten, 3.25% chromium, and 0.40% vanadium. *Uses:* For extrusion dies and molds, dummy blocks on extrusion presses, hot-heading punches, hot-swaging dies, forging-die inserts, brass-forging dies, die-casting dies for copper-base alloys, spike dies, shear blades and trimmer dies, hot bolt and rivet dies, shell-piercing punches, etc. ATLAS STEELS LTD.

Hoistphone[NE]. An FM carrier system which provides instant 2-way voice communication. Designed for use in operation and maintenance of mine hoists.
MINE SAFETY APPLIANCES CO.

Holdfast®. The trademark for a line of letterpress, non-scratch, halftone inks. INTERCHEMICAL CORP., PRINTING INK DIV.

Hollandale Margarine[NE]. A margarine made of hydrogenated soybean and cottonseed oils, nonfat dry milk, water, salt, LECITHIN, 0.1% sodium benzoate added as a preservative, artificial coloring, and 15,000 units of VITAMIN A per lb.
ANDERSON, CLAYTON & CO. FOODS DIV.

Holostud. *See* GOLD BOND® HOLOSTUD.

Home-Tex®. An insulating siding material with a striated design. MASTIC ASPHALT CORP.

Homoclad[NE]. A moisture-resistant sealer for wood furniture and other wood products, used for improving the dimensional stability of wood on exposure to high humidity atmospheres. SHERWIN-WILLIAMS CO.

Honduras Rosewood△. *Same as* COCOBOLA△.

Honeywood. *See* AFRICAN HONEYWOOD[NE].

Hopcalite®. Chemical materials for use as a catalyst.
MINE SAFETY APPLIANCES CO.

Hortondome Roof[NB]. A special roof for reducing evaporation loss from standing storage tanks. It consists of a cone roof with a welded steel dome mounted at the center. A flexible membrane, hemispherical in shape, having the same diameter as the dome, is attached at its outer edge to the inside of the steel dome, and is free to hang downward in the form of a hemisphere.
CHICAGO BRIDGE & IRON CO.

Hortonsphere®. A spherical vessel used for the storage of volatile high pressure liquids and gases. It is built of steel plates fabricated to the proper form, cut to size and welded. The HORTONSPHERE is used in the petroleum and petro-chemical industries and in municipal gas distribution systems.
CHICAGO BRIDGE & IRON CO.

Hortonspheroid®. A vessel used for the storage of volatile low-pressure liquids. The HORTONSPHEROID prevents excessive evaporation losses which occur when such products are placed in conventional storage tanks. The distinctive shape of the HORTONSPHEROID provides the most efficient utilization of the steel plates to resist the liquid and gas pressures inside the vessel. The HORTONSPHEROID is used principally in the petroleum industry for storing motor gasolines and natural gasolines.
CHICAGO BRIDGE & IRON CO.

Horton® Vaportank. A tank designed to reduce evaporation loss of stored liquids. It is a dome-roof tank with a flexible hemispherical membrane attached at the top of the vertical shell.
CHICAGO BRIDGE & IRON CO.

Hoskins® Alloy 502. Formerly known as CHROMEL® ALLOY 502 (*HBMTN* p. 132). HOSKINS MFG. CO.

Hospital V[NB]. (*Supp.* I p. 105). No longer available.
U. S. SANITARY SPECIALTIES CORP.

Hot Top Moldit. See R & I HOT TOP MOLDIT®.

Houdrane. (*HBMTN* p. 281). No longer available.
HOUDRY PROCESS CORP.

Houdresid[NB]. A continuous, moving-bed cracking process which utilizes, in contradistinction to other types of cracking processes, residual crude as charge stock. Production of heavy fuel is eliminated by this process.
HOUDRY PROCESS CORP.

Houdriflow[NB]. A continuous, moving-bed catalytic cracking process by which high yields of top quality gasoline and other products are obtained from a variety of charge stocks ranging from the lightest gas oil to vacuum gas oils.
HOUDRY PROCESS CORP.

Houdriforming[NB]. A fixed-bed catalytic reforming process utilizing a catalyst containing platinum for conversion of straight-run and cracked petroleum naphthas to high octane motor gasoline, aviation blending stocks, and aromatics. The process normally operates continuously, although the catalyst may be regenerated in place as the occasion demands.
HOUDRY PROCESS CORP.

Houdry Chrome Alumina Catalyst[NB]. A specifically-developed catalyst for use in the HOUDRY DEHYDROGENATION PROCESS. This catalyst features very high selectivities and outstanding stability for the dehydrogenation of light hydrocarbons.
HOUDRY PROCESS CORP.

Houdry Cobalt Molybdate Catalyst[NB]. An alumina-base catalyst commercially proven in many desulfurization and hydrotreating operations. This catalyst offers high hardness and excellent activity and stability at low cost.
HOUDRY PROCESS CORP.

Houdry Dehydrogenation[NB]. A fixed-bed cyclic catalytic process in which it is possible to produce diolefins directly from paraffins in a single step. The HOUDRY DEHYDROGENATION process uses a chrome-alumina catalyst at reduced pressures and is capable of producing butene or butadiene from butane, propene from propane, isobutene from isobutane, isoprene from mixed pentanes, and a number of other olefin-diolefin mixtures from either mixed paraffins or paraffin-olefin mixtures.
HOUDRY PROCESS CORP.

Houdry Hard Alumina[NB]. An extremely-hard, high-purity, cylindrically extruded alumina catalyst support. It is commercially produced in several pellet sizes and various grades, differing principally in surface area and sodium content. These aluminas are currently being used for the mfg. of many alumina-base catalysts. These include COBALT MOLYBDATE HYDRODESULFURIZATION CATALYSTS; PLATINUM and MOLYBDENA REFORMING CATALYSTS; PLATINUM, PALLADIUM and MOLYBDENUM SULFIDE HYDROGENATION CATALYSTS; and CHROMIUM OXIDE DEHYDROGENATION CATALYSTS.
HOUDRY PROCESS CORP.

Houdry Mineral Kaolin Cracking Catalyst[NB]. A natural cracking catalyst for HOUDRIFLOW and TCC MOVING BED CATALYTIC CRACKING UNITS. Offers maximum octane at low cost. Other features include: high activity, sulfur resistance, superior thermal stability and excellent regeneration characteristics.
HOUDRY PROCESS CORP.

Houdry Platinum Hydrogenation Catalyst[NB]. A platinum hydrogenation catalyst mfg'd to maintain high catalytic activity and yields over long periods of service. High purity products are thereby achieved.
HOUDRY PROCESS CORP.

Houdry Silica Alumina Catalyst[NB]. A highly-acid, pelleted silica alumina catalyst employed in numerous reactions where acidic catalytic properties are required.
HOUDRY PROCESS CORP.

Houdry Type 3-D Platinum Catalyst[NB]. A pelleted platinum catalyst employed in catalytic reforming operations. This advanced HOUDRY catalyst offers increased activity and selectivity. For any reforming operation, octane number and selectivity are increased. The economics of this catalyst are unusually attractive to petroleum refiners.
HOUDRY PROCESS CORP.

Houghto-Safe®. A fire-resistant hydraulic fluid for use in hydraulic equipment operating under pressure near open flames, high heat, molten metal, or other potential fire hazards.
E. F. HOUGHTON & CO.

House of Resistors, The®. The trademark for ballast resistors, adjustable resistors, metal tube resistors, power resistors, fixed resistors, resistor potentiometers, rheostats, volume controls, attenuators, electrical resistance heating elements, voltage dividers, ballast tubes, line ballasts, voltage regulators, decade boxes, shunts, fuses, chokes, switches, ion traps, synchronous motors, and parts thereof. (Registration No. 595,833; Class 21; Sept. 28, 1954).　　　Clarostat Mfg. Co.

Hrdflakes®. The trademark for flaked hydrogenated vegetable oils used in shortening and oleomargarine.
　　　Anderson, Clayton & Co. Foods Div.

H-R Tex Top[NE]**.** A carpet cushion consisting of 100% pure sponge rubber with an anti-friction fiber top.　　　Hewitt-Robins, Inc.

H. T.®. A clay used for paper coating.
　　　Minerals & Chemicals Corp. of America

H.T.M.[NE]**.** A high-tensile-strength heat-treated pearlitic malleable iron. Brinell hardness (air-quenched and tempered), 163–228; yield strength, 48,000 lb./sq.in.; ultimate strength, 70,000 lb./sq.in.; elongation, 4%.
　　　National Malleable & Steel Castings Co.

Huetex®. A low-maintenance, high-quality spandrel glass that may be used for curtain-wall construction, on storefronts, and as an interior paneling. It is made in the form of a panel, the outer surface of which is a textured-surface, tempered, $^5/_{16}$" glass; a ceramic enamel is fused to the back of this glass to give it the desired color; and aluminum welded to the back of the panel protects the enamel and reflects heat. Available in 12 standard colors.
　　　Mfg'd by Blue Ridge Glass Corp.
　　　Distributed by Libbey-Owens-Ford Glass Co.

Huewhite®. A glare-reducing glass developed for use where light diffusion with max. of glare reduction and true color transmission are desired. It is translucent white in color and delivers very wide light distribution that is almost uniform down to incidence of 15 degrees. Particularly useful for daylighting schools, work shops, studios, museums, etc.
　　　Mfg'd by Blue Ridge Glass Corp.
　　　Distributed by Libbey-Owens-Ford Glass Co.

Humdinger®. The trademark for variable electrical resistors. (Registration No. 568,849; Class 21; Jan. 6, 1953.)　　　Clarostat Mfg. Co.

Hunt-Spiller® Gun Iron. Incorrectly listed as Gun Iron (*HBMTN* p. 264)　　　Hunt-Spiller Mfg. Corp.

Hyazyme®. An enzyme, hyaluronidase, used in medicine to accelerate the diffusion and absorption of subcutaneously injected fluids and drugs.
　　　Abbott Laboratories

Hy-Base®. An all-vegetable, fully hydrogenated shortening for use in baking, frying and pastry making.
　　　Anderson, Clayton & Co. Foods Div.

Hy-Chill Salad Oil®. A winterized cottonseed oil. It has a light golden color, bland neutral flavor, and good stability against oxidation. Its exceptionally long chill test (resistance to crystallization at low temp.) makes it ideal for use in salad dressings of all kinds.　　　Anderson, Clayton & Co. Foods Div.

Hyco-Span[NE]**.** The trade name for a line of wire rope, strand and cable.　　　United States Steel Corp.

Hydeltra®. Prednisolone, or *delta*-1-dehydrohydrocortisone. A medicinal for the treatment of rheumatoid arthritis, bronchial asthma, and various inflammatory skin diseases including atopic dermatitis, contact dermatitis, urticaria and dermatitis herpetiformis.
　　　Merck Sharp & Dohme

Hydeltracin®. A medicinal, each cc. of which contains 5.0 mg. Hydeltra® (prednisolone, Merck) and 5.0 mg. neomycin sulfate in 5% isopropyl alcohol. *Uses:* For the treatment of nonspecific anogenital pruritis; allergic dermatoses such as contact dermatitis (e.g. poison ivy); atopic dermatitis (allergic eczema); neurodermatitis; pruritus with lichenification; eczematoid dermatitis; food eczema; infantile eczema; seborrheic dermatitis; actinic dermatitis; insect bites; and miliaria.　　　Merck Sharp & Dohme

Hydra-Magic®. The trademark for a hand lotion.
　　　Max Factor & Co.

Hydramine®. A water-soluble synthetic resin for general use in the industrial arts.
　　　Pennsylvania Salt Mfg. Co.

Hydrimix[NE]**.** (*Supp.* I p. 106). No longer available.
　　　Metal Hydrides, Inc.

Hydrin®. A water-soluble rust-preventive chemical for preventing rust on dry metal between operations and during short term storage. It is a dry, stable, crystalline powder; very soluble in water.
　　　Daubert Chemical Co.

Hydro-Bilein®. A choleretic and hydrocholeretic consisting of tablets containing bilein and dehydrocholic acid. Used to improve digestion and absorption of fat and fat-soluble vitamins; in treating chronic inflammatory diseases of the gall bladder, bile ducts, etc.　　　Abbott Laboratories

Hydrocide®, Hydrocide® No. 633, Hydrocide® Paste, *and* **Hydrocide® Powder.** (*HBMTN* p. 286). The name Hydrocide® is now a registered trademark.　　　L. Sonneborn Sons, Inc.

Hydrocord[NE]**.** (Trademark registration pending). A backing for resilient flooring.
　　　Armstrong Cork Co.

Hydrocortone®-T.B.A. Hydrocortisone *tertiary*-butylacetate, Merck, or 17-hydroxycorticosterone-21-*tertiary* butylacetate, or Compound F *tertiary*-butylacetate. A white crystalline powder, very slightly soluble in water. *Use:* In medicine for the treatment of rheumatoid arthritis and osteoarthritis.
　　　Merck Sharp & Dohme

Hydrocure[NE]**.** (*Supp.* I p. 117). Now a product of The Borden Co., Chemical Div., successor to Pioneer Latex & Chemical Co.

Hydroderm®. (*Supp.* I p. 107). Now a registered trademark and a product of Merck Sharp & Dohme, Div. of Merck & Co.

Hydrodyne[NE]**.** Compressed tablets each of which contains 2.5 mg. of Hydrocortone® (hydrocortisone, U.S.P., Merck) and 0.3 g. Aspirin. *Use:* In medicine for maintenance therapy in patients with rheumatoid arthritis. It is also of value in the treatment of collagen diseases.　　　Merck Sharp & Dohme

Hydrolyzed Vegetable Proteins 43-A *and* **52-A**[NE]**.** Liquid hydrolyzates produced from corn protein by acid hydrolysis followed by refinement processing.

They contain all the amino acids (either as free acid or amino acid salts) normally found in corn protein. The two grades offered differ only in solids concentration. *Uses:* In processed foods, to supply flavor and also to balance and blend other natural food flavors. A. E. STALEY MFG. CO.

Hydromagma®. (*Supp.* I p. 107). No longer available. SHARP & DOHME DIV., MERCK & CO.

Hydron®. A line of dyestuffs mfg'd. like sulfur dyes but dyed like vat dyes, and which give very economical navy-blue shades on RAYON and COTTON. These dyeings are as fast to light as are dyeings of true sulfur colors but they are considerably faster to chlorine and somewhat brighter in shade.
GENERAL DYESTUFF CO.

Hydrone®. (*HBMTN* p. 288). This trademark has been assigned by the E. I. DU PONT DE NEMOURS & Co. to CUTTER-HAMMER, INC.

Hydroptic®. (*Supp.* I p. 107). Now a registered trademark and a product of MERCK SHARP & DOHME, DIV. OF MERCK & CO.

Hydropurge®. A water-wash spray-booth purgant for periodic clean up. It is an excellent general-purpose, hot alkaline stripper.
FIDELITY CHEMICAL PRODUCTS CORP.

Hydrosperse® Foam Depressant. A non-caking, non-dusting, readily-soluble, powder for the control of overspray in water-wash spray booths. It eliminates objectionable foaming over a broad range of operating conditions and quickly disperses the overspray. From ¾ to 2 oz. of this material are used per gal. of operating water capacity of the booth.
FIDELITY CHEMICAL PRODUCTS CORP.

Hydrospray®. (*Supp.* I p. 107). Now a registered trademark and a product of MERCK SHARP & DOHME, DIV. OF MERCK & CO.

Hydrotex. (*HBMTN* p. 288). No longer available. BEACON CO.

Hydrozets[NE]. Medicinal troches, each of which contains 2.5 mg. HYDROCORTONE® acetate, 50 units zinc bacitracin, 1 mg. tyrothricin, 5 mg. neomycin sulfate, and 5 mg. benzocaine. *Use:* In suppressing the inflammatory response of tissue to a variety of agents including spider venom, tuberculin, histamine, and trauma. MERCK SHARP & DOHME

Hyfilm®. (*Supp.* I p. 107). Now a registered trademark. ACME WIRE CO.

Hyflo® Super-Cel. One of a series of CELITE® FILTER-AIDS made of exceptionally pure diatomaceous silica. HYFLO SUPER-CEL will completely screen fine solid matter out of suspension while permitting a high flow rate. It is especially useful in the pressure filtration of such materials as animal fats and oils, dyestuffs, fish oils, grape juice, liquid soap, maltose, molasses, shellac, vegetable oils, dry cleaners' solvents, sugar syrups, etc. (*See also* STANDARD SUPER-CEL). JOHNS-MANVILLE SALES CORP.

Hyform Emulsion[NE]. Aqueous emulsions of various waxes, including pure paraffin wax, pure microcrystalline wax, or a modification of one of these waxes. In the ceramic field, these emulsions are used as binders for pressed pieces, lubricants for die or mold release, and plasticizers during mold forming.
AMERICAN CYANAMID CO.

Hygrolized Oil 221[NE]. A WOOL top oil that provides positive static elimination, reduced fly, and excellent lubrication for WOOL and other yarns. COLLOIDS, INC.

Hylene® M Organic Isocyante. (*Supp.* I p. 107). The name HYLENE is now a registered trademark.
E. I. DU PONT DE NEMOURS & CO.

Hylene® M-50 Organic Isocyante. (*Supp.* I p. 107). The name HYLENE is now a registered trademark.
E. I. DU PONT DE NEMOURS & CO.

Hyline®. Mixtures of clay, silica sand, gravel, a flux and a binder for use as a refractory lining for cupolas, furnaces containing molten metal, and the like.
INTERNATIONAL MINERALS & CHEMICAL CORP.

Hylo®. An 85%-magnesia pipe and block insulation for both high and low temps., ranging down from 1,600°F. to 100°F. It has extremely low thermal conductivity, yet this characteristic actually improves after exposure to high temps. Being remarkably durable, it is easy to handle; withstands packing, shipping, and handling with minimum, if any, breakage. It does not scratch, cut, itch or otherwise irritate applicators' hands and skin. Its internal shrinkage is low; and it retains its high level of efficiency because it does not crack or break apart from shrinkage. It can be easily and quickly fitted over irregular areas and around projections; it may be cut and trimmed with an ordinary knife. It trims precisely and squarely. The edges remain neat and intact for tight, secure joints that prevent heat leakage. *Uses:* For ovens, boiler walls, breechings, oil stills, and other equipment. EAGLE-PICHER CO.

Hynite®. A high-grade, natural organic form of nitrogen for use in fertilizer mixtures.
UNITED FERTILIZER CO.

Hyonic[NE]. A line of detergents, wetting agents, and foam-stabilizing additives. NOPCO CHEMICAL CO.

Hyotole®-12. A palatable hematinic syrup of B-complex vitamins. Each 30 cc. (1 fluid oz.) contains 1.3 g. ferrous sulfate, 25 mcg. cyanocobalamin (VITAMIN B$_{12}$), 19 mg. thiamine hydrochloride (VITAMIN B$_1$), 2 mg. riboflavin (VITAMIN B$_2$), 1 mg. pyridoxine hydrochloride (VITAMIN B$_6$), 2 mg. panthenol, 30 mg. niacinamide, 20 mg. choline chloride, 5 mg. folic acid, and 1 g. liver fraction (Whipple). *Use:* As a nutritional supplement in subclinical VITAMIN B complex deficiency states, and in the treatment of nutritional or secondary anemias.
MERCK SHARP & DOHME

Hypertencin[NE] *and* **Hypertencin Mild[NE].** Medicinals for the treatment of essential hypertension. Both contain 32 mg. mannitol hexanitrate per tablet. Each tablet of HYPERTENCIN MILD also contains 16 mg. phenobarbital. CONSOLIDATED MIDLAND CORP.

Hy-Phos®. A water-treating composition adapted for use as a water softener, wetting agent, sequestering agent; and in detergents.
PENNSYLVANIA SALT MFG. CO.

Hypobeta®-20. A VITAMIN B complex injectable preparation for veterinary use. Each cc. contains 10 mg. thiamine hydrochloride (VITAMIN B₁), 2 mg. riboflavin (VITAMIN B₂), 1 mg. pyridoxine hydrochloride (VITAMIN B₆), 100 mg. niacinamide, 4 mg. panthenol, 0.005 cc. liver injection U.S.P., and 20 mcg. cyanocobalamin (VITAMIN B₁₂). *Use:* For treatment of VITAMIN-B deficiency states.
MERCK SHARP & DOHME

Hyprophen[NE]. Parahydroxypropiophenone (paraoxypropiophenone). A compound having utility as a hypophyseal regulator. SUMNER CHEMICAL CO.

Hy-Sheen. A liquid, water-emulsion, self-polishing floor wax. It is water resistant, slip resistant, and scuff resistant. J. I. HOLCOMB MFG. CO.

Hysol® Concrete Floor Enamels. (*HBMTN* p. 290). No longer available.
HOUGHTON LABORATORY, INC.

Hysol® Rack Coating. (*HBMTN* p. 290). No longer available. HOUGHTON LABORATORY, INC.

Hy-Temp Refracto[NE]. A refractory cement containing zirconium.
INTERNATIONAL MINERALS & CHEMICAL CORP.

Hy-Tox Insect Dust. A 4% MALATHION dust for use in poultry houses to control chicken red mite, northern fowl mite, and chicken body louse; on vegetables, flowers, and shrubs to control a wide variety of insects including Mexican bean beetle, red spider mite, leaf hopper, aphis, cabbage hopper; and on cats and dogs to control fleas.
MILLER CHEMICAL & FERTILIIZER CORP.

Hytrophen[NE]. An oval yellow tablet containing 250 mg. dehydrocholic acid, 2.5 mg. homatropine methylbromide, and 8.0 mg. phenobarbital. Used in medicine for the treatment of dyspepsia, biliary stasis, constipation of biliary origin, cholecystitis, cholangitis, and bilary dyskinesia; and for postoperative treatment, in the absence of a mechanical biliary closure. CHICAGO PHARMACAL CO.

Hyzin[NE]. (*HBMTN* p. 291). No longer available.
ABBOTT LABORATORIES

I

I-Beam-Lok®. The trademark for a line of open steel flooring, and armored steel flooring.
UNITED STATES STEEL CORP., AMERICAN BRIDGE DIV.

Iberol®. A hematinic with vitamin supplement. Consists of intrinsic factor concentrate, B₁₂, iron and other vitamins, in tablet form. ABBOTT LABORATORIES

IC®. Registered trade name for products mfg'd by the INTERCHEMICAL CORP.

I. C. Degreaser[NE]. (*Supp.* I p. 108). No longer available. ULTRA CHEMICAL WORKS

Ice Machine Oil. *See* No. 1 ICE MACHINE OIL *and* No. 210 ICE MACHINE OIL.

Ichthyamer[NE]. Ichthammol ointment in 10% and 20% concentrations, packaged in 1-oz. collapsible tubes. AMERICAN PHARMACEUTICAL CO.

Ictotest®. A diagnostic composition for the determination of bilirubin in urine. AMES CO.

Ideal®. The trademark for a line of nails and brads.
UNITED STATES STEEL CORP.

Illini Red[NE]. The resinated Sodium Lithol Red variety of GRAPHIC RED. SHERWIN-WILLIAMS CO.

Illinois®. The trademark for a line of steel rails, and steel joint bars. UNITED STATES STEEL CORP.

Immedial®. A group of sulfur dyestuffs for COTTON and RAYON usually dyed with soda ash and sodium sulfide. GENERAL DYESTUFF CO.

Immunovac®. An injectable material for prevention against and treatment of respiratory tract infections.
PARKE, DAVIS & CO.

Imperial[NE]. (Trademark registration pending). A vinyl-plastic flooring material. ARMSTRONG CORK CO.

Implenal[NE]. (*HBMTN* p. 293). No longer available. GENERAL DYESTUFF CO.

Imulary[NE]. (*HBMTN* p. 293). No longer available.
ONYX OIL & CHEMICAL CO.

Inco-Rod "A"®. (*Supp.* I p. 110). Now a registered trademark. INTERNATIONAL NICKEL CO.

Indo Carbon®. A group of sulfur dyestuffs used primarily for dyeing black shades on COTTON and RAYON. They differ from dyeings of ordinary sulfur blacks in not causing tendering of the substrate upon exposure to warm humid conditions, and by their improved fastness to light, washing, and chlorine.
GENERAL DYESTUFF CO.

Indoil®. (*HBMTN* p. 294). Now a product of AMOCO CHEMICALS CORP., successor to INDOIL CHEMICAL CO.

Indoil® Detergent Alkylate. (*Supp.* I p. 110). Now a product of AMOCO CHEMICALS CORP., successor to INDOIL CHEMICAL CO.

Indoil® Isooctyl Alcohol. (*Supp.* I p. 110). Now a product of AMOCO CHEMICALS CORP., successor to INDOIL CHEMICAL CO.

Indoil® Sulfonates. (*HBMTN* p. 294). Now a product of AMOCO CHEMICALS CORP., successor to INDOIL CHEMICAL CO.

Indoine®. A line of basic blue dyestuffs derived from safranine. GENERAL DYESTUFF CO.

Indopol®. (*HBMTN* p. 295). Now a product of AMOCO CHEMICALS CORP., successor to INDOIL CHEMICAL CO.

Indulin® A and C. (*HBMTN* p. 296). No longer available. WEST VIRGINIA PULP & PAPER CO., INDUSTRIAL CHEMICAL SALES DIV.

Industrial®. (*HBMTN* p. 296). Now a registered trademark. ARMOUR AND CO.

Industrial No. 39[NE]. An alkaline cleaner for use in tumble washers. WYANDOTTE CHEMICALS CORP., J. B. FORD DIV.

Industrial "S"[NE]. An alkaline soak cleaner.
WYANDOTTE CHEMICALS CORP., J. B. FORD DIV.

Infallible®. A smokeless powder.
HERCULES POWDER CO.

Infantovit® Drops. A pediatric multivitamin preparation for infants and children. It is virtually undetectable in water, milk, orange juice, cereals, and other foods. CONSOLIDATED MIDLAND CORP.

Infantovit® *and* **Infantovit® Chewable.** A preparation of vitamins A, D and C for diet supplementation, and prophylaxis or treatment of these vitamin deficiencies, especially in children. Supplied as easily swallowed spheres, and as chewable and palatably-flavored spheres which obviate the swallowing problem; useful in rickets, tetany, osteomalacia, xerophthalmia, night blindness, retarded growth and malnutrition, cutaneous keratotic lesions, and scurvy.
CONSOLIDATED MIDLAND CORP.

Infantovit® Plus. A multivitamin preparation used as a dietary vitamin supplement for growing children as well as adults. Supplied in chewable, tasty form. It serves as a convenient source of necessary vitamins for supplemental or replacement therapy.
CONSOLIDATED MIDLAND CORP.

Infatabs®. PARKE-DAVIS tablets of various kinds specifically designed for use by children.
PARKE, DAVIS & CO.

Infazyme®. (*HBMTN* p. 298). Temporarily withdrawn from the market. WM. S. MERRELL CO.

Inferol H-138[NE]. A combination of a wetting and a rewetting agent and a defoamer. Used in the textile industry for any process where max. penetration and min. foaming are desired.
PIONEER CHEMICAL WORKS, INC.

Infra®. A group of vat dyestuffs, in paste form, that have been especially prepared by a new process which insures more uniform dispersion. This is especially important in pigment padding and in circulation before reduction in circulating machines.
GENERAL DYESTUFF CO.

Infusorial Earth[△]. *Also known as* FOSSIL FLOUR[△] *and* KIESELGUHR[△]. A siliceous or diatomaceous earth. Essentially siliceous frustules and fragments of various species of diatoms. A white to light gray to pale buff powder; insoluble in water, acids or dilute alkalis. Used as a clarifying agent for oils, varnishes, etc.; absorbent for liquids; filter aid; filler for paper and paints; adsorbent for nitroglycerine in mfg. of dynamite; in mfg. of heat insulators, fire brick, and fire- and acid-proof packing materials.

Inhibitex[NE]. A durable type of atmospheric gas-fading inhibitor. It is applied directly in the dye-bath during the dyeing of ACETATES. It imparts durable protection against atmospheric gas fading without causing yellowing. It disperses readily in water.
TEX-CHEM CO.

Inhibitor 225[NE] *and* **Inhibitor 226**[NE]. Now products of PENNSYLVANIA SALT MFG. CO., which has absorbed SHARPLES CHEMICALS, INC.

Inhibitor 250[NE]. 1,3-Diisopropylthiourea. $(CH_3)_2CHNHCSNHCH(CH_3)_2$; mol.wt. 160.3. A corrosion inhibitor for HCl, H_2SO_4, H_3PO_4, and other acids used in pickling baths. A grayish white to light gray powder; freezing point, 136°C. (min.).
PENNSYLVANIA SALT MFG. CO.

Initial Line®. The trademark for a line of botanical drugs and herbs. S. B. PENICK & CO.

Ink-Sav. A colorless, liquid anti-skinning agent for printing, lithography, and silk-screen inks. One part per 64 parts ink effectively prevents hardening and skinning of the ink. It is volatile, and does not interfere with the normal drying rate of the ink.
AMES LABORATORIES, INC.

Inositol[△]. *Also known as* MEAT SUGAR[△], DAMBOSE[△], *and* NUCITE[△]. Hexahydroxycyclohexane. $C_6H_6(OH)_6 \cdot 2H_2O$; mol.wt. 216.9. It is widely distributed in plants and animals and is considered to be a growth factor for animals and micro-organisms. Sweet tasting, efflorescent crystals that melt anhydrous at 100°C.; very soluble in water; insoluble in ether or absolute alcohol. In medicine it is used for the treatment of cirrhosis and fatty infiltration of the liver and diseases associated with alterations in lipid metabolism.

Insecote®. A non-toxic larvacide and residual insecticide. It kills fly and mosquito larvae and crawling insects, and leaves an invisible, long-lasting film of toxicants on surfaces. J. I. HOLCOMB MFG. CO.

Insekil 100®. An insecticide for flying and crawling insects—flies, mosquitoes, fleas, gnats, clothes moths, bed bugs, roaches, ants, silverfish, spiders, etc. It contains activated PYRETHRINS, METHOXYCHLOR and other active ingredients. (*See also* AEROSOL INSEKIL®.) J. I. HOLCOMB MFG. CO.

Insekil E.C.® An insecticide for use in the food industry. J. I. HOLCOMB MFG. CO.

Inselock®. Aluminum roof shingles designed so they lock and seal on all four sides.
MASTIC ASPHALT CORP.

Install-it-Yourself[NE]. (Trademark registration pending.) The trademark for a line of linoleum.
ARMSTRONG CORK CO.

Instant Evergreen[NE]. A non-toxic, green colorant for dormant or faded lawns, shrubs and foliage. It retains the color for a complete season with a single application. It does not fade, rub off or wash off.
KRIEGER COLOR & CHEMICAL CO.

Instant-Jel®. (*Supp.* I p. 111). Now a registered trademark. NATIONAL STARCH PRODUCTS INC.

Insta-Sol. An instantly soluble, free-flowing powdered cream especially for use in coffee and chocolate vending machines.
M & R DIETETIC LABORATORIES, INC.

Insulation Seal 820[NE]. An asphalt cut-back type coating, reinforced with asbestos fibers, for use as a protective coating for insulated pipes and tanks. Supplied in either spray or trowel consistency. Provides great resistance to vapor transmission where the temp. is lower at inside of insulation than at outside surface. PHILIP CAREY MFG. CO.

Insulcrete®. (*HBMTN* p. 299 & *Supp.* I p. 112). Should have been listed as PLASTIC INSULCRETE®.
QUIGLEY CO.

Insul-Master Vaporseal. A protective coating for low-temp. thermal insulation. (*See* POLY-CELL®).
INSUL-MASTIC CORP. OF AMERICA

Insurok® T-725. (*HBMTN* p. 300 & *Supp.* I p. 112). No longer available. RICHARDSON CO.

In-Tag®. The trademark for a line of gravure inks for magazines, newspaper supplements, mail order catalogues, etc. INTERCHEMICAL CORP., IN-TAG DIV.

Intalox Saddle Packing. A ceramic tower packing with greater surface area (78 sq.ft./cu.ft.), greater free space (77.5%), and lower weight 38 lb./cu.ft.) than Raschig rings and Berl saddles. It is also characterized by low pressure drop and high flooding limit. UNITED STATES STONEWARE CO.

Interchem®. The trademark for: (1) dispersed dyes for COTTON, RAYON, ACETATE, NYLON, WOOL, and other fibers; and (2) dispersions for mildewproofing textiles.
INTERCHEMICAL CORP., IN-TAG DIV.

Interchem®. (*HBMTN* p. 300). Should have been listed as a registered trademark.
INTERCHEMICAL CORP., TEXTILE COLORS DIV.

Intraplast.[NB] A grouting aid usually used in the proportions of 1 lb. per bag of cement together with a volume of low-carbon fly ash equal to the volume of cement and sufficient water to give the desired plasticity. The INTERPLAST causes an expansion of 8–12%. The mixture is used for grouting prestressed cables in place; and for grouting fissures and rock. Available in two types: A and B. A has only a very slight retarding action on the cement, but B delays the set by about 50% and is used where slow set is not objectionable and highest structural quality is desired. SIKA CHEMICAL CORP.

Invadine B® and Invadine N Conc.®. (*HBMTN* p. 301). No longer available. CIBA CO.

Inversine[NB]. A brand of mecamylamine hydrochloride. It is a ganglionic blocking agent which is completely absorbed from the gastrointestinal tract. *Use:* In the management of hypertensive vascular disease.
MERCK SHARP & DOHME

Invert Sugar△. A mixture of approx. 50% dextrose and 50% levulose obtained by the hydrolysis of sucrose either with dilute acids or enzymes. Commercial INVERT SUGAR is made by hydrolyzing a 96% solution of cane sugar with invertase and dilute HCl at a pH of 3 to 4. The acid is generally neutralized with sodium carbonate to a pH of 6.5, at which point the dextrose crystallizes. The entire mass is then beaten into a creamy, plastic product. INVERT SUGAR is slightly levorotatory, reduces Fehling's solution, and can be fermented.

Ionex®. (*HBMTN* p. 301). No longer available.
SHELL CHEMICAL CORP.

Ionol® Antioxidant. Listed as IONOL® (*HBMTN* p. 301). SHELL CHEMICAL CORP.

Ionol®, C. P. An especially purified form of IONOL acceptable to the Food and Drug Administration and the Bureau of Animal Industry for use in lard, shortenings, tallow, vegetable oils, essential oils, VITAMIN A preparations, cosmetics, and similar food and drug products requiring protection against oxidation. Rubber, paraffin, and plastic materials intended for use in processing, handling, and packaging of food and drug products may be stabilized effectively by IONOL, C.P. Incorporation of IONOL, C.P. in paper and in paper-board packaging for fat-containing foodstuffs greatly extends their shelf life by retarding rancidification of fat migrating to the inner surface of the package. SHELL CHEMICAL CO.

Ionosol®. A solution containing sodium chloride, potassium chloride, calcium chloride, magnesium chloride and sodium lactate which conforms in composition to the average electrolyte concentrations found in fluids of the small intestine. It is administered intravenously as a replacement fluid for losses of electrolytes and fluid incurred by various illnesses.
ABBOTT LABORATORIES

Ion-O-Trate®. The trademark for a line of special concentrated solutions designed to be added aseptically to suitable infusion solutions.
ABBOTT LABORATORIES

Iowa®. The trademark for a line of barb wire.
UNITED STATES STEEL CORP.

IPI®. The trademark for an extensive line of printing inks: (1) typographic and lithographic inks for newspapers, magazines and books, and commercial printing, and for packaging materials of all types—wrappers, boxes, cartons, bags, cans and containers, bottles, crowns, labels; (2) flexographic and gravure inks for packaging materials; and (3) screen-process inks. INTERCHEMICAL CORP., PRINTING INK DIV.

IPI-Isofoam. A foamed-in-place, polyisocyanate expansible resin, which is self-cured to produce a low density product. A number of 2-component formulations are available which, upon mixing just before use, will expand to foams ranging from resilient foams with a density of 2 lb./cu.ft. to rigid foams with a density of 20 lb./cu.ft. The IPS-ISOFOAM compound and catalyst are mixed at room temp., and the slightly viscous mixture is poured or sprayed into cavities of almost any size and shape desired. The chemical reaction liberates CO_2, which expands the resin, and heat, which effects the cure. During foaming, the resin expands to fill the shape of the container, and, after curing, it bonds strongly to the sides. It has good adhesion to metals, glass, FIBERGLAS® laminates, wood, fabrics, and most plastics; high moisture resistance; a thermal conductivity of about 0.25 B.t.u.-inch/hr. x sq.ft. x °F.; high electrical resistance; excellent resistance to oils, greases, and most petroleum products; and will not settle or sag under vibration. *Uses:* As thermal insulation for home freezers, refrigerators, water coolers, refrigerated trucks and railroad cars, and other refrigerated units; as pipe covering for low-temp. lines and low-pressure steam lines; as a core material for sandwich construction of building panels; as a core material for radomes in aircraft and guided missiles; and for potting and encapsulating radio and electronic circuits. ISOCYANATE PRODUCTS, INC.

Iradogen®. PARKE-DAVIS vaccines of several types prepared by ultraviolet irradiation technique.
PARKE, DAVIS & CO.

Irish Moss△. *Also known as* CHONDRUS△; PEARL MOSS△, *and* CARAGEEN△. A variety of brown seaweed, *Chondrus crispus*, found off the Hebrides, the west coast of Ireland, and New England. The brown kelp seaweed *Laminaria saccharium, L. dilatata*, and other species found off the Hebrides, is used principally for the production of ALGIN. The seaweed *Gigartina stellata*, found in the North Atlantic, is also used to produce AGAR-AGAR and ALGIN. A purified, edible material obtained from IRISH MOSS is used in pharmaceuticals and foodstuffs. It differs from AGAR-AGAR in that it contains the natural salts of potassium, sodium, calcium, and magnesium.

Irisol®. A line of reddish-blue anthraquinone dyestuffs, of good light fastness, used in unsulfonated form to color oils and in sulfonated form to dye WOOL.   GENERAL DYESTUFF CO.

Iron Clad. *See* BOSTON IRON CLAD.

Iron Shot△. An abrasive material made by pouring molten iron into water. It is used in tumbling barrels, and in the cutting and grinding of stones.

Isadoxol[NB]. A combination of 100 mg. dioctyl sodium sulfosuccinate plus 1.0 mg. DIACE (diacetyldihydroxyphenylisatin, Blair). Indicated for the treatment of constipation where it is desirable to obtain response within 6 to 12 hr. without the usual laxative side effects.   BLAIR LABORATORIES, INC.

Isco Bohemia Montan Wax[NB]. (*HBMTN* p. 303). No longer being mfg'd by INNIS, SPEIDEN & Co.

Isinglass△. A gelatin material made from the dried swimming bladders of sturgeon and other fish. It is made by softening the bladder in water and cutting it into long strips. Used in glues and cements, and in printing inks.

Isocrin®. A medicinal for the treatment of chronic constipation or cathartic addiction, particularly when immediate, demonstrable action is necessary to insure the continued cooperation of the patients, or in any other instances where prompt overnight action is desired. Each ISOCRIN tablet contains 5 mg. of diacetylhydroxyphenylisatin.
    WARNER-CHILCOTT LABORATORIES

Isocyanate Resins△. *Also known as* POLYURETHANE RESINS△ *and* URETHANE RESINS△. Resins made by reacting various compounds containing two or more "active" hydrogen groups with diisocyanates. The principal compounds used presently for reaction with diisocyanates are polyesters that terminate primarily in hydroxyl groups. Linear polyesters usually lead to elastic polyurethanes, whereas highly branched polyesters give rigid polyurethanes. The major applications for isocyanate resins include flexible and rigid foams, coatings, synthetic elastomers, and adhesives.
    POLYURETHANE FOAMS. These cellular materials are made principally by the reaction of polyisocyanates, ALKYD RESINS and water. The polyisocyanate reacts with the water, liberating carbon dioxide which is immediately entrapped by the product resulting from the simultaneous polymerization and cross-linking of the polyisocyanate and the alkyd resin. The density of the foam is, therefore, controlled by the quantity of water and the excess polyisocyanate used in the formulation. Because these materials normally react rather slowly, tertiary amines are used as catalysts to accelerate the foaming and curing reactions. These urethane foams can be foamed in place and they are self-curing because of the heat generated in the foaming reactions. Flexible, semi-rigid and rigid foam-type materials, with densities ranging from 1.5 to 40 lb. per cu.ft., can be produced by varying the type of alkyd resin used and the reaction conditions. Foams of the flexible type are used for clothing interliners, shoulder pads, rug underlays, sponges, cushions, mattresses, acoustical tile, etc. Semi-rigid foams, because of their high impact absorption properties, are used for automobile crash pads, shoe inner soles, athletic padding, etc.
    URETHANE COATINGS. These coating materials are formulated with partially reacted isocyanates (adducts) and are used in one- and two-component systems. The one-component coatings are made with a "blocked" isocyanate and they are stable at room temp.; at elevated temps. (bake), the blocking agent is driven off and the isocyanate is available for reaction. Two-component systems have a practical work or container life of 24–48 hr. after mixing but this can be extended by modifying the mixing and storage procedures. They cure at room temp. but cure can be accelerated by heat. Like the foams, the chemical and physical properties of the coatings are dependent to a large degree on the type of polyester used in the reaction. These coatings have good abrasion, impact, chemical, solvent, salt water and moisture resistance, and good weathering properties.
    ISOCYANATE ELASTOMERS. These rubber-like materials are made from linear polyesters and an excess of diisocyanate; generally without any catalysts and emulsifiers. Some agent, such as water, a glycol, an amino alcohol, or a diamine is used in small amount to insure adequate urethane or urea groups, which are potential points for cross-linking with the excess diisocyanate. The isocyanate-polyester rubbers have outstanding abrasion and tear resistance, as well as excellent tensile strength, ozone resistance, and oil resistance. However, they have only limited resistance to dry heat. They are available in a considerable range of hardness and other properties.
    ISOCYANATE ADHESIVES. These adhesives are made in much the same way as are the urethane coatings. They are used extensively in formulating adhesives for the rubber industry. They promote excellent adhesion to metallic and non-metallic surfaces.

Isodine®. A detoxified, complexed form of iodine formulated for use as a topical antiseptic, mouthwash, etc.   ISODINE PHARMACAL CORP.

Isodrin△. The *endo-endo* isomer of ALDRIN. 1,2,3,-4,10,10 - Hexachloro - 1,4,4a,5,8,8a, hexahydro - 1,4-*endo-endo*-5,8-dimethanonaphthalene. $C_{12}H_8Cl_6$; mol. wt. 364.94. A white, crystalline solid that slowly decomposes at temps. above 100°C. Insoluble in water; soluble in aromatic hydrocarbons, but less soluble in paraffinic hydrocarbons; compatible with commonly-used pest control materials. It is an insecticidal agent that is non-phytotoxic at the concentrations generally employed. Has shown promise against lepidopterous, hemipterous, and homopterous insects.

Isofoam. *See* IPI-ISOFOAM.

Isohalant®. (*HBMTN* p. 305). No longer available.
    ABBOTT LABORATORIES

Isolastane®. An elastomeric isocyanate-type polymer which possesses a high degree of thermal stability, and is used for forming an electrical insulating barrier. This is accomplished by coating ISOLASTANE® on web materials such as FIBERGLAS® cloth, tubular FIBERGLAS® braid, asbestos, etc. It has essentially the same characteristics as the coating used on ISOGLAS®, but its rubbery nature results in improved resistance to creasing and ability to conform to the shape of irregular objects. NATVAR CORP.

Isomica®. Built-up Muscovite sheet mica (SA-MICA®) impregnated with epoxy or silicone resins, shellac, or other organic or inorganic binders. Available in various forms: tapes, tubes, plates; and in various thicknesses. It can be punched, sawed, drilled, or turned. *Use:* As electrical insulation. MICA INSULATOR CO.

Isopacin®. A tuberculostatic used for the treatment of tuberculosis, particularly in streptomycin-resistant cases. Supplied in the form of tablets, each of which contains a balanced combination of 0.5 g. sodium para-aminosalicylate and 12.5 mg. isoniazid, designed to permit the administration of these two anti-tuberculous drugs in convenient dosage form. CONSOLIDATED MIDLAND CORP.

Isoplex®. A group of completely integrated, multi-base, isocyanate-treated electrical insulating materials. Multiple plies of treated, heat-resisting fabrics and/or papers are cured into a composite sheet of indefinite or continuous length. The resulting web or sheet can be further cut and handled as tape, sheets, or rolls, or fabricated to required shapes for a particular application. A typical application is as slot-cell insulators or liners for electric motors or generators designed for service at high temp. NATVAR CORP.

Iso-Plus Houdriforming[NE]. A combined catalytic process employing the advantages of HOUDRIFORMING plus any of three additional adjunct processing schemes to produce high-quality motor fuel. HOU-DRIFORMING, in the Iso-PLUS variation, may be combined with aromatic extraction with subsequent reforming of paraffinic raffinate. It may also be combined with aromatic extraction and subsequent recycling of the paraffinic raffinate. Iso-PLUS HOUDRI-FORMING may also be achieved by thermal reforming of the effluent of the normal HOUDRIFORMING operation. HOUDRY PROCESS CORP.

Isotox® PMA Seed Treater. A wettable powder formulation that effectively controls smut and damping-off disease on wheat, oats, barley and rye, and prevents destruction of seed by wireworms, maggots and false wireworms. It also provides protection against seed decay in the soil. Contains 50% LIN-DANE, 2.5% phenyl mercuric acetate, and 47.5% inerts. CALIFORNIA SPRAY-CHEMICAL CORP.

Isotox® Spray No. 200. A LINDANE-base insecticide for the control of termites, for the protection of stored grain against weevils and other storage insects, etc. It is a concentrated liquid that mixes readily with water to form an emulsion that can be used with any type of spraying equipment. CALIFORNIA SPRAY-CHEMICAL CORP.

Isotron[NE]. A fluorinated hydrocarbon. PENNSYLVANIA SALT MFG. CO.

Itrumil® Sodium. A powerful antithyroid agent that blocks thyroxin formation without goitrogenic action. It is the sodium derivative of 5-iodo-2-thiouracil, and is used in the treatment of hyperthyroidism prior to thyroidectomy, or for medical management when surgery is not feasible. CIBA PHARMACEUTICAL PRODUCTS INC.

Iversine[NE]. (*Supp.* I p. 113). No longer available. SHARP & DOHME DIV., MERCK & CO.

Ivy-Kil[NE]. A ready-to-use oily paste containing a blend of low volability 2,4-D and 2,4,5-T. Packed in 4-oz. jars with brush and plastic arm guards. *Use:* Specifically for killing poison ivy growing intermingled with wanted plants. It does this without injury to wanted plantings. Applied by brushing on a few ivy leaves and on a few stem areas. LETHELIN PRODUCTS CO.

J

J-1190[NE]. (Trademark registration pending). An adhesive primer. ARMSTRONG CORK CO.

Jack Rabbit®. An all-vegetable, fully hydrogenated shortening for use in baking, frying and pastry making. ANDERSON, CLAYTON & CO. FOODS DIV.

Japan Tallow[△]. Same as JAPAN WAX[△].

Japan Wax[△]. *Also known as* SUMAC WAX[△] *and* JAPAN TALLOW[△]. A vegetable fat found between the kernel and outer skin of the berries of plants of the genus *Rhus*, which grow in Japan but are also cultivated in California. The fat, erroneously called wax, is extracted by steaming the berries and then pressing them, and is then refined by melting, filtering, and bleaching. Sp.gr. about 0.975; m.p. about 51°C.; contains principally palmitic, stearic and oleic acids and some Japonic acid. Used in candles and polishes, and as an extender for BEESWAX.

Japtox®. (*Supp.* I p. 114). No longer available. GENERAL CHEMICAL DIV., ALLIED CHEMICAL & DYE CORP.

Jasmonene®. The trademark for aromatic chemicals for perfumes. S. B. PENICK & CO.

Jaxmor®. An all-vegetable, fully hydrogenated shortening for use in baking, frying and pastry making. ANDERSON, CLAYTON & CO. FOODS DIV.

Jaylene®. The trademark for a group of products classified as olefins used as raw materials for the mfg. of many organic chemicals. ENJAY CO.

Jaysol®. The trademark for a proprietary solvent. ENJAY CO.

J-Cool. See #230 J-COOL[NE].

J-Cut. See #123 J-CUT[NE].

Jelliff Alloy "30"®. A copper-nickel electrical resistance alloy. Resistivity, 60 ohms/circular mil-ft. Sp.gr., 8.92. C. O. JELLIFF MFG. CORP.

Jelliff Alloy "45"®. An electrical resistance alloy of 55% copper and 45% nickel. Has constant electrical resistance over a wide temp. range; resistivity, 294 ohms/circular mil-ft.; temp. coeff. ±0.00002

ohms/°C. Operating temp., 930°F. Used in the winding of precision resistors, in electrical measuring and testing instruments, radio and electronic equipment, controlling devices, etc.
C. O. Jelliff Mfg. Corp.

Jelliff Alloy "60"®. A copper-nickel electrical resistance alloy. Resistivity, 60 ohms/circular mil-ft. Sp.gr. 8.92.
C. O. Jelliff Mfg. Corp.

Jelliff Alloy "1000"®. (*Supp.* I p. 114). Temporarily withdrawn from the market.
C. O. Jelliff Mfg. Corp.

Jelliff Alloy "A"®. An electrical resistance alloy of 80% nickel and 20% chromium. Resistant to oxidation at extreme temps., and to chemical corrosion. Resistivity, 650 ohms/circular mil-ft. Operating temp. 2,100°F. *Use:* For resister elements.
C. O. Jelliff Mfg. Corp.

Jelliff Alloy "C"®. An electrical resistance alloy containing 60% nickel, 15% chromium, and the balance iron. Resistivity, 675 ohms/circular mil-ft. Used in electric heating elements for toasters, flat irons, percolators and other domestic appliances; and in fixed and variable resisters for radio and electronic equipment. Max. operating temp., 1,700°F.
C. O. Jelliff Mfg. Corp.

Jelutong△. Same as Pontianak△.

Jersanese®. The trademark for a line of fabrics made wholly or partially of cellulose derivatives.
Celanese Corp. of America

Jet Cleaners[NE]. A series of economical, efficient, low-foaming spray cleaners for use on zinc, copper, brass, and steel. They are non-toxic, dust-free, and non-caking; and harmless to rack coatings and equipment.
Northwest Chemical Co.

Jewett®. (*Supp.* I p. 115). Now a registered trade mark.
Johns-Manville Sales Corp.

J-M No. 302 Insulating Cement[NE]. An insulating finishing cement made of asbestos fiber and binding materials. It produces a hard, durable and attractive surface which does not crack, break or peel off. Suitable for temps. up to 1,000°F.
Johns-Manville Sales Corp.

J-M Weather-Protected® Insulation. (*Supp.* I p. 115). No longer available.
Johns-Manville Sales Corp.

"John Crane" Chemlon®. A line of pipe-joint compound, braided and molded packings, and gaskets made from chemically inert Teflon®. Used for positive sealing of acids, alkalis, other corrosive chemicals and solvents within the temp. range of —120° to +500°F.
The pipe compound can be used on iron and steel, stainless steel, Monel, aluminum and other non-ferrous metals, plastics, synthetic rubber, and carbon. It remains plastic for the life of the connection, thus permitting easy disassembly.
The packings are recommended for service in the chemical, refinery, food, and other industries.
Chemlon braided packings are available in 3 types: (1) braided Teflon® tape; (2) braided Teflon® tape jacket over a blue asbestos case; (3) braided Teflon® fiber yarn; and (4) braided asbestos with Teflon® suspensoid impregnation or surfacing.
Chemlon molded packings are available in a variety of types, the most popular of which are the C-V Rings, molded from virgin Teflon® in "V" form. Other types include solid rings, split rings, endless rings of sponge Teflon®, and endless rings of interlocked shreds of Teflon®.
Chemlon gaskets are available for a wide variety of pipe service, including Pyrex®, glass-lined steel pipes, and porcelain; and for standard and special connections on distillation columns, retorts, reactor kettles, nozzles, etc. Types include solid gaskets, "O" rings, and FreeFlow envelope-type gaskets which are constructed so that they do not extend beyond the pipe I.D., and thus do not offer resistance to the flow or create turbulence. Crane Packing Co.

"John Crane" PLS (Plastic Lead Seal). A leak-proof, seize-proof, non-hardening, insoluble pipe joint compound for use at temps. up to 550°F. and pressures up to 6,000 lb./sq.in. Insoluble in gas, oil, steam, Freon®, ammonia, petroleum products, and many other chemical products. Available in various grades, including: PLS No. 1, a heavy consistency product for pipe sizes over 1", and for use on flanges or machined surfaces to eliminate gaskets; PLS No. 2, not as thick as No. 1, used for most industrial service —Freon®, natural gas, petroleum, steam, air, water, etc.; PLS No. 4, which contains a special insoluble vehicle, for such service as acetone, alcohol, glycerol, methyl ethyl ketone, and amyl, butyl, and ethyl alcohol.
Crane Packing Co.

"John Crane" Thred-Gard. A high-temp. thread compound that prevents seizing and galling at operating temps. up to 1,200°F. Joints can be easily disassembled even after prolonged exposure to extreme heat. Thred-Gard can also be used as a high-temp. protective coating and as a lubricant for cutting dies and taps, broaching and spinning tools, wire-drawing dies, lathe centers, steady rests, rock drill and bit threads.
Crane Packing Co.

Johnson's®. A trademark used to identify wax and other products of S. C. Johnson & Son, Inc., for household maintenance, industrial and agricultural uses.

Johnson's Cream Wax®. A liquid wax polish for furniture, composed of a blend of waxes, solvent, neutral soaps and a small percentage of water. Used to clean and polish light and dark furniture, painted and varnished surfaces, plastic, etc.
S. C. Johnson & Son

Jojoba Wax△. A liquid wax obtained from the seed beans of the evergreen shrub *Simmondsia californica* that grows in northern Mexico and in the semiarid region of southwest United States. The bean contains about 50% oil, which is recovered by pressing or by solvent extraction. It contains high-molecular-weight acids and alcohols and is free of glycerin. It is used as a substitute for sperm oil in lubricants, in leather dressings, and in cosmetics.

J. R. Joint Sealer[NE]. *See* Nervastral J. R. Joint Sealer[NE].

Jubilee®. A liquid product used to clean and give a protective wax finish to enamel and porcelain kitchen

surfaces, woodwork, walls, refrigerators, cabinets, etc. Contains no harsh abrasives or strong detergents that dull the surface. Removes yellowing caused by cooking fumes, dirt, food stains, etc.
S. C. JOHNSON & SON

Jumbo Junior. The trade name for a bubble bath composition. It consists of sodium sulfate, sodium alkyl aryl sulfonate, and sodium alkyl lauryl sulfonate.
ROBERT H. CLARK CO.

J-Wax®. A one-step, paste-type auto cleaner and wax composed of cleaning agents and protective waxes. It imparts good gloss and water resistance. It is effective on both lacquer and enamel finishes.
S. C. JOHNSON & SON

K

K-7. A grinding fluid and coolant in concentrate form. It dissolves readily in water to form clear, transparent, colorless solutions that are non-foaming and rust-inhibiting. Density, 10.5 lb./gal.; pour point, 20°F.; pH (75:1 solution), 8.8.
F. E. ANDERSON OIL CO.

K-87 Asphalt Tile Cement[NB]. (*Supp.* I p. 115). Now a product of THE BORDEN CO., CHEMICAL DIV., successor to PIONEER LATEX & CHEMICAL CO.

K-99®. A finish used on felt-base floor-covering materials. ARMSTRONG CORK CO.

Kalex Cul[NB]. A sequestering agent of the polyamino carboxylic acid type used as a chelating agent for calcium, magnesium, zinc, copper, and ferrous and ferric iron. Used in textile processing.
HART PRODUCTS CORP.

Kalex G[NB]. A chelating agent, of the polyamino carboxylic acid type, with high sequestering power for ferric iron, nickel, cobalt, and copper ions. It will sequester 0.90 grains ferric ion per gram of sequestering agent at pH of 7.0; 1.7 grains ferric iron per gram at pH of 11.0; 0.44 grains nickel; and 0.52 grains copper. HART PRODUCTS CORP.

Kalex V[NB]. A sequestering agent of the polyamino carboxylic acid type used as a chelating agent for hard water salts, ferrous iron and other metal ions. It is soluble on the acid side. HART PRODUCTS CORP.

Kalinex® Dust. (*HBMTN* p. 309). No longer available. GENERAL CHEMICAL DIV., ALLIED CHEMICAL & DYE CORP.

Kaliscour®. A nonionic textile scouring compound for use in combination with either cationic or anionic agents to improve wetting, penetration and detergency; in hard water; where quick and efficient removal of grease is required; where cleaning and wetting action are required simultaneously; and where good emulsifying properties are required. It can be used in combination with tetrasodium pyrophosphate, sodium hexametaphosphate, sodium tetraphosphate, trisodium phosphate, sodium silicates and carbonates. It is effective on WOOL and all other fibers including synthetics. KALI MFG. CO.

Kalista[NB]. (*HBMTN* p. 309). Should have been listed as a registered trademark. However, this product is no longer available. GODFREY L. CABOT, INC.

Kalsitex. A water-ground mica for use as a filler in the textile industry.
FRANKLIN MINERAL PRODUCTS CO.

Kantstik. A dry-film type mold-release agent for plastic molding. It is an aqueous solution of complex, high polymers which leaves, on the surface of the processed work, a dry film which need not be removed before painting, plating, or other operations. It can be used on all thermosetting and thermoplastic molding and casting resins. SPECIALTY PRODUCTS CO.

Kaolin[△]. *Also known as* CHINA CLAY[△]. A hydrated aluminum silicate clay, consisting principally of KAOLINITE, $Al_2O_3 \cdot 2SiO_2 \cdot 2H_2O$. It is a decomposition product of granite and feldspar and generally contains some quartz, feldspar or mica as impurities. Sp.gr. 2.6; m.p. about 3,200°F. Used for making porcelain; as a refractory in bricks and for furnace linings; as a pigment and filler in paints, plastics, etc.

Kaolinite[△]. *See* KAOLIN[△].

Kapco[NB]. A line of building products including:
KAPCO FOUNDATION COATING. A product for dampproofing footings, weather-exposed sides of bricks, stone, cinder blocks, concrete blocks, or concrete foundations that come in contact with back-filling.
KAPCO STONE BACKING. A heavy, black liquid made of asphalt and petroleum solvents. Used for coating foundations before they are back-filled; and for coating unexposed sides of stone before laying. It prevents water penetration.
KAPCO COLORLESS WATERPROOFING. For application by spray or brush to wood, brick, concrete or stucco to prevent water absorption where pressure is not involved.
KAPCO CONCRETE PRIMER. A black product for painting over concrete structures to prevent the absorption of moisture and to protect the concrete from the effects of moisture, freezing, and loosening of particles; and for priming concrete roofs before application of built-up materials or roof coatings.
KAPCO CAULKING COMPOUNDS. A complete line of waterproof, weather-resistant compounds for sealing open cracks around window casings, door frames, and where the roof joins the main structure or the house joins the foundation. Available in knife and gun grades, and in the form of cartridges.
KAPCO GLAZING COMPOUND. A heavy paste used to replace putty. It remains plastic for years; can be painted immediately; will not bleed through or discolor paint; and will not sag or pull out.
KAPCO PLASTER BOND. A tough, elastic, and durable dampproof compound that retains its adhesive qualities indefinitely. For use on interior surfaces of weather-exposed walls to which hard plaster is to be applied without laths.
KAPCO FLOOR PATCHING COMPOUND. A product for repairing rough, broken, and irregular floor surfaces. For use on concrete floors, sidewalks, driveways, loading platforms, trucking aisles, stair treads, and other places subjected to constant traffic. Dries in 24 to 36 hr.
PRESSTITE-KEYSTONE ENGINEERING PRODUCTS CO.

Kapok[△]. A silky fiber obtained from the seed pods of the SILK-COTTON trees of the genera *Ceiba*, *Bombax*, *Chorisia* and *Ochroma*, which are grown in most tropical countries. The fibers are extremely light and resilient and resemble COTTON in appearance, but they are too brittle for spinning. Most of the commercial KAPOK is obtained from Java. It is used principally as an insulation material, and for fine padding work.

Kap XX[NE]. (*HBMTN* p. 310). No longer available.
SPENCER KELLOGG & SONS

Karbko Core & Mold Wash[NE]. A carbon-type refractory powder suitable for coating gray iron and brass cores and molds. Tends to produce a reducing atmosphere in the mold cavity and prevent burned-on or adhering sand. It is a finished wash in which the binder and suspending agent are already incorporated.
M. A. BELL CO.

Karma®. An alloy for the mfg. of electrical resistors. It has very high resistance—800 ohms/circular mil-ft.—and an extremely low temp. coefficient of resistance—0.00002 ohms/°C.
DRIVER-HARRIS CO.

Kasenit Keepbryte[NE]. An anti-scaling powder for use in the heat treatment of steel at temps. up to 1,650°F. Applied as a powder or as a solution in methylated spirits, it forms a protective film which prevents oxidation and thus keeps the surface bright.
KASENIT CO.

Kaukit®. (*HBMTN* p. 311). Now a registered trademark.
L. SONNEBORN SONS, INC.

Kauri Gum△. A fossil gum that is found buried in the ground in areas of New Zealand and New Caledonia. It is the exudation of the Kauri tree that has been buried for long periods of time. Sp.gr. 1.05; m.p. 182–235°C.; soluble in turpentine, benzol, and alcohol. Used principally in varnishes and enamels to increase body, elasticity and hardness; it is also used in adhesives, and in linoleum.

Kayquinone®. (*HBMTN* p. 311). No longer available.
ABBOTT LABORATORIES

K-Cemo®. (*HBMTN* p. 312). No longer available.
UNITED STATES GYPSUM CO.

Kearsarge® Gaskets. A line of asbestos-metallic gaskets for sealing boiler manholes, handholes, and tube plates. The manhole and handhole gaskets are made by folding and forming to the proper size and shape, plies of strong, durable, wire-inserted asbestos cloth treated with a rubber heat-resisting compound. The edges of the folds are on the inner side, leaving an unbroken, rounded shoulder on the outer side where the gasket is exposed to pressure. For service against oil, gasoline, kerosene and other rubber solvents, the gaskets are treated with a special synthetic rubber compound. The tube plate gaskets are made of the same treated asbestos-metallic cloth but are seamless and without a joint.
JOHNS-MANVILLE SALES CORP.

Kearsarge® Sheet Packing. A packing material made of tightly twisted asbestos yarn spun with brass wire for additional strength, woven into asbestos-metallic cloth and impregnated with a special heat-resisting compound. Furnished in 48″-wide rolls, $1/32″$ and $1/4″$ thick, and as cut gaskets. Available in several styles. STYLE No. 100 is designed for use on rough flanges against low-, medium-, or high-pressure steam, water and air. STYLE No. 98 is recommended for use on rough flanges against oil, gasoline, and other petroleum derivatives; it is similar to STYLE No. 100 except that it is impregnated with a synthetic rubber compound to provide max. resistance to oil.
JOHNS-MANVILLE SALES CORP.

Kectil® Suspension. A medicinal for the treatment of specific and non-specific bacterial diarrheas. Each 5 cc. teaspoonful contains 50.0 mg. dihydrostreptomycin sulfate, 250.0 mg. sulfaguanidine, 250.0 mg. sulfadiazine, 0.033 mg. CENTRINE® hydrogen sulfate, 250.0 mg. bismuth subcarbonate, 500.0 mg. kaolin, 25.0 mg. pectin.
BRISTOL LABORATORIES INC.

Keepbryte. See KASENIT KEEPBRYTE[NE].

Kel-F®. (*HBMTN* p. 312 and *Supp.* I p. 117). All of the KEL-F products, formerly mfg'd by the M. W. KELLOGG Co., are now mfg'd by the MINNESOTA MINING & MFG. CO.

Kelube®. An amine alginate derivative for thickening alcohol, glycerin, or glycol solutions, or mixtures of these with other hydroxylated solvents or water. Used for such applications as sizing of synthetic yarns, suspension of pigments for textile, tile, and fabricated board products, plasticizing of hydrocarbon resistant lubricants, dispersion of inks, dyes, stains, and finishes, and as ingredients of cosmetic creams, detergent formulations, polishes, etc.
KELCO CO.

KEM®. (*HBMTN* p. 313). No longer available; company being liquidated.
KEM PRODUCTS CO.

Kem®. The trademark for a line of paints, enamels, finishes, and coatings for home and industrial uses.
SHERWIN-WILLIAMS CO.

KEM® #222. (*HBMTN* p. 313). No longer available; company being liquidated.
KEM PRODUCTS CO.

Kemak[NE]. A machine tool finish.
SHERWIN-WILLIAMS CO.

Kem Cati-Coat[NE]. An air-dry finish with baked-finish characteristics. It has excellent chemical resistance, hardness and toughness. It is used on concrete, steel, wood and brick for general industrial maintenance where chemical resistance is essential.
SHERWIN-WILLIAMS CO.

Kem-Cut[NE]. A metal-cutting coolant and lubricant in concentrate form. It contains rust preventives and special detergents, and will not turn rancid. It forms a stable emulsion in water. For use, 1 part is diluted with 25 parts water.
PARK CHEMICAL CO.

Kem-Grind[NE]. A metal-grinding concentrate consisting of synthetic emulsifying, detergent, and rust-proofing agents combined with a highly refined paraffin stock. It will not turn rancid. Used in dilutions of 1 part KEM-GRIND to 30–60 parts water.
PARK CHEMICAL CO.

Kem-Kold-Bild®. A high-build, one-coat synthetic enamel for freight cars. It replaces conventional hot spray and two-coat enamels.
SHERWIN-WILLIAMS CO.

Kem-Krete®. A finish for concrete blocks.
SHERWIN-WILLIAMS CO.

Kem-Namel® Snow White. (*HBMTN* p. 314). The name KEM-NAMEL® should have been listed as a registered trademark.
SHERWIN-WILLIAMS CO.

Kem-O-Kleen. A cleaner for tile, marble, porcelain, and enameled surfaces. *Uses:* For cleaning toilet bowls, urinals, swimming pools, lavatories, drinking fountains, shower rooms, granite, tile, brick, porcelain and terra cotta; and for removing lime and magnesium incrustations and deposits from laundry and institutional wash wheels, pumps, evaporators, pipe lines, and other types of equipment.
BELL-RAY CHEMICAL CORP.

Kem-O-Lite[NR]. A finish for exterior applications.
SHERWIN-WILLIAMS CO.

Kemplate®. A roller coat aluminum enamel for interior and exterior applications, such as storage tanks. SHERWIN-WILLIAMS CO.

Kemprint[NR]. A textile printing material.
SHERWIN-WILLIAMS CO.

Kem® Rayon Super-Size VC and V-10. (*HBMTN* p. 314). No longer available; company being liquidated. KEM PRODUCTS CO.

Kem® Rol. (*HBMTN* p. 314). No longer available. SHERWIN-WILLIAMS CO.

Kem Transport[NR]. A synthetic enamel for transportation equipment such as cars, trucks, busses.
SHERWIN-WILLIAMS CO.

KEM®ulsion. (*HBMTN* p. 314). No longer available; company being liquidated. KEM PRODUCTS CO.

Kendall, The 2000 Mile Oil®. A motor oil refined from Pennsylvania crude. Available in SAE Grades 10W through 50 and combined SAE 5W-10W-20W-20.
KENDALL REFINING CO.

Kendall All-Oil Gear Lube[NR]. A pure mineral oil gear lubricant refined from 100% Pennsylvania crude. It is refined and dewaxed to zero pour point; and has high-viscosity index, and excellent resistance to oxidation, thickening, and foaming.
KENDALL REFINING CO.

Kendall Automatic Transmission Fluid[NR]. A fluid for automatic transmissions and power steering hydraulic systems requiring a Type "A" fluid. Completely compatible with all approved automatic transmission fluids. KENDALL REFINING CO.

Kendall Lemon Oil[NR]. A light-colored, low-pour-test oil for high-speed, light machinery, floors, molds, furniture, leather, high-speed fractional horsepower motors, and some hydraulic hoists; also for plunger lubrication in vacuum boosters.
KENDALL REFINING CO.

Kendall Motor Oil Non-Detergent[NR]. (Trademark registration pending.) A lubricating oil for aviation, automotive, natural gas, low-pressure gas, and other engines where a non-detergent oil is recommended. Has high stability and resistance to oxidation, corrosion, and foaming. Available in SAE Grades 10W through 50G, and Grades J-60 and GG-70.
KENDALL REFINING CO.

Kendall Multi-Purpose Hypoid Gear Lube, SCL[NR]. A dewaxed gear lubricant with rust- and foam-preventive characteristics. Protects hypoid gears at high speeds and under heavy loads.
KENDALL REFINING CO.

Kendall Outboard Gear Grease[NR]. A waterproof grease that protects outboard motor gears against rusting and insures proper lubrication. Can also be used for automotive steering gears.
KENDALL REFINING CO.

Kendall Outboard Hypoid Gear Lube[NR]. An SAE 90 lubricant made from Pennsylvania crude and blended with oiliness and load-carrying additives. Possesses rust- and foam-preventing characteristics. Can also be used for automotive steering gears.
KENDALL REFINING CO.

Kendall Outboard Motor Oil[NR]. A special non-detergent oil, refined from Pennsylvania crude, for use in outboard and all other 2-cycle gasoline engines. Fortified to prevent rusting in fresh- or salt-water operation. KENDALL REFINING CO.

Kendall Super-D Oil[NR]. A lubricating oil for supercharged diesels or engines operating on fuels having a high sulfur content and for gasoline engines under unusual service conditions that promote sludge and varnish deposits. Refined from Pennsylvania crude. Available in SAE Grades 10W through 40.
KENDALL REFINING CO.

Kenface®. A cemented carbide, hard-surfacing material. KENNAMETAL INC.

Kenflex® A, B, L, N. A series of synthetic aromatic hydrocarbon resins with softening points ranging from 28°F. to 158°F. They act as polymeric plasticizers and process aids for all the rubbers and vinyls, as well as other thermoplastic materials; impart good heat aging; improve electrical characteristics; improve ozone resistance of BUTYL and NEOPRENE; and retard crystallization and bin set up of NEOPRENE. They do not affect rate of cure. KENRICH CORP.

Kenmix® Dispersions. A series of dispersions of all the more commonly used accelerators in KENFLEX N. They reduce heat formation and milling time; overcome the problem of handling toxic and explosive dust; and avoid master batching. KENRICH CORP.

Kerba®. An all-hydrogenated vegetable shortening processed to give it exceptionally high stability. It is a specialty shortening for frying, and for extra long shelf life in biscuits and crackers.
ANDERSON, CLAYTON & CO. FOODS DIV.

Kerodex®. Skin protective creams that form elastic, invisible, strong films to protect hands, face, or other areas against contact-dermatitis due to a wide variety of irritants commonly found in industry. Two types (for wet or for dry work) are effective against acids, alkalis, oils, solvents, synthetic resins and "curing" agents, tars, pitches, rubber compounds, chromates, solutions, etc. They also provide protection against poison ivy and other plant irritants. A light-deflectant type is available for protection against ultraviolet, infrared, and other actinic rays, natural or artificial. AYERST LABORATORIES

Kerodor®. (*Supp.* I p. 118). No longer available.
SINDAR CORP.

Kerozone®. (*HBMTN* p. 316 and *Supp.* I p. 118). No longer available. SINDAR CORP.

Keryl®. Synthetic organic chemicals, including aromatic hydrocarbons and derivatives of aromatic hydrocarbons. PENNSYLVANIA SALT MFG. CO.

Ke-Tone®. A product for treating water used in cooling towers, boilers, and other industrial installations to prevent and remove scale. It combines the features of the polymerized phosphates and the amino acid chelates. It not only inhibits scale formation but loosens, suspends, and, in some cases, dissolves scale already present.
UNITED CHEMICAL CORP. OF NEW MEXICO

Key Abso-Lute®. (*Supp.* I p. 119). Now a product of W-K-M MFG. CO., KEY PRODUCTS DIV., a subsidiary of ACF INDUSTRIES, INC.

Key Graphite Paste®. A pipe-joint compound for use in sealing joints and devices handling gasoline or petroleum products.
W-K-M MFG. CO., KEY PRODUCTS DIV.

Keystone®. The trademark for a line of copper-bearing steel sheets. UNITED STATES STEEL CORP.

Keystone No. 29 Cartridged Grease[NB]. An adsorptive, heat-resistant, and water-, acid-, and alkali-repellent grease for open gears under severe conditions of pressure, dust, and high temp. Applied in ribbon form with a gun applicator or by paddle from bulk containers. KEYSTONE LUBRICATING CO.

Keystone® No. 44 and No. 45 Greases. Smooth, non-fibrous greases for the lubrication of ball and solid roller bearings in motors, fans, blowers, pumps, etc. over the temp range of 0–225°F. No. 44 has an ASTM penetration at 77°F. of 280; No. 45 has a penetration of 325. KEYSTONE LUBRICATING CO.

Keystone No. 122 Grease[NB]. A tacky, water-repellent grease for open gears on excavating equipment and other equipment. It does not crack or peel, and does not cause unnecessary drag or starting torque. M.p., approx. 190°F. Available in various densities.
KEYSTONE LUBRICATING CO.

Keystone All Purpose Hypoid Lubricant[NB]. A lubricant for hypoid and all other types of gears in cars and trucks, and for industrial hypoid gears. Harmless to copper-alloy bearings. Available in SAE 80 and SAE 90 grades. KEYSTONE LUBRICATING CO.

Keystone® Ammonium Carbonate. A sublimed, highly purified U.S.P. grade of ammonium carbonate ($NH_4HCO_3 \cdot NH_2COONH_4$) containing approx. 30% NH_3 and 52% CO_2. A white-to-translucent solid which upon exposure to air decomposes with loss of NH_3 and CO_2, becoming white and powdery. Soluble in cold water; decomposed by hot water; partially soluble in alcohol. Available in chip, lump and powder forms. *Uses:* As a leavening agent in bakery goods; in pharmaceuticals, smelling salts, and malt preparations; as an analytical reagent; as an ingredient of hair waving preparations; as a mordant in dyeing; in feedstuffs; in mfg. of foam rubber; in fermentation of wines; in textile processing; etc.
AMERICAN AGRICULTURAL CHEMICAL CO.

Keystone Clay[NB]. (*HBMTN* p. 317). No longer available. UNITED CLAY MINES CORP.

Keystone® Gelatin. Gelatin ($C_{102}H_{151}O_{39}N_{31}$) available in the following grades:
EDIBLE, in granulated and flake types, for use in meats, candy, bakery products, ice cream, gelatin desserts, jellied foods, and other food products.
PHOTOGRAPHIC, in film and emulsion types, for use in photographic films, plates, papers; photo-lithography and photo-gelatin engraving; collotype printing, and silk screen stencils.
PHARMACEUTICAL, for use in making hard and soft capsules, suppositories, pill coatings, emulsions, and culture media.
TECHNICAL, for use on print rollers; in sizings, emulsions, and decalcomanias; and as a protective colloid. AMERICAN AGRICULTURAL CHEMICAL CO.

Keystone U. W. Grease[NB]. A high-melting-point, adhesive and cohesive grease for wheel bearing rollers and races. Available in light and medium grades.
KEYSTONE LUBRICATING CO.

Key Tite®. A plastic, waterproof pipe-joint compound for use in gas, water, steam, compressed air, and other lines.
W-K-M MFG. CO., KEY PRODUCTS DIV.

Kieselguhr△. Same as INFUSORIAL EARTH△.

Kil-Klatter®. A typewriter pad, 11″ x 13″, composed of 100% cattle hair. It has a pressure-resisting top which prevents machine legs from digging in, and its under surface is treated to prevent the machine from slipping. AMERICAN HAIR & FELT CO.

Kill-All[NB]. A 40% sodium arsenite solution for total weed control on driveways, walks, and storage yards, and for tree and stump killing. For use, one part of KILL-ALL is diluted with from 3 to 20 parts water, depending on the application.
MILLER CHEMICAL & FERTILIZER CORP.

Kil-O-Mist[NB]. A non-poisonous, stainless, non-explosive insect spray concentrate for killing flies, mosquitoes, moths, carpet beetles, silver fish, buffalo bugs, roaches, ants, fleas, bed bugs, spiders, wasps, and other insects. Contains piperonyl butoxide, petroleum distillate, and pyrethrins. *Uses:* For insect control in homes, restaurants, food-processing plants, mills, elevators, warehouses, stores, granaries, etc.; and on cattle. CENTRAL O-B PRODUCTS CO.

Kimfect[NB]. A line of coated papers.
KIMBERLY-CLARK CORP.

Kimpak®. A registered trademark for a line of creped wadding products. KIMBERLY-CLARK CORP.

Kimsul®. A registered trademark for construction materials made of wood or paper.
KIMBERLY-CLARK CORP.

King O' Chef's[NB]. A brand of charcoal.
CHARCOAL CORP. OF AMERICA

Kino Resin△. *Also known as* GUM KINO△. The red exudation of the tree *Pterocarpus marsupium*, of India and Ceylon, and of *P. erinaceus*, of West Africa. This resin was at one time extensively used in the mfg. of colored varnishes and lacquers, and in the formulation of throat medicinals.

Kiss-O'-Flavor®. A line of food products including mushroom extract food seasoning (Registration No.

628,395, Class 46; June 5, 1956); fruit juices; garlic, onion and celery salt; maple syrup; and other flavoring and food products.
CONTINENTAL SPECIALTIES CO.

Kladak[NE]. A water-white, crystal clear, fast-drying wood and linoleum finish that is particularly useful on oak floors. It may be applied over new or old wood wherever varnish, lacquer or shellac can be used. It provides a very tough, durable film.
WURDACK CHEMICAL CO.

K. L. C. Oils[NE]. A group of highly-refined paraffin-base oils for deisel engine lubrication, steam engine crankcases and bearings, and air-compressor service; and for lubrication of machine tools by hand or automatic oilers. Available in SAE grades of 10 to 60.
KEYSTONE LUBRICATING CO.

Kleenex®. A registered trademark for a line of creped wadding and other paper products, including cleansing tissues.
KIMBERLY-CLARK CORP.

Kleen Floor®. A non-flammable, concentrated blend of neutral soaps and detergents which when mixed with hot water effectively removes accumulated wax, dirt, oil, etc., from floors. Will not harm hands or clothing, and can be used for cleaning linoleum, vinyl plastic, rubber and asphalt tile, terrazzo, marble, and other masonry-type floors.
S. C. JOHNSON & SON

Kleen-Flush. A concentrated detergent for cleaning and flushing machine-tool coolant systems and machine surfaces. Mixed with water in the ratio of 4 oz. concentrate to 5 gal. water, it removes grease, oil, and scum.
DOALL CO.

Kleen-Grip. An adhesive for adhering labels to polyethylene, polystyrene, and similar plastics.
ADHESIVE PRODUCTS CO.

Kleen-It. A non-flammable cleaning fluid.
SLOMONS LABORATORIES, INC.

Kleen-Kool. A grinding oil and coolant in concentrate form. It is a synthetic product that emulsifies with water. Has no unpleasant odor, will not rancify, requires no water conditioner, is transparent, and inhibits rust.
DOALL CO.

Klen-Olax®. A fluid soap for use in wet-cleaning processes in dry-cleaning plants.
PENNSYLVANIA SALT MFG. CO.

K-Lens-M® **Tissue**. A strong, interfolded, long fiber, absorbent and lint-free tissue for cleaning eyewear.
WILKINS CO., INC.

Klinch[NE]. (*HBMTN* p. 318). No longer available.
HANSON-VAN WINKLE-MUNNING CO.

Klinger-Acidit®[Brit.]. A compressed asbestos sheet packing material for hot nitric, hydrochloric, sulfuric, and all other organic and inorganic acids. Not damaged by oils, gasoline, and other solvents. Suitable for temps. up to 500°F. and pressures up to 1,000 lb./sq.in.
RICHARD KLINGER, LTD.

Klingerit®[Brit.]. A compressed asbestos sheet packing for super-heated and saturated steam, acids, alkalies, and other chemicals, oils, solvents, hydrocarbons, etc. *Use:* For flange gaskets for high-pressure hydraulic and gas service, and similar applications.
RICHARD KLINGER, LTD.

Kingerit-1000®[Brit.]. A sheet packing material made from an asbestos compound and close-mesh wire gauze. It is more resistant to blowing out than sheet packings without the wire reinforcement. Particularly useful for extremely high-temp. service.
RICHARD KLINGER, LTD.

Klinger-Oilit®[Brit.]. A compressed asbestos sheet packing material for use in the oil industry, suitable for trichlorethylene, carbon tetrachloride, naphtha, and many other chemicals up to 900°F. Composed principally of inorganic materials, it is suitable for highest temps. and pressures. RICHARD KLINGER, LTD.

Klondyke®. A clay used as a filler for paper.
MINERALS & CHEMICALS CORP. OF AMERICA

Klotogen F®. A VITAMIN K preparation consisting of menadione sodium bisulfite. Designed as a supplement for poultry feeds.
ABBOTT LABORATORIES

Knight®. (*HBMTN* p. 318). No longer available.
WITCO CHEMICAL CO.

Knight No. 2 Cement[NE]. An especially compounded silicate-type mortar, resistant to all acids, both inorganic and organic, except those containing fluorine. It is also resistant to neutral salts, and is entirely unaffected by organic salts. It consists of a liquid binder and an inert ceramic filler. It sets by chemical action which converts the binder into insoluble silica. It will not shrink or grow in the joints after it has set, and will not spall, vitrify, or soften at temps. up to 1,800°F., and it is water resistant after it has been acid treated, usually with 15% sulfuric acid or hydrochloric acid. Compressive strength, 3,200 lb./sq.in.; tensile strength, 400 lb./sq.in. *Use:* As a mortar for acid-proof brick.
MAURICE A. KNIGHT

Knightbond #6 Cement[NE]. A plasticized sulfur-sand cement mfg'd under license from the TEXAS-GULF SULPHUR CO. It is melted and poured at 265°F. *Uses:* This acid-proof cement is used for joining acid-proof brick and tile in the construction of acid-proof floors in chemical plants, steel plants, food plants, and dairies; and in the construction of pickling plants, galvanizing tanks, acid-storage tanks, sewers, gutters, and pits; and for grouting foundations and anchor bolts.
MAURICE A. KNIGHT

Knightbond #7 Cement[NE]. A sulfur-carbon base cement which is inert to hydrofluoric as well as to other acids. It is used for the same purposes as KNIGHTBOND #6 CEMENT.
MAURICE A. KNIGHT

Knight Super XX Cement[NE]. A refractory-type acid-proof mortar. It can be used at temps. in excess of 2,300°F. without vitrification or softening; it does not shrink, spall, craze, or grow in the joints during repeated heating and cooling cycles; and is chemically inert at high temps. It is unaffected by all mineral and organic acids, except those containing fluorine, and to acid and neutral salt solutions of pH 10 or lower.
MAURICE A. KNIGHT

Knight-Ware®. The trademark for acid-proof chemical stoneware, including filters, jars, kettles, tanks, pipe, towers, heat-exchangers, scrubbers, absorbers, and other process equipment.
MAURICE A. KNIGHT

Knox-Out® **Moths**. (*HBMTN* p. 319). No longer available.
PENNSYLVANIA SALT CO.

Kodachrome®. The trademark for a line of sensitized photographic film, and photographic transparencies, prints, and enlargements. EASTMAN KODAK CO.

Kodafix®. A concentrated, photographic, single-solution fixer for films, plates, and papers.
EASTMAN KODAK CO.

Kodak®. A trademark for organic and inorganic chemicals, photographic chemicals, and materials for use in photography, including lacquers, varnish, oil and water colors, dyes, lubricating oil, cement, and cleaning compounds. EASTMAN KODAK CO.

Kodalak®. (*HBMTN* p. 319). No longer available.
EASTMAN KODAK CO.

Kodalk®. A balanced alkali for use in photographic developers. EASTMAN KODAK CO.

K. O. Grease[NR]. A smooth, amber-colored, translucent, adhesive, water-repellent grease for plain and anti-friction bearings, cams, slides, etc. in beverage and food plants, laundries, etc. Available in various densities. KEYSTONE LUBRICATING CO.

K Oil[NR]. (*HBMTN* p. 319). No longer available.
BAKER CASTOR OIL CO.

Kold-Bild. See KEM-KOLD-BILD®.

Kold Dip Metal Cleaner. See GLOBE KOLD DIP METAL CLEANER.

Komyrj®. (*HBMTN* p. 320). No longer available.
ATLAS POWDER CO.

Kon-Toor® Wheel. A polishing wheel composed of coated abrasive cloth mounted on a metal hub.
BEHR-MANNING CO.

Kontrex®. A cleaning compound designed for use in bakeries. DIVERSEY CORP.

KopeSeal®. A permanently soft compound used for sealing metal-casting molds. It is a heavy mastic compound, extruded and furnished in bead or rope-like form. It is made of special non-hardening synthetic resins and other inert modifiers with asbestos fiber binder; and it gives off no gas which might cause blow holes.
PRESSTITE-KEYSTONE ENGINEERING PRODUCTS CO.

Koreline Core Wash[NR]. A PLUMBAGO-base, foundry blacking that can be used on any type of gray iron or brass castings as well as on cores and molds. It is a powdered material containing suspending agents and binders. M. A. BELL CO.

Korex®. A germicidal cleaner for cleaning, disinfecting, and deodorizing floors, walls, instruments, and fabrics in schools, hospitals, and other institutional buildings. HUNTINGTON LABORATORIES, INC.

Kor-Flo®. An agent in the nature of a core oil, added to foundry sand compositions, particularly to core sand compositions, to prevent the compositions from sticking to a flask or core box and to aid in the release of the same.
INTERNATIONAL MINERALS & CHEMICAL CORP.

Korox #1. A chemical product for the bright dipping of metals. J. F. HENRY CHEMICAL CO.

Kostico®. (*HBMTN* p. 322). No longer available.
HANSON-VAN WINKLE-MUNNING CO.

Kote-Aid®. (*HBMTN* p. 322). No longer available.
NOPCO CHEMICAL CO.

Kote-Rax® Grade M. (*Supp.* I p. 121). No longer available. HANSON-VAN WINKLE-MUNNING CO.

Kot-Masq[NR]. (*HBMTN* p. 322). No longer available. HANSON-VAN WINKLE-MUNNING CO.

KP-120[NR]. (*HBMTN* p. 322). No longer available.
OHIO-APEX DIV.

KP-150[NR]. (*HBMTN* p. 323). No longer available.
OHIO-APEX DIV.

KP-220[NR]. A primary plasticizer for most resins and plastics—vinyls, nitrocellulose, polystyrene, ethyl cellulose—and for synthetic rubbers. Mol.wt. 358 (approx.); sp.gr. (20°/20°C.), 0.906; moisture, 0.1% (max.); color (A.P.H.A.), 100 (max.); odor, mild; acidity (as acetic acid), 0.06% (max.).
OHIO-APEX DIV.

KP-550[NR]. A primary plasticizer for most resins and many synthetic rubbers. Particularly useful in synthetic rubbers of the acrylonitrile type and heavy-gage vinyl plastics. It is bis-(dimethyl benzyl) ether. $[(CH_3)_2C_6H_3CH_2]_2O$; mol.wt. 254. Sp.gr. (20°/20°C.), 1.008; moisture, 0.1% (max.); color (A.P.H.A.), 200 (max.); odor, mild; acidity (as acetic acid), 0.1% (max.). OHIO-APEX DIV.

KPR®. Photographic chemicals, namely, resist developer, resist, resist thinner, and resist dye.
EASTMAN KODAK CO.

Krameria△. Same as RHATANY△.

Krene®. Flexible vinyl film and sheeting in thicknesses from 0.004″ to 0.025″. The film may be clear or colored, transparent, translucent, or opaque. Available in a range of standard and special colors. Resistant to mold, grease, water, alcohol, and many chemicals. *Uses:* For tablecloths, draperies, shower curtains, rainwear, garment bags, nursery items, baggage, swimming pools, and wall coverings.
BAKELITE CO.,
DIV. OF UNION CARBIDE CORP.

Kresola. (*HBMTN* p. 324). No longer available.
TILDEN CO.

K-R Hand Rubbing Compound. See PARKO® K-R HAND RUBBING COMPOUND.

Kriegr-O-Dip Universal[NR]. (*HBMTN* p. 324). No longer available. KRIEGER COLOR & CHEMICAL CO.

Kriegr-O-Dip V[NR]. (*HBMTN* p. 324). No longer available. KRIEGER COLOR & CHEMICAL CO.

Kriegr-O-Tex[NR]. (*HBMTN* p. 324). No longer available. KRIEGER COLOR & CHEMICAL CO.

KR Lubricant[NR]. An industrial gear lubricant for speed reducers and enclosed gears. It does not have extreme-pressure properties but it does have anti-corrosion and non-sludging features.
KEYSTONE LUBRICATING CO.

Krumbhaar Resins. A line of resins for varnishes and enamels, lacquers, printing inks, etc. Included in the line are:

Rosin Base Hard Resins

K-303. Polypenta rosin ester. For white enamels, pale varnishes, flush colors, decorative coatings, alkyd modification.

K-404. Maleic lacquer resin. For pale lacquers, wood lacquers, sanding sealers, nitrocellulose-type fillers.

K-414. Maleic varnish resin. For baking varnishes and enamels, Venetian blind vehicles, furniture finishes, rubbing lacquers, overprint varnishes.

K-444. Rosin-base polyhydric polymer. For rubbing varnishes, pale grinding liquids, baking enamels, soya-oil vehicles, traffic paints.

K-606. Phenolic printing ink resin. For overprint varnishes, gloss ink liquids, metallic ink vehicles, non-scratch ink vehicles, heat-set ink vehicles.

K-707. Phenolic varnish resin. For floor varnishes and enamels, rubbing and polishing varnishes, primers, shopcoats, traffic marking paints, overprint varnishes.

Pure Phenol Formaldehyde Resins

K-254. Pure phenyl phenol formaldehyde resin. For specification finishes in the marine, structural, and transportation fields, and chemical-resistant floor and spar varnishes.

K-1010. Pure butyl phenol formaldehyde resin. For finishes for ships, rust-preventive primers, railroad finishes, iron structure finishes, floor finishes.

K-1111. Pure alkyl phenol formaldehyde resin. For spar varnishes, floor finishes, porch and deck enamels, primer and enamel vehicles.

K-1717. Pure hydrogenated phenol formaldehyde resin. For vinyl coatings, cellulose lacquers, label coatings, specialty inks, grease-resistant finishes, adhesives, rubber compositions.

Copal Type Synthetics

K-222. High polymer copal-type synthetic resin. For overprint varnishes, gloss inks, gloss-mixing varnishes, and lithographic vehicles.

K-333. Low polymer copal-type synthetic resin. For colorless, clear varnishes, white enamel vehicles, silk screen liquids, impregnating liquids, printing ink vehicles, wax compounding.

K-666. Reactive copal-type synthetic resin. For medium and low priced varnishes and enamels, non-penetrating vehicles for flats, undercoats, and primers, finishes for walls, floors, woodwork and implements.

K-777. Phenol base copal-type synthetic. For rubbing varnishes, furniture finishes, industrial specialties, overprint varnishes, metallic inks, rub-proof ink vehicles.

Alcohol Soluble Resin

K-1515. Fumaric resin. For steam-setting inks for food labels and packages, bread and meat wrappers, milk containers. KRUMBHAAR CHEMICALS, INC.

Krylon® Cleaner and Degreaser. A cleaner for dissolving oil and grease deposits from automobile and truck engines and underframes, aircraft and diesel engines, marine engines and engine rooms, aircraft fuselages, materials-handling equipment, painted surfaces, clothing and upholstery, asphalt tile floors, etc. It consists of a mixture of solvents in an aerosol spray dispenser. KRYLON, INC.

Krylon® Dulling Spray. A product for eliminating glare on shiny surfaces in TV, movie, and photographic studio use. Available in an aerosol spray container; dries rapidly; is harmless to fine finishes; is easily removed. KRYLON, INC.

Krylon® Hide-a-Mark®. A paint in "kraft-paper" color, for covering old stencil marks and thus making old drums, crates, and cartons reusable. Available in aerosol spray containers; dries rapidly making new stencilling possible almost immediately. KRYLON, INC.

Krylon-Houghton® Rust Veto Spray. A soft, dry, waxy surface coating for protecting metal parts from rust and corrosion during long periods of storage. Available in aerosol spray dispensers; dries in 15 min. KRYLON-HOUGHTON RUST VETO SPRAY is packaged and marketed by KRYLON, INC., under license from E. F. HOUGHTON & Co. KRYLON, INC.

Krylon-Houghton® Tenac Open Gear and Cable Lubricant. A heavy-duty lubricant spray in an aerosol dispenser. Will not crack or flake at low temps.; provides exceptional adhesiveness and oilness at high temps.; resists leaching action of water and mild alkalis and acids. *Use:* For lubrication of wire rope, cables, and open gears under adverse conditions of high humidity, dust, etc. KRYLON-HOUGHTON TENAC OPEN GEAR AND CABLE LUBRICANT is packaged and marketed by KRYLON, INC., under license from E. F. HOUGHTON & Co. KRYLON, INC.

Krylon® Metal Primer. A rust-inhibitive zinc chromate primer in an aerosol spray dispenser.
KRYLON, INC.

Krylon® Rust Release. A formulation of chemicals and oils in an aerosol spray dispenser, for penetrating and loosening rusty bolts and nuts and "frozen" movable parts. Releases parts made tight because of corrosion, paint, dirt, scale, gum residues, etc.
KRYLON, INC.

Krylon® Spray Enamels. A line of fast-drying enamels in aerosol spray dispensers. Used for equipment, furniture, etc., both indoors and outdoors. Available in 18 colors. KRYLON, INC.

Krylon® Stencil Ink Sprays. Stencil inks, in 6 colors, available in aerosol spray containers.
KRYLON, INC.

Kryoflux®. The trademark for a brand of cryolite.
PENNSYLVANIA SALT MFG. CO.

Kuik Kore Kompound[NR]. A dry-powder foundry-core binder formulated with readily-available, non-strategic compounds. These compounds, in water solution, precipitate at the ultimate heat reached and then set the binder for the core. The precipitation is carried out during the mulling cycle when water is added to or is already present in the core sand. Once the precipitation has occurred, the core is formed and the binder set in the presence of moisture in a conventional core oven at temps. of 350°–400°F.
M. A. BELL CO.

Kupred®. The trademark for a line of nails and dowel pins. UNITED STATES STEEL CORP.

Kwell®. A medicinal consisting of 1% gamma benzene hexachloride in a hydrophilic cream or lotion base. The cream is available in 2 oz. and 1 lb. jars, the lotion in 2 oz. and 1 pint bottles. *Uses:* For the prompt cure of scabies, pediculosis and chigger infestations. REED & CARNRICK

Kwik Wash. *See* PARKO® KWIK WASH.

Kyanite△. An aluminum silicate mineral having the composition $Al_2O_3 \cdot SiO_2$. It generally occurs in combination with other minerals. High-grade KYANITE comes principally from India and Kenya. In the United States, it is produced in North Carolina, Georgia, Virginia and California. Sp.gr. 3.56–3.67; hardness on the Moh scale, 6–7. *Uses:* As a refractory, especially for linings of glass furnaces and foundry furnaces handling non-ferrous metals; low-grade KYANITE is sometimes used in the mfg. of glass as a source of alumina, and in ceramics.

Kylan[NE]. Deacetylated Chitin. A glucose amine similar in structure to that of cellulose. *Uses:* For woolen shrinkage control; in water repellents and textile sizes; for increasing the wet strength of paper; as a constituent of adhesives; and as a synthetic fiber. MORTEX CHEMICAL PRODUCTS, INC.

Kymene®. A strongly cationic synthetic resin for use in the mfg. of wet strength paper.
HERCULES POWDER CO.

L

L-30. (*HBMTN* p. 327). No longer available.
VEGETABLE OIL PRODUCTS CO.

L-60, L-61, L-70, L-18-8, *and* **L-201**[NE]. Electrode wires for automatic welding.
  L-60 is a low carbon steel wire with approx. 0.12% carbon.
  L-61 is a low carbon steel wire with approx. 0.12% carbon, silicon killed for single-pass, light gage material.
  L-70 is a low carbon alloy steel wire with approx. 0.14% carbon and 0.5% molybdenum, for high tensile strength applications. Tensile strength, 70,000 lb./sq.in. (min.) when stress relieved.
  L-18-8 is a chromium-nickel stainless steel.
  L-201 is a medium carbon steel of approx. 0.50% carbon, used for surfacing. LINCOLN ELECTRIC CO.

Label-Rite®. A line of prescription bottles with large, smooth label surfaces, flat backs, and funnel shoulders for easy pouring. Available in sizes from ½ to 32 oz. ARMSTRONG CORK CO.

Lacacap[NE]. Bottle cap coatings of cellulose base. These coatings contract around the cork and bottle.
MAAS & WALDSTEIN CO.

Lacca△. *Same as* SHELLAC△.

Lacet Resin[NE]. (*HBMTN* p. 328). No longer available. AMERICAN CYANAMID CO.

Lacquer-Flo®. A lacquer solvent for general use.
SHERWIN-WILLIAMS CO.

Lamb Air Mover[NE]. A ventilation device for moving large volumes of air by utilizing the power of a compressed air or steam line.
MINE SAFETY APPLIANCES CO.

Lami-Rock®. Laminated tubular goods made from mats and cloths with polyester resins; and fittings and accessories for the tubes. FIBERCAST CORP.

Lanaseal[NE]. A water-soluble emulsion, containing lanolin and waxes, used as a softener and lubricant for hosiery, particularly for full fashion and seamless NYLON hose. It imparts a weighty softness along with lubrication. It is compatible with other hosiery finishes. W. F. FANCOURT CO.

Lanaset® Resin. A melamine-formaldehyde condensate finish for WOOL fabrics. Designed to reduce wool shrinkage and felting. It can be applied as an acid colloid without requiring curing at high temps.
AMERICAN CYANAMID CO.

Lanaset® Resin MW. A melamine-formaldehyde condensate finish for WOOL fabrics. Designed to reduce wool shrinkage and felting. It can be applied as an acid colloid without requiring cure at high temps.
AMERICAN CYANAMID CO.

Lanazine Tip[NE]. A product, composed of fatty esters, used to promote level dyeing on tippy WOOL. It is designed for use particularly in the dyeing of loose WOOL, because of its good penetrating and leveling properties. It is also useful in the dyeing of yarn, tops and piece goods. It gives equally good results with both acid and chrome colors.
ORGANIC CHEMICAL CORP.

Lanese®. The trademark for a line of fabrics made wholly or partially of cellulose derivatives.
CELANESE CORP. OF AMERICA

Lanolin△. *See* DEGRAS△.

Lanoseal[NE]. An aqueous emulsion containing lanolin, for imparting softness, lubrication and body to NYLON hose. It aids in the exhaustion and leveling of delustering agents to produce even, uniform dulling. In conjunction with other conventional hosiery finishes, it can be varied to produce extreme body and fullness or soft sheer hose which board and pair easily.
W. F. FANCOURT CO.

Lanthanol® LAL. (*Supp.* I p. 124). Should have been listed as LATHANOL® LAL.
NATIONAL ANILINE DIV.,
ALLIED CHEMICAL & DYE CORP.

Lanum®. (*Supp.* I p. 124). No longer available.
SHARP & DOHME DIV., MERCK & CO.

Lapidolith®. (*HBMTN* p. 329). Now a registered trademark. L. SONNEBORN SONS, INC.

Laptite[NE]. An asphaltic sealing compound used for sealing the longitudinal laps of ANTI-SWEAT® cold water pipe insulation. JOHNS-MANVILLE SALES CORP.

Laqua®. A water-dip lacquer that has the property of displacing water from the surface of metals and at the same time depositing a thin protective film. It prevents oxide and sulfur stains, and finger printing and staining during handling and storage. The coating does not interfere with electrical contacts; it eliminates drying after plating; and it does not interfere with subsequent spot welding or soldering operations. A LAQUA-coated surface can be finished with

lacquers or synthetics. Applied by dip or spray. It is especially useful in plating and finishing operations.
FIDELITY CHEMICAL PRODUCTS CORP.

Lariat®. (*Supp.* I p. 124). No longer available.
GENERAL CHEMICAL DIV.,
ALLIED CHEMICAL & DYE CORP.

Larvacide®. A High-purity (over 99%) chlorpicrin manufactured especially for fumigating soils and foodstuffs. CCl$_3$NO$_2$; mol.wt. 164.39; sp.gr. 1.6579; b.p. 112°C.; insoluble in water; soluble in alcohol, gasoline and other organic solvents. It is a heavy, almost colorless liquid which, when injected under the soil surface in liquid form, vaporizes and diffuses through the soil. Soil fumigation with LARVACIDE® kills most soil fungi detrimental to plants. It is also very effective for insect fumigation in warehouses, mills, food plants and homes, and for rodent control in buildings and outside burrows.
LARVACIDE PRODUCTS, INC.

Larvacover[NE]. A plastic cover for use in greenhouses and outdoor areas to seal in the vapors of volatile type fungicides and herbicides. (*See Bromex*).
LARVACIDE PRODUCTS, INC.

Larva-Tectant[NE]. A non-toxic formulation of pyrethrins and synergists for treating grain before storage. It insures insect-free storage for periods up to 12 months.
LARVACIDE PRODUCTS, INC.

Larvonil[NE]. (*HBMTN* p. 329). No longer available.
ONYX OIL & CHEMICAL CO.

Lastiglas®. A smooth, glossy, corrosion-resistant, thermosetting, phenolic tank- and pipe-lining material. It is tasteless, odorless, and resistant to solvents, alcohols, oils, salt solutions, many acids, and other corrosive materials. *Use:* For lining equipment in the food, beverage, pharmaceutical and chemical industries.
BISHOPRIC PRODUCTS CO.

Lathanol® LAL. Incorrectly listed as LANTHANOL® LAL (*Supp.* I p. 124).
NATIONAL ANILINE DIV.,
ALLIED CHEMICAL & DYE CORP.

Lavamenthe[NE]. A proprietary synthetic aromatic chemical. A practically colorless liquid, with a fresh minty top note having a woody background.
DOW CHEMICAL CO.

Leader Flakes. (*HBMTN* p. 331). No longer available.
NATIONAL MILLING & CHEMICAL CO.

Leadstar[NE]. Normal lead stearate. Pb(C$_{17}$H$_{35}$COO)$_2$; mol.wt. 774. A fine white, unctuous powder; insoluble in all common solvents. *Use:* As a lubricant and supplementary stabilizer for vinyl resins.
NATIONAL LEAD CO.

Learok®. (*HBMTN* p. 332). Now a registered trademark.
LEA MFG. CO.

Leather-Care. See LECTON® Leather-Care.

Leatheroid® Fibre. The trademark for a vulcanized fiber.
NATIONAL VULCANIZED FIBRE CO.

Leather Product 612[NE]. A resin retanning agent for use in the mfg. of white or colored leather. It tightens the grain surface and at the same time adds fullness and roundness to the leather.
AMERICAN CYANAMID CO.

Leather Product UF[NE]. A urea-formaldehyde resin tanning agent. It is particularly useful when used as a "filler." It may be used to replace part of the cationic-type resins, or it may be used as an additional resin to further increase fullness. When used in conjunction with cationic-type resins, it relaxes the grain and reduces grain draw to an appreciable extent.
AMERICAN CYANAMID CO.

Leatherwood®. A TEMPERED PRESDWOOD® product that simulates Spanish-grain leather. *Uses:* In offices, lounges, recreation rooms, and other places where a rich, leather-like treatment is desired.
MASONITE CORP.

Lecithin△. A complex glyceride obtained by solvent and steam extraction of soyabeans, and cottonseed. It is a soft, light-brown, salve-like material with a bland taste and odor; insoluble in water; soluble in oils and in alcohol. It melts at about 150°F. *Uses:* As an antioxidant in chocolate and other foods; as an emulsifier, softener, and wetting agent; as a viscosity regulator in casein paints; as a curing accelerator in synthetic rubber; etc.

Lecton® Car-Care. A patented, high-quality, cleaner-polish for automobiles.
CANNON CHEMICAL CO.

Lecton® Easy-Care. A high-quality, cleaner-polish for automobiles. Similar to LECTON® CAR-CARE except that it contains a mild scratch-free filler to remove road film, oxidation, etc.
CANNON CHEMICAL CO.

Lecton® Furniture-Care. A high-quality furniture cleaner and polish.
CANNON CHEMICAL CO.

Lecton® Leather-Care. A liquid cleaner for leather. It effectively removes dust and other spots, and leaves an anti-static, water-repellent film.
CANNON CHEMICAL CO.

Lecton® Plastic & Leather Cleaner. A concentrated, liquid cleaner for plastics and leather. Can be used safely for cleaning of white as well as any other colored surfaces.
CANNON CHEMICAL CO.

Lecton® Solvent. A solvent cleaner for automobiles, designed to effectively remove tar, wax, silicone, etc.
CANNON CHEMICAL CO.

Lecton® Super-Care. A patented, protective coating for new automobiles. It is used after LECTON® CAR-CARE has been applied to the body.
CANNON CHEMICAL CO.

Lectraseal[NE]. Incorrectly listed as LECTRASEEL (*HBMTN* p. 332).
PEMCO CORP.

Lectraseel. (*HBMTN* p. 332). Should have been listed LECTRASEAL[NE].
PEMCO CORP.

Lectro "60"[NE]. A lead chloro-silicate complex used as an economical stabilizer for vinyl electrical and calendered products. It is a fine white powder; sp.gr. 4.0; refractive index, 2.1; insoluble in all common solvents.
NATIONAL LEAD CO.

Lectro-Clad®. Nickel-plated steel plate made by electroplating pure nickel by the Bart Process. Used for equipment where contamination of a product is to be avoided. Working temp. up to 1,000 F.
COLORADO FUEL & IRON CORP.,
CLAYMONT STEEL PRODUCTS DEPT.

Led-Plate® Anti Seize Compound No. 250. (*HBMTN* p. 332). The name LED-PLATE® is now a registered trademark. ARMITE LABORATORIES

Legsure®. A non-buffing type, slip-resistant floor polish for all resilient floors in corridors, lobbies, and other heavy-duty areas. Can be used on linoleum, cork, asphalt, tile, rubber, wood, and vinyl floors.
WALTER G. LEGGE CO.

Lektroset®. An electronic process for the treatment of RAYON cord to prevent kinking and curling in fabric mfg. It sets the twist uniformly as the cones or spools of cord pass between electrodes.
INDUSTRIAL RAYON CORP.

Lemac 7, 15, 40, 150, 1,000 and 6,000[NE]. A series of polyvinyl acetate beads available in the six grades of increasing viscosity. Used in the formulation of adhesives, inks and paper coatings.
AMERICAN MONOMER CORP.

Lemac WD[NE]. An alkali-soluble vinyl acetate copolymer used in the mfg. of textile finishes, textile sizes, adhesives, paints and paper coatings.
AMERICAN MONOMER CORP.

Lemol 65-98[NE]. A high-viscosity, completely polymerized polyvinyl alcohol resin that is especially useful in the mfg. of adhesives and textile finishes.
AMERICAN MONOMER CORP.

Lemongrass Oil[△]. A pale reddish essential oil used as a stabilizer and perfume in the mfg. of soaps and cosmetics. It is obtained by distilling various species of the *Cymbopogon* grass of the East Indies, Malaya and tropical America. In the U. S., it is obtained from grasses grown in Florida. The oil is composed principally of about 75% citral, $C_9H_{15}CHO$, together with some citronellal, $C_{10}H_{18}O$, geraniol, $C_{10}H_{17}OH$, and ionone, $C_{13}H_{20}O$.

Lentin®. (*Supp.* I p. 125). No longer available.
SHARP & DOHME DIV., MERCK & CO.

Levant Storax[△]. *See* STORAX[△].

Levelon[NE]. A leveling agent for wax and resin emulsions. It is a water-soluble, resinous system containing water and alcohol-type solvents. pH, 9.0–9.5; solids content, approx. 60%. It has the ability to improve and increase gloss in many formulations and, therefore, finds use in the formulation of latex-based products, resin emulsions, paints, varnishes, inks, and protective coatings. ABCO CHEMICAL CO.

Lexan®. Thermoplastic polycarbonate resins which may be used as molding or extrusion compounds, or in films, varnishes or coatings. The resins possess an unusual combination of toughness, impact strength, heat resistance, dimensional stability, and good electrical properties. GENERAL ELECTRIC CO.

Libeplex®. An injectable vitamin B complex for the prevention and treatment of macrocytic anemia, beriberi, pellagra, ariboflavinosis, polyneuritis, gastrointestinal disturbances, cardiovascular disorders, and other forms of vitamin B complex deficiencies. The vitamin B_{12} and liver content makes this preparation suitable for the treatment of various marcrocytic anemias. CONSOLIDATED MIDLAND CORP.

Liberty®. The trademark for a line of agricultural dusts for orchards and gardens.
APOTHECARIES HALL CO.

Liberty Liquid Parting[NE]. A thin, waterproof coating that spreads evenly on all surfaces, is stable over a reasonable temp. range, and provides a clean, slick surface on match plates. It is not recommended where a wax fillet is used on the pattern. For use in metal foundries. M. A. BELL CO.

Liberty Red Rubber Sheet Packing[NE]. A red rubber sheet packing material made from a heat-resisting rubber compound and designed for use against hot and cold water, air, and medium- or low-pressure steam up to 150 lb. per sq. in. Available in several styles, with and without wire insertions, in sheets and in cut gaskets. JOHNS-MANVILLE SALES CORP.

Life® for Fabrics. A textile water repellent and conditioner. It is a white, stable, wax emulsion that is readily dispersible in water. It is designed primarily for treating LINENS but it may be used on any fabric that is washable in water. FRANKLIN RESEARCH CO.

Lightning®. A smokeless powder for use in shot guns, rifles, and small arms. HERCULES POWDER CO.

Light/Stop®. Light-impervious partitions extending laterally along the top surface of heater-ventilator units and flanking cabinets. AMERICAN AIR FILTER CO.

Lignite Wax[△]. *Same as* MONTAN WAX[△].

Lignophol®. (*HBMTN* p. 335). Now a registered trademark. L. SONNEBORN SONS, INC.

Lignophol® Quick-Drying. (*HBMTN* p. 335). The name LIGNOPHOL® is now a registered trademark.
L. SONNEBORN SONS, INC.

Ligno-sote[NE]. The trade name for a line of shingle stains. BURGESS, FOBES CO.

Lignum Vitae[△]. A very hard, heavy, tough wood of the guayacum trees, *Guaiacum officinale* and *G. sanctum*, of tropical America. The best quality comes from Cuba, Haiti, Yucatan, Dominican Republic, and the west coast of Mexico and Central America, although species of the tree grow as far south as Paraguay. The wood is brown to greenish black in color, has a greasy feel, and a very finely twisted grain. It is used for applications requiring a very hard wood, as for pulley blocks, bearings, rollers, mallet heads, etc. It has a density of 72–88 lb. per cu. ft. and a crushing strength of about 10,000 lb. per sq. in.

Lik-Wid®. A winterized cottonseed oil. It remains clear and free-flowing longer at low temps. than ordinary salad oils. Does not separate when refrigerated. Used in salad dressings, mayonnaise, for seasoning and for frying.
ANDERSON, CLAYTON & CO. FOODS DIV.

Lily®. Sublimed flowers of sulfur, N.F.
OLIN MATHIESON CHEMICAL CORP.

Limelite. (Trademark registration pending). A white, free-flowing moderately alkaline powder for use as an additive to high caustic bottle washing solutions. OAKITE PRODUCTS, INC.

Lime Sulfur[△]. *Also known as* EAU GRISON[△]. An aqueous solution containing calcium polysulfides.

Prepared by solution of sulfur in calcium hydroxide suspensions, preferably under pressure in absence of air. It is a deep orange, malodorous liquid with a sp.gr. of not less than 1.28 (60°F.). It acts as a direct fungicide on powdery mildew; it is phytotoxic, especially on "sulfur-shy" varieties.

Lincide 2. (*Supp.* I p. 127). Should have been listed as LINCIDE 20. THOMPSON CHEMICALS CORP.

Lincide 20. Incorrectly listed as LINCIDE 2 (*Supp.* I p. 127). THOMPSON CHEMICALS CORP.

Lionblast®. A tough, sharp aluminum oxide for pressure blasting. Used in foundries for cleaning and descaling; in the stone industry for sharp, clear lettering and delicate shading of scroll-work; for pottery and glass etching. GENERAL ABRASIVE CO.

Lipo Gantrisin®. A medicinal for the treatment of systemic and urinary tract infections. Consists of 20% GANTRISAN® ACETYL emulsified in a readily digestible vegetable oil. Each teaspoonful (5 cc.) contains the equivalent of 1 g. sulfisoxazole (GANTRISIN®) in the form of acetyl sulfisoxazole.
HOFFMANN-LA ROCHE INC.

Lipoiodine®. An organic iodide preparation supplied in the form of pleasant-tasting tablets containing 41% iodine organically bound. Used in the treatment of all conditions in which iodide medication is of value. CIBA PHARMACEUTICAL PRODUCTS INC.

Liqua-Leaf[NB]. A fertilizer for application by spray through the leaves of plants. Total nitrogen, not less than 10%; available phosphoric acid, not less than 10%; water-soluble potash, not less than 8%; together with boron, molybdenum, magnesium, manganese, iron copper, and zinc, and the plant hormone, naphthalene acetic acid.
MILLER CHEMICAL & FERTILIZER CORP.

Liquid C.H.Q.[NB]. (*Supp.* I p. 130). No longer available. EDWAL SCIENTIFIC PRODUCTS CORP.

Liqui-Det. (Trademark registration pending). A general-purpose, highly concentrated, liquid detergent.
OAKITE PRODUCTS, INC.

Liquid Rosin△. Same as TALL OIL△.

Liquid Shineze. A blend of Carnauba and synthetic waxes in a fast-evaporating solvent carrier, used to clean, wax, and polish wood floors in one operation. It buffs to a velvet-like, scuff-resistant sheen. It can also be used as a sealer coat on cork tile, and for cleaning and polishing furniture, paneled walls, etc.
J. I. HOLCOMB MFG. CO.

Liqui-Fry®. A winterized cottonseed oil. It remains clear and free-flowing longer at low temps. than ordinary salad oils. Does not separate when refrigerated. Used in salad dressings, mayonnaise, for seasoning and for frying. ANDERSON, CLAYTON & CO. FOODS DIV.

Liquizinc[NB]. Incorrectly listed as LIQUIZINE[NB] (*Supp.* I p. 130). RUBBA, INC.

Liquizine[NB]. (*Supp.* I p. 130). Should have been listed as LIQUIZINC[NB]. RUBBA, INC.

Lira[NB]. A line of infrared gas and liquid analyzers. *Use:* For selective sensitive high-speed analysis of complex streams. MINE SAFETY APPLIANCES CO.

Lissephen®. A muscle relaxant in capsule form. Chemically it is mephenesin. ABBOTT LABORATORIES

Lite®. A winterized cottonseed oil. It remains clear and free-flowing longer at low temps. than ordinary salad oils. Does not separate when refrigerated. Used in salad dressings, mayonnaise, for seasoning and for frying. ANDERSON, CLAYTON & CO. FOODS DIV.

Lithocrome®. The trademark for a line of coatings for metal decorating.
INTERCHEMICAL CORP., FINISHES DIV.

Lithoday®. The trademark for a line of pre-packaged lithographic inks.
INTERCHEMICAL CORP., PRINTING INK DIV.

Lithofect[NB]. A line of coated papers.
KIMBERLY-CLARK CORP.

Lithogem®. A line of lithographic inks.
INTERCHEMICAL CORP., PRINTING INK DIV.

Litholite®. An aluminum oxide abrasive which is heat treated, washed, dried and graded into sizes 54 to 240. Used for lithographic plate graining.
GENERAL ABRASIVE CO.

Litmus△. A dyestuff prepared from several varieties of the lichen, *Variolaria*, principally *Rocella tinctoria*. The dyestuff is obtained by fermenting the lichen in the presence of ammonia and potassium carbonate. LITMUS has a deep blue color in an alkali medium and a red color in an acid medium. It is used as an acid-alkali indicator, and for dyeing textiles, staining wood, and coloring foods. The coloring principle in LITMUS is azolitmin, $C_7H_7O_4N$.

Livestock Self Dewormer®. A flavored phenothiazine powder for deworming cattle, sheep, goats, horses, mules, and swine. For application, it is mixed with the animal's feed. Composition: phenothiazine, 53% by wt. (240 g. per lb.); flavoring media, 47% by wt.
ATOMIC BASIC CHEMICALS CORP.

Livitol®. A combination of vitamins, liver, and iron for the treatment of hypochromic microcytic anemias due to loss of blood or chronic infections. Supplied in capsule form. CONSOLIDATED MIDLAND CORP.

Livitol® Syrup. A combination of vitamin B complex, liver, and iron for the treatment of nutritional anemias. CONSOLIDATED MIDLAND CORP.

Livrex[NB]. An injectable liver extract for the treatment of pernicious anemia, sprue, and severe secondary anemias. It aids in restoring normal red cell count and hemoglobin content in the blood. It is available as: (1) Livrex-2, which has, per cc., crude liver extract equivalent in vitamin B_{12} activity to 2 mcg. cyanocobalamine; (2) Livrex-10, which has, per cc., refined liver extract equivalent in vitamin B_{12} activity to 10 mcg. cyanocobalamine; (3) Livrex-BB, which is the same as Livrex-10 with the addition of 5 mg. vitamin B_1 and 5 mcg. crystalline B_{12} per cc.; and (4) Livrex-BF, which is the same as Livrex-2 with the addition of 5 mg. folic acid and 15 mcg. crystalline vitamin B_{12} per cc.
CONSOLIDATED MIDLAND CORP.

Lixa-Beta®. A VITAMIN B preparation. Each fluid ounce contains: VITAMIN B_1 (thiamine hydrochloride)

2664 U.S.P. units (8.0 mg.) in a flavored elixir; alcohol content, 15%. WARNER-CHILCOTT LABORATORIES

Lock-Ease®. A graphited lock fluid designed to prevent sticking of the lock, minimize rusting and wear, and protect against freezing.
AMERICAN GREASE STICK CO.

Lock-Seal®. The trademark for a line of spring-head roofing nails. UNITED STATES STEEL CORP.

Lo-Fat®. The trademark applied to various soy products such as Powdered Soya and Soy Flour. Aside from their many food applications, LO-FAT Soy products are used as stabilizing agents in asphalt emulsions, and as sticking and spreading agents in insecticide sprays. They are also used as fillers and binders in linoleum, and as stabilizers in latex-type paints.
A. E. STALEY MFG. CO.

L.O.F. Super-Fine[NR]. A glass fiber thermal and acoustical insulation material made of extremely fine, long and uniform fibers. Available in rolls of various widths, thicknesses and densities, either plain or faced with a choice of several standard facing materials, including aluminum foil, vinyl, plain or reflective vapor barrier papers. The thermal conductivity of L.O.F. SUPER-FINE of 1.0 lb./cu.ft. density is 0.20 B.t.u.-inch/(hr. × sq.ft. × °F.) at a mean temp. of 50°F. L.O.F. GLASS FIBERS CO.

Log Cabin®. An all-vegetable, fully hydrogenated shortening for use in baking, frying and pastry making.
ANDERSON, CLAYTON & CO. FOODS DIV.

Log Cabin® Margarine. A margarine made of hydrogenated soybean and cottonseed oils, nonfat dry milk, water, salt, LECITHIN, 0.1% sodium benzoate added as a preservative, artificial coloring, and 15,000 units of VITAMIN A per lb.
ANDERSON, CLAYTON & CO. FOODS DIV.

Logolube[NR]. (*HBMTN* p. 338). No longer available. BEE CHEMICAL CO.

Lok-Bevel®. Wood fiberboard materials with a special joint. ARMSTRONG CORK CO.

Lok-Crete[NR]. A bonding agent that is used to lock new concrete to old concrete, and new plaster to old plaster. It is also used to mend broken stone, marble, and tile. HALLEMITE MFG. CO.

Lonchocarpus△. Known as BARBASCO in Spanish speaking countries of South America, as CUBE in Peru, as HAIARI in British Guiana, as NEKOE in Dutch Guiana, and as TIMBO in Brazil. An insecticidal material prepared from the dried roots of certain leguminous shrubs and trees, principally *L. utilis, L. urucu,* and *L. nicou.* The principal insecticidal compound of LONCHOCARPUS is ROTENONE, which is present in amounts from 8–11%, together with smaller amounts of related compounds.

Lonco #42. (*Supp.* I p. 131). No longer available. LONDON CHEMICAL CO.

Lonco Copperbrite #48. A cleaner and brightener for printed circuits. LONDON CHEMICAL CO.

Lonco PC #33 Solder Resist. An organic coating designed to make possible elective soldering of printed circuits. It is screened onto certain areas of a circuit to mask out solder "take" while other areas are left uncoated to permit soldering. It cures in 30–35 min. at 200–230°F.; and leaves a hard, tough film that does not peel, pit or blister in the soldering operation at temps. as high as 600°F.
LONDON CHEMICAL CO.

Long Reach®. The trademark for: (1) jute bagging and jute bagging patches used for covering bales of COTTON; and (2) COTTON bale marking ink.
ANDERSON, CLAYTON & CO.

Long Ternes△. *See* TERNE PLATE△.

Loosol®. (*HBMTN* p. 339). No longer available. TENNESSEE EASTMAN CO.

Lorfan Tartrate[NR]. A potent narcotic antagonist used in obstetrics for the prevention of maternal and fetal respiratory depression from narcotics; for the treatment and prevention of narcotic-induced depression during nitrous oxide-oxygen anesthesia with narcotic supplementation, and when narcotics are used preoperatively or postoperatively for the relief of pain. Chemically, LORFAN TARTRATE is 1–3 hydroxy-N-allylomophinan tartrate.
HOFFMANN-LA ROCHE INC.

Lorig-Aligner®. The trademark for a line of self-centering rolls and pulleys. UNITED STATES STEEL CORP.

Lotocreme®. A soothing body rub and emollient for hospital use. ABBOTT LABORATORIES

LowAmp®. The trademark for a line of arc-welding electrodes that require much lower current than conventional electrodes. For example, a ⅛" LOW-AMP electrode requires 80–90 amps. as compared to the usual 165–180 amps.
EUTECTIC WELDING ALLOYS CORP.

LowTemp®. The trademark for a line of torch-welding electrodes that can be used at lower temps. than conventional rods. EUTECTIC WELDING ALLOYS CORP.

L-P Industrial Spray[NR]. A knock-down, non-poisonous, synergized pyrethrin, oil-base spray for the control of grain insects, flies, cockroaches, etc.
LARVACIDE PRODUCTS, INC.

LSD. *See* OAKITE® LSD.

LT-Minus Thirty®. *See* ARMSTRONG LT PIPE COVERING.

LT-Thirty®. *See* ARMSTRONG LT PIPE COVERING.

LT-Zero®. *See* ARMSTRONG LT PIPE COVERING.

Lubeway®. A high-quality, dual-purpose hydraulic oil that also serves as a way lubricant. Possesses good stability and non-sludging characteristics of a good hydraulic oil and also the ability to wet the metal and provide the extreme-pressure qualities of a good lubricant for machine ways. Intended primarily for use in hydraulically operated milling, grinding and boring machines in which the ways are fed from the hydraulic-oil reservoir. SUN OIL CO.

Lubricant 105. *See* CD LUBRICANT 105.

Lubritine[NR]. A sterile, convenient and efficient, non-greasy lubricant for hands, gloves or instruments.
ABBOTT LABORATORIES

Lukens Clad Steels[NR]. A line of clad steels including various types of stainless clad; nickel clad, MONEL-clad, INCONEL-clad; and copper clad.
LUKENS STEEL CO.

Lukens "T-1" Steel®. A low-carbon, high-strength, quenched and tempered, readily weldable alloy plate steel possessing a combination of properties that make it especially useful for pressure vessels, bridges, shipbuilding, construction machinery, and general industrial equipment. The typical chemical composition of this steel is as follows: carbon, 0.15%; manganese, 0.75%; phosphorus, 0.026%; sulfur, 0.030%; silicon, 0.24%; nickel, 0.85%; chromium, 0.50%; molybdenum, 0.45%; vanadium, 0.05%; copper, 0.31%, and boron, 0.0029%. Tensile strength, 105,000 lb./sq.in.; yield strength under load, 90,000 lb./sq.in. (min.); modulus of elasticity in tension, 30,000,000 lb./sq.in.; atmospheric corrosion resistance, 4 times greater than that for carbon steel.
LUKENS STEEL CO.

Lullamin® **Drops.** A medicinal consisting of 16.0 mg. methapyrilene hydrochloride (N.N.R.) per teaspoonful (5 cc.) in a pleasantly flavored syrup. *Use:* To combat daytime irritability and overactivity, and to help re-establish the normal sleep pattern at bedtime. It is non-habit forming because it is free of bromides, barbiturates and narcotics.
REED & CARNRICK

Lumatex®. A line of pigment colors suitable for machine and screen printing. They have excellent fastness to light and very good all-round fastness, particularly to dry cleaning.
Mfg'd by BADISCHE ANILIN-U. SODA-FABRIK AG.
Dist'd by NOVA CHEMICAL CORP.

Lumatex® **Binder F.** A binder for use in conjunction with the LUMATEX pigment colors for padding on COTTON and synthetic piece goods. It requires only the addition of water, no auxiliaries or catalysts are necessary. Any of the standard resins used in finishing may be added for a one-bath operation.
Mfg'd by BADISCHE ANILIN-U. SODA-FABRIK AG.
Dist'd by NOVA CHEMICAL CORP.

Lumattin SL. A substantive delustering agent for RAYON and staple fiber. It is a white paste, easily dilutible with warm water to a milky-white, finely dispersed suspension. The suspension can be diluted with soft or hard water. The delusterings produced with LUMATTIN SL are fast to rinsing, do not dust, and give RAYON and staple fiber a full soft feel. It is not compatible with all normally applied anion active detergents, softeners, wetting and levelling agents; these products must therefore be removed by thorough rinsing if they are on the materials to be delustered.
NOVA CHEMICAL CORP.

Lume-Brite[NR]. A viscous, odorless liquid for cleaning and brightening aluminum and stainless steel. Used on aircraft and truck trailer exteriors. Approved by U. S. Air Force.
BRULIN & CO.

Lumicel®. Translucent, sound-absorbing elements used in building construction.
CELOTEX CORP.

Lumifect®. A registered trademark for a book paper.
KIMBERLY-CLARK CORP.

Luminite®. A quick-hardening, calcium-aluminate cement characterized by its excellent resistance to corrosion and resistance to disintegration by heat. It is used for making corrosion-resistant concrete for floors and structures, refractory concrete, cement linings for iron and steel pipe, mortar protective coatings for steel and concrete tanks, insulating concrete, and overnight concrete.
UNIVERSAL ATLAS CEMENT CO.

Lumisol. (*Supp.* I p. 132). No longer available.
CARLISLE CHEMICAL WORKS, INC.

Lundite®. A wide-graded aluminum oxide abrasive grain used for buffing operations. Available in sizes 100/120, 180/220, 240F, and 320F.
GENERAL ABRASIVE CO.

Lunetzol A. A nonfrothing wetting and leveling agent. It is a clear, yellowish brown, slightly viscous liquid of practically neutral reaction. It is readily and rapidly dispersed in water, yielding slightly opalescent solutions. It is particularly useful with direct sulfur and vat dyestuffs.
NOVA CHEMICAL CORP.

Luracel®. The trademark for a line of fabrics made wholly or partially of cellulose derivatives.
CELANESE CORP. OF AMERICA

Luridine△. *Same as* CHOLINE△.

Lusterlite®. (*HBMTN* p. 344 and *Supp.* I p. 132). No longer available.
MINNESOTA & ONTARIO PAPER CO., INSULITE DIV.

Lustracrystal®. An economical, heavy sheet glass for glazing large areas. It is 2½ times as resistant to surface abrasion as plate glass, and transmits 4 times as much ultraviolet light and slightly more visible light. It is a very light colored glass, free from a greenish cast, and has a fire-polished, scratch-resistant surface.
AMERICAN WINDOW GLASS CO.

Lustragray®. A gray-tinted, heat-absorbing and glare-reducing glass for glazing where a reduction of sun glare and heat transmission is desirable. LUSTRAGRAY® (¼" thick) transmits only 55.0% of visible light, 68.5% of the infra red, and 62.6% of solar radiation.
AMERICAN WINDOW GLASS CO.

Lustrakool®. A green-tinted, heat-absorbing and glare-reducing glass for glazing where a reduction of sun glare and heat transmission is desirable. A ¼" thickness transmits only 78.7% of visible light, 19.1% of the infra red, and 43.6% of solar radiation.
AMERICAN WINDOW GLASS CO.

Lustral®. A machine dishwashing compound.
DIVERSEY CORP.

Lustrawhite®. A picture glass of exceptional clarity and flatness.
AMERICAN WINDOW GLASS CO.

Lustreflex®. (*Supp.* I p. 132). Now a registered trademark. A product of UBS CHEMICAL CORP., successor to UNION BAY STATE CHEMICAL CO.

Lustre-N-Dure[NR]. A line of waxes and polishes.
SHERWIN-WILLIAMS CO.

Lustrocel®. The trademark for a line of fabrics made wholly or partially of cellulose derivatives.
CELANESE CORP. OF AMERICA

Lycoid®. Formulations of galactomannan colloids incorporating such materials as guar gum, locust bean gum, etc. *Use:* For paper mill applications ranging from internal bonding to surface sizing.
STEIN, HALL & CO.

Lyfanite®. Phosphate and other complex coatings for steel and aluminum alloys for imparting greater corrosion resistance and better paint adherence.
NEILSON CHEMICAL CO.

Lyman®. The trademark for a galvanized 4-point (round point) barbed wire, with barbs spaced 5″ apart.
UNITED STATES STEEL CORP.

Lyofix® EW Conc. A product used for improving the fastness of dyes to water, perspiration, hot pressing, washing, sea water, sizing, fulling and finishing. It improves the fastness of direct, diazo, sulfur, and union dyeings, and prints produced with direct and acid colors on COTTON, LINEN, spun and filament VISCOSE, SILK, and mixed materials containing WOOL. It is a fine, cream-colored, somewhat hygroscopic powder. It is cation-active, and is precipitated by soap, sulfonated oils, sulfates, direct and acid dyes, and other high-molecular-weight anion-active compounds.
CIBA CO.

M

M6[NE]. (*HBMTN* p. 345). Now a product of THE BORDEN CO., CHEMICAL DIV., successor to PIONEER LATEX & CHEMICAL CO.

M-58 Dust[NE]. (*HBMTN* p. 345). No longer available.
MILLER CHEMICAL & FERTILIZER CORP.

M-75[NE]. (*Supp.* I p. 133). Now a product of THE BORDEN CO., CHEMICAL DIV., successor to PIONEER LATEX & CHEMICAL CO.

Mabco Aluminum Flux[NE]. An aluminum flux for use in foundry work. Available in two grades, No. 1 and No. 2. The No. 1 FLUX is designed to remove most of the oxides and impurities from molten aluminum, increasing the strength and elongation of the finished casting. It is economical to use since only 2 to 4 oz. per 100 lb. of metal are necessary. The No. 2 FLUX has a milder action than No. 1 and also acts as a protective covering during the melting process.
M. A. BELL CO.

Mabco Core Oils[NE]. The trade name for an extensive line of laboratory-controlled core oils.
M. A. BELL CO.

Mabco Iron Filler[NE]. A compound used to fill blow holes in iron or steel castings, smoothing surface blemishes, and closing pores in spongy places. When hard, it has the color and luster of cast iron. Furnished in light and dark colors.
M. A. BELL CO.

Mabco Mineral Facing[NE]. A finely-ground, high-carbon facing material used in the mfg. of car wheels. It is applied to the face of the mold through a dust bag.
M. A. BELL CO.

Mabco Pattern Paint[NE]. A quick-drying paint designed to provide a coating on wood patterns that is impervious to moisture and most solvents. It leaves a smooth metallic finish to which hot sand does not stick. The paint may also be used to coat wax and leather fillets so that a liquid parting agent may be used. *Uses:* To build up and revamp metal or wood patterns; coat wood patterns for longer life and a slick draw; make cast stone patterns work like metal; coat iron patterns to prevent rusting; coat wood flasks to prevent sticking and swelling; and to coat metal sand bins.
M. A. BELL CO.

Mabco Quality Pitch Core Compound[NE]. A finely ground, pure, coal tar pitch pulverized to a mesh which has been proven to be most suitable for foundry purposes. Only crude pitch which meets rigidly maintained specifications (m.p. 285° to 315°F.) is used in the mfg. of this product. May be used as a dry sand facing.
M. A. BELL CO.

Mabco Seacoal Facing[NE]. A foundry facing material made of specially selected bituminous coal. Available in six standard grade sizes, although special grades are also available on order. Designed to prevent sand grains from burning into the metal, with a resultant improvement in the casting finish.
M. A. BELL CO.

Mabcotherm 23 IS[NE]. An exothermic, carbon-free, hot top material for use in the casting of gray iron, steel, and stainless steel. The exothermic and insulating action of this material promotes feeding of the casting with smaller risers than would ordinarily be used.
M. A. BELL CO.

Mabcotherm Pipe Eliminator[NE]. A foundry anti-piping compound that is used to keep the risers open on either gray iron or steel castings. It contains a heat-producing compound as well as an insulating material designed to keep the heat in a position to do the most good. With this compound, piping will be uniform and the action will continue until the metal casting has completely solidified. Does not contain carbon or graphite, or any agents which are detrimental to steel or gray iron castings.
M. A. BELL CO.

Macco Finish 6000[NE]. A paste-type product for weighting and finishing textiles in one operation. Especially useful for tubular knit goods.
MAC CHEMICAL CO.

Maccowax Softener[NE]. A textile softener for use on tubular knit fabrics to give additional body and finish to the fabric. It also can be used on piece goods of both natural and synthetic fibers.
MAC CHEMICAL CO.

Magcal[NE]. (*Supp.* I p. 133). No longer available.
SHARP & DOHME DIV., MERCK & CO.

Magikil® Ant and Roach Duster. A duster equipped with removable rubber bulb for easy refilling, and filled with 1½ oz. of 5% CHLORDANE dust. Also packed in refill containers. *Use:* For the control of all types of ants and roaches.
LETHELIN PRODUCTS CO.

Magikil® Jelly Ant Bait. A jelly ant bait containing 1% thallium sulphate. Packed in traps, tubes and in bulk. *Use:* To control sweet eating ants and Brown Banded roaches.
LETHELIN PRODUCTS CO.

Magitrack Mouse Duster[NE]. A duster equipped with removable rubber bulb for easy refilling, and filled with 1¼ oz. of dust containing 50% micronized DDT.

Also packed in refill containers. *Use:* For the control of mice infested buildings.
LETHELIN PRODUCTS CO.

Maglite®. (*Supp.* I p. 133). No longer available.
SHARP & DOHME DIV., MERCK & CO.

Magnel[NE]. (*HBMTN* p. 347). No longer available.
NATIONAL MALLEABLE & STEEL CASTINGS CO.

Magno®. (*HBMTN* p. 347). No longer available.
NATIONAL MALLEABLE & STEEL CASTINGS CO.

Maintinets®. (*Supp.* I p. 133). No longer available.
SHARP & DOHME DIV., MERCK & CO.

Majestic[NE]. (*Supp.* I p. 133). No longer available.
HANSON-VAN WINKLE-MUNNING CO.

Malathion[△]. An insecticidal compound. S-(1,2-dicarbethoxyethyl)*o,o*-dimethyl phosphorodithioate. $C_{10}H_{19}O_6PS_2$; mol.wt. 330.37. The pure compound is a yellowish oil with a b.p. of 156–157°C. (7 mm.Hg); the technical grade, 95–98% pure, is a dark brown liquid with a strong garlic odor. It is water soluble to the extent of 145 ppm., and is miscible with most organic solvents but of limited solubility in petroleum oils. Rapidly hydrolyzed at pH above 7.0 or below 5.0, but stable in aqueous solution buffered at pH 5.26. MALATHION is highly toxic to certain phytophagus mites and to certain insects, including aphids, Mexican bean beetle, several species of scale insects and houseflies.

Malglyn® Compound Tablets. A combination of the antacid, ALGLYN®, with ¼ grain phenobarbital and ¹/₄₀₀ grain Belladonna alkaloids. Used for the treatment of peptic ulcer and hyperacidity.
BRAYTON PHARMACEUTICAL CO.

Malikil®. A residual fly killer, particularly for use in industrial and business establishments.
J. I. HOLCOMB MFG. CO.

Mallory 1000®. A sintered, high-density alloy of 4% copper, 6% nickel, and the balance tungsten, for use as rotating inertia members, counterbalances, and shielding material for radioactive products. Density, 16.96 g./cc.; ultimate tensile strength, 112,000 lb./sq.in.; modulus of rupture, 220,000 lb./sq.in.; hardness, Rockwell "C," 24–30; electrical conductivity, 14.0% I.A.C.S.; yield strength, 75,000 lb./sq.in.; shear strength, 51,000 lb./sq.in.
P. R. MALLORY & CO.

Mallory 1000 Gyromet®. A very dense alloy of tungsten, nickel, copper, and other elements developed for rotor applications, particularly in the aviation industry. Density, 16.70–17.05 g./cc.; hardness, Rockwell "C," 30–36; endurance limit, 55,000 lb./sq.in.; electrical conductivity, 14% I.A.C.S.; thermal conductivity, 0.235 g.-cm./cm.^{2} × sec. × °C.; ultimate compressive strength, 170,000 lb./sq.in.; yield strength, 120,000 lb./sq.in.; ultimate tensile strength (room temp.), 135,000 lb./sq.in.; modulus of rupture (flexure), 230,000 lb./sq.in.
P. R. MALLORY & CO.

Mallory Mallosil® Process. This patented process was originally developed for depositing a thick silver deposit on electrical contacts. It is now used for silver plating aircraft bearings and for other plating requirements in the electrical, electronic, and mechanical industries where excellent thermal and electrical conductivity are required. The MALLOSIL PROCESS bonds a homogenous and highly pure (99.90%) silver coating or lining to ferrous and nonferrous metals and alloys including low- or medium-carbon steel, cartridge brass, stainless steel, and most other lead-free metals and alloys. Parts up to 20″ × 14″ × 14″ can be coated with coatings from 0.0003″ to 0.060″.
P. R. MALLORY & CO.

Mallosil®. See MALLORY MALLOSIL® PROCESS.

Maltese Cross®. (*Supp.* I p. 134). This trademark for various types of rubber goods is also registered in Bolivia, Brazil, Chile, Cuba and Peru.
HEWITT-ROBINS, INC.

Maltine®. (*HBMTN* p. 348). Now a product of WARNER-CHILCOTT LABORATORIES, successor to THE MALTINE CO.

Malto® Yerbine. A soothing expectorant for the relief of coughs due to colds and bronchitis. Each fluid ounce contains 2 g. extract yerba santa (Eriodictyon) and MALTINE® (concentrated extract of malted barley). It contains no cane sugar or opiates.
WARNER-CHILCOTT LABORATORIES

Manartal®. A medicinal. Mannitol hexanitrate and phenobarbital tablets.
ABBOTT LABORATORIES

Mang-Arc®. Bare and coated nickel-manganese electrodes for the welding of manganese steel. Composition: 0.55% carbon, 13.0% manganese, 0.65% silicon, 3.5% nickel, balance iron.
ALLOY RODS CO.

Mangrove[△]. A leather tanning extract from the bark of the mangrove tree, *Rhizophora mangle,* of Venezuela and Colombia; the red mangrove, *R. racemosa,* of Nigeria; the East African mangrove, *R. mucronata,* and other species of Africa, the East Indies, southern Asia, and tropical America. The tannin content varies from as little as 5% to as much as 45%. The tanning material is marketed as a solid extract in the form of blocks containing about 50% tannin, as a solution containing about 50% tannin, and as a solution containing from 25 to 35% tannin.

Manila Copal[△]. See COPAL[△].

Manolator®. The trademark for a sifter cartridge insufflator.
ABBOTT LABORATORIES

Mantalloy®. Crusher parts, such as the head mantle and concave ring, of gyratory crushers, made from an abrasion-resisting alloy.
ALLIS-CHALMERS MFG. CO.

Man-Ten®. See U.S.S.® MAN-TEN®.

Manumatic®. A patented brass multiport valve specifically designed for domestic and light industrial pressure water softeners and filters. It incorporates four operating positions in a single valve, and each position is clearly marked on a stainless steel face plate provided. It is very compact and easy to operate.
CLACK WATER TREATMENT, INC.

Mapleagenda[NR]. A compound of vegetable origin recommended for use in conjunction with MAPLE-AROME.
FLORASYNTH LABORATORIES, INC.

Maplearome[NE]. An imitation maple flavor base with the flavor and aroma of maple sap. Used for the mfg. of maple-flavored syrup.
FLORASYNTH LABORATORIES, INC.

Maraset®. A line of epoxy resins for casting, bonding, laminating, and other production applications.
MARBLETTE CORP.

Mark C®. An organic chelating agent recommended for use in conjunction with metallic compounds for the stabilization of polyvinyl chloride. It is a clear liquid, soluble in esters, ethers, and most other organic solvents; insoluble in water.
ARGUS CHEMICAL CORP.

Mark WS®. A barium-cadmium organic soap for the stabilization of rigid and plasticized polyvinyl chloride. A fine white powder; sp.gr. 1.27; moisture content, 1.0% (max.); used in conc. of 0.75–1.5 parts per 100 parts resin.
ARGUS CHEMICAL CORP.

Marrakesh. *See* ROSE MARRAKESH.

Marvalon®. The registered trademark for a line of coated and/or impregnated fibrous sheet materials.
KIMBERLY-CLARK CORP.

Maskfone[NR]**.** A sound-powered wire communication system for direct telephone contact with protective mask wearers.
MINE SAFETY APPLIANCES CO.

Masland Duran®. Incorrectly listed as DURAN® (*HBMTN* p. 190).
MASLAND DURALEATHER CO.

Masland Duran® Clad. Semi-rigid vinyl sheeting designed for laminating to steel and non-ferrous metals. The sheeting, which is available in a number of patterns and colors, can be laminated to flat metal sheets or continuous coils, and shaped or formed as the metal itself. Bonding is secure and unimpaired after forming.
MASLAND DURALEATHER CO.

Masland Durasol®. Incorrectly listed as DURASAL® (*HBMTN* p. 191).
MASLAND DURALEATHER CO.

Master of Flame®. (*Supp.* I p. 138). No longer available.
ANSUL CHEMICAL CO.

Mastolyn®. A phenolic-modified resin.
HERCULES POWDER CO.

Match Box®. A kit for matching printing ink colors.
INTERCHEMICAL CORP., PRINTING INK DIV.

Mattolin. (*HBMTN* p. 352). No longer available; Company liquidated as of Oct. 1, 1955.
GENERAL DRUG CO.

Mawco[NR]**.** Lacquers, synthetics and enamels of miscellaneous compositions for various products.
MAAS & WALDSTEIN CO.

Maxlite®. An essentially clear CORRULUX® panel which permits the highest light transmission in the CORRULUX range of colors (approx. 85% of available sunlight). It is used primarily for industrial flat glazing, industrial skylighting, and a major new market—greenhouses.
L-O-F GLASS FIBERS CO., CORRULUX DIV.

Maxilets[NR]**.** A multi-vitamin and mineral tablet used in the treatment of vitamin deficiencies. Available in the form of bright green tablets which contain VITAMIN A (synthetic), VITAMIN D, thiamin mononitrate, riboflavin, nicotinamide, pyridoxine hydrochloride, VITAMIN B_{12}, folic acid, pantothenic acid, ascorbic acid, iron, copper, iodine, cobalt, manganese, magnesium, potassium, zinc, and molybdenum. One tablet daily is the prophylactic dose.
ABBOTT LABORATORIES

Mazic® No. 2 Anodes. (*HBMTN* p. 352). No longer available.
HANSON-VAN WINKLE-MUNNING CO.

Mazic® Brightener. (*HBMTN* p. 352). No longer available.
HANSON-VAN WINKLE-MUNNING CO.

MC (Mold and Cavity Steel)[NR]**.** A medium carbon-alloy steel with very deep hardening qualities. Carbon, 0.35%; silicon, 0.40%; manganese, 0.85%; chromium, 0.85%; molybdenum, 0.40%. It is provided heat-treated and ready-for-use for plastic-mold cavities, die-casting dies, and a wide range of other uses where a highly polished finish is desirable. Painstaking production is made to avoid sulfides and other non-metallic inclusions, permitting high polish in plastic-mold cavities without pits or blemish. It is used for die-casting dies for white-metal alloys, plastic-mold cavities, boring bars, gears, arbors, milling cutter bodies, reamer bodies, and spindles.
VANADIUM-ALLOYS STEEL CO.

MC-1®. A washing powder for use as a general-purpose cleaner.
PENNSYLVANIA SALT MFG. CO.

MC-3®. A detergent composition especially adapted for dairy and home use.
PENNSYLVANIA SALT MFG. CO.

McCaa®. A self-contained breathing apparatus for use in poisonous or oxygen deficient atmospheres. U. S. Bureau of Mines approved.
MINE SAFETY APPLIANCES CO.

MCC® Flake Bottle Wash. A caustic soda cleanser for dairy and bottling plants.
OLIN MATHIESON CHEMICAL CORP.

McKay Tube-Alloy®. Welding wires for automatic and semi-automatic hardsurfacing applications. Available in sizes from $1/8''$ to $5/32''$ in various grades as follows:

Tube-Alloy Grade	Typical weld metal analysis, % (elements other than iron)								Hardness, Rockwell "C"
	C	Cr	Mn	Ni	Si	V	Mo	W	
BU	0.25	0.40	1.25	....	0.75	....	0.35	....	25–30
218	0.70	....	14.00	3.50	....	....	....	....	
252	0.30	3.75	1.75	....	0.75	0.30	0.50	....	45–50
258	0.30	5.00	0.75	....	0.75	....	1.50	1.50	50–54
239	2.25	15.00	2.00	....	1.30	....	....	....	50–54
420	0.35	13.00	0.45	0.20	0.50	....	....	....	47–52

MCKAY CO.

MCPA△. A weed killer and growth-regulating compound. 4 - Chloro - 2 - methylphenoxyacetic acid. $C_9H_9ClO_3$; mol.wt. 200.63. A crystalline product made by the chlorination of *o*-cresol and coupling with monochloroacetic acid. The chlorination of *o*-cresol gives a mixture of 4-chloro-2-methyl phenol and 6-chloro-2-methyl phenol; however, only the 4-chloro-2-methyl derivative is effective as a weed killer and growth-regulating compound. In these properties, it closely resembles 2,4-D. The technical product is a light, granular solid, with a m.p. of 99–107°C. The sodium salts and salts of inorganic bases are water soluble; oil-soluble esters may be readily prepared.

Meadolake® Margarine. A margarine made of hydrogenated soybean and cottonseed oils, nonfat dry milk, water, salt, LECITHIN, 0.1% sodium benzoate added as a preservative, artificial coloring, and 15,000 units of VITAMIN A per pound.
ANDERSON, CLAYTON & CO. FOODS DIV.

Mearlin®. (*HBMTN* p. 354). No longer available.
MEARL CORP.

Mearlmaid[NR]. A natural pearl essence.
MEARL CORP.

Meat Sugar△. *Same as* INOSITOL△.

Mechbond Felts[NR]. A group of filter felts made from pressed staple synthetic fibers. The pressed structure gives smooth, non-raveling edges without sewing or heat sealing; the felts retain finer particles than most woven fabrics; and these chemical-resistant filter felts, which are graded as to porosity, are lower in cost than comparable woven filter fabrics.
BROSITES PRODUCTS CORP.

Mechling®. (*HBMTN* p. 354). No longer available.
GENERAL CHEMICAL DIV.,
ALLIED CHEMICAL & DYE CORP.

Medinal®. A hypnotic-sedative which is rapidly absorbed and produces prolonged, refreshing sleep. Completely soluble in water and aqueous vehicles, it is convenient to administer. Each tablet contains 0.33 g. barbital sodium; each teaspoonful (4 cc.) contains 0.12 g. barbital sodium.
WARNER-CHILCOTT LABORATORIES

Meerschaum△. A soft, white or gray, claylike mineral that is mined principally in Asia Minor. It has a hardness of about 2 on the Moh scale, and a sp.gr. of 1.28. It can be easily cut when wet, and it can withstand relatively high temps. Chemically, it is $3SiO_2·2MgO·2H_2O$. It is used for making pipes and cigar holders, as a filler in soaps, etc.

Mei-Wei-Fen[NR]. Food savoring powders comprising monosodium glutamate.
INTERNATIONAL MINERALS & CHEMICAL CORP.

Melanogen®. A line of blue dyestuffs that are made like a sulfur color but designed for application on COTTON and RAYON from a bath containing salt but no sodium sulfide. Aftertreatment with copper sulfate fixes the dye on the fiber.
GENERAL DYESTUFF CO.

Mellisol®. A compatible lanolin for use in liquid and powdered skin cleaners. It can be added to liquid soaps without sacrifice of clarity or richness of lather.
U. S. SANITARY SPECIALTIES CORP.

Mellitone[NR]. A proprietary synthetic aromatic chemical. A compounded specialty, designed to supply a particular unique note or character to certain finished perfumes.
DOW CHEMICAL CO.

Mello-Green®. The trademark for a line of fertilizers.
INTERNATIONAL MINERALS & CHEMICAL CORP.

Melostrength® Resin. The trademark for a melamine-formaldehyde paper resin designed to improve wet- and dry-strength properties of the paper. It is a pulp additive.
AMERICAN CYANAMID CO.

Mema®. A liquid seed disinfectant containing 11.4% methoxy ethyl mercury acetate (equivalent to 0.6 lb. metallic mercury per gal.). Applied in liquid or slurry treater. *Use:* For the seed treatment of wheat, barley, oats, flax, COTTON and sorghum, to control certain seedborne diseases.
CHIPMAN CHEMICAL CO.

Mepherin. A medicinal tablet containing 300 mg. mephensin, 60 mg. betaine hydrochloride, and 6 mg. ethaverine hydrochloride. It is a combined skeletal muscle and smooth muscle relaxant used in the treatment of low back pain, disc syndrome, myositis, torticollis, lumbosacral strain, lumbago, Parkinsonism, alcoholism, tension headaches, biliary syndrome, mild ureteral spasm, pylorospasm, and spastic colitis.
G. F. HARVEY CO.

Merac® #225. A water-soluble, rubber latex accelerator. A dark brown liquid; sp.gr. 1.025–1.035 (20°/20°C.); viscosity, 9.78 cps. (25°C.); flash point, 185°F.; freezing point, –25°C. (max.); soluble in water, methanol, acetone, and ethyl acetate; insoluble in ethyl ether, benzene, and hexane.
PENNSYLVANIA SALT MFG. CO.

Merfenel 51[NR]. A microorganism control product composed of 71.4% MERFENEL PMA and 28.6% VANCIDE 51 (powder). *Use:* As a fungicide and bactericide.
R. T. VANDERBILT CO.

Merfenel PMA[NR]. Industrial grade phenylmercuric acetate (powder), $C_6H_5HgOCOCH_3$. *Use:* As a fungicide and bactericide.
R. T. VANDERBILT CO.

Mergamma®. A seed protectant containing 40% gamma isomer of BHC and 1.93% phenyl mercury urea. In powder form; applied dry or as a slurry. *Use:* To control wireworms and certain seedborne diseases on small grains, flax, sorghum and corn.
CHIPMAN CHEMICAL CO.

Merix® Stabilite. A light stabilizer for plastics. It is transparent to visible light but absorbs ultraviolet, and thus prevents darkening or discoloration. It also acts as an antistatic agent to prevent dust attraction caused by static electricity.
MERIX CHEMICAL CO.

Merix® Stabilite A. An ultraviolet light absorber and antistatic agent for plastics. A film 0.001″ thick on plastics filters out 99.8% of incident ultraviolet light at wave length 400, and 100% at all wave lengths below 390. Its antistatic property makes plastics dust free.
MERIX CHEMICAL CO.

Merlenate[NR]. A smooth, white ointment and a white, light, fluffy powder for the treatment of Athlete's Foot (tinea pedis), superficial epidermophytosis of the skin, ring worm, and other parasitical

and bacterial infections of the skin. Contains 5% undecylenic acid and 1:1500 phenylmercuric nitrate.
CHICAGO PHARMACAL CO.

Mermix[NB]. (*Supp.* I p. 140). No longer available.
SHARP & DOHME DIV., MERCK & CO.

Mersoclean 540[NB]. A diphase solvent-type metal cleaner for removing buffing compounds and other heavy soils. It contains solvents, emulsifiers, and corrosion inhibitors. WYANDOTTE CHEMICALS CORP., J. B. FORD DIV.

Mersorb®. Respirator cartridges. *Use:* For protection against light concentrations of metallic mercury vapors. MINE SAFETY APPLIANCES CO.

Meta Cine® Douche Powder. A cleansing, soothing, physiologically sound acid douche (pH, 3.5) for routine douching needs, and, in combination with other therapy, in the treatment of various vaginal complaints. BRAYTEN PHARMACEUTICAL CO.

Metafos®. An alternate or companion product to QUADRAFOS® (*HBMTN* p. 471). It is a condensed sodium polyphosphate in the form of a soluble glass. Composition: P_2O_5, 67.0% (min.); Na_2O, 33.0% (max.); titratable Na_2O, 3.2%; H_2O, 0.5% (max.); insolubles (in water), 0.002% (max.). The physical properties of METAFOS are very similar to those of QUADRAFOS, as are their industrial applications. For some special uses, as in the formulation of detergents and as a viscosity controller in oil-well drilling muds, METAFOS may be preferred because of its higher P_2O_5 content and its lower pH.
RUMFORD CHEMICAL WORKS

Metagel-811, 811-32, 820, 860[NB]. A series of co-polymered water-phased resins especially adapted to the printing of metallics as well as for the adhesion of pigments and oxides to textiles. They are quick drying, and require no curing. Available in various viscosities. EASTERN COLOR & CHEMICAL CO.

Metaglow-303[NB]. A copolymerized water-phased resin especially adapted for printing of metallics on textiles. It is quick-drying, does not dull metallic prints, requires no curing, and is fast to washing and dry cleaning. EASTERN COLOR & CHEMICAL CO.

Metagrip. A crystal clear, waterproof, fast-drying cement for bonding plastics to plastics or plastics to metals. For use in the jewelry trade.
ADHESIVE PRODUCTS CORP.

Metalace[NB]. Coating materials systems either of nitrocellulose or synthetic resin base that produce a web or lace-like pattern. MAAS & WALDSTEIN CO.

Metalan®. The trademark for a line of dyestuffs.
GENERAL DYESTUFF CO.

Metalguild®. A lacquer enamel formulated with metal powders that dry out to a lustrous, extremely attractive metal-like finish that are durable, tough, perspiration resistant, and possess excellent adhesion. Available in air-dry and bake types and in a wide range of colors and sheens. Used as a finish coat over lacquer undercoats, synthetic primers, surfacers, and as a finish coat over wrinkles.
FIDELITY CHEMICAL PRODUCTS CORP.

Metallan. *See* ORCO METALLAN[NB].

Metallum. *See* PROTEX METALLUM®.

Metal Luster. A non-flammable cleaner and polish for copper, brass, bronze, nickel, stainless steel, and other metals. It combines solvent, detergent, and abrasive action; and contains no acid.
J. I. HOLCOMB MFG. CO.

Metalplex. A series of coatings for plastics, designed primarily for the metallizing phase of plastic decorating. METALPLEX coatings for both the first and second surface application are available. Only the base coat requires baking; both coatings, however, can be dyed to obtain any desired color tone.
SULLIVAN CHEMICALS DIV., SULLIVAN VARNISH CO.

Metalprep®. A rust remover and metal cleaner.
NEILSON CHEMICAL CO.

Metalsium[NB]. Incorrectly listed as METALSUM[NB] (*HBMTN* p. 360). CERESIT WATERPROOFING CORP.

Metalsum[NB]. (*HBMTN* p. 360). Should have been listed as METALSIUM.[NB]
CERESIT WATERPROOFING CORP.

Metalweld® Joints. A special process, using metal mesh, for making strong, flexible joints in abrasive belts. BEHR-MANNING CO.

Metalweld Plasticote[NB]. (*Supp.* I p. 141). No longer available. METALWELD, INC., PROTECTIVE COATINGS DIV.

Metalyn®. A methyl ester of tall oil.
HERCULES POWDER CO.

Metasap®. A line of metallic soaps, including the following:
  METASAP DP. A special grade of calcium stearate used in the drawing of steel wire.
  METASAP 537. An aluminum stearate used in the mfg. of firm greases.
  METASAP 539. A calcium stearate used for waterproofing and plasticizing masonry cement.
  METASAP 546. A specially-prepared zinc stearate. A neutral white powder, passing 100% through a 325 mesh screen. *Uses:* In cold-water paints, it eliminates excessive settling and caking, imparts water repellency to the finished coating, and reduces the tendency toward formation of floats, spotting and glazing. Especially useful in sanding sealers due to its ability to remain in suspension. Also used as a mold lubricant.
  METASAP 569. A 30% aluminum stearate solution for waterproofing porous surfaces, such as paper containers, shingles, and concrete.
  METASAP 571. A low-bodying metallic soap in the form of a powder consisting essentially of aluminum stearate. Toluol solution containing 30% of this soap has the viscosity of molasses at room temp. In this condition it is used to suspend small quantities of solids in lacquer or for suspension of pigments for flat wall paints.
  METASAP 576. A grade of zinc stearate for use in paints, varnishes and lacquers, especially where a relatively dense material is required.
  METASAP 579. A 30% aluminum stearate solution used in paint mfg. where grinding is objectionable; and for waterproofing porous surfaces, such as paper containers, shingles, and concrete.

METASAP 598. An aluminum stearate grease base used when extreme bodying is desired.

METASAP 602. A fused calcium stearate used as a mold lubricant; in wire-drawing compounds; and in the mfg. of cement, asphalt and asphalt products, grease, candles and crayons.

METASAP 611. A fused lead stearate in the form of a white powder. Used as a stabilizer for vinyl resins.

METASAP 613-A, 613-B, *and* 613-B-1. A group of specialty products formulated as heat and light stabilizers for vinyl resins.

METASAP 620. A water-dispersible type of zinc stearate used as a mold lubricant and as a dusting agent.

METASAP 630. A U.S.P. grade of zinc stearate used in cosmetics, for salves and creams; as an external and internal lubricant in plastics and rubber; as a flatting agent for varnishes and lacquers; as a filler in sanding sealers, where it gives tough, durable films; for increased waterproofing of rock wool; etc. METASAP CHEMICAL CO.

Metasert® Inserts. A combination of papain, sodium lauryl sulfate, succinic acid, phenyl mercuric acetate, and tyrothricin. Kills Trichomonas Vaginalis and other vaginal invaders immediately on contact.
BRAYTEN PHARMACEUTICAL CO.

Metavis® 540. An aluminum stearate grease base designed to be used with the palest oils to produce tackiness and stringiness without changing the clarity or color of the original compounding oil. Used to produce low viscosity greases for agricultural and industrial machinery where a semi-fluid, adhesive-type lubricant is desired. METASAP CHEMICAL CO.

Metavis® 543. An aluminum stearate grease base designed to give stringiness and body to oils. Especially useful with the heavier oils. With pale-colored, heavy, steam-refined oils, METAVIS 543 produces thick, viscous, transparent lubricants. As little as 4% of METAVIS 543 adds considerable body to black oils. Such lubricants are used for differential and transmission lubrication which does not require extreme-pressure lubricants. METASAP CHEMICAL CO.

Methajade®. (*Supp.* I p. 142). Now a registered trademark and a product of MERCK SHARP & DOHME, DIV. OF MERCK & CO.

Methanite®. An ammonium nitrate blasting composition. HERCULES POWDER CO.

Methionine[NE]. An amino acid for the treatment of infectious or toxic hepatitis and cirrhosis of the liver. Supplied in tablet form.
CONSOLIDATED MIDLAND CORP.

Methium®. A medicinal for the treatment of hypertension. It consists of hexamethonium chloride, in tablet form. WARNER-CHILCOTT LABORATORIES

Methium® with Reserpine. A medicinal for the oral treatment of hypertension, reduction of blood pressure and relief of hypertensive symptoms. Supplied in the form of tablets containing 125 mg. hexamethonium chloride and 0.125 mg. reserpine; and tablets containing 250 mg. hexamethonium chloride and 0.125 mg. reserpine. WARNER-CHILCOTT LABORATORIES

Methoxychlor△. *Also known as* DIMETHOXY-DDT *and* DMDT. An analog of DDT. 2,2-Bis-(*p*-methoxyphenyl)-1,1,1-trichloroethane. $C_{16}H_{15}Cl_3O_2$; mol.wt. 345.65. Prepared by condensing anisole with chloral in the presence of sulfuric acid or aluminum chloride. Contains about 88% of the *p,p'*-isomer, and the remainder largely the *o,p'*-isomer. The pure *p,p'*-isomer is a white, crystalline solid with a m.p. of 89°C.; practically insoluble in water; soluble in alcohol; somewhat less soluble in petroleum oils than DDT. METHOXYCHLOR is preferred to DDT for use on animals and animal forage and in dairy barns because it is not accumulated in fatty tissues and excreted in milk, and is only from $1/25$ to $1/50$ as toxic to mammals. It is especially effective against the Mexican bean beetle, and gives a more rapid knockdown than DDT.

Met-L-Brite Clear. *See* TUF-ON® MET-L-BRITE CLEAR.

Met-L-Kote. *See* ADELPHI MET-L-KOTE MACHINERY ENAMEL.

Metlseel®. An inert, inorganic and non-metallic compound for selective carburizing, neutralizing and nitriding as well as for protecting tools and parts that are repeatedly subjected to high temps. during heat treatment. It is easily applied to any surface to be protected and establishes an effective bond to the parts that are heat treated. It matures at about 1,500°F. It is also effective as a protective coating on the inner surfaces of such articles as aluminum melting pots, goosenecks used in die casting, etc.
PEMCO CORP.

Meva[NE]. A blend of meat and hydrogenated vegetable fats, with stabilizers added, for use in frying tasks that require a fat mfg'd under exacting standards but competitively priced. Stability and high smoke point make MEVA ideal for quantity frying in bakeries, restaurants, hotels and other institutions.
ANDERSON, CLAYTON & CO. FOODS DIV.

M-F-21[NE]. (*Supp.* I p. 142). Now a product of THE BORDEN CO., CHEMICAL DIV., successor to PIONEER LATEX & CHEMICAL CO.

M. F. Acid[NE]. A powdered acid product for removing heat-treat scale from stainless steel and titanium, and for brightening heat-treated aluminum alloys. It is a white, free-flowing mixture of powdered ingredients, 100% soluble in water. It contains fluorides and other ingredients. WYANDOTTE CHEMICALS CORP., J. B. FORD DIV.

MGK® Repellent 11. A repellent for German, American and Oriental roaches, horn flies, stable flies, mosquitoes, and gnats. Chemically, it is 2,3,4,5-bis (Δ 2-butylene)-tetrahydrofurfural. Sp.gr. 1.121; refractive index (25°C.), 1.5262; color (Gardner), 9. It is less toxic than pyrethrins to warm-blooded animals. Usually used in combination with other toxicants in insect sprays for the home, bakeries, food plants and other industrial establishments; and for use on cattle and other animals. McLAUGHLIN GORMLEY KING CO.

Mica△. A group of minerals with a monoclinic crystalline structure and ranging in color from colorless to black. MICA breaks easily into thin, tough scales, with a sp.gr. of 2.7–3.1 and a hardness of 2–3 on the Moh scale. The most common variety of MICA is MUSCOVITE, $H_2KAl_3(SiO_4)_3$; magnesium mica, known as PHLOGOPITE, has the chemical composition $H_2KMgSi(SiO_4)_3$. MICA is marketed as cut or uncut block, sheet, and splittings, and in ground form. The value of sheet mica is affected materially by the extent of staining, due to the presence of impurities. The largest production of block mica comes from India, Brazil and Argentina. *Uses:* As an electrical and thermal insulation material; as a filler in plastics, paints, etc.

Miccroloid®. (*HBMTN* p. 363). Now a registered trademark. MICHIGAN CHROME AND CHEMICAL CO.

Miccromask®. (*HBMTN* p. 363). Now a registered trademark. MICHIGAN CHROME AND CHEMICAL CO.

Miccropeel®. (*Supp.* I p. 143). Now a registered trademark. MICHIGAN CHROME AND CHEMICAL CO.

Miccrosol®. (*Supp.* I p. 143). Now a registered trademark. MICHIGAN CHROME AND CHEMICAL CO.

Miccrosol® E-1003. (*HBMTN* p. 363). The name MICCROSOL® is now a registered trademark. MICHIGAN CHROME AND CHEMICAL CO.

Miccro Supreme® Better Seal Compound. (*HBMTN* p. 364). The name MICCRO SUPREME® is now a registered trademark. MICHIGAN CHROME AND CHEMICAL CO.

Miccro Supreme® Layout and Identification Dye. Incorrectly listed as MICCRO® SUPREME LAYOUT and IDENTIFICATION DYE (*Supp.* I p. 143). MICHIGAN CHROME AND CHEMICAL CO.

Miccro Supreme® Spatterproof. Incorrectly listed as MICCRO® SUPREME SPATTERPROOF (*Supp.* I p. 143). MICHIGAN CHROME AND CHEMICAL CO.

Miccrotex®. (*HBMTN* p. 364). Now a registered trademark. MICHIGAN CHROME AND CHEMICAL CO.

Miccrotube®. (*HBMTN* p. 364). Now a registered trademark. MICHIGAN CHROME AND CHEMICAL CO.

Miccrowax®. (*HBMTN* p. 364). Now a registered trademark. MICHIGAN CHROME AND CHEMICAL CO.

Michigan No. 40. An extra-light, calcined technical magnesium oxide, MgO; mol.wt. 40.32; density of solid, 3.65 g./cc.; bulk density, 5 lb./cu.ft. Screen size, 99.5% through 200 mesh, 99.9% through 200 mesh. Analysis: 98.0% MgO, 0.4% SiO_2, 0.4% Al_2O_3, 0.2% Fe_2O_3, 1.0% CaO, 0.009% Mn. *Use:* As an accelerator and antiscorch agent in the compounding of NEOPRENE rubber. MICHIGAN CHEMICAL CORP.

Michigan Metal. (*HBMTN* p. 365). No longer available. GREAT LAKES STEEL CORP.

Mico Spreader[NB]. (*HBMTN* p. 365). No longer available. MILLER CHEMICAL & FERTILIZER CORP.

Mico® Sulphur. (*HBMTN* p. 365). The word MICO should have been listed as a registered trademark. MILLER CHEMICAL & FERTILIZER CORP.

Micratized®. A vitamin-containing product for fortifying foods and feeds with vitamins. NOPCO CHEMICAL CO.

Micris[NB]. A line of microcrystalline, amorphous-type waxes. COMMERCE OIL CORP.

Microballoon®. *See* COLFOAM MICROBALLOON® SPHERES.

Microcast®. The trademark used in connection with industrial metal castings made of ferrous and nonferrous metals and alloys. Also used to describe a process for the production of industrial component parts by investment casting. AUSTENAL, INC.

Micro-Fast[NB]. A line of chrome greens noted for their very fine particle size and exceptional light fastness. SHERWIN-WILLIAMS CO.

Microflex®. A glass fiber cushioning and vibration mounting. It is made of a springy mass of closely interlaced glass fibers, compressed and cured with a stable bonding agent to provide abrasion resistance. Its operating characteristics are practically constant over a temp. range of $-65°$ to $+165°F$.; it recovers immediately after compression; can be worked similar to wood; and is resistant to moisture, oils, and fungus growth. L.O.F. GLASS FIBERS CO.

Microlite®. A glass fiber thermal and acoustical insulation material made of extremely fine, long and uniform fibers. Available in rolls of various widths, thicknesses and densities, either plain or faced with a choice of several standard facing materials, including aluminum foil, vinyl, plain or reflective vapor barrier papers. The thermal conductivity of MICROLITE of 1.0 lb./cu.ft. density is 0.20 B.t.u.-inch/(hr. x sq.ft. x °F.) at a mean temp. of 50°F. L.O.F. GLASS FIBERS CO.

Micronex®. The trademark for a series of impingement carbon blacks produced from natural gas. They impart good tensile strength, abrasion resistance, and crack-and-tear resistance. Used primarily in natural rubber truck treads and carcasses, mining cable covers, wire jacket compounds, camel back, and heavy-duty footwear. Available in the following grades: STANDARD MICRONEX, a medium-processing channel; MICRONEX W-6, and easy-processing channel; MICRONEX MARK II, a hard processing channel; and HIGH TEAR MICRONEX, designed for use in heavy-duty cable covers. COLUMBIAN CARBON CO.

Micro Nu-Cop. A fixed, neutral, finely divided copper fungicide for the effective control of persistent diseases of fruits and vegetables. Particle size, 0.5–1.0 microns. Used in water suspension as a spray; or as a dusting powder. FAESY & BESTHOFF, INC.

Micropaint. *See* RS14 SHIELDING MICROPAINT[NB], RS17 POLYSHIELD MICROPAINT[NB], SC12 AND SC13 SILVER MICROPAINTS[NB], *and* SS12-B SILVER SHIELDING MICROPAINT[NB].

Micro-Quartz[NB]. A lightweight, high-temp. insulation material composed of 98% pure quartz. May be used at temps. up to 2,000°–2,500°F. It is resilient, and resistant to vibration and air flow. Available in felted form, in bulk, and as a paper which can be impregnated or coated for electrical applications. L.O.F. GLASS FIBERS CO.

Microsulfon[NB]. A sulfonamide preparation for the oral treatment of infections. Supplied in the form of tablets, each of which contains 0.5 g. sulfadiazine. CONSOLIDATED MIDLAND CORP.

Microtex[NE]. A glass fiber thermal and acoustical insulation material. L.O.F. Glass Fibers Co.

Micro-Tex[NE]. A line of red color pigments noted for their extremely fine particle size.
Sherwin-Williams Co.

Microveer. A pre-finished, flexible thin wood veneer for decorative use. Available in some sixty different species of wood, and supplied in sheets or rolls to the user's size requirements. The polyester surface of Microveer renders it scratch-resistant and impervious to water and the ordinary chemical preparations found around the house, while its aluminum underside makes it resistant to cigarette burns. It can be bent back against itself (i.e., 180°) without fracture, and may be cleaned with only a damp cloth. Its thickness varies from 0.012″ to 0.019″. David Feldman & Associates

Microverter®. An apparatus for the production of diazo-duplicates of photographic microfilm. It handles, 16, 35, 70 and 105 mm. microfilm, and accommodates lengths up to 1,000 ft. It operates in conjunction with any continuous-type, ammonia-developing diazotype processing machine. Tecnifax Corp.

Microwood. (*Supp.* I p. 144). No longer available.
David Feldman & Associates

Midas Gold®. The trademark for a line of transparent, permanent gold pigment dispersions for lacquers and synthetics.
R-B-H Dispersions Div. of Interchemical Corp.

Midget Impinger[NE]. A portable hand-operated instrument which uses the impingement method for collection of dust samples from the atmosphere.
Mine Safety Appliances Co.

Mildex[NE]. A yellow, wettable powder (25% active) for application as a spray or dust for the eradication of powdery mildew on flowers, fruits, vegetables, and nursery stock. Larvacide Products, Inc.

Mil Du-Rid®. (*Supp.* I p. 144). No longer available.
Ultra Chemical Works

Mil-Etch[NE]. A non-scaling alkaline aluminum etchant for producing an attractive, uniform etch on extrusions, wrought sheets and bar stock. Also for chemically milling or deep etching aluminum alloys. It is a yellow, free-flowing granular product. Total alkalinity (as Na_2O), 72%.
Wyandotte Chemicals Corp., J. B. Ford Div.

Mill Bearing-Metal. See Hewitt Mill Bearing-Metal.[NE]

Milne AMC[NE]. Incorrectly listed as AMC[NE] (*HBMTN* p. 41). A. Milne & Co.

Minaplex V-P 721. Organic mineral tablets containing colloidal minerals of sea lettuce (Dulse) and alfalfa, especially high in organically combined potassium and manganese. *Use:* As a nutritional supplement. Vitamin Products Co.

MinePhone[NE]. An FM carrier system providing instant 2-way voice communication. Designed for use in mining operations.
Mine Safety Appliances Co.

Mineral Wax△. *Same as* Ozokerite△.

Minerovit®. A combination of minerals and vitamins for the treatment of multivitamin and mineral difficiency, especially during pregnancy, lactation, and convalescence. Supplied in capsule form.
Consolidated Midland Corp.

Minit Cleaner®. A free-flowing powder floor and wall cleanser with a color indicator to enable the user to readily determine the concentration of solutions: pale pink for light jobs, vivid pink for normal floor cleaning, and red for hard-to-clean surfaces. It is non-abrasive, and contains no free alkali.
J. I. Holcomb Mfg. Co.

Miokon® **Sodium.** (*Supp.* I p. 145). The name Miokon® is now a registered trademark.
Mallinckrodt Chemical Works

Miracle Metal. See Parko® Miracle Metal.

Miramesh[NE]. (*HBMTN* p. 370). No longer available. National Research Corp.

Miravar[NE]. Incorrectly listed as Mirvar[NE] (*Supp.* I p. 145). C. J. Osborn Co.

Mirvar[NE]. (*Supp.* I p. 145). Should have been listed as Miravar[NE]. C. J. Osborn Co.

Mist[NE]. A dry-cleaning spotting compound.
Pennsylvania Salt Mfg. Co.

Mistofume®. The trademark for a line of insecticides. S. B. Penick & Co.

Mitis Green△. *Same as* Paris Green△.

Mix-Ezy®. A specially prepared, emulsifier type all-hydrogenated vegetable fat for use in whipped toppings and bakers' toppings. It adds the following qualities to toppings: a rich flavor, free from any greasy taste; high volume and excellent body; a surface that will not shatter or dry out; and uniformity.
Anderson, Clayton & Co. Foods Div.

Mix-I-Go. A gasoline additive which helps keep the cylinder heads, valves, spark plugs, and pistons clean; leaves a thin lubricant film on the surfaces; absorbs moisture in fuel tanks, lines, and carburetors; and slows down combustion, resulting in more uniform power. Used in the ratio of 1 gal. Mix-I-Go to 300 gal. gasoline, it adds a small, but desirable, amount of water, in permanent suspension, to the fuel.
Bell Laboratory, Inc.

MM 6 & 6[NE]. A tungsten-molybdenum, high-speed steel developed to obtain good cutting ability and toughness. Typical analysis: 0.85% carbon, 4.15% chromium, 6.40% tungsten, 5.00% molybdenum and 1.90% vanadium. It is particularly suitable for tools subject to shock. A. Milne & Co.

Mobilene®. A sheet and cut gasketing material made of strong asbestos fabric interwoven with fine brass wire, and impregnated with a special compound to withstand high temps. and pressures. *Uses:* For packing cylinder heads, exhaust manifold flanges, and water-jacket connections on gas and gasoline engines, especially in marine service.
Johns-Manville Sales Corp.

Mobil-Roll[NE]. (Trademark registration pending). A fiberglass insulation material for mobile homes.
Armstrong Cork Co.

Mocar[NR]. An automobile BABBITT. It is a lead-base alloy that has replaced tin-base BABBITS in automobile main, connecting-rod, and cam-shaft bearings. It has a very close grained structure, is hard yet ductile, and bonds well to brass, copper, bronze, and steel. It is lower in cost than tin-base BABBITTS, yet gives better performance. HEWITT METALS CORP.

Modernedge Slatekote[NR]. A variety of SLATEKOTE with a split through the center of the roll in a pyramid pattern to effect thatch-like roof lines. Furnished in 32″-wide rolls to cover 100 sq.ft. of roof area. JOHNS-MANVILLE SALES CORP.

Moderntred[NR]. (Trademark registration pending). A rubber runner for floors. ARMSTRONG CORK CO.

Moebiquin®. A medicinal preparation that is active against the protozoon and the cysts of endamebahistolytica. Used in the treatment of intestinal amebiasis. Supplied in the form of tablets, each of which contains 210 mg. diiodohydroxyquinoline. CONSOLIDATED MIDLAND CORP.

Moistop. See SISALKRAFT MOISTOP®.

Molding Wax #583. (*HBMTN* p. 373). No longer being mfg'd by INNIS SPEIDEN & Co.

Moldit. See R & I MOLDIT-D® and R & I HOT TOP MOLDIT.®

Mold Release A. See CD MOLD RELEASE A.

Mold Release B. See CD MOLD RELEASE B.

Mold Release B-2. See CD MOLD RELEASE B-2.

Mo-Max®. A trademark applied to: (1) a steel in the form of ingots, billets, bars, rods, wire, sheets, castings or forging, usually having a basic composition of 0.65–1.05% carbon, 3.5–4.35% chromium, 1.2–2.0% tungsten, 7.5–9.5% molybdenum, and 0.9–2.0% vanadium; and (2) metallic tools and machine elements, namely, drills, reamers, milling cutters, counterbores, hacksaw blades for both power and handsaws, dies and gears. CLEVELAND TWIST DRILL CO.

Monabond[NR]. A complex polyvinyl alcohol-based resin. It is added to resin textile finishes for reduction of residual shrinkage, improved flat abrasion resistance, better durability of finish to washing and dry-cleaning, and for added bulk, weight and fullness in the finished fabric. MONA INDUSTRIES, INC.

Monabond C[NR]. A complex cationic polyvinyl alcohol-based resin. Its properties and uses are the same as for MONABOND. MONA INDUSTRIES, INC.

Mona® **Catalyst M.** A catalyst for use with MONASET, a thermosetting resin textile finish. MONA INDUSTRIES, INC.

Monapal T[NR]. A nonionic wetting agent and penetrant used to improve the penetration of resin textile finishes. It is an ethylene oxide condensate. MONA INDUSTRIES, INC.

Monapolene A®. An anionic polyethylene emulsion. It is a softener and plasticizer for thermosetting resin finishes. It imparts excellent draping qualities, and enhances hydrophobicity. MONA INDUSTRIES, INC.

Monapolene Concentrates[NR]. Solid self-emulsifiable polyethylene complexes, 100% active. They are efficient softeners and plasticizers for thermosetting resin finishes used on RAYON and COTTON fabrics. They improve tear strength and flat abrasion resistance. MONA INDUSTRIES, INC.

Monapolene N[NR]. A nonionic polyethylene emulsion used as a softener and plasticizer for thermosetting resin finishes on RAYON and COTTON fabrics. It improves the tear strength and flat abrasion resistance. MONA INDUSTRIES, INC.

Monaquest E[NR]. A liquid sequestering agent, used to improve and facilitate the emulsification of MONAPOLENE CONCENTRATES. MONA INDUSTRIES, INC.

Monar. A welding wire consisting of 67.0% nickel and 30.0% copper. ARCOS CORP.

Monarch[NR]. (*Supp.* I p. 147). The trade name MONARCH is a registered trademark in Argentina, Bolivia, Cuba and South Africa, for hose, belting and packing materials. HEWITT-ROBINS, INC.

Monares Paste[NR]. An acid-stable urea-formaldehyde resin paste, containing 50% solids. It is used in combination with MONASET to impart excellent dimensional stability and crease resistance to wash and wear finishes used on RAYON and RAYON-blended fabrics. MONA INDUSTRIES, INC.

Monaset[NR]. A cyclic methylol urea resin for use as a textile finish. It imparts excellent dimensional stability and durable crease resistance to RAYON and RAYON-blended fabrics. MONA INDUSTRIES, INC.

Monasoft S[NR]. A highly effective cationic softener and plasticizer for cellulosic fibers and fabrics. MONA INDUSTRIES, INC.

Monatose[NR]. A cold-water-soluble starch-type additive which is added to thermosetting resins to impart a full, firm hand to RAYON, RAYON blend and COTTON fabrics. MONA INDUSTRIES, INC.

Monitan®. A medicinal fat emulsifier used in the treatment of steatorrhea. Each teaspoonful (5 cc.) contains 1½ g. of sorbitan monooleate polyoxyethylene derivative in a flavored aqueous sugar and glycerin base. IVES-CAMERON CO.

Monitor®. The trademark for a line of woven wire fencing and wire rope. UNITED STATES STEEL CORP.

Monitor A[NR]. An organic sequestrant and solubilizer for use in routine scouring, bleaching, dyeing, printing and finishing operations in the textile industry. In scouring and washing it will solubilize iron and other metals which discolor and tender yarns and fabrics. It can replace oxalic acid for iron removal, and has a stabilizing effect on peroxides. In the dyebath, it usually eliminates difficulties due to poorness of shade or intensity or streakiness. It has a stabilizing effect on printing pastes and a plasticizing effect on gums. GLOBE COMPOUND CO.

Monolac. A clear varnish for use over MONOLAC VARNISH STAIN. GILLESPIE VARNISH CO.

Monolac Varnish Stain. A transparent stain that duplicates the tones of natural woods such as oak, walnut, mahogany, maple, etc.

GILLESPIE VARNISH CO.

Monolate®. (*HBMTN* p. 375). No longer available.
ABBOTT LABORATORIES

Monolux Supreme White Enamel. A non-yellowing enamel for walls, woodwork, etc. It brushes easily, and dries to a porcelain-like finish.
GILLESPIE VARNISH CO.

Mono-Man®. A refined manganese sulfate monohydrate. It is a stable, white, free-flowing, water-soluble powder. *Uses:* In the mfg. of manganese compounds, textile dyeing compounds, calico printing compounds; as an ingredient in drying compositions for paints and varnishes and boiled linseed oil; in the mfg. of oxalate and borate driers; and in ceramics and ore flotation.
TENNESSEE CORP.

Monopeen®. (*HBMTN* p. 375). Now a registered trademark.
INTERCHEMICAL CORP., FINISHES DIV.

Monoplast®. A trowelled-on monolithic insulation finish for use at temps. as low as 80°F. below zero. Only a single coat is required for a durable finish that will not crack, craze, become brittle, or chip. It is white in color and reflects 72% of the light that strikes it. It is odorless when dry; and is easily cleaned.
ARMSTRONG CORK CO.

Monox®. A combination organic scale preventive and corrosion inhibitor which has proved effective in removing and inhibiting deposition of hard-water scales.
TRETOLITE CO.

Montan Wax△. *Also known as* LIGNITE WAX△. A wax, similar to OZOKENTE△, obtained by solvent extraction of lignite coal. It is white to dark brown in color and has a m.p. of 80° to 90°C. *Uses:* In the mfg. of leather finishes, polishes, phonograph records, insulation compounds, candles, etc.

Moraine Porous Metal®. Formerly marketed as POREX® (*Supp.* I p. 191).
MORAINE PRODUCTS DIV. OF GENERAL MOTORS CORP.

Moran's®. A line of round belt couplings in sizes from 1/8" to 1" o.d. Used on sewing, business, textile, and printing machines, and other equipment.
GREENE, TWEED & CO.

Morepel RW^NE. A renewable, textile water repellent of extremely fine particle size. It can be run hot or cold, is stable to freezing, and will not affect color fastness.
MORETEX CHEMICAL PRODUCTS, INC.

Moretex Napping Softener A^NE. A textile assistant which gives excellent lubrication for napping wires and produces a soft silky hand to the fabric. It can be exhausted from a bath or padded to wet or dry fabric, eliminating one or two drying operations. It does not affect light fastness.
MORETEX CHEMICAL PRODUCTS, INC.

Morin△. *See* FUSTIC△.

Morindone△. *See* FUSTIC△.

Moropol 600^NE. A nonionic polyethylene emulsion of extremely fine particle size, used in resin finishing of textiles as a durable softener to increase crease recovery, and tear and tensile strengths.
MORETEX CHEMICAL PRODUCTS, INC.

Moropol 700^NE. A nitrogen-free, nonionic polyethylene used in conjunction with thermosetting resins to maintain tear and tensile strength of fabrics. It imparts a durable softening effect, increases the angle of recovery, and eliminates the necessity of using fat-based softeners. It is compatible with dye fixatives, metal salts, acids, etc.
MORETEX CHEMICAL PRODUCTS, INC.

Moropon LC^NE. A textile detergent containing no tall oil or rosins. It prevents crack and crush marks; and provides all of the advantages of cocoanut amine condensates at a much lower cost.
MORETEX CHEMICAL PRODUCTS, INC.

Motletone^NE. A one-coat hammered-effect finish based on synthetic and lacquer compositions.
MAAS & WALDSTEIN CO.

Mound City Paints^NE. The trademark for a line of consumer paints.
GLIDDEN CO.

M-P-A^NE. A paint additive that develops a thixotropic gel structure in paints, and imparts sag resistance, better brushability, improved pigment suspension, and controlled penetration. It withstands high processing temp. in high-speed mills; and does not grain, seed, or undergo unfavorable change at elevated processing or storage temp.
BAKER CASTOR OIL CO.

MPS-500® Plasticizer. A stabilized chlorinated ester of a fatty acid used as a plasticizer for synthetic resins. The chlorine content is controlled to give an optimum balance between compatibility and plasticizing efficiency. It is compatible with butadiene copolymers, alkyds, ethyl cellulose, NEOPRENE, polyvinyl acetate, polyvinyl chloride, and polystyrene; not compatible with cellulose acetate, nitrocellulose; and polyvinyl butyral; soluble in chlorinated hydrocarbons, aliphatics, aromatics, alcohols, esters, ketones; insoluble in water. It has a freezing point of −39°C., a pour point of −18°C., a fire point of 252°C., a viscosity of 243 centistokes at 100°F. It is of special interest in the formulation of electrical extrusion compounds. Its permanence on heat aging, water aging, oil aging, and gasoline aging, and its resistance to migration insure a flexible stock at elevated temps. Its excellent electrical properties are also of importance, as well as its high strength, flame retardance and low-temp. flexibility.
HOOKER ELECTROCHEMICAL CO.

MpT^NE. Methyl para-toluate. A white, crystalline solid with a characteristic aromatic odor; melts at 34°C. to a clear, mobile liquid. *Uses:* In the synthesis of dyestuffs and organic pigments; in essential oils, insecticides, and pharmaceuticals.
HERCULES POWDER CO.

MR®. A line of thermosetting, liquid polyester resins that can be cured or solidified, in the presence of peroxide catalysts, to stable infusible solids at no pressure and at low temp. *Uses:* For laminating, molding, casting, potting, coating, and impregnating.
CELANESE CORP. OF AMERICA

Mr. Charcoal^NE. A brand of charcoal. The name is a registered trademark in the state of West Virginia; and application for registration has been made with the U. S. Patent Office.
CHARCOAL CORP. OF AMERICA

Mrs. Tucker's Salad Oil® *and* **Mrs. Tucker's Shortening®.** *See* TUCKER'S, MRS., SALAD OIL® *and* TUCKER'S, MRS., SHORTENING®.

M-S-A®. A trademark used to denote goods manufactured or sold by MINE SAFETY APPLIANCES CO.

MSA Comfo Cap®. Caps or helmets made of synthetic resin, interiorly reinforced with woven material. *Use:* As protective headwear for miners and other industrial workers. MINE SAFETY APPLIANCES CO.

MSA Self-Rescuer®. An emergency respirator which affords respiratory protection against carbon monoxide for a period of 30 min. or more in concentrations likely to be found after fire or explosion. U. S. Bureau of Mines approved.
MINE SAFETY APPLIANCES CO.

MSS 32. An inhibited acid cleaner for use on metals.
J. P. HENRY CHEMICAL CO.

MTE (Concentrate). Same as MYSTIKIL® TERMITE EMULSION.

M. T. Emery[NE]. (*HBMTN* p. 377). No longer available. HANSON-VAN WINKLE-MUNNING CO.

Mucigel®. (*HBMTN* p. 377). Now a product of WARNER-CHILCOTT LABORATORIES, successor to THE MALTINE CO.

Mucker. See BOSTON MUCKER.

Mucotin®. A medicinal for the treatment of peptic ulcer and gastric hyperacidity. Each MUCOTIN tablet contains 0.16 g. gastric mucin, 0.45 g. magnesium trisilicate, and 0.25 g. aluminum hydroxide gel.
WARNER-CHILCOTT LABORATORIES

Mule®. A commercial flour sulfur.
OLIN MATHIESON CHEMICAL CORP.

Mulsafact®. (*Supp.* I p. 150). No longer available.
SHARP & DOHME DIV., MERCK & CO.

Mulsivon®. (*HBMTN* p. 378). Now a registered trademark. L. SONNEBORN SONS, INC.

Mulsoid 815M[NE]. A non-ionic dispersing agent that is not affected by alkalis, acids or metal salts. It is non-foaming, and stable at high temps. and pressures. Especially useful with pigment colors and metallic colors. It is effective as a dye-leveler and a crock-inhibitor. COLLOIDS, INC.

Mulsolv[NE]. (*HBMTN* p. 378). No longer available.
BEE CHEMICAL CO.

Multi-B-Plex. A vitamin-mineral preparation. Each cc. contains 100 mg. THIAMIN HCl, 100 mg. nicotinamide, 10 mg. pyridoxine, 1 mg. riboflavin, 10 mg. pantothenic acid, 0.35% chlorobutanol, 0.02 g. benzyl chloride, plus calcium and magnesium chlorides.
TESTAGAR & CO.

Multi-Chlor®. A germicide and deodorant used in laundries, dry-cleaning plants, and rug-cleaning plants. It is similar to STERI-CHLOR® (*HBMTN* p. 538) except that it has four times as much available chlorine.
WYANDOTTE CHEMICALS CORP., J. B. FORD DIV.

Multicolor[NE]. A lacquer-type finish which produces, with one application, two or three different colors on the same surface. SHERWIN-WILLIAMS CO.

Multicord®. The trademark for a line of fabrics made wholly or partially of cellulose derivatives.
CELANESE CORP. OF AMERICA

Multi-Duty®. Mechanical, viscous-type, ventilating air filters of the automatic self-cleaning type.
AMERICAN AIR FILTER CO.

Multifax. See TEXACO® MULTIFAX.

Multifect®. A registered trademark for book and printing papers. KIMBERLY-CLARK CORP.

Multigrip[NE]. The trade name for steel floor plates.
UNITED STATES STEEL CORP.

Multisafety[NE]. The trade name for a line of highway guard cable. UNITED STATES STEEL CORP.

Multi-Super®. A phosphatic fertilizer or phosphatic ingredient for mixed fertilizers.
INTERNATIONAL MINERALS & CHEMICAL CORP.

Mulvitol® *and* Multivitol® Strong. Potent multivitamin preparations for patients with faulty dietary habits and restricted diets such as are prescribed for diabetes, obesity, food allergy, and colitis. Especially useful for growing children, and during pregnancy. Supplied in the form of spheres.
CONSOLIDATED MIDLAND CORP.

Munising®. A registered trademark for bond and waxed papers. KIMBERLY-CLARK CORP.

Murillo Bark△. Same as QUILLAJA△.

Muscovite△. See MICA△.

M-X. See U.S.S.® M-X®.

My-B-Den®. A therapeutic composition consisting of adenosine-5-monophosphate. AMES CO.

Mycalex® 385. An arc-resistant glass-bonded mica, with excellent resistance to thermal shock, for continuous operating temp. up to 700°F. Readily machinable but not moldable. Used for electrical applications. MYCALEX CORP. OF AMERICA

Mycalex® 400®. A standard compression molded glass-bonded mica for operating temps. up to 700°F. Readily machinable but not moldable. Used for electrical applications. MYCALEX CORP. OF AMERICA

Mycalex® 410®. Glass-bonded mica precision-molded with or without inserts, for electrical applications involving temps. up to 650°F.
MYCALEX CORP. OF AMERICA

Mycalex® 410X®. A lightweight precision-molded glass-bonded mica with a somewhat higher loss factor than MYCALEX® 410®. MYCALEX CORP. OF AMERICA

Mycalex® K *and* KM. Glass-bonded mica capacitor dielectrics. K is machinable; KM is moldable.
MYCALEX CORP. OF AMERICA

Mylase®. Fungal amylase preparations, furnished in different grades, for use in the preparation of dextrose syrups and crystalline dextrose, and for other food and pharmaceutical end uses. WALLERSTEIN CO.

Myrj®. (*HBMTN* p. 382). This product is also mfg'd in England and Germany. The trademark is registered in Germany but not in England.
ATLAS POWDER CO.
HONEYWILL-ATLAS, LTD.
ATLAS-GOLDSCHMIDT G.M.B.H.

Mysterious Roach Killer Outfit[NB]. A duster equipped with removable rubber bulb for easy refilling, and filled with 1½ oz. of dust consisting of a blend of PYRETHRUM, boric acid and DDT. Total active ingredients, 63.23%. Also packed in refill containers. *Use:* For the control of roaches, fleas, silverfish, bedbugs, and ants. LETHELIN PRODUCTS CO.

Mystikil® Rose Duster. A duster equipped with removable rubber bulb for easy refilling, and filled with 4 oz. of dust containing 1% LINDANE, 5% DDT, 3.9% ZINEB and 20% sulfur. Also packed in refill containers. *Use:* As an insecticide and fungicide for rose and general garden use. LETHELIN PRODUCTS CO.

Mystikil® Termite Emulsion. A water-emulsifiable concentrate. Contains 72.3% CHLORDANE. Packed in quarts, half and one gallon containers. *Uses:* For the control of subterranean termites, lawn insects, and crab grass. LETHELIN PRODUCTS CO.

Mytinic®. A hematinic, in liquid and tablet forms, for the treatment of secondary anemias. Each teaspoonful (5 cc.) of the liquid contains 111.0 mg. ferric ammonium citrate, 1.7 mg. thiamine hydrochloride (VITAMIN B_1), 0.7 mg. riboflavin (VITAMIN B_2), 17.0 mg. niacinamide, 170.0 mg. liver fraction 1, N.F., and 3 mcg. VITAMIN B_{12}. Each tablet contains 225.0 mg. ferrous sulfate (exsiccated), 330.0 mg. liver powder concentrate, 1.3 mg. riboflavin (VITAMIN B_2), 0.5 mg. pyridoxine HCl (VITAMIN B_6), 2.0 mg. calcium pantothenate (Filter Factor), 10.0 mg. nicotinamide (PP Factor), 5.0 mcg. VITAMIN B_{12}, 50.0 mg. ascorbic acid (VITAMIN C), and 3.3 mg. thiamine HCl (VITAMIN B_1). BRISTOL LABORATORIES INC.

Myvacet®. Distilled acetylated monoglycerides prepared from fats and oils for particular use in the cosmetic and industrial chemical fields.
DISTILLATION PRODUCTS INDUSTRIES,
DIV. OF EASTMAN KODAK CO.

Myva-Dry®. A dry VITAMIN A preparation for food and drug usage. DISTILLATION PRODUCTS INDUSTRIES,
DIV. OF EASTMAN KODAK CO.

Myvamix®. A VITAMIN E feed supplement for fortifying animal and poultry feeds.
DISTILLATION PRODUCTS INDUSTRIES,
DIV. OF EASTMAN KODAK CO.

Myvapack®. A VITAMIN A preparation for fortifying foods, particularly margarine.
DISTILLATION PRODUCTS INDUSTRIES,
DIV. OF EASTMAN KODAK CO.

Myvatex®. Food emulsifiers, containing monoglycerides as the active ingredient, used in bread, ice cream and similar food products.
DISTILLATION PRODUCTS INDUSTRIES,
DIV. OF EASTMAN KODAK CO.

Myvax®. A VITAMIN A preparation for food, drug, and cosmetic usage.
DISTILLATION PRODUCTS INDUSTRIES,
DIV. OF EASTMAN KODAK CO.

Myverol®. Distilled monoglycerides, prepared from various fats and oils, for a variety of edible and industrial usages.
DISTILLATION PRODUCTS INDUSTRIES,
DIV. OF EASTMAN KODAK CO.

N

Nabor[NB]. (*Supp.* I p. 152). No longer available.
NATIONAL ANILINE DIV.,
ALLIED CHEMICAL & DYE CORP.

Nacconate®. The trademark for a complete line of diisocyanates employed in the mfg. of flexible, semi-rigid and rigid urethane forms, elastomers, coatings, adhesives, molding compounds, fibers, textile finishes, water repellents; in the tanning of leathers; etc.
NATIONAL ANILINE DIV.,
ALLIED CHEMICAL & DYE CORP.

Nacconate® 65, 80, 100, and 300. (*Supp.* I p. 152). The name NACCONATE® is now a registered trademark.
NATIONAL ANILINE DIV.,
ALLIED CHEMICAL & DYE CORP.

Nacconate® 310. A brand of DMMDI△. 3,3'-Dimethyldiphenylmethane 4,4'-diisocyanate; or 4,4'-methylenebis(2-methylphenylene isocyanate). A light-cream colored crystalline solid solidifying at 31.4°C.; soluble in benzene, mixed xylenes, solvent naphtha, SKELLYSOLVE C, kerosene, monochlorobenzene, o-dichlorobenzene, carbon tetrachloride, ethyl acetate, methyl ethyl ketone, and 1,2-dimethoxyethane. This diisocyanate has an unusually low reactivity and vapor pressure which are important advantages in its use as a curing agent for urethane elastomers and plastics; and in aqueous emulsions useful for treating various textile fibers and fabrics, in impregnating paper, and in the tanning of soft leathers. NATIONAL ANILINE DIV.,
ALLIED CHEMICAL & DYE CORP.

Nacconate® 1080-H. A partially reacted NACCONATE® 80 used in the mfg. of rigid urethane foams. It is a clear liquid with a viscosity of 150–200 cps. at 25°C.; f.p. —40°C.; b.p. 247°C.; NCO-equivalent, 120; amine-equivalent, 118–123.
NATIONAL ANILINE DIV.,
ALLIED CHEMICAL & DYE CORP.

Nacconate® 1300-50. A 50% solution of NACCONATE® 300 in chlorobenzene. *Use:* As a primer on substrates which are to be treated with urethane coatings or adhesives, and a major ingredient of urethane adhesives. NATIONAL ANILINE DIV.,
ALLIED CHEMICAL & DYE CORP.

Nacromer® Pearl Pigments. Nacreous, translucent pigments which, when added to a transparent coating material, create a deep lustrous finish. Developed as an economical substitute for natural pearl essence. NACROMER® pigments are composed of many tiny plate-like crystals each of which reflects light rays and make possible a wide variety of pleasing finishes. Special effects can be obtained by the addition of spirit soluble dyes. Supplied in the form of a 35% dispersion. The vehicle is a combination of lacquer, solvent, and plasticizer specially formulated to give good dispersion and to be completely compatible with the system in which the dispersions are to be used. A few of the available dispersions are as follows:

NACROMER XNC, for use in cellulose nitrate lacquers, and in pyroxylin plastics.

NACROMER XVA, for dispersion in vinyl lacquers that are to be used to coat vinyl plastics.

NACROMER XDO, prepared in dioctyl phthalate, is for incorporation into vinyl sheeting and in polystyrene.

NACROMER XPE, for use in casting operations with most polyester resins.

NACROMER XTH, a special dispersion for incorporation into methyl methacrylate monomer.

Uses: In formulating the base and top coats for simulated pearls; plastic pearl buttons; decorative finish on statuary, jewelry, sporting goods, sea shells, etc.; coating glass, wood, plastic, leather, or metal.
MEARL CORP.

Nacrosol[NR]. The trademark for organic pigments, other than phthalocyanine and vat colors. These are used in plastics, rubber, spin dyeing, and industrial coatings. NATIONAL ANILINE DIV., ALLIED CHEMICAL & DYE CORP.

Nalex®. (*HBMTN* p. 383). Now a registered trademark. NATIONAL STARCH PRODUCTS INC.

Nalplex. See "DUTCH BOY" NALPLEX®.

Nalzin[NR]. A zinc organic complex especially developed for co-use with barium-cadmium stabilizers in vinyl products to eliminate sulfur staining. It is a clear, pale yellow liquid, miscible in mixtures of hydrocarbon solvents with ketones, esters, CELLOSOLVES®, etc.; sp.gr. 0.916. It should never be used alone without supplementary stabilization.
NATIONAL LEAD CO.

Namiglo. An all-purpose built soap for fabric cleaning. It is fortified with alkalis and water conditioners, and contains a whitening agent. *Use:* As a laundry detergent, particularly in launderettes.
NATIONAL MILLING & CHEMICAL CO.

Nami-Lo®. A low-sudsing, fast-acting, all-purpose detergent for home and commercial uses. It is effective in either hard or soft water; and contains a whitening agent. *Uses:* As a laundry detergent, and for cleaning dishes, glassware, windows, and painted surfaces. NATIONAL MILLING & CHEMICAL CO.

Napped Leather△. Same as SUEDE△.

Narcoil® 10. A diffusion pump fluid. A chlorinated diphenyl; mol.wt. 326.0; sp.gr. 1–538–1.548; max. temp. for exposure to atmospheric pressure, 300°F.; vapor pressure, 0.01 mm. Hg at 70°C. and 1.0 mm. at 150°C. *Use:* Particularly for vacuum application where tolerance to air while hot is important.
NATIONAL RESEARCH CORP.

Narcoil® 40. A diffusion pump fluid. A di-nonyl phthalate ester, specially distilled, purified, and tested for high vacuum service. $C_6H_4(COOC_9H_{19})_2$; mol.wt. 418.60; sp.gr. (25°C.), 0.973; max. temp. for long exposure to atmospheric pressure, 140°F.; vapor pressure, 10^{-4} mm. Hg at 85°C. and 1.0 mm. at 215°C. NATIONAL RESEARCH CORP.

Naremide®. (*Supp.* I p. 154). No longer available.
SHARP & DOHME DIV., MERCK & CO.

Narescoil®. An oil for use in high-vacuum mechanical pumps. NATIONAL RESEARCH CORP.

Narliner® Type 5018. A synthetic strippable film coating material designed for use as a tank liner on high vacuum coating equipment. Applied by brush; dries in approx. 8 hr.; easily removed from the walls of the tank. NATIONAL RESEARCH CORP.

Na-Sul[NR]. A product consisting of dinonyl naphthalene sulfonates. *Use:* As a corrosion inhibitor for petroleum products. R. T. VANDERBILT CO.

National[NR]. (*HBMTN* p. 384). No longer available.
DELAWARE TOOL STEEL CORP.

National®. The trademark for steel pipes, boiler tubes, casings and plastic pipe.
UNITED STATES STEEL CORP., NATIONAL TUBE DIV.

National® Anhydrous Ammonia. (*Supp.* I p. 155). No longer available.
E. I. DU PONT DE NEMOURS & CO.

Natopherol®. A VITAMIN E preparation consisting of mixed tocopherols in capsule form. Used in the treatment of habitual abortion, muscular dystrophies and amyotrophic lateral sclerosis.
ABBOTT LABORATORIES

Natox[NR]. Incorrectly listed as NOXATE® (*Supp.* I. p. 161). VICTOR CHEMICAL WORKS

Natrona Brand® Bicarbonate of Soda. A brand of sodium bicarbonate. PENNSYLVANIA SALT MFG. CO.

Navalon®. (*Supp.* I p. 155). Now a registered trademark. JOHNS-MANVILLE SALES CORP.

N-A-X®. (*HBMTN* p. 285). Now a registered trademark. GREAT LAKES STEEL CORP.

Naxol[NR]. The proprietary name for a distilled commercial cyclohexanol of high purity. It is a clear, colorless liquid of faintly-phenolic aromatic odor, having a boiling range of 160.1° to 161.1°C.; f.p. 25.0°C.; sp.gr. 0.943 (20/4°C.). *Uses:* As a solvent for rubber, rosin, metal soaps, certain dyes, fats, oils, waxes and other substances used in various formulations; blending and stabilizing agent for emulsions, greases and creams; homogenizing agent; antifoaming material; paint and lacquer solvent for improving flowout and gloss; important chemical intermediate in the mfg. of plasticizers, pesticides, fruit-thinning agents, petroleum additives, dielectrics, rubber-processing agents, rust inhibitors, and surfactants; as a cosmetic ingredient; etc. NATIONAL ANILINE DIV., ALLIED CHEMICAL & DYE CORP.

Naxol D[NR]. The same as NAXOL[NR] except that it is protected from freezing by the addition of small amounts of pure methanol. Used for the same purposes as NAXOL. NATIONAL ANILINE DIV., ALLIED CHEMICAL & DYE CORP.

NBA△. N-bromoacetamide. $CH_3CONHBr$; mol.wt. 137.97; active bromine, 57%. A white powder with a bromine odor; m.p. 105–108°C. *Use:* As a brominating agent for allylic brominations, side-chain brominations. etc.; and as a source of HOBr in aqueous media.

NBS△. N-bromosuccinimide. $C_4H_4NO_2Br$; mol.wt. 178.0. A white, fine crystalline powder with a faint odor of bromine; active bromine, 44.5%; m.p. 174–178°C.; sparingly soluble in water, ether, benzene, carbon tetrachloride, chloroform; freely soluble in acetone, ethyl acetate, acetic anhydride. *Use:* As a brominating agent where it is desired to substitute bromine for active hydrogen without adding bromine to an unsaturated linkage.

NCS△. N-chlorosuccinimide. $C_4H_4O_2NCl$; mol.wt. 133.54; active chlorine, 26.2%; decomposes about 145°C. A white powder with a mild odor of chlorine. *Uses:* As a chlorinating agent; for the oxidation of primary and secondary alcohols to aldehydes and ketones; as a water disinfectant.

N-dure[NR]. A 12% nitrogen, urea-formaldehyde solution for making chemically blended mixed fertilizers with a wide variety of ratios between quickly soluble and slowly soluble nitrogen. NITROGEN DIV., ALLIED CHEMICAL & DYE CORP.

Neatsfoot Oil△. An inedible, pale-yellow oil obtained by boiling the feet of cattle and sheep. Contains about 80% oleic acid and some BONE OIL. Sp.gr. 0.916; iodine no. 74; saponification no. 97. Used in leather finishing, and as a fine lubricant.

Neenah®. A registered trademark for a line of writing and printing papers. KIMBERLY-CLARK CORP.

Nekanil. A line of surface-active agents for use as textile detergents, wetting-agents, penetrating and dye-leveling agents. Available as liquid solutions and water-soluble powders. NOVA CHEMICAL CORP.

Nekanil AC Special. A cleansing and dispersing agent particularly suitable for ACETATE dyeing. It is a light brown, clear liquid of slightly alkaline reaction. Soluble in water in any proportion; stable in hard water, acids and alkalis, and metal salts. It is particularly efficient in removing impurities during the soaping operation. NOVA CHEMICAL CORP.

Nekoe. *See* LONCHOCARPUS△.

Nelson, Herman. *See* HERMAN NELSON®.

Nemagon[NR] **Soil Fumigant.** A halogenated propane for the control of nematodes in soils in which citrus fruits, peaches, figs, walnuts, grapes, beans, ornamentals, and many other crops are grown. It is applied by soil injection, as a drench, and in granular form. It can be applied where certain plants are growing without causing injury to the plants.
SHELL CHEMICAL CORP.

Nemazene®. A veterinary medicinal consisting of tablets of phenothiazine, Parke-Davis. *Use:* For removing various types of worms from animals.
PARKE, DAVIS & CO.

Nembudeine®. Analgesic-sedative combination of aluminum salt, phenacetin, caffeine, and pentobarbital, in tablet form. Also available with codeine.
ABBOTT LABORATORIES

Nembu-Donna®. A medicinal consisting of pentobarbital sodium and extract belladonna in capsule form.
ABBOTT LABORATORIES

Nembu-Fedrin®. A medicinal consisting of pentobarbital sodium and ephedrine hydrochloride in capsule form. ABBOTT LABORATORIES

Nembu-Gesic®. A medicinal consisting of pentobarbital sodium and acetylsalicylic acid in capsule form.
ABBOTT LABORATORIES

Nembusen®. A veterinary medicinal consisting of pentobarbital sodium and mephensin.
ABBOTT LABORATORIES

Nembu-Serpin®. Tranquilizer and hypotensive preparation of pentobarbital calcium and reserpine, in tablet form. ABBOTT LABORATORIES

Nembutal®. A sedative and hypnotic consisting of pentobarbital calcium or pentobarbital sodium, in tablets, elixir, capsules and intravenous solution.
ABBOTT LABORATORIES

Nemex[NR]. A soil fumigant containing ethylene dibromide. It is especially effective against nematodes and wire worms. LARVACIDE PRODUCTS, INC.

Neobon®. A nutritional supplement, in capsule form, for the geriatric patient. It is a complex mixture of enzymes, hormones, vitamins, and minerals. Three capsules a day is the normal dosage.
J. B. ROERIG & CO.

Neobon® **Liquid.** A nutritional supplement, in liquid form, for the geriatric patient. Each cc. contains 30 mg. ferrous gluconate, 50 mg. ascorbic acid, 0.5 mg. *d*-amphetamine sulfate, 167 mcg. folic acid, 2.5 mcg. VITAMIN B_{12}, 0.1 mg. *l*-thyroxine, 1 mcg. ethinyl estradiol, 1 mg. methyl testosterone, 25 mg. liver fraction 1, and 0.5 cc. ethyl alcohol. J. B. ROERIG & CO.

neo Bromth® **Tablets.** A medicinal for treatment of symptoms of premenstrual tension.
BRAYTEN PHARMACEUTICAL CO.

Neoferrum®. (*HBMTN* p. 388). Now a product of WARNER-CHILCOTT LABORATORIES, successor to THE MALTINE CO.

Neohetramine®. A brand of thonzylamine hydrochloride. An antihistamine medicinal used for the treatment of hay fever, allergic rhinitis and dermatitis, urticaria, angioneurotic edema, serum sickness and other allergies. NEPERA CHEMICAL CO.

Neolan® **Salt P.** A non-ionic textile dyeing assistant. A clear, yellowish solution with a neutral reaction.
CIBA CO.

Neonicotine△. Same as ANABASINE△.

Neopilate Dyestuffs. A line of WOOL dyestuffs of the metal complex series. They have very good fastness properties, particularly to light and rubbing, and have good solubility and excellent leveling properties. The group comprises nine types representing one yellow, one orange, one red, several violets and blues and one brown. NOVA CHEMICAL CORP.

Neopon[NR]. (*Supp.* I p. 156). No longer available.
ROYCE CHEMICAL CO.

Neopone LO Beads®. A non-ionic detergent composed of an ethylene oxide condensate and a builder. *Uses:* As a laundry detergent, and as a detergent for textiles. ULTRA CHEMICAL WORKS

Neoprene W. A single-package, synthetic rubber coating that air cures to a tough, vulcanized rubber at room temp. Solids content, 38%. Has excellent resistance to weathering, abrasion, high humidity, oils, grease, acids, and alkalis. A 3-mil film thickness can be deposited with a single application by brush, dip, or roller. *Use:* As a paint for equipment, floors, etc., in chemical processing, water treatment and sewage, pulp and paper, food processing, and petroleum plants; for marine maintenance; and for railway equipment. CARBOLINE CO.

Neoprime A®. A pigmented, chlorinated rubber-base paint which may be applied to metal and wood surfaces prior to coating with synthetic rubber-base coating materials. PENNSYLVANIA SALT MFG. CO.

Neoprime B®. A non-pigmented, chlorinated rubber-base paint which may be applied to metal and wood surfaces prior to coating with synthetic rubber-base coating materials. PENNSYLVANIA SALT MFG. CO.

Neo Size[NE]. A complete size for synthetic filament yarns. It has excellent flexibility and film-forming characteristics, and is readily soluble in water. TEX-CHEM CO.

Neosol® **Proprietary Solvent.** Listed as NEOSOL® (*HBMTN* p. 388). SHELL CHEMICAL CORP.

Neo Spectra®. The trademark for a series of jet impingement carbon blacks for automotive enamels and all types of applications requiring high jetness. Available as:

NEO SPECTRA MARK I, designed for specialty applications requiring a powdered carbon black of very high jetness.

NEO SPECTRA MARK II. This is a standard black for top quality enamels and lacquers. Characterized by high gloss and blackness and rapid dispersion in the vehicle. Available in powdered and bead forms.

NEO SPECTRA III. A medium-high color that is economical in price yet high in quality. Used in enamels, lacquers, and synthetic fibers and plastics. COLUMBIAN CARBON CO.

Neothren Spray. (*Supp.* I p. 157). Should have been listed as NEOTHRIN SPRAY. THOMPSON CHEMICALS CORP.

Neothrin Spray. Incorrectly listed as NEOTHREN SPRAY (*Supp.* I p. 157). THOMPSON CHEMICALS CORP.

Neovadine® **AL.** A dyeing and printing assistant identical with NEOVADINE® AN in all properties except that it is non-foaming. CIBA CO.

Neovadine® **AN.** A non-ionic dyeing and printing assistant that is highly effective as a leveling, retarding and stripping agent in dyeing textile and leather. It is a viscous liquid or paste, readily soluble in hot water. Solutions are neutral and stable to acids, alkalis, and hard water. CIBA CO.

Neowite #10. A porcelain enamel frit for application on refrigerator doors, refrigerator liners, washing machine tubs, reflectors, signs, table tops, holloware, etc. It is a titania opacified, acid-resisting, white covercoat of unusual opacity, color stability, and abrasion-resistance. Applied by spraying, drain diping or by tong dipping. Median burning temp. 1,550°F.; median burning time, 3–4 min. PEMCO CORP.

Neowhite D Liquid[NE]. A liquid textile whitener and brightener. It is stable, powerful, and freely soluble, and may be used in liquid soaps, detergents, and starches. FIBER CHEMICAL CORP.

Nephritin®. (*HBMTN* p. 389). No longer available. REED & CARNRICK

Nerofil®. A filteraid processeed from carbonaceous materials. It is a very finely divided, grayish-black powder having a cake density of approx. 14–18 lb. per cu.ft. Its principal use is in the filtration of highly alkaline solutions. It is practically insoluble in boiling 50% caustic. High flow rates and excellent clarity are obtained with this filteraid. GREAT LAKES CARBON CORP.

Nerva-Kote®. (*Supp.* I p. 157). Now a registered trademark. RUBBER & PLASTICS COMPOUND CO.

Nerva-Seal®. (*HBMTN* p. 389). No longer available. RUBBER & PLASTICS COMPOUND CO.

Nervastral J. R. Joint Sealer[NE]. A hot-pour elastomeric compound, resistant to the solvent action of jet fuels. Used for sealing concrete joints in warming aprons and refueling stations at jet airports; and for sealing breaks in macadam surfaces in parking lots, driveways, service stations, bridge abutments and other pavement and floor surfaces subject to the action of spilled gasoline, oil or grease. RUBBER & PLASTICS COMPOUND CO.

Nervastral Seal-Pruf® **H-D.** A non-reinforced, homogeneous, waterproof and impermeable elastomeric sheet, 0.020" thick, and flexible over the temp. range of −10°F. to +180°F. *Uses:* For window flashing, spandrel beam and column waterproofing, membrane waterproofing, through-wall flashing, cavity wall flashing, box and valley gutters, and other construction work; and for protection against corrosion of buried pipe lines and conduits and equipment exposed to acid fumes and spillings. RUBBER & PLASTICS COMPOUND CO.

Nervastral Seal-Pruf® **Tape 30** *and* **60.** An unsupported, waterproof, impermeable sheeting composed of rubber hydrocarbons and high melting oxidized asphalt. TYPE 30 weighs 22 oz./sq.yd.; TYPE 60 is twice as thick and twice as heavy. *Uses:* For window and door flashing, spandrel beam waterproofing, and perimeter flashing. RUBBER & PLASTICS COMPOUND CO.

Nervatape®. (*Supp.* I p. 158). Now a registered trademark. RUBBER & PLASTICS COMPOUND CO.

Nervatape® **#7.** (*Supp.* I p. 158). The name NERVATAPE is now a registered trademark. RUBBER & PLASTICS COMPOUND CO.

Neuro-Centrine®. A combination medicinal tablet which incorporates an effective antispasmodic-anticholinergic agent with a sedative and tranquilizer. Each sugar-coated tablet contains 15.00 mg. phenobarbital, 0.25 mg. CENTRINE® hydrogen sulfate (a brand of aminopentamide), and 0.05 mg. reserpine. Used in the treatment of anxiety states and emotional tension, either of psychogenic origin or as concomitants of various somatic diseases. Also recommended for the relief of symptoms associated with functional disorders of the gastrointestinal and cardiovascular systems. BRISTOL LABORATORIES INC.

Neutranyl Colors[NR]. A line of dyestuffs made especially for the neutral dyeing of NYLON. The colors dye level and leave ACETATE unstained. Ex-

cellent fastness to washing is obtained when the dyeings are after-treated with BELLEFIX N-100.
BELLE CHEMICAL CO.

Neutrascour. See CLARAPENT® NEUTRASCOUR.

Neutrazoic® Dyestuffs. See ATLANTIC NEUTRAZOIC® DYESTUFFS.

Neutrotone®. (*HBMTN* p. 390). Formerly mfg'd by OLIN MATHIESON CHEMICAL CORP., now a product of ENDRISS CHEMICALS.

Nevamar®. A high-pressure laminate surfacing material that will not crack, craze, or peel in normal use; and is resistant to alcohol, fruit acids, ammonia, ordinary inks, cigarette burns, and boiling water. Used as a building material for surfacing furniture, cabinets, etc.
NATIONAL PLASTIC PRODUCTS CO.

Nevasota®. (*HBMTN* p. 390). No longer available.
NEVILLE CHEMICAL CO.

Nevastain A *and* B. Two non-staining rubber antioxidants having the following properties:

	Nevastain A	Nevastain B
Physical state	liquid	solid, flaked
Color	9 (max.), Gardner	light amber
Sp.gr. (30°C.)	1.08–1.09	1.137
Flash point (C.O.C.),°F.	275 (min.)	—
Viscosity, S.U.S. at 210°F.	50–60	—
M.p., °C.	—	55 (min.)

They are soluble in the usual rubber solvents and insoluble in water.
NEVILLE CHEMICAL CO.

Nevillac 10°®. *Also known* as PHO. A light-colored viscous liquid for use as an anti-skinning agent for paint, varnish, and printing ink, and as a plasticizer for most synthetic resins including nitrocellulose, ethylcellulose, cellulose acetate, vinyl acetate, vinyl butyral, ZEIN, NYLON, and others. Sp.gr. 1.075–1.10; distillation range, 300–370°C., refractive index (25°C.), 1.597; flash point, above 290°F.; acid no. less than 5; saponification no. less than 5; mol.wt. 240; odor, phenolic; viscosity (25°C.), 235 poises.
NEVILLE CHEMICAL CO.

Nevillac OA, RT, RX *and* ZC®. (*HBMTN* p. 291). No longer available.
NEVILLE CHEMICAL CO.

Neville "G" Resin®. (*HBMTN* p. 391). No longer available.
NEVILLE CHEMICAL CO.

Nevoll®. (*HBMTN* p. 392). No longer available.
NEVILLE CHEMICAL CO.

Nevtar®. (*HBMTN* p. 392). No longer available.
NEVILLE CHEMICAL CO.

New Diokem®. A non-organic, chlorine-base cleaner-sanitizer that is especially useful for cleaning and sanitizing pipeline milking system, farm tanks, milking machines, and utensils.
DIVERSEY CORP.

New Plastic Mix[NE]**.** (*HBMTN* p. 392). Now a product of THE BORDEN CO., CHEMICAL DIV., Successor to PIONEER LATEX & CHEMICAL CO.

Newray®. A linoleum flooring material, 0.070" thick, for light residential service.
ARMSTRONG CORK CO.

New Solnus® Oils. A line of specially compounded lubricating oils designed for general lubrication of such parts as plain bearings, antifriction bearings, linkages, slides, cams and gears. They can be used in the so-called "once-through" appliances, "continuous-use" appliances, miscellaneous oil-circulating systems, reservoirs and bath lubrication. They resist oxidation, prevent rusting and corrosion, and give excellent performance for long periods of time. Available in a wide variety of viscosity grades to meet the requirements of various industrial applications.
SUN OIL CO.

New Utah. See BOSTON NEW UTAH.

Niagathal®. (*HBMTN* p. 393). Now a product of HOOKER ELECTROCHEMICAL CO. successor to NIAGARA ALKALI CO.

Niagrite[NE]**.** A commercially pure asbestos felted tape used as an electrical cable fireproofing in conjunction with ASBESTOMENT S refractory powder. NIAGRITE is supplied in widths of 1½", 2", and 3", and in thicknesses of ⅛" and ³/₁₆", and in the following 3 types: NIAGRITE B, backed with a heavy, strong, open-mesh fabric reinforcement; and NIAGRITE C and NIAGRITE D, without reinforcement. NIAGRITE D is not as high in quality as the other types, and, especially when wet, is not as flexible or strong.
JOHNS-MANVILLE SALES CORP.

Nialk®. The brand name for: (1) caustic potash, (KOH), (2) carbonate of potash (K_2CO_3), and (3) trichlorethylene.
HOOKER ELECTROCHEMICAL CO.

Nicamin®. A medicinal consisting of monoethanolamine nicotinate ampoules.
ABBOTT LABORATORIES

'n icer®. Ice buckets of inert, flexible, unbreakable expanded polyvinyl chloride (SPONGEX® PLASTIC). Capacity, 1 gal. It keeps 90% of ice after 4 hr.; and 40% after 19 hr.
B. F. GOODRICH SPONGE PRODUCTS DIV.

Niconyl®. Tablets of isoniazid, PARKE-DAVIS, for the treatment of tuberculosis.
PARKE, DAVIS & CO.

Nicothiamin®. Nicotinamide and THIAMINE elixir for oral use.
ABBOTT LABORATORIES

Nicotine Pyrox®. A combined insecticide, fungicide, and aphicide designed for use as a spray on vegetables, small fruits, and flowers. Contains nicotine to combat sucking insects, arsenic poison to control leaf-eating insects, and a copper ingredient to provide protection against fungus diseases. Supplied in the form of a paste which is mixed with water prior to spraying.
AMERICAN AGRICULTURAL CHEMICAL CO.

Nicouline△**.** *Same as* ROTENONE△.

Nicuar. A welding wire consisting of 30.0% nickel and 69.0% copper. Type 803.
ARCOS CORP.

Nigron®. A black enamel for application by spray or dip. It will air dry to a hard finish in 4 hr., or it can be baked hard in 15 min, at 325°F. It has good resistance to oils and greases, good adhesion, good gloss, and good durability. *Use:* For water-heater bases and tops, kick plates, appliance parts, wrought-iron or tubular-steel furniture, machinery, automotive parts, etc. INTERCHEMICAL CORP., FINISHES DIV.

Nile®. A line of basic dyestuffs characterized by good wet fastness and fair light fastness and which are used for the dyeing or color-discharge printing of bright greenish blues on SILK. As these bright blues hold their shade in artificial light, they are especially useful for evening wear. GENERAL DYESTUFF CO.

Nilstain C-20®. (*Supp.* I p. 159). No longer available. WILBUR B. DRIVER CO.

Nilustre®. Lacquers, air-drying and baking enamels and varnishes of miscellaneous composition that are very dull after air drying or baking. MAAS & WALDSTEIN CO.

Ninate 411. An alkylamine dodecyl benzene sulfonate for making kerosene emulsifiable degreasers, and clear blends of kerosene and water. A yellow, viscous liquid; mol.wt. 400; 95% active; density, 8.5 lb./gal.; pH of 1% solution in water, 4.0; surface tension of 0.1% solution in water, 30 dynes/cm.; soluble in kerosene, Stoddard solvent, chlorinated and aromatic solvents, alcohol, pine oil; insoluble in mineral oils; forms clear solutions in water at concentrations below 1%, and is dispersible in water at higher concentrations. NINOL LABORATORIES, INC.

Ninex 21. A high-foaming liquid detergent for use in applications such as dishwashing, carwashing, bubble baths, shampoos; and for rubber foaming and air entrainment. This foam-stabilized product is essentially a combination of a nonionic alkalolamide and an alkyl aryl sulfonate. NINOL LABORATORIES, INC.

Ninex 303. A sodium xylene sulfonate solution used as a coupling agent to help dissolve nonionic detergents in alkali solutions. NINOL LABORATORIES, INC.

Ninol 1281. A 100%-active, nonionic detergent for use in liquid all-synthetic floor- and wall-cleaning concentrates, and in soap-synthetic blends. It is a coconut diethanolamide; and is an amber liquid, weighing 8.5 lb./gal.; soluble in water, alcohol, benzene, and pine oil; insoluble in kerosene. NINOL LABORATORIES, INC.

Ninol AA62. A foam-stabilizing amide for use with alkyl aryl sulfonates or lauryl sulfates to improve sudsing in the presence of grease, as in dishwashing detergents and shampoos. NINOL LABORATORIES, INC.

Ninox BJO. An acid- and alkali-stable nonionic detergent for low-priced bar-glass cleaners; and, with quaternary ammonium compounds for making detergent-sanitizers. NINOL LABORATORIES, INC.

Nipoxin®. A black, baking enamel based on epoxy resins and characterized by excellent resistance to acids, alkalis, chemicals, salt spray, humidity, and water immersion. When properly baked, they yield very hard, marproof, highly resistant films with excellent toughness, flexibility, and adhesion. Enamels, identical to NIPOXIN but in colors other than black are sold under the name EPOXIN®. INTERCHEMICAL CORP., FINISHES DIV.

NIS△. N-iodosuccinimide. $C_4H_4O_2NI$; mol.wt. 225.00; active iodine, 56.4%; m.p. 200–201°C. An off-white, nearly odorless powder; soluble in acetone and methanol, moderately soluble in dioxane; insoluble in carbon tetrachloride and in ether; decomposes in water. It is a chemical reagent used to convert enol acetates to alpha-iodo ketones; and in the mfg. of other iodo compounds.

NiTectic®. An all-purpose, all-position, DC arc-welding rod for joining nickel alloys. EUTECTIC WELDING ALLOYS CORP.

Nitramac® Tablets. (*HBMTN* p. 398). Now a product of WARNER-CHILCOTT LABORATORIES, successor to THE MALTINE CO.

Nitri-Cast-Iron. See FCC® NITRI-CAST-IRON.

Nitrocycle[NE]. The trade name for a patented pressure nitriding process using ammonia. UNITED STATES STEEL CORP., OIL WELL SUPPLY DIV.

Nitro-Dur[NE]. A high-solids, catalyzed epoxy-resin-based coating used as a protective coating for metal, wood, and concrete which are exposed to corrosive conditions. It is resistant to most acids, alkalis, and solvents. ELECTRO-CHEMICAL ENGINEERING & MFG. CO.

Nitrogation Ammonia[NE]. Incorrectly listed as NITROGEN AMMONIA® (*HBMTN* p. 398). SHELL CHEMICAL CORP.

Nixon. The tradename for a line of thermoplastics including cellulose nitrate (NIXON C/N), cellulose acetate (NIXON C/A), vinyl (NIXON V/L), ethyl cellulose (NIXON E/C), and cellulose acetate butyrate (NIXON C/AB). C/A, V/L and C/AB are available as sheeting; C/A and E/C as molding powders; C/A, E/C, C/N and C/AB as extrusions in the form of rods, tubes, and profiles; and C/N and C/AB as spiral-wrapped and butt-welded tubing. These plastics are used for the mfg. of display containers, tool handles, toothbrushes, toys and novelties, optical frames, playing cards, shoe heels, pens and pencils, and many other articles. NIXON NITRATION WORKS

NNO®. (*HBMTN* p. 399). This product is also mfg'd in England, Germany and Canada. The trademark is registered in Canada but not in England and Germany. ATLAS POWDER CO.
HONEYWILL-ATLAS, LTD.
ATLAS-GOLDSCHMIDT G.m.b.H.
ATLAS POWDER CO., CANADA, LTD.

NNOR®. (*HBMTN* p. 399). This product is also mfg'd. in England, Germany, and Canada. The trademark is registered in Canada but not in England and Germany. ATLAS POWDER CO.
HONEYWILL-ATLAS, LTD.
ATLAS-GOLDSCHMIDT G.m.b.H.
ATLAS POWDER CO., CANADA, LTD.

NOBS No. 1 Accelerator®. The proprietary name for N-oxydiethylene benzothiazole-2-sulfenamide. A delayed-action accelerator for use in furnace black-rubber stocks where processing safety is important. Imparts greater scorch protection than NOBS No. 1. AMERICAN CYANAMID CO.

No-Buff®. See BROWN LABEL® NO-BUFF®.

No-Fil®. A line of coated abrasive papers with special non-loading treatment. BEHR-MANNING CO.

No-Glo Oil®. A specially treated, highly refined oil which, when emulsified with a conventional oil-free, water-base mud by means of agitation with a suitable emulsifier, produces a non-fluorescent emulsion drilling fluid which does not mask or change the fluorescence of cutting and/or core sections from an oil zone when these are examined under an ultraviolet light of 2,600–3,700 Ångstrom units. OIL BASE, INC.

No-Glo Thread Lubricant®. A non-fluorescent thread lubricant for use when a non-fluorescing drilling mud is being employed. It contains powdered copper, lead, graphite and molybdenum disulfide in a heat-resistant bentonite grease base. OIL BASE, INC.

Noisefoe[NE]. Noise eliminating ear cushions with spring-type head suspension. *Use:* For effective protection in high level noise areas.
MINE SAFETY APPLIANCES CO.

Noisemaster®. The trademark for a line of acoustical products. SIMPSON LUMBER CO.

Nois-Stop Baffles[NE]. Plastic-wrapped boards of interbonded fibrous glass to be suspended in enclosures for absorbing sound.
OWENS-CORNING FIBERGLAS CORP.

No Karb®. A clay used as a filler for paper.
MINERALS & CHEMICALS CORP. OF AMERICA

Nonic® #218. A straw-colored liquid, non-ionic, surface-active agent possessing good surface activity, detergency and foam properties. It is a polyethylene glycol tert-dodecylthioether. Sp.gr. 1.05 (20°/20°C.); viscosity, 1.33 cps. (25°C.); soluble in water; at least 5% soluble in ethyl alcohol, acetone, ethyl acetate, amyl acetate, diethyl ether, and pyridene. *Uses:* As a household detergent; textile detergent, and wetting agent; for grease removal; in mfg. of paper; etc.
PENNSYLVANIA SALT MFG. CO.

Nonic® #234. A straw-colored liquid, non-ionic, surface-active agent particularly useful as a textile detergent and wetting agent. It is a polyethylene glycol tert-dodecylthioether. Sp.gr. 1.04 (20°/20°C.).
PENNSYLVANIA SALT MFG. CO.

Nonic® #259. A clouding agent. It is a straw-colored surface-active liquid that is very slightly soluble in water. PENNSYLVANIA SALT MFG. CO.

Nonic® #260. A yellow-colored liquid, non-ionic surface-active agent possessing excellent wetting properties. Consists of 98% polyethylene glycol tert-dodecylthioether. PENNSYLVANIA SALT MFG. CO.

Nonic® #261. A wetting and emulsifying agent. It is a yellow-colored liquid composed of polyethylene glycol tert-dodecylthioether and a max. of 2% water.
PENNSYLVANIA SALT MFG. CO.

Nonic® #300. A surface-active agent characterized by excellent stability to acids, alkalis, and oxidizing agents. It is a polyethylene glycol alkyl-phenyl ether and is used as a wetting agent, detergent, and emulsifier. A pale, straw-colored liquid; sp.gr. 1.06 (20°/20°C.); cloud point, 56°C. (min.); flash point (open cup), greater than 400°F.; soluble in alcohols, ketones, esters, aromatic hydrocarbons, water, and many chlorinated compounds.
PENNSYLVANIA SALT MFG. CO.

Non-Shrinkable®. (*HBMTN* p. 401). Should have been listed as COLONIAL No. 6 NON-SHRINKABLE®.
VANADIUM-ALLOYS STEEL CO.

Non-Sweat®. (*HBMTN* p. 401). Now a registered trademark. KEASBEY & MATTISON CO.

Non-Vac[NE]. The trademark for a blood bottle without vacuum. ABBOTT LABORATORIES

Nopcaine®. An antibiotic-containing product for fortifying foods and feeds with vitamins.
NOPCO CHEMICAL CO.

Nopco 75[NE]. (*HBMTN* p. 401). No longer available. NOPCO CHEMICAL CO.

Nopco 99®. (*HBMTN* p. 401). No longer available.
NOPCO CHEMICAL CO.

Nopco 800®. (*HBMTN* p. 401). No longer available. NOPCO CHEMICAL CO.

Nopco ESI[NE]. A paper-coating compound containing 45% active material, used in both starch and casein coatings. NOPCO CHEMICAL CO.

Nopco FM®. (*HBMTN* p. 402 and *Supp.* I p. 161). No longer available. NOPCO CHEMICAL CO.

Nopcofoam[NE]. A line of polyurethane foamed plastics. NOPCO CHEMICAL CO.

Nopco KFC[NE]. A 100%-active defoaming agent, in flake form, for paper-mill applications.
NOPCO CHEMICAL CO.

Nopcol MDP®. (*HBMTN* p. 402 and *Supp.* I p. 161). No longer available. NOPCO CHEMICAL CO.

Nopcolube[NE]. A line of lubricants used in textile-treating operations. NOPCO CHEMICAL CO.

Nopcom®. Antibiotic- and vitamin-containing products for fortifying foods and feeds for poultry and animals. NOPCO CHEMICAL CO.

Nopco-Pak®. Vitamin-, mineral- and antibiotic-containing products for fortifying foods and feeds for poultry and animals. NOPCO CHEMICAL CO.

Nopcosize[NE]. Water-soluble, synthetic polymer-type sizing agents. NOPCO CHEMICAL CO.

Nopcosol®. Stabilized vitamin concentrates for use in animal and poultry feeds. NOPCO CHEMICAL CO.

Nopcostat®. A series of products, having antistatic properties, used in the treatment of textiles.
NOPCO CHEMICAL CO.

Nopcosulf[NE]. A sulfated oil used for general industrial purposes. NOPCO CHEMICAL CO.

Nopcotal®. Sulfonated tallow products for general industrial use and particularly for use in the treatment of textiles. NOPCO CHEMICAL CO.

Nopcote®. Synthetic resins for use in the protective and decorative coating of paper, CELLOPHANE and similar sheet materials. NOPCO CHEMICAL CO.

Nopcotex®. Textile-finishing compounds for use in the treatment of fibers and fabrics.
NOPCO CHEMICAL CO.

Nopcovar®. (*HBMTN* p. 402 and *Supp.* I p. 161). No longer available. NOPCO CHEMICAL CO.

Nopcowax®. The trademark name for a line of synthetic waxes. NOPCO CHEMICAL CO.

Nopdex. *See* SUPER NOPDEX®.

Nopvite®. The trademark name for a VITAMIN E concentrate. NOPCO CHEMICAL CO.

Norisodrine®. A bronchial antispasmodic consisting of isopropylarterenol sulfate for oral inhalation only. ABBOTT LABORATORIES

Normasal®. Normal lead salicylate. (C_6H_5) $(COOPbOCO)(C_6H_4)(OH)$; mol.wt. 481. A soft, creamy white, crystalline powder; sp.gr. 2.36; refractive index, 1.78; soluble to the extent of 0.5% in water; soluble in glycols and glycol ethers; slightly soluble in methyl and ethyl alcohol. *Use:* As an anti-oxidant and light-screening agent for vinyl resins. NATIONAL LEAD CO.

Norvan[NB]. Emulsions of polyvinyl acetate, polymer and copolymer, containing 50–55% solids. *Use:* For making emulsion paints. R. T. VANDERBILT CO.

Nostyn®. A pharmaceutical preparation for calming tensive and anxiety states, containing 2-ethylcrotonylurea. AMES CO.

Novaculite[△]. *See* OILSTONE[△].

Novafix CA. A fixing agent for aftertreatment of direct dyestuffs. It improves the fastness properties of this group of dyestuffs. NOVA CHEMICAL CORP.

Novafix CU. A resinous copper complex salt for aftertreatment of direct dyestuffs to improve the fastness properties in dyeing or printing. NOVA CHEMICAL CORP.

Novafix WW. An amino condensate used in aftertreatment of direct colors to improve the fastness to washing. NOVA CHEMICAL CORP.

Novagen Black II BN. A fast, acid-aging, neutral-developing azoic printing black of reddish shade with good fastness to all agencies. It produces a full, bloomy black. It can be printed alongside pigment colors as it is not appreciably affected by the presence of formaldehyde. NOVA CHEMICAL CORP.

Novalan. A line of metallized acid dyestuffs, with excellent solubility, leveling, and fastness properties, for use on WOOL and polyamide fibers. NOVA CHEMICAL CORP.

Novanol AO *and* B Powders. Products for softening water and removing insoluble metal compounds from textiles. They are almost white, slightly hygroscopic powders, readily soluble in warm and cold water. The aqueous solutions have an alkaline reaction, but not stronger than that of soda solutions. They are stable against boiling and alkalis. NOVA CHEMICAL CORP.

Novanol Nap. A dyeing assistant used for aftertreatment of naphthol dyeings to improve fastness to crocking. It is in powder form, readily wetted out and dissolved in water. It is stable to hard water, acids and alkalis. NOVA CHEMICAL CORP.

Novanol R. A textile detergent based on a fatty alcohol sulfonic acid condensation product. NOVA CHEMICAL CORP.

Novanol WS Powder. An acid-stable protective colloid and dyeing auxiliary. It is a brownish, somewhat hygroscopic powder which may be readily dissolved in water of any degree of hardness. It is stable against alkalis, acids and salts. It is not surface active, and therefore does not show any wetting-out, lathering, or scouring effects. It has a certain affinity for animal fibers (WOOL, SILK, etc.), as well as for NYLON. NOVA CHEMICAL CORP.

Novanthrene Brilliant Green 3B. An anthraquinone dyestuff available as a dispersed powder and in paste form. It has excellent fastness properties, including a light rating of 7 in darker shades. Tinctorially, it exhibits a strong bluish green shade. NOVA CHEMICAL CORP.

Novapon A. A detergent based on a condensation product of protein derivatives with fatty acids. It is an excellent wetting and emulsifying agent, as well as a dyeing assistant. NOVA CHEMICAL CORP.

Novapon NE. A printing and dyeing assistant for WOOL. It improves the appearance of woolen material, increase penetration, and promotes level dyeing. It has an affinity for dyestuffs and, therefore, is an efficient stripping agent. NOVA CHEMICAL CORP.

Novasoft A. A cationic textile softener with a pH of 6.5. It can be used under acid or alkaline conditions; and does not cause yellowing of whites or affect the light fastness of dyestuffs. NOVA CHEMICAL CORP.

Novatol. An aromatic nitro compound. It is a mild oxidizing agent. Primarily used to prevent "facing" of goods in discharge printing. It is in powder form and readily soluble in water. NOVA CHEMICAL CORP.

No-Vent®. The trademark for a line of blasting caps. HERCULES POWDER CO.

Novex®. An alkaline compound used in mechanical can washing equipment where water hardness is below 200 p.p.m. Contains complex phosphates possessing water-softening properties. DIVERSEY CORP.

Novocore®. A particle board construction or building panel. UNITED STATES PLYWOOD CORP.

Novon[NB]. A weed killing composition containing 2-(2,4,5 - trichlorophenoxy) ethyl-2,2 - dichloropropionate. DOW CHEMICAL CO.

Novotile®. A floor tile made of bonded wood shavings. UNITED STATES PLYWOOD CORP.

Novowall[NB]. A particle board partition panel. UNITED STATES PLYWOOD CORP.

Novulphor A Oil-Soluble. An emulsifier for mineral and fatty oils. It is a fluid, brown oil of neutral reaction, stable against hard water. It is easily soluble in most technical fatty and mineral oils and emulsifiable in water. NOVA CHEMICAL CORP.

Novulphor EL. An emulsifying agent. It is a yellowish-brown oil which becomes pasty at low temps. It is readily soluble in water, liquid or melted paraffin

waxes and fats, other waxes, and a variety of organic solvents. It and its solutions give a neutral reaction. It has excellent stability against hard water. It is saponified by strong alkalis, but is compatible with weak alkalis and acids, particularly at low temps.
NOVA CHEMICAL CORP.

Novusol®. (*HBMTN* p. 403). No longer available.
NOPCO CHEMICAL CO.

Noxate®. (*Supp.* I p. 161). Should have been listed as NATOX[NE].
VICTOR CHEMICAL WORKS

Nox-Carbon®. A chemical carbon remover for automobile engines. It is introduced into the combustion chamber to dissolve carbon and lead deposits.
DAUBERT CHEMICAL CO.

Nox-Sound®. A mastic coating for use as a sound deadener for automobiles, appliances, and other equipment. NOX-SOUND is a paste-like, black mastic in 3 grades. Can be applied with pressure-pot or barrel-type pumps; or by trowel, brush, or flow gun. It covers in one coat; it stays tough and flexible; and it insulates, waterproofs, and rustproofs in addition to deadening sound.
DAUBERT CHEMICAL CO.

NP-10[NE]. A polymeric plasticizer which is a condensation product of neopentyl glycol and adipic acid. It has a mol.wt. of 1,200–1,300; color, A.P.H.A., of 100(max.); sp.gr. of 1.060; flash point of 535°F.; and viscosity at 70°F. of 5,000 cps. *Uses:* As a primary or secondary plasticizer in vinyls; and for the preparation of plastisols.
EASTMAN CHEMICAL PRODUCTS, INC.

NPD (in monogram)®. The trademark for a line of subsurface pumps and parts.
UNITED STATES STEEL CORP.

NT (in circle)®. The trademark for a line of pressure vessels.
UNITED STATES STEEL CORP.

Nu Aero®. A penetrating oil consisting of a blend of oils, solvents, wetting agents and molybdenum disulfide. *Use:* For loosening nuts, bolts, fittings, sheaves, etc.
PRESSURE PRODUCTS CO.

Nu Aero® Chain Life. A lubricant for motorcycle and bicycle chains, high-speed roller chains, and timing chains. It adheres to chains at high speeds, penetrates deeply into the links, lubricates, and prevents rust.
PRESSURE PRODUCTS CO.

Nualets®. The trademark for a phosphorus-free vitamin-mineral diet supplement in tablet form.
ABBOTT LABORATORIES

Nucite[△]. Same as INOSITOL[△].

Nu-Film®. (*HBMTN* p. 405). Now a registered trademark.
MILLER CHEMICAL & FERTILIZER CORP.

Nu-Film®. (*Supp.* I p. 162). Now a registered trademark.
NATIONAL STARCH PRODUCTS INC.

Nu-Finish. A liquid furniture and woodwork cleaner and polish. It is also used to treat yarn dusters and sweepers to improve dirt and dust pick-up.
J. I. HOLCOMB MFG. CO.

Nu-Iron®. A nutritional iron compound containing the equivalent of 30% total iron, and 10% chelated iron (expressed as metal). It is a dry, neutral powder which suspends readily in water; and is compatible with insecticidal and fungicidal materials. Used in the form of a spray for application to ornamentals, grasses, fruits and vegetables to correct iron chlorosis and to stimulate growth.
TENNESSEE CORP.

Nu-M®. A neutral manganese compound, containing 41% metallic manganese, designed to correct nutritional deficiencies of truck crops, grain crops, and fruits. It is a light brown, water-insoluble, noncrystalline powder that is compatible with organic insecticides. Safe for direct application on plants and fruit by spray or dust methods.
TENNESSEE CORP.

Nu-Manese®. A water-insoluble, acid-soluble, brownish-black powder consisting essentially of MnO. A source of manganese as a nutritional trace element; suitable for direct soil application by spray or dust methods.
TENNESSEE CORP.

Nupercaine®. A local anesthetic of high potency and prolonged effect. It is a crystalline, colorless, odorless, and tasteless compound that is readily soluble in water and alcohol. Used as a spinal anesthesia as well as for topical application in urology, laryngology, and ophthalmology. Supplied in ampuls for spinal anesthesia, in solution form for topical application, and tablets for preparation of solutions. (*See also* HEAVY SOLUTION NUPERCAINE® *and* NUPERCAINE® IN OIL).
CIBA PHARMACEUTICAL PRODUCTS INC.

Nupercaine® In Oil. An anesthetic agent for relief of painful anal conditions. Contains 0.5% NUPERCAINE® hydrochloride 1.0%, phenol 10%, benzyl alcohol, and oil of sweet almond.
CIBA PHARMACEUTICAL PRODUCTS INC.

Nuporals®. Pleasant-tasting throat lozenges designed to provide prolonged anesthesia of mucous membrane of mouth and throat. Each lozenge contains 1.0 mg. NUPERCAINE® hydrochloride.
CIBA PHARMACEUTICAL PRODUCTS INC.

Nurex®. (*HBMTN* p. 407). No longer available.
NATIONAL MALLEABLE & STEEL CASTINGS CO.

Nu-Set[NE]. A 2,4,5-T hormone spray for preventing pre-harvest drop of apples. Used in the ratio of 2 to 4 oz. per 100 gal. water.
MILLER CHEMICAL & FERTILIZER CORP.

Nushank. See ATLAS NUSHANK[NE].

Nuva B[NE]. (*HBMTN* p. 408). No longer available.
GENERAL DYESTUFF CO.

N. V. Medium[NE]. A soft, semi-solid petroleum grease for protecting metal surfaces from rust and corrosion. It leaves a non-drying greasy surface which lasts indefinitely.
KEYSTONE LUBRICATING CO.

Nyagene Black 3B Conc[NE]. A textile dye suitable for direct or developed dyeing of light grays and blacks. It is especially useful as a direct dyeing color on RAYON material containing ACETATE and WOOL effects which must be left white. It shows no change in shade on fabrics when treated with resin or resin with copper salts.
NYANZA COLOR & CHEMICAL CO.

Nyalite Fast Blue NPC[NE]. A member of the NYALITE FAST COLORS. It produces bright shades of blue

on Cotton and Rayon and possesses excellent fastness to light. When aftertreated with resin and copper complexes, the wash fastness is greatly improved. It withstands urea-formaldehyde treatment; the wash and light fastness are both improved; and Acetate fibers are left unstained.
Nyanza Color & Chemical Co.

Nyanthrene[NR]. A line of anthraquinone dyes for the dyeing and printing of textiles.
Nyanza Color & Chemical Co.

Nyapon FP[NR]. An effective fulling and scouring agent for woolen fabrics, especially when used with soda ash or phosphates. It is a viscous liquid consisting of a modified amine condensate. It is fast to lime soaps, alkalis and acids in concentrations generally encountered in acid fulling and dyeing. Nyapon FP is characterized by its fast and free-rinsing properties. Also recommended for souring Nylon and Rayon material. Nyanza Color & Chemical Co.

Nygen® Tolex®. A Nylon® -base vinyl plastic fabric that stretches in all directions, and therefore, conforms to any shape without pleating, folding, or wrinkling. *Uses:* As a furniture upholstery fabric; for covering luggage, handbags, wallets and toilet cases; as an upholstery and trim material for automotive and aircraft uses.
Textileather Div., General Tire & Rubber Co.

Nylene®. A pure, refined, all-hydrogenated lard. It is used generally where a very stable lard shortening, competitively priced, is required in bakery production. The hydrogenated lard maintains its stability under adverse frying and baking conditions.
Anderson, Clayton & Co. Foods Div.

NYQ (in design)®. The trademark for medicinals, vitamins and other products mfg'd by the New York Quinine & Chemical Works, Inc.

Nytal[NR]. A powder consisting of finely divided Tremolitic talc, with a formula ranging between $H_2Mg_3(SiO_3)_4$ and $Ca_2Mg_5H_2(SiO_3)_8$; a soft, relatively inert and infusible powder; sp.gr. 2.6 (approx.). *Uses:* As a filler and extender in paints; constituent of wall and other tiles; filler in rubber, paper and other products.
R. T. Vanderbilt Co.

O

O₂ Cub[NR]. A name used to designate a self-contained oxygen breathing apparatus of relative short service time, for use in poisonous of oxygen-deficient atmospheres.
Mine Safety Appliances Co.

O₂ Mask[NR]. A self-contained, demand-type oxygen-breathing apparatus. *Use:* To supply oxygen on demand under the worst respiratory conditions.
Mine Safety Appliances Co.

Oakite®. The name applied to all cleaning and related materials mfg'd by Oakite Products, Inc.

Oakite® Aviation Cleaner. A fine, buff-colored powder containing soap. Especially safe on aluminum and aluminum alloys. *Uses:* For cleaning aluminum and delicate alloys, without tarnishing or corrosion; and for pre-cleaning in spot welding processes.
Oakite Products, Inc.

Oakite® Bactericide. A fine, white, free-flowing powder with a chlorine odor. Dissolves instantly to a clear solution. *Uses:* For disinfecting, sterilizing, and deodorizing equipment. Used in practically all types of food processing plants.
Oakite Products, Inc.

Oakite® Bottle-Soak. A coarse, white powder containing a germicidal agent. Has excellent detergent and rinsing properties. Used for bottle washing, in soaker and spray-type machines.
Oakite Products, Inc.

Oakite® Composition No. 97. Incorrectly listed as Composition No. 97 (*HBMTN* p. 142).
Oakite Products, Inc.

Oakite® Composition No. 98. Incorrectly listed as Composition No. 98 (*HBMTN* p. 142).
Oakite Products, Inc.

Oakite® Composition No. 99. Incorrectly listed as Composition No. 99 (*HBMTN* p. 143).
Oakite Products, Inc.

Oakite® Di-Sanite. A tan-colored powder with excellent detergent and odor-destroying properties. Used for general cleaning and deodorization.
Oakite Products, Inc.

Oakite® General Cleaner. A white free-flowing powder. Forms adequate suds with lasting quality. Possesses excellent water softening and rinsing qualities. *Uses:* For regular maintenance cleaning in food processing plants by manual, machine or tank methods.
Oakite Products, Inc.

Oakite® Hand Cleaner. A tan-colored, coarse, powdered material partially soluble in hot or cold water. Readily removes oil, grease, graphite inks and other soils from the hands.
Oakite Products, Inc.

Oakite® LSD. A liquid detergent for steam-cleaning in the medium-to-heavy duty range. Specially compounded to prevent clogging of steam generating equipment coils. It is pleasant to use because it gives off no irritating fumes.
Oakite Products, Inc.

Oakite® Penetrant®. A coarse, yellow-brown powder with a light-pine odor. It penetrates caked-on grease, cleans very fast, and is very effective in small quantities. *Uses:* For floor cleaning, general cleaning, steam cleaning, radiator flushing, and as a break material for laundries.
Oakite Products, Inc.

Oakite® Pickle Control No. 5. A viscous, red-brown liquid which combines inhibition with controlled foam blanket. It is a neutral inhibitor for sulphuric, hydrochloric and phosphoric acid pickles.
Oakite Products, Inc.

Oakite® Platers' "A" Special. A moist, light-tan powder for cleaning metals prior to plating; for barrel cleaning of steel stampings; and for other metal cleaning applications.
Oakite Products, Inc.

Oakite® Railroad Cleaner. An excellent heavy-duty equipment cleaner. It is an exceptionally good steam-cleaning material for most soils.
Oakite Products, Inc.

Oakite® Sanitizer No. 1. A clear, light-yellow liquid containing 20% of an active quaternary ammonium germicide. It effectively destroys algae in air conditioning and humidifying systems. It is also used to control slime and algae in holding vats, for sanitizing-food-processing equipment after cleaning, for mold control on walls, etc. OAKITE PRODUCTS, INC.

Oakite® Scald-Aid. An alkaline, powdered product for effective hog-scalding. It provides complete penetration of the scurf and the wetting of the skin so that the hair follicles open wide. This minimizes the need for shaving, singeing, or scraping; and it maintains the scald water within the optimum pH range without the need for lime or other additives.
OAKITE PRODUCTS, INC.

Oakite® Shield. A paint-spray-booth coating designed to catch and hold overspray. It is applied by brush or spray. The coating is readily peeled from walls. OAKITE PRODUCTS, INC.

Oakite® Soluble Oil. An amber-colored oil which forms a stable, milky emulsion when mixed with water. Used for machining and grinding operations, drawing operations, and as an anti-rust compound.
OAKITE PRODUCTS, INC.

Oakite® Special Drawing Compound. A light, cream-colored neutral paste which forms an emulsion when mixed with water. Gives a high degree of lubrication in deep drawing and heavy machining operations. OAKITE PRODUCTS, INC.

Oakite® Special Protective Oil. A corrosive-preventive, amber-colored liquid which quickly and easily displaces water, leaving a thin protective coating on metal surfaces. OAKITE PRODUCTS, INC.

Oakite® Steel Preserver. A reddish-brown, heavy-bodied oil for protecting steel, iron, brass and other metals from corroding and oxidizing under outdoor storage conditions. OAKITE PRODUCTS, INC.

Oakite® Stripper, Stripper M-3, Stripper R-6, Stripper No. 110, *and* **Stripper S-A.** A group of materials for paint stripping operations.
OAKITE PRODUCTS, INC.

Oakite® Stripper Additive. A translucent, brown liquid for use with OAKITE STRIPPERS. It improves the stripping properties of the latter materials.
OAKITE PRODUCTS, INC.

Oakite® Test Q. A slightly moist, light-brown powder containing soap. It is a good, all-around metal cleaner for fast, thorough cleaning.
OAKITE PRODUCTS, INC.

Oakite® Test X. A dry, coarse, off-white powder for heavy-duty metal cleaning. It is especially useful for cleaning power plant surface condensers; for boiling out radiators; and for cleaning steel molds in the rubber, plastic and glass industries.
OAKITE PRODUCTS, INC.

Oakum△. A caulking material made by treating hemp fiber with tar. Generally, fibers are obtained by unravelling old hemp ropes. OAKUM is used for caulking the seams of vessels and wood tanks and as a caulking material for water pipes.

O-B®. Registered trademark for a line of cleaners, polishes, waxes, insecticides, and other products including O-B CLEANER, O-B DISH WASH, O-B SUPER MACHINE DISH WASH, O-B POWDERED SOAP HAND CLEANSER, O-B WATERLESS HAND CLEANSER, O-B CAR WASH, O-B LIQUID CAR WASH-CONCENTRATE, O-B SELF POLISHING SUPER FLOOR WAX, O-B LIQUID CLEANER, O-B LIQUID DETERGENT-CONCENTRATED, O-B LIQUID GLASS CLEANER, O-B LIQUID HAND SOAP, O-B DEODORANT SPRAY, O-B GERMICIDE (a pine oil disinfectant), O-B INSECT SPRAY—5% D.D.T., O-B INSECT SPRAY—SEMI-CONCENTRATE, O-B INSECT SPRAY-CONCENTRATE, O-B SWEEPING COMPOUNDS (sand type, no-grit type, wax-base type and liquid type), O-B STEAM CLEANING COMPOUNDS (medium, heavy-duty, and extra-heavy-duty types), O-B CONVEYOR LUBE LIQUID, O-B CONTROLLED SUDS (a soap for automatic washing machines), O-B RUG SHAMPOO.
CENTRAL O-B PRODUCTS CO.

OB Gel®. (*HBMTN* p. 409). Now a registered trademark. OIL BASE, INC.

OB Gen®. (*HBMTN* p. 409). Now a registered trademark. OIL BASE, INC.

OB Hevywate®. (*HBMTN* p. 409). Now a registered trademark. OIL BASE, INC.

OB Mix Fix®. (*HBMTN* p. 409). Now a registered trademark. OIL BASE, INC.

OB Wate®. (*HBMTN* p. 409). Now a registered trademark. OIL BASE, INC.

OB Well Pack[NR]. A mixture which is placed around the outside of the oil-well pipe at the time the casing is set to prevent exterior corrosion of the casing in formations bearing corrosive salts, sulfides, and other damaging compounds. OB WELL PACK consists of a mixture of OB GEN, CHEMICAL "W," and an asphalt-base crude oil of low gravity. OIL BASE, INC.

OB Zero®. (*HBMTN* p. 409). Now a registered trademark. OIL BASE, INC.

Occultest®. A diagnostic composition for the determination of occult blood in urine. AMES CO.

Octagon (Hippocrates)®. The trademark for: (1) waxes; (2) botanical drugs and drug extracts; and (3) food products, etc. S. B. PENICK & CO.

Octo-Solve®. A general-purpose floor cleaner and wax stripper. Safe to use on all composition floors. Meets requirements of all national flooring institutes.
BRULIN & CO.

Odo-Kakes®. (*HBMTN* p. 409). No longer available HILLYARD CHEMICAL CO.

Odor Crystals. A product for revitalizing musty, stale air. The crystals are sprinkled in closets, locker rooms, vaults, store rooms, and around toilets and urinals to neutralize objectionable odors and leave a fresh, floral aroma. J. I. HOLCOMB MFG. CO.

Odrene®. A trademark for a series of fragrant additives for household, chemical and maintenance products. SINDAR CORP.

Off![NR]. A liquid insect repellent that provides hours of protection from mosquitoes and biting insects. It is the most effective repellent ingredient ever developed, and the formula is recommended by the

United States Department of Agriculture. It resists perspiration, is not greasy, and is safe to use on NYLON, ORLON, COTTON and WOOL.
S. C. JOHNSON & SON

Ogden Process. See OROXALYDE LIQUID[NR].

Ohmstone®. An electrical insulating board composed of asbestos fiber, cement and a water-repellent, bonded under pressure and impregnated with a non-carbonizing insulating compound. It has a min. arc-resistance of 230 sec., and a dielectric strength of 38,000 volts for 1″-thick material; weighs approx. 120 lb./cu. ft.; and has a safe working temp. of 175°F. It can be readily drilled and machined to accommodate elaborate control equipment. Used primarily as a base material for switchboards, controller plates, switch bases, bus-bar supports, etc. which are used under unusually dusty conditions.
JOHNS-MANVILLE SALES CORP.

Oilex. A granular porous carbon especially processed to adsorb the emulsified oil from steam condensate without the addition of a coagulant feed and pH control. It may be used in standard pressure-type filter tanks on downflow operations. It should be supported on a graded bed of anthracite coal rather than gravel to prevent pickup of silica by the hot condensate. A bed depth of 30″ to 36″ is recommended, and a freeboard space of at least 50% of the bed depth is necessary for adequate backwashing. The adsorption flow rate may vary from 1 to 4 gal./min. per sq.ft. of bed area depending on local conditions of temp., degree of dispersion, and oil concentration.
CLACK WATER TREATMENT, INC.

Oilit. See KLINGER-OILIT®[Brit.].

Oil of Santal△. Same as SANDALWOOD OIL△.

Oil of White Birch△. Same as BIRCH OIL△.

Oil-Solv. A liquid which is added to fuel-oil tanks to prevent sludge deposits that might result in clogged lines, heaters, fuel pumps, screens and burner orifices.
ANDERSON-STOLZ CORP.

Oilstone△. A fine-grained, slaty, silica rock used principally for making sharpening stones for edged tools. In the United States, major deposits of oilstone are found in Arkansas. NOVACULITE is a hard, fine-grained, bluish-white and opaque-white oilstone mined in Arkansas and composed of about 99.5% of chalcedony silica. Another type, called WASHITA OIL-STONE is mined near Hot Springs, Arkansas. It is a hard, compact, white stone of uniform texture.

Oilwell®. The trademark for a line of well drilling and production apparatus, machinery and tools; and petroleum-processing equipment.
UNITED STATES STEEL CORP., OIL WELL SUPPLY DIV.

Oiticici Oil△. An oil obtained from the kernels of the nuts of the tree *Licania rigida* of northeastern Brazil. The oil contains about 80% licanic acid; sp.gr. 0.944–0.971; saponification no. 187–193; iodine no. 142–155. It is used as a substitute and extender for tung oil in the mfg. of paints and varnishes.

OK®. An alkyd resin lacquer for automotive use.
SHERWIN-WILLIAMS CO.

Okemco®. A slightly moist, light-brown powder containing soap. Makes a very powerful cleaning solution. *Uses:* As a heavy-duty tank cleaner for metal plants and railroads; for cleaning carburetors and fuel pumps before overhaul; and for removing burned-on food deposits.
OAKITE PRODUCTS, INC.

Old American®. (*HBMTN* p. 411). Now a product of OLD AMERICAN ROOFING MILLS, DIV. OF THE RUBEROID CO.

Old Dr. Stork's[NR]. A line of preparations for the care of babies. Included in the line are aspirin tablets; baby powder; a syrup, containing saccharated extract of thyme, for the relief of minor bronchial irritations and coughs due to colds; and infants suppositories.
AMERICAN PHARMACEUTICAL CO.

Oleacid®. (*HBMTN* p. 411). No longer available.
NOPCO CHEMICAL CO.

Olho Wax△. See CARNAUBA WAX△.

O-Lube. See PARKER O-LUBE[NR].

Olympian Grease. See TEXACO® OLYMPIAN GREASE.

O & M Compound. See TROY O & M COMPOUND.

Omni-Beta®. A vitamin preparation for use as an appetite stimulant for children or adults; and therapeutically or prophylactically in the treatment of VITAMIN B deficiencies. Each teaspoonful contains: 2.0 mg. VITAMIN B$_1$ (thiamine hydrochloride), 2.0 mg. VITAMIN B$_2$ (riboflavin), 10.0 mg. niacinamide, 1.87 mg. d-panthenol (equiv. to 2.0 mg. pantothenic acid), 0.2 mg. VITAMIN B$_6$ (pyridoxine hydrochloride), 1.0 mcg. VITAMIN B$_{12}$, crystalline, 23.05 mcg. choline chloride (equiv. to 20.0 mg. choline), 10.0 mg. inositol, and 150.0 mg. liver concentrate, N.F.
WARNER-CHILCOTT LABORATORIES

OMPA△. Same as SCHRADAN△.

Ondal® A Oxidizing Agent. (*Supp.* I p. 165). The name ONDAL is now a registered trademark.
E. I. DU PONT DE NEMOURS & CO.

One-A-Day®. A line of vitamin tablets including A and D tablets, B-complex, and multiple vitamins.
MILES LABORATORIES, INC.

ONYX 10®. (*HBMTN* p. 412). No longer available.
GODFREY L. CABOT, INC.

Opal-Glo®. An opalescent interior wall finish. Available in seven colors.
SHERWIN-WILLIAMS CO.

Opalite®. A line of white, ceramic-coated, flint glass ointment jars available in sizes from ½ oz. to 16 oz.
ARMSTRONG CORK CO.

Opaltone®. (*HBMTN* p. 413). No longer available.
TRUSCON LABORATORIES

Opalwax®. (*Supp.* I p. 165). Now a registered trademark.
BAKER CASTOR OIL CO.

Openteine®. The trademark for a perfume base.
S. B. PENICK & CO.

Opticleer®. Synthetic and other resins in solid form and solutions thereof in organic solvents intended for incorporation with other constituents to form lacquers and synthetic-resin coating compositions that are very clear and practically colorless.
MASS & WALDSTEIN CO.

Optilets®. A therapeutic, multivitamin preparation in tablet form. ABBOTT LABORATORIES

Optilite®. A safety lens made of compounded resins. It weighs only half as much as conventional safety glass, and has approx. twice the strength. It provides more comfort, better appearance, and greater protection to workers. UNITED STATES SAFETY SERVICE CO.

Optimus® **Electric Cleaner.** (*HBMTN* p. 413). No longer available.
HANSON-VAN WINKLE-MUNNING CO.

Optonic®. (*HBMTN* p. 413). Now a registered trademark. ARCO CO.

Ora-Lutin®. (*HBMTN* p. 413). No longer available. PARKE, DAVIS & CO.

Orcanette△. Same as ALKANET△.

Orco Antifoam AF[NR]. A defoaming agent that is especially useful wherever excessive foam is found to be troublesome. It is a stabilized-emulsion-type silicone complex that has a wide range of applications in textile processing. ORGANIC CHEMICAL CORP.

Orcoboil #15[NR]. A product consisting of a sulfated alcohol and fatty condensate, designed for the boiling-off and pre-scouring of WOOL. It can also be used in the finishing of WOOL, and as a general detergent. It promotes levelness in dyeing and greatly improves the hand of the goods. ORGANIC CHEMICAL CORP.

Orcoceylene #30[NR]. A complex polyester condensate with a vegetable-oil base. It is essentially a neutral, salt free, nonionic detergent. It is especially effective in the soaping off of heavy vat prints, preventing completely the redeposition on the fabric of color onto white or pastel designs or stripes.
ORGANIC CHEMICAL CORP.

Orcochromate Mordant[NR]. A mordant for use in the metachrome process for dyeing worsted piece goods. ORGANIC CHEMICAL CORP.

Orcochrome Black P New[NR]. A chrome dyestuff for WOOL yarn, stock or piece goods. It can be used where a rating of 4 to 5 is required in fastness to cross dyeing, fulling, potting, washing, and crocking. It possesses a light fastness rating of 7, and, due to its exceptional solubility, it has very good leveling properties. ORGANIC CHEMICAL CORP.

Orco Ferrosol Powder WS *and* **Orco Ferrosol Liquid**[NR]. A sequestering agent having a very high combining power with unwanted metal ions. It is the tetrasodium salt of ethylenediamine tetra acetic acid. Can be used directly in a dyebath to give bright and more level shades on WOOL goods; as a general water softener; as a printing assistant; and as an aid in dye-stripping baths.
ORGANIC CHEMICAL CORP.

Orcolana Strip NA[NR]. An agent which, when added to the dyebath in small amounts, promotes level dyeing and prevents the "tippy" dyeing of wool. When used with NYLON, "barre" effect is reduced to a minimum. This agent can also be used in discharge work on COTTON and RAYON with naphthol and vat dyes, creating whiter whites by preventing redeposition of color. ORGANIC CHEMICAL CORP.

Orcolon Black #55 Paste[NR]. A black dyestuff for use where extreme fastness is required on NYLON yarn, piece goods and lace. When used in conjunction with ORCO DEVELOPER VII, it produces on NYLON a bloomy, jet black, which has excellent fastness to cross dyeing and good fastness to fulling against other white fibers. ORGANIC CHEMICAL CORP.

Orco Metallan[NR]. A line of neutral-dyeing, premetallized dyestuffs. ORGANIC CHEMICAL CORP.

Orcomine Black RBM Conc[NR]. A direct black dyestuff that produces a deep full black on COTTON and RAYON. It is highly recommended for use where an ACETATE RAYON decoration is to remain white.
ORGANIC CHEMICAL CORP.

Orcopal #18[NR]. A fatty acid tallow condensate formulated specifically for acid fulling of woolen goods. With this material, woolen goods are carbonized in the grease, then fulled and neutralized in one operation using a fulling solution containing this product and enough alkali to neutralize the carbonizing acid plus a small additional amount to assist in the fulling and later scouring. This method produces better whites and brighter pastel shades, eliminates fulling mill wrinkles, decreases flocking and reduces residual grease and soap in the fabric as much as 70% compared to traditional procedures with other soaps.
ORGANIC CHEMICAL CORP.

Orco Pentro PS[NR]. A product especially designed for wetting and rewetting of pile fabrics. It can be used in all phases of normal processing, and helps to assure more even bottoming, dyeing, and finishing.
ORGANIC CHEMICAL CORP.

Orco Scour 48[NR]. A cold scour produced especially for the woolen and worsted trade. Designed for use on piece goods where general all-round scouring ability is required. It is exceptionally effective in removing old sizing and misc. dirt for the efficient handling of goods in subsequent processes.
ORGANIC CHEMICAL CORP.

Orco Synthrowite FWN[NR]. An optical bleach in a blended solvent for the whitening of NYLON, ACETATE and WOOL from a bath where the pH ranges from 7 up.
ORGANIC CHEMICAL CORP.

Orco Synthrowite GNW[NR]. An optical bleach in easy-to-use liquid form. It produces a desirable white or greenish cast on NYLON. It can also be used on WOOL and SILK, and being fast to a peroxide bleach bath, serves to reduce the process time.
ORGANIC CHEMICAL CORP.

Orcowet #33[NR]. An extremely versatile wetting agent that can be used in a variety of operations in wet processing of textiles. It is a sulfonated ester, and is recommended for use in dyeing to promote penetration and levelness, as a dispersant for dyestuffs, and as an emulsifying agent.
ORGANIC CHEMICAL CORP.

Orcquesol LHN[NR]. A cresylic acid-base detergent for use as a cold scour and as an aid to soap where mineral oil and grease are present in the processing of woolen worsted piece goods and raw stock.
ORGANIC CHEMICAL CORP.

Orel® Rubber Lubricant. (*Supp.* I p. 166). The name ORE L is now a registered trademark.
E. I. DU PONT DE NEMOURS & CO.

Or-Fer-Gro[NR]. A fertilizer.
PENNSYLVANIA SALT MFG. CO.

Organosol[△]. A dispersion of a polyvinyl chloride resin similar to a PLASTISOL. The important difference is that solvents are added to improve the flow properties of compounds where a lower plasticizer loading is desired.

Orion Red[NE]. A yellowish-red color pigment with excellent heat resistance and good light resistance. Available in dry form and dispersed in various organic vehicles for paint, printing inks and plastics.
SHERWIN-WILLIAMS CO.

Or-Lo. A lubricating oil additive for use in internal-combustion engines. Added to the oil in the crankcase, it helps keep the engine clean, thus increasing engine life.
BELL LABORATORY, INC.

Ornatox®. (*Supp.* I p. 166). No longer available.
GENERAL CHEMICAL DIV.,
ALLIED CHEMICAL & DYE CORP.

Oroxalyde Liquid[NE]. A stripping agent for woolen piece goods and shoddy. Chemically, it is a zinc formaldehyde sulfoxolate solution. It works best on the acid side, and is especially recommended for the OGDEN PROCESS of simultaneously stripping and dyeing in one bath. With this method, not only is there an immense saving in time, but, due to the reduced amount of handling of the goods, the results are superior to the usual two or more bath systems of stripping and redyeing. The tensile strength of the treated goods remains very high, and a soft hand is retained.
ORGANIC CHEMICAL CORP.

Ortar®. (*Supp.* I p. 166). Formerly known as ORTAR®-D.S.
FLINTKOTE CO.

Ortar®-D.S. (*Supp.* I p. 166). Now known as ORTAR®.
FLINTKOTE CO.

Ortar® Emulsion-Type P. C. (*Supp.* I p. 166). No longer available.
FLINTKOTE CO.

Ortazol® and Ortazol® Powder. (*HBMTN* p. 414). The name ORTAZOL® is now a registered trademark.
MILLER CHEMICAL & FERTILIZER CORP.

Orthophen® #278. A special blend of mixed amylphenols used as a paint anti-skinning agent. A straw-colored liquid; sp.gr. 0.95–0.97 (30°C.); distillation range, 95% between 235° and 270°C.; flash point, 200°F.; solidification point, below −10°C.
PENNSYLVANIA SALT MFG. CO.

Orthosil®. An alkaline detergent used in general industrial operations.
PENNSYLVANIA SALT MFG. CO.

Orthosolv®. (*Supp.* I p. 168). Now known as OZENE®.
SOLVAY PROCESS DIV.,
ALLIED CHEMICAL & DYE CORP.

Ortol. A line of textile colors for use in combination with the ORTOLAN neutral dyeing dyestuffs, for the production of clear, brilliant shades on WOOL, NYLON, and WOOL and NYLON mixtures.
NOVA CHEMICAL CORP.

Ortolan®. A group of neutral-dyeing metal complex dyestuffs for use on WOOL, as well as for union shades with NYLON. They are fast to light, and have excellent leveling properties.
NOVA CHEMICAL CORP.

Orzan® AH-3. *Formerly known as* ORZAN® AH (*Supp.* I p. 168).
CROWN ZELLERBACH CORP.,
CHEMICAL PRODUCTS DIV.

Osmoplastic®. (*HBMTN* p. 415). Now a registered trademark. OSMOSE WOOD PRESERVING CO. OF AMERICA

Osmosalts®. (*HBMTN* p. 415). Now a registered trademark. OSMOSE WOOD PRESERVING CO. OF AMERICA

Ospho®. A liquid for treating ferrous metals, galvanized iron, and aluminum to form a rust- and corrosion-preventive surface to which paint adheres strongly. It forms an inert, hard, gray, iron phosphate surface on ferrous metals, and imparts a slight etch which holds the paint film.
RUSTICIDE PRODUCTS CO.

Ottawa®Can.. *See* ATLAS OTTAWA®Can..
ATLAS STEELS LTD.

Ouricury Wax[△]. Also known as URUCURY WAX[△]. A green-colored wax obtained from the leaves of the palm tree *Syagrus coronota* or *Cocos coronata*, of northern Brazil. Except for its color, this wax is similar in its properties to CARNAUBA WAX and has the same uses where color is not important. M.p. approx 85°C.; iodine no. 16.9; acid no. 10.6; saponification no. 78.8.

Ovalclene®. (*HBMTN* p. 416). No longer available.
E. I. DU PONT DE NEMOURS & CO.

Ovale®. A line of nursing bottles oval in shape.
ARMSTRONG CORK CO.

Oxamine®. A group of direct dyes for use on COTTON, RAYON, paper, and leather. GENERAL DYESTUFF CO.

Oxiblak®. *See* DU-LITE® OXIBLAK®.

Oxynate No. 7. A chemical blackening compound for mass blackening of steel parts. Designed primarily for the firearms and gunsmith industry. It is a granular material that is dissolved in water and the solution used at 294°F. to produce a deep, durable black finish on all ferrous metals. BOB BROWNELL'S

Oxyseal[NE]. (*HBMTN* p. 416). No longer available.
PARKER APPLIANCE CO.

Oxythane[△]. *Same as* DCPM[△].

Ozark[NE]. A line of zinc sulfates.
SHERWIN-WILLIAMS CO.

Ozene®. Formerly known as ORTHOSOLV®. (*Supp.* I p. 168).
SOLVAY PROCESS DIV.,
ALLIED CHEMICAL & DYE CORP.

Ozide[NE]. A line of low-lead and lead-free zinc oxides for general industrial use, including activation of rubber accelerators.
SHERWIN-WILLIAMS CO.

Ozite®. A line of hair-felt products including:
ALL HAIR CARPET CUSHION. A soft non-spongy pad for use under carpets and rugs.
PADDING FELT. Available in rolls, 36″, 54″, and 108″ wide x 60′ long, in thicknesses from ⅛″ to 1″.

Used as thermal insulation for ice cream shippers, milk cans, etc.; as padding for furniture, sports equipment, bicycle and tractor seats; and for protection of equipment during shipment.

LAUNDRY FELT. Supplied in roll form, up to 108" wide, in thicknesses of ¼" to 1". Used on commercial laundry ironers.

INSULATING HAIR FELT. An insulating material for cold pipes, ducts and equipment. Thermal conductivity, 0.24 B.t.u.-inch/hr. x sq.ft. x °F. Available in thicknesses of ¼" to 2".

SHOE AND SLIPPER FELT. A product used in the shoe trade.

GYM MAT FELT. For use under mats in gymnasiums. Available in rolls, 9' x 30', in thicknesses of 1" to 2½". AMERICAN HAIR AND FELT CO.

Ozlo[NR]. A line of leaded zinc oxides used in the paint industry. SHERWIN-WILLIAMS CO.

Ozokerite[△]. Also known as MINERAL WAX[△] and EARTH WAX[△]. A natural, greasy solid, yellowish to black paraffin material found in Utah and in Central Europe. Occurs in rocks which are crushed and heated to melt the wax. Melts at 55°–110°C.; sp.gr. 0.85–0.95; soluble in alcohol, benzol and naphtha; insoluble in water. Uses: As an extender and substitute for beeswax; in the mfg. of polishes, candles, printing inks, crayons, sealing waxes, phonograph records, etc.

P

P-33®. (*HBMTN* p. 417). Should have been listed as a registered trademark of THERMATOMIC CARBON CO.

P-179. A free-flowing, urea-formaldehyde, tan, powdered adhesive containing a catalyst. It is mixed with water for use in glueing wood and certain urea and phenolic plastics. Can also be used to bond MASONITE® and many of the PRESDWOOD® type of boards. WILROSS PRODUCTS CO.

P-204. A synthetic resin-rubber emulsion primer for use with P-222 adhesive in the mfg. of vinyl-type pressure-sensitive tapes. The primer acts as a tie coat between the adhesive layer and the film surface. This primer forms a clear, non-tacky dried film that will not block. It weighs about 8 lb./gal. and has a viscosity of about 3,500 centipoises. Applied by roller coat, gravure roll, brush or spray. WILROSS PRODUCTS CO.

P-222. A synthetic resin-rubber polymer adhesive used in combination with P-204 primer in the mfg. of vinyl-type, pressure-sensitive tapes. Deposits a clear, colorless film when dried; has a combination of aliphatic hydrocarbons as the solvent carrier which is released very rapidly. Applied by roller coat, gravure roll, and knife methods; a temp. of 220°F. is sufficient to dry the film. WILROSS PRODUCTS CO.

P-268. A synthetic resin adhesive designed specifically for bonding ethyl cellulose plastics. The solvent used in this formulation consists of a mixture of ketones and hydrocarbons. Has excellent water resistance. WILROSS PRODUCTS CO.

P-269. A synthetic-resin wood glue in emulsion form. Non-volatile content, approx. 50%; viscosity, 3,800–5,000 centipoises; block shear test, 2,800–3,000 lb./sq.in.; excellent freeze resistance and good water resistance. WILROSS PRODUCTS CO.

P-297. A contact-type adhesive, consisting essentially of a co-reacted resin-rubber complex dispersed in aromatic hydrocarbons. Applied by brush, roller coat or spray; for spray applications it is diluted 20% by volume with a special thinner. Uses: For bonding metals, plastic laminates, wood, cloth, paper, hardboard, plastics, rubber, and concrete to themselves and to each other. WILROSS PRODUCT, CO.

P-323. A rubber latex-resin complex adhesive in the form of a white to cream-colored emulsion. The dried adhesive film has a light yellow color, good water and heat resistance. Applied by brush, spray or roller coat. Uses: For bonding paper, cloth, wood, MASONITE®, felt, canvas, etc. to themselves and each other; as a laminating adhesive; and for bonding CELLOPHANE and cellulose acetate to any porous surface. WILROSS PRODUCTS CO.

P-354. An emulsion-type adhesive designed expressly for bonding fabric—particularly canvas—to fabric, paper, wood, etc. When properly cured, the bond is water and dry-cleaning resistant. Applied by brush or trowel; after application with firm contact pressure, the adhesive is cured at 275°F. for at least 30 min. WILROSS PRODUCTS CO.

P-360. A general-purpose adhesive for bonding metals, wood, rubber, etc. Consists of two parts: Part A contains the curing agent and Part B the catalyst. The well-mixed adhesive is applied to the objects to be bonded, and the parts are clamped lightly in position. Air curing requires about 24 hr., but max. strength is obtained only by heat curing. WILROSS PRODUCTS CO.

P-380. A synthetic resin cement for bonding flexible, semi-rigid or rigid vinyls to metals, wood, MASONITE®, etc. Applied by brush, spray or roller coat. Its use is not recommended where excessive amounts of migratory plasticizer are present in the vinyl film. WILROSS PRODUCTS CO.

Padrina®. (*Supp.* I p. 169). No longer available. SHARP & DOHME DIV., MERCK & CO.

Padrophyll®. (*Supp.* I p. 169). No longer available. SHARP & DOHME DIV., MERCK & CO.

Painter Craft[NR]. A line of finishes designed for use by painting and decorating contractors. SHERWIN-WILLIAMS CO.

Painticator®. Solvents for removing oil, tar, paint, and the like. PENNSYLVANIA SALT MFG. CO.

Paint-Sav. A colorless, liquid, anti-skinning agent for paints, varnishes, and enamels. It effectively prevents hardening of the paint, yet evaporates along with the paint solvent, and does not affect the drying rate. AMES LABORATORIES, INC.

Pakseal[NR]. A stiff-type sealing compound which can be applied only by caulking tools. It is highly water resistant and unaffected by continuous temps. up to 140°F. or intermittent exposures up to 200°F. It withstands weathering without effect except for a slight surface hardening. Can be used on metals and painted surfaces but is not suitable for use on rubber

insulation. Used largely in marine work to seal openings in bulkheads, tube glands, etc., as well as to prevent passage of dust, vermin, and gases.
JOHNS-MANVILLE SALES CORP.

Palanthrene® Brown LG Double Paste. A homogeneous brown vat dyestuff in highly dispersed form for piece goods dyeing, pad and jig applications, and for use by the pad-steam process, on RAYON and COTTON. It is very fast to light, washing, chlorine and peroxide. Particularly useful for awnings, work clothes and shirtings, straight and in combinations.
Mfg'd by BADISCHE ANILIN-U. SODA-FABRIK AG.
Dist'd by NOVA CHEMICAL CORP.

Palapent®. A palatable elixer containing 2 gr. pentobarbital sodium U.S.P. in each fluid oz. Used for the treatment of insomnia, as pre-operative medication to calm patients and induce sleep the night before the operation, and for the treatment of psychoneuroses.
BRISTOL LABORATORIES INC.

Palatine®. A group of metalized acid dyes, of very good fastness properties, that are applied on WOOL from a strongly acid bath. They can also be used on SILK, NYLON, and leather. GENERAL DYESTUFF CO.

Palay Rubber△. *See* CRYPTOSTEGIA RUBBER△.

Palco® Industrial Fibers. A line of redwood and redwood bark fibers used in oil filters; for the mfg. of special papers; as soil conditioners; for packaging; for toy stuffing; as fillers for lightweight concrete and as ceramic burnout fillers; as adhesive extenders; for thermal insulation; for sealing porous formations in oil-well-drilling; etc. PALCO® FIBER PS is a processed wood fiber; PALCO® FIBER PW, is shredded redwood bark; and PALCO® FIBERS A and AR are refined bark fibers. PACIFIC LUMBER CO.

Palconate®. A brown-black product consisting of the sodium salts of phenolic acids extracted from redwood bark. It is similar to PALCOTAN® and is used for many of the same purposes. It is also used as a partial replacement for phenol in phenolic resin mfg.
PACIFIC LUMBER CO.

Palco Seal®. A fibrous redwood product used for preventing loss of circulation in drilling operations. It mixes readily with mud, disperses thoroughly, remains in suspension, is easily pumped, forms a dense cross-hatch matting for an effective seal, and is resistant to rot and decay. PACIFIC LUMBER CO.

Palcotan®. A dark brown reactive chemical product derived from redwood bark. It consists of the sodium salts of phenolic acids extracted from the bark. *Uses:* As a drilling-mud conditioner for controlling viscosity, gel strength, and water loss; as an ingredient of commercial boiler-water compounds; as a binder for ceramic clays and as a deflocculent for casting slips and glazes; as a depressant for calcite in the flotation of fluorspar and scheelite-bearing ores and as a pulp conditioner in the benefication of iron ores by flotation; in leather tanning; as a dispersant for carbon black in the mfg. of synthetic rubber; and as a dispersant for cement, gypsum, asphalt emulsions and many other organic and inorganic slurries.
PACIFIC LUMBER CO.

Palha Wax△. *See* CARNAUBA WAX△.

Pal-lite[NE]. A smoothly sanded, asbestos sheet material used as a pallet in the drying of ceramic ware, especially special refractory shapes, abrasive wheels, graphite crucibles, large-size wall tile, chinaware, etc. Consists of selected asbestos fibers with an inorganic binder formed into solid homogeneous sheets which are light in weight and have an unusually low rate of heat transmission. While it is more absorptive than other pallet materials, including PLASTER OF PARIS, it will not disintegrate even when subjected to prolonged immersion in water. Approx. density, 36 lb./cu.ft. (3 lb./board ft.); av. transverse strength, 900 lb./sq.in.; recommended temp. limit, 500°F.
JOHNS-MANVILLE SALES CORP.

Palmetto G-T® Ring. A molded packing seal for piston and rod assemblies, so constructed that the packing material will not be extruded. Designed originally for aircraft hydraulic service, it is now used for many industrial applications. It has been used at pressures up to 15,000 lb./sq.in.
GREENE, TWEED & CO.

Palm Wax #1. (*HBMTN* p. 419). No longer being mfg'd by INNIS, SPEIDEN & CO.

Pamak[NE]. The trademark for tall oil fatty acids.
HERCULES POWDER CO.

Pamisc®. The trademark for a line of insecticides.
PENNSYLVANIA SALT MFG. CO.

Panaflex®. A line of low-cost, completely hydrocarbon plasticizers derived from petroleum. Normally they are high boiling liquids; available in light or dark colors; compatible with natural and synthetic rubbers, and many synthetic and natural resins. Used in vinyl compounding as secondary plasticizers in conjunction with primary plasticizers such as dioctyl phthalate; and as the sole plasticizer in rubber compounding. AMOCO CHEMICAL CORP.

Panalene[NE]. The tradename for a line of aromatic solvents, including heptene, nonene, and propylene tetramer. AMOCO CHEMICALS CORP.

Panama Bark△. *Same as* QUILLAJA△.

Panapol®. A series of low-cost hydrocarbon drying oils derived from petroleum, available in a wide range of physical properties. Products of the polymerization of petroleum unsaturates, they normally have a high degree of unsaturation and thus the ability to dry by absorption of oxygen. Color, viscosity, and drying properties can be varied by the mfg. technique and by changing the stock employed. Completely hydrocarbon in nature, they are neutral and nonsaponifiable and are therefore of value in those applications where such properties are desirable. They are used extensively as replacements in whole or in part for vegetable and marine drying oils. *Uses:* In printing ink applications, core oil formulations, paints and varnishes, adhesive formulations, rubber compounding, paper saturants, and floor coverings. AMOCO CHEMICALS CORP.

Panarez®. A series of low-cost hydrocarbon resins derived from petroleum, available in a wide color range from pale lemon to dark brown and in a wide softening point range up to 300°F. Readily soluble in aliphatic and aromatic hydrocarbons and compatible with a wide variety of resins, oils, and waxes.

Because of their hydrocarbon nature, they are neutral and non-saponifiable and are therefore of value in applications where resistance to attack by alcohol, alkali, and water is desired and where good electrical properties are required. They are used extensively in paints and varnishes to improve film resistance to water and alkali and increase film hardness and adherence. PANAREZ resins are used in rubber compounding as softeners and aids to improve processing and effect improvements in the physical properties of the compound. They are also used in printing ink varnishes, adhesive compositions, aluminum paint formulations, floor tile, and caulking compounds.
AMOCO CHEMICALS CORP.

Panasol®. A series of high-solvency aromatic hydrocarbon solvents derived from petroleum. Available in differing boiling ranges and degrees of solvency to suit the requirements of a variety of applications. They are used extensively in the formulation of paints and varnishes, baking enamels, insecticide compositions and other products where a high degree of solvency is required. AMOCO CHEMICALS CORP.

Panbiotic®. A crystalline medicinal for the treatment of upper and lower respiratory infections, urogenital-renal infections, gonorrhea, syphilis. It is a dry crystalline product which is dissolved in water and administered by deep intramuscular injection. The standard clinical dosage is 1 or 2 cc. Each 2 cc. dose contains 300,000 units of potassium PENICILLIN G and procaine PENICILLIN G, and 600,000 units of dibenzylethylenediamine (dipenicillin G).
BRISTOL LABORATORIES INC.

Panelcoustic[NE]. An easily-removed, perforated metal, sound-absorbing ceiling panel. Made of sound-absorbing mineral wool pads encased with 2' × 4' protective panels of perforated metal. The pads are available in 3 thicknesses, giving noise reduction ranges from 0.60 to 0.90. The sound-absorbing pads behind the PANELCOUSTIC units are supported by built-in ribs. No spacer grid is necessary. The units are finished with a baked enamel and contain $7/_{64}$" perforations spaced $21/_{64}$" on centers. The units are easily lifted up and out of carrying runners for access to utilities behind the ceiling. NATIONAL GYPSUM CO.

Panelply[NE]. A rigid ½"- or ⅜"-thick smooth-surfaced panel made by bonding together two or more thicknesses of PRESDWOOD® with special adhesives. The panel is smooth on both sides. *Use:* For cabinet construction, hinged and sliding doors, etc.
MASONITE CORP.

Pantopaque®. A radiopaque contrast medium for myelography, cholangiography, etc.
DISTILLATION PRODUCTS INDUSTRIES, DIV. OF EASTMAN KODAK CO.

Papain[△]. The dried extract obtained from the fruit and sap of the papaya tree, *Carica papaya,* of tropical America, East Africa, and Asia. It is an enzyme marketed as a dry, friable powder. *Uses:* In medicine as a digestive aid; as a meat tenderizer; in beer mfg. to remove haze; in degumming SILK; for softening WOOL that is to be used in mixed fabrics.

Paper Machine Oil HD. *See* TEXACO® PAPER MACHINE OIL HD.

P.A.R.®. A highly water-repellent finish for redwood, red cedar, Philippine mahogany, and other woods of similar color characteristics. It imparts a warm glossless finish, and minimizes grain-raising, checking, warping and splitting caused by weather exposure.
PROTECTION PRODUCTS MFG. CO.

Para[NE]. The tradename for a group of dyes specially prepared for the dyeing of leather.
NATIONAL ANILINE DIV., ALLIED CHEMICAL & DYE CORP.

Paradione®. A brand of paramethadione in capsule and solution forms for oral administration. It is an anticonvulsant used in the treatment of petit mal, myoclonic and akinetic epilepsy. ABBOTT LABORATORIES

Paradyne®. A trademark for a line of anti-icing additives for gasoline, jet fuels, and No. 2 fuel oils.
ENJAY CO.

Paraffin Jelly[△]. Same as PETROLATUM[△].

Paraflow®. (*HBMTN* p. 421). This product is marketed by the ENJAY CO., INC., an affiliate of the ESSO STANDARD OIL CO.

Parallel-O-Plate®. A polished plate glass made by a specially developed twin-grinding process whereby both sides of the glass are ground simultaneously by extremely accurate grinders. This produces a glass of highly uniform thickness with surfaces that are parallel to a very high degree. Available in ¼" thickness only. *Mfg'd by* BLUE RIDGE GLASS CORP.
Dist'd by LIBBEY-OWENS-FORD GLASS CO.

Paramul® Repellent 115. A re-treatable, textile water repellent in aqueous emulsion form.
AMERICAN CYANAMID CO.

Paramul® Repellent DC-1, *and* DC-2. A two-package textile water repellent. It provides a finish having good durability to dry cleaning on all fabrics, and durability to mild washing on synthetic hydrophobic fabrics. AMERICAN CYANAMID CO.

Paranox®. (*Supp.* I p. 171). This product is marketed by the ENJAY CO., INC., an affiliate of the Esso STANDARD OIL CO.

Paraplex® P-444. A polyester resin for the mfg. of glass fiber-reinforced laminates of great transparency. When blended with styrene monomer or vinyl toluene and cured, the product has a refractive index of 1.546 compared with 1.548 for glass. Therefore, there is little evidence of the glass fibers in the laminate. PARAPLEX P-444 resists discoloration by ultraviolet light and outdoor erosion. ROHM & HAAS CO.

Parapoid®. (*Supp.* I p. 171). This product is marketed by the ENJAY CO., INC., an affiliate of the ESSO STANDARD OIL CO.

Parapol®. (*Supp.* I p. 171). This product is marketed by the ENJAY CO., INC., an affiliate of the ESSO STANDARD OIL CO.

Para-Syllium®. A laxative consisting of a palatable, demulcent emulsion of mineral oil and psyllium seed jelly. ABBOTT LABORATORIES

Paratac®. (*Supp.* I p. 171). This product is marketed by the ENJAY CO., INC., an affiliate of the ESSO STANDARD OIL CO.

Parathion△. A highly toxic, agricultural insecticide. o,o-Diethyl o-p-nitrophenyl phosphorothioate. $C_{10}H_{14}NO_5PS$; mol.wt. 259.21. When pure, it is a colorless, nearly odorless liquid with a m.p. of 6.1°C. and a b.p. of 157–162°C. (0.6 mm. Hg). The technical product is a dark brown liquid with a garlic odor. Slightly soluble in water (20–25 ppm.); miscible with acids and alcohols up to 6 carbon atoms, esters, ketones, ether, benzene, toluene, chloroform, carbon tetrachloride, and animal and vegetable oils; only slightly soluble in paraffinic hydrocarbons. It is extremely insecticidal by stomach or contact to most insects and phytophargous mites; and has some fumigant action.

Paratone®. (*Supp.* I p. 171). This product is marketed by the ENJAY CO., INC., an affiliate of the ESSO STANDARD OIL CO.

Parchkin®. The trademark for a vegetable parchment for use in art work.
PATERSON PARCHMENT PAPER CO.

Parchment△. A writing material which at one time was made from goat and sheep skins which were specially tanned and prepared with a smooth, hard finish. It was used for legal documents, maps, books, etc. At present, parchment is made from a base paper of COTTON rags or alpha cellulose and containing no size or filler. This so-called Waterleaf base is treated carefully with sulfuric acid which converts it to a gelatin-like material. The dried paper, called VEGETABLE PARCHMENT, is used for documents, as a food-packaging material, etc.

Parene®. See ACE® PARENE®.

Parez® **Resins.** A line of synthetic resins especially useful in the mfg. of paper. Available in the following types:

Parez Designation	Description and uses
607	A dry, powdered melamine-formaldehyde resin for improving the wet and dry strength properties of paper.
608	A liquid, 66% urea-formaldehyde resin syrup used in starch-resin paper coating and special paper and fiber treatments.
611	A dry, powdered, melamine-formaldehyde resin of good storage stability designed to improve the wet rub resistance of starch-pigment paper coatings.
612	A dry, powdered, urea-formaldehyde resin of good storage stability. Used for starch-resin paper coating and special paper and fiber treatments.
613	An 80% syrup of methylated, trimethylol melamine of good storage stability. Used to improve water resistance of protein-pigment coatings.
614	A 37% cationic, urea-formaldehyde resin syrup used to impart wet strength to paper. It is added either directly to the beater or diluted with water and applied at the tub.

Parez Designation	Description and uses
620	A dry, powdered urea-formaldehyde resin having good storage stability. Used to impart wet-strength to paper either as a beater or tub size additive.

AMERICAN CYANAMID CO.

Parez® **Resins 605, 609, 610.** (*HBMTN* p. 423). No longer available. AMERICAN CYANAMID CO.

Parian®. See ACE® PARIAN®.

Parical® **Dust.** (*HBMTN* p. 423). No longer available.
GENERAL CHEMICAL DIV.,
ALLIED CHEMICAL & DYE CORP.

Paris Green△. *Also known as* EMERALD GREEN△, FRENCH GREEN△, MITIS GREEN△, and SCHWEINFURTERGRUN△. Copper aceto-arsenate. Approx. $3\,Cu(AsO_2)_2\cdot Cu(CH_3COO)_2$; mol.wt. 1014.11. It is a poisonous, green powder prepared by interacting sodium arsenite, copper sulfate and acetic acid. Insoluble in water; soluble in dilute acids. *Uses:* As a pigment, particularly in paints used on ships and submarines; as a wood preservative; and as an insecticide of the stomach-poison type.

Parisul® **Dust.** (*HBMTN* p. 423). No longer available.
GENERAL CHEMICAL DIV.,
ALLIED CHEMICAL & DYE CORP.

Parith®. See ACE® PARITH®.

Park-Cut M.P.[NR]. A multi-purpose oil for use as a lubricant, cutting oil, and hydraulic oil.
PARK CHEMICAL CO.

Par-Kem Cleaners[NR]. A line of metal cleaners primarily for use in heat-treating departments. Included in the line are:
PAR-KEM CLEANER No. 7. A medium-duty cleaner for use in soak tanks.
PAR-KEM CLEANER No. 9. A cleaner primarily for use in power washers, but also suitable for use in soak tanks or electrolytic tanks.
PAR-KEM CLEANER No. 11. A heavy-duty cleaner for use in soak tanks; may also be used in electrolytic tanks.
PAR-KEM CLEANER No. 15. A combination of alkalis and synthetic detergents for use in tanks and power washers. Especially useful for cleaning oily work before and after carbo-nitriding operations.
PAR-KEM EMULSION CLEANER. A solvent-type cleaner which can be used "as-is," or emulsified with 20–50 parts water at temps of 140–170°C.
PARK CHEMICAL CO.

Parker O-Lube[NR]. A lubricant used to extend the life of synthetic rubber O-rings on exposed cylinder rods, valve plungers, etc., especially in low-pressure pneumatic and vacuum systems. Operating temp. range, −20° to +400°F. (Application has been made for registration of the name "O-LUBE.")
PARKER APPLIANCE CO.

Parker Unipar®. An all-purpose thread and gasket compound for water, steam, air, and petroleum lines at temps. from −70° to +300°F. It forms a flexible, vibration-proof seal that is easy to disconnect.
PARKER APPLIANCE CO.

Parko®. A line of automotive chemicals and polishing compounds, including cleaners, polishes and waxes, leather cleaner and preservative, anti-static polish for plastics, chrome cleaners, fabric cleaners, detergents, tire cleaners and paints, radiator cleaners, stop leak and rust preventives, fire extinguisher fluid, automatic transmission fluid, shock absorber fluid, penetrating oil, rubber lubricants, solvent cleaners, gasket and weatherstrip cements, paint masking compounds, buffing compounds, "cold solder," etc.
PARK CHEMICAL CO.

Parko® Beauty Coat. A liquid wax product for cleaning, polishing and waxing automobile bodies in one operation. It is long lasting, sunproof, waterproof, and weatherproof. PARK CHEMICAL CORP.

Parko® Blue Foam Upholstery Cleaner. A cleaner for draperies, tapestry, and upholstered furniture.
PARK CHEMICAL CO.

Parko® Eze Cleaner. A mildly abrasive pre-wax or pre-polish cleaner for automobile bodies.
PARK CHEMICAL CO.

Parko® Eze-Wax. A polishing wax for automobile bodies. PARK CHEMICAL CO.

Parko® K-R Hand Rubbing Compound. A fast cleaning and polishing compound, free from wax and harsh abrasives, used for cleaning automobile bodies.
PARK CHEMICAL CO.

Parko® Kwik Wash. A concentrated, neutrol, heavy sudsing, soapless powder for washing cars, trucks, and buses. PARK CHEMICAL CO.

Parko® Miracle Metal. A plastic metal, or "cold solder" for filling dents and cracks in automobile bodies. It adheres to steel, brass, copper, aluminum, magnesium, glass, and wood; and can be sanded, filed, and ground to a feather edge without cracking, peeling or checking. PARK CHEMICAL CO.

Parko® Protex-It. A non-drying masking compound for windows, enameled parts, chrome plating and other areas of automobiles to protect against lacquer overspray during painting.
PARK CHEMICAL CO.

Parko® Silcoseal. A cleaner and polish for automobile bodies. Contains 4% silicones.
PARK CHEMICAL CO.

Parko® Static-Stop. A detergent and anti-static agent for cleaning plastic seat covers and preventing static charges. PARK CHEMICAL CO.

Parko® Super-Dri. A chemical solvent for absorbing water accumulations in gasoline tanks and gas lines due to condensation. PARK CHEMICAL CO.

Parko® Tank-O-Lene. A non-evaporating, fast-acting, general-purpose cleaner for all automotive, aviation, and general repair shop use.
PARK CHEMICAL CO.

Parko® Tank-Solv. A powerful, concentrated, non-evaporating, penetrating solvent for use in mechanically or air agitated cleaning tanks for the rapid cleaning of carburetors, fuel pumps, roller bearings, air cleaners, etc. It removes paint, carbon, and sludge.
PARK CHEMICAL CO.

Parnal®. *See* ACE® PARNAL®.

Parnol[NE]. A line of direct dyes for COTTON, VISCOSE, etc., characterized by their excellent light fastness and good wash fastness.
NYANZA COLOR & CHEMICAL CO.

Parresine®. A protective surgical dressing. It is a lace-mesh dressing impregnated with pliable paraffin.
ABBOTT LABORATORIES

Parsan®. *See* ACE® PARSAN®.

Parsidol®. A medicinal for the control of symptoms in parkinsonism. It is a brand of ethopropazine hydrochloride [N-(2-diethylaminopropyl) phenothiazine hydrochloride] in tablet form.
WARNER-CHILCOTT LABORATORIES

Par-Ten®. A low-alloy, high-strength steel.
UNITED STATES STEEL CORP.

Partex[NE]. A mold soap used as a parting compound for plaster molds in the ceramic industry.
R. T. VANDERBILT CO.

Particle Board△. *Also known as* WOOD PARTICLE BOARD△. A composition board made up largely of individual, essentially dry wood particles which have been coated with a resin binder and formed into shape by pressure. Heat is applied to cure, or harden, the binder which is generally urea- or phenol-formaldehyde. The board may possess a homogeneous-type structure, or it may be made up of layers possessing dissimilar particle types. Almost any type or species of wood may be used as the source of chips, although many of the characteristics of the product are influenced by the chip size and shape. The board may be made as a flat sheet or in a wide variety of shapes. At present, the largest use of PARTICLE BOARD is as a core stock for ¾" to ⅞" thick veneered furniture parts. Plastic-surfaced countertops and cabinet sections frequently are made with PARTICLE BOARD as a core material. High-density, flake-surfaced PARTICLE BOARD is also used for interior wallboard with natural finish. It is also used to some extent as subflooring, subroofing and sheathing.

Partingkote No. 832. *See* PREPOXY PARTINGKOTE No. 832.

Par-T-Kreme. An instantly soluble, free-flowing powdered cream, especially for use in coffee dispensing machines. M & R DIETETIC LABORATORIES, INC.

Patapar®. A high-wet-strength, grease-resisting vegetable parchment. It is made by treating high quality paper, made from wood pulp, with sulfuric acid. *Uses:* For packaging and protecting foods, wrapping surgical instruments, dressings, and other articles to be sterilized in the autoclave; as master sheets for direct-print copying machines; as backing sheets for pressure-sensitive tapes; etc.
PATERSON PARCHMENT PAPER CO.

Patax®. The trademark for a waxed paper.
PATERSON PARCHMENT PAPER CO.

Paterson®. The trademark for a line of industrial filter papers. PATERSON PARCHMENT PAPER CO.

Patheba® Tablets. A calcium-iron-mineral gestational supplement for pregnant and lactating women.

Also used in postoperative recovery, and treatment of the aged. BRAYTEN PHARMACEUTICAL CO.

Pathex®. (*Supp.* I p. 172). No longer available.
GENERAL CHEMICAL DIV., ALLIED CHEMICAL & DYE CORP.

Patterson Phenothiazine, Drench Grade[NE]. A veterinary medicinal for deworming sheep and goats, calves, swine, horses, and poultry. Consists of 98.5% phenothiazine N.F. and 1.5% wetting agent.
PEARSON-FERGUSON CHEMICAL CO.

Patterson's Copper Carbonate, 20%[NE]. A fungicide used in the ratio of 3 to 4 oz. per bushel of seed (wheat, sorghum, etc.) to control smut. Contains 20% copper in the form of basic copper carbonate. PEARSON-FERGUSON CHEMICAL CO.

Patterson's Creosote Dip and Disinfectant[NE]. A disinfectant and deodorant for floors, sinks, urinals, water closets, barns, kennels, animal pens and sties; for treating garbage; and as a stock dip for killing lice on horses, cattle, and hogs, and to treat sarcoptic and psoroptic mange and scabies in sheep. Contains 90% coal tar neutral oils, soap, and phenols; and 10% water. PEARSON-FERGUSON CHEMICAL CO.

Patterson's Hand Cleaner and Conditioner[NE]. A rolling, cleansing type of skin cream which cleans the pores as well as the surface of the skin. It is mildly medicated, and soothes and softens the skin and promotes healing. Contains Microderm. Packaged in an aerosol bomb dispenser.
PEARSON-FERGUSON CHEMICAL CO.

Patterson's Livestock Fly Spray with Crag® Fly Repellant. A ready-to-use product for repelling and killing horse flies, stable flies, horn flies, mosquitoes, and gnats on dairy and beef cattle, and in the barn and pasture. Active ingredients: 8.60% butoxypolypropylene glycol; 0.03% pyrethrins; 0.2% piperonyl butoxide, technical; 1.01% methoxychlor, technical; and 90.11% petroleum distillate. CRAG® is a registered trademark of UNION CARBIDE CO.
PEARSON-FERGUSON CHEMICAL CO.

Patterson's Pine Oil Disinfectant[NE]. A powerful, yet pleasant, disinfectant, deodorant, germicide cleaner. Contains 90% steam distilled pine oil and soap and 10% water. *Uses:* For disinfecting and cleaning floors, toilet rooms, urinals, cuspidors, etc., and beds, clothes, and utensils in sick rooms; and for treating garbage to prevent breeding of flies and other vermin.
PEARSON-FERGUSON CHEMICAL CO.

Patterson's Water Soluble Pivalyn[NE]. A rat and mouse killer. Active ingredient: 0.14% sodium salt of 2-pivalyl-1,3-indandione. Three tablespoonfuls are dissolved in a quart of water to prepare a liquid bait.
PEARSON-FERGUSON CHEMICAL CO.

Pave[NE]. A heat-stable, surface-active asphalt additive which gives greatly increased bonding properties to asphalt for any type of aggregate. It remains effective even at the high temps. required to handle hot mixes. It is a dark brown liquid containing 80% active ingredients. Sp.gr. 0.9482; wt. per gal. 7.9 lb.; pour point, 15°F.; flash point (open cup), 200°F.; fire point (open cup), 220°F.; viscosity, S.U.S.: 750.8 at 100°F., and 246.0 at 140°F.
CARLISLE CHEMICAL WORKS, INC.

Pax® No. 11. (*Supp.* I p. 174). No longer available.
G. H. PACKWOOD MFG. CO.

Pax® No. 31. (*Supp.* I p. 174). No longer available. G. H. PACKWOOD MFG. CO.

Pax® No. 119. A fast, effective, granulated, buffered skin cleanser, with an all corn-meal scrubber, having free-flowing bulk and efficient cleansing action. It is extra mild in action, yet it quickly cleanses the skin of industrial soil, grease and grime.
G. H. PACKWOOD MFG. CO.

Pax® Chlorinated Dish Wash. A powdered, non-foaming cleanser for use in electric dishwashers. It is rapid acting; and the chlorine destroys food odors.
G. H. PACKWOOD MFG. CO.

Paxcide[NE]. (*Supp.* I p. 175). No longer available.
G. H. PACKWOOD MFG. CO.

Pax® C. M. 118. A granulated skin cleanser with a combination corn meal and corn derivative scrubber. Used to remove industrial soil, grime, and grease.
G. H. PACKWOOD MFG. CO.

Pax® C-P Dispenser. See PAX® DEODORANT CREAM SOAP.

Pax® Deodorant Cream Soap. A gentle and mild deodorant soap for use on all body areas: hands, face, under-arms, etc. It eliminates the waste ordinarily associated with liquid and bar soaps in shower rooms and lavatories. Applied from a PAX® C-P DISPENSER.
G. H. PACKWOOD MFG. CO.

Pax® Dictator Special. A low-cost, industrial, granulated skin cleanser containing an inorganic scrubber. For use in industrial plants to remove heavy grease and soil from the hands. G. H. PACKWOOD MFG. CO.

Pax® Formula TL-13 Floor Cleaner. A concentrated cleaner used in water solution to clean floors, walls, woodwork, windows, automobile and other engines, various types of equipment, and other washable surfaces. G. H. PACKWOOD MFG. CO.

Pax® Hand Cleaning Lotion. A fragrant lotion for removing all types of office stains, grime, and ink; aniline and other types of dyes; food stains; and numerous types of household, office, factory, and hospital stains and grime. It contains no harsh chemicals or abrasives. G. H. PACKWOOD MFG. CO.

Pax® Liquid Antiseptic Hand Soap with Emollient. (*Supp.* I p. 175). No longer available.
G. H. PACKWOOD MFG. CO.

Pax® Liquid Dish Wash. A concentrated dish-washing detergent. It can also be used for washing NYLONS, RAYONS, and other fabrics.
G. H. PACKWOOD MFG. CO.

Pax® Liquid Hand Soap Regular (with Emolient). (*Supp.* I p. 176). No longer available.
G. H. PACKWOOD MFG. CO.

Pax® Repeater Hand Cleanser. A cleaner designed especially for cleaning the hands and forearms of garage mechanics. It is a combination of scrubbers and detergents which give a rich cream-like lather. Contains lanolin to reduce chapping and protect the hands against drying, cracking, and soreness.
G. H. PACKWOOD MFG. CO.

Pax® Stock #70. (*Supp.* I p. 176). No longer available. G. H. PACKWOOD MFG. CO.

Pax® White Wall Tire Cleaner. An easy-to-use cleaner that is sprayed on the white sidewall, allowed to remain for a few minutes, and then rinsed off with water. G. H. PACKWOOD MFG. CO.

Payta△. *Same as* RHATANY△.

PC #33 Solder Resist. *See* LONCO PC #33 SOLDER RESIST.

PC&C[NE]. The trade name for various products of the PIGMENT, COLOR and CHEMICAL DIV. OF THE SHERWIN-WILLIAMS CO.

PDO-40[NE]. A free-flowing, liquid petroleum polymer which will film-dry at room temp. to a solid thermoplastic resin. The transparent film which it forms is resistant to water, dilute acid, 40% formaldehyde and many other products which attack the more conventional surface coatings. It is composed of polymerized olefinic hydrocarbons that are generally cyclic in character and average more than one double bond per molecule. Drying proceeds primarily by evaporation and oxygenation. Sp.gr. 0.9554; fire point (C.O.C.), 205°F.; pour point, −35°F.; initial b.p., 375°F.; miscible with petroleum spirits, petroleum naphtha, linseed oil, mineral oil, acetone, and benzol; not miscible with water. *Uses:* As a corrosion-resistant surface coating, metal primer, aluminum bronze vehicle, concrete curing compound; in the formulation of core oils; as a concrete floor paint; and as a reclaiming agent for rubber. SUN OIL CO.

P.D.Q Mechanics Soap. *See* TROY P.D.Q. MECHANICS SOAP.

P-D Tungsten[NE]. (*HBMTN* p. 426). No longer available. DELAWARE TOOL STEEL CORP.

Pearl Moss△. *Same as* IRISH MOSS△.

Pearson®. The trademark for a cement coating applied to wire nails after mfg. UNITED STATES STEEL CORP.

Peausan®. The trademark for a medicinal preparation in liquid form, used as a local external application in the treatment of eczematous conditions, skin disorders, sun burn, chapped hands, and dry scaling and rough skin. CHICAGO PHARMACAL CO.

Peel-Pak®. The trademark for a line of strippable coatings. FIDELITY CHEMICAL PRODUCTS CORP.

Peerless[NE]. Nitrocellulose lacquers for protecting brass and other metals from tarnishing. MAAS & WALDSTEIN CO.

Peerless Clay[NE]. A kaolin clay. *Use:* As a filler for adhesives, wallboard, paint, paper, fertilizer, etc. R. T. VANDERBILT CO.

Peerless Kaolin[NE]. A South Carolina kaolin used in most types of ceramic bodies. It is a very good casting clay. R. T. VANDERBILT CO.

Peganone®. The trademark for an anticonvulsant intended for use in the treatment of Grand Mal and related convulsive disorders. (Registration No. 627,656; Class 18; May 29, 1956). ABBOTT LABORATORIES

Pen-Aqua®. A dual-acting PENICILLIN for intramuscular injection in the treatment of upper and lower respiratory infections, subacute bacterial endocardites, urogenital-renal infections, gonorrhea, cellulitis, mastitis, and erysipelas. Each cc. contains 100,000 units potassium PENICILLIN G and 300,000 units crystalline procaine PENICILLIN G. BRISTOL LABORATORIES INC.

Penasoid® Suspension. (*Supp.* I p. 177). No longer available. PARKE, DAVIS & CO.

Penbrite®. A heavy-duty alkali sold to the laundry trade, and used primarily as a soap builder. PENNSYLVANIA SALT MFG. CO.

Penbrom®. Metal bromates sold as chemical reagents, chemical raw materials, or chemical processing agents. PENNSYLVANIA SALT MFG. CO.

Pencal®. A low-lime calcium arsenate. PENNSYLVANIA SALT MFG. CO.

Penchlor FCC®. The trademark for a construction cement of the hardened silicate type, and also for certain ingredients therefor, namely, a mixture of filler and setting agent adapted to be admixed by the user with a silicate solution to produce a mortar for forming said hardened silicate cement. PENNSYLVANIA SALT MFG. CO.

Penclor®. The trademark for a line of insecticides. PENNSYLVANIA SALT MFG. CO.

Penco®. The brand name for herbicides, insecticides, and other agricultural chemicals. PENNSYLVANIA SALT MFG. CO.

Pendit® WA Cosmetic. A brand of sodium lauryl sulfate primarily for use in cream shampoos, either liquid; MV (medium viscosity), a clear syrupy liquid LV (low viscosity), a clear, practically water-white liquid; MV (medium viscosity), a clear syrupy liquid at room temp.; and HV (high viscosity), a white, opaque paste. In addition to its principal use as a constituent of shampoos (20–60% by wt.), PENDIT® WA COSMETIC is also used as an emulsifying agent in dishwashing compositions, car washes, personal cleansing products, etc. RAYMOND LABORATORIES, INC.

Pendit® WA-D. A cosmetic base consisting of 40-42% triethanolamine lauryl sulfate. Free fatty alcohol, 1–3%; pH (10% solution), 8.0–8.7. RAYMOND LABORATORIES, INC.

Pendit® WA-T. A cosmetic base consisting of 40-42% triethanolamine lauryl sulfate. Free fatty alcohol, 1–3%; pH (10% solution), 6.5–7.5. RAYMOND LABORATORIES, INC.

Penequick®. (*HBMTN* p. 429). Now a registered trademark. L. SONNEBORN SONS, INC.

Penesolve 901[NE]. (*Supp.* I p. 178). No longer available. PENETONE CO.

Penetralene®. (*HBMTN* p. 429). Now a registered trademark. L. SONNEBORN SONS, INC.

Penetrant Y[NE]. A neutral dyeing assistant which produces good unions on NYLON hose. It is an ex-

cellent dispersing agent for dyestuffs, and its retarding and leveling action cause good color unions between NYLON monofilament and multi-filament yarn.
W. F. FANCOURT CO.

Penetrating Oils No. 1 and No. 1A[NB]. Oil No. 1 is a rapid rust solvent for use on rusted nuts and bolts, bearings, pulleys, etc. It penetrates readily but contains no highly volatile solvent which might create a fire hazard. OIL No. 1A is used for cleaning machine tools. It leaves a light, rust-preventing film.
KEYSTONE LUBRICATING CO.

Penetrell[NB]. A solvent used to improve the flowing qualities of dipping enamels. GLIDDEN CO.

Penetron Conc[NB]. A wetting and rewetting agent containing over 60% active ingredients. It is used for wetting of COTTON before stock dyeing, as a dispersing agent for dyestuffs in order to give them color value, for plasticizing and leveling adhesives, and for wetting out in desizing RAYON, COTTON and ACETATE. HART PRODUCTS CORP.

Penflour®. The trademark for a line of insecticides.
PENNSYLVANIA SALT MFG. CO.

Penford Finishing Gum 3XL and 3XP[NB]. Patented film-forming starch ethers for use, in place of starch, in textile finishing. The films have greater clarity, strength, and abrasion resistance than starch. These starch ethers have a reactive hydroxyl radical that enables them to react with urea formaldehyde resins. The cross-linked starch ether-urea resin compounds provide a much more durable finish than can be obtained with starch alone. PENICK & FORD LTD.

Pen-Gleam®. A mild alkaline detergent composition primarily adapted for the cleaning of painted and other surfaces, such as metal.
PENNSYLVANIA SALT MFG. CO.

Pen-Glo®. An acid detergent used for the removal of acid-soluble material from paint, enamel, or metal surfaces. It is sold particularly for the cleaning of railroad and trucking equipment.
PENNSYLVANIA SALT MFG. CO.

Pen Hob[NB]. (*HBMTN* p. 430). No longer available. PENINSULAR STEEL CO.

Penicel®. The trademark for a nutritional preparation for use as an ingredient of animal feeds.
ABBOTT LABORATORIES

Penicillin△. A powerful antibacterial derived from the mold, *Penicillium notatum*. Commercially, PENICILLIN is made by growing, under aerobic submerged fermentation conditions, a special strain of *Penicillin chrysogenum* on a medium consisting principally of corn steep liquor and lactose. The mass is agitated during the growth cycle with sterile air. At 25° to 27°C., the fermentation requires from 50 to 100 hr. The liquor is then clarified by filtration and the antibiotic is separated from the filtrate by extraction with an organic solvent at a pH of 2.0 to 2.5. The PENICILLIN is then separated from the solvent phase by means of a small quantity of an aqueous alkaline solution and then isolated by vacuum freeze drying.

The chemical composition of penicillin is:

$$\begin{array}{c} H_3C \\ \diagdown \\ C \\ H_3C\diagup \diagdown \\ S \\ \diagdown \\ C - H \\ | \\ H \end{array} \quad \begin{array}{c} H \\ | \\ C - COOH \\ | \\ N \\ \diagdown \\ CO \\ | \\ NH \cdot CO \cdot R \end{array}$$

Five different penicillins, differing only in the composition of the R group, have been isolated from the natural medium as follows:

Penicillin Type	R Group
F	2-pentyl
Dihydro F	n-amyl
G	benzyl
X	p-hydroxybenzyl
K	n-heptyl

A large number of PENICILLIN preparations are commercially available today including products for oral, inhalation, parenteral, sublingual, and topical applications. PENICILLIN G is perhaps the most desirable chemically. It is available as PENICILLIN G POTASSIUM CRYSTALLINE, PENICILLIN G PROCAIN, PENICILLIN G SODIUM, etc. *Uses:* For the treatment of infections caused by PENICILLIN-susceptible organisms, including streptococcic, staphylococcic and pneumococcic infections, Vincent's stomatitis, gonorrhea, syphilis, etc.

Penick, S. B., & Company®. The trademark for insecticides and incense. S. B. PENICK & CO.

Peninsular Black Label[NB], **Gray Label**[NB], **and Green Label**[NB]. (*HBMTN* p. 430). No longer available. PENINSULAR STEEL CO.

Penite®. A sodium arsenite in concentrated liquid form, used for killing weeds.
PENNSYLVANIA SALT MFG. CO.

Penitracin®. A Penick brand of Bacitracin U. S. P. A polypeptide antibacterial substance produced by the growth of a Gram-positive, spore-forming organism of a strain of Bacillus Subtilis. *Uses:* For the treatment of pyrogenic skin infections, open wounds, eye and nasal infections, mild pharyngeal and tonsillar infections, amebic and bacillary dysenteries.
S. B. PENICK & CO.

Pennant[NB]. (*HBMTN* p. 431). No longer available. DELAWARE TOOL STEEL CORP.

Penncoat®. The trademark for an asphalt, both in bulk and sheet form, sold for use primarily in forming protective linings and inner-linings.
PENNSYLVANIA SALT MFG. CO.

Pennex®, **Pennex A**; *and* **Pennex B**®. Trademarks for industrial chemicals sold only in bulk; namely, caustic alkali, calcium hypochlorite, ammonium persulphate, sodium perborate, potassium permanganate, etc. PENNSYLVANIA SALT MFG. CO.

Pennply®. A fiber-glass sheet material used to reinforce asphaltic or similar plastic coatings.
PENNSYLVANIA SALT MFG. CO.

Pennprime®. A liquid primer for treating concrete and metal surfaces for the reception of bituminous coatings and linings. PENNSYLVANIA SALT MFG. CO.

Pennsalt A-27®. The trademark for an industrial cleaning composition. PENNSYLVANIA SALT MFG. CO.

Pennsalt AE-16®. A strongly alkaline composition adapted primarily for cleaning and etching aluminum.
PENNSYLVANIA SALT MFG. CO.

Pennsalt EC-7®. A solvent emulsion cleaner for cleaning metal, ceramic, plastic, painted, and like surfaces. PENNSYLVANIA SALT MFG. CO.

Pennsalt EC-51®. A solvent emulsion cleaner for cleaning metal, ceramic, plastic, painted and like surfaces. PENNSYLVANIA SALT MFG. CO.

Pennsalt EC-54®. A liquid cleaning composition for industrial use. PENNSYLVANIA SALT MFG. CO.

Pennsalt LF-42®. The trademark for fluoboric acid.
PENNSYLVANIA SALT MFG. CO.

Pennsalt MS-1®. Adhesives used in molding and core-binder solutions. PENNSYLVANIA SALT MFG. CO.

Pennsalt PB-1®. An additive used with water for water-curtain applications in paint-spray boths.
PENNSYLVANIA SALT MFG. CO.

Pennsalt SC-25[NE]. A solubilizing organic cleaning agent for Diesel engine rooms and automotive engines.
PENNSYLVANIA SALT MFG. CO.

Pennsalt Scale Remover 4®. A metal cleaner and descaler. PENNSYLVANIA SALT MFG. CO.

Pennsalt Whirlaway®. A cleaning composition particularly adapted for clearing drains.
PENNSYLVANIA SALT MFG. CO.

Pennsorb®. An absorbent detergent used to absorb oils, greases, and water from garages, factories, machine shops, and the like.
PENNSYLVANIA SALT MFG. CO.

Penofen®. (*HBMTN* p. 432). No longer available.
CIBA CO.

Penphate®. A chemical with surface-active, hydrotropic, and wetting properties, used to assist the wetting and detergent action of aqueous solutions.
PENNSYLVANIA SALT MFG. CO.

Penphene®. The trademark for insecticides, particularly TOXAPHENE formulations.
PENNSYLVANIA SALT MFG. CO.

Penprim[NE]. A dry-cleaning, water-repellent, sizing agent. PENNSYLVANIA SALT MFG. CO.

Penresina®. The trademark for a powdered resin with diluent. S. B. PENICK & CO.

Pensal Cleans All®. A general-purpose cleansing preparation with water softening properties.
PENNSYLVANIA SALT MFG. CO.

Penso®. An alkaline detergent for bottle-washing and related uses in dairies, breweries, beverage-bottling plants, and other food- and beverage-processing plants. PENNSYLVANIA SALT MFG. CO.

Pensuds®. A wet-cleaning soap for use in dry-cleaning plants. PENNSYLVANIA SALT MFG. CO.

Pent-Acetate® #28. Synthetic amyl acetate. A highly uniform ester solvent with an ester content of over 85%. A water white liquid; sp.gr. 0.86–0.87 (20°/20°C.); b.p. range, 126°–155°C.; viscosity, 0.683 cps. (40°C.); flash point (open cup), 105°F. *Uses:* As a lacquer solvent, extractant for penicillin and other antibiotics; and as a general solvent.
PENNSYLVANIA SALT MFG. CO.

Pent-Acetate® #29. A special high-acetate-content grade (over 92%) of synthetic amyl acetate produced for extraction and lacquer uses. A water white liquid; sp.gr. 0.86–0.87 (20°/20°C.); b.p. range, 130°–152°C.; flash point, (open cup), 115°F.
PENNSYLVANIA SALT MFG. CO.

Pentalarm "A"®. Odorizing compositions which are injected into gases to warn of the presence of leaks.
PENNSYLVANIA SALT MFG. CO.

Pentalene® #95. A crude, undistilled mixture of mono-, di-, and polyamyl derivatives of naphthalene used as an intermediate in the mfg. of anionic surface-active agents where dark color is not objectionable. A dark green to brown liquid; av. mol.wt. 231–256; sp.gr. 0.93–0.96 (20°/20°C.); not less than 85% distills between 250° and 400°C.; viscosity, 112 cps, (20°C.); flash point (open cup), 315°F.; soluble in most organic solvents; insoluble in water and methyl alcohol.
PENNSYLVANIA SALT MFG. CO.

Pentalene® #195. A distilled mixture of about 20% mono-, 55% di-, and 25% polyamyl naphthalenes used as an intermediate for the mfg. of anionic surface-active agents. An amber-colored liquid; sp.gr. 0.92–0.94 (20°/20°C.); b.p. range, 290–400°C.; flash point, 300°F.; soluble in most organic solvents, insoluble in water and methyl alcohol.
PENNSYLVANIA SALT MFG. CO.

Pentaphen® #67. Para-tert-amylphenol. $C_5H_{11}C_6H_4OH$; mol.wt. 164.2. A white solid that may be tinged with pink or yellow; freezing point, 90°C. (min.); soluble in most organic solvents; insoluble in water. *Uses:* In the mfg. of oil-soluble resins and pharmaceutical preparations; and in organic synthesis.
PENNSYLVANIA SALT MFG. CO.

Pentasol® #26. A special esterification grade of synthetic amyl alcohol used for organic synthesis. A water-white liquid; sp.gr. 0.81–0.82 (20°/20°C.); b.p. range, 120°–140°C.; flash point (open cup), 105°F.
PENNSYLVANIA SALT MFG. CO.

Pentasol® #27. Synthetic amyl alcohol consisting of a mixture of isomeric amyl alcohols: primaries, secondaries and some tertiaries. A water-white liquid; sp.gr. 0.81–0.82 (20°/20°C.); b.p. range, 118°–140°C.; flash point (open cup), 115°F.; slightly soluble in water; soluble in organic solvents. *Uses:* As a solvent for nitrocellulose lacquer formulations, urea-formaldehyde resins, and many organic compounds; as a flotation reagent in the concentration of non-ferrous ores; as an intermediate in organic synthesis; and in hydraulic fluids. PENNSYLVANIA SALT MFG. CO.

Pentasol® #258. A special blend of alcohol for use as a solvent in the lacquer industry. A water-white liquid; sp.gr. 0.803–0.819 (20°/20°C.); b.p. range, 110°–138°C.; flash point (open cup), 75°F.
PENNSYLVANIA SALT MFG. CO.

Pentasol® Frother #124. A mixture of amyl alcohols used as a solvent, and as a frother in the concentration of non-ferrous ores. A light yellow liquid; sp.gr. 0.81–0.82 (20°/20°C.); 95% distills below 140°C.; flash point (open cup), 110°F.; av. wt. per gal. 6.8 lb.   PENNSYLVANIA SALT MFG. CO.

Pentergent®. (*HBMTN* p. 434. No longer available.
NOPCO CHEMICAL CO.

Pentex 44[NE]. A concentrated, pine oil-base penetrant that has been solubilized on a non-ionic system. It is unusually stable to pressure and to acids, alkalis and other materials commonly encountered in textile processing. Since it is non-scumming, it yields max. absorbency and rinsability, very bright colors, and freedom from crocking.   COLLOIDS, INC.

Penthanco®. The trademark for bulk perfume compounds for industrial uses.   S. B. PENICK & CO.

Penton[NE]. A chlorinated polyether thermoplastic polymer.   HERCULES POWDER CO.

Pentothal®. An anesthetic that is administered intravenously. Chemically, it is thiopental sodium.
ABBOTT LABORATORIES

Pentrete®. A seed disinfectant composition for protecting seeds and young plants against decay.
PENNSYLVANIA SALT MFG. CO.

Pentro PS. See ORCO PENTRO PS[NE].

Penval®. The trademark for bulk perfume compounds.   S. B. PENICK & CO.

Pen-Wood 176[NE]. The trade name for a sealer for wood surfaces.   BURGESS, FOBES CO.

Peptex®. A general-purpose, dairy farm cleaner. It is a granular material which is dissolved in water in an amount of one tablespoon to a gal. of water. Used for cleaning milk pails and utensils, milking machines, floors, walls, dishes, silverware, glassware, etc.   DIVERSEY CORP.

Peptomagic®. A white, free-flowing powder which is mixed with crude oil to make a general-purpose oil-well drilling fluid that is used for completing wells to prevent water blocking and mudding off the producing zone, and as a corrosion inhibitor.
OIL BASE, INC.

Perabeta®. (*HBMTN* p. 435). No longer available.
SHARP & DOHME, INC.

Peralga®. An effective synergistic combination of an analgesic-antipyretic and a sedative-hypnotic for sedation, hypnotic action, and relief of pain. Each tablet contains 1.5 gr. barbital, 2.0 gr. acetophenetidin, and 3.5 gr. acetylsalicylic acid. *Use:* For the treatment of restlessness and sleeplessness due to or associated with pain.   WARNER-CHILCOTT LABORATORIES

Perapret A. A binder for pigment and bronze printing; and a textile finishing agent. It is a low-viscosity, milky white dispersion of slightly ammoniacal reaction, and with a dry content of approx. 25%. It may be diluted with water in any proportion. On drying, it yields a tough, elastic, very slightly tacky, colorless film, which will swell but not dissolve in water. It is used as a binder for preparing pure white or pastel shade mat prints with pigments or pigment dyestuffs. It has good fastness to washing.
NOVA CHEMICAL CORP.

Perapret AX 45. A finishing agent for brushing and padding processes and a binder for printing with bronzes. It is a dispersion of low viscosity, with a dry content of about 40%, and gives a slightly alkaline reaction. It can be diluted with water in any proportions. When dry, it yields a flexible, slightly tacky film, which is insoluble in water. It is suitable for the production of brushing and padding finishes, and as a binder for metallic powder prints.
NOVA CHEMICAL CORP.

Perapret LN 25. A finishing agent for spreading and padding processes. It is supplied in the form of a white dispersion of low viscosity and approx. 40% solids content. It reacts slightly alkaline and, on drying, yields a flexible film which is insoluble in water. The solutions are stable in hard water. It is suitable for the preparation of spreading finishes, especially for final coats. It can also be used for the preparation of pad finishes which are stable against repeated mild washings. It can be applied together with other finishing agents.   NOVA CHEMICAL CORP.

Perapret PN. A finishing agent for NYLON. It is supplied in the form of a fluid dispersion of plastics, and can be diluted with cold or warm water in any proportion. It imparts good firmness and firm stability to NYLON hose in preboarding.
NOVA CHEMICAL CO.

Perf-A-Bead®. A metal corner reinforcement for gypsum wallboard. Applied with PERF-A-TAPE® cement.   UNITED STATES GYPSUM CO.

Perf-A-Tape®. A joint system for reinforcing and concealing gypsum wallboard joints. Consists of a cement, which is prepared for use by mixing the dry cement powder with lukewarm water; and a tape, in roll form, which is forced down on the wet cement.
UNITED STATES GYPSUM CO.

Perfection Cord. See BOSTON PERFECTION CORD.

Perfolite[NE]. An acoustical plaster for application over properly prepared interior basecoat surfaces of gypsum or portland cement-lime-sand. It is mixed with water just before it is applied with a trowel. The acoustical properties are secured by opening the surface with a stippling brush and a special perforating tool. PERFOLITE forms a cellular structure of lime, bound with mineral fibers, hardened by drying. Additional hardness develops with time by exposure to normal room temp.   NATIONAL GYPSUM CO.

Perfon®. An acid-type polishing and cleaning compound for nearly all surfaces. Easily and quickly removes stains from copper, stainless steel, tile and porcelain without damaging the finishes. Contains no soap, alkalis or harsh abrasives.   DIVERSEY CORP.

Perforall®. A line of perforated panels for decorative, utility, and display purposes. Available in sizes of 2′ × 3′, 2′ × 4′, 3′ × 4′, 4′ × 4′, 4′ × 6′ and 4′ × 8′; in thicknesses of ⅛″ and ³⁄₁₆″; with ³⁄₁₆″ holes on ½″ and on 1″ centers; and in the following materials: STANDARD and TEMPERED PRESWOOD®, STANDARD and TEMPERED DUOLUX®, LEATHERWOOD®, and PERFORATED LAMIDALL®.
WOODALL INDUSTRIES, INC.

Perforated Fibretex[NR]. A low-cost, decorative, insulating board, made of wood fibers. Especially suitable for ceilings of small stores, offices, game rooms, etc. where an expensive acoustical treatment is not required. JOHNS-MANVILLE SALES CORP.

Perilla Oil[△]. A light yellow oil obtained from the seeds of the plant *Perilla ocimoides* of China and Japan. It contains 41–46% linolenic acid, 31–42% linoleic acid, and 3–10% oleic acid. It is used in place of linseed oil in varnishes, core oils, printing inks, linoleum, etc. It dries to a harder, tougher and glossier film than linseed oil, and when blown in dries more rapidly and has greater weather resistance than linseed oil. Sp.gr. about 0.935; iodine no. 200; saponification no. 91.

Perimsul®. A thermal insulation composed of spun mineral wool fibers processed from a molten state to form a semi-rigid felt. It does not rot, decay, or support combustion; is not damaged by fungi or termites; and water will not travel through it by capillary action. Thermal conductivity, 0.27 B.t.u.-inch/hr. × sq.ft. × °F. Used as a perimeter-type structure insulation, it effectively prevents excessive heat loss from foundations, especially from cast concrete floor slabs, and from walls of crawl spaces used as heating plenums. BALDWIN-HILL CO.

Peritrate®. A medicinal used to prevent attacks in agina pectoris; to reduce the number and severity of those attacks not prevented; and to reduce nitroglycerin requirements. Consists of pentaerythritol tetranitrate, the nitric acid ester of the tetrahydric alcohol, pentaerythritol.
WARNER-CHILCOTT LABORATORIES

Permachlor Red[NR]. A yellowish-red color pigment suitable for exterior paints and enamels. Notable for its good exterior durability. SHERWIN-WILLIAMS CO.

Permachrom Red[NR]. A series of red color pigments with good light resistance, recommended especially for exterior paints, enamels, stains, lacquers. Available in medium red, bluish-red and maroon shades.
SHERWIN-WILLIAMS CO.

Permagel®. An inorganic perified colloidal form of the mineral attapulgite, a hydrated magnesium silicate. It is used as a thickening or gelling agent for aqueous and organic liquids; emulsifier and emulsion stabilizer; suspending agent for pigments and abrasives; and flatting agent for paint. PERMAGEL is composed of needle-like particles, which makes it very efficient for producing thixotropic gels. *Uses:* In paints, polishes, wax emulsions, adhesives, cosmetics, pharmaceuticals, metal-drawing lubricants, etc.
MINERALS & CHEMICALS CORP. OF AMERICA

Permagrid[NR]. The trademark for nickel grid wires for electronic tubes. WILBUR B. DRIVER CO.

Permaloid 155[NR]. An alkali-soluble, plasticized, vinyl acetate copolymer used in textile sizing, finishing and other operations where good luster, hand and water resistance are required. It produces clear, tough, water- and grease-resistant films. COLLOIDS, INC.

Permaloid 170V20[NP]. An alkali-soluble polyvinyl acetate co-polymer dispersion used for textile finishing. It has excellent stability and water resistance and is compatible with other finishes. COLLOIDS, INC.

Permamix®. A ready-to-use floor patching material for making permanent repairs on concrete, brick, tile, or asphalt floor surfaces. The area to be repaired is cleaned and coated with PERMAMIX® PRIMER, and then PERMAMIX® is poured on the area and tamped solidly into place. It is ready for traffic immediately.
PERMAMIX CORP.

Permanite® and **Permanite® Resin Cement.** (*HBMTN* p. 437). The name PERMANITE® is now a registered trademark. MAURICE A. KNIGHT

Permansa®. A line of yellow, orange, red and green color pigments for use in paints, printing inks, wallpaper, paper coating, etc. They have good light resistance and heat resistance. They are available in dry form and dispersed in various organic vehicles.
SHERWIN-WILLIAMS CO.

Perma-Ply®. A roofing material in the form of glass fiber mats impregnated or saturated with asphalt.
OWENS-CORNING FIBERGLAS CORP.

Permel® Finish. *See* CYANA® PERMEL® FINISH.

Permel Plus® Finish. *See* CYANA® PERMEL PLUS® FINISH.

Permel® Resin B. A durable water repellent for COTTON, RAYON, WOOL and synthetics. Frequently used as a hand modifier. AMERICAN CYANAMID CO.

Permigels®. The trademark for a line of permissible explosives, based on U. S. Bureau of Mines standards, approved for mining of coal. Recommended where wet conditions are encountered.
AMERICAN CYANAMID CO.

Persian Insect Powder[△]. *Same as* PYRETHRUM[△].

Persorb®. A sweat band. *Use:* To absorb perspiration from the forehead. It can also be moistened to cool the forehead. MINE SAFETY APPLIANCES CO.

"PE" Series. *See* CLAREMONT "PE" SERIES.

Pestroy®. A line of insecticides for household and garden use. SHERWIN-WILLIAMS CO.

Petitgrain[△]. An essential oil obtained by the distillation of the leaves and small twigs of the bitter orange tree *Citrus aurantium*, which is native to tropical Asia but is also grown now in other countries. The best quality of this oil comes from Paraguay. It is used as a fixative for fine perfumes and in flavoring extracts.

Petreco®. The registered tradename for petroleum-treating processes of PETRECO, a DIVISION OF PETROLITE CORP. Among the processes are PETRECO® DESALTING, PETRECO® ELECTROFINING, PETRECO® LUBE OIL TREATING, PETRECO® DESAPONIFICATION, and BENDER PROCESS.

Petreco® Electrofining[NE]. A fast, continuous, automatically controlled process for treating petroleum distillates such as straight-run gasoline, reformed gasoline, naphtha, diesel oil, lube oil, kerosene, burning oils, etc. It is used for acid contacting, caustic and doctor treating, water washing, Dualayer treating, and naphthenic acid removal. Sharp, clean separation is effected by electric precipitation. PETRECO

Petreco® Electrosphere[NE] **Desalting Process.** A process for desalting crude oil. It consists of heating the crude, emulsifying it with water, and dispersing the emulsion in a high-potential electric field in an ELECTROPHERE. In the electric field, the salts and other impurities are caused to be closely associated with the fresh water by the coalescing action of the field, and the water carrying the impurities is then rapidly separated from the oil. Other PETRECO® ELECTRIC DESALTING PROCESSES are similar but employ the CYLECTRIC[NE] (horizontal desalter) or VERTELECTRIC[NE] (vertical desalter) in place of the ELECTROSPHERE. PETRECO

Petrofac. (*HBMTN* p. 439). No longer available. SUN OIL CO.

Petrohol®. A trademark for isopropyl alcohol in various concentrations. *Uses:* As a raw material in the mfg. of chemical derivatives such as acetone and esters; as a solvent for many oils, resins, and surface-coating materials; as an extraction solvent; and in the formulation of cosmetics, varnishes and lacquers, cleaning compositions, antiseptics and astringents, insecticides and disinfectants. ENJAY CO.

Petrolatum△. *Also known as* PETROLEUM JELLY△ *and* PARAFFIN JELLY△. A yellowish to light-amber or white, semisolid, unctuous mass obtained from petroleum, composed of hydrocarbons, chiefly of the methane series of the general formula C_nH_{2n+2} and ranging between $C_{17}H_{36}$ and $C_{21}H_{44}$. It is practically odorless and tasteless; sp.gr. 0.802–0.865; insoluble in water, glycerol, alcohol; soluble in benzene, chloroform, ether, petroleum ether, carbon disulfide, and oils. Available in technical and U.S.P. grades. *Uses:* In pharmacy as an ointment base and in cosmetics; as a lubricant for firearms and machinery; in leather greases, shoe polishes, rust preventives; as a softener for rubber; etc.

Pet-Rolax®. A paste soap for use in petroleum solvent systems. PENNSYLVANIA SALT MFG. CO.

Petrolene®. (*Supp.* I p. 182). Should have been listed as PETROTHENE®. U. S. INDUSTRIAL CHEMICALS CO.

Petroleum Jelly△. *Same as* PETROLATUM△.

Petrolite®. A line of microcrystalline waxes. Typical members of the line are: PETROLITE C-700 and PETROLITE C-1035, which have the following properties, respectively: m.p. 190°F. (min.) and 195°F. (min.); penetration (100 g.) at 77°F. (ASTM D1321-54T), 4 (max.) and 7 (max.); color (N.P.A.), amber, 1½ (max.), for both. These waxes are used for polishes, crayons, electrical insulation, paper coatings, candles, and other uses. PETROLITES C-15, C-23, C-36, PE-100, and R-50 are emulsifiable waxes used in water emulsion formulations for floor, furniture, and leather polishes. C-15, C-23, and C-36 all have a m.p. of 180°F. (min.), and PE-100 and R-50 have a m.p. of 195–200°F. Penetration (100 g.) at 77°F. (ASTM D1321-54T) varies from 4–6 to 2 (max.); color (N.P.A.), 4½ (max.) to 6 (max.); acid no., 15–20 to 40–50; saponification no. 45–55 to 65–80. Of these waxes, R-50 is not strictly a microcrystalline wax, but a blend of an oxidized microcrystalline wax and a high-melting phenolic terpene resin. BARECO WAX CO.

Petronate®. (*HBMTN* p. 439). Now a registered trademark. L. SONNEBORN SONS, INC.

Petrothene®. Incorrectly listed as PETROLENE® (*Supp.* I p. 182). U. S. INDUSTRIAL CHEMICALS CO.

Petrox®. An all-petroleum motor-fuel additive. It burns completely, leaves no deposits, and "plates" each engine part with a protective anti-rust, anti-wear film. TEXAS CO.

Pexol®. A fortified rosin size for paper. HERCULES POWDER CO.

P-F®. A form of fibrous glass wool bonded together with a thermosetting resin and used for insulating buildings, vehicles and appliances such as refrigerators. OWENS-CORNING FIBERGLAS CORP.

Phantocube®. The trademark for a container and absorber for radioactive capsules and solutions used in quantitating against uptake in the thyroid gland. ABBOTT LABORATORIES

Phenac®. (*HBMTN* p. 439). No longer available. AMERICAN CYANAMID CO.

Phe-Ni-Met®. (*HBMTN* p. 439). No longer available. NATIONAL DRUG CO.

Phenix®. A line of nursing and prescription bottles. ARMSTRONG CORK CO.

Pheno® Direct Color Dyes. The trademark for a group of direct dyes used for coloring paper. AMERICAN CYANAMID CO.

Phenoform®. A group of dyestuffs of good heat stability. The are recommended for coloring thermosetting and thermoplastic molding resins such as urea-formaldehyde, melamine-formaldehyde, cellulose acetate, polystyrene, and especially phenol-formaldehyde. GENERAL DYESTUFF CO.

Phenurone®. A synthetic anticonvulsant used in the treatment of epileptic disorders. Consists of phenacemide, in tablet form. ABBOTT LABORATORIES

Philblack® A. A fast-extrusion, oil-furnace black used in rubber compounding. It increases the modulus and hardness, and provides excellent dimensional stability and smooth extrusion. PHILLIPS CHEMICAL CO., RUBBER CHEMICALS DIV.

Philblack® O. A high-abrasion, oil-furnace black with excellent balance and physical properties for molded and extruded rubber products. PHILLIPS CHEMICAL CO., RUBBER CHEMICALS DIV.

Phlogopite△. *See* MICA△.

Phloxine. *See* AZO PHLOXINE®.

PHO. *Same as* NEVILLAC 10°®.

Phos-Feed®. A feed-grade of dicalcium phosphate containing from 18.5–21% phosphorus, a minimum of 25% calcium, and a maximum of 40 ppm. fluorine. It is designed as a mineral supplement for animal and poultry feeds. AMERICAN AGRICULTURAL CHEMICAL CO.

Phosflake®. Incorrectly listed as PHOSPHLAKE® (HBMTN p. 443).
COLUMBIA-SOUTHERN CHEMICAL CORP.

Phosgene△. Carbonyl or chloroformyl chloride. $COCl_2$; mol.wt. 98.92. A colorless, highly toxic gas that irritates the eyes strongly and has a suffocating odor. Prepared by passing a mixture of chlorine and excess carbon monoxide over activated carbon. Condenses at about 0°C. to a clear, colorless, fuming liquid. Slightly soluble in water; freely soluble in benzene, toluene, glacial acetic acid, and most liquid hydrocarbons. *Uses:* In the mfg. of metal chlorides and anhydrides, pharmaceuticals, perfumes, and other organic chemicals; and as a poison war gas.

Phos-It®. A liquid product used as a cleaner for removing light soils and rust from steel surfaces, and as a metal conditioner for preparing steel, zinc, and aluminum alloy surfaces for painting. It is a clear, buff-colored liquid; density, 10.2 lb./gal.; acidity (as phosphoric acid), 37–38%. It is diluted with 3 or 4 parts of water before using.
WYANDOTTE CHEMICALS CORP., J. B. FORD DIV.

Phos-Kleen®. A sanitizing cleaning composition for use in the food-processing industries, particularly in the dairy trade. PENNSYLVANIA SALT MFG. CO.

Phosphlake®. (HBMTN p. 443). Should have been listed as PHOSFLAKE®.
COLUMBIA-SOUTHERN CHEMICAL CORP.

Phosphodust®. A diluent for insecticidal dusts and sprays. AMERICAN AGRICULTURAL CHEMICAL CO.

Phosphosil®. A metal cleaner comprising a compound of phosphorus. PENNSYLVANIA SALT MFG. CO.

Phosteem®. A cleaning and phosphating process, employing steam, for ferrous and aluminum alloy surfaces. NEILSON CHEMICAL CO.

Phylladrine®. Ephedrine, glucophylline and NEONAL® capsules for medicinal use.
ABBOTT LABORATORIES

Phytin®. A brand of calcium-magnesium salt of inositol hexaphosphoric acid, discovered and isolated from green plants in 1903. In PHYTIN®, the percentages of the three important elements are: phosphorus, 22; calcium, 12; and magnesium, 1.5. Designed to supply additional calcium, phosphorus and magnesium in the treatment of chronic illnesses, debilitated states and various nutritional deficiencies.
CIBA PHARMACEUTICAL PRODUCTS INC.

Phytomycin[NR]. A 20% streptomycin nitrate, for use as a bactericide. OLIN MATHIESON CHEMICAL CORP.

Pick-A-Shaft®. The trademark for a line of variable electrical resistors and parts thereof. (Registration No. 595,120; Class 21; Sept. 14, 1954.)
CLAROSTAT MFG. CO.

Pickle Control No. 5. *See* OAKITE® PICKLE CONTROL NO. 5.

Pickling Acids△. Solutions of various acids used for cleaning, or pickling, of metal castings and fabricated articles. Sulfuric, hydrochloric, nitric, and phosphoric acids are the common pickling acids of commerce. To minimize metal brittleness due to hydrogen absorption during pickling, various types of inhibitors are added to the pickling baths, which are generally used at temps. of 140–180°F. The common pickling bath for iron and steel is a sulfuric acid solution; hydrofluoric acid baths are sometimes used for pickling iron.

Pigmentar®. A consistently uniform pine tar extender and substitute. It is a viscous, dark-colored oil of pine origin, miscible in all proportions with pine tar and with most other softeners and plasticizers. Used in rubber compounding and reclaiming, marine paints, and roof coatings. GLIDDEN CO.

Pilate. A line of metallized acid dyestuffs with excellent solubility, leveling properties, and fastness to light and washing. *Use:* For dyeing WOOL and polyamide fibers. NOVA CHEMICAL CORP.

Pilate Fast Salt O Solution. An auxiliary for PILATE FAST COLOR dyeings. It is a yellow, clear liquid of low viscosity with practically neutral reaction. Miscible with water in any proportion. It improves fastness to decatizing and perspiration and the fastness to rubbing of heavy shades.
NOVA CHEMICAL CORP.

Pine Air. A room deodorizer, in an aerosol bomb dispenser, for washrooms, toilets, and wardrobes. It has a crisp woodsy fragrance. CLAIRE MFG. CO.

Pinealco®. The trademark for an Extract White Pine Compound. S. B. PENICK & CO.

Pine Emulso. *See* TROY PINE EMULSO.

Pine-Ola. A disinfectant-deodorant for rest rooms, locker rooms, showers, toilets, urinals, etc. Used as a spray, a floor rinse, or in scrubbing solutions. Phenol coefficient, 5. J. I. HOLCOMB MFG. CO.

Pioneer #202[NR]. *Formerly known as* WITCOTE® #202 (HBMTN p. 625). A metal protector and sound deadener consisting principally of asphalt, asbestos, inorganic fillers and petroleum solvents. Used extensively in applications where corrosion resistance, water and vapor sealing, insulating and sound deadening are required, such as in waterproofing outdoor structures, in thermal-insulation coatings for tanks, and as a vapor seal over concrete and cement. Has excellent flexibility and adhesion in the temp. range of −30°F. to +300°F. WITCO CHEMICAL CO.

Pioneer #214[NR]. A high efficiency sandless deadener. A fluid-type deadener consisting principally of selected asphalt, resins, special inert fillers, asbestos and nontoxic petroleum solvents. Used for eliminating vibration and reducing sound properties of metals. Used on all sheet metal surfaces subjected to vibration where outstanding dampening is desired. May be applied over dry, slightly oily, primed or painted surfaces. WITCO CHEMICAL CO.

Pioneer #216[NR]. A high efficiency fluid-type sandless deadener consisting principally of asphalt, asbestos, inorganic fillers and non-toxic thinner. Used for automobile doors, floors, deck lids and fenders, bus side panels and roof panels, railroad cars, metal cabinets, sinks, etc., to deaden sound. Also provides protection against rust and corrosion. It is resistant to salts and chemicals; and is waterproof and fungus proof. WITCO CHEMICAL CO.

Pioneer #301[NB]. *Formerly known as* WITCOTE® #301 (*HBMTN* p. 625). A sewer-joint compound which is applied cold in any weather condition. Seals joints in concrete or vitrified clay sewer pipe. Resists acid, alkalis, salts, and roots. Withstands temps. from −1°F. to +300°F. without hardening or cracking.
WITCO CHEMICAL CO.

Pioneer #401-P[NB]. A vapor barrier and thermal-insulating coating developed for use in the railroad-car building and maintenance industry. It combines anti-sweating properties with excellent metal protection. WITCO CHEMICAL CO.

Pioneer #406[NB]. A roof-coating material. It is an asphaltic compound of spray or brushing consistency, composed of special asphalts, asbestos fillers, mineral stabilizers and solvents. It is used on new or old prepared roofing or on built-up roofs to provide a tough, durable elastic coating of superior adhesion and high resistance to the elements. PIONEER #406 is also an excellent coating for maintaining metal roofs. WITCO CHEMICAL CO.

Pioneer #500[NB]. *Formerly known as* WITCOTE® #500 (*HBMTN* p. 625). A crate topcoating. A smooth, homogeneous mixture of asphalt and fiber asbestos blended with petroleum solvents. Used to weatherproof the tops, sides and ends of cases especially for export shipping. When sprayed, raked or trowled over the case it forms a thin continuous film that covers separation of the sheathing boards due to shrinkage. The coating is stable at temps. from below 0°F. to 140°F. PIONEER #500 conforms to government specifications MIL-C-102Z, Type I.
WITCO CHEMICAL CO.

Pioneer #507 Aluminum Mastic[NB]. An asphaltic aluminum paint easily applied by brush or spray equipment. It serves as a protective coating against rust and corrosion, provides insulation for piping or wherever humid areas and moisture occur. It reflects the sun's heat to decrease inside temps. and minimize heat expansion. WITCO CHEMICAL CO.

Pioneer #607 and #609[NB]. *Formerly known as* WITCOTE® #607 *and* #609 (*HBMTN* p. 626). General-purpose coatings for metal, such as structural steel, storage tanks, pipes etc. When dry, the paint resists water and acid, is stable, tough and elastic. Conforms to government specifications JAN-P-450, Types I and II. WITCO CHEMICAL CO.

Pioneer #610 Adhesive[NB]. An asphalt tile adhesive which provides damp-proofing to porous and cementaceous surfaces. It is resistant to rust and corrosion, acids, alkalis, and salts, as well as water-resistant and fungus proof. WITCO CHEMICAL CO.

Pioneer #622 Asphalt Paint[NB]. A general utility and maintenance metal paint used as a seal coating over porous surfaces and as a protective coating for metal surfaces. It is used as a blending ingredient for other paints, enamels and japans, and as a vehicle for roof coatings and cements. WITCO CHEMICAL CO.

Pioneer #630 Primer[NB]. A black fluid asphaltum preparation. Used as a primer or base for asphalt and mastic coatings. Applied over cementaceous materials, porous and dried out roofing and siding felt.
WITCO CHEMICAL CO.

Pioneer #820 Cork Insulation[NB]. A cold-application-type of spray-on insulation formulated for use on heated storage tanks where conservation of heat is required. Also applicable for rundown, expansion-type and floating-roof tanks. Prevents corrosion, is water-resistant, and acid and termite resistant.
WITCO CHEMICAL CO.

Pioneer #1008 Vapor Seal[NB]. A bituminous coating for all surfaces of structural materials. Serves as a waterproofing agent, vapor seal, rust and corrosion protector. Resists weathering and abrasion.
WITCO CHEMICAL CO.

Pipizan®. (*Supp.* I p. 184). Now a registered trademark and a product of MERCK SHARP & DOHME, DIV. OF MERCK & CO.

Pittabs®. Compressed tablets of PITTCHLOR® (*HBMTN* p. 445), a calcium hypochlorite containing 70% available chlorine. Used for the control of bacteria, algae, and odors in swimming pools, ponds, out-door reservoirs, and wells. Added directly to the pool water, PITTABS provide a continuous and uniform supply of available chlorine for 18 hr.
COLUMBIA-SOUTHERN CHEMICAL CORP.

Placco[NB]. (*Supp.* I p. 186). Now a product of THE BORDEN CO., CHEMICAL DIV., successor to PIONEER LATEX & CHEMICAL CO.

Placidyl®. A nonbarbiturate hypnotic, ethchlorvynol, BORDEN CO., CHEMICAL DIV., successor to PIONEER LATEX & CHEMICAL CO.

Placidyl®. A nonbarbiturate hypnotic, ethchlorvynol, in capsule form. ABBOTT LABORATORIES

Planifoline[NB]. An imitation vanilla concentrate containing pure vanilla and other plant extractions and fortified with vanillin.
FLORASYNTH LABORATORIES, INC.

Plantarome®. *See* ENTRAPPED® PLANTAROME® FOAM PRODUCER.

Plantex[NB]. An anti-traspirant designed for treating nursery stock herbaceous transplants to reduce moisture loss and wilting, and for protecting ornamentals in exposed positions against "winter burn." It is a liquid dispersion of modified vinyl resins containing a stabilizer. It forms a harmless plastic coating which greatly reduces transpiration water loss from leaves without altering the normal exchange of oxygen and carbon dioxide. LARVACIDE PRODUCTS, INC.

Plastamine®. A synthetic organic chemical condensation product. PENNSYLVANIA SALT MFG. CO.

Plastergrip. A sealer for bare plaster walls and ceilings, wallboard, concrete, stucco, brick, etc. It can be applied to damp walls; dries in 24 to 36 hr.; resists alkali; and forms an excellent base for paint.
GILLESPIE VARNISH CO.

Plaster-Weld®. A liquid product, similar to WELD-CRETE®, used for bonding new plaster to old plaster or almost any structurally sound surface, including glass.
LARSEN PRODUCTS CORP.

Plasti-Calk[NR]. Plastic caulking compounds that are heat and cold resistant.   MAAS & WALDSTEIN CO.

Plastic Chrome. See R & I PLASTIC CHROME®.

Plastic Insulcrete®. Incorrectly listed as INSULCRETE® (HBMTN p. 299 and Supp. I p. 112).
QUIGLEY CO.

Plasticizer #239. (HBMTN p. 447). No longer available.   GENERAL CHEMICAL DIV., ALLIED CHEMICAL & DYE CORP.

Plasticizer BD-8. See DC PLASTICIZER BD-8[NR].

Plasticizer E-S. See RC PLASTICIZER E-S[NR].

Plasticizer LP and Plasticizer MP[NR]. Light-colored, petroleum-based plasticizers. Aniline points, below 25°C.; sp.gr. 0.95–0.97 and 0.97–1.00 for LP and MP, respectively. They are primary plasticizers for neoprene and other rubbers, and secondary plasticizers for polyvinyl chloride compounds. Up to 100 parts of either plasticizer can be used per 100 parts neoprene without blooming. In vinyl compounding, 10 to 20 parts of LP or 15 to 30 parts of MP can often be used per 100 parts of polymer.
AKRON CHEMICAL CO.

Plasticizer O-16. See RC PLASTICIZER O-16[NR].

Plasticizer TG-8. See RC PLASTICIZER TG-8[NR].

Plasticizer TG-9. See RC PLASTICIZER TG-9[NR].

Plasticizers VA[NR]. (HBMTN p. 447). No longer available.   ADVANCE SOLVENTS & CHEMICAL CORP.

Plasticone Red®. A line of red color pigments especially recommended for plastics, paints, enamels, lacquers, rubber, printing inks, etc. Available in dry form and dispersed in alkyd resins, litho varnish and plasticizers. Good heat resistance, non-bleeding, good light resistance. Available in the following grades: light red, opaque; medium red, transparent; medium red, opaque; and maroon.   SHERWIN-WILLIAMS CO.

Plastic Peel No. 3601. A hot-dip, strippable coating for the protection of finished machined parts during processing, storage, and shipping. It is supplied in solid form, and is heated to 190°C. for application. Articles are dipped in the melt for about 5 seconds.
ADHESIVE PRODUCTS CORP.

Plasti-Gum®[Can.]. (Supp. I p. 87). The name PLASTI-GUM is registered in the Canadian Patent Office.
CANADA ROOF PRODUCTS LTD.

Plastiplex. A series of coatings for plastics, developed primarily for application on general-purpose, molded polystyrene as well as on high-impact and high-temp. molded polystyrene. Applied by spray or dip methods; have good adhesion, hardness, and flexibility. PLASTIFLEX coatings also possess excellent adhesion to phenolic and other thermosetting plastics.
SULLIVAN CHEMICALS DIV., SULLIVAN VARNISH CO.

Plasti Sand Process®. A patented process using liquid phenolic resin-coated sand in foundry shell molding. The process is easily adapted to every shell-molding method, including cold mulling for blowing and roll-over where a strike-off bar is used, and hot mulling for dump box operations. In the cold process, the liquid resin, sand and certain catalysts are mulled in any standard foundry muller, but in the hot process, specially designed equipment is necessary. With either process, clean finishes and strong, lightweight molds are obtained more economically and efficiently than with conventional processes.   ACME RESIN CORP.

Plasti-Seal®[Can.]. (Supp. I p. 87). The name PLASTI-SEAL is registered in the Canadian Patent Office.
CANADA ROOF PRODUCTS LTD.

Plastisol△. A polyvinyl chloride resin dispersed in a liquid plasticizer along with colorants, stabilizers and other modifying agents. The resulting compound may be either a liquid or a paste. The most common molding PLASTISOLS are relatively low viscosity liquid formulations that are pourable for ease of handling. They may be poured, pumped, or sucked into a mold, or a mold may be dipped into the liquid. Essentially, they are 100%-solids materials; therefore, there are no solvents or diluents to be evaporated and cause shrinkage problems. The PLASTISOL which lines, fills, or coats the mold is converted to an elastomeric compound by raising its temp. to 350°–400°F. Once this temp. is attained by the mass, conversion or fusion is practically instantaneous. A recent development in the PLASTISOL field has been the commercial production of VINYL sponge and foam. Various expanded or cellular PLASTISOLS, with a wide range in density, are being made by different methods. PLASTISOLS are used for coating many consumer and industrial products, and for molding a variety of products by dip, slush, rotational, and low-pressure injection techniques.

Plastite®. A polyvinyl chloride thermoplastic insulation used in the mfg. of various types of flexible insulated electric cable.   WHITNEY BLAKE CO.

Plastoid Plastic Rope. (HBMTN p. 450). No longer available.   PLASTIC PRODUCTS CO.

Plastolein® 9110, 9114, and 9128. (HBMTN p. 450). No longer available.   EMERY INDUSTRIES, INC.

Plastolite®. (Supp. I p. 188). Should have been listed as a registered trademark.   CELOTEX CORP.

Plastolith®. A plasticizer for concrete. Formulated in three types similar to Portland cement. It aids in the placement of all concrete, and assures maximum durability under the most extreme conditions.

TYPE I PLASTOLITH. For use where Type I cement is required: single lift foundation pours, sidewalks, highways, etc.

TYPE III PLASTOLITH. For use where high-early-strength is required. It can be used with both Type I and Type III cements.

TYPE IV PLASTOLITH. For use where low heat of hydration and/or a controlled initial set delay is desired. The most wide-spread application of TYPE IV PLASTOLITH is found where multi-lift or jacked-

form placements require an initial set delay to insure proper vibration and integration of successive pours.
FORT PITT CHEMICAL CO.

Platers "A" Special. See OAKITE® PLATERS "A" SPECIAL.

Plenco. A line of phenolic molding compounds including general-purpose heat-resistant, electrical-insulating, and high-impact grades.
PLASTICS ENGINEERING CO.

Pleogen®. A line of polyester resins for laminating, molding, and casting. By the use of catalysts, they will set in a short time at room temp. They are used for such purposes as boat building, mfg. of corrugated panels, etc. Sp.gr. 1.15–1.26; shrinkage, 6.5–10%; water absorption, 0.15–0.30%; Barcol hardness, 40–55; tensile strength, 1,400–8,250 lb./sq.in.; flexural modulus, 5.0–6.2 $\times$ 10^5.
MOL-REZ DIV., AMERICAN PETROCHEMICAL CORP.

Plestran®. A metalbolic regulator for middle-age slowdown, states of chronic depletion and debilitation, and other effects of endocrine imbalance. Each tablet contains 0.005 mg. ethinyl extradiol, 2.5 mg. methyltestosterone, and 15.0 mg. Proloid®.
WARNER-CHILCOTT LABORATORIES

Plexichrome[NE]. A colorful, long-lasting, acrylic-based finish for asphalt driveways, sidewalks, tennis courts, and parking areas. Easily applied by pouring or brushing; hardens in an hour to an attractive flexible coat that will not crack or peel; that fills small crevices, and protects the surface against acids, alkalies, gasoline, oil, and ultraviolet rays.
CALIFORNIA STUCCO PRODUCTS OF N. E., INC.

Plexicolor[NE]. An acrylic emulsion, exterior, flat paint for masonry, stucco, painted wood, and unglazed tile; and over asphalt and asbestos shingles. It is quick drying, non-flammable, odorless, non-toxic, and scrubbable. Available in various colors.
CALIFORNIA STUCCO PRODUCTS OF N. E., INC.

Plexiglas® R. An acrylic plastic sheet, lower in cost than regular PLEXIGLAS, but with the same chemical and physical properties. Supplied in unmasked, untrimmed, transparent sheets.
ROHM & HAAS CO.

Plexon® Pigtail. (*HBMTN* p. 451). Now a registered trademark.
PLEXON, INC.

Pliapak[NE]. The trademark for a disposable plastic blood container.
ABBOTT LABORATORIES

Plimasin®. An antiallergic and stimulant used in the relief of hay fever, allergic rhinitis, drug and serum reactions, etc. Supplied in form of tablets, each containing 25 mg. PYRIBENZAMINE® hydrochloride and 5.0 mg. RITALIN® hydrochloride.
CIBA PHARMACEUTICAL PRODUCTS INC.

PLS. See "JOHN CRANE" PLS (PLASTIC LEAD SEAL).

Plush[△]. A term designating fabrics woven of COTTON, SILK, LINEN or WOOL, and having a pile that is deeper than that of VELVET. It is used principally as an upholstery material. Brocade designs are made by "bruning" the pile with rollers to form a lower background. PLUSH is also dyed and curled to simulate furs.

Plyacein®. (*Supp.* I p. 189). Should have been listed as PLYACIEN®.
REICHHOLD CHEMICALS, INC.

Plyacien®. Incorrectly listed as PLYACEIN® (*Supp.* I p. 189).
REICHHOLD CHEMICALS, INC.

Plyokem®. A general-purpose, neutral liquid cleaner.
DIVERSEY CORP.

Plyowax®. A self-polishing, water-emulsion floor wax.
DIVERSEY CORP.

PMA Seed Treater. See ISOTEX® PMA SEED TREATER.

Pneolator®. A resuscitator. *Uses:* As a portable automatic device for administering artificial respiration. It operates from its own oxygen cylinder or spare large cylinder. An auxiliary attachment for treatment of a second patient simultaneously is also available.
MINE SAFETY APPLIANCES CO.

Pneophone[NE]. A device which provides efficient inhalational therapy and effective artificial respiration for cases of suspended breathing.
MINE SAFETY APPLIANCES CO.

Polaris Red[NE]. A bluish-red color pigment suitable for plastics, printing inks, and rubber. Notable for its good light resistance in full shade and tints; is nonbleeding; and has an exceptionally clean shade. Available in dry form, and dispersed in various organic vehicles.
SHERWIN-WILLIAMS CO.

Poly-A9 Cast Film. Cast polystyrene film for electrical insulation. Thicknesses from 0.0004" to 0.0012"; widths from ½" to 16"; softening point, 90°C.; dielectric strength, 3,200 volts/mil; dielectric constant, 2.55–2.65; power factor, 0.0001–0.0005.
DIELECT INC.

Poly-Cell®. A polyurethane, foamed-in-place, low-temp. insulation. Consists of two liquids which can be mixed and applied by special spray equipment, or mixed and poured into molds to conform to the shape of the object to be insulated. The resulting semi-rigid, low-density foam can be further protected after one hour with INSUL-MASTIC VAPORSEAL.
INSUL-MASTIC CORP. OF AMERICA

Polychem. The trade name for polyester resins and allied materials made in Canada by arrangement with INTERCHEMICAL CORP. of the United States.
CHEMICAL OIL & RESIN CO.

Polycizer® 532. A plasticizer for polyvinyl chloride plastics. Octyl decyl adipate. Mol.wt. 398; sp.gr. (25/25°C.), 0.918; refractive index, (25°C.), 1.440; viscosity (25°C.), 17 cps.; flash point (C.O.C.), 390°F.; fire point, 465°F.
HARWICK STANDARD CHEMICAL CO.

Polycizer® 562. A plasticizer for polyvinyl chloride plastics. Octyl decyl phthalate. Mol.wt. 418; sp.gr. (25/25°C.), 0.970; refractive index (25°C.), 1.484; viscosity (25°C.), 65 cps.; flash point (C.O.C.), 415°F.; fire point, 485°F.; pour point, −45°C.
HARWICK STANDARD CHEMICAL CO.

Polycizer® 632. A plasticizer for polyvinyl chloride plastics. Didecyl adipate. Mol.wt. 426; sp.gr. (25/25°C.), 0.9155; refractive index (25°C.), 1.4505; viscosity (25°C.), 19.2 cps.; flash point (C.O.C.), 415°F.; fire point 495°F.
HARWICK STANDARD CHEMICAL CO.

Polycizer® 662. A plasticizer for polyvinyl chloride plastics. Didecyl phthalate. Mol.wt. 446; sp.gr. (25/

25°C.), 0.964; refractive index, (25°C.), 1.4835; viscosity (25°C.), 1.4835 cps.; flash point, 435°F.; fire point, 510°F.; pour point, −46°C.
HARWICK STANDARD CHEMICAL CO.

Polycizer® DBP. Dibutyl phthalate. Mol.wt. 278.3. A low-toxicity plasticizer for cellulose acetate film, nitrocellulose lacquers, and textile coatings. Also used in paper coatings, insect repellent formulations, explosives, and synthetic rubbers. A clear, transparent, odorless liquid; color (A.P.H.A.), 25 (max.); sp.gr. (20/20°C.), 1.045; b.p. 340°C.; crystallizing point, less than 35°C.; flash point, 170°C.; refractive index (20°C.), 1.4889.
HARWICK STANDARD CHEMICAL CO.

Polycizer® DBS. Dibutyl sebacate. A plasticizer for polyvinyl chloride, vinyl copolymers, polyvinyl butyral, cellulose nitrate, cellulose acetate-butyrate, acrylic resins, and synthetic rubbers. Color (A.P.H.A.), 25–30; flash point, 400°F.; refractive index (23°C.), 1.4403; vapor pressure, 1 mm. Hg at 160°C.
HARWICK STANDARD CHEMICAL CO.

Polycizer® DOS. Dioctyl sebacate. A plasticizer for polyvinyl chloride and its copolymers, cellulose nitrate, cellulose acetate-butyrate, and synthetic rubbers. Color (A.P.H.A.), 50 (max.); flash point (C.O.C.), 445°F. (min.); refractive index (30°C.), 1.4473–1.4483; vapor pressure, 1 mm. Hg at 211°C.
HARWICK STANDARD CHEMICAL CO.

Poly-Coupler®. A water-miscible, nonionic, resin copolymer, used in combination with urea- and melamine-formaldehyde resin baths to prevent the excessive liberation of free formaldehyde after cure, and to help prevent the formation of methyl amines on un-neutralized resinated fabrics. It does not discolor, modify hand, or contribute disagreeable odors to finished materials. It is applied with the resin in the pad bath, or as an after-wash on freshly resinated and cured finishes. It does not alter standard resination techniques, except that the wash may be eliminated; and it does not alter curing time for the resin-treated fabrics.
TEXTILE ADJUNCTS CORP.

Polycycline®. A broad-spectrum antibiotic product from a species of *Streptomyces*. This brand of tetracycline is used in medicine for the treatment of many infections including pneumonia and other pneumococcal infections, streptococcal infections, urinary tract infections, broncho-pulmonary infections, acute otitis media, scarlet fever, bacillary dysentery, epidermal abscesses, gonorrhea, and many others.
BRISTOL LABORATORIES INC.

Polycycline® Aqueous '250'. A cherry-flavored medicinal, each 5 cc. teaspoonful of which contains calcium tetracycline equivalent to 250 mg. tetracycline hydrochloride. It is effective against a large variety of Gram-positive and Gram-negative organisms, certain rickettsiae, and large viruses.
BRISTOL LABORATORIES INC.

Polycycline® Intramuscular. A brand of crystalline tetracycline hydrochloride in single-dose vials each of which contains 100 mg. tetracycline hydrochloride and 2% procaine hydrochloride buffered with ascorbic acid and magnesium chloride. Its antibacterial activity compares favorably with that of chlortetracycline or oxytetracycline with the advantage of minimum side effects.
BRISTOL LABORATORIES INC.

Polycycline® Intravenous. A brand of crystalline tetracycline hydrochloride in 3 concentrations: 100 mg., 250 mg., and 500 mg. tetracycline hydrochloride per vial. The broad-spectrum antibiotic is used in severe illness when the patient is unable to take medication by mouth.
BRISTOL LABORATORIES INC.

Polycycline® Ointment. A medicinal for the treatment of pyogenic skin infections and as a prophylactic measure against secondary infection of abrasions, open wounds, and complications following surgery. Contains 30 mg. tetracycline hydrochloride, and 20 mg. lidocaine in a petrolatum-lanolin base. Has a wide range of activity against Gram-negative and Gram-positive organisms as well as rickettsiae and large viruses.
BRISTOL LABORATORIES INC.

Polycycline® Ophthalmic Ointment. A broad-spectrum antibiotic that is effective against Gram-negative and Gram-positive bacteria, certain rickettsiae and large viruses. Contains 10 mg. tetracycline and 20 mg. lidocaine in a light mineral oil base.
BRISTOL LABORATORIES INC.

Polyester Resins△. Synthetic resins made by the esterification of polyhydric alcohols and polybasic acids. Saturated polyesters result from the interaction of a saturated dihydric alcohol and a saturated dibasic acid under controlled conditions. These saturated polyesters undergo further intermolecular condensations but cannot be cross-linked. When a dihydric alcohol and a dibasic acid, either or both of which contain a double-bonded pair of carbon atoms, are reacted, an unsaturated polyester is obtained. The double bonds render the unsaturated polyester capable of subsequent cross-linking. Generally, unsaturated polyesters are blended with a reactive monomer, such as styrene, and reacted in the presence of special catalysts. The polyester and the monomer polymerize to form a thermosetting resin. The dihydric alcohols most commonly used are glycols of ethylene, propylene, 1,3- and 2,3-butylene, diethylene, and dipropylene. Unsaturated dihydric alcohols are not commercially available and, therefore, the dibasic acids must supply the necessary unsaturation or double bonds to the polyester-base resin. The unsaturated dibasic acid is usually maleic anhydride or fumaric acid. The most common saturated dibasic acid components are phthalic anhydride and adipic and azelaic acids. The polymerizable monomer can be styrene, vinyl-toluene, diallyl phthalate, methyl methylacrylate or triallyl cyanurate. Polymerizable polyesters are characterized by their ease of handling —in the uncured state they are liquids. They cure rapidly to thermosetting resins, they can be colored easily, they have excellent dimensional stability, and good electrical and physical properties. Some of the major uses of polyester resins include architectural sheeting, electrical equipment parts, automotive parts, matched-metal moldings, filled castings, buttons, etc. Among the many applications for saturated polyester resins are the following: plasticizers, fibers and films, foams, polyurethane elastomers, etc.

Polyfax® Process. (*HBMTN* p. 457). The word POLYFAX is now a registered trademark.
INTERCHEMICAL CORP., FINISHES DIV.

Poly-Flex 100[NE]. A cold-setting flexible mold compound. It is a two component system: (A) a combination of low-viscosity liquid polymers, and (B) a hardening agent. The mixture hardens rapidly to a tough, flexible compound from which duplicate models and patterns of great fidelity can be made. It can also be used for making molds for epoxy resin castings. Tensile strength, 130 lb./sq.in. after 16 hr.; elongation, (Scott), 600%. (Registration applied for.)
SMOOTH-ON MFG. CO.

Polyfluoron®. *See* ACME POLYFLUORON® LIQUID DISPERSION, *and* ACME POLYFLUORON® MOLDING POWDER.

Poly-G®. The group name for polyethylene glycols used as humectants and in the production of surface-active agents, cosmetics, and pharmaceuticals. They are heat stable, have low vapor pressures, and are soluble in water, aliphatic ketones, alcohols, esters, and aromatic hydrocarbons.
OLIN MATHIESON CHEMICAL CORP.

Polygriptex. A plastic adhesive for adhering paper labels to polyethylene containers using conventional labeling machines. ADHESIVE PRODUCTS CORP.

Polymel® **6, 7, C-128, D,** *and* **H-2.** (*HBMTN* pp. 457, 458). The name POLYMEL® should have been labeling machines. ADHESIVE PRODUCTS CORP.

Polymel® **C-130.** A light amber, solid, friable terpene-copolymer resin for plasticizing highly loaded GR-S and natural rubber stocks. Sp.gr. 1.03; m.p. 208–210°F. It increases flex-crack growth resistance, increases Shore hardness, and maintains abrasion resistance. POLYMEL CORP.

Polymel® **D-Tac.** Incorrectly listed as D-TAC (*HBMTN* p. 185). POLYMEL CORP.

Polymel® **DX.** A polystyrene resin-type plasticizer for natural and synthetic rubbers. It is a medium-soft, friable resin, amber to brown in color; sp.gr. 1.01; m.p. 200–215°F. POLYMEL CORP.

Polymel® **DX-111 Powder.** A polystyrene resin-type plasticizer, in powder form, for natural and synthetic rubbers. Color, amber to brown; sp.gr. 1.11.
POLYMEL CORP.

Polymeric BGA. *See* RC POLYMERIC BGA[NE].

Polymerin®. (*HBMTN* p. 458). Now a registered trademark. INTERCHEMICAL CORP., FINISHES DIV.

Polymix®. A line of dry-blended, colored, polyethylene molding compounds. GERING PRODUCTS INC.

Polymul[NE]. A series of polyethylene emulsions designed for use in many industrial treating operations.
NOPCO CHEMICAL CO.

Polyplex. A series of coatings for plastics, designed for application on articles fabricated of high-impact polystyrene, acrylics, and certain types of acetate. These coatings possess max. adhesion, flexibility and hardness, and they withstand vacuum-forming operations. Under normal atmospheric conditions, POLYPLEX coatings dry rapidly, and can be adjusted to any type of automatic spray applications.
SULLIVAN CHEMICALS DIV.,
SULLIVAN VARNISH CO.

Poly-Po-Nitro®. The trademark for a line of fertilizers and fertilizer materials.
INTERNATIONAL MINERALS & CHEMICAL CORP.

Polyprene®. A vinyl organosol-type material characterized by extreme toughness and resistance to abrasion, and excellent resistance to acids, alkalis, most chemicals, perspiration, soaps, and detergents. Used for coating applications where resistance to mechanical impact and abrasion are important factors.
INTERCHEMICAL CORP., FINISHES DIV.

Polyrad®. A family of ethylene oxide derivatives of HERCULES ROSIN AMINE D. They are mildly cationic surface-active agents. They are used as wetting agents, emulsifiers, and demulsification agents; as corrosion inhibitors for mineral acids and brines in petroleum-refinery and oil-well applications; and for anti-cratering action and bath mud control in rayon manufacture. HERCULES POWDER CO.

Polyseal. *See* SUNOCO POLYSEAL®.

Polyshield Micropaint[NE]. *See* RS17 POLYSHIELD MICROPAINT[NE].

Poly-Solv®. The group name for ethylene glycol ethers used as solvents for dyestuffs, oils, waxes and resins; as components of brake fluids, metal and glass cleaners, dry cleaning soaps, "soluble" textile and metal cutting oils; and as intermediates for a number of plasticizers. Available in the following grades:

Grade	Compound	Formula
EM	Ethylene glycol monomethyl ether	$CH_3OCH_2CH_2OH$
DM	Diethylene glycol monomethyl ether	$CH_3OCH_2CH_2OCH_2CH_2OH$
EE	Ethylene glycol monoethyl ether	$CH_3CH_2OCH_2CH_2OH$
DE	Diethylene glycol monoethyl ether	$CH_3CH_2OCH_2CH_2OCH_2CH_2OH$
EB	Ethylene glycol monobutyl ether	$CH_3CH_2CH_2OCH_2CH_2OH$
DE	Diethylene glycol monobutyl ether	$CH_3CH_2CH_2CH_2OCH_2CH_2OCH_2CH_2OH$

OLIN MATHIESON CHEMICAL CORP.

Polysty-Lac®. Ready-mixed paints, paint primers, clear lacquers and pigmented lacquers for use on polystyrene. MAAS & WALDSTEIN CO.

Poly-Tergent[NE]. The group name for non-ionic detergents and surface-active agents.
OLIN MATHIESON CHEMICAL CORP.

Polytherm®. (*HBMTN* p. 459). Now a registered trademark. INTERCHEMICAL CORP., FINISHES DIV.

Polyurethane Resins△. *Same as* ISOCYANATE RESINS△.

Ponkote®. An epoxy ester protective-decorative coating in attractive colors. This enamel is designed specifically to improve the beauty and wearing qualities of nonsubmerged metal, wood, and plaster.
INERTOL CO.

Pontianak△. *Also known as* JELUTONG△. A rubbery gum obtained from the trees *Dyera costulata* and *D. laxifolia* of Borneo and Malaya. The commercial gum is a grayish-white material, resembling burnt lime and containing up to 60% water. It is used in formulating friction compounds used to coat belting; in varnishes and insulations; and for mixing with GUTTA PERCHA.

Poppy ®. The trademark for a line of wheelbarrows.
UNITED STATES STEEL CORP.

Poppy Oil△. *Also known as* POPPY-SEED OIL△. An oil expressed from poppy seeds. It is free of morphine and other opium alkaloids. It is a pale-yellow drying oil with a pleasant odor. Sp.gr. 0.925; solidifies at about −18°C.; saponification no. 188–197; iodine no. 133–158. *Use:* In the mfg. of paints, varnishes, and soaps.

Poppy-Seed Oil△. *Same as* POPPY OIL△.

Porete® Prestressed Beams. A line of beams for roofs and floors, made from concrete and prestressed with from 4 to 12 wires per beam depending on load factor and span required. Compressive strength, 2,000 lb./sq.in.　　　　　PORETE MFG. CO.

Porex®. (*Supp.* I p. 191). Now marketed as MORAINE POROUS METAL®.
MORAINE PRODUCTS DIV. OF GENERAL MOTORS CORP.

Por-Lox®. (*HBMTN* p. 460). No longer available.
TRUSCON LABORATORIES

Porocel®. (*HBMTN* p. 460). Now mfg'd by MINERALS & CHEMICALS CORP. OF AMERICA, successor to ATTAPULGUS CLAY CO.

Poro-Cel®. (*HBMTN* p. 460). No longer available.
MINNESOTA MINING & MFG. CO.

Porofos®. (*HBMTN* p. 460 and *Supp.* I p. 191). No longer available.　　　GENERAL CHEMICAL DIV.,
ALLIED CHEMICAL & DYE CORP.

Potato Fix®. (*Supp.* I p. 191). Should have been listed as a registered trademark.
THOMPSON CHEMICALS CORP.

Potentox®. (*Supp.* I p. 192). No longer available.
GENERAL CHEMICAL DIV.,
ALLIED CHEMICAL & DYE CORP.

Potpot®. The trademark for a line of electrical controls and resistors. (Registration No. 628,177; Class 21; June 5, 1956).　　　CLAROSTAT MFG. CO.

Potters' Flint△. A ground flint of about 140 mesh used in ceramics for mixing with clay to reduce the firing and drying shrinkage and to prevent deformation.

Potting Compounds P-415, P-420, P-430, *and* **P-460.** *See* HELIX POTTING COMPOUNDS.

Pourite®. The trademark for a line of container spouts and containers, including large size pails, on which the same are mounted. (Registration No. 628,045; Class 2; June 5, 1956.)
CROWN CORK & SEAL CO.

Powdalator®. The trademark for a device and package for the administration of penicillin and sulfonamide powder by insufflation.　ABBOTT LABORATORIES

Power. A line of oak-tanned flat leather belting for power transmission. Available in thicknesses of $^{11}/_{64}''$ to $^{23}/_{64}''$ and in widths of 6″ to 7″.
J. E. RHOADS & SONS

Power-Cut®. A concentrated, fortified, cutting fluid and coolant base. Used for high-speed sawing and most other machinery operations. Used in dilutions of 1 part concentrate to 3 to 30 parts water.
DOALL CO.

Power-Pak[NE]. A dry-cleaning detergent for charged systems.　　　PENNSYLVANIA SALT MFG. CO.

Powminco Asbestos. A line of asbestos fibers for use as fillers in phenolic and other plastics, as a filter fiber in Gooch crucibles, and for numerous other industrial applications.　　POWHATAN MINING CO.

Prairie®. The trademark for a line of woven wire fence.　　　　UNITED STATES STEEL CORP.

Prasco® High Temperature. A diatomaceous earth and asbestos high-temp., steam-pipe covering and insulation block.　FIBREBOARD PAPER PRODUCTS CORP.

Pratt's Shot Gun Spray *or* **Dust.** An all-purpose garden insecticide and fungicide for use on fruits, vegetables and flowers. It contains MALATHION, METHOXYCHLOR, CAPTAN, and sulfur. It can be used as a dust or, dispersed in water, as a spray. It is non-toxic to animals.　　　　B. G. PRATT CO.

Pream®. A powdered cream product for use in place of liquid cream in coffee, soups, frostings, puddings and other food products. It is made essentially from fresh sweet cream and other milk products.
M & R DIETETIC LABORATORIES, INC.

Pre-Daylin®. The trademark for VITAMIN A, C and D drops for infants.　　ABBOTT LABORATORIES

Pre-mens®. A non-hormonal treatment for the prevention or relief of the premenstrual tension syndrome. It provides ammonium chloride for its diuretic action, homatropine methylbromide for its anti-spasmodic effect, the mildly stimulating effect of caffeine, and the dual effect of VITAMIN B complex in increasing the breakdown of estrogens by the liver and by increasing the utilization of protein. Also available as PRE-MENS WITH *d*-AMPHETAMINE for those patients in whom depression constitutes a prominent symptom which may be refractory to usual therapy.
PURDUE FREDERICK CO.

Premier®. The trademark for a line of spring wire and welding wire.　　UNITED STATES STEEL CORP.

Premium Producer®. The trademark for a line of fertilizers.
INTERNATIONAL MINERALS & CHEMICAL CORP.

Prenasup®. A pre-natal dietary supplement in tablet form used for therapy in care of pregnant and lactating women and adapted for use as a tonic and for the treatment of nausea.
CHICAGO PHARMACAL CO.

Prentalin[NR]. An aromatic specialty having a very tenacious flowery odor somewhat like the nerolidol-farnesol type. DOW CHEMICAL CO.

Prentice[NR]. A line of coated papers. KIMBERLY-CLARK CORP.

Prep-N-Cote®. An iron phosphate coating and cleaning product for use on steel. It imparts corrosion-resisting properties to metal surfaces, and provides an excellent paint bond. NEILSON CHEMICAL CO.

PrEpoxy Partingkote No. 832. A clear, liquid-type, mold-parting agent that dries at room temp. It is a ready-to-use, clear, transparent, film-forming plastic solution that is especially useful as a parting medium for room-temp. epoxy casting and laminating resins using plaster, wood, plastic, or metal molds. REZOLIN, INC.

Prep-Pik-L®. A cleaner for removing heavy rust and light scale from ferrous metal surfaces. NEILSON CHEMICAL CO.

Presdwood®. A line of building boards and panels made from "exploded" wood chips re-united under heat and pressure. Available in various types, including:
STANDARD PRESDWOOD®. Panels of medium density compared to other PRESD-WOOD products, but denser than most woods. They have excellent finishing qualities; and are suitable for interior use such as walls, ceilings, cabinets, etc., where extreme or fluctuating humidity conditions or exceptional hard usage may be encountered.
TEMPERED PRESDWOOD®. STANDARD PRESDWOOD impregnated with a tempering compound polymerized by baking. This treatment improves the durability, strength, and rigidity, and makes the product suitable for both interior and exterior applications.
BLACK TEMPERED PRESDWOOD®. Similar to TEMPERED PRESDWOOD but treated with a black dye at time of mfg. Not suitable for exterior use. MASONITE CORP.

Preserv-A-Post®. (*HBMTN* p. 462). Now a registered trademark. OSMOSE WOOD PRESERVING CO. OF AMERICA

Prestige 40 Greases. See SUN® PRESTIGE 40 GREASES.

Prestix Contact Cement. A liquid cement which, when brushed onto wood or metal and allowed to dry for 30 min. or longer, will bond instantly to materials such as plastic, fabric, leather, and paper. Used for contact decorating of fabric, plastic, or leather. ADHESIVE PRODUCTS CORP.

Presto Flavor Bases[NR]. A line of 20 concentrated soluble imitation fruit flavor bases for the mfg. of flavoring extracts. FLORASYNTH LABORATORIES, INC.

Pride®. A furniture polish composed of solvent, waxes and a cleaning agent. It removes oil, grease spilled food, etc., and leaves a protective wax finish without rubbing. Can be used on light or dark wood surfaces, leather top tables, metal furniture, stainless steel, etc. S. C. JOHNSON & SON

Primafresh®. Wax emulsions that reduce shrinkage and provide a high shine on a variety of vegetables and citrus fruits. They contain a balance of waxes and other ingredients that are easily applied to vegetables and fruits after washing. They are milky white in color when applied but dry to a bright, transparent luster without polishing. Effective on avacados, grapefruit, lemons, limes, oranges, apples, and other deciduous fruit. S. C. JOHNSON & SON

Primatube®. An electric blasting cap fastened inside a rigid cardboard tube. HERCULES POWDER CO.

Printable "TS" Ger-Pak®. A polyethylene film with the same low-temp. flexibility, toughness, moisture-vapor retention, and heat-sealing properties of GER-PAK® but with a surface which permits non-rub-off printing. Available in thicknesses from 0.005" to 0.008". *Uses:* As a packaging material for fruits and vegetables, other food products, and manufactured articles. GERING PRODUCTS INC.

Proco®. Trademark for a paper toilet seat cover in folded form. (*See also* CONSECO®). CONSOLIDATED COVER CO.

Product G. L. (*HBMTN* p. 463). No longer available; Company liquidated as of Oct. 1, 1955. GENERAL DRUG CO.

Produral®. (*Supp.* I p. 193). No longer available. SHARP & DOHME DIV., MERCK & CO.

Pro-Gen®. An animal feed supplement consisting of arsanilic acid. ABBOTT LABORATORIES

Prohexinol®. (*Supp.* I p. 193). No longer available. SHARP & DOHME DIV., MERCK & CO.

Proketuss®. A antihistaminic expectorant syrup for symptomatic control of productive and nonproductive cough. Each cc. (approx. 1 teaspoonful) contains 10 mg. methapyrilene hydrochloride, 15 mg. PROPADRINE® hydrochloride, 150 mg. potassium citrate, 15 mg. chloroform, and 1 mg. menthol. MERCK SHARP & DOHME

Proloid®. (*HBMTN* p. 464). Now a product of WARNER-CHILCOTT LABORATORIES, successor to THE MALTINE CO.

Promacetin®. Tablets of acetosulfone, Parke-Davis, for the treatment of leprosy. PARKE, DAVIS & CO.

Prosein®. An industrial soybean flour used in wallpaper coatings, adhesives, and felt-base products; as an extender for casein; and as an emulsion stabilizer. GLIDDEN CO.

Prospector®. The trademark for a line of fabrics made wholly or partially of cellulose derivatives. CELANESE CORP. OF AMERICA

Pro-Stat[NR]. A poultry coccidiostat consisting of dodecylamine salt of para-chlorophenylarsonic acid. ABBOTT LABORATORIES

Protective Coating #621. An unmodified epoxy resin coating for the protection of all types of materials against moisture permeability and chemical action. It has excellent adhesion, even without a primer coat; has high melting point; and remains flexible at both high and low temps. No baking is required: the coating cures dust free in 1 hr. at room temp., and reaches full cure in 6 hr. It resists solvents, acids, caustics, and boiling water. CARL H. BIGGS CO.

Pro-Tecto-Cape®. A line of welder's chrome leather safety clothing. EASTERN EQUIPMENT CO.

Protector®. The trademark for a line of wire fencing. UNITED STATES STEEL CORP.

Protedyn V-P 726. A nutritional supplement containing food protein concentrates high in heat liable amino acids known to be essential to life, plus 60 mg. of ribo-nucleic acid per capsule. VITAMIN PRODUCTS CO.

Protein Insecticide Baits #2 and #7[NR]. Liquids, rich in amino acids, which are used as baits or attractants in insect sprays. They contain, respectively, 31.2% and 29.0% amino acids and amino acid salts. Both contain 49% total solids and both contain sufficient sodium chloride to provide them with excellent keeping qualities. They may be applied by plane or ground spraying equipment. *Uses:* As effective attractants for the Mediterranean, oriental and melon fruit flies, the walnut husk fly, apple maggot, cherry fruit fly, housefly, Mexican fruit fly, mosquito and olive fly. A. E. STALEY MFG. CO.

Protektol®. (*HBMTN* p. 464). Now a registered trademark. INTERCHEMICAL CORP., FINISH DIV.

Protektuss®. (*Supp.* I p. 194). No longer available. SHARP & DOHME DIV., MERCK & CO.

Protex. (*Supp.* I p. 194). No longer available. IOWA SOAP CO.

Protex Gel W®. (*HBMTN* p. 465). No longer available. CIBA CO.

Protex-It. See PARKO® PROTEX-IT.

Protex Metallum®. A compound designed for cleaning bake pans. DIVERSEY CORP.

Protobore®. A Penick brand of Protoveratrine A & B. A mixture of the alkamine ester alkaloids, protoveratrine A and protoveratrine B, obtained from Veratrum Album or Veratrum Viride. *Uses:* For the treatment of high blood pressure and toxemia of pregnancy. S. B. PENICK & CO.

Protovan®. An imitation vanilla flavor. It imparts an aroma and taste similar to that of Bourbon beans. FLORASYNTH LABORATORIES, INC.

Protovanol "C"[NR]. A flavoring material for use as a replacement for coumarin. It has a flavored strength more than 50% greater than that of coumarin; and is soluble in alcohol, propylene, and essential oils. FLORASYNTH LABORATORIES, INC.

Protovanol "C" Powdered[NR]. A coumarin replacement for use as a flavoring material in dry mixes. It has about one-half the flavoring strength of coumarin fine crystals. FLORASYNTH LABORATORIES, INC.

Provinite[NR]. A barium-cadmium organic complex, supplied in a two-component system (PROVINITE A and PROVINITE B), which physically resembles CLARITE. It is used as a general-purpose, clear, heat and light stabilizer for vinyl resins for calendering, extrusion and dispersion resin applications. Its stabilizing characteristics are different from those of CLARITE in several respects. While its heat stability is comparable, PROVINITE is readily distinguished by its stronger anti-oxidant action, its excellent light stability, and its exceptional freedom from yellowing. It has slightly less lubricating action than CLARITE and it develops lower viscosity in plastisols. Furthermore, it has the best electrical properties of the barium-cadmium type stabilizers. Although its electrical properties are not equal to those of the standard lead stabilizers, PROVINITE is highly satisfactory for clear and brightly colored jacketing stocks for instrument wires, novelty Christmas tree wire, and other low requirement wire coatings. For most applications, from 0.75 to 2 parts of PROVINITE A (a soft white powder) and 1 part of PROVINITE B (a clear, straw-colored liquid) are used per 100 parts of resin. NATIONAL LEAD CO.

Prulose® Complex. A medicinal for the treatment of chronic constipation. Each PRULOSE COMPLEX tablet contains 130 mg. dehydrated prune concentrate, 390 mg. methylcellulose, and 1 mg. diacetylhydroxyphenylisatin. Each 15 cc. (approx. one tablespoonful) of PRULOSE COMPLEX liquid contains 3,370 mg. liquid prune concentrate (70% solids), 2 mg. diacetylhydroxyphenylisatin, and 750 mg. sodium carboxymethylcellulose. WARNER-CHILCOTT LABORATORIES

PSM-35®. A meat fat and vegetable shortening mfg'd specifically for use where a standard type shortening is required. This product has unusual stability in mixes such as rolls, biscuits, etc. ANDERSON, CLAYTON & CO. FOODS DIV.

PT Pine Tar Products[NR]. A line of pine products used in the rubber industry as softeners and solvents. Included in this line are the following: PT 800, a heavy pine tar; PT 600, a medium pine tar; PT 400, a light pine tar; PT 101, a pine tar oil; PT 67, a light pine oil; and PT 150, a pine solvent. GODFREY L. CABOT, INC.

Pumice△. A complex silicate material of volcanic origin. It is a gray-colored, light but hard, rough, porous material that is found chiefly in the Lipari islands and in the Greek achipelagos. In the United States it is produced in California and New Mexico. Powdered pumice is used as an abrasive for fine polishing; in the mfg. of metal polishes, scouring compounds, and soaps; and in plaster, lightweight concrete and puzzuolonic cement; in fireproofing and insulating compounds; and as a carrier for metal catalysts.

Puradrin®. A seed protectant for the control of fungus diseases and wireworms. It is a combination of PURASEED® and ALDRIN. Contains 2.5% phenyl amino cadmium dilactate, 2.5% phenyl mercury formamide, and 40% ALDRIN Technical. GALLOWHUR CHEMICAL CORP.

Puraseed®. A wettable powder which can be used either as a dust or slurry for the control of seedling blights, damping-off, and seed-borne diseases of wheat, oats, barley, rye, sorghum, and flax. Contains 6.25% anilinocadmium dilactate and 6.25% phenylmercury formamide. GALLOWHUR CHEMICAL CORP.

Puritine®. A 100%-active, non-sudsing, free-flowing, non-abrasive powder cleanser for use in cleaning floors, walls, windows, store fixtures, etc. J. I. HOLCOMB MFG. CO.

Purtone®. (*HBMTN* p. 468). No longer available.
WITCO CHEMICAL CO.

Py-Eze®. A meat fat-vegetable fat shortening designed and developed for tender, flaky pie crusts. It has a wide plastic range which makes it especially good for use in pies of all types.
ANDERSON, CLAYTON & CO. FOODS DIV.

Pylex®. An all-vegetable, fully hydrogenated shortening for use in baking, frying and pastry making.
ANDERSON, CLAYTON & CO. FOODS DIV.

Pyoktanin®. (*Supp.* I p. 195). No longer available.
SHARP & DOHME DIV., MERCK & CO.

Pyrasteel®. (*HBNTN* p. 468). No longer available. Company out of business.
CHICAGO STEEL FOUNDRY CO.

Pyrethrin. *See* PYRETHRUM△.

Pyrethrum△. *Also known as* DALMATION POWDER△ *and* PERSIAN INSECT POWDER△. An insecticidal material made by the grinding or extraction of the dried flowers of *Chrysanthemum cineraefolium*. However, the use of the ground flower has been largely replaced by that of extracts. The insecticidal components of the flower heads, amounting to 0.7–3%, are the esters of two acids and two ketones as follows:
PYRETHRIN I. Pyrethrolone ester of chrysanthemum monocarboxylic acid. $C_{21}H_{28}O_3$; mol.wt. 328.43. A viscous liquid that oxidizes readily and becomes inactive in the presence of air; practically insoluble in water; incompatible with alkalis; soluble in alcohol, petroleum ether, kerosene, carbon tetrachloride, ethylene dichloride, and nitromethane.
PYRETHRIN II. Pyrethrolone ester of chrysanthemum dicarboxylic acid monomethyl ester. $C_{22}H_{28}O_5$; mol.wt. 372.44. A viscous liquid with properties that are very similar to those of PYRETHRIN I.
CINERIN I. 3-(2-Butenyl)-4-methyl-2-oxo-3-cyclopenten-1-yl ester of chrysanthemum monocarboxylic acid. $C_{20}H_{28}O_3$; mol.wt. 316.42. A viscous liquid with properties similar to those of the Pyrethrins.
CINERIN II. 3-2(Butenyl)-4-methyl-2-oxo-3-cyclopenten-1-yl ester of chrysanthemum dicarboxylic acid monomethyl ester. $C_{21}H_{28}O_5$; mol.wt. 360.43. A viscous liquid similar in properties to the PYRETHRINS.
PYRETHRUM concentrates are prepared from the ground flowers by extracting with petroleum ether, ethylene dichloride, glacial acetic acid, methyl alcohol, or acetone. Considerable quantities of waxes and coloring matter are also extracted and must be removed by precipitation, adsorption on charcoal, or by cooling and filtration. The crude extracts may be reextracted with nitromethane, followed by adsorption on activated carbon, to produce concentrates containing 90–100% pyrethrins.
The constituents of pyrethrum flowers are unique among insecticides in the rapidity with which they paralyze insects affected. They are widely used in fly sprays, household insecticides, grain protectants, and for the control of certain agricultural pests.

Pyribenzamine®-Ephedrine Tablets. A combination of PYRIBENZAMINE® hydrochloride and ephedrine sulfate, for the relief of asthma and the control of certain cases of hay fever and other allergies not relieved by PYRIBENZAMINE® alone.
CIBA PHARMACEUTICAL PRODUCTS INC.

Pyribenzamine® Expectorant. A combination of four agents which have proved useful in alleviating or controlling severe cough, both allergic and nonallergic. Supplied as an orange-colored, peach-flavored liquid, each 4-ml. teaspoonful of which contains: 30 mg. PYRIBENZAMINE® citrate, 8.0 mg. codeine phosphate, 10 mg. ephedrine sulfate, and 80 mg. ammonium chloride. Also available without the codeine.
CIBA PHARMACEUTICAL PRODUCTS INC.

Pyribenzamine® Injectable Solution. A solution containing 2.5% PYRIBENZAMINE® hydrochloride for preventing blood transfusion reactions.
CIBA PHARMACEUTICAL PRODUCTS INC.

Pyribenzamine® Ointment and Cream. An ointment and a cream for effective relief in allergic skin conditions. Both contain 2% PYRIBENZAMINE® hydrochloride.
CIBA PHARMACEUTICAL PRODUCTS INC.

Pyricidin®. A brand of isonicotinic acid hydrazide. $C_6H_7N_3O$; mol.wt. 137.14. A medicinal used in the treatment of tuberculosis.
NEPERA CHEMICAL CO.

Pyroceramik®. A flame-sprayed coating that is resistant to high wind erosion and to temps. up to 1,700°F.
PYROCOTE CHEMICALS, INC.

Pyrocote-AC® (Anti-Corrosive). A general-purpose marine and industrial steel protective coating. It is a rubber-base coating with strong adhesion. Applied by flame spraying.
PYROCOTE CHEMICALS, INC.

Pyrocote-CR® (Chemical Resistant). A coating material for protection against hot caustic at 73% concentration and 140°F.
PYROCOTE CHEMICALS, INC.

Pyroflex® *and* **Pyroflex® Lacquer.** (*HBMTN* p. 470). The name PYROFLEX® is now a registered trademark.
MAURICE A. KNIGHT

Pyrolux Maroon[NB]. A maroon color pigment suitable for plastics, paints, enamels, etc. Especially noted for its good light resistance, good heat resistance, non-bleeding characteristics, and clean shade.
SHERWIN-WILLIAMS CO.

Pyrometalik®. An improved, economical metallizing compound that is applied in liquid form by flame spraying.
PYROCOTE CHEMICALS, INC.

PyroPanl®. A fire-resistant panel mfg'd with resins which extinguish themselves when the source of flame is removed. For use in areas governed by strict building and fire codes and where Underwriters' Laboratory label and/or Factory Mutual approval is required.
L-O-F GLASS FIBERS CO., CORRULUX DIV.

Pyropo®. The trademark for a line of insecticides.
S. B. PENICK & CO.

Pyrosan A[NB]. A renewable flame retardant finish for COTTON, WOOL, RAYON and LINEN.
LAUREL SOAP MFG. CO.

Pyroset® D *and* **N.D.** (*HBMTN* p. 470). No longer available.
AMERICAN CYANAMID CO.

Pyroset® DO Fire Retardant. An agent designed to impart a fire-retardant finish to COTTON, VISCOSE, RAYON and WOOL. The finish is durable to commercial dry cleaning.
AMERICAN CYANAMID CO.

Pyroset® Fire Retardant N-2. An agent designed to produce a durable, stiff, non-flammable finish on NYLON. Lightweight NYLON fabrics treated with PYROSET FIRE RETARDANT N-2 will pass the requirements of the Federal Flammable Fabrics Act.
AMERICAN CYANAMID CO.

Pyrote®. (*HBMTN* p. 470). No longer available.
GENERAL CHEMICAL DIV.,
ALLIED CHEMICAL & DYE CORP.

Pyrothene[NE]. A polyethylene coating for field application by a simplified flame spray technique. It is compounded with special additives which enable it to be melted and sprayed on surfaces heated to only 150–190°F. This results in adherent coatings with little chance of decomposition. The coatings are very inert to dilute and concentrated HCl and H_2SO_4 as well as to many other chemicals.
PYROCOTE CHEMICALS, INC.

Pyrox®. An arsenical insecticide for the control of leaf-eating insects. *See also* NICOTINE PYROX®.
AMERICAN AGRICULTURAL CHEMICAL CO.

Q

Q Cock Lubricant[NE]. A lubricant for plug-type valves. It is water repellent and resistant to some petroleum distillates and acids. Working range, 20°–130°F. Available in several densities.
KEYSTONE LUBRICATING CO.

Quadrol®. N,N,N',N'-tetrakis (2-hydroxypropyl) ethylenediamine used as a humectant, plasticizer, chelating agent and organic intermediate.
WYANDOTTE CHEMICALS CORP.,
MICHIGAN ALKALI DIV.

Quali-Kote®. An interior wall and ceiling paint that produces a soft, velvet smooth finish.
SHERWIN-WILLIAMS CO.

Quassia△. *Also known as* BITTERWOOD△ *and* BITTER ASH△. The wood of the Jamaica quassia tree, *Picroena excelsa*, and of the Surinam quassia tree, *Quassia amara*, of the West Indies and northern South America. The wood is light yellow, dense and tough, and is odorless but has an immensely bitter taste. An extract obtained from chips of this wood is used in formulating the poison used on flypaper.

Quebracho△. *Also known as* ASPIDOSPERMA△. The wood of the Quebracho Colorado, or red quebracho tree, *Aspidospera quebracho,* found along the west bank of the Parana and Paraguay rivers in Argentina and Paraguay. The wood contains about 25% tannin and is used principally as a source of QUEBRACHO extract, a hard resinous, brownish black material obtained by water extraction and used as a tanning material. The extract is also used in boiler compounds, and for the treatment of oil-well drilling muds.

Quelicin®. A muscle relaxant, succinylcholine chloride, in intravenous solution. ABBOTT LABORATORIES

Quertine®. An antihemorrhage preparation. A brand of quercetin for investigational use in the treatment of abnormal capillary fragility. Supplied in tablet form with and without the addition of ascorbic acid. ABBOTT LABORATORIES

Quick-Set. A patching material for concrete, wood block, asphalt, brick and stone floors. The area to be covered is first treated with QUICK-SET PRIMER and then the QUICK-SET is trowelled and tamped in place.
ACORN REFINING CO.

Quick-Set. *See* CASPRO® QUICK-SET.

Quickwall Primer. A fast-drying, odor-free, emulsion-type, pigmented primer and sealer. Dries in 2 hr. to very low luster with excellent hiding, holdout, and adhesion. Can be applied directly on unpainted plaster, dry wall, masonry, concrete and cinder block, wallboard, plasterboard, and similar surfaces, as well as over existing oil-base paints and tightly secured water-base paints. BARRELED SUNLIGHT PAINT CO.

Quillaja△. *Also known as* SOAP BARK△, PANAMA BARK△, CHINA BARK△, *and* MURILLO BARK△. The dried, inner bark of the tree *Quillaja saponaria* Molina, *Rosaceae,* of the west coast of South America. It is also cultivated in northern Hindustan. Composed of quillaic acid, quillajasaponin, sucrose and tannin. The bark, marketed in the form of brownish-white pieces produces suds in water. It is used in the mfg. of saponin; as a foam producer; in liquid shampoos; and in mineral water.

Quilt®. A line of rubber sundries—fountain syringes and combination syringes—for sale by druggists.
ARMSTRONG CORK CO.

Quilticel®. The trademark for a line of permanently-bonded batting made wholly or partially of cellulose derivative fibers. CELANESE CORP. OF AMERICA

Quinorgo®. High dielectric, heat-resistant sheet materials designed for use on electric equipment operating up to 130°C., the upper limit for Class "B" electrical insulation. They are made with a highly purified type of selected asbestos fiber, completely free of dust, and containing less than 0.5% free magnetic iron, bonded with selected organic materials. QUINORGO insulations may be readily combined with organic or inorganic reinforcing materials, such as CAMBRIC, glass cloth or completely organic electrical papers. Two types of the insulation are available:

QUINORGO No. 3,000 is an absorptive type, especially in the thinner calipers. This permits impregnation by many of the conventionally used oil-base or synthetic-base dielectrics.

QUINORGO No. 4,000 is a slightly modified version of No. 3,000 in that it contains about 3% of resin, which slightly reduces its absorption and penetration characteristics. No. 4,000 may be coated on one surface with shellac or varnish to permit bonding or cementing to it such mechanically or dielectrically stronger materials as inorganic woven cloth and mica or organic cellulose films and sheets.

QUINORGO insulations are available in either roll or tape form. The standard roll is 100 lb., 36" wide.
JOHNS-MANVILLE SALES CORP.

Quso. A pure white, soft, finely divided silica. It is an extremely lightweight, free-flowing powder, with a surface area of 100–260 sq. meters per gram. Bulk density, 3–13 lb./cu.ft.; thermal conductivity, 0.27 B.t.u.-in./hr. × sq.ft. × °F.; sp.gr., 1.99–2.10; refractive index, 1.46; pH, 6.3–9.3. *Uses:* As an ingredient of high-temp lubricating greases; as a flatting agent in varnishes and lacquers; as a thickening and bodying

agent in printing inks, pharmaceuticals and cosmetics and as a filler in resins and plastics.
PHILADELPHIA QUARTZ CO.

R

"R"^NR. A 200-mesh water-ground mica for use as a filler in the rubber industry.
FRANKLIN MINERAL PRODUCTS CO.

R-66^NR. (*Supp.* I p. 196). Now a product of THE BORDEN CO., CHEMICAL DIV., successor to PIONEER LATEX & CHEMICAL CO.

R-313. (*HBMTN* p. 472). No longer available.
WESTERN SEALANT CO.

Rachromate®. The trademark for a radioactive sodium chromate used in diagnostic procedures.
ABBOTT LABORATORIES

Racobal^NR. Radioactive cobalt for use as a radioactive source in radiation therapy.
ABBOTT LABORATORIES

RADA^NR. The tradename for a ROSIN AMINE D ACETATE.   HERCULES POWDER CO.

Radapon^NR. A weed killing composition containing DALAPON (d,d'-dichloropropionic acid) for industrial use.   DOW CHEMICAL CO.

Radio®. A group of acid dyestuffs for WOOL. They level well and give dyeings with good fastness to light and washing.   GENERAL DYESTUFF CO.

Radiocaps®. The trademark for capsules embodying radioactive substances for diagnosis and medical treatment.   ABBOTT LABORATORIES

Radul D®. (*HBMTN* p. 473). No longer available.
CIBA CO.

Ra-Grid® Heater Plates. An electrical heating plate made of a sheet of tempered rolled glass coated with metallic aluminum on one side. This aluminum coating is in the form of a grid to carry the current. It is approx. 0.001" thick and permanently fused to the glass in the process of mfg. The grid is protected from atmospheric corrosion and abrasion by a coat of heat-resisting enamel. The enamel also partially insulates the grid electrically from accidental contact or grounding. It has an operating temp. up to 300°F. Excellent for low-temp. heating and drying where uniform radiation is desirable over large areas; and for space heating. *Mfg'd by* BLUE RIDGE GLASS CORP.
Dist'd by LIBBEY-OWENS-FORD GLASS CO.

Raid®. The family name for a complete line of insecticides. Products include RAID HOUSE AND GARDEN BUG KILLER, RAID ROACH AND ANT KILLER, RAID INSECT SPRAY, and RAID MOTH PROOFER. RAID HOUSE AND GARDEN BUG KILLER is unique in that it can be used on plants as well as for control of household insects. RAID ROACH AND ANT KILLER is a residual-type product to be sprayed around baseboards, under sinks and cabinets, etc. It is available in both aerosol and liquid form. RAID INSECT SPRAY is a liquid space-spray-type insecticide which is effective on all kinds of insects. RAID MOTH PROOFER is an aerosol product which is safe for all fabrics. One application is effective for 12 months.   S. C. JOHNSON & SON

Raiflex. A high-pressure melamine-surfaced flexible laminate. *Uses:* For edge-banding on tables; to surface sides and fronts of furniture, cabinets, etc.; and to line the insides of china cabinets and other furniture items. Available in a variety of patterns and woodgrains.   REISS ASSOCIATES INC.

Railite. A high-pressure melamine-surfaced flexible laminate, 1/16" thick, for counter tops and table tops. Available in a variety of patterns and woodgrains.
REISS ASSOCIATES INC.

Rainbow®. The trademark for a line of fertilizers.
INTERNATIONAL MINERALS & CHEMICAL CORP.

Rain-Shield®. A water-repellent thermal-insulation-board finish.   ARMSTRONG CORK CO.

Rajah Brand®. The trademark for raw henna, etc.
S. B. PENICK & CO.

Ramie△. A fiber used for cordage and for making various course fabrics. It is obtained from the plant *Urtica nivea* found in countries with temperate climates, and from the plant *U. tenacissima*, found in countries with tropical climates. RAMIE fibers are much stronger than COTTON, FLAX or HEMP. They are not very flexible but they have a high wet-strength and are resistant to mildew. RAMIE yarn is used for making strong, wear-resistant canvas, in fire hose, and in marine gland packings.

Ranch Style^NR. A fireproof asbestos shingle made with an integral color and finished with a transparent plastic coating. Available in 4 different colors: Bolero Black, Cactus Green, Adobe Red, and Hacienda White.   NATIONAL GYPSUM CO.

Ranedare®. A line of highly durable water repellents for fabrics. RANEDARE C, designed specifically for cotton, is durable to repeated washings and dry-cleanings. RANEDARE R, designed specifically for synthetics, is used with crease-resistant and stabilizing resins to provide water repellancy, shrinkage control, and wrinkle- and spot-resistant effects. RANEDARE S, formulated with General Electric's silicone DRI-FILM®, is primarily for synthetics but also works well on cottons and woolens. It is exceptionally durable to dry cleaning, even on velvets and sheer fabrics.   METRO-ATLANTIC INC

Rantier^NR. An all-purpose, medium-duty alkaline cleaner for locomotives, trucks, and freight cars. *Uses:* For cleaning radiator and water jackets on Diesel locomotives; steam cleaning of trucks and miscellaneous parts, interior cleaning and deodorizing of freight cars; floor cleaning and deodorizing; and vat and filter cleaning. WYANDOTTE CHEMICALS CORP.,
J. B. FORD DIV.

Rape Oil△. *Same as* RAPESEED OIL△.

Rapeseed Oil△. *Also known as* RAPE OIL△ *and* COLZA OIL△. An oil expressed from the seed of a species of the turnip, *Brassica Campestris*, grown in Europe, India, Canada, and Argentina. It is a pale yellow, rather viscid liquid composed of palmitic, oleic, lanoleic and stearic acids, and from 43 to 50% of erusic or brassidic acid, $C_{22}H_{42}O_2$. Sp.gr. 0.915; iodine no. 97–105; saponification no. 170–177; flash point, 455°F.; soluble in chloroform, ether, and carbon disulfide. *Uses:* As an edible oil; as a lubricant; in the mfg.

of margarine, rubber substitutes, cutting oils, quenching oils, soft soaps; for oiling woolens; etc.

Rapidogen®. A line of dyestuffs containing a stabilized diazotized organic base and a naphthol AS type of developer, which, when printed on COTTON and RAYON and aged in a steam and acid atmosphere or in neutral steam in the presence of an acid-splitting substance, couple to form an insoluble azo dyestuff on the fiber. GENERAL DYESTUFF CO.

Ratany△. Same as RHATANY△.

Rat-A-Way Bait[NB]. A ready-to-use bait for killing rats and mice. Contains 0.025% WARFARIN, 3-(alpha-acetonylbenzyl) 4-hydroxycoumarin.
MILLER CHEMICAL & FERTILIZER CORP.

Rat-A-Way Concentrate[NB]. A rat and mouse killer containing 0.5% WARFARIN, 3-(alpha-acetonylbenzyl) 4-hydroxycoumarin. Four oz. of RAT-A-WAY CONCENTRATE makes 5 lb. of bait.
MILLER CHEMICAL & FERTILIZER CORP.

Ratmaster[NB]. (*HBMTN* p. 474). No longer available. MICHIGAN CHEMICAL CO.

Rattan△. The long slender stem of the palm *Calamus rotang* and a number of other species grown in Ceylon, Malaya, and Indo China. The stems are tough, flexible, strong and durable and are used to make canes, umbrella handles, furniture, etc. Split RATTAN is used for weaving baskets, car seats, etc; for whips, heavy cordage, etc.

Rauwicon[NB]. A hypotensive tranquillizer used in the treatment of hypertension and anxiety and tension states. Supplied in the form of tablets, containing 50 mg. or 100 mg. of alkaloids that are prepared from powdered whole root of *Rauwolfia serpentina*.
CONSOLIDATED MIDLAND CORP.

Raydex®. A powdered or granular detergent composition for use in dairy and other food-processing plants. PENNSYLVANIA SALT MFG. CO.

Raygomm®. A modified starch used as a pure finish for textile fabrics, or used in conjunction with urea-formaldehyde and melamine-formaldehyde resins.
STEIN, HALL & CO.

Raylite[NB]. A rubber-latex, interior, flat paint. Dries in about 30 min. Very abrasion resistant; can be scrubbed after 3 days. Excellent for basement walls or playrooms subject to hard usage.
CALIFORNIA STUCCO PRODUCTS OF N. E., INC.

Rayotint[NB]. An alkyd-latex, interior, flat paint for one-coat coverage, especially on rough or irregular surfaces such as masonry block. Available in light pastel colors only.
CALIFORNIA STUCCO PRODUCTS OF N. E., INC.

R-B-H Fast Yellow[NB]. A line of organic pigment dispersions for coloring cellulose acetate and other coating materials. Available in the following grades:

FAST YELLOW P6 E151. Pigment, 30%; GLYPTAL® 1247, 20%; aromatic thinner, 50%.

FAST YELLOW P661 E922. Pigment, 20%; VINYLITE® VYHH, 20%; methyl ethyl ketone, 60%.

FAST YELLOW P944 E243. Pigment, 25%; ¼ sec. nitrocellulose, 20%; ethyl acetate, 25%; toluol, 25%; tricresyl phosphate, 5%.
R-B-H DISPERSIONS,
DIV. OF INTERCHEMICAL CORP.

RC Plasticizer BD-8[NB]. A plasticizer for synthetic resins and rubbers, etc. Butanediol dicaprylate. $(CH_2)_2(CH_2OCOC_7H_{15})_2$; mol.wt. 342. A clear liquid with a mild characteristic odor; sp.gr. 0.929; acid no. 1.0; distillation range (5 mm. Hg), 211°–222°C.; flash point, 390°F.; freezing point, 10.5°C.; soluble in most organic solvents; compatible with most synthetic and natural resins and rubbers except water-soluble polymers. RUBBER CORP. OF AMERICA

RC Plasticizer E-S[NB]. An epoxidized triester with an average mol.wt. of 975. It is an ester-type plasticizer characterized by its excellent heat stability and solvation rate and low migration. A liquid with a mild odor; sp.gr. 0.994; acid no. 1.2; saponification no. 129; epoxy oxygen content, 6.1%; soluble in most organic solvents; incompletely soluble in ethyl alcohol and certain glycols; compatible with most synthetic and natural resins and rubbers except water-soluble polymers and some cellulose esters.
RUBBER CORP. OF AMERICA

RC Plasticizer O-16[NB]. A plasticizer for polyvinyl chloride compositions and other vinyls, including organosols and plastisols. Chemically it is iso-octyl palmitate. $C_{15}H_{31}COOC_8H_{17}$; mol.wt. 368. A clear liquid with a mild odor; sp.gr. 0.863; distillation range (5 mm. Hg), 218–235°C.; flash point, 415°C.; acid no. 0.03; soluble in most organic solvents; compatible with most synthetic and natural resins and rubbers except water-soluble polymers. As a secondary plasticizer in polyvinyl chloride compositions, it adds antiblocking properties and increases the heat stability by functioning as an internal lubricant; in organosols and plastisols it reduces initial viscosity and tends to increase the viscosity stability on storage. It can also be used as a plasticizer for nitrocellulose and synthetic rubbers. RUBBER CORP. OF AMERICA

RC Plasticizer TG-8[NB]. A solvent-type plasticizer. An ester of triethylene glycol and a mixture of fatty acids, in which caprylic acid predominates. Triethylene glycol dicaprylate. $(CH_2OCH_2)_2(CH_2OCOC_7H_{15})_2$; av. mol.wt. 406; a clear liquid with a mild characteristic odor; sp.gr. 0.973; distillation range (5 mm. Hg), 212°–254°C.; acid no. 1.0; flash point, 400°F.; freezing point, −3°C.; soluble in most organic solvents; compatible with most synthetic and natural resins and rubbers except water-soluble polymers. *Uses:* As a plasticizer for synthetic resins, plastisols, etc.; and as a mild lubricant in lacquers, rubbers, etc.
RUBBER CORP. OF AMERICA

RC Plasticizer TG-9[NB]. A plasticizer for synthetic resins, rubbers, etc. Triethylene glycol dipelargonate. The diester of triethylene glycol and pelargonic acid. $(CH_2OCH_2)(CH_2OCOC_8H_{17})_2$; av. mol.wt. 438. A clear liquid with a mild characteristic odor; sp.gr. 0.964; acid no. 1.0; distillation range (5 mm. Hg), 225°–255°C.; flash point, 420°F.; freezing point, +1° to −4°C.; soluble in most organic solvents; compatible with most synthetic and natural resins and rubbers except water-soluble polymers.
RUBBER CORP. OF AMERICA

RC Polymeric BGA[NE]. A poly-adipate with a mol. wt. of about 2,500. It is a primary, high-molecular-weight plasticizer for polyvinyl chloride used in compounds for electrical tapes, metal laminates, surgical tubing, gaskets, non-marring film and sheeting, etc. It is a clear viscous liquid with a very mild odor. Sp.gr. 1.108; saponification no. 515; flash point (C.O.C.), 555°F.; soluble in most organic solvents; incompletely soluble in ethyl alcohol, and certain glycols; compatible with most synthetic and natural resins and rubbers except water-soluble polymers, polystyrene, and some cellulose esters.
RUBBER CORP. OF AMERICA

Red Acaroid△. *Also known as* RED GUM△ *and* GRASS TREE GUM△. An ACAROID RESIN obtained from *X. Australis* and about 15 other species of the tree of southeastern Australia.

Reddon[NE]. A brush killing composition containing 2,4,5-trichlorophenoxyacetic acid, for farm use.
DOW CHEMICAL CO.

Reddy Core Paste[NE]. A conventional-type core paste in convenient, ready-to-use form. It is very economical and efficient. M. A. BELL CO.

Red-E-To-Use®. (*Supp.* I p. 199). No longer available. HANSON-VAN WINKLE-MUNNING CO.

Red Gum△. *Same as* RED ACAROID△.

Red H®. A series of slow permissible explosives particularly adapted for the production of coarse coal.
HERCULES POWDER CO.

Red Hoop®. The trademark for a line of galvanized nails. UNITED STATES STEEL CORP.

Redigram®. (*Supp.* I p. 199). No longer available.
SHARP & DOHME DIV., MERCK & CO.

Redilev®. (*Supp.* I p. 199). No longer available.
SHARP & DOHME DIV., MERCK & CO.

Reditrin[NE]. Capsules containing hemopoietic agents effective in the treatment of commonly occurring anemias. Used in the treatment of hypochromic microcytic anemia, in the management of the macrocytic anemia of pregnancy, nutritional macrocytic anemia, and tropical and nontropical sprue. Each capsule contains ½ U.S.P. oral units of VITAMIN B$_{12}$ with intrinsic factor concentrate, 10 mcg. crystalline VITAMIN B$_{12}$, 300 mg. ferrous sulfate, 50 mg. ascorbic acid, 1 mg. folic acid, 2 mg. thiamine mononitrate, 2 mg. riboflavin, 1 mg. pyridoxine hydrochloride, 10 mg. niacinamide, 50 mg. liver fraction 2 N.F., and 50 mg. desiccated stomach. MERCK SHARP & DOHME

Redium Selenium[NE]. A pure grade of metallic selenium used in the glass industry as a decolorizer, and in ruby glass. R. T. VANDERBILT CO.

Red Label. *See* AIRKEM® RED LABEL.

Red Label Gym Finish[NE]. An oleo-resinous material used as a top finish on wood floors. It resists rubber burns, marring, and scuffing, and withstands the action of alkaline cleaners. S. C. JOHNSON & SON

Red Label Mist. *See* Airkem® RED LABEL MIST.

Redo®. (*HBMTN* p. 476). Now mfg'd by GOODALL-SANFORD, INC., successor to GOODALL FABRICS, INC.

Redratsquill®. A RED SQUILL rat and mouse poison.
S. B. PENICK & CO.

Red Skin. (*HBMTN* p. 476). No longer available.
DENNIS CHEMICAL CO.

Red Squill△. A rat poison. It is a powdered material prepared from the bulbs of the plant *Urginea (Scilla) maritima*. It is less toxic to humans than some of the other rat poisons; dogs and cats readily vomit it; fowls tolerate large quantities of this material. Its activity as a rat poison is probably due to the inability of rodents to vomit.

Red Tag®. The trademark for chain-link fencing, lawn fencing, picket fencing, trellises, fence posts and gates; wire screen cloth, wire mesh partitions and window guards; wire baskets, flexible steel mats and conveyor belting. UNITED STATES STEEL CORP., AMERICAN STEEL & WIRE DIV., CYCLONE FENCE DEPT.

Red Tiger[NE]. (*HBMTN* p. 477). No longer available. BETHLEHEM STEEL CO.

Red Wing®. Ground refined sulfur, N.F.
OLIN MATHIESON CHEMICAL CORP.

Red Writing Hood. *See* THE RED WRITING HOOD®.

Ree-Drape®. (*Supp.* I p. 199). Now a registered trademark. RIVERSIDE MFG. CO.

Refax®. A low-alloy, nickel-chromium cast iron which is resistant to oxidation at the high operating temps. encountered in the melting of metals. *Use:* In the form of pots, for melting and holding applications in aluminum foundries, die-casting operations, battery plants, and smelting works.
ACF INDUSTRIES, INC.

Refined Vegetable Wax #717[NE]. (*HBMTN* p. 478). No longer being mfg'd by INNIS, SPEIDEN & CO.

Refined Wax #648A[NE]. (*HBMTN* p. 478). No longer being mfg'd by INNIS, SPEIDEN & CO.

Reflex-Sol[NE]. An aluminum paint designed for brush or spray application on metal, concrete, or built-up roofs. It provides a heat-reflective as well as a protective surface. UPCO CO.

Reflin Pipe. Pipe and fittings made from FIBERGLAS®-reinforced polyester resin. Pipe is available in sizes from 4″ to 12″ o.d., and fittings include reducers, laterals, tees, elbows and flanges. Working pressure, 200 lb./sq.in.; bursting pressure 1,000 lb./sq.in. It is highly resistant to most salts, acids, hydrocarbons, moisture, and soil solutions. Sp.gr. 1.55; tensile strength, 14,000 lb./sq.in.; compressive strength, 22,000 lb./sq.in.; water absorption (24 hr.), 0.3%; thermal conductivity, 1.5 B.t.u.-inch/hr. $\times$ sq.ft. $\times$ °F. *Uses:* As piping in the chemical, petroleum, and mining industries; food and beverage plants; for water service; and for irrigation purposes. REFLIN CO.

Refracto. *See* HY-TEMP REFRACTO[NE].

Regal®. The trademark for henna leaves.
S. B. PENICK & CO.

Regal® Cap Sheet. A rag-felt roofing cap sheet, furnished in 1-sq. rolls (108 sq.ft.), 36″ wide, and weighing 43 lb. JOHNS-MANVILLE SALES CORP.

Regal® Roof Coating. A smooth-bodied, asphalt coating for roofs which have started to dry out. It is also used for preventing rust and preserving metal roofs, as a surface finish on J-M BONDED BUILT-UP ROOFS, and as a valuable adjunct in coating the valley flashings of shingle roofs.
JOHNS-MANVILLE SALES CORP.

Reginol HNP[NR]. This 100%-active nonionic product for all textile detergency, wetting and penetrating applications where stability to acids, alkalies, salt and heat is a requirement. It is also an excellent emulsifier for natural oils, greases, and solvents, and finds a wide variety of uses in the textile, metal-cleaning and formulated-detergent fields.
HART PRODUCTS CORP.

Regitine®. A potent antiadrenergic drug for the diagnosis and therapy of pheochromocytoma, a tumor which causes sustained or paroxysmal hypertension.
CIBA PHARMACEUTICAL PRODUCTS INC.

Re-juv-nal®. (*HBMTN* p. 479). No longer available.
HILLYARD CHEMICAL CO.

Release Agent "G"[NR]. An agent developed to readily free foundry core mixes of core and molding sand in the hoppers and during the molding and core-making operations. Only ½ lb. or less is required per 100 lb. of sand. Can also be used in molding of synthetic plastics.
M. A. BELL CO.

Reliance®. The trademark for a line of electrical wire and cable.
UNITED STATES STEEL CORP.

Relion®. A caustic-base, bottle-washing compound. It quickly and effectively removes dried-on chocolate, orange pulp, etc., and it drains free.
DIVERSEY CORP.

Remox®. A rare earth oxide composition for use in metallurgy.
MALLINCKRODT CHEMICAL WORKS

Renex®. (*Supp.* I p. 200). This product is also mfg'd in England, and the trademark is also registered in that country.
ATLAS POWDER CO.
HONEYWILL-ATLAS, LTD.

Renovator. (Trademark registration pending). A light-greenish liquid solvent which forms a milky emulsion when mixed with water. Particularly safe on paints, lacquers, and enamels. *Use:* For washing painted surfaces such as walls and machinery.
OAKITE PRODUCTS, INC.

Rep®. A concentrated liquid synthetic detergent, with sustained sudsing action, for cleaning floors. It is particularly useful for removing wax.
J. I. HOLCOMB MFG. CO.

Repeator Hand Cleanser. See PAX® REPEATOR HAND CLEANSER.

Resiloid 250[NR]. A synthetic textile-sizing agent, especially suitable for ACETATE, RAYON, ORLON and similar yarns. No additives, softeners, or penetrants are required with this size.
COLLOIDS, INC.

Resiloid B[NR]. A polyvinyl alcohol resin, textile finishing agent. It is compatible with other resins, starches, and gums. Can be insolubilized with usual polyvinyl alcohol setters or with melamine or urea formaldehyde resins to produce crisp and springy finishes.
COLLOIDS, INC.

Resin 107[NR]. A 55% polyvinyl acetate emulsion for stiffening of fabrics such as COTTONS, NYLONS and LINENS.
JERSEY STATE CHEMICAL CO.

Resin 300[NR]. A modified urea-formaldehyde resin for use in textile finishing. It imparts a crisp finish of excellent dimensional stability. *Use:* For crushproofing NYLON, DACRON and ORLON.
JERSEY STATE CHEMICAL CO.

Resin 529®. An especially refined odor- and taste-free version of RESIN 510® (*HBMTN* p. 483). It is a high melting resin mined in Utah where it is found in clear yellowish flakes as a 2% to 5% component in certain large coal deposits. It is recovered by flotation and purified by solvent extraction. *Use:* Especially in rubber compounds and sealants used in connection with food packaging.
R-B-H DISPERSIONS,
DIV. OF INTERCHEMICAL CORP.

Resin-Glas. A clear, lightweight, thermoplastic cast polymethyl methacrylate sheet in ultra-violet and non-ultra-violet grades. It is shatter- and heat-resisting; and it can be fabricated by machining, pressure forming, or vacuum drawing. *Uses:* For aircraft canopies and blisters, signs and displays, etc.
REX CORP.

Resin MS2. An alicylic ketone resin for enamels, lacquers, vinyls, plastisols, and textile finishes. It is a pale yellow, brittle solid; color, X; acid no., practically zero; softening point (ball & ring), 85–95°C.; sp.gr., 1.078. Soluble in many solvents including mineral spirits, benzene, toluene, xylene, acetone, methyl isobutyl ketone, ethyl acetate, aliphatic alcohols, dipentene, ethers, and chlorinated hydrocarbons; compatible with cellulose nitrate, ethyl cellulose, vinyl chloride resins, polystyrene, epoxide resins, alkyd resins, urea-formaldehyde resins, shellac, and many other resins.
Mfg'd by HOWARDS & SONS (CANADA) LTD.
Sole U. S. Distributor, BAIRD CHEMICAL CORP.

Resin Release N. A mold-release agent for releasing plastic parts from all types of molds including metal and plastic. It can be used with all types of plastics—phenolic, polyester, epoxy, alkyd, urea, melamine, etc. It can also be used as a lubricant for guide rods on presses and other parts subjected to high temp. It contains no silicone, yet melts at a temp. far above that necessary for processing plastic products.
SPECIALTY PRODUCTS CO.

Resin RF *and* **Resin 112**[NR]. Alkyd resins for use as ribbon finishes in the textile industry. They impart a crisp, firm hand to ACETATE SATINS without mark-off or decrease in original luster.
JERSEY STATE CHEMICAL CO.

Resin Syrup J S[NR]. A textile finishing agent consisting of a high solids urea-formaldehyde polymer, used for imparting a desirable firm hand to suitings.
JERSEY STATE CHEMICAL CO.

Resistal-Weld®. A line of plastic bags.
BEMIS BROTHERS BAG CO.

Resiston[NR]. A preparation of VITAMIN B complex for the prophylaxis and treatment of VITAMIN B complex deficiencies in children and in adults. Sup-

plied in palatable, sugar-coated tablets and capsules, and in liquid form for parenteral use.
CONSOLIDATED MIDLAND CO.

Resiweld Adhesives. A line of structural adhesives based on epoxy resins. They will bond almost any type of material to itself or to any other material. They give high-strength bonds with metals, including aluminum, steel, bronze, brass, copper, magnesium, lead, iron, and titanium; and with non-metals such as wood, glass, plastics, ceramics, rubber, concrete, and leather. The bonds are resistant to water, chemicals, and solvents; have high strength and excellent impact and thermal shock resistance; have negligible shrinkage; and do not weaken or become brittle with age. RESWELD ADHESIVES No. 1 and 2 are two-component systems (separate resin and hardener) with a pot life of 1–4 hr. after mixing; RESWELD ADHESIVES No. 101 and 102 are one-component systems with a pot life of over 6 months.
H. B. FULLER CO.

Resizet®. A liquid enzymic compound used for adding luster, body, and weight to fabric garments.
TAKAMINE LABORATORIES

Reslube[NB]. A NYLON hosiery finish consisting of a combination of a modified resin emulsion and a lubricative dulling emulsion. It gives the hose a full bodied, crisp, silk-like hand, imparts remarkable resiliency and shape retention, gives smooth uniform dulling, allows for easy boarding, and improves snag resistance.
FABRIC CHEMICALS CO.

Res-N-Dex[NB]. A combination resin and dextrine remoistening gum for the front seal of envelopes.
PAISLEY PRODUCTS INC.

Res-N-Seal[NB]. A resin remoistening gum for envelope front seals. It is a vinyl polymer resin emulsion. It has good nonblocking properties; and retains remoistening and adhesive qualities when subjected to engraving and thermographic printing.
PAISLEY PRODUCTS INC.

Resodor®. A trademark for a series of fragrant additives for use in plastics.
SINDAR CORP.

Resoflex® R-296. A resinous, non-volatile, non-migrating plasticizer for polyvinyl acetate. Has excellent resistance to oils, fats, greases, gasoline; and excellent flexibility and toughness.
CAMBRIDGE INDUSTRIES CO.

Resoform®. The trademark for: (1) a group of pigments; (2) water-soluble dyes; (3) spirit-soluble dyes; and (4) hydrocarbon-soluble dyes standardized for coloring plastics.
GENERAL DYESTUFF CO.

Resolite. Shatterproof translucent panels molded from polyester resins reinforced with OWENS-CORNING FIBERGLAS mat. Available either flat or corrugated, and in standard semi-clear, pale green and ice blue colors, as well as colors for decorative purposes. Also available as a security panel, composed of polyester resins, FIBERGLAS, and a sheet of flat, expanded metal, for use where maximum impact resistance is desired. *Uses:* As structural panels for roofs and walls where it is desired to let daylight into buildings or rooms; and for glazing factory and shop windows.
RESOLITE CORP.

Resolite Fire-Snuf®. Panels similar to regular RESOLITE (*see above*) but made with special resins which permit the panels to be used where codes call for a flame spread rating below 75 or where fire hazard is severe.
RESOLITE CORP.

Restfoam®. The trademark for latex foam in the form of sheets and unfinished molded shapes, and foam rubber backed on one side with fabric, plastic, or other material. *Uses:* For mattresses, cushions, upholstery, etc. The trademark RESTFOAM is also registered in Canada and Cuba.
HEWITT-ROBINS INC.

Resthane[NB]. (*Supp.* I p. 201). This product, a polyurethane foam in the form of sheets and unfinished molded shapes, is now marketed under the trade name of HEWITEX[NB].
HEWITT-ROBINS INC.

Restocrat®. The trademark for a line of reclining chairs.
T. BAUMRITTER CO.

Restolic[NB]. Medicinal tablets, each of which contains 30 mg. mannitol hexanitrate, 0.1 mg. reserpine, and 20 mg. rutin. *Use:* In the treatment of essential hypertension to decrease blood pressure and for effective sedation.
MERCK SHARP & DOHME

Rest-Ore-Nap®. (*HBMTN* p. 484). No longer available.
NOPCO CHEMICAL CO.

Retarder PD[NB]. The proprietary name for a modified phthalic anhydride. Effective as a retardant for premature cure or setup during processing of rubber compounds. Normally used in combination with thiazole or mixtures of thiazole-guanidine accelerators.
AMERICAN CYANAMID CO.

Retinol△. Same as ROSIN OIL△.

Rexobase. A concentrated emulsifier for kerosene and VARSOL. One part base and four parts kerosene (or VARSOL) mix together to give a bright soluble oil which will not separate on storing. This mixture is used as a scouring agent for removing obstinate oil and grease from RAYON, NYLON, and ACETATE fabrics.
EMKAY CHEMICAL CO.

Rexobase GA[NB]. A synthetic detergent and concentrated emulsifier for kerosene and VARSOL® (*HBMTN* p. 599). One part REXOBASE GA and four parts kerosene (or VARSOL) are mixed to give a bright soluble oil which will not separate on storing. This mixture is used as a scouring agent for removing obstinate oil and grease in RAYON, NYLON, and ACETATE fabrics. It is particularly useful where acid conditions prevail.
EMKAY CHEMICAL CO.

Rexobase TR-3. A bright oil, easy to apply. When mixed with pine oil and allied solvents it is an efficient grease and oil remover for woolen blankets and piece goods.
EMKAY CHEMICAL CO.

Rexobase XX. A 100%-active emulsifier for VARSOL or STODDARD SOLVENT. Five gal., mixed with 50 gal. solvent in a dry drum, forms a bright soluble oil. This mixture is used in water solution for the removal of stubborn soil and grease in the textile industry.
EMKAY CHEMICAL CO.

Rexobond. A resin-gum prepared textile weighter and body builder finish compatible with softeners, blues, etc. It is an excellent lining finish.
EMKAY CHEMICAL CO.

Rexobond 46 Concentrate. A highly active, non-slip textile finish in liquid form. It easily disperses in water; imparts non-slip without stiffness; is compatible with dye-fixing agents, cationic softeners, weighters, etc. EMKAY CHEMICAL CO.

Rexobond E-12[NR]. A viscous emulsion of thermoplastic resins based on polyvinyl acetate. It imparts, to textiles, a stiff, flexible hand which is highly resistant to washing. Compatible with softeners, starches and similar materials. Requires no curing. EMKAY CHEMICAL CO.

Rexobond E-24, E-36, E-48, E-60 and E-72[NR]. A series of modified thermoplastic resins designed to give a flexible bodied finish to textiles. They reduce "pilling" of DACRON and DACRON-WOOL mixtures; are highly resistant to abrasion and washing; and require no curing. EMKAY CHEMICAL CO.

Rexobond N-8. A water-dispersed NYLON resin for use in textile finishing. It improves resistance to abrasion and imparts a NYLON coating on other fibers. EMKAY CHEMICAL CO.

Rexoclean. A complete textile scouring agent composed of synthetic detergents, terpenes, and solvents. Contains 85% active matter. Used as a cleaner for stubborn oil and grease stains, and for removal of NYLON warp size. EMKAY CHEMICAL CO.

Rexodull CNY[NR]. A homogenized dispersion of pigments combined in a cationic resin carrier and binder. May be applied on padder or quetsch or exhausted from dye bath. This textile finish is durable, resistant to washing, and resistant to yellowing from heat and storage. EMKAY CHEMICAL CO.

Rexodull DK. A formulation of dispersed pigments for use as a dark shade textile duller. EMKAY CHEMICAL CO.

Rexodull M. A textile dulling agent suitable for both light and dark shades. It is compatible with waxes, gums and softeners. EMKAY CHEMICAL CO.

Rexodull XX. A blended formulation of titanium dioxides and lithopone pigments. Readily mixes with gums, soluble waxes, hydrosulfite, albumen, and printing gums. Used as a textile dulling agent. EMKAY CHEMICAL CO.

Rexofos. A blend of phosphate powders for water softening and conditioning. Used in the textile industry. EMKAY CHEMICAL CO.

Rexogel. A purified gelatin-base product used as a stiff textile finish that requires no curing. EMKAY CHEMICAL CO.

Rexogum. A clear, transparent gum-resin mixture, soluble in warm water, compatible with softening agents. Used as an all-round textile weighter and body builder. EMKAY CHEMICAL CO.

Rexole CJ. A glycerin substitute used for textile finishing. It is a clear plasticizer for gelatins and gums, used to prevent dusting and powdering. EMKAY CHEMICAL CO.

Rexole ESC. An amino complex recommended as a scroop finish for silk skeins and fabrics. EMKAY CHEMICAL CO.

Rexole GR. A high gravity liquid product with excellent moisture-retaining properties. It is an economical substitute for glycerin in plasticizing glues and gelatins, for use in the paper trade and allied industries. EMKAY CHEMICAL CO.

Rexole MC-2. A sulfonated blend of vegetable oils used in throwing and in textile sizing as a glue or gelatin plasticizer. EMKAY CHEMICAL CO.

Rexole TW. A highly efficient oil softener used for paper products. EMKAY CHEMICAL CO.

Rexoloid. A clear, water-soluble resin textile finish that requires no curing. Used in the finishing of ACETATE ribbon materials. It imparts a heavy bodied finish giving a high luster; and will not mark off. EMKAY CHEMICAL CO.

Rexolube. A textile lubricant and chafe eliminator, stable in acid. Used in the diazotizing bath to eliminate chafes on developed black and navy colors. EMKAY CHEMICAL CO.

Rexonite D. A protein-resin mixture used as a heavy finish for RAYON and ACETATE fabrics. It will not mark off or dust off when a high concentration of finish is used with REXOWAX CNN. EMKAY CHEMICAL CO.

Rexopene. An alkyl aryl sulfonate, in liquid form, with excellent wetting and leveling properties. Used in the textile industry as a general wetting and dye leveling agent, highly resistant to acid solutions. It is also an excellent carbonizing wetting agent. EMKAY CHEMICAL CO.

Rexopon E. An amide amino condensate, synthetic detergent in popular strength. It is an efficient after wash for prints in the textile industry. EMKAY CHEMICAL CO.

Rexopon V. A synthetic detergent, in paste form, with excellent foaming properties. Retains its foam for extended periods when used as a boil-off compound in Hinnekens and other types of continuous boil-off machines. It is an excellent after wash for vats and naphthols; and an excellent scour for synthetic fabrics in jigs and boxes. EMKAY CHEMICAL CO.

Rexoscour. A solvent-soap detergent widely used for scouring RAYON, ACETATE, and NYLON fabrics in jigs, boxes and continuous machines. EMKAY CHEMICAL CO.

Rexoslip. An amino complex resin mixture used to impart weight and non-slip properties to RAYON and ACETATE fabrics. It withstands aging and high temp. drying without discoloration. It is also an excellent satin finish. EMKAY CHEMICAL CO.

Rexoslip Concentrate. A double-strength product which gives weight and non-slip properties to RAYON and ACETATE fabrics. EMKAY CHEMICAL CO.

Rexosolve. A blend of petroleum solvents and terpenes, soluble in water. Used to cleanse oil or grease soils, dirty knots, etc., in the textile industry. EMKAY CHEMICAL CO.

Rexosolve 150. A blend of terpenes and petroleum solvents easily dispersible in water. It contains 100%-active matter, and in combination with REXOPON V

has become part of a popular process for the cleaning of dirty knots and obstinate soil in NYLON and NYLON-and-DACRON combination fabrics.
EMKAY CHEMICAL CO.

Rexosolve CR. An emulsified blend of solvents and cresylic acid. Used as an assistant in WOOL scouring for removing mineral oils. EMKAY CHEMICAL CO.

Rexosolve EP[NR]. A highly efficient mixture of synthetic detergents and concentrated solvents designed for cleaning textiles. It is stable under acid, neutral and alkaline conditions, and has excellent penetrating properties. EMKAY CHEMICAL CO.

Rexosolve GA[NR]. A mixture of liquid detergents and aliphatic solvents that is stable in acid solutions. It is recommended as a solvent wash for cleaning oil and grease soils from textiles, particularly when oxalic acid or ammonium biflouride must be used in the same procedure or when an acid bath must follow this treatment directly without an intermediate rinse.
EMKAY CHEMICAL CO.

Rexosolve HP. A concentrated cleaner containing soluble high-flash solvents; 100% active. Used for the removal of stubborn tars and greases in the textile industry. EMKAY CHEMICAL CO.

Rexosolve TR. A mixture of mineral spirits, terpenes, and soaps. It is a good tar remover for WOOL and COTTON mixtures. EMKAY CHEMICAL CO.

Rexowax CNN. A water-dispersible synthetic wax and resin, combining, into one product, excellent non-slip, fullness, and luster properties when used as a finish for RAYON and ACETATE satins.
EMKAY CHEMICAL CO.

Rexowax DR. An emulsified blend of waxes in liquid form. Compatible with weighters, gums and starches. Used in textile finishing. EMKAY CHEMICAL CO.

Rexowax W-19. A selected mixture of lubricants for use in paper-yarn mfg. Take-up on yarn is uniform and consistent from package to package.
EMKAY CHEMICAL CO.

Rexowax WS. A mixture of waxes, plasticizers, and fatty matter, with good solubility in water. Used as a lubricant for paper-yarn mfg.
EMKAY CHEMICAL CO.

Rexowet A Concentrate, Rexowet A *and* Rexowet A-25. A series of powerful surface-tension depressants. Sulfonated dioctyl succinates. Stable in acid, alkaline and neutral baths, highly resistant to hydrolysis. Used in the textile industry.
EMKAY CHEMICAL CO.

Rexowet CR[NR]. A cresylic-base, textile wetting agent and penetrant. Also used in scouring to remove mineral-oil stains. EMKAY CHEMICAL CO.

Rexowet GR[NR]. A highly concentrated liquid penetrant and wetting agent especially useful in textile processing. EMKAY CHEMICAL CO.

Rexowet MS. A special penetrant for textile sizing formulations. It is non-foaming, and helps the sizing to penetrate the yarn finish, giving an even application of sizing. EMKAY CHEMICAL CO.

Rexowet RW. A highly efficient textile wetting and rewetting agent with good stability to salts, acids and alkalis. Used as a general all-around dyeing assistant. It is also very effective in the re-wetting SANFORIZING process of cotton-fabric finishing.
EMKAY CHEMICAL CO.

Rez[NR]. Chemically treated perlite used as a conditioning, purifying, decolorizing, and filter aid material for solvents used in the dry-cleaning industry.
INTERNATIONAL MINERALS & CHEMICAL CORP.

Rezamul®. A solvent-free alkyd emulsion used as a vehicle in the formulation of high-gloss, water-based industrial enamels of either the air-drying or baking types. REICHHOLD CHEMICALS, INC.

Rezlok®. A moisture-proof and thermoplastic closure for bags. BEMIS BROTHERS BAG CO.

RG® Soya Lecithin. A granular lecithin packaged for consumer use as a dietary supplement.
GLIDDEN CO.

Rhatany△. *Also known as* RATANY△, PAYTA△ *and* KRAMERIA△. The dried root of the plant *Karmeria triandria*, of Peru, Bolivia and Brazil. It contains about 40% tannin, which is extracted with hot water and used for tanning leather. At one time RHATANY was used in medicine as an internal astringent for diarrhea.

Rheotol[NR]. A solution of a polymerized alkyl phosphate in mineral spirits, containing 73% solids. *Use:* In paint, to promote luster and leveling.
R. T. VANDERBILT CO.

Rhoads JE-538 Waterproof and Oil-Resistant Cement. A waterproof and oil-resistant adhesive for joining leather belting. It dries rapidly, and belts can be run within an hour after application.
J. E. RHOADS & SONS

Rhoduline®. A line of: (1) blue basic dyestuffs useful in the coloring of aqueous and spirit wood stains, spirit varnishes, aniline printing inks, aqueous and spirit paper stains, and coating, brushing and spraying film-forming lacquers; and (2) direct dyestuffs for dyeing bright, bluish-red shades on COTTON, RAYON, and paper. GENERAL DYESTUFF CO.

Rhoplex® B-15. An acrylic binder for pigmented paper coatings, particularly for coatings for folding boxboard. It gives excellent gloss and printing qualities, and good mechanical and chemical stability. Coatings prepared with this binder dry rapidly, have good water resistance, do not shrink, and are highly flexible. Solids content, 46%; particle size, less than 1 micron; pH, 6.0 to 6.5; stable to acids and alkalis, light and freezing. ROHM & HAAS CO.

R & I Aluminacrete®. A high-alumina castable refractory. REFRACTORY & INSULATION CORP.

Rich Tone Oil Stain. A wood stain, applied by wiping onto the surface and then wiping off the excess when the desired shade has been attained. Available in 10 wood colors. GILLESPIE VARNISH CO.

Ridgeline[NR]. Formerly known as RIDGEWOOD[NR] (*Supp.* I, p. 202). MASONITE CORP.

Ridgewood[NE]. (*Supp.* I, p. 202). Name changed to Ridgeline. Masonite Corp.

R & I Hot Top Moldit®. A patented (U. S. Pat. No. 2,407,135) castable refractory for hot topping steel ingots. It is used in place of refractory brick for lining cast-iron heads and casings of permanent-type ingot molds. Refractory & Insulation Corp.

Riji-Tuf®. An impact-resistant, resin-reinforced rubber compound that is used in such diversified products as football helmets, furniture trim, acid vent ducts, textile bobbins, bowling pin bases, trays, clicker blocks, tool handles, and pipe and fittings. It is harder and more rigid than Ace-Hide® and slightly more flexible than hard rubber. Strong inorganic acids and alkalis or salt solutions have little or no effect on this material. It also has good electrical properties and low thermal conductivity. Produces a smooth, shiny surface in molds. Tensile strength, 2,000–3,500 lb./sq.in.; sp.gr. 1.20–1.40; heat distortion temp. 125–140°F. Available in black, green, brown, red and gray. American Hard Rubber Co.

Rimifon®. An antituberculous drug. It is a brand of isoniazid. Available in scored 50-mg. and 100-mg. tablets. Hoffmann-La Roche Inc.

R & I Moldit Chrome Castable Refractory®. Formerly known as R & I Moldit Chrome Refractory Cement® (*HBMTN* p. 490). Refractory & Insulation Corp.

R & I Moldit-D®. A castable refractory cement for repairing furnace walls, for new wall construction, and for shape molding of burner blocks, arch units, baffles, etc. It has a m.p. of 2,656°F., and can be used at temps. up to 2,400°F. Refractory & Insulation Corp.

Rincontroller®. A catalyst designed for use with Rincontrol® textured enamels. Interchemical Corp., Finishes Div.

Ring-Tite® Coupling. A specially-designed coupling for Transite® Pressure Pipe. This coupling provides easy aligning and automatic adjustment for expansion, assuring max. tightness and joint flexibility to withstand shock and vibration, relieve line stresses, and permit conformance to curves. Johns-Manville Sales Corp.

Rinse-Away. A remover for paint, varnish, lacquer, and stains. Brushed on a painted surface, it softens the finish in a few minutes and the softened finish can be washed away with water. Gillespie Varnish Co.

Rinse-Kleen. A rapid-acting, water-rinsable paint brush and roller cleaner. The brush or roller is soaked until the paint is softened, and then rinsed in water. It removes oil-base paint, enamel, rubber-base paint, varnish, shellac, polyvinyl, acetate, and acrylics. Sterling Quality Products, Inc.

Rinse-Off. A smooth, heavy-bodied, non-flammable liquid paint and varnish remover. It is brushed on in a thick layer and then rinsed off with water, taking the paint film with it. No scraping is necessary. It is safe to use on metal, wood, glass, plaster, and masonry. Sterling Quality Products, Inc.

Rinsite. (Trademark registration pending). A light-yellow liquid in concentrated form. Its excellent draining properties prevent water spotting and protect steel and plated articles with a rust-retarding film. Useful as a rinsing aid in the final hot or cold rinse after plating or other metal cleaning operations. Oakite Products, Inc.

R & I Plastic Chrome®. A chrome-base refractory ramming mix. Refractory & Insulation Corp.

Ripp-Nipp®. A quick opening feature for multiwall paper bags. Bemis Brothers Bag Co.

Ripp-Tabb. See Bemis Ripp-Tabb®.

Risa®. The trademark for radioactive iodine for use in blood and plasma volume determination, tumor localization, and other physiological techniques. Abbott Laboratories

Ritalin®. A mild psychomotor stimulant. It restores mental and physical activities to normal levels without producing hyperexcitability or depressive rebound. Administered orally in divided doses. Ciba Pharmaceutical Products Inc.

Rival®. The trademark for a steel spoke wire. United States Steel Corp.

Riviclor®. See Ace® Riviclor®.

Riz®. An odorless liquid disinfectant for floors, toilets, rest rooms, and showers. Phenol coefficient, 16. Used in a dilution of 1 part Riz to 320 parts water. J. I. Holcomb Mfg. Co.

R-Mor-Plate®. A combination of catalyzed, synergistic chemicals, supplied as a dry powder, used for hardening and toughening all grades of ferrous metals. It is non-poisonous, non-explosive, fast and safe. When activated at heat-treating temps.—1,650–1,700°F.—it forms atomic carbon and hardening and toughening elements. It is applied by sprinkling on the metal that has been heated to 1,650°F. Service Industries

Roachmaster®. (*HBMTN* p. 491). No longer available. Michigan Chemical Co.

Roboline®. (*HBMTN* p. 491). No longer available. Reed & Carnrick

Rock-Tex®. A stone-faced siding material consisting of an insulation board that is first sealed with a waterproof saturant, coated with asphalt and embedded with colored mineral granules. This siding has the texture and character of real stone. Mastic Asphalt Corp.

Rocou△. Same as Annatto△.

Roco Wall Size. (*Supp.* I p. 203). No longer available. Reardon Co.

Rogepel[NE]. A proprietary synthetic aromatic chemical. A practically colorless liquid with a rose character. Dow Chemical Co.

Rogette®. A mild, abrasive hand cleaner specifically developed for female factory workers, duplicating machine operators, etc. It contains an antiseptic agent and a perfume. J. I. Holcomb Mfg. Co.

Roll Fire-Felt. See Asbestos Roll Fire-Felt®.

Roll-O-MAT®. A flexible air cleaning web of fiber glass, of expansible-contractible air flow depth, wound in a compressed condition. AMERICAN AIR FILTER CO.

Roll-O-MATIC®. An automatic, self-cleaning, viscous-type, ventilating air filter having disposable type media. AMERICAN AIR FILTER CO.

Roloy. See FCC® ROLOY.

Roly-Poly Dry Cleaner. A cleaner for suede, shoes, bags, gloves, felt hats and similar items.
SLOMONS LABORATORIES, INC.

Ronagen Black IL. An azoic black dye with excellent fastness to light, chlorine and bleaching. It is also fast to formaldehyde, which will not cause change of shade. Unlike most stabilized azoic blacks, RONAGEN BLACK IL will not bleed out and stain whites during the soaping operation. It is developed in acid fumes. Available in powder form.
NOVA CHEMICAL CORP.

Ronagen Black IL Powder. An azoic printing color which possesses excellent fastness to light, chlorine, peroxide and formaldehyde on COTTON and RAYON and does not bleed out and stain whites. It is applied by the normal procedure for azoic colors, and produces grays, as well as blacks. *Mfg'd by* ROHNER LTD. *Dist'd by* NOVA CHEMICAL CORP.

Roomates®. The trademark for a line of contemporary furniture. T. BAUMRITTER CO.

Rooticate. A product used for destroying and preventing tree and shrub root growth and fungus growths in sewer pipes from the house to street sewers, thus preventing noxious odors and backed-up sewers resulting from root clogging. It does not affect the health and vigor of trees and shrubs.
FAESY & BESTHOFF, INC.

Rosaryl[NB]**.** A proprietary synthetic aromatic chemical. A practically colorless liquid with a rose character. DOW CHEMICAL CO.

Rose Marrakesh[NB]**.** A proprietary synthetic aromatic chemical. A practically colorless liquid with a rose character. DOW CHEMICAL CO.

Rosetone®. (*HBMTN* p. 492). No longer available.
AMERICAN CHEMICAL PAINT CO.

Rosin△**.** *Also known as* COLOPHONY△ *and* YELLOW RESIN△. A resin obtained from several varieties of the pine tree, including *Pinus palustris* and other species of *Pinus Pinaceae*. Two types of ROSIN are available: GUM ROSIN, which is the residue that remains after distilling off the volatile oil from the collected exudations of the pine tree; and WOOD ROSIN, which is obtained from the destructive distillation, steam distillation or extraction of the wood or stumps. Many grades of ROSIN are on the market, classified according to color, clarity, saponification number, and softening point. It is a pale yellow to amber, translucent, brittle solid with a slight turpentine taste and odor. It is composed chiefly of abietic acid, together with sapinic, primaric, and similar acids. Sp.gr. 1.08; m.p. ranges from 100° to 140°C.; acid no., not less than 150; insoluble in water; freely soluble in alcohol, benzene, ether, glacial acetic acid, carbon disulfide, oils, and dilute alkali solution. *Uses:* In the mfg. of varnishes, varnish and paint driers, printing inks, cements, soaps, sealing wax, wood polishes, floor coverings, paper sizes, rosin oil, plastics, fireworks, belt dressings, tree waxes, etc.; and for waterproofing cardboard, wall paper, etc.

Rosin Amine D[NB]**.** Two fungicidal agents. ROSIN AMINE D PENTACHLOROPHENATE, and ROSIN AMINE D ACETATE. The former, which is chemically inert and non-toxic to warm-blooded animals, is used as a fungicide in paper for soap wrappings, and as a preservative for cotton; the latter is used in special textiles where its lack of color and strengthening effect are desirable. HERCULES POWDER CO.

Rosin Oil△**.** *Also known as* ROSINOL△ *and* RETINOL△. The oil produced by the dry distillation of ROSIN△ at a temp. of 200°–360°C. It is a yellow, viscid, fluorescent, oily liquid; sp.gr. 1.020; flash point, 160–170°C.; insoluble in water; soluble in ether, turpentine, and other oils; dissolves phosphorus, sulfur, camphor, phenols, and many other organic compounds. *Uses:* In the mfg. of printing inks; in varnishes, RETINOL colors, lacquers, brewers' pitch, and axle greases; as a plasticizer for rubber; as a tack agent in rubber cement; etc.

Rosinol△**.** *Same as* ROSIN OIL△.

Rosottone[NB]**.** A proprietary synthetic aromatic chemical. An aromatic specialty replacement for ATTAR OF ROSE in compounding perfumes.
DOW CHEMICAL CO.

Rosottone Savon[NB]**.** A proprietary synthetic aromatic chemical. An aromatic specialty replacement for ATTAR OF ROSE, especially suited to soap and detergent perfuming. DOW CHEMICAL CO.

Rotenone△**.** *Known also as* DERRIN△, NICOULINE△, *and* TUBATOXIN△. $C_{23}H_{22}O_6$; mol.wt. 394.43. A selective contact insecticide possessing some acricidal action. Prepared by crystallization from extracts of DERRIS or LONCHOCARPUS. Colorless crystals with a m.p. of 163°C.; and a dimorphic form with a m.p. of 181°C. Practically insoluble in water; slightly soluble in petroleum oils, and carbon tetrachloride; soluble in polar organic solvents. Readily oxidized, especially in presence of light or alkali, to less insecticidal compounds. It is non-phytotoxic and relatively harmless to warm-blooded animals. Rotenone insecticides are especially valuable for controlling plant-feeding pests, especially where toxic residues are not desired, and for the control of cattle grubs.

Roto-Clone®. Centrifugal dust separators of the dynamic precipitator type, and of the hydrostatic precipitator type. AMERICAN AIR FILTER CO.

Rotofect®. A registered trademark for a book paper.
KIMBERLY-CLARK CORP.

Rottenstone△**.** A light-gray to olive-colored, soft, friable, earthy stone composed of 80–85% alumina, 4–15% silica, and 5–10% iron oxides. In powdered form it is used as an abrasive for metal and wood finishing, and as a filler for molding compounds. It is also molded into bricks and used for oil-on-rag wheel polishing.

Rouge△**.** A hydrated iron oxide made by calcining ferrous sulfate, and used as a fine abrasive for polishing metals. ROUGE is available in varying shades of red; the darker colors are harder than the lighter material. The hardness varies from 5.5 to 6.5 on Moh's scale. (*See also* SATIN ROUGE.)

Rough Top. See BOSTON ROUGH TOP.

Roxel[NE] *and* **Roxel Forte**[NE]. Medicinals for the management of hypertension, psychoneuroses, psychoses, and some gynecologic and dermatologic disorders with associated psychogenic factors. Each 15 cc. (approx. one teaspoonful) of ROXEL contains 0.1 mg. reserpine, 5 mg. thiamine hydrochloride (VITAMIN B$_1$), 5 mg. pyridoxine hydrochloride (VITAMIN B$_6$), 25 mcg. cyanocobal (VITAMIN B$_{12}$), and 10 mg. niacinamide in 17% ethyl alcohol. ROXEL FORTE contains 0.25 mg. reserpine per 15 cc., and the same amounts of the other ingredients.
MERCK SHARP & DOHME

Royal® Paints. The trademark for a line of consumer paints. GLIDDEN CO.

Royal Purple[NE]. A line of purple color pigments for use in printing inks, paints, etc. They have excellent strength and good permanence. Available in dry form, and dispersed in various organic printing ink vehicles. SHERWIN-WILLIAMS CO.

"RP" Series. See CLAREMONT "RP" SERIES.

RS[NE]. (*Supp.* I p. 206). No longer available.
HANSON-VAN WINKLE-MUNNING CO.

RS12 Conductive Shielding Micropaint[NE]. (*Supp.* I p. 206). No longer available. MICRO-CIRCUITS CO.

RS14 Shielding Micropaint[NE]. A very low-resistance paint for coating the inside of non-metallic areas of TV-receiver and instrument cabinets to reduce RF radiation to an acceptable level. It is a metal pigment-fortified carbon coating; and provides shielding at much lower cost than when aluminum foil shielding is used. MICRO-CIRCUITS CO.

RS17 Polyshield Micropaint[NE]. An electrically conductive coating for polyethylene. Used principally for TV-receiver parts made of polyethylene. In one application, it forms the two plates of a high-voltage condenser on the polyethylene boot covering color picture tubes; in another, it forms an RF shield over polyethylene-insulated parts. MICRO-CIRCUITS CO.

R T V®. The trademark for a line of electrical resistors and controls. (Registration No. 623,979; Class 21; March 27, 1956). CLAROSTAT MFG. CO.

Rubanox Red[NE]. A series of Lithol Rubine color pigments characterized by their great strength. Available in resinated and non-resinated grades, in dry form and dispersed in various organic vehicles. *Uses:* In paints, enamels, printing inks, plastics and rubber.
SHERWIN-WILLIAMS CO.

Rubba-Coat[NE]. (*HBMTN* p. 494). Should have been listed as RUBBAKOTE[NE]. RUBBA, INC.

Rubbakote[NE]. Incorrectly listed as RUBBA-COAT[NE] (*HBMTN* p. 494). RUBBA, INC.

Rubber-Coat® Liquid Neoprene. A coating material in jet black, tile red, light gray, and aluminum. Applied by brush or spray to metal equipment, concrete, and other materials to provide a chemical-, corrosion-, oil-, and abrasion-resistant surface of low vapor permeability. It has long shelf life.
WILBUR & WILLIAMS CO.

Rubberlith®. (*HBMTN* p. 495). No longer available. WITCO CHEMICAL CO.

Rubber Red[NE]. (*HBMTN* p. 495). No longer available. SHERWIN-WILLIAMS CO.

Rubinol®. A group of level-dyeing fast-to-light anthraquinone-type acid dyes for WOOL.
GENERAL DYESTUFF CO.

Rub-Once. A cream emulsion that cleans and polishes furniture in one operation. It gives the wood a rich, mirror-like sheen, and leaves no oily film for dirt and dust to cling to. J. I. HOLCOMB MFG. CO.

Rub-R-Kleen®. A highly soluble, alkaline cleaner designed for cleaning and soaking the rubber tubes and inflations of dairy milking machines. Contains at least 85% sodium hydroxide. DIVERSEY CORP.

Rub-R-Lon. A line of exterior-interior, chlorinated rubber-base enamels that are resistant to acids, alkalis, and other chemicals, fumes, oils, fungi, gases, grease, and moisture. Recommended particularly for industrial use in chemical plants, steel mills, paper mills, warehouses, etc.; in schools, hospitals, hotels, dairies, laundries, bakeries, bottling plants; and in other industrial and institutional buildings. Also available in a non-skid grade for use as a safety coating on factory ramps, steps, and dangerous floor areas.
ACORN REFINING CO.

Rucoam®. The trademark for rubber latex and other products mfg'd by the RUBBER CORP. OF AMERICA.

Rufert®. A nickel catalyst for hardening margarine.
HARSHAW CHEMICAL CO.

Ruf-Grip®. A special paper for large bags to prevent slipping when the bags are filled and stacked.
BEMIS BROTHERS BAG CO.

Ru Glide®. A rubber lubricant especially suitable for use when changing tubeless tires on passenger cars and trucks. It prevents scuffing of rim-seal ridges and bead toes when mounting and demounting the tires either with hand tools or tire machines. Recommended also for lubricating and preserving other rubber parts. AMERICAN GREASE STICK CO.

Run-Rite®. The registered trademark of NATIONAL PLASTICS, INC. for their line of textile machinery, such as harness loom sheaves, idlers and twisters for spinning, separators for spinning, spinning drives, etc.

Runwel®. A commercial grade mechanical packing for rods, shafts, etc. GREENE, TWEED & CO.

Rust-Oleum® Mer-Q-Ree. (*Supp.* I p. 208). No longer available. RUST-OLEUM CORP.

Rustripper®. A heavy-duty, off-white granular alkaline stripper. In a single operation it removes rust and light scale, paint, grease and shop soils. Will not attack sound metal or cause hydrogen embrittlement.
OAKITE PRODUCTS, INC.

Rust-Veto. See KRYLON-HOUGHTON® RUST VETO SPRAY.

Rutaplex A V-P 729A. A nutritional supplement containing dehydrated buckwheat juice. Used for correcting VITAMIN P deficiency where not associated with hypercholesteremia. VITAMIN PRODUCTS CO.

Rutaplex V-P 729. A nutritional supplement containing dehydrated extract of buckwheat seed and green leaf. Each tablet contains 20 mg, inositol. Used for correcting VITAMIN P deficiency states where associated with hypercholesteremia.
VITAMIN PRODUCTS CO.

Ryania△. An insecticidal material prepared from the ground stems and roots of *Ryania specioca* Vahl (Flacourtiacee), a tropical shrub native to Trinidad and the Amazon basin. The insecticidal principles are extractable by water, methyl alcohol, or chloroform. The most important of the *Ryania* alkaloids is RYANODINE, $C_{25}H_{35}NO_9$ (mol.wt. 493.56), the structure of which has not been fully determined. It is a selective stomach poison, especially effective against the European corn-borer.

Ryanodine△. See RYANIA△.

S

S-32. (*HBMTN* p. 497). No longer available.
VEGETABLE OIL PRODUCTS CO.

Sabadilla△. *Also known as* CEVADILLA. The seeds of SABADILLA, *Schoenocaulon officinale*, family Liliaceae, have been used for centuries as louse powders by the natives of South and Central America. The ground seeds and their extractives are now of considerable commercial importance as selective contact insecticides for the control of plant feeding Hemiptera and Homoptera and thrips. They are also effective against domestic pests and house flies. SABADILLA seeds contain about 2–4% of a crude mixture of alkaloids termed VERATRINE, from which about 13% CEVADINE ($C_{32}H_{49}O_9N$; mol.wt. 591.75; m.p. 205°C.), 10% VERATRIDINE ($C_{36}H_{51}O_{11}N$; mol.wt. 673.81; m.p. 160°–180°C.), and smaller amounts of CEVADILLINE, SABADINE, and SABATINE have been isolated. The crude alkaloids are slightly soluble in water and in petroleum solvents, fairly soluble in dilute acids, and most organic solvents.

Sabadine△. *See* SABADILLA△.

Sabatine△. *See* SABADILLA△.

Sadler Clay^NR. (*HBMTN* p. 498). No longer available. UNITED CLAY MINES CORP.

Saf-Drive®. The trademark for automotive seat belts. Available in 3 models: SD-100, for driver seat only; SD-200, individual belts for driver and one front seat passenger; and SD-300, individual belts for driver and two front seat passengers.
ANSUL CHEMICAL CO.

Safe-T-Sheen®. A no-wax floor finish.
J. I. HOLCOMB MFG. CO.

Safety-Solv^NR. An industrial grease and oil remover. Used by diluting with water to produce a non-flammable product. Eliminates the use of flammable petroleum solvents. Non-toxic and non-irritating to the skin. Used for removing oil, grease, dirt, and soft carbon deposits from plant machinery and equipment and aircraft exterior engine-exhaust areas.
BRULIN & CO.

Safflower△. Red and yellow coloring materials obtained from the orange-colored, thistle-like heads of the plant *Carthamus tinctorius*. The heads are dried and pressed into cakes. The plant is grown in France and in India. In India, it is produced commercially for the seeds, which yield up to 35% of an oil that is used in paints, leather dressings, and foods. SAFFLOWER finds extensive use as a food color, in cosmetic rouge, and for the dyeing of textiles.

Saffron△. A water-soluble, yellow dye used to color foods and medicinals. Contains crocin, $C_{44}H_{70}O_{28}$, a bright-red, alcohol-soluble powder. Extracted from the dried flowers and tips of the saffron crocus.

Saf-T-Dek®. A non-slip coating for floors, catwalks, and metal decks. Applied by trowel to a thickness of $1/32''$ to $1/16''$. TRUSCON LABORATORIES

Saftepak®. A specially-designed plastic bottle for reagent A.C.S. hydrofluoric acid. It eliminates all of the hazards inherent in the old-fashioned wax bottle for HF. GENERAL CHEMICAL DIV.,
ALLIED CHEMICAL & DYE CORP.

Saf-T-Klenz. *See* BULL FROG® SAF-T-KLENZ.

Saf-T-Pak® Torpedo Tube. The trademark for a rigidly-constructed, spirally wound laminated tube of KRAFT and asphalt papers which serves as both cartridge and shipping container. This tube is charged with four cartridges of NITRO OIL GELATIN DYNAMITE, and a lowering bail is provided for safe shooting of deep oil and gas wells. AMERICAN CYANAMID CO.

Sago Flour△. A tan-colored starch material extracted from the pith of the sago palm, *Metroxylon sagu*, of the East Indies and Malaya. It is used as a textile size and filler.

Sagrotan®. (*HBMTN* p. 498). No longer available.
LEHN & FINK PRODUCTS CORP.

Salamac. Salammoniac in brick form for use in soldering operations. J. F. HENRY CHEMICAL CO.

Salihexin®. Hexamethylenamine-acetaminosalicylic acid, for intravenous use. ABBOTT LABORATORIES

Salioca®. (*HBMTN* p. 498). Should have been listed as a registered trademark.
AMERICAN MAIZE PRODUCTS CO.

Salnide®. (*Supp.* I p. 209). Now a registered trademark. CHEMO PURO MFG. CO.

Samica®. Continuous sheet mica in roll form. Thicknesses, from 0.0015″ to 0.004″; dielectric strength, 500–800 volts/mil.; power factor (60 cycles at 25°C.), 0.04–0.10%. It is made by partially dehydrating flake Muscovite mica by heat treatment, followed by treatment with sodium carbonate or bicarbonate solution and then sulfuric acid. After being washed, the treated mica is formed into continuous sheets on a Fourdrinier-type machine. *Use:* As electrical insulation. (*See also* ISOMICA®). MICA INSULATOR CO.

Samplair®. A portable hand-operated instrument

for quick estimation of concentrations of chromic acid mist in working atmospheres.
MINE SAFETY APPLIANCES CO.

San-A-Jon-Liquid[NE]. A toilet bowl cleaner.
CENTRAL O-B PRODUCTS CO.

Sandalwood Oil[△]. *Also known as* OIL OF SANTAL[△]. A yellowish, volatile oil obtained from the distillation of the dried heartwood of the evergreen tree *Santalum album* L. *Santalaceae*, and other species of southern Asia. It is a somewhat viscid liquid with a characteristic SANDALWOOD odor and taste. Sp.gr. 0.953–0.985; slightly soluble in water. *Uses:* Formerly as a urinary antiseptic; in perfumery; in the mfg. of soap.

Sandarac[△]. *Also known as* WHITE GUM[△] *and* AUSTRALIAN PINE GUM[△]. A white to light-yellow, brittle resin obtained as an exudation from various species of the coniferous tree *Callitris quadrivalvis*, Vent. *Pinaceae*, of Morocco, and from the Austrailian tree *C. arenosa*. It consists of about 80% pimaric acid, 10% callitrolic acid, and some sandaricinic acid. It crumbles to a powder when masticated; m.p. 135°–140°C.; insoluble in water, benzene, and petroleum ether; soluble in alcohol, ether, acetone, hot caustic alkalis; partially soluble in chloroform, volatile oils, carbon disulfide, and oil turpentine. *Uses:* In tooth cements, lacquers, and varnishes; and as an incense.

Sandopan® DTC. A surfactant for textile processing. Combines advantages of both anionic soap and nonionic detergent. Removes oil and graphite from synthetics; gives faster and more uniform bleach; increases abrasion resistance and crease retention of resin-finished goods. SANDOZ CHEMICAL WORKS, INC.

Sandseal Core & Mold Wash[NE]. A plastic-type, finished core and mold wash with a fusion temp. above 3,100°F. It is an economical wash that has most of the properties of HI-RESIST CORE & MOLD WASH but not as high a refractory value. M. A. BELL CO.

Sanek®. The trademark for a line of creped wadding and other paper products. KIMBERLY-CLARK CORP.

Sanforized®. This registered trademark of CLUETT, PEABODY & CO. is applied to fabrics treated by a compressive shrinking process. The Company permits the use of this trademark, adopted in 1930, only on fabrics which meet its rigid shrinkage requirements. Fabrics bearing the trademark SANFORIZED® will not shrink more than 1% by the Government's standard test. It is permissible to use SANFORIZED® as an adjective, *e.g.*, SANFORIZED® broadcloth, SANFORIZED® shirt, etc. It is a misuse of the trademark SANFORIZED® to employ it as a verb or participle, or to vary the spelling, *e.g.*, SANFORIZE, SANFORIZING, SANFORIZER, SANFORIZATION, etc. CLUETT, PEABODY & CO.

Sanforizing Oil S-261-C[NE]. (*Supp.* I p. 209). Should have been listed as COMPRESSIVE SHRINKING OIL S-261-C[NE]. JACQUES WOLF & CO.

Sanforlan®. This registered trademark of CLUETT, PEABODY & CO. is used to identify wool items which conform to specific shrinkage requirements. The Company permits the use of this trademark only on woolen fabrics or garments which have been treated by procedures approved by this Company and which meets its rigid requirements. When washed in accordance with recommended procedures for WOOL garments bearing the trademark SANFORLAN® will not mat, felt, or shrink. CLUETT, PEABODY & CO.

Sanicyl®. An ointment of salicylanilide and PHEMEROL chloride (benzethonium chloride, Parke-Davis) for treatment of ringworm of the scalp.
PARKE, DAVIS & CO.

Sani-Tate[NE]. A milky white emulsion for cleaning, disinfecting, and deodorizing toilet bowls, urinals, and similar porcelain items. This sanitizing agent flushes away organic particles, grease, oil, and gummy sludge, as well as encrustations of lime and rust.
HUNTINGTON LABORATORIES, INC.

Sanitizer No. 1. *See* OAKITE® SANITIZER No. 1.

Sapamine A®. (*HBMTN* p. 503). No longer available. CIBA CO.

Sapamine FL®. (*HBMTN* p. 503). *Now known as* SAPAMINE® FLK. CIBA CO.

Sapamine® FLK. *Formerly known as* SAPAMINE FL® (*HBMTN* p. 503). CIBA CO.

Sapamine® OC. A cationic softening agent for raw stock, yarns, and fabrics of natural and synthetic fibers, including NYLON, VISCOSE, ORLON, BEMBERG, ACETATE, WOOL, COTTON, LINEN and SILK. It is a smooth, cream-colored paste which readily forms an opalescent solution or dispersion in hot water.
CIBA CO.

Saponaria[△]. *Also known as* SOAPWORT[△], SOAPROOT[△], FULLER'S HERB[△], BRUISEWORT[△], *and* BOUNCING BET[△]. The herb and root of the plant *Saponaria officinalis* L., *Caryophyllaceae*, that grows in Europe and Middle Asia, and has been naturalized in the United States. Contains saponin, sapotaxin, and saponarin. Used as a detergent for cleansing silk and fine woolens.

Sapphirol®. A group of very level-dyeing acid dyestuffs for WOOL. They give bright blue shades with very good fastness to light. GENERAL DYESTUFF CO.

Saran Wrap[NE]. The trade name for SARAN film.
DOW CHEMICAL CO.

Satinol® Finish. One of several types of surface finishes for glass mfg'd by the BLUE RIDGE GLASS CORP. A SATINOL FINISH on one or both surfaces of the glass provides a soft satin-like appearance, increases obscurity, and spreads transmitted light uniformly over a wide area.
Mfg'd by BLUE RIDGE GLASS CORP.
Dist'd by LIBBEY-OWENS-FORD GLASS CO.

Satin Rouge[△]. A grade of lampblack used as a polishing medium, in the form of bricks, for silverware.

Satisfaction at Harvest Time®. The trademark for a line of fertilizers.
INTERNATIONAL MINERALS & CHEMICAL CORP.

Saturol. (Trademark registration pending). A solvent-type, dark brown liquid for removing carbon, soil and paint deposits from aviation, automotive and railroad transportation equipment.
OAKITE PRODUCTS, INC.

Sav-It®. *See* CUPRINOL® SAV-IT®.

Savon. *See* ROSOTTONE SAVON.

Saw Eez. A colloidal graphite lubricant for band, hack, and circular saws; and for metal spinning, bearing surfaces, lathe centers, etc. DoAll Co.

SC[NR]. A mineral wool, available in loose and granulated forms. Celotex Corp.

SC12 and SC13 Silver Micropaints[NR]. High electrical conductivity paints for painted and printed wires, shields, contacts, etc. Used for conductors, tube shields, circuit shielding, conducting hardware, printed circuits, etc. SC12 is used for rigid and semi-rigid surfaces. SC13 is tough and very flexible; and is used for paper and thin laminates. Micro-Circuits Co.

SC-50[NR]. A water-soluble alkali-metal siliconate used to render various materials water-repellent. General Electric Co.

Scald-Aid. See Oakite® Scald Aid.

Scale Free®. The trademark for a line of steel pipes, tubes, casing and couplings. United States Steel Corp.

Scale-Tox. A dormant spray for fruit trees, shade trees, shrubs, and evergreens. Used for the control of various insect infestations including oyster shell scale, juniper scale, San Jose scale, maple scale, red spider mite eggs, leaf roller and pear psylla, etc. Miller Chemical & Fertilizer Corp.

Schradan[△]. Also known as OMPA. An organic phosphorus insecticide first prepared by Schrader in 1947. Bis(dimethylamino) phosphorus anhydride. $C_8H_{24}N_4O_3P_2$; mol.wt. 286.26. It is a colorless, viscous liquid with a b.p. of 118–122°C. (0.3 mm. Hg); miscible with water and most organic solvents; slightly soluble in petroleum oils. The commercial product is a dark brown, viscous liquid that is stable to water and alkali but hydrolyzed under acid conditions to orthophosphoric acid and dimethylamine. Schradan is relatively inert as a direct contact insecticide but is absorbed by leaves and translocated, rendering the plant systemically toxic to many sap-feeding insects and mites. It is toxic to mammals.

Schweinfurtergrun[△]. Same as Paris Green[△].

Scotch'em[NR]. An aerosol insecticide for household use. Pennsylvania Salt Mfg. Co.

Scotchgard® Stain Repeller. A fluorochemical-type textile finish that repels oil and water-borne stains and improves the crease retention of woolens, worsteds, worsted blends, etc. Minnesota Mining & Mfg. Co.

Scotch-Top[NR]. (HBMTN p. 506). No longer available. Minnesota Mining & Mfg. Co.

Scourlon-Pentalon[NR]. A one-bath scouring and dyeing process for Nylon hosiery or piece goods, combining in two products an alkaline powdered detergent with a penetrating-leveling organic dyeing assistant. With Scourlon-Pentalon, Nylon hosiery or piece goods can be scoured and dyed in the same length of time previously required for scouring. W. F. Fancourt Co.

Screen-Bak®. An open-mesh coated abrasive cloth. Behr-Manning Co.

Screwlock®. A screw-holding gypsum board. It is a composite panel. Celotex Corp.

Sealed Lok-Joint Lath®. (HBMTN p. 507). No longer available. Minnesota & Ontario Paper Co., Institute Div.

Sealmore®. (HBMTN p. 507). Now a registered trademark. Armite Laboratories

Sealon[NR]. Incorrectly listed as Selon[NR] (HBMTN p. 509). Maurice A. Knight

Seal-Pruf H-D. See Nervastral Seal-Pruf® H-D.

Seal-Pruf Tape 30 and 60. See Nervastral Seal-Pruf Tape 30 and 60.

Seal-tite®. (HBMTN p. 507). No longer available. Hillyard Chemical Co.

Sea Ring Packing[NR]. A molded rod and plunger packing made of asbestos fabric or duck, or a combination of the two, impregnated with heat- and oil-resisting compounds. The rings are made to fit any reciprocating rod and stuffing box where the rod is not less than ¾″, and the width of the packing space is not less than $^5/_{16}$″. Johns-Manville Sales Corp.

Sebacol®. A depilatory for hides and skins. Use: To produce clean uniform quality leather under a variety of beamhouse practices. Wallerstein Co.

Sebb®. The trademark for a non-toxic, non-irritating greenish colored, transparent liquid, containing a white sediment dispersed by shaking, and having a mild, pleasant odor. Uses: For the treatment of seborrheic dermatitis, particularly dandruff and other seborrheic conditions of the scalp. Max Factor & Co.

Secal[NR]. (HBMTN p. 508). No longer available. Emulsol Chemical Corp.

S.E.C.O. Same as Sunoco® Emulsifying Cutting Oils.

S.E.C.O. HD "F." Same as Sunoco® Emulsifying Cutting Oil HD "F."

Securit® Glass. A special glass made by subjecting an annealed patterned glass to a special process of heat treatment and rapid cooling that creates a highly compressed zone at the outer surface. Securit Glass has a tensile strength of 3 to 5 times that of similar non-treated glass, and it is extremely resistant to temp. variations.
  Mfg'd by Blue Ridge Glass Corp.
  Dist'd by Libbey-Owens-Ford Glass Co.

Securit® Interior Glass Doors. A decorative all-glass door that transmits softly diffused light without sacrificing privacy. The glass is heat tempered and is patterned on both surfaces.
  Mfg'd by Blue Ridge Glass Corp.
  Dist'd by Libbey-Owens-Ford Glass Co.

Seed-Less-Set®. (HBMTN p. 508). No longer available. Plant Products Corp.

Seed-O-Lax®. A brand of psyllium seed, N. F. American Pharmaceutical Co.

Selbalith®. (HBMTN p. 508). Now a registered trademark. Selby, Battersby & Co.

Selectotherm®. Automatically controlled heating systems of the type wherein low-pressure steam flows from a stream supply system through a control valve to a heating system. AMERICAN AIR FILTER CO.

Seleen®. A selenium sulfide suspension for effective control of nonspecific dermatoses.
ABBOTT LABORATORIES

Self-Rescuer. See MSA SELF-RESCUER®.

Sellogen® AS. (*Supp.* I p. 212). No longer available. JACQUES WOLF & CO.

Sellogen® P. (*Supp.* I p. 212). No longer available. JACQUES WOLF & CO.

Selon[NE]. (*HBMTN* p. 509). Should have been listed as SEALON[NE]. MAURICE A. KNIGHT

Selsun®. A selenium sulfide suspension for treating seborrheic dermatitis of the scalp.
ABBOTT LABORATORIES

Senecal Gum[△]. See GUM ARABIC[△].

Sennar Gum[△]. See GUM ARABIC[△].

Senokap®. A medicinal, each gelatin capsule of which contains the total active constituents of 450 mg. of cassia acutifolia pods. Used for the corrective treatment of constipation. PURDUE FREDERICK CO.

Senokot®. A standardized concentrate of the active principals of cassia acutifolia pods, in tablet and granule dosage forms, for the corrective treatment of constipation. PURDUE FREDERICK CO.

Separan 2610®. A synthetic, water-soluble polymer which is useful as a coagulent or flocculating agent.
DOW CHEMICAL CO.

Sepia[△]. A dark brown pigment made from the black secretion found in an internal sac of the *Sepia* mollusk. Used in the mfg. of India inks of SEPIA or dark brown color.

Seqlene®. A mixture of sodium salts of closely related, non-toxic polyhydroxy acids. Chemically it consists of the alpha and beta isomers of sodium hexahydroxyheptonate. These salts are very efficient chelating or sequestering agents for various metallic ions, especially strongly alkaline solutions. It effectively chelates calcium and iron, aluminum, copper, nickel, etc. *Uses:* In bottle-washing and metal-cleaning compositions; in textile processing to prevent iron stains; in electroplating baths; for the purification and separation of organic salts; in the purification of organic compounds; in the refining of fats and oils, etc.
PFANSTIEHL LABORATORIES, INC.

Serafume[NE]. A grain fumigant composition for farm use. DOW CHEMICAL CO.

Serenacel®. The trademark for a line of fabrics made wholly or partially of cellulose derivatives.
CELANESE CORP. OF AMERICA

Serene Green[NE]. A line of light and dark green color pigments suitable for use in paints, enamels, rubber, plastics, printing inks, etc. Recommended for their good light resistance, good heat resistance, and non-bleeding characteristics. SHERWIN-WILLIAM CO.

Serpasil®. A tranquilizer and antihypertensive drug. It is a pure crystalline alkaloid of rauwolfia root, a medicinal shrub of India. Useful for the gradual, sustained lowering of blood pressure in patients with hypertension. CIBA PHARMACEUTICAL PRODUCTS, INC.

Serpasil®-Apresoline®. A tranquilizer-antihypertensive combination containing in each tablet either 0.2 mg. SERPASIL® and 50 mg. APRESOLINE® hydrochloride, or 0.1 mg. SERPASIL® and 25 mg. APRESOLINE® hydrochloride. Useful for lowering blood pressure in patients with moderate to severe forms of hypertension. CIBA PHARMACEUTICAL PRODUCTS, INC.

Serphedrine®. A medicinal used for the treatment of bronchial asthma, pulmonary emphysema and other chronic bronchopulmonary disorders. Each oral tablet contains 0.1 mg. reserpine, crystalline; 10.0 mg. (1½ gr.) aminophylline in enteric-coated core to avoid gastric irritation and prolong protection; plus 16 mg. (¼ gr.) ephedrine sulfate.
BLAIR LABORATORIES, INC.

Serphylline®. A medicinal used for the treatment of various cardiac disorders, including hypertension, arterio-sclerotic and hypertensive heart disease, angina pectoris, paroxysmal dyspnea and pulmonary emphysema. Each oral tablet contains 0.1 mg. aminophylline in enteric-coated core to avoid gastric irritation and prolong protection. BLAIR LABORATORIES, INC.

Serpicon[NE]. A hypotensive tranquilizer used in the treatment of hypertension, and anxiety and tension states. Supplied in the form of tablets containing 0.1 mg. and 0.25 mg. of reserpine, respectively.
CONSOLIDATED MIDLAND CORP.

Servacide[NE]. An oil-base insecticidal spray containing pyrethrin, a non-toxic synergist and carbon tetrachloride. It is especially effective for killing insects that hide in cracks and other inaccessible places.
LARVACIDE PRODUCTS, INC.

Service® Sheet Packing and Cut Gaskets. A general-purpose sheet packing material made from selected long fiber asbestos and heat-resisting compounds bonded together under heat and pressure. The finished product is a tough, durable sheet without plies or laminations; it is pliable and resilient; and it does not dry out in storage. Available graphited on one side (Style No. 60) and ungraphited (Style No. 61). Can be used for service against superheated steam, air, gas, water, hot oil, ammonia, and many acids and chemicals. Also available in cut gaskets for flanges. JOHNS-MANVILLE SALES CORP.

Sesame Oil[△]. A pale-yellow, almost odorless oil with a bland taste obtained from the seeds of cultivated varieties of *Sesamum indicum* L., *Pedaliaceae*, grown in India, China, and Latin America. The oil from Nigeria is called BENNE OIL[△], in India it is known as TEEL or TIL OIL[△]; in Madras it is called GINGELLY or GINGILLI OIL[△], and in Mexico it is known as AJONJOLI[△]. The seeds contain about 50% of the oil which has a sp.gr. 0.920–0.925, and solidifies at about −5°C. Saponification no. 188–193; iodine no. 103–122; insoluble in water; soluble in chloroform, ether, petroleum ether, carbon disulfide; slightly soluble in alcohol. *Uses:* In the mfg. of oleomargarine, cosmetics, soaps; for blending with industrial oils; and as a vehicle for intramuscular medication.

Sesamin△. A constituent (about 0.25%) of sesame oil, which enhances the toxicity of pyrethrum. $C_{19}H_{18}O_6$; mol.wt. 342.35. SESAMIN is a crystalline solid with a m.p. of 122.7°C. However, it is not necessary to isolate SESAMIN for its use as a pyrethrum synergist since sesame oil has been found to be equally as effective as SESAMIN by itself. SESAMIN is *dextro*-rotatory, and is converted by hydrochloric acid to isosesamin, its geometric isomer. A number of other natural plant constituents have similar structure. These include ASARININ, the *levo*-rotatory isomer of SESAMIN, which is found in the bark of the southern prickly ash, and in various oriental plants.

Setamol® WSN. (*HBMTN* p. 510). No longer available. GENERAL DYESTUFF CO.

Setsit-9[NR]. A liquid, activated dithiocarbamate-type latex accelerator. Designed with a lower precure rate than SETSIT-E (*HBMTN* p. 510). Used for dipped goods and latex foam compounding.
R. T. VANDERBILT CO.

SFC®. A combination stain and filler for wood.
INTERCHEMICAL CORP., FINISHES DIV.

SGS®. The trademark for a line of steel strapping equipment and machines. UNITED STATES STEEL CORP.

Shadow Crest[NR]. Square butt asphalt strip shingles.
CELOTEX CORP.

ShadowGrain®. A grained, lap insulating siding for building construction. CELOTEX CORP.

Shadowvent® Siding. (*Supp.* I p .213). The name SHADOWVENT® is now a registered trademark.
MASONITE CORP.

Shamrock. A metal-working coolant and lubricant for drawing, stamping, threading, tapping, rolling, broaching, and similar applications. It is an emulsion concentrate, one part of which is diluted with 3 to 25 parts water. Density, 7.9 lb./gal.; pour point, 5°F.; pH (at operating dilutions), 8.6.
F. E. ANDERSON OIL CO.

Shamrock Green[NR]. A line of green color pigments for use in paints and plastics. They have excellent resistance to light, heat, acid and alkali. They are non-bleeding in varnish and water. Available in the following grades: SHAMROCK GREEN LIGHT 11184, and SHAMROCK GREEN DARK 11185.
SHERWIN-WILLIAMS CO.

Sharples Accelerator 52[NR]. Tetramethylthiuram disulfide. $[(CH_3)_2NCS_2]_2$; mol.wt. 240.4. A white powder; sp.gr. 1.44; m.p. 142.5°C. (min.); soluble in carbon disulfide, benzene and chloroform; insoluble in water, gasoline and 1% sodium hydroxide. Also available in extruded form. *Uses:* As an insecticide and fungicide; vulcanization accelerator; retarder for NEOPRENE; lubricating oil additive.
PENNSYLVANIA SALT MFG. CO.

Sharples Accelerator 57[NR]. Zinc dimethyldithiocarbamate. $Zn[(CH_3)_2NCS_2]_2$; mol.wt. 305.8. A rubber vulcanization accelerator. A white powder; sp.gr. 1.66; m.p. 243°C. (min.); soluble in 1% sodium hydroxide, carbon disulfide, benzene, and chloroform; insoluble in water and gasoline. Also available in aqueous dispersion and extruded forms.
PENNSYLVANIA SALT MFG. CO.

Sharples Accelerator 62[NR]. Tetraethylthiuram disulfide. $[(C_2H_5)_2NCS_2]_2$; mol.wt. 296.4. A cream-colored powder; sp.gr. 1.29; f.p. 66.5°C. (min.); soluble in carbon disulfide, benzene, and chloroform; insoluble in water, gasoline, and 1% sodium hydroxide. Also available in extruded form. *Uses:* As a vulcanization accelerator; retarder for NEOPRENE; insecticide and fungicide; lubricating oil additive.
PENNSYLVANIA SALT MFG. CO.

Sharples Accelerator 66[NR]. A mixture containing equimolar quantities of selenium diethyldithiocarbamate and tetraethylthiuram disulfide, used as a rubber vulcanization accelerator. A yellow powder; sp.gr. 1.32; m.p. 60°C. (min.); soluble in carbon disulfide, benzene, and chloroform; insoluble in water, gasoline, and 1% sodium hydroxide.
PENNSYLVANIA SALT MFG. CO.

Sharples Accelerator 67[NR]. Zinc diethyldithiocarbamate. $Zn[(C_2H_5)_2NCS_2]_2$; mol.wt. 361.9. A rubber vulcanization accelerator. A white powder; sp.gr. 1.44; m.p. 171°C. (min.); soluble in 1% sodium hydroxide, carbon disulfide, benzene and chloroform; insoluble in water and gasoline. Also available in aqueous dispersion and extruded forms.
PENNSYLVANIA SALT MFG. CO.

Sharples Accelerator 77[NR]. Zinc dibutyldithiocarbamate. $Zn[(C_4H_9)_2NCS_2]_2$; mol.wt. 474.1. A white powder; sp.gr. 1.24; melting point, 104°C. (min.); soluble in gasoline, carbon disulfide, benzene and chloroform; insoluble in water and 1% sodium hydroxide. Also available in aqueous dispersion and extruded forms. *Uses:* As a rubber vulcanization accelerator; and a lubricating oil additive.
PENNSYLVANIA SALT MFG. CO.

Sharpshooter®. A smokeless powder used for shotguns, rifles, and small arms. HERCULES POWDER CO.

Sharsol®. The trademark for amines and mixtures thereof. PENNSYLVANIA SALT MFG. CO.

Sharstop® 204. Sodium dimethyldithiocarbamate. $Na[(CH_3)_2NCS_2]$; mol.wt. 143.2. A 40% aqueous solution used as a shortstop in the mfg. of synthetic rubber. An amber-to-light green liquid; sp.gr. 1.17–1.20 (25°/25°C.); f.p. —1.5°C.
PENNSYLVANIA SALT MFG. CO.

Sharstop® 268. Potassium dimethyldithiocarbamate. $K[(CH_3)_2NCS_2]$; mol.wt. 159.2. A 50% aqueous solution used as a shortstop in the mfg. of synthetic rubber. An amber-to-light-green liquid; sp.gr. 1.22–1.24 (25°/25°C.); f.p. —14.2°C.
PENNSYLVANIA SALT MFG. CO.

Shed-A-Leaf®. A sodium chlorate defoliant and desiccant. Available in liquid form (SHED-A-LEAF "L"), and powder form (SHED-A-LEAF "D"). Applied as spray or dust by airplane or ground applicators. *Uses:* As a defoliant on cotton, bean, tomato and other plants to hasten maturing of the crops, and to reduce rot and late insect infection; and as a rice desiccant. CHIPMAN CHEMICAL CO.

Sheele's Mineral△. Same as SWEDISH GREEN△.

Sheen®. (*Supp.* I p. 213). Now a registered trademark. HEATBATH CORP.

Sheerset® Resin. (*HBMTN* p. 511). No longer available. AMERICAN CYANAMID CO.

Shelby®. The trademark for a line of seamless steel tubing. UNITED STATES STEEL CORP., NATIONAL TUBE DIV.

Shelf-X®. (*HBMTN* p. 511). No longer available. UNITED STATES GYPSUM CO.

Shell-105 and Shell-205 Catalysts. *See* 105® CATALYST *and* 205® CATALYST.

Shellac△. *Also known as* LACCA△. A resinous excretion of the insect Laccifer (*Tachardia*) *lacca* Kerr, order *Homoptera*, family *Coccidae*. The larva of the lac insect settle on the branches of various trees of southern Asia, pierce the bark, and feed on the sap. The lac secretion forms a thick secretion over the twigs. This is scraped off and dried. The whitest grade of shellac is produced when the Kusum tree (*Schleichera trijuga*) is the host. The dried material, known as STIC-LAC, contains lac resin, woody matter, lac dye, bodies of insects, etc. The STICK-LAC is screened, ground and washed, forming SEED LAC from which SHELLAC is prepared by melting or by solvent extraction. It is marketed in the form of brittle, yellowish, transparent sheets, or crushed. Most SHELLAC is produced in the central and United provinces of India and in the states of Bihar and Orissa.

SHELLAC is a unique plastic resin because it possesses thermosetting and thermoplastic properties. Heat curing increases its mechanical and electrical strength. Sp.gr. 1.035–1.140; m.p. 115–120°C.; saponification no. 185–210; iodine no. 10–18; insoluble in water; soluble in aqueous solutions of ethanolamines, alkalis, and borax. *Uses:* Principally in lacquers and varnishes; in mfg. of adhesives, insulating compounds, some molding compounds, buttons, grinding wheels, sealing wax, cements, inks, phonograph records; for stiffening hats; in medicinal tablets and coatings; in finishing leather; etc.

Shelldie. A 5.00% chromium-2.00% molybdenum hot-work die steel furnished in both annealed and heat-treated conditions. A FINKEL & SONS CO.

Sherdye®. A line of pigment emulsions for printing on textiles. Advantages are sharpness of print, fidelity of reproduction of engravings, brilliancy of shade, excellent light resistance, and ease and economy of application. SHERWIN-WILLIAMS CO.

Sher-Glide[NE]. A line of zone-marking paints recommended for use on concrete and bituminous surfaces. SHERWIN-WILLIAMS CO.

Shielding Micropaint. *See* RS14 SHIELDING MICROPAINT[NE], *and* SS12-B SILVER SHIELDING MICROPAINT[NE].

Shine®. An all-vegetable, fully hydrogenated shortening for use in baking, frying and pastry making. ANDERSON, CLAYTON & CO. FOODS DIV.

Shirayuki®. Food savoring powders comprising monosodium glutamate. INTERNATIONAL MINERALS & CHEMICAL CORP.

Shockgard[NE]. A protective head covering of the hat or cap type, primarily designed to provide protection to the wearer from high voltage electricity. MINE SAFETY APPLIANCES CO.

Shorewood[NE]. A line of coated papers. KIMBERLY-CLARK CORP.

Short Ternes△. *See* TERNE PLATE△.

Shu-Glo®. (*Supp.* I p. 215). Now a registered trademark. SIGMA CHEMICAL CO.

Shurflo®. The trademark for high quality filter cloths made from cotton flannel material, bleached or unbleached, for milk filters; and for filter cloths for all commercial coffee making equipment. AMERICAN URN BAG CO.

Shur-Tred®. A self-polishing floor finish having slip-retardant characteristics. It can be buffed to remove scuffs, and possesses good durability and water resistance. It can be used on linoleum, rubber tile, asphalt tile, vinyl, sealed cork and wood, terrazzo, and sealed or painted concrete. S. C. JOHNSON & SON

Sikacrete®. (*HBMTN* p. 514). Now a registered mark. SIKA CHEMICAL CORP.

Silcoseal. *See* PARKO® SILCOSEAL.

Silcotite. A clear, colorless, silicone-type water repellent for above-grade masonry walls. Contains 4½% silicone solids in a petroleum solvent. CERESIT WATERPROOFING CORP.

Silicones△. A group of materials produced by the condensation of organo-silicon halide intermediates. The intermediates may be made by different methods, including a direct process, the Grignard method, and the olefin method. Modified silicones are prepared by reacting a silicone intermediate with an organic compound containing more than one hydroxyl group and then reacting the final product with fatty acids or phthalic anhydride to give alkyd-type polymers containing siloxane groupings. Organopolysiloxanes are made up of a molecular skeleton of silicon-oxygen linkages, with organic groups completing the molecule. Structurally, organopolysiloxanes may be linear or crosslinked. The degree of crosslinking and the type of organic groups in the molecule determine, to a large extent, the physical form of the finished SILICONE. Dependent on the structure and composition, a SILICONE may be fluid, resinous or elastomeric.

SILICONES are characterized by a unique combination of desirable properties: they retain their basic physical properties at elevated temps., yet are serviceable at very low temps.; they are highly resistant to oxidation and weathering, and to the action of many corrosive chemicals; most SILICONES are water repellent and have excellent dielectric properties; and many SILICONES have excellent adhesive properties. Some of the important applications for SILICONE products are as follows:

SILICONE FLUIDS: As antifoaming agents, release agents, lubricating fluids, damping fluids, hydraulic fluids, dielectric fluids, diffusion pump fluids, ingredients in polishes and cosmetics, and for the treatment of leather, textiles, and paper.

SILICONE COMPOUNDS: For pressure-sensitive adhesives, anti-foaming agents, release agents, adhesives, sealing compounds for electrical applications, lubricants, dielectric compounds.

SILICONE RESINS: As vehicles for formulating paints, enamels, varnishes, masonry water repellents; in electrical varnishes for bonding, cloth coatings, wire coatings, and impregnating; in molding compounds; for ready-to-use foaming powders; for high- and low-pressure laminating and bonding.

SILICONE ELASTOMERS: In rubber pastes for caulking, sealing, coating, and encapsulation; rubber dispersions; gums for compounding; and rubber stocks for extruding, molding, calendering, laminating, wire coverings, and sponging.

Silicote Skin Protectant Ointment®. A 30%-silicone oil in a petroleum base used to protect the skin against cutting oils, detergents, soap and water, and other industrial irritants. ARNAR-STONE LABORATORIES, INC.

Siligen A. A textile-finishing auxiliary for use in imparting anti-slip and dirt-resistant properties. It is an odorless liquid of neutral reaction, which is readily miscible with water in any proportion. It is unaffected by hard water, and it may be applied at any temp. It is compatible with most of the usual softening, creaseproofing, water-repellent and other finishing agents. NOVA CHEMICAL CO.

Silk△. A fibrous material produced by the exudation of a liquid from the head canals of the silkworm, or larva of the moth *Bombyx mori*. The liquid solidifies to a flexible filament immediately upon being exposed to the air. The cultivation of silkworms is a major industry in the Mediterranean countries and in parts of the Orient, particularly China and Japan. Eggs are laid by the silkmoth on strips of cloth, which are kept in rooms for several months under controlled conditions of temperature and humidity. After about a month, the worm hatches and it is fed on mulberry leaves for about 40 days, when it is ready to spin its cocoon. The cocoons are placed in warm water to soften the SILK glue and the SILK filaments are unwound. The filaments from several cocoons are reeled off and twisted together into a thread and finally made up into a skein. The raw SILK fiber, known as FIBROIN, consists largely of the amino acid alanine, $CH_3CH(NH_2)COOH$. Most crude SILK has a cream color, but some SILKS are a brilliant yellow. This color is removed in the degumming operations. Individual crude SILK fibers are about 0.018 mm. in diameter. Each cocoon provides from 2,000 to 3,000 yards of filament.

Silkoat[NE]. (*Supp.* I p. 216). No longer available. BURGESS, FOBES CO.

Silkos. A line of water-ground micas for use in the wallpaper and coated paper industries. Included are: No. 4 SILKOS, a 160-mesh product; and No. 8 SILKOS, 200-mesh. FRANKLIN MINERAL PRODUCTS CO.

Silvatrim®. A plastic molding that simulates chrome. It consists of a clear plastic body with a mirror-bright foil imbedded in it. These cored-foil extrusions are available in various sizes and shapes; and can be used in place of metal molding for such applications as counter tops, etc. GLASS LABORATORIES, INC.

Silverbrite[NE]. A ready-mixed aluminum paint for general exterior and interior use. SHERWIN-WILLIAMS CO.

Silver King. See BOSTON SILVER KING.

Silver King Rotocord. See BOSTON SILVER KING ROTOCORD.

Silverline®. The trademark for a cold-drawn seamless steel tubing used for one-piece subsurface pump barrels by the oil-producing industry.
UNITED STATES STEEL CORP., OIL WELL SUPPLY DIV.

Silver Micropaints. See SC12 *and* SC13 SILVERMICROPAINTS[NE], *and* SS12-B SILVER SHIELDING MICROPAINT[NE].

Simex®. A line of lightweight, rigid-type, reinforced resin-bonded grinding wheels for heavy-duty, severe jobs where stock removal is given preference over finish. Designed for use on portable disc sanders and right-angle portable grinders. These are laminated wheels; the grinding section consists of resin-bonded abrasive particles reinforced with alpha cellulose fibers, the grinding side is covered with a reinforcing fabric, and the wheel is backed with a spiral safety web backing. *Use:* For grinding welds, removing flash and bead, and cleaning up rough, ragged surfaces and edges, especially on stainless steel.
SIMONDS ABRASIVE CO.

Simplex®. A specialty corn starch used in the paper industry for laminating and bag pasting.
A. E. STALEY MFG. CO.

Simpson®. The trademark for: (1) lumber, plywood, doors, insulating board products, hardboard, and acoustical products; (2) redwood lumber; and (3) paper and paper products. SIMPSON LUMBER CO.

Sincaline△. *Same as* CHOLINE△.

Singletone. *See* CRAFTINT SINGLETONE.

Sinker®. The trademark for a line of cement-coated nails. UNITED STATES STEEL CORP.

Sioux. *Same as* ATLAS®Can.. KK.

Sippyplex®. A preparation for the treatment of peptic ulcer and other gastrointestinal disorders associated with hyperacidity. It consists of antcids for the control of gastric acidity; high-protein defatted milk solids for its acid buffering action and nutritional support; and vitamins to protect against ulcer stress and dietary invalidism. PURDUE FREDERICK CO.

Sisal△. The hard, strong, light-yellow to reddish fibers from the large leaves of the sisal plant, *Agave sisalana*, and the HENEQUEN plant *A. fourcroydes*. The plant grows best in semiarid regions. The agave plant is native to Mexico, but most SISAL comes from Haiti. East Africa, and the East Indies. YUCATAN SISAL, known as HENEQUEN, is obtained from the HENEQUEN plant and is reddish in color and much stiffer and coarser than regular SISAL. About 80% of all binder twine is made from SISAL. Ropes made of SISAL have only about 75% of the strength of MANILA rope and are not as resistant to moisture. *Uses:* For cordage and rope; for sacking material; as a substitute for hair in cement wall plaster; and in laminated plastics.

Sisalkraft Moistop®. A permanent vapor barrier for use under concrete floors and for crawl spaces. It consists of a top layer of black polyethylene, which is acid- and alkali-proof, and a bottom layer of tough, impregnated kraft paper treated to resist fungus and mold. Available in rolls up to 8 ft. wide.
AMERICAN SISALKRAFT CORP.

Sisalkraft Vaporstop®. A reinforced waterproof paper used as a moisture barrier under concrete floors and as a ground cover for crawl spaces under homes without basements. Available in rolls 3 to 8 ft. wide.
AMERICAN SISALKRAFT CORP.

Skat®. (*HBMTN* p. 517). No longer available.
GALLOWHUR CHEMICAL CORP.

Skiabaryt®. (*Supp.* I p. 218). No longer available.
SHARP & DOHME DIV., MERCK & CO.

Skimkote[NE]. A "feather-edge" floor-surfacing material designed for patching, leveling and smoothing rough floors. HALLEMITE MFG. CO.

Skin-Cote. A waterless hand cream containing a solvent buffered by emollient oils, petrolatum and lanolin. It changes to a liquid, loosening dirt, grime, rubber cement, etc. BOYER-CAMPBELL CO.

Skullgard[NE]. A head covering of the hat or cap type designed to protect the wearer from head injuries.
MINE SAFETY APPLIANCES CO.

Sky Chief® Marine Gasoline. A high-octane motor fuel for inboard or outboard engines. It is supercharged with PETROX for full, knockless power.
TEXAS CO.

SL®. (*HBMTN* p. 518). Now a registered trademark. MALLINCKRODT CHEMICAL WORKS

Slatekote[NE]. A mineral-surfaced, ready-to-lay asphalt roofing material. Available in several different colors. It is 36″ wide with a 2″ selvedge edge for lap. (*See also* SLATEKOTE DUPLEX *and* MODERNEDGE SLATEKOTE). JOHNS-MANVILLE SALES CORP.

Slatekote Duplex[NE]. A style of SLATEKOTE roofing for use where a longer lasting roof is desired on pitches as low as 1″ to the foot, where built-up roofing is not available. It is 36″ wide, with a 17″ slate surfacing and 19″ selvedge for cementing.
JOHNS-MANVILLE SALES CORP.

Sliprite®. A line of vegetable shell dusting powders for use during the shaving of hides in the tanning industry; and as dusting powders in the rubber industry. AGRASHELL, INC.

Slip-Screen®. A sheet of flexible, plastic-like material, with thousands of tiny perforations, for use in ammonia-developing photographic tanks. It rests on top of the developer tank, providing a smooth, almost zero-frictional surface between the tank and the sleeve. When sensitized materials are inserted in the developer, they slide easily across the screen without sticking or binding. Ammonia fumes readily pass through the screen, and develop the diazotype material. TECNIFAX CORP.

Smo-Cloud. A fog-type insecticide, designed for killing roaches, waterbugs, ants, flies, mosquitoes and other flying insects. A fine fog, resembling heavy white smoke, is released when the contents of the can are lighted with a match. There is no flame. The lighted match starts a rapid vaporizing process that continues until all of the material in the can has been converted into a penetrating insecticidal fog. When used as directed, it is non-injurious to humans and animals. CONTINENTAL CHEMISTE CORP.

Smokescope®. An optical instrument. *Use:* For comparatively estimating the density of smoke.
MINE SAFETY APPLIANCES CO.

Snofos®. (*HBMTN* p. 519 and *Supp.* I p. 218). No longer available. GENERAL CHEMICAL DIV., ALLIED CHEMICAL & DYE CORP.

Sno Gard®. The trademark for a line of fence posts.
UNITED STATES STEEL CORP.

Snow Floss[NE]. A grade of CELITE® MINERAL FILLERS especially suitable as a non-scratching, polishing abrasive for fine polishes. The thin-walled cellular structure of this material causes the individual particles to collapse under pressure before they can scratch. In addition, this highly porous powder absorbs residual oil, dirt or other solid matter and leaves a coating that can be easily and completely removed from the polished surface. The average particle size of SNOW FLOSS is 1–2 microns; sp.gr. 2.00; fineness, 1% (max.) on 325-mesh screen; free moisture content, 6% (max.); bulking value, lb./cu.ft., 8 (loose) and 22 (wet). JOHNS-MANVILLE SALES CORP.

Soap Bark△. *Same as* QUILLAJA△.

Soaperior®. A liquid toilet soap made from cocoanut and other vegetable oils, and containing lanolin. It is mildly perfumed.
U. S. SANITARY SPECIALTIES CORP.

Soaproot△. *Same as* SAPONARIA△.

Soapstone△. A massive variety of TALC or hydrous magnesium silicate. It can be cut readily, and on being heated it becomes very hard due to the loss of its combined water. It is used for electric panels, gasjet tips, stove linings, tank linings, as an abrasive, and for chemical laboratory tabletops and sinks.

Soapure[NE]. An industrial liquid antiseptic hand soap, containing 3% hexachlorophene on the dry soap basis. Active ingredient: bis(3,5,6 trichloro-2-hydroxyphenyl) methane. It also contains lanolin.
U. S. SANITARY SPECIALTIES CORP.

Soapwort△. *Same as* SAPONARIA△.

Sobo® Adhesive. (*HBMTN* p. 520). The name SOBO is now a registered trademark.
SLOMONS LABORATORIES, INC.

Soda Ash△. Anhydrous sodium carbonate. Na_2CO_3; mol.wt. 106.00. A white, odorless, hygroscopic powder made by the Solvay process in which a purified brine solution is treated successively with ammonia gas and carbon dioxide. Under controlled operating conditions, high purity sodium bicarbonate precipitates. This is then calcined to the anhydrous sodium carbonate. SODA ASH is marketed in three grades: extra-light, light and dense. The extra-light grade has a density of 23 lb./cu.ft.; the dense grade, 63 lb./cu.ft. *Uses:* In the mfg. of sodium salts, glass, and soap; for softening water; as an analytical reagent; in textile scouring and wool washing; in oil refining, etc.

Soda Lime△. A mixture of calcium oxide and from 5 to 20% sodium hydroxide and containing from 6 to 18% water. It absorbs 25–35% of its weight of carbon dioxide. *Uses:* As an absorbent for carbon dioxide in basal metabolism tests, in rebreathing anesthesia systems, and in carbon determinations.

Sodan® Solution. (*Supp.* I p. 219). No longer available. NITROGEN DIV., ALLIED CHEMICAL & DYE CORP.

Softex Y[NE]. An amphoteric type of softener for cellulosic fabrics. It exhausts readily on the material from a dilute aqueous solution; it imparts a soft full hand to fabrics; and does not yellow when exposed to the usual temps. employed in dyeing textiles. W. F. FANCOURT CO.

Soft Silica△. Same as TRIPOLI△.

Soilox®. (*Supp.* I p. 219). No longer available. CROWN ZELLERBACH CORP.

Solar®. A group of fast-to-light water-dispersible pigments prepared from the phosphotungsto molybdate-type lakes of basic dyes and used for tinting paper in the beater, especially white paper, and for tinting paper coatings. GENERAL DYESTUFF CO.

Solasol[NE]. Sodium lauryl sulfate in needle form which eliminates dust irritation that occurs when the powdered form of this compound is used. It is a dispersing agent, dyeing assistant, and textile finishing assistant. ACETO CHEMICAL CO.

Solasol USP Extra[NE]. A surface-active agent consisting of sodium lauryl sulfate U.S.P., in powder form, made by sulfation of a distilled lauryl alcohol to insure a product whose alkyd group contains a max. of C_{12} molecules. *Uses:* As an anionic wetting agent, dispersing agent, and penetrating agent; in cleaners, scouring products, etc. ACETO CHEMICAL CO.

Solbrol M & P. (*HBMTN* p. 521). No longer available; Company liquidated as of Oct. 1, 1955. GENERAL DRUG CO.

Solfast®. A line of red, green and blue pigment colors, available in dry form, and dispersed in litho varnish, printing ink vehicles, alkyd varnishes, plasticizers, etc. Available in the following grades:

Solo Brand[NE]. A line of 20 concentrated, water-soluble imitation fruit flavors for the mfg. of flavoring extracts. FLORASYNTH LABORATORIES, INC.

Solomides®. (*Supp.* I p. 219). No longer available. SHARP & DOHME DIV., MERCK & CO.

Solon F[NE]. An amino polycarboxylic acid sequestering agent specifically compounded to remove iron during kier boiling. Its use results in elimination of troublesome rust spots or yellowing due to presence of metallic salts (particularly iron) in the kier water. EASTERN COLOR & CHEMICAL CO.

Solpon KD[NE]. A textile fulling, dyeing and scouring assistant consisting of a protein-fatty acid condensate. It protects animal fibers against damage during alkaline processing. PIONEER CHEMICAL WORKS, INC.

Sol-Speedi-Dri®. An oil and grease absorbent for floors. It is an inorganic product, essentially a highly adsorbent clay.
MINERALS & CHEMICALS CORP. OF AMERICA

Soluble Oil CX. See TEXACO® SOLUBLE OIL CX.

Sol-U-Lube[NE]. A soapless compound for the removal of a wide variety of stains from fabrics. It is stable in both acids and alkalis; and it will not react chemically with either the fabric or dye. HUNTINGTON LABORATORIES, INC.

Sol-U-Soap[NE]. A dry-cleaning soap. It contains a corrosion inhibitor which helps to prevent corrosion in the system due to hydrolysis. HUNTINGTON LABORATORIES, INC.

Solutized®. (*HBMTN* p. 522). No longer available. NOPCO CHEMICAL CO.

Solvacera[NE]. A wax for use in the preparation of solvent-type floor polishes for linoleum and wood floors. INTERNATIONAL WAX REFINING CO.

Color	Properties	Uses
SOLFAST RED (medium and bluish-red shades)	Good light resistance Good heat resistance Good chemical resistance Non-bleeding Very strong	Printing inks Paints and enamels Rubber Plastics
SOLFAST GREEN (light and dark shades)	Excellent light resistance Excellent heat resistance Excellent chemical resistance Non-bleeding Very strong	Paints and enamels Lacquers Printing inks Rubber Plastics
SOLFAST SKY BLUE (green and reddish shades)	Excellent light resistance Excellent heat resistance Excellent chemical resistance Non-bleeding Very strong	Paints and enamels Lacquers Printing inks Rubber Plastics

SHERWIN-WILLIAMS CO.

Soligens®. (*HBMTN* p. 521). No longer available. ADVANCE SOLVENTS & CHEMICAL CORP.

Solinox®. (*HBMTN* p. 521). No longer available. SPENCER KELLOGG & SONS

Solnus® Oils. See NEW SOLNUS® OILS.

Solvent 101. A combination of solvents which will gradually soften cured epoxy resins. CARL H. BIGGS CO.

Solvent Degreaser[NE]. A very high flash point, degreasing solvent which replaces carbon tetrachloride and flammable petroleum solvents. Dries residue-free; approved by U. S. Coast Guard and major insurance companies; listed by Underwriters Laboratories. Used for cleaning electric motors and electronic equipment, and dewaxing bread wrapping machinery. BRULIN & CO.

Sol-Vet. A water-treatment service for the elimination and prevention of scale, prevention of corrosion, and elimination of foaming and priming in boilers, condensers, refrigerating brine systems, etc; and for algae control. The service includes a survey of the plant, and the formulation of treatment chemicals for the specific conditions encountered.
ANDERSON-STOLZ CORP.

Somatovite®. A preparation consisting of reserpine, in safe, low-level dosage, combined with VITAMINS B_1 and B_{12}, in tablet and liquid dosage forms. Used to improve appetite and eating habits, normalize sleeping patterns, reduce the appetite-depressing and growth-inhibiting factors of tension, irritability, hyperactivity, and emotional unrest.
PURDUE FREDERICK CO.

Sonaquol®. (HBMTN p. 523). Now a registered trademark. L. SONNEBORN SONS, INC.

SonNoMar®. A sealer and protective coating for concrete floors. Composed of a blend of synthetic resins possessing high chemical resistance and hardness and combined with high elastic plasticizing agents. Protects and seals concrete floors by providing max. abrasion resistance and immunity to attack by most chemicals. L. SONNEBORN SONS, INC.

Sonocor®. Thin, flexible, soft blankets of interbonded fibrous glass used as a sound-absorbing medium behind perforated ceilings.
OWENS-CORNING FIBERGLAS CORP.

Sonofaced® Acoustical Tile. An acoustical tile having a vibratable plastic membrane covering.
OWENS-CORNING FIBERGLAS CORP.

Sono-Grip®. A non-slip, plastic brush coating that provides safe footing on concrete, metal or wood. It is an aggregate-reinforced, non-slip, plastic coating that is applied by brush to walkaways, stairs, ramps, platforms, decks, and other slippery areas to reduce danger of falls. Provides sure footing on concrete, wood or metal surfaces, for the prevention of accidents. L. SONNEBORN SONS, INC.

Sono-Jell®. (HBMTN p. 523). Now a registered trademark. L. SONNEBORN SONS, INC.

Sonotard®. A retarding admixture for concrete, mortar and stucco. It is a dry, free-flowing, powdered, lime-reactive composition containing puzzuolanic, plasticizing, and water ratio-reducing agents designed to impart highly colloidal properties to Portland cement pastes, to delay early hydration, and to densify the concrete. Its use makes possible more effective control in designing, mixing, placing and finishing cementitous mixes over a wide range of job conditions. L. SONNEBORN SONS, INC.

Soot-Solv. A product for the removal of carbon deposits on the heating surfaces of boilers, in stacks, etc. It is a solid, which is spread over the bed of hot coal or blown directly into the boiler if the boiler is oil-heated. ANDERSON-STOLZ CORP.

Sorbistat®. Sorbic acid. $CH_3(CH)_4COOH$; mol.wt. 122.12. A white, fluffy crystalline powder, sorbic acid is a selective growth inhibitor for many molds and yeasts and certain bacteria which cause spoilage in food products. Low levels of sorbic acid are used in such products as carbonated beverages, fruit-flavored syrups, fruit and vegetable juices, wines, vinegars, salad dressings, pickles and related products, margarine and other acidic foods. It has been reported to be of value in aqueous sugar solutions, cheeses and baked goods. Certain food products such as cheese and margarine may be protected by the use of wrapping material impregnated with sorbic acid. CHAS. PFIZER & CO.

Sorlate®. Sorbitan monooleate polyoxyethylene. A digestant possessing good emulsifying and wetting properties. Used in the treatment of malnutrition due to faulty fat absorption. ABBOTT LABORATORIES

Soundscope®. A precision sound-level meter and analyzer. *Use:* For direct measurement and analysis of noise. MINE SAFETY APPLIANCES CO.

Southern Queen®. A standard type shortening made from hardened vegetable oils processed for a wide variety of uses. It is uniform in quality and has a bland, neutral flavor and a wide plastic range which makes it suitable for use in many food products.
ANDERSON, CLAYTON & CO. FOODS DIV.

Span®. (*Supp.* I p. 221). This product is also mfg'd in England, Germany, and Canada, and the trademark is also registered in these countries.
ATLAS POWDER CO.
HONEYWILL-ATLAS, LTD.
ATLAS-GOLDSCHMIDT G.M.B.H.
ATLAS POWDER CO., CANADA, LTD.

Sparta 80®. (HBMTN p. 525). No longer available. UNIVERSAL-CYCLOPS STEEL CORP.

Special A. R. Roof Putty®. A highly adhesive black roof putty especially suitable for quick repairs on smooth-surface asphalt roofs where it is necessary to seal plies of felt together. Packed in containers holding 1, 5 and 15 gal. JOHNS-MANVILLE SALES CORP.

Special Flexible Fyrex®. (HBMTN p. 527). No longer available. VICTOR CHEMICAL WORKS

Special Nutrient 4-S®. A derivative of soybeans, used as a nutrient in microbiological processes, particularly in the production of antibiotics.
A. E. STALEY MFG. CO.

Special Nutrient 22® and Special Nutrient 114®. Liquids, rich in amino acids, refined from corn steep liquor. They are used as nutrients in microbiological processes, particularly in the production of antibiotics.
A. E. STALEY MFG. CO.

Specification®. (HBMTN p. 527). No longer available. NOPCO CHEMICAL CO.

Speco Bleach Assist®. A white, powdery, stable compound for use in conjunction with sodium chlorite in both stripping and bleaching of synthetic fabrics. It serves to slow down the release of CO_2 gas, thus inhibiting odor and increasing the efficiency of the chlorite. It also inhibits rusting and corrosion of machinery and equipment.
INDEPENDENT CHEMICAL CORP.

Specon #33[NE]. A 33%-active nonionic alkylaryl polyether alcohol for use in household and industrial cleaners; in textile processing; as an emulsifying agent for insecticides and herbicides; in electroplating baths; and as a dispersing agent for industrial products. INDEPENDENT CHEMICAL CORP.

Specon X 13[NE]. A 100%-active, nonionic polyoxyethylene ether of fatty alcohol for use as an emulsifying agent at low pH. It is also used to promote level dyeing of textiles. INDEPENDENT CHEMICAL CORP.

Speco Pal EO 33[NE]. A 33%-active, nonionic alkyl phenol polyethylene oxide condensate. It is a textile detergent for removal of all types of soil. It has high wetting action at very low conc., and, therefore, is particularly beneficial for use in wetting out and in dyeing. INDEPENDENT CHEMICAL CORP.

Speco Sodium Chlorite[NE]. A pure-white, high-quality sodium chlorite of 80% conc. for use in the bleaching and stripping of all types of synthetic fibers. It is especially suited for bleaching ORLON. INDEPENDENT CHEMICAL CORP.

Spec-Pro-Tector[NE]. A welder's and chipper's coverall goggle. EASTERN EQUIPMENT CO.

Spec-Tak®. A liquid bottle-washing compound. It is a caustic material that controls scale and produces clean, sparkling bottles even in hard water areas. DIVERSEY CORP.

Specti-Goggle[NE]. A line of spectacle-type goggles. EASTERN EQUIPMENT CO.

Spectra-Glaze®. Concrete blocks with one or more faces glazed with a thermosetting resinous compound permanently bonded by heat treatment. Resistant to chemicals and stain. Available in a range of colors. BURNS & RUSSELL CO.

Spectrum. A line of paints including:
SPECTRUM ALKYD WALL PAINTS. Flat, semi-gloss, and gloss paints for interior walls, ceilings, and woodwork.
SPECTRUM RUBBERIZED WALL PAINT. A water-emulsion paint for interior walls, woodwork, brick, concrete, plaster, wall board, etc.
SPECTRUM RUBBERIZED MASONRY PAINT. A synthetic vinyl resin emulsion primer and finish for both interior and exterior masonry such as stucco, concrete, brick, cement block, asbestos-cement, etc.
SPECTRUM HOUSE PAINT. An oil-base paint for exterior wood siding.
SPECTRUM SASH AND TRIM PAINT. An alkyd resin paint for exterior trim such as sash, doors, shutters, etc.
SPECTRUM SHINGLE AND SHAKE PAINT. An alkyd-type flat oil-base primer and finish for exterior wood shakes and shingles and other exterior wood siding where a flat finish is desired.
BARRELED SUNLIGHT PAINT CO.

Speculum Metal[△]. An alloy of 55 to 67% copper and the balance tin. It is a hard, tough alloy that takes a high surface polish, and is corrosion resistant. It is used as a surface coating on food-processing equipment and on optical reflectors for it retains its reflectivity better than silver.

Speed Cut®. A free-machining die steel furnished heat-treated ready-for-use for die-casting dies for white-metal alloys, plastic-mold plates, die shoes, backing plates and many other applications. Its alloy content is sufficient to produce hardnesses of 275 to 325 Brinell for sizes as large as 20″ × 10″ on cooling in still air, and it machines very readily at such hardness. It has proved outstanding for press brake dies due to its excellent wear resistance and non-galling properties. It is used for plastic molds, cavity plates, backing plates, die-casting dies for white metal, reamer bodies, boring bars, collets, bushings, shafts and spindles. Composition: carbon, 0.43%; silicon, 0.30%; manganese, 0.85%; chromium, 1.15%; molybdenum, 0.50%. VANADIUM-ALLOYS STEEL CO.

Speedee White Sidewall Tire Cleaner. A tire cleaner that is sprayed on and then flushed off. It requires no rubbing or scrubbing. DORAN CHEMICAL CO.

Speedex[NE]. An iron powder welding material. METAL & THEMIT CORP.

Speedex. See DICALITE® SPEEDEX.

Speedflow. See DICALITE® SPEEDFLOW.

Speedframe[NE]. A head hardness with welding goggles attached. MINE SAFETY APPLIANCES CO.

Speed-Glos®. A polish for fine silver. FRANKLIN RESEARCH CO.

Speed King® Printing and Lithographic Inks. (*Supp.* I p. 222). Formerly a product of CHARLES ENEU JOHNSON COMPANY; now mfg'd and dist'd by INTERCHEMICAL CORP., PRINTING INK DIV., under their trademark IPI®.

Speedline®. A line of stainless steel fittings especially designed for Schedules 5 and 10 stainless steel pipe. The fittings are low in cost and light in weight, and are easily and quickly installed by expanding the pipe into the fittings. HORACE T. POTTS CO.

Speed-Lite. See BOSTON SPEED-LITE.

Speedplus. See DICALITE® SPEEDPLUS.

Speed-Rex®. An industrial maintenance paint for handling equipment, metal partitions, conveyor lines, hand trucks, machinery, tools, motors, etc., in bakeries, paper mills, breweries, textile mills, packing houses, chemical plants, and other plants. It is based on DEVRAN® epoxy resins, and is resistant to vegetable oils and greases, alkalis, water, cleaning compounds and many other chemicals. It dries to the touch in 15 min.; and is very tough and adherent.
TRUSCON LABORATORIES

Speed-Wax®. A furniture polish formulated with CARNAUBA wax and silicones. It cleans and polishes in a single operation. FRANKLIN RESEARCH CO.

Spellerized®. The trademark for a line of steel pipes, tubes, casings and couplings. UNITED STATES STEEL CORP.

Spermacetti[△]. *Also known as* CETACEUM[△]. A waxy substance that separates from SPERM OIL on cooling after boiling. Consists chiefly of cetyl palmitate, free cetyl alcohol, esters of lauric, stearic, and myristic acids, and esters of higher alcohols. It is a white, somewhat translucent, slightly unctuous material with a crystalline fracture and pearly luster; practically odorless and tasteless; turns yellow and rancid on long exposure to air. Sp.gr. 0.938–0.944; m.p. 42–50°C.; saponification no. 120–136; iodine no. 3–4.4; insoluble in water and cold alcohol; soluble in chloroform, ether, carbon disulfide, oil, boiling alcohol; slightly soluble in petroleum ether. *Uses:* As a base for ointments; in mfg. of candles, soap, cosmetics, and laundry wax; in finishing and lustering of linen.

Sperm Oil△. A thin, yellow, waxy oil obtained from the head cavity of the sperm whale, *Physeter breviceps* and the Bottlenose whale, *P. macrocephalus*. Composed of esters of fatty acids and some SPERMACETTI. Sp.gr. 0.875–0.885; saponification no. 123–147; iodine no. 80–84; flash point, above 440°F.; insoluble in water, cold alcohol, and petroleum ether; soluble in chloroform and ether. *Uses:* As a lubricant; in mfg. of soap; for hardening steel; as a lamp oil; and when sulfonated, as a wetting agent in textile mfg.

Sperse[NE]. Carboxymethylcellulose (HERCULES® CMC) designed for use as an ingredient in laundry starch. HERCULES POWDER CO.

Spice Air. A room deodorizer, in an aerosol bomb dispenser, for dining rooms and kitchens. It has a tangy fragrance. CLAIRE MFG. CO.

Spicearomes[NE]. A line of highly concentrated, water-soluble spice flavors. FLORASYNTH LABORATORIES, INC.

Spider®. A rubbermaker's grade of ground crude sulfur with conditioner added.
OLIN MATHIESON CHEMICAL CORP.

Spiralok®. Specially constructed cartridges used for high explosives, which enable the joining of several cartridges to make a rigid column of any reasonable length. HERCULES POWDER CO.

Spirapoint®. A spirally wound abrasive cloth with a conical-tapered point used on threaded mandrels for polishing hard-to-reach areas and difficult radii.
BEHR-MANNING CO.

Spirotallic®. Metal-asbestos gaskets made of interlocked plies of preformed metal, cushioned with asbestos strip spirally wound. When compressed in service, the central spring-like corrugation of the metal strip is held under constant tension, compensating for expansion and contraction due to frequent and extreme changes of temp. This action creates and maintains a perfect seal. Available in a number of different styles. JOHNS-MANVILLE SALES CORP.

Spongex®. (*HBMTN* p. 529). Now a product of B. F. GOODRICH SPONGE PRODUCTS DIV., B. F. GOODRICH Co., successor to SPONGE RUBBER PRODUCTS CO.

Spongex® Handi-Floats[NE]. Floats of expanded polyvinyl chloride (SPONGEX® PLASTIC) for flotation requirements such as life-lines, marker buoys, swimming aids, and, in assembly, as marine fenders. They are lightweight, permanently buoyant, rot-proof, and resistant to marine growth.
B. F. GOODRICH SPONGE PRODUCTS DIV.

Spongex® Plastic. Incorrectly listed as SPONGE PLASTIC® (*HBMTN* p. 529). Now a product of B. F. GOODRICH SPONGE PRODUCTS DIV., B. F. GOODRICH Co., successor to SPONGE RUBBER PRODUCTS CO.

Spongex® Ring Life Buoys. Lightweight, mildew-resistant buoys of expanded polyvinyl chloride (SPONGEX® PLASTIC) for use as life-saving equipment approved by the United States Coast Guard. Available in rings of 18", 20", 24", and 30" diam.
B. F. GOODRICH SPONGE PRODUCTS DIV.

Spor-Co®. (*Supp.* I p. 222). No longer available.
GENERAL CHEMICAL DIV.,
ALLIED CHEMICAL & DYE CORP.

Spot-Clor®. The trademark for spotting compounds having bleaching properties.
PENNSYLVANIA SALT MFG. CO.

Spotticator®. A cleaning fluid for fabrics.
PENNSYLVANIA SALT MFG. CO.

Spradri®. A patented water-displacing chemical, with a rust inhibitor and preservative, packaged in an aerosol container. When sprayed on damp or wet surfaces, it penetrates, creeps into pores and crevices, displaces and drives out water, and leaves a microscopic, molecular, protective film. *Uses:* To dry out damp or flooded electrical and mechanical equipment and machinery; and to protect metal parts from rust and corrosion. SPRADRI CO.

Spra-Gard®. A peelable, plastic-type spray-booth coating that can be removed in large sheets. Applied by conventional spray equipment. The coating is non-flammable when dry.
FIDELITY CHEMICAL PRODUCTS CORP.

Spray Flo®. A detergent composition particularly adapted for circulation and spray cleaning of food-processing equipment, including piping, pressure tanks, storage tanks, and the like.
PENNSYLVANIA SALT MFG. CO.

Spraylat® SC-1071B. A temporary, protective coating for painted, lacquered and enameled surfaces. It is a viscous, water-base compound composed of plasticized resins emulsified in water. When sprayed onto the surface to be protected it forms a tough, strippable, elastic film that is resistant to oils, rust, grease, alkalis, acids, and fats; and it is inert to plastics, rubber, glass, metal, etc. When desired, the plastic coating is removed by simply peeling it off from the surface.
SPRAYLAT CORP.

Spray-Lube[NE]. A black, heavy-duty lubricant for open gears, open chains, cables, etc. on industrial, mining, construction, and maritime equipment. It is packaged in an aerosol container for rapid, non-messy application. It has extreme-pressure characteristics, high m.p. (will not run off under 200°F.), and stays flexible and retains its lubricity at low temps. Fire point, approx. 500°F. PRESSURE PRODUCTS CO.

Spray Mask A. *See* CD SPRAY MASK A.

Sprayolite. *See* GOLD BOND® SPRAYOLITE.

Spray-Satin®. A clay used for paper coating.
MINERALS & CHEMICALS CORP. OF AMERICA

Spraysoy[NE]. (*HBMTN* p. 530). No longer available.
MILLER CHEMICAL & FERTILIZER CORP.

Sprayway® First Aid. An antiseptic spray that soothes sunburn, insect bites, etc. It has anesthetic and germicidal properties. Leaves a dry petrolatum-like coating. SPRAYWAY, INC.

Sprayway® Plastic Spray. A clear acrylic plastic coating packaged in a pressurized self-spraying container. The coating dries in less than a minute, leaving a clear finish that is flexible and resists water, alcohol, alkalis, acids, mineral oils, grease, etc. Used to protect ornamental silver, brass, and copper; to waterproof automobile ignition wires, battery cables, distributors, and other electrical parts; and to weatherproof leather articles, etc. SPRAYWAY, INC.

Sprayway® Tru-Nox. A non-poisonous insect spray containing PYRENONE® (*HBMTN* p. 468). Effective against flies, ants, mosquitoes, gnats, roaches, silverfish, etc. SPRAYWAY, INC.

Spred® Patch. A 100%-latex spackling compound. GLIDDEN CO.

Spring Aire. A room deodorizer, in an aerosol bomb dispenser, for powder rooms and living rooms. It has a dainty floral scent. CLAIRE MFG. CO.

SPS-245®[Can.]. A machinery steel designed especially for those applications requiring the following tensile strengths:

Diam. of sections, in.	Tensile strength, lb./sq.in. after heat treatment
1	175,000
2	150,000–175,000
4	125,000–150,000
6	100,000–125,000

The typical analysis of this steel is as follows: 0.40% carbon, 0.75% manganese, 0.030% phosphorus (max.), 0.030% sulfur (max.), 0.20% silicon, 0.60% chromium, 1.25% nickel, and 0.15% molybdenum. ATLAS STEELS LTD.

SR-10[NE]. A powdered acid product for food-processing equipment cleaning. *Uses:* In dairies for removing milkstone, cleaning plate pasteurizers, can washing, and cleaning evaporating pans; in hotels and restaurants for removing stains and films from dishes and glassware, and for cleaning copper utensils, exteriors of dishwashing machines, etc. Acidity (as H_2SO_4), 30%. WYANDOTTE CHEMICALS CORP., J. B. FORD DIV.

SRHS®. A line of various chromium plating materials. METAL & THERMIT CORP.

SR Lubricants[NE]. A line of lubricants for speed reducers and enclosed gears. They have very high load-carrying capacities. Available in SAE grades 10 to 20. They are also used for drawing of stainless steel. KEYSTONE LUBRICATING CO.

S.R.P.®. (*HBMTN* p. 530). Now a registered trademark. L. SONNEBORN SONS, INC.

SS12-B Silver Shielding Micropaint[NE]. A flexible, air-drying paint for electromagnetic and static shielding of hearing-aid cases, meter cases, radio and TV cabinets, vacuum tubes, electronic components; for conducting lines and areas; for grounding and capacitance applications; and for special antenna elements. Resistance, approx. 1 ohm. per square and up. For brush or silk-screen application. MICRO-CIRCUITS CO.

ST-760, 780, 781, and 840[NE]. A line of mild steel fluxes for use with L-60, L-61, L-70, L-18-8, *and* L-201 automatic welding wires. LINCOLN ELECTRIC CO.

Stabelan®. The trademark for a line of stabilizers for synthetic resins. METASAP CHEMICAL CO.

Stabilite. *See* MERIX® STABILITE.

Stabilite A. *See* MERIX® STABILITE A.

Stabilized®. (*HBMTN* p. 531). Formerly mfg'd by U. S. FINISHING CO., now a product of USF-ASPINOOK FINISHING DIV., GERA CORP.

Stabilizers No. 1 and No. D-17[NE]. (*HBMTN* p. 531 and *Supp.* I p. 223). No longer available. SINDAR CORP.

Stabilizers[NE] **21, 53, 85, 85X and 6162X.** (*Supp.* I p. 223). Now known as VICTOR STABILIZERS[NE] 21, 53, 85, 85X *and* 6162X. VICTOR CHEMICAL WORKS

Stabilizers JCX, SN and V-1-N[NE]. (*HBMTN* p. 531). No longer available. ADVANCE SOLVENTS & CHEMICAL CORP.

Staclipse®. A line of thin-boiling corn starches of especially low viscosity. They are used industrially as binders; for example, in the mfg. of matches. They are special finishing agents for the textile industry; and in the paper industry they are used in calender sizing, coating, laminating and combining, and in bag pasting operations. A. E. STALEY MFG. CO.

Stacolloid®. A line of noncongealing gums derived from corn starch. Their pastes possess excellent viscosity stability and superior flow properties. They produce strong, clear, flexible films. STACOLLOID GUMS have many applications throughout the textile industry, particularly in the warp sizing of spun synthetics and combed cottons, and in special finishing operations in which they are used in conjunction with resins. They are also extensively used in the paper industry. A special use in this latter field is in the surface sizing of direct process paper. A. E. STALEY MFG. CO.

Sta-Cream[NE]. A thermophile-free, low-viscosity canner's corn starch, modified to resist curdling. It is used in cream style corn and in other thickened food products. A. E. STALEY MFG. CO.

Stadex®. A complete line of dextrins manufactured by an exclusive process to produce dextrins of great uniformity and improved color. *Uses:* In prepared adhesives and in various industrial applications, such as in foundry cores and in the mfg. of match heads. They provide plasticity and strength in ceramic processing and are used as adhesives for gummed tape and in leather pasting. Applications in the paper industry include sizing, high-solids paper coating, bag pastings and tube winding. In the textile industry, they are used as finishing agents and print-paste thickeners. A. E. STALEY MFG. CO.

Staflex®. A line of plasticizers and stabilizers for the plastics industry. The plasticizers include high-mol.-wt. phthalates, dialkyl phthalates, ricinoleates, azelates, sebacetes, adipates, and stearates. STAFLEX

QMXA is a rapid acid absorber type stabilizer; and STAFLEX OY, a liquid cadmium salt, is used to improve the color stability of vinyl chloride resins.
DEECY PRODUCTS CO.

Sta-Gel®. A line of starch products developed from corn starch, particularly for warp sizing of spun RAYON and blends containing RAYON. They are also used on combed and worsted yarns and in finishing.
A. E. STALEY MFG. CO.

Staley's®. The trademark for a number of diversified products, many of which are produced from corn and soybeans. The products include corn syrups, starches, soy oils, soy flours, sauce bases, phytic acid, inositol, and various protein-rich materials used in insecticide baits, nutrients, food supplements, etc.
A. E. STALEY MFG. CO.

Sta-Mino®. A refined mixture of natural amino acids offered in two grades. TYPE A, a technical grade, contains *l*-leucine, 49%; *l*-isoleucine, 10%; *l*-tyrosine, 14%; *l*-methionine, 5%; *l*-phenylalanine, 5%. TYPE B, a refined grade, contains *l*-leucine, 75%; *l*-isoleucine, 13%; *l*-methionine, 8%; *l*-phenylalanine, 3%; *l*-tyrosine, trace. *Uses:* As a raw material for the isolation of individual amino acids and in the preparation of mixed amino acid derivatives. They are used in pharmaceutical preparations, and for amino acid supplementation of foods and feeds. They are a source of nutrient for microbiological processes, particularly in the production of antibiotics. STA-MINO is also used as a brightener in electroplating baths and in similar applications.
A. E. STALEY MFG. CO.

Standard "400". *See* ASBESTONE® STANDARD "400".

Standard Super-Cel[NR]. One of a series of CELITE® FILTER-AIDS made of exceptionally pure diatomaceous silica. Considerably higher rates of flow are obtained with this grade than with the FILTER-CEL® grade. However, the rates of flow are considerably lower through STANDARD SUPER-CEL than through HYFLO® SUPER-CEL. This Standard grade is especially useful in the filtration of beer, cider, extracts, fruit juices, gelatine, glue, organic chemicals, wine, sugar refinery liquors, etc.
JOHNS-MANVILLE SALES CORP.

Standee®. The trademark for a line of power resistors. (Registration No. 564,192; Class 21; Sept. 16, 1952).
CLAROSTAT MFG. CO.

Stanley 40X-610[NR]. A wash primer for use under vinyls, alkyds, varnishes, nitrocellulose lacquers, Japans and other finishes. Applied by spray, brush, or dip. It provides excellent adhesion of the paint to iron, steel, aluminum, and magnesium; and allows outdoor storage of steel or iron parts up to one year without topcoating.
STANLEY CHEMICAL CO.

Stanley Hand Save[NR]. A hand-protective cream. Rubbed on the hands before starting work, it prevents contact of the skin with dirt, oil, paint, grease, ink, dust, or solvents. It is readily washed off with water.
STANLEY CHEMICAL CO.

Stannochlor®. (*HBMTN* p. 534). Should have been listed as a registered trademark and a product of METAL & THERMIT CORP.

Stanolex® **Furnace Oil.** (*HBMTN* p. 534). No longer available.
STANDARD OIL CO. (INDIANA)

Stansets[NR]. The trade name for a line of durable crease- and shrink-resistant textile-finishing agents.
STANDARD CHEMICAL PRODUCTS, INC.

Stansol®. The trademark for a line of standard volumetric solutions used in analytical chemistry. The solutions are in the form of concentrates, and in the majority of cases are packaged in 4-oz. polyethylene bottles. Reagents which attack polyethylene are sealed in glass ampoules.
Mfg'd by STANDARD SOLUTION CO.
Dist'd by CHICAGO APPARATUS CO.

Stanteosine[NR]. (*HBMTN* p. 534). This product is now known as STANTONE[NR].
STANDARD CHEMICAL PRODUCTS, INC.

Stantone[NR]. Formerly known as STANTEOSINE[NR] (*HBMTN* p. 534).
STANDARD CHEMICAL PRODUCTS, INC.

Staphene®. A concentrated, non-specific germicide recommended for general hospital sanitation.
VESTAL, INC.

Star[NR]. A rubbermaker's grade of ground refined sulfur.
OLIN MATHIESON CHEMICAL CORP.

Star®. The trademark for copper-bearing galvanized steel sheets.
UNITED STATES STEEL CORP.

Starcor®. An oil-well cement used for cementing wells with high gas or oil pressures. It forms a heavy, dense slurry of excellent pumpability; and contains no tricalcium aluminate, which means that it has max. resistance to sulfate attack. Composition, % by wt.: SiO_2, 23.8; Al_2O_3, 3.2; Fe_2O_3, 7.8; CaO, 62.0; MgO, 0.9; SO_2, 1.3; loss on ignition, 0.4.
LONE STAR CEMENT CO.

Star Facing[NR]. A foundry facing material consisting of a pure white, non-carbonaceous shake-on powder, composed primarily of zircon flour. It is widely used in gray iron foundries. It is applied by shaking through a porous bag; no slicking or brushing is required. The use of this facing eliminates the necessity of mold drying. It presents no silicosis hazard.
M. A. BELL CO.

Starguar[NR]. A powdered guar gum, in refined grades, for food use. This cold-water-dispersible hydrocolloid is used as a thickener and stabilizer in cheese spreads, ice cream, salad dressings, strained foods, processed meats, and other food products; and is also used in cosmetics, lotions, creams, etc.
PAISLEY PRODUCTS, INC.

Stargum®. A chlorinated potato starch.
PAISLEY PRODUCTS, INC.

Starwax®. A high-melting-point microcrystalline wax for use in polishes, crayons, electrical insulation, paper coatings, candles, and other uses. M.p. 180°F. (min.); penetration (100 g.) at 77°F. (ASTM 1321-54T), 16 (max.); color (N.P.A.), amber, 2 (max.).
BARECO WAX CO.

Sta-Rx®. A corn starch meeting U.S.P. specifications, and mfg'd specifically for the pharmaceutical industry.
A. E. STALEY MFG. CO.

Sta-Sol®. Commercial soybean lecithin concentrate. A complex fat-like material consisting of approx.

65% soybean phosphatides and 35% soybean oil. It is an emulsifying agent and antioxidant, offered in four grades, two grades each of bleached and unbleached, which differ only in their degree of fluidity. *Uses:* As a softener, emulsifier, and stabilizer in soaps and cosmetics; as a penetrating agent in leather processing; as a wetting and stabilizing agent in oil-base paints; as an emulsifier and softener in the textile industry; and as an antioxidant in pharmaceutical products. STA-SOL LECITHIN is used extensively in the food and allied industries: as an antioxidant and emulsifier in the baking industry; as an antioxidant in lard, margarine, and shortenings; to reduce stickiness in candies; for its emulsifying and gloss improving properties in fountain syrups and toppings, etc. A. E. STALEY MFG. CO.

Sta-Thik®. A high-strength modified corn starch which is thicker boiling than native corn starch. *Uses:* In low-cost adhesives; in the briquetting of charcoal, coal, ore, etc.; in the paper industry, at the wet-end and in bag pasting; in the textile industry, for finishing, in back-filling, padding, and for binding clays and other fillers. A. E. STALEY MFG. CO.

Static-Stop. *See* PARKO® STATIC-STOP.

Staybind®. A line of specialty starches used in the corrugating and paper industries. STAYBIND WATERPROOF CORRUGATING STARCH 5030 is used extensively in the mfg. of waterproof corrugated board; GRADES A, B, and C are used in the paper industry for laminating and bag pasting. A. E. STALEY MFG. CO.

Staycal®. A low-cost specialty corn starch for paper and board sizing. Available in two viscosity grades. A. E. STALEY MFG. CO.

Stayco®. A line of oxidized, thin-boiling corn starches available in five viscosity grades. *Uses:* In the mfg. of non-congealing, high-viscosity adhesives; as a thickener and stabilizer in latex-type paints; and in the paper industry at the wet end, in tub and press sizing, in calender sizing, and in coating; in premium finishes in the textile industry, particularly on white fabrics; and to provide plasticity and strength in ceramic processing, and as crayon binders. A. E. STALEY MFG. CO.

Stayrite®. The trademark name for a line of vinyl resin stabilizers, including the following:

Stayrite No.	Composition	Physical state	Sp. gr.	Uses
10	Normal lead stearate	White to light cream-colored-powder	1.37	Medium efficiency heat stabilizer for polyvinyl chloride resins where clarity of finished product is not essential.
15	Dibasic lead stearate	White powder	2.00	Heat stabilizer for most translucent or opaque vinyl films.
20	Precipitated barium stearate	Fluffy, white powder	1.23	Medium efficiency heat stabilizer for polyvinyl chloride formulations of high clarity. Also used as mold lubricant and dusting powder where temps. of molds and surfaces to be dusted are above m.p.s of other stabilizers.
22	Precipitated cadmium stearate	Fluffy, white powder	1.21	Heat and light stabilizer for polyvinyl chloride-type compounds, especially for use in transparent films, sheets, and extruded items where max. clarity is desired.
25	Precipitated calcium stearate	Fluffy, white powder	1.03	General-purpose lubricating agent for polyvinyl chloride resins; gives medium to good light stability. Also as a non-toxic stabilizer for transparent food-packaging films.
26	Precipitated calcium stearate	Slightly off-white fluffy powder	1.03	Same as for #25
70	Co-precipitated cadmium-barium soap	Ivory powder	1.23	Combination heat and light stabilizer for vinyl compounds.
71	Co-precipitated cadmium-barium soap	White powder	—	Excellent heat and light stabilizer for vinyl compounds, with high degree of clarity.
75	Synergist for use with #70 and #71	Clear, amber-colored liquid	—	Materially increases heat stability of polyvinyl chloride-type resins.
76	Synergist for use with #70 and #71	Clear, amber-colored liquid	—	Gives max. protection against heat and light degradation of polyvinyl chloride resins, with excellent clarity at moderate cost.

Stayrite No.	Composition	Physical state	Sp. gr.	Uses
80	Barium-cadmium soap plus synergist	Yellow liquid	1.18	Excellent heat and light stabilizer for polyvinyl chloride resins; excellent clarity; particularly efficient under calendering and extrusion operations, and for plastisols and organosols.
90	Combination of metallic soaps	Fluffy, white powder	1.05	Non-toxic product which imparts good initial color and clarity to transparent films; for food wrappers, cap linings, toys, and beverage and surgical tubings. Also for plastisol formulations.
95	Non-toxic "booster" for #90	Colorless liquid	—	Provides good light and heat stabilization for polyvinyl chloride items such as surgical tubing, wrapping films, plastisols, etc.
229	Basic lead salt	Cream-colored powder	5.9	Heat stabilizer for opaque and rigid polyvinyl chloride compounds; as ultraviolet light screening agent; for stabilization of chlorinated paraffins; as curing agent for chloro-sulfonated polythene.

WITCO CHEMICAL CO.

Staysize®. A specialty thin-boiling corn starch for the paper industry. Used in tub and press sizing and as a binder for all-carbonate paper coating.
A. E. STALEY MFG. CO.

Stazon. *See* TEXACO® STAZON.

Stazyme®. Neutral corn starches for general industrial application wherever enzyme conversion is performed in the individual plant. They are used extensively in prepared adhesives, for paper coating, and in the textile industry for warp sizing, finishing, etc.
A. E. STALEY MFG. CO.

STCA△. The sodium salt of TCA (trichloroacetic acid). A selective weedkiller which is less corrosive than TCA, and stable in the presence of moisture.

Steam-O. *See* TROY STEAM-O.

Stearin Pitch△. A brown to black residue obtained in the distillation of animal and vegetable oils and fats. It is used in the formulation of paints and varnishes, insulating compounds, floor coverings, and cold-molding compositions.

Steelacoustic®. Metal-faced sound-absorbing units used in building construction.
CELOTEX CORP.

Steelyfe®. (*HBMTN* p. 538). No longer available.
BEE CHEMICAL CO.

Steller®. A clay used for paper coating.
MINERALS & CHEMICALS CORP. OF AMERICA

Sterilair®. The trademark for a moth preventive.
PENNSYLVANIA SALT MFG. CO.

Sterilope®. The trademark for special double envelopes containing sterile sulfanilamide powder.
ABBOTT LABORATORIES

Sterisil[NE]. A vaginal gel for use in the treatment of vaginitis or leukorrhea caused by Trichomonas, Monilia or Hemophilus vaginalis. It consists of 0.1% hexetidine incorporated in a colorless, non-staining vaginal gel.
WARNER-CHILCOTT LABORATORIES

Sterling® T-653-LB Thermopoxy. A clear-baking, thermosetting, electrical insulation material based on epoxy resins. Applied by brush, dip, spray, or vacuum impregnation. It requires no catalyst and, therefore, has unlimited tank life. Withstands temps. from —55° to 200°C.; sp.gr. 0.989; viscosity at 21°C. (Stormer), 8.2; drying time at 105°C., 5 min. *Use:* For insulation of industrial and aircraft motors and other electrical equipment operating in corrosive atmospheres or subject to high temp.
STERLING VARNISH CO.

Sterling® Thermobonds. A line of synthetic resin baking varnishes for insulating motors, generators, transformers and other electrical equipment. They are chemical and oil resistant, and withstand high overload temps., are elastic, and have excellent bonding strength and electrical resistance. Baking temp. 105°C. (min.). The THERMOBONDS range from low viscosity, clear varnishes to black, opaque heavy-bodied products.
STERLING VARNISH CO.

Ster-L-Yzer. *See* TROY STER-L-YZER.

Ster-O-Mint®. (*HBMTN* p. 538). No longer available.
HILLYARD CHEMICAL CO.

Steropes[NE]. (*HBMTN* p. 538). No longer available.
UNIVERSAL-CYCLOPS STEEL CORP.

Sterozol®. A germicide for use in the leather industry. *Use:* To inhibit bacterial and fungal growth on raw stock and on leather during processing.
WALLERSTEIN CO.

Stic-Lac△. *See* SHELLAC△.

Stigmonene®. A medicinal for prevention or treatment of postoperative urinary retention and abdominal distention; for the treatment of simple, delayed menstruation; and as a convenient, accurate office

test for early pregnancy. It consists of benzpyrinium bromide in 1 cc. ampuls for injection.
WARNER-CHILCOTT LABORATORIES

Stik-Wax. See #140 STIK-WAX[NE].

Stillingia Oil[△]. A drying oil obtained from the kernels of the seeds of the tree *Stillingia sebifera*, of China. It is a light-yellow oil resembling linseed oil but it has a lower drying power than linseed oil. Sp.gr. 0.943–0.946; iodine no. 160. It is used in the mfg. of paint.

Stilphostrol®. An anticarcinogenic composition containing the sodium salt of diethylstilbestrol diphosphate.
AMES CO.

Stimavite® **Tastitabs**®. An appetite and growth stimulant for children. Each TASTITAB contains 15 mg. *l*-lysine, 10 mg. VITAMIN B_1, 3 mg. VITAMIN B_6, 20 mcg. VITAMIN B_{12}, and 25 mg. VITAMIN C (as sodium ascorbate).
J. B. ROERIG & CO.

Stim-Root®. (*HBMTN* p. 539). No longer available.
PLANT PRODUCTS CORP.

Stix No. 555 Cement[NE]. (*Supp.* I p. 226). Now known as STIX-GRIP[NE].
ADHESIVE PRODUCTS CORP.

Stix-Grip[NE]. Formerly known as STIX No. 555 CEMENT[NE] (*Supp.* I p. 226).
ADHESIVE PRODUCTS CORP.

S. T. O. Lubricant[NE]. A clear, practically colorless type of so-called "stainless oil," for use on sewing and other textile machinery, and as a thread saturant to prevent needle breakage. Available in medium (approx. SAE 20) and light (approx. SAE 10) grades.
KEYSTONE LUBRICATING CO.

Stoncote[NE]. A plastic-base, acid-resistant coating, in colors, of brushing consistency. Can be sprayed, upon dilution with STONCOTE THINNER. Specially formulated for surfaces where corrosion is a special problem. Provides a tough, stable, non-oxidizing, acid-, alkali- and oil-resistant film over concrete, metal or wood. Withstands sulphuric acid up to 50% concentration, phosphoric acid up to 60%, sodium hydroxide up to 15%. Also resists cyanides; formaldehyde; latic, muriatic, and oleic acids; ammonia, brine and salt solutions. *Uses:* For floors, walls, machinery, tanks, pipes, etc.
STONHARD CO.

StoneTex®. (*HBMTN* p. 539). No longer available.
TRUSCON LABORATORIES

Stonfast®. A specialized asphaltic formulation fixed on a specific grade of mineral aggregate and used with a tamper for the quick repair of rutted concrete and black-top structures. There is no waiting period for curing and the repair can be opened to traffic immediately. A primer is furnished with the unit. Formulated for patching blacktop, macadam, asphalt, concrete, brick and other hard surfaces. *Uses:* For emergency repairs to roads, driveways, ramps, parking areas and factory floors.
STONHARD CO.

Stonfil[NE]. A dry, powdery mixture which, when mixed with water, forms a quick-patching compound that sets in 15 min. and cures ready for service in 30 to 40 min. It also has excellent patching properties at sub-freezing temps. *Uses:* For making fast repairs to small ruts, holes or cracks in concrete floors; and for permanently anchoring bolts, hand rails, ornamental iron work and machinery in concrete bases. It is stronger than concrete, and resistant to heavy strain and vibration.
STONHARD CO.

Stonpach®. A dry granular mixture which, when mixed with water, forms an acid-, grease- and oil-resistant mortar. *Uses:* For patching or overlaying concrete floors subjected to severe conditions and disintegration. It can be applied as thin as ½ inch. Available in concrete gray, red or green.
STONHARD CO.

Stontite®. A specially formulated water-repelling liquid which is mixed with sand and cement to form an impervious mortar for the effective sealing of leaks and water-seepage in above- and below-grade masonry surfaces. Mixed directly with fresh Portland cement, it stops water flow almost instantly, even against hydrostatic pressure. In plaster coating it provides a smooth, non-porous finish, leaving no fine hairline cracks to allow further seepage. *Uses:* To repair cracks and breaks in underground foundations, tunnels, dams, spillways and reservoirs; and to overcome water-seepage in basements, elevator pits, sewers and vaults.
STONHARD CO.

Stontreet[NE]. A pitch-base bituminous resin of liquid consistency for protecting and sealing bituminous-concrete, asphalt, macadam or blacktop surfaces from the penetration of oil drippings and gasoline. Resists acid fumes and sediment from exhaust blasts; also prevents heaving and breaks in the surface caused by ice formation. It is black with a velvety appearance. Easily applied by long-handled brush. *Uses:* For driveways, parking lots, airfields, bus depots, terminal loading areas, platforms and ramps.
STONHARD CO.

Stoody Automatic and Semi-Automatic Wires[NE]. Welding wires produced in 10 different analyses, suitable for hard-facing and building-up of carbon, low-alloy and manganese steels. Supplied in sizes $7/64''$ to $3/16''$. They operate through all standard automatic heads and semi-automatic welders.
STOODY CO.

Stoody Build-Up[NE]. A low-alloy, manual, coated welding electrode, generally used for rebuilding steel parts preliminary to hard-facing.
STOODY CO.

Stoody Wear-Resistant Castings[NE]. Non-ferrous (generally chromium, cobalt and tungsten) castings produced by a centrifugal casting process. They have high abrasion resistance and moderate resistance to most corrosive media, and retain their physical properties at elevated temps.
STOODY CO.

Stopleak® **#1008**. A fuel-gas warning agent. A blue-colored liquid-injection type odorant; mercaptan sulfur, 33% (min.); sp.gr. 0.827 (68°F.); distillation range, 95% below 270°F.; viscosity, 0.52 centistokes (77°F.); av. mol.wt. 91.
PENNSYLVANIA SALT MFG. CO.

Stopleak® **#1009**. A fuel-gas warning agent. It is an evaporation by-pass and liquid-injection type odorant. A green-colored liquid; mercaptan sulfur, 35% (min.); distillation range, 95% below 180°F.; viscosity, 0.64 centistokes (77°F.); av. mol.wt. 86.
PENNSYLVANIA SALT MFG. CO.

Stopomat®. Photographic stop bath especially adapted for continuous paper processing.
EASTMAN KODAK CO.

Storax△. *Also known as* STYRAX△, LEVANT STORAX△, *and* AMERICAN STORAX△. An aromatic balsam obtained from the trunk of the tree *Liquidambar orientalis* (Levant Storax), or from the tree *L. styraciflua L.* (American Storax). LEVANT STORAX is produced in Asia Minor; AMERICAN STORAX comes chiefly from Honduras, although it is also produced in the southern United States and in Central America. STORAX contains 33–50% of the α- and β-storesin and its cinnamic ester, 5–10% styracin, 10% phenypropyl cinnamate, small quantities of ethyl cinnamate, benzyl cinnamate, and styrene, 5–15% free cinnamic acid, 0.4% of the levorotatory oil, $C_{10}H_6O$, and traces of vanillin. Levant STORAX is a semi-liquid, grayish, sticky, opaque mass; AMERICAN STORAX is a semi-solid or solid mass that is softened on warming. It is transparent in thin layers; is denser than water; and has a characteristic taste and odor. Insoluble in water; almost completely soluble in benzene, ether, acetone, carbon disulfide, and 1 part warm alcohol. *Uses:* In cough medicines; as a parasiticide on the skin; a fixative for heavy perfumes; a flavoring agent for tobacco and soap; in fumigating pastilles and powders; and as an imbedding material in microscopy.

Storcavite®. A vitamin-mineral preparation, in tablet form, containing: phosphate-free calcium, minerals and hematinic factors, prepared especially for women during pregnancy and lactation. Contains VITAMINS A, B_1, B_2, B_6, B_{12}, C, D, E, NIACINAMIDE, calcium pantothenate, folic acid, iron, copper, cobalt, calcium, manganese, molybdenum, magnesium, zinc and potassium. J. B. ROERIG & Co.

Storm King. (*HBMTN* p. 540). Formerly mfg'd by SAYLES FINISHING Co., now mfg'd by SAYLES FINISHING PLANTS, INC.

Storm Seal®. The trademark for steel roofing and siding sheets. UNITED STATES STEEL CORP.

StrapLbond[NE]. (*Supp.* I p. 224). No longer available. HANSON-VAN WINKLE-MUNNING Co.

Strata-Fiber®. A drilling mud additive. It is a selected, dehydrated, inner-rind fiber from sugar cane bagasse that has been blended with wood fibers and other cellulose materials, resulting in a fibrous material that has one of the lowest moisture contents of any fibrous lost-circulation material used by the oil industry today. It is resistant to fermentation. GREAT LAKES CARBON CORP.

Stratalets®. (*Supp.* I p. 227). No longer available. SHARP & DOHME DIV., MERCK & Co.

Strata-Lite®. A pre-mixed oil-well cement for lightweight slurries. GREAT LAKES CARBON CORP.

Strata-Seal®. A perlite aggregate for plugging or bridging formation voids in oil wells. It is one of the most versatile and valuable products available to the oil industry for combating lost circulation. It is chemically inert and has no effect on the pH or chemical properties of the mud. Its action is purely mechanical. GREAT LAKES CARBON CORP.

Streptoconin®. A powerful tuberculostatic agent which combines streptomycin with isoniazid. Supplied in powder form for intramuscular use only. CONSOLIDATED MIDLAND CORP.

S-t-r-e-t-c-h®. A color concentrate for coloring polyethylene. It consists of pigments dispersed in polyethylene, and is available as uniform-size pellets in brown, black, and various bright colors. GERING PRODUCTS INC.

Striatone[NE]. A striated, sound-absorbing mineral tile used in building construction. CELOTEX CORP.

Stride®. A liquid, self-polishing floor finish containing a high percentage of hard waxes. Designed to give a self-polishing floor finish that protects like paste wax and can be buffed to remove scuff marks. It is extremely water-resistant, and can be damp mopped repeatedly. It can be used on linoleum, asphalt and rubber tile, vinyl plastic, sealed wood and cork, terrazzo, and sealed or painted concrete. S. C. JOHNSON & SON

Strip 100. *See* CD STRIP 100.

Strip A. *See* CD STRIP A.

Strip B. *See* CD STRIP B.

Strip-Eze. A purgant for water-wash paint-spray booths. It is a powerful stripper which is added to the water in the booth to remove adherent paint build up in lines, nozzles, etc., at the end of a week's run or other predetermined period. NATIONAL RESEARCH & CHEMICAL Co.

Stripltex®. Lacquers, enamels and varnishes that have a strippled surface after air drying or baking. MAAS & WALDSTEIN Co.

Stripper, Stripper M-3, Stripper R-6, Stripper 110, *and* **Stripper S-A.** *See* OAKITE STRIPPER M-3, STRIPPER R-6, STRIPPER 110, *and* STRIPPER S-A.

Stripping Agent Soluble Conc. A stripping agent for textiles. It is supplied in the form of a white water-soluble powder. It has good reducing action, and in acidic and neutral aqueous solutions it is stable for several days. It does not tender any of the usual textile fibers and is, therefore, particularly suitable for stripping shoddy, reclaimed WOOL, WOOL, NYLON, ACETATE RAYON and mixed fabrics of all kinds. It develops its highest efficiency at 160–200°F. in presence of acids. NOVA CHEMICAL CORP.

Striprite. A heavy-duty remover for varnish, enamel, lacquer, paint, and primers. Applied by spray, brush, or swab to metals or wood, this non-flammable stripper softens the finish in 5–15 min. The loosened paint is then scrubbed with a stiff brush, and finally washed away with water or steam. NATIONAL RESEARCH & CHEMICAL Co.

Striptex®. A compound used in stripping organic finishes from metal and other surfaces. It is particularly useful on oil-base paints which have remained on surfaces for a considerable period of time and are hard to remove with ordinary materials of a solvent nature. DIVERSEY CORP.

Strobane△. A chlorinated hydrocarbon insecticide made by chlorinating a mixture of terpenes to a chlorine content of about 68%. It is a viscous, straw-colored liquid with a mild aromatic odor; practically insoluble in water; soluble in alcohol to 12–14%; readily soluble in petroleum and aromatic oils and in most organic solvents. Possesses some acaricidal properties.

Strocillin®. An antibiotic preparation consisting of Penicillin G procaine in dihydrostreptomycin sulfate solution. It is used for intramuscular administration. Abbott Laboratories

Stronghold. A line of oak-tanned flat leather belting for power transmission. Available in thicknesses of $^{11}/_{64}''$ to $^{23}/_{64}''$ and in widths of 6″ and 7″. Will withstand dry temps. up to 212°F., and moist heat up to 175°F. J. E. Rhoads & Sons

Strux△. *Same as* CCA△.

Style®. A clear, transparent wax-free plastic floor finish for asphalt tile, linoleum, rubber and vinyl floors. Vestal, Inc.

Styrad 205. A water-white, synthetic resin adhesive designed solely for bonding polystyrene plastic. Can also be used to bond paper and cloth to the plastic. The bond is practically instantaneous. Wilross Products Co.

Styrax△. *Same as* Storax△.

Styromix®. A line of dry-blended, colored, premixed polystyrene molding compounds. Gering Products Inc.

Styrroid. *See* Certified Styrroid®.

Styrroidite. *See* Certified Styrroidite®.

Subrote®. (*Supp.* I p. 228). No longer available. General Chemical Div., Allied Chemical & Dye Corp.

Suconox[NE]. A line of acyl *p*-amino phenols useful as anti-oxidants and as ultra-violet sunscreening agents. Sumner Chemical Co.

Suede△. *Also known as* Napped Leather△. A soft, chrome-tanned leather made of calf, kid, split cowhide or sheepskin. After tanning, the skin is worked on the staking machine until it is soft and supple; it is then buffed or polished on an abrasive wheel. The polished side has a soft nap. Suede is used for shoe uppers, hats, pocketbooks, clothing, etc.

Suganilla®. The trademark for a line of flavoring extracts, namely pure vanilla blended with specially processed sugars. S. B. Penick & Co.

Sugar®. The trademark for a brand of iron sulfate in a granulated form. United States Steel Corp.

Sulestrex®. An oral estrogen preparation used in the treatment of symptoms due to the menopause and postmenopausal conditions. Consists of piperazine estrone sulfate sublingual tablets. Abbott Laboratories

Sulfanone A[NE]. A liquid anionic surfactant for scouring and dyeing operations on synthetic fabrics. It has high detergency, wetting, penetrating and leveling properties, and exhibits excellent stability to acid, alkaline and hard-water salts. Hart Products Corp.

Sulfast®. (*Supp.* I p. 229). No longer available. General Chemical Div., Allied Chemical & Dye Corp.

Sulfastrep®. Veterinary medicinal tablets containing 2.0 g. Sulfathalidine® phthalylsulfathiazole, 125 mg. Streptomycin, 0.5 g. sulfamethazine, and 1.0 g. Kaolin. *Use:* For the control of diarrhea caused by bacterial intestinal infections. Particularly useful in the prophylaxis and treatment of calf scours. Merck Sharp & Dohme

Sulfa-Ter Tablets[NE]. Medicinal tablets, each of which contains 0.167 g. sulfadiazine, 0.167 g. sulfamerazine, 0.167 g. sulfamethiazine. American Pharmaceutical Co.

Sulfedex®. An antibacterial preparation consisting of a stabilized solution of sulfathiazole sodium and desoxyephedrine, for medicinal use. Abbott Laboratories

Sulfedexan®. A vasoconstrictor consisting of a stabilized sulfacetamide-desoxyephedrine solution. Used as a local decongestant for local application to the nose and throat. Abbott Laboratories

Sulfole®. Tertiary dodecyl mercaptan. A mercaptan modifier for control of emulsion polymerization systems including those to produce cold rubber (41°F. SBR), hot rubber (122°F. SBR) and many other elastomeric polymers. Phillips Chemical Co., Rubber Chemicals Div.

Sul-Fon-Ate®. The trademark for a line of surface-active agents.

Sul-Fon-Ate AA-9. A 90+% dodecylbenzene sulfonate, sodium salt, in a white, odorless, dustless flake form. An all-purpose wetting agent and detergent.

Sul-Fon-Ate AA-10. A 96+% sodium dodecylbenzene sulfonate in flake form.

Sul-Fon-Ate OA-5. The sodium salt of a sulfonate of oleic acid, designed especially for use in acid media. Tennessee Corp.

Sulfonate OS[NE]. A low cost, highly purified, oil-soluble petroleum sulfonate, used as a detergent, lubricating-oil additive, and surface-active agent. Sun Oil Co.

Sulfonate WS[NE]. A low-cost, water-soluble, petroleum sodium sulfonate that can be used as a wetting agent, rewetting agent, air-entraining agent, foaming agent, and ore flotation agent. This anionic, surface-active agent dissolves in hot or cold water to form a clear amber solution. Sp.gr. 1.2; consists of 25% sodium sulfonate, 15% mineral oil, 0.4 sodium carboxylate, 0.4% free NaOH, 9% inorganic salts, and the balance water. It has a combining weight of 380. *Uses:* In the formulation of insecticides, herbicides and fertilizers; as a dispersing agent for carbon black master batches; in ore flotation; in formulation of chemicals for fire fighting; in leather processing; and in waste-paper processing. Sun Oil Co.

Sulf-Opto®. A topical sulfonamide preparation consisting of a stabilized ophthalmic solution containing sulfathiazole sodium and desoxyephedrine. Used as a local antibacterial and vasoconstrictor in the treatment of conjunctivitis, blepharitis, etc. Abbott Laboratories

Sullvyne-Clad®. A pre-finished panel made of smooth or embossed vinyl sheeting laminated on steel, aluminum, or magnesium. It is completely flexible; and

can be stamped, punched, crimped, deep-drawn, or bent 180° without damaging the vinyl or breaking the bond. The coating resists abrasion and corrosion, and will not chip, crack or craze. Available in sheets up to 52″ × 120″. *Uses:* For the mfg. of luggage, furniture, sporting goods, vending machines, tables, appliances, wall panels, radio and TV cabinets and many other types of equipment.
O'SULLIVAN RUBBER CORP.

Sulphon Azurine®. A group of acid dyestuffs for WOOL. They dye best from a neutral bath and give blue shades with good fastness to milling. They also dye COTTON reasonably well. GENERAL DYESTUFF CO.

ditions; loose fitting or worn bearings; bearings subject to high unit pressures; bearings with low surface speeds; and equipment with parts that operate reciprocally or intermittently. SUN OIL CO.

Sunaptic® Acids. A group of saturated, high-molecular-weight naphthenic acids that have been specially processed to a low unsaponifiable content. Chemically, they are monocarboxylic derivatives of naphthene hydrocarbons. They are distinguished from fatty and rosin acid mixtures by the absence of olefinic unsaturation, high resistance to oxidative rancidity, higher hydrocarbon solubility, and low freezing or pour points. Available in three grades, A, B, and C, typical properties of which are as follows:

SUNAPTIC ACIDS	A	B	C
Average molecular formula	$C_{19}H_{34}O_2$	$C_{21}H_{37}O_2$	$C_{29}H_{49}O_2$
Average mol. wt. of de-oiled acids	297	330	415
Density (20°/4°C.)	0.988	0.987	0.992
Viscosity, S.U.S. at 210°F.	106	159	624
Pour point, °F.	25	40	75
Acid no., mg KOH per gram	178	159	122
Unsaponifiables, wt. %	5.6	6.3	9.1
Bromine no.	10.0	10.7	12.1
Distillation range °F. (2 mm. Hg)	315–485	287–530	408–596

Sulphopet®. (*HBMTN* p. 544). Now a registered trademark. L. SONNEBORN SONS, INC.

Sulvetil®. A PENICILLIN-STREPTOMYCIN, mineral oil suspension with sulfanilamide, for the treatment of mastitis infections. ABBOTT LABORATORIES

Sulvetil-Es^{NE}. An erythromycin-streptomycin, mineral oil suspension with sulfanilamide, for treatment of mastitis and other infections. ABBOTT LABORATORIES

Sumac[△]. The dried leaves of a bush *Rhus coriaria* of Sicily, and of the bush *R. typhina* that grows in the eastern part of the United States. The leaves contain from 30–40% tannin in the form of gallotannin and ellagitannin. Used as a source of tannin in leather mfg. It produces a light, strong leather with a fine, soft grain.

Sumac Wax[△]. *Same as* JAPAN WAX[△].

Sun® 1300 *and* 1301 Greases. Lime-base greases especially compounded for general applications at temps. from 0° to 150°F. They are fortified to provide max. protection against rust and corrosion under wet or humid operating conditions. They are ideal, multipurpose lubricants for machine tools, textile machines, and other machines equipped with gun fittings or grease cups. They are also suitable for use in all types of pressure systems. SUN OIL CO.

Sun® 1893 *and* 1897 Greases. Highly-adhesive, lime-base greases that have been fortified to provide max. protection against rust and corrosion under wet or humid operating conditions and to maintain their body and high adhesiveness even in the presence of excessive moisture. Recommended for the lubrication of bearings and other parts in "hard-to-get-at" places; bearings operating under wet or humid con-

Uses: Their major applications are closely related to those of the fatty acids and rosin acids. They are used in driers, emulsifying and flotation agents, and in the preparation of esters, plasticizers, and preservatives. Thus, the sodium and potassium soaps of the SUNAPTIC ACIDS are good emulsifiers, detergents and surface-active agents; they are useful in textile processing, as corrosion inhibitors, flatting agents, dye dispersants and solubilizers, intermediates in the preparation of alkaline earth and heavy metal soaps, etc. The non-alkali metal soaps have a wide variety of applications including anti-skinning agents for paint, stabilizers for vinyl chloride polymers, fungicides for wood, dispersants for pigments, fabric mildewproofing agents, paper sizes, pigment grinding aids, etc. SUN OIL CO.

Sun® C-850 EP Greases. Two water-resistant, calcium-lead base greases that are fortified with extreme-pressure additives that greatly increase their film strength. Specially useful for lubricating services under heavy loads, shock loads and overloads. GRADE C-850 EP has an NLGI consistency of zero and GRADE C-852 EP of 2. Both grades may be applied by pressure gun, centralized pressure system, brush or swab. SUN OIL CO.

Sun® C-891T Grease. A high-adhesive grease specially suited for the lubrication of bearings and parts in "hard-to-get-at" places, gears, chains or slides operating in dirty or dusty surroundings, loose-fitting or worn bearings which would consume large quantities of ordinary grease, bearings with relatively slow surface speeds, or which are subject to high unit pressures, etc. Applied by brush, swab, pressure gun, or through a central pressure system. SUN OIL CO.

Sundex®-41. A 100% petroleum-base, cold-rubber process aid. It is a complex, dark-colored blend of high-molecular-weight fractions and a specially prepared asphaltum, all derived from selected sources. When properly applied in the production of stocks from cold GR-S, it helps to prevent scorching during mixing, milling, and extruding, aids dispersion of compounding ingredients, reduces power consumption. and contributes to improved wear resistance and flex life of cured products. It is especially useful in the production of tread stocks and similar rubber compounds. Sun Oil Co.

Sundex®-53. A low-cost, relatively aromatic, liquid petroleum derivative similar in consistency to Circosol®-2XH. It is highly compatible with natural rubber and GR-S polymers. Used as a process aid in the mfg. of oil-extended polymers; especially suited for processing rubber footwear, matting, toys and semi-hard rubbers. Sp.gr. 0.9792; viscosity, 85 SUS at 210°F.; aniline point, 115°F.; aromatics (% by wt.), 75. Sun Oil Co.

Sundex®-85. A rubber process aid. It is a highly aromatic oil that is very compatible with natural rubber, GR-S type polymers, Neoprenes, and acrylonitrile polymers. Sp.gr. 1.0165; viscosity, 14.4 centistokes (210°F.). Used in the mfg. of oil-extended polymers, particularly in extending Neoprene WHV with exceptionally high loading of oil. Sun Oil Co.

Sundex®-170. A relatively aromatic product with a high molecular weight. Sp.gr. 0.9874; viscosity, 37.9 centistokes (210°F.). Used as a processing aid in the mfg. of mastic floor tile, battery cases, and resinous binders. Sun Oil Co.

Sunep® Oils. A high-quality, lead naphthenate-type, extreme pressure lubricant for heavy-duty gears and other applications including the lubrication of gear-reduction units driving rolling mills, strip-mill reel drives, rubber mills, calenders and conveyors, etc. Has high film strength, strong adhesion to metal, excellent stability, and rust preventive and non-corrosive properties. Available in several viscosities, from about 300 to 3000 SUS at 100°F. Sun Oil Co.

Sunform®. A line of reinforced polyester resins for use in low-pressure laminating. The reinforcing material, which is impregnated with the resin, may be cloth or matting of cotton, Dacron®, Orlon®, Nylon, or other fibers, but the most widely used reinforcement is fiber glass cloth. Sunform® is supplied to laminators in ready-to-mold form, that is, it is pre-impregnated with the resin and catalyst. Sheets are cut from rolls, layed-up in the desired number of plies, and heated at 250°–300°F. to effect the cure. Molding time varies from about 1 to 2 min. for $1/16''$ thickness to 20 to 30 min. for $1/2''$ thickness. Products are strong and tough, resistant to solvents. acids, alkalis, water, outdoor weathering, rot and mildew, and have excellent electrical properties. *Uses:* For mfg. of aircraft parts, tote boxes, drill jigs, shaping jigs, structural laminates, light doors, trays, trunks, luggage, furniture, etc. Electro-Technical Products Div., Sun Chemical Corp.

Sunicut® 11-S. A non-emulsifying, low viscosity cutting oil for medium duty on automatic screw machines cutting non-ferrous metals and free-machining steels. Because of its low viscosity and excellent cooling properties, it is particularly suitable for high-speed production. Sun Oil Co.

Sunicut® 85. A light, free-flowing, transparent, heavy-duty, sulfurized cutting oil especially designed for production threading of tubing, pipe, and couplings made from high-alloy steels. Characterized by its fast runoff, high heat absorption, fast metal-wetting action, excellent extreme-pressure lubrication, and high rust prevention. Sun Oil Co.

Sunicut® 102-S and **Sunicut® 110-S.** Non-emulsifying, heavy-duty, active-type sulfur cutting oils that contain a special-type of additive which greatly increases their effectiveness when used for heavy-duty automatic screw-machine work and for other heavy-duty operations. Sunicut® 102-S is especially recommended for heavy-duty work on automatic screw machines where a dual-purpose lubricating and cutting oil is not desired. It is also an excellent general-purpose oil. Sunicut® 110-S is recommended for heavy-duty and relatively slow-speed cutting operations, such as broaching, gear-hobbing, threading, and tapping. Sun Oil Co.

Sunicut® 105. A heavy-duty, transparent, sulfurized, straight cutting oil for such operations as gear-cutting and broaching and for use with turret lathes and hand screw machines doing turning, threading and tapping on alloy steels. Sun Oil Co.

Sunicut® 171. A heavy-duty, sulfur-chlorine type, straight cutting oil. It is used extensively for pipe mill threading operations. Sun Oil Co.

Sunicut® 209-S. A non-emulsifying cutting oil intended primarily for use on automatic screw machines doing heavy-duty cutting on alloy steels and tough non-ferrous metals. It is a stainless, heavy-duty cutting oil that can also be used as a general-purpose cutting oil on lathes and other machine tools. Sun Oil Co.

Sunicut® 216. A cutting oil developed especially for thread-grinding operations. It is heavily compounded to produce mirror-like finishes and to eliminate burning and checking. Sun Oil Co.

Sunicut® 793. A transparent, low-viscosity, straight cutting oil possessing excellent cooling and lubricating properties which make high-speed production possible. It does not stain steel, aluminum, magnesium or copper. It is especially useful in machining aluminum, magnesium and their alloys. Sun Oil Co.

Sunicut® 5534. A transparent, non-emulsifying cutting oil containing sulfur, chlorine, and a fatty oil. Has high film strength, excellent metal-wetting properties, fast run-off, and high cooling capacity. Designed for general service on automatic screw machines, turret lathes, chucking machines, gear cutters, drill presses, milling machines, light stamping presses, etc.; particularly suited for medium alloy and free-machining steels with machinability ratings of 70 or over; can also be used on brass where a slight staining of the parts can be tolerated. Sun Oil Co.

Sunicut® "W" Series Cutting Oils. A line of free flowing, non-emulsifying, cutting oils containing an all-mineral additive which imparts to these oils excellent metal-wetting and oiliness properties. Presently available are the following grades:

SUNICUT® 11W, a light-colored, non-staining cutting oil for use on free-machining steels, brass, and aluminum. It gives the work fine finishes on all types of single and multiple spindle automatics as well as on milling machines, turret lathes, boring machines, etc.

SUNICUT® 105W, a transparent-type sulfurized cutting oil for general-duty on lathes, milling machines, drill presses and similar equipment doing turning, thread and gear cutting, and average machining of free-machining steels and medium-alloy steels.

SUNICUT® 110W, also a transparent-type sulfurized cutting oil designed for heavy-duty machining of tough, hard alloy steels. The heavy-duty feature of this oil makes it particularly valuable for broaching, gear cutting, tapping and threading operations.

SUNICUT® 812W, a light-colored, mildly sulfurized cutting oil of low viscosity recommended for use at all practical speeds and feeds on a wide range of steels. It is widely used in the antifriction bearing industry for machining SAE 51200 steel.
SUN OIL CO.

Suniso® Refrigeration Oils. A line of high-quality lubricating oils designed for use in refrigerating and air-conditioning equipment. They are characterized by extremely low pour points, extremely low wax-separating characteristics, high stability, and long life. They are initially neutral and resistant to formation of detrimental acids in service. Available in grades to meet all low, normal, and high-temp. conditions.
SUN OIL CO.

Sunkote A. A metal-coating oil used to protect hot- or cold-rolled sheet or strip steel and large ferrous castings and assemblies against rusting and staining while in process, storage or shipment. It is an all-petroleum product containing corrosion inhibitors. It forms a transparent, non-drying, adherent film that is easily removed by any of the usual cleaning processes, including alkali- or solvent-type degreasers. The viscosity of SUNKOTE A is approx. 100 SUS at 100°F. Applied by dip, roller or spray methods.
SUN OIL CO.

Sunland®. A needleloom carpeting composed of carpet fibers needled and bonded to a reinforced fabric base. Available in leaf green, dove gray, desert beige, parana nutria, American beauty rose, and sea mist green.
AMERICAN HAIR & FELT CO.

Sun® N-52X Grease. A high-melting-point (340°F.), short-fibered grease, compounded to resist oxidation at temps. up to 250°F. It is of medium consistency and has an NLGI Number of 2. *Uses:* For lubricating plain and anti-friction bearings where the lubricant must withstand unusually high temps. for long periods, such as in electric motors; open bearings operating at high-temp. conditions; and bearings of life-time lubricated appliances.
SUN OIL CO.

Sunoco® Anti-Check. A highly-refined, snow-white, petroleum wax designed especially to prevent rubber products from surface cracking and checking caused by sunlight, ultraviolet light and ozone. It is a primary product and not a blend. It blooms at a precise rate that insures max. protection without excessive film thickness of brittleness. *Uses:* For protecting black tire stock, white sidewall stock, automotive weather stripping, mechanical goods, wire insulation, etc.
SUN OIL CO.

Sunoco® Emulsifying Cutting Oil HD "F". (*Also known as S.E.C.O. HD "F"*). A heavy-duty, emulsifying cutting oil developed especially for difficult machining operations on alloy steels. It is a medium-viscosity, transparent oil which emulsifies easily with water to form stable white emulsions; contains extreme-pressure, stainless-type additives which increase the film strength to more than double that of regular emulsifying oils; also contains a germicide to prevent deterioration.
SUN OIL CO.

Sunoco® Emulsifying Cutting Oils. (*Also known as S.E.C.O.*). An all-petroleum, emulsifying-type cutting oil that is an efficient and economical cooling and lubricating medium for turning, milling, drilling and other metal-working operations on ferrous and non-ferrous metals. It is stable, does not turn rancid, and mixes easily with water. It is also an excellent grinding coolant.
SUN OIL CO.

Sunoco Polyseal®. A plastic-blended dairy wax. It is a carefully formulated blend of waxes and polyethylene for the coating of milk and milk-product containers. It gives a satin-smooth, uniform coating that is highly resistant to lactic and citric acids. Available in both slab and liquid forms.
SUN OIL CO.

Sunoco® Waxes. A complete line of fully refined paraffin and microcrystalline waxes, available in a wide range of physical properties.
SUN OIL CO.

Sunoco Way® Lubricant. A high-quality mineral oil especially compounded to eliminate "stick-slip" of tables and scoring of machine tool ways. This non-corrosive lubricant contains special compounds that coat the sliding surfaces with a microscopically thin, chemically bonded film that keeps the high spots of the two surfaces from touching, thereby preventing metal-to-metal contact. This results in smooth table action even at low speeds and under heavy loads. Available in several viscosities.
SUN OIL CO.

Sunolax®. A fluid dry-cleaning soap.
PENNSYLVANIA SALT MFG. CO.

Sunotex® Machine Oil. A general-purpose lubricant that can be used with nearly every type of textile machine. It is a high-quality mineral oil compounded to prevent rust, cling to moving parts, and minimize wear. It scours out of all kinds of fabrics easily and completely, leaving no discoloration.
SUN OIL CO.

Sunotex® Machine Oil *Light*. A lubricant that is essentially the same as SUNOTEX MACHINE OIL except that it is lighter in viscosity. It is recommended especially for lubricating needles, sinkers and related parts of knitting machines.
SUN OIL CO.

Sun® Prestige 40 Greases. A group of high-quality greases designed for all types of industrial lubricating applications at temps. of 0 to 300°F., in wet, moist, or dry surroundings. They are compounded with lithium soaps; have high melting points, exceptional chemical and mechanical stability; strong resistance to water; do not separate in storage or in service; and are easy to pump. These greases are available in the following consistencies: NGLI 0, NLGI 1, and NLGI 2. In addition, three similar greases, the SUN PRESTIGE 740 EP SERIES, are also available. These grades are designed for use under extra-heavy duty, high load or shock conditions. They have a Timken Test rating of 40 lb. SUN OIL CO.

Sun® Process Oil 515. A highly paraffinic-type of process aid used in the mfg. of butyl inner tubes. Also useful in light-colored products to minimize staining and discoloration. Sp.gr. 0.8686; viscosity, 5.3 centistokes (210°F). SUN OIL CO.

Sunquench 78. A high-speed quenching oil. It is a highly-refined, paraffinic oil which has been compounded especially to increase the rate of heat transfer from steel. It rapidly cools the steel through the critical hardening range, producing a high degree of hardness. The steel is hardened uniformly and deeply, with minimum risk of distortion and cracking even if the parts are thick or of widely varying cross-section. API gravity (60°F.), 30.5–32.5; viscosity, 90–100 SUS (100°F.); flash point (open cup), 340°F. (min.); fire point, 380°F. (min.); pour point, 0°F. (max.). SUN OIL CO.

Sun® Quenching Oil No. 11. A highly-refined paraffinic oil characterized by a high thermal stability and high boiling range, which make it particularly suitable for use in quenching systems where a high-flash-point oil is required. It is also suitable for bright quenching from controlled atmosphere furnaces. API gravity, 3.10–33.0 (60°F.); viscosity, 100–120 SUS (100°F.); flash point (open cup), 370°F. (min.); fire point, 420°F. (min.); pour point, 0°F. (max.). SUN OIL CO.

Sun® Quenching Oil Light. A well-refined, low-sludging, high-detergent naphthenic oil with a viscosity of 100–115 SUS at 100°F. Recommended for quenching systems in which the average temp. of the oil does not exceed 150°F. Designed primarily for large-scale production work, especially where steel is heat treated in a salt or cyanide bath before quenching. SUN OIL CO.

Suntac® Oils. A line of high-quality, exceptionally stable mineral oils that are oxygen-inhibited and contain additives designed to reduce leakage. They are especially suited for hydraulic and circulating systems where excessive leakage is a problem, loose-fitting or worn bearings which would consume large quantities of ordinary oil, all types of moving parts where excessive "throw-off" must be avoided, and equipment containing parts which operate reciprocally or intermittently. SUN OIL CO.

Sunvis Oils[NE]. A line of paraffinic-type lubricating oils characterized by their uniform high viscosity index, low pour point, and low carbon content. *Use:* In all types of industrial reservoirs and circulating systems operating at normal temps. SUN OIL CO.

Sunvis 700 Oils[NE]. A line of premium-quality oils for circulating systems, hydraulic systems, gear boxes, and compressors. These lubricants are specially formulated for applications requiring a detergent-dispersant type oil. They clean out dirty systems and keep them clean; and on regular-duty machines subject to continuous contamination, they keep oil lines from clogging with foreign matter. Available in a number of viscosities. SUN OIL CO.

Sunvis 900 Oils[NE]. A line of solvent-refined, paraffinic-type oils with an inherently high viscosity index. They are specially fortified to resist deterioration and provide maximum protection against corrosion and rusting. Specially suited for use in hydraulic systems and in turbines and other circulating lubricating systems where an exceptionally stable oil is desired. Available in a range of viscosities. SUN OIL CO.

Super-12®. A 12-inch, rotary floor-maintenance machine that will scrub, polish, and shampoo. It has a ¼ h.p. motor and heavy cast aluminum housing. S. C. JOHNSON & SON

Super-16®. A 16-inch, rotary floor-maintenance machine that can be used for scrubbing, polishing and steel wooling all types of floors, and shampooing rugs. It is driven by a ¾ h.p. motor, and has a heavy cast aluminum housing. S. C. JOHNSON & SON

Superaid. See DICALITE® SUPERAID.

Super-Beckamine®. An aromatic, solvent-soluble melamine-formaldehyde resin which produces low viscosity enamels of exceptional hardness. [*See also* BECKAMINE® (*HBMTN* p. 79)] REICHHOLD CHEMICALS, INC.

Super-Bondsit®. A liquid latex emulsion which is substituted for most of the mixing water in cementitious mixtures to form a durable topping for concrete floors. A SUEPR-BONSIT topping—usually about ¼" thick—provides a chemical-resistant, non-dusting, chip-proof, slip- and spark-resistant surface. *Uses:* For topping and patching industrial and commercial floors, playgrounds, tennis courts, etc. A. C. HORN CO.

Supercarbovar®. (*HBMTN* p. 545). Should have been listed as a registered trademark. GODFREY L. CABOT, INC.

Super-Care. See LECTON® SUPER-CARE.

Super-Cel. See HYFLO® SUPER-CEL *and* STANDARD SUPER-CEL.[NE]

Super-Crete-X[NE]. (*Supp.* I p. 230). Now a product of THE BORDEN CO., CHEMICAL DIV., successor to PIONEER LATEX & CHEMICAL CO.

Super-D Oil. See KENDALL SUPER-D OIL.

Superdraw®. The trademark for a coated tin plate, coated by the hot-dipped process. UNITED STATES STEEL CORP.

Super Drex®. High potency vitamin-containing solids for fortifying foods and feeds with vitamins. NOPCO CHEMICAL CO.

Super-Dri. See PARKO® SUPER-DRI.

Super Exsize-T®. *Same as* EXSIZE-T® except that it is more concentrated. PABST BREWING CO., INDUSTRIAL PRODUCTS DIV.

Super-Fine. See L.O.V. SUPER-FINE.[NE]

Superflo Boiled Oil[NE]. (*HBMTN* p. 546). No longer available. SPENCER KELLOGG & SONS

Super Floss[NE]. Similar to SNOW FLOSS except that the particles have an average size of 2-4 microns and a max. moisture content of 1%. Used for the same purposes as SNOW FLOSS. JOHNS-MANVILLE SALES CORP.

Super-G®. A diglyceride and monoglyceride mixture used as an emulsier ingredient in vegetable-oil food products and/or bakery goods. ANDERSON, CLAYTON & CO. FOODS DIV.

Supergard[NE]. A head-supported protective face-shield. *Use:* To protect the face and eyes from chemical splash or chips of metal or other solids in grinding operations. MINE SAFETY APPLIANCES CO.

Superheat[NE]. (*Supp.* I p. 231). No longer available. JOHNS-MANVILLE SALES CORP.

Superior Curtain Rods[NE]. Flat steel curtain rods in white or bronze, in single, double and with extension; drapery hardware of ⅜" round rodding with brackets and accessories; and seam and edge binding for carpets and linoleum. YOUNGSTOWN MFG., INC.

Superior[NE] **Foam Killer.** A defoamer consisting of a sulfonated tallow base. HERCULES POWDER CO.

Superior Metal Mouldings®. A complete line of extruded aluminum mouldings: nosings for counter and sink tops, wall covering mouldings, stair nosings, carpet and doorway edging, threshold plates, price tag mouldings, and commercial extrusions. YOUNGSTOWN MFG. CO.

Superior Nu-Oil®. A dormant and delayed dormant spray for the control of red mites, scale insects, aphids and leaf rollers on apples, peaches and cherries. Viscosity, Saybolt (100°F.), 90–120 sec.; A.P.I. gravity, 31; pour point, not greater than 30°F. MILLER CHEMICAL & FERTILIZER CORP.

Superior Red[NE]. A yellowish-red color pigment for printing inks where requirements are not severe and inexpensive pigmentation is paramount. SHERWIN-WILLIAMS CO.

Superise®. An enzymic preparation for use in bread making or as yeast food. TAKAMINE LABORATORIES

Super-Kem-Tone®. A latex emulsion paint designed for use on interior walls and ceilings. It dries in less than an hour. The painted surface can be cleaned easily with ordinary wall-washing cleaners. Available in a wide range of colors. SHERWIN-WILLIAMS CO.

Super King Bomb-Lube. A silicone-base mold lubricant for the molding of all types of plastics—phenolic, urea, acrylic, cellulose acetate, ethyl cellulose, polyethylene, polystyrene, polyamide, etc. It is packaged in self-dispensing aerosol container that discharges a fine, penetrating mist of particles in the 50-micron range. PRICE-DRISCOLL CORP.

Superkore®. The trademark for a carburizing alloy steel. UNITED STATES STEEL CORP.

Super-Lap. A lapping compound composed of graded diamond particles formulated into a special paste-like base. It is a fast-cutting material for roughing to super-finishing operations on plastic molds, ceramic parts, carbide dies, cutting tools, plug and ring gages, knitting and spinning tools, etc. Can be used for either hand- or mechanical-finishing operations. ACME SCIENTIFIC CO.

Superline®. Mixtures of clay, silica sand, gravel, a flux, and a binder for use as a refractory lining for ladles and cupolas and furnaces containing molten metal. INTERNATIONAL MINERALS & CHEMICAL CORP.

Superlok®. A patented price tag moulding with built-in rubber insert to hold the tag in place. YOUNGSTOWN MFG., INC.

Super Mafos®. (*HBMTN* p. 547). Formerly mfg'd by OLIN MATHIESON CHEMICAL CORP., now a product of ENDRISS CHEMICALS.

Super Metalsium[NE]. A metallic hardener for heavy-duty concrete floors. It consists of METALSIUM (*HBMTN* p. 360) with the addition of a puzzolanic cement dispersing and water-reducing admix. This makes it possible to use up to 120 lb. of the hardener per 100 sq.ft. and gives a more wear-resisting surface. CERESIT WATERPROOFING CORP.

Super Nopdex®. High potency vitamin-containing solids for fortifying foods and feeds with vitamins. NOPCO CHEMICAL CO.

Super Nufos®. (*HBMTN* p. 547). Formerly mfg'd by OLIN MATHIESON CHEMICAL CORP., now a product of ENDRISS CHEMICALS.

Superoxol®. (*Supp.* I p. 231). No longer available. SHARPE & DOHME DIV., MERCK & CO.

Super Redo®. (*HBMTN* p. 548). Now mfg'd by GOODALL-SANFORD, INC., successor to GOODALL FABRICS, INC.

Superseal®. An envelope resin seal adhesive. STEIN, HALL & CO.

Superset Finish. See CYANA SUPERSET® FINISH.

Supersolve[NE]. An engine-cleaning compound for removing oil, and for softening and removing carbon deposits and paint from engine parts by immersion in heated solution. It is a clear, free homogeneous liquid at ordinary temp.; pH, 7.5–7.8 at 68°F.; completely soluble in kerosene; one part soluble in 4 parts water at 131°F.; does not corrode or discolor steel, polished copper, or anodized aluminum alloys. WYANDOTTE CHEMICALS CORP., J. B. FORD DIV.

Super Stod-Sol®. A petroleum solvent consisting of 11.6% aromatics, 41.9% naphthenes, and 46.5% paraffins. Initial b.p., 305–315°F.; end point, 340–350°F.; flash point (TCC), 100°F. (min.); color, water white; sp.gr. (60°F.), 0.779; odor, mild; viscosity (60°F.), 0.98 centipoises. *Use:* As a dry-cleaning fluid. ANDERSON-PRICHARD OIL CORP.

Super-Tens®. The trademark for a steel wire for pre-stressed concrete. UNITED STATES STEEL CORP.

Super Tru-Sorb®. An absorbent for oil, grease, water and other liquids on floors of chemical plants and refineries, machine shops and garages, paint and printing shops, dairies, breweries, bottling plants, etc. It eliminates slippery and hazardous conditions, and keeps floors clean and dry. TRU-SORB CORP.

Super White "37". *See* CRAFTINT SUPER WHITE "37".

Super XX Cement. *See* KNIGHT SUPER XX CEMENT[NR].

Suprafix®. A group of vat-dye pastes that have been especially prepared to resist drying out and freezing. GENERAL DYESTUFF CO.

Suprak® Tanning Agents. The trademark for a line of tanning agents classified as synthetic phenolic resins. Used in the leather industry as tanning agents. AMERICAN CYANAMID CO.

Supralan®. A group of neutral-dyeing, pre-metallized acid dyestuffs recommended primarily for dyeing very fast shades on wool by a short dyeing procedure. They preserve the fiber quality much better than do other dyestuffs of equal fastness. They are also useful for dyeing fast shades on leather, NYLON, PERLON®, SILK, and ACRILAN®; and for printing all textile fibers that they dye satisfactorily. GENERAL DYESTUFF CO.

Supranyl[NR]. A synthetic textile size for continuous filament NYLON warps. A light amber liquid, of uniform viscosity and controlled concentration. STEIN, HALL & CO.

Sur-Bex®. A VITAMIN-B complex preparation, available in syrup and tablet forms. ABBOTT LABORATORIES

Sure-Foot[NR]. An anti-slip paint for concrete, metal, or wood surfaces. It contains carbide crystals. It is applied by brush or trowel, and dries overnight to a tough film that resists traffic wear. It can be used on floors, stairs, treads, catwalks, platforms, truck beds, etc. Available in black, blue, gray, green, red, and traffic yellow. FROST PAINT & OIL CORP.

Surett®. A line of black petroleum products used as adhesive gear shields and wire rope dressings. Available in six grades designated, respectively: 135, 310, 1500, 3000, 5000, and U-1500. The numerical suffix is indicative of the viscosity in Saybolt seconds at 210°F. GRADE U-1500 is compounded to resist water and is often used in place of SURETT 1500 for wet operating conditions. At ordinary temps., only grades 135 and 310 can be applied directly. The heavier grades, 1500, U-1500, 3000 and 5000 are so thick they must be heated to approx. the boiling point of water before application. When these grades cool, they thicken into a coating that sticks to the lubricated part and resists being displaced. *Uses:* As a coating for open gears, wire rope, and other wearing parts that cannot be provided with a continuous supply of lubricant. ESSO STANDARD OIL CO.

Surett® Fluid. A lubricant similar to SURETT® but compounded with a volatile, non-flammable solvent to make it easier to handle under normal temp. conditions. In addition to the solvent content, SURETT FLUID contains a lead soap to improve the extreme-pressure and rust-preventive properties. Available in 2 grades: SURETT FLUID 30 and SURETT FLUID 50. The viscosities of these grades are 500 and 700 Saybolt seconds at 210°F., respectively. After evaporation of the solvent, the respective viscosities are the same as those of SURETT 3000 and SURETT 5000, the two heaviest grades. ESSO STANDARD OIL CO.

Surett® P-65. A special flotation-type rust retarder designed to check corrosion of marine ballast tanks, coffer dams, telescoping gas holder sections, and similar structures that are in intermittent contact with water and for which other means of protection are not practical. Gravity (°API), 18.0; flash point, 425°F.; pour point, 0°F.; viscosity, S.U.S.: 918 at 100°F. and 66.4 at 210°F. ESSO STANDARD OIL CO.

Surfonic® Adducts. A line of intermediates used in preparing surface-active agents and as surface-active agents themselves. JEFFERSON CHEMICAL CO.

Surital®. An ultrashort-acting anesthetic agent for intravenous use. It is thiamylal sodium, Parke-Davis. PARKE, DAVIS & CO.

Surplex®. A hematinic with vitamin supplement used in the treatment of secondary anemia, especially when associated with VITAMIN B deficiency. Consists of ferrous sulfate and crystalline vitamins in a VITAMIN B complex syrup. ABBOTT LABORATORIES

Surtreat Process. A chromate-type surface treatment for cadmium and zinc. It is used to produce a high luster or a colored chromate film on pure electrodeposited surfaces. It also produces colored chromate films on zinc alloys used in the mfg. of zinc-base die-castings. When used for brightening the SURTREAT PROCESS is a two-dip operation with an intermediate rinse. The first dip (SURTREAT) forms a colored chromate film on the surface, and the second dip (SURTREAT LEACH) leaches the color, leaving an extremely bright surface, covered by a thin, practically invisible passivating film. This film will retard the formation of white corrosion, delay tarnishing and provide a good base for paint and lacquer. UDYLITE CORP.

Swedish Green△. *Also known as* SCHEELE'S MINERAL®. Copper arsenite. $CuHAsO_3$ (approx.); mol.wt. 187.5; usually contains from 35 to 40% Cu and 40 to 45% As_2O_3. A poisonous, yellowish green powder; insoluble in water or alcohol; soluble in dilute ammonia and in dilute acids. *Uses:* As an insecticide; as a base for various green copper pigments; in medicine, it has been used as an intestinal antiseptic.

Sweet Birch Oil△. *Also known as* WINTERGREEN OIL△, BETULA OIL△ *and* TEABERRY OIL△. Methyl salicylate. $C_8H_8O_3$; mol.wt. 152.14. It is found in the leaves of the plant *Gaultheria procumbens,* and the bark of the tree, *Betula* lenta; however, it is prepared principally by esterifying salicylic acid with methanol. A colorless, yellowish or reddish, oily liquid with the odor and taste of gaultheria. Slightly soluble in water; soluble in chloroform and in ether; miscible with alcohol, and glacial acetic acid. *Uses:* In perfumery; for flavoring candies, etc.

Sweetose®. A high-conversion, low-viscosity corn syrup mfg'd by acid-enzyme conversion in a patented process. It is low in color and bland in flavor. Available in two grades and in various densities. The average composition of 43° Bé SWEETOSE SYRUP is as follows: moisture, 18.2%; total solids, 81.8%; dextrose, 30.6%; maltose, 28.0%; higher sugars, 13.2%; dextrin, 10.0%; ash, 0.02%; dextrose equivalent, 63; fermentable extract (dry basis), 70%; pH, 5; viscosity, 52 poises at 100°F. SWEETOSE "C" SYRUP is an economical grade of approx. the same analysis

except that it contains 0.3% ash. *Uses:* As a sweetening agent and humectant in tobacco; as a reducing agent in chrome leather tanning; as a conditioner for sole leather; as a brightener in metal plating; as a plasticizer in dextrin and animal glue adhesives; and as a finishing agent in the textile industry. In the food industry, it is used extensively in the confectionery, baking, brewing, and meat-packing industries; in canned and frozen fruits, jams, jellies, preserves; in dairy products; in the mfg. of vinegar; in frozen eggs; etc.
A. E. STALEY MFG. CO.

S W P®. A general-purpose house paint for all wood surfaces subject to exterior exposure. Available in 17 colors and white. SHERWIN-WILLIAMS CO.

Synalol E[NE]. A proprietary synthetic aromatic chemical. A practically colorless liquid with a peppery pungent floral odor. DOW CHEMICAL CO.

Synalyl D[NE]. A proprietary synthetic aromatic chemical. A practically colorless liquid with an aroma quite like a highly refined linalyl acetate from bois de rose. DOW CHEMICAL CO.

Syndex[NE]. A general-purpose floor cleaner and wax stripper. Safe to use on all composition floors. Meets requirements of all national flooring institutes. Tested and approved as a cleaner for electrically conductive floors in hospital operating rooms, powder factories, etc. BRULIN & CO.

Synhibit "AQ". A water-soluble, corrosive-inhibitive, organic coating solution which produces a water-insoluble film, about 20 millionths of an inch thick on drying. These extremely thin films provide temporary corrosion protection and are also used as a base for painting. SYNHIBIT "AQ" has excellent adhesion to metals and all classes of organic film-formers. THOMPSON & CO.

Synite®, Synite® Aluminum Paint, *and* **Synite® Enamels.** (*HBMTN* p. 532). The name SYNITE® is now a registered trademark. ARCO CO.

Synpex[NE]. Lacquers, enamels and varnishes that contain nitrocellulose and synthetic resins, and that combine the properties of both constituents; *i.e.* they are fast drying and have flexible toughness.
MAAS & WALDSTEIN CO.

Synpra®. The trademark for a line of synthetic rubber finishes. FIDELITY CHEMICAL PRODUCTS CORP.

Syntemp®. The trademark for a line of bake-type synthetic finishes.
FIDELITY CHEMICAL PRODUCTS CORP.

Synterge 748[NE]. A non-ionic condensate detergent and dispersing agent especially adapted for boiling off or dyeing waxed griege goods, especially NYLONS, ORLONS, and DACRONS as well as RAYONS and ACETATES. COLLOIDS, INC.

Synterge 750[NE]. A coconut oil amide processing excellent detergent, emulsifying, wetting and dye-leveling properties. It is an excellent textile detergent that can be used with all types of fibers in acid or alkali solutions, and in all textile processes, including bleaching, scouring, stock or package dyeing, jig or box work, etc. Available in 100%, 75%, 33^1/$_3$% and 25% concentrations. COLLOIDS, INC.

Syntex L-852. (*Supp.* I p. 234). No longer available. FLINTKOTE CO.

Synthabond®. (*Supp.* I p. 234). No longer available. SYNTHETIC MICA CORP.

Synthamica[NE]. (Trademark registration pending). A synthetic mica made from a stoichiometric ratio of magnesium oxide, aluminum oxide, silicon dioxide, potassium silica fluoride, and potash feldspar. The dry mix is heated in an electric-arc furnace to 2,500°F. in 20-ton batches, and the melt is allowed to cool slowly over a 7–12 day period. The crystalline mass of fluor-phlogopite mica is removed from the unreacted portion of the charge and broken up. This synthetic mica withstands temps. of 800–1,000°C., compared to 500–600°C. for natural mica. Available in sintered, hot-pressed, bonded and unbonded sheets, and three dimensional and crystalline forms. Used for many high-temp. electrical insulation applications in electron tubes, capacitors, etc.
SYNTHETIC MICA CORP.

Syntharome Flavors®. A line of concentrated imitation flavors based on fruit and vegetable extractions, fortified with SYNTHAROME Oils.
FLORASYNTH LABORATORIES, INC.

Syntharome Oils®. A line of flavoring oils made from natural essential oils.
FLORASYNTH LABORATORIES, INC.

Syntharome Oils® (Imitation). A line of: (1) full strength flavoring oils, consisting of essential oils and aromatics, used for the mfg. of high grade imitation flavoring extracts, and available in 37 fruit flavors; and (2) flavoring oils in butter, cheese, and butterscotch flavors. FLORASYNTH LABORATORIES, INC.

Synthe-Copal®. (*HBMTN* p. 553). Now a registered trademark. REICHHOLD CHEMICALS, INC.

Synthofruit Oils® (Imitation). A line of 13 imitation fruit-flavored oils for the mfg. of flavoring extracts. Approx. the same strength as SYNTHAROME OILS® but lower in price.
FLORASYNTH LABORATORIES, INC.

Synthramine® A 50% Paste. Cetyl trimethyl ammonium bromide with fatty compounds and water. It is an assistant used in the stripping of azoic colors from textiles. ARNOLD, HOFFMAN & CO.

Synthrapol® N-380. (*Supp.* I p. 234). Now known as SYNTHRAPOL® NX. ARNOLD, HOFFMAN & CO.

Synthrapol® NX. Formerly known as SYNTHRAPOL® N-380 (*Supp.* I p. 234). ARNOLD, HOFFMAN & CO.

Synthrowite. See ORCO SYNTHROWITE FWN *and* GNW[NE].

Syntilon®. A soft and flexible, wetproof vinylized fabric for baby pants, crib sheets, and children's clothing. It is tear resistant, will not crack or peel, and is acid and alkali resistant. PLASTIC FILM CORP.

Syphon Seal[NE]. The trade name for a roofing material. UNITED STATES STEEL CORP.

T

T®. The trademark for a line of steel bars, concrete reinforcing bars, cotton tie buckles, nails, track spikes, and bolts. UNITED STATES STEEL CORP.

T-1®. See U.S.S.® T-1®.

T-653-LB Thermopoxy. See STERLING® T-653-LB THERMOPOXY.

Tabatonka[NE]. An aromatic liquid blend with a natural tonka character, used as tonka replacement in tobacco products. DOW CHEMICAL CO.

Tabcin®. An antihistaminic analygetic compound used for the treatment of colds, headaches, grippe, influenza, neuralgia, and other aches and pains. MILES LABORATORIES, INC.

Tacanols®. A series of nonionic surfactants possessing modified scouring, wetting, and emulsifying properties. They have excellent pigment dispersing properties with extremely low foaming characteristics. Available in odorless and scented forms. TEXTILE ADJUNCTS CORP.

Tackmaster®. Pressure-sensitive film adhesives consisting of lightweight, porous, essentially transparent paper carriers which have been saturated and coated on both sides with a clear, aggressive, pressure-sensitive adhesive. TACKMASTER TYPE "A" has a highly aggressive tack, relatively soft, and is recommended for use on porous or semi-porous surfaces where adhesive flow is desirable. TACKMASTER TYPE "B" has an aggressive tack, firmer than for Type "A," and is used where restricted flow is desired. Available in standard rolls, 36" wide and 100 yards long. RUBBER AND ASBESTOS CORP.

Tadpole Gasketing Tape[NE]. A tape made of asbestos cloth wrapped over a core of asbestos rope or wick, depending upon the size and degree. Designed for use as a door gasket where a groove is not provided. This tape provides a tight seal with a minimum pressure, for service on oven doors, sterilizers, safes, vaults, plenum chambers, dust collectors, hinged tank covers, cooking kettles, kiers, etc. JOHNS-MANVILLE SALES CORP.

Takabate®. An enzyme preparation used to remove undesirable proteinaceous substances from animal hides. TAKAMINE LABORATORIES

Talamine M. A.[NE] A surface-active agent possessing good detergent, penetrating, and dispersing properties. It is a sulfated amide ester that is widely used in textile processing to remove grease and graphite from hosiery, as a vat dyeing assistant, and in package dyeing. MAC CHEMICAL CO.

Talc△. Also known as TALCUM△ and FRENCH CHALK△. A native hydrous magnesium silicate of the approx. composition $4SiO_2 \cdot 3MgO \cdot H_2O$, and occurring in white, gray, green, brown or red colors. TALC has a hardness of 1 on Moh's scale and a sp.gr. of 2.8. It is a very fine, odorless, crystalline powder that adheres readily to the skin; insoluble in water, cold acids or alkalis. FRENCH CHALK is a high-grade talc that occurs in massive block form and is found in the United States in the Appalachian region from Vermont to Georgia. *Uses:* As a dusting powder either alone or with starch or boric acid, for medicinal and toilet preparations; as an excipient and filler for medicinal pills and tablets and for dusting tablet molds; for clarifying liquids by filtration; as a pigment for paints, varnishes and rubber; as a filler for paper, rubber, and soap; in fireproof and cold-water paints for wood, metal and stone; as a lubricant for molds; as a glove and shoe powder; for molding into ceramic insulators, heater parts, and chemical ware; as a thermal-insulation material; etc.

Talco Gum△. See GUM ARABIC△.

Talcum△. Same as TALC△.

Talha Gum△. See GUM ARABIC△.

Talh Gum△. See GUM ARABIC△.

Talisman®. The trademark for a line of prefabricated homes. UNITED STATES STEEL HOMES, INC.

Talleol△. Same as TALL OIL△.

Tall Oil△. Also known as LIQUID ROSIN△, TALLOL△ and TALLEOL△. A dark brown, oily, resinous liquid, with an odor similar to that of burnt rosin, that is recovered as a by-product from the pine wood "black liquor" of the sulfate or KRAFT paper process. Refined TALL OIL is reddish-yellow and nearly odorless. Sp.gr. 0.97–0.99; flash point, 350°–370°F.; acid no. 160–170; saponification no. 172–185; iodine no. 120–188; contains 30–40% rosin acids, 5–10% unsaponifiable matter, and 45–60% linoleic acid, 20% linolenic acid, and some palmitic acid. *Uses:* In the mfg. of soap pastes, flotation agents, asphalt emulsions, rust preventives, animal dips, insecticides, cutting oils, paints, alkyd resins, rubber formulations, etc.

Tallol△. Same as TALL OIL△.

Tallowene[NE]. (*HBMTN* p. 555). No longer available. HANSON-VAN WINKLE-MUNNING CO.

Tamarix®. The trademark for food flavoring products. S. B. PENICK & CO.

Tamptite®. A dynamite in special cartridge form for use in explosive operations. TAMPTITE permits max. density in the drill hole without the usual slitting of the cartridge. HERCULES POWDER CO.

Tanamer® Product 370. A dry sodium polyacrylate that is readily adaptable to the paste drying operation in the tanning of leather. It is highly compatible with methyl cellulose, thereby eliminating the necessity of soaking the methyl cellulose in hot water to obtain solution. It also eliminates the necessity for washing of full grain leathers after drying. Furthermore, with the use of this product, plate washing is held to a minimum. AMERICAN CYANAMID CO.

Tando®. (*HBMTN* p. 556 and *Supp.* I p. 236). No longer available. CLACK WATER TREATMENT SERVICE

Tank Clad®. A chemical-resistant coating for exterior steel surfaces such as tanks, and for general industrial maintenance. SHERWIN-WILLIAMS CO.

Tank-O-Lene. See PARKO® TANK-O-LENE.

Tank-Solv. See PARKO® TANK-SOLV.

Tannate. (1) A line of flat leather belts for power transmission in the textile, pulp and paper, flour-processing and other industries. Available in thicknesses of $^{11}/_{64}''$ to $^{34}/_{64}''$ and in widths of 8" to 76". (2) Rounded leather belting in sizes from ⅛" to ⅝". (3) Solid round leather belts in diameters of ⅜" to 1". (4) Leather V belting. (5) Leather packings for shafts, pistons, etc. (6) BICUT® leather check straps for use in the textile industry. J. E. RHOADS & SONS

Tanoyl HDF®. A line of fat liquoring and finishing compositions. NOPCO CHEMICAL CO.

Tarcortin®. A synergistic combination of Tarbonis and hydrocortisone (0.5%). It is particularly valuable in the treatment of chronic and subacute dermatoses such as nummular eczema, hand eczemas, atopic eczemas, seborrhea, etc. It is far more effective than either tar or steroid therapy alone. REED & CARNRICK

Tarophen[NE]. A series of tarry aromatic or aliphatic residues. DOW CHEMICAL CO.

Tashan Cream[NE]. A multivitamin skin cream. Each gram contains, in a vanishing cream base, 10,000 U.S.P. units of VITAMIN A, 50 mg. d-panthenol, 1,000 U.S.P. units VITAMIN D, and 5 mg. VITAMIN E (dl-alpha-tocopheryl acetate). Used for symptomatic relief of sunburn, diaper rash, itching, poison ivy, prickly heat, minor burns, cracked skin, insect bites, dry skin, and other skin conditions.
HOFFMANN-LA ROCHE INC.

Tasti[NE]. Food savoring powders comprising monosodium glutamate.
INTERNATIONAL MINERALS & CHEMICAL CORP.

Tastitabs®. See STIMAVITE® TASTITABS® and VITERRA® TASTITABS®.

Taylor[NE]. The trade name for a line of adjustable rail braces. UNITED STATES STEEL CORP.

Taylor Laminated Plastics[NE]. An extensive line of laminates, available in a large selection of resins and bases, including phenol laminates, melamine laminates, silicone laminates, epoxy laminates, and combination laminates. TAYLOR FIBRE CO.

Taylor Vulcanized Fibre[NE]. A hard, dense material made by passing a number of layers of paper through a bath of zinc chloride. This solution gelatinizes the paper, causing the individual fibers in the several layers to cohere into a homogeneous sheet. The thickness of the finished sheet is determined by the number of layers of paper used in the make-up.

After gelatinization, the zinc chloride is removed by leaching with water. The sheet material passes through a drying operation and, as water is removed, shrinks in thickness to form a hard, dense product. Calender rolls then produce the desired surface finish.

Available in a large number of grades for specific uses, such as washers, terminal blocks, switch and appliance insulation, insulating plates, gears and cams, bushings and grommets, switch handles, trunks, refrigerator hardware, washer plates, etc.
TAYLOR FIBRE CO.

TCA[△]. Trichloroacetic acid. $CCl_3 \cdot COOH$; mol.wt. 163.40. Prepared by the oxidation of chloral with nitric or nitrous acids, and by the direct chlorination of acetic acid. Hygroscopic, colorless crystals that melt at 56.9°C.; highly soluble in water, ether, and alcohol. Very corrosive to the skin; corrosive to iron, zinc, aluminum, etc. *Uses:* As a selective weedkiller that is effective against quack grass (*Agropyron* spp.); as a precipitant of protein; as a decalcifier and fixative in microscopy; in medicine as a caustic, astringent, and antiseptic. (*See also* STCA[△]).

T-C Hydro®. A dry, white, free-flowing, crystalline sodium hydrosulfite. Purity, 94% $Na_2S_2O_4$ (min.).
TENNESSEE CORP.

TCI Tool Steel®. The trademark for a high grade tool, drill, and channeler steel in bar form.
UNITED STATES STEEL CORP.,
TENNESSEE COAL & IRON DIV.

TDE[△]. Same as DDD[△].

Teaberry Oil[△]. Same as SWEET BIRCH OIL[△].

Teal®. (*HBMTN* p. 557). No longer available.
E. I. DU PONT DE NEMOURS & CO.

Teca®. (*HBMTN* p. 557). No longer available.
TENNESSEE EASTMAN CO.

Technicolor®. A registered trade and service mark identifying the products and services of the TECHNICOLOR CORP., including color consulting service and three-color subtractive still and motion pictures in which the color components are printed in registry in one layer by dye transfer or are formed respectively in three superposed layers of emulsion by direct or reversal color development.

Technirama®. A registered trademark identifying the products of the TECHNICOLOR CORP., including color motion pictures.

Techniscope®. A registered trademark identifying the products of the TECHNICOLOR CORP., including color motion pictures.

Technivision®. A registered trademark identifying the products of the TECHNICOLOR CORP., including color motion pictures.

Tech-Var®. A varnish for the furniture industry.
SHERWIN-WILLIAMS CO.

Tecmangam®. Technical manganese sulfate, consisting primarily of manganese sulfate and, in lesser quantity, ammonium sulfate. It is completely soluble in water, and is used as a source of manganese in fertilizers and nutritional sprays.
EASTMAN CHEMICAL PRODUCTS, INC.

Teco Polychrome Rabake. (*HBMTN* p. 557). No longer available. THOMPSON & CO.

Tecosteel. (*HBMTN* p. 557). No longer available.
THOMPSON & CO.

Tecsol®. A proprietary solvent.
EASTMAN CHEMICAL PRODUCTS, INC.

Tectant. See LARVA-TECTANT[NE].

Tedral®. (*HBMTN* p. 558). Now a product of WARNER-CHILCOTT LABORATORIES, successor to THE MALTINE CO.

Teebacin®. A tuberculostatic which may be used alone or in combination with streptomycin or isoniazid. Supplied in the form of tablets, each of which contains 0.5 g. sodium para-aminosalicylate. Also available in strengths of 0.6 g. or 1.0 g. sodium para-aminosalicylate. CONSOLIDATED MIDLAND CORP.

Teebacin® Acid. A tuberculostatic which may be used alone or in combination with streptomycin or ioniazid. Supplied in the form of tablets, each of which contains 0.5 g. para-aminosalicylic acid. The tablets are either plain (TEEBACIN® ACID) or buffered (TEEBACIN® ACID BUFFERED).
CONSOLIDATED MIDLAND CORP.

Teebaconin®. A tuberculostatic used alone or in combination with other agents. Supplied in the form of tablets, each of which contains 50 mg. isonicotinic acid hydrazide. Also available as a parenteral solution for intramuscular administration.
CONSOLIDATED MIDLAND CORP.

Teebazone[NR]. A tuberculostatic agent. It is a brand of 4-acetyl amino benzaldehyde thiosemicarbazone; a pale yellow crystalline powder. It is most effective when the disease is primarily a mucous membrane condition; it is ineffective in miliary and meningeal tuberculosis. Supplied in the form of 25 mg. tablets. CONSOLIDATED MIDLAND CORP.

Teel Oil[△]. See SESAME OIL[△].

T.E.E.P.[△]. Same as T.E.P.[△].

Teglac® Resins. (*HBMTN* p. 558). No longer available. AMERICAN CYANAMID CO.

Teko[NR]. A special liquid emulsifying agent containing non-ionic synthetic detergents and an effective grease solvent for faster grease, oil, and stain removal in washing of coveralls, linen supplies, rags, industrial wipers, and commercial work.
WYANDOTTE CHEMICALS CORP.
J. B. FORD DIV.

Tel-A-Pipe. A line of self-adhering, pre-painted, identification markers for pipe, tubing, conduit and electrical cable. It combines color coding with identification of pipe contents. Standard wordings in four types, available from stock. Special wordings, colors, sizes available on order.
WESTERN LITHOGRAPH CO.
WESTLINE PRODUCTS DIV.

Telecrane®. An interplant frequency-modulated carrier communication system. *Use:* To provide direct voice communication between crane operator and ground stations. MINE SAFETY APPLIANCES CO.

Tell-Board[NR]. A name used to designate a line of bulletin boards. MINE SAFETY APPLIANCES CO.

Tellerette®. A polyethylene tower packing made in the form of rosettes. This packing weighs about ¼ as much as conventional packing; and has high efficiency, high free volume, and low pressure drop.
HARSHAW CHEMICAL CO.

Tembrite®. A fast-working, thorough-cleaning, strongly alkaline compound that contains no free caustic. It is used to clean dairy pasteurizers and heaters, remove baked-on grease and carbonized deposits from smokehouses, etc. DIVERSEY CORP.

Tempogen® Forte. A medicinal for the treatment of patients with rheumatoid arthritis and related diseases. Each tablet contains 2.0 mg. HYDELTRA®, 0.3 g. acetylsalicylic acid, 60 mg. sodium ascorbate, and 0.2 g. dried aluminum hydroxide gel.
MERCK SHARP & DOHME

Tempro (Formula CI-103)[NR]. (*Supp.* I p. 237). No longer available. JOHN B. MOORE CORP.

Tempron®. A synthetic (BUNA N) rubber especially suited for the fabrication of hard rubber. Sp.gr. 1.24–1.29; tensile strength, 7,100–8,500 lb./sq.in.; heat distortion temp. 275°–300°F.; excellent resistance to weak and strong acids and alkalis, and good resistance to organic solvents. Can be molded into parts, sheets, tile, etc. Available as pipe in sizes from 1″ to 4″ and fittings from 2″ to 4″.
AMERICAN HARD RUBBER CO.

Tenac. See KRYLON-HOUGHTON® TENAC OPEN GEAR AND CABLE LURICANT.

Tenamene® 1, 2, and 3. Incorrectly listed as TENEMENE® 1, 2, and 3 (*Supp.* I p. 237).
TENNESSEE EASTMAN CO.

Tenamene® 30. N, N′-di-secondary-octyl-*p*-phenylenediamine. A tan to dark red liquid at room temp.; sp.gr., 0.90. *Use:* As an antiozonant for use in rubber compounding.
EASTMAN CHEMICAL PRODUCTS, INC.

Tenamene® 31. N,N′-di-3-(5-methyl-heptyl)-*p*-phenylenediamine. A tan to dark red liquid at room temp.; sp.gr., 0.90. *Use:* As an antiozonant for use in rubber compounding.
EASTMAN CHEMICAL PRODUCTS, INC.

Tenamene® 60. A copper deactivator for motor fuels and aviation gasolines, and a sludge inhibitor for fuel oils. It is composed of disalicylal propylene di-imine (80%) and toluene (20%).
EASTMAN CHEMICAL PRODUCTS, INC.

Ten-B-Low. A sweetened food mix for use in making ice cream, puddings, pie fillings, etc.
M & R DIETETIC LABORATORIES, INC.

Tenelon[NR]. The trade name for a stainless steel.
UNITED STATES STEEL CORP.

Tenemene® 1, 2, and 3. (*Supp.* I p. 237). Should have been listed as TENAMINE® 1, 2, and 3.
TENNESSEE EASTMAN CO.

Tenite® Acetate. A thermoplastic material composed primarily of cellulose acetate. It is characterized by toughness, high impact strength, uniform texture, permanent luster, and unlimited range of transparent, translucent, variegated, and opaque colors which are an integral part of the material. It is supplied in the form of pellets for molding and extruding into finished products. It is exceptionally light in weight; under ordinary conditions of heat and humidity, it has a high degree of dimensional stability and may be molded and extruded to very close tolerances; it is insoluble in most vegetable and mineral oils, and soluble in some ketones and esters; it is damaged by acids, alkalis, and alcohol. TENITE ACETATE is suitable for the production of a wide variety of products, ranging from automotive parts, pipe, sporting goods, home appliances, toys, tool handles, etc. EASTMAN CHEMICAL PRODUCTS, INC.

Tenite® Butyrate. A thermoplastic material composed primarily of cellulose acetate-butyrate. Its properties are similar to those of TENITE ACETATE although it is lighter in weight than the latter, has greater resistance to distortion under varying degrees of heat and humidity, its moisture absorption is lower, and its finish is more lustrous. It is suitable for the production of the same wide variety of products as is TENITE ACETATE.
EASTMAN CHEMICAL PRODUCTS, INC.

Tenite® Polyethylene. A polyethylene thermoplastic which is offered in the form of ⅛-in. spherical pellets in formulas of varying melt indexes. It is supplied in natural, and in any color within the limitations of the inherent translucence of the base material, with or without antioxidant. Color and black concentrates are offered, as are antioxidant concentrates, which can be mixed with natural material by the user. It is odorless and tasteless, remains flexible over a wide temp. range, and is virtually unbreakable. It is resilient; it resists the attack of most chemicals and solvents; and it is easily molded. TENITE POLYETHYLENE applications include packaging film, molded products, wire and cable insulation, pipe and tubing, bottles, and paper coatings.
EASTMAN CHEMICAL PRODUCTS, INC.

Tenlo®. A polyhydroxy alcohol-fatty acid ester used as a wetting agent and spreader for agricultural chemicals. NOPCO CHEMICAL CO.

Tenneseal®. The trademark for uncoated or galvanized steel sheet roofing and siding.
UNITED STATES STEEL CORP.,
TENNESSEE COAL & IRON DIV.

Tennessee®. The trademark used to designate a type of open hearth basic slag, steel cotton ties, structural shapes, plates, bars, rails, tie plates and splice bars.
UNITED STATES STEEL CORP.,
TENNESSEE COAL & IRON DIV.

Tennessee Tri-Basic® Copper. Tri-basic copper sulfate. $CuSO_4·3Cu(OH)_2·H_2O$; mol.wt. 470.290; copper content, 53–54%. An aqua-colored powder of fine particle size; insoluble in water; stable in storage; forms essentially neutral water dispersions; compatible with DDT, arsenicals, organic insecticides, sulfur and cryolite; does not inhibit photosynthesis; adheres well to foliage and does not require the addition of lime. Applied by spray or dust. *Uses:* As a fixed copper agricultural fungicide that is toxic to pathogenic fungi, but does not injure the fruits and vegetables. It also serves as a nutritional trace element for plants. TENNESSEE CORP.

Tenox®. EASTMAN food-grade antioxidants for edible fats and oils. Available in a number of formulations containing various combinations of butylated hydroxyanisole (BHA), butylated hydroxytoluene (BHT), and propyl gallate. A typical formulation, TENOX II, is a propylene glycol solution of BHA plus propyl gallate and citric acid as synergists. TENOX is particularly effective in stabilizing fats and oils which are used to prepare baked and fried foods. Its antioxidant properties carry through the heat of the baking oven and frying vat to protect the finished product. EASTMAN CHEMICAL PRODUCTS, INC.

Ten-Ten®. Weed killing composition containing propylene glycol butyl ether esters of 2,4-D.
DOW CHEMICAL CO.

T.E.P.△. Also known as T.E.E.P.△ Tetraethyl pyrophosphate. $(C_2H_5)_4P_2O_7$; mol.wt. 290.20. A hygroscopic, mobile liquid that hydrolyzes in water; miscible with water, acetone, alcohol, benzene, chloroform, glycerol, toluene, and xylene; not miscible with petroleum ether, kerosene and other petroleum oils. *Uses:* As an insecticide, especially to control aphids, thrips, and mites.

Tergenol S Liquid Conc[NE]. A clear liquid containing at least 33% sodium-N-methyl-N-oleyltaurate. It has good detergency, wetting, emulsifying and dispersing properties; and excellent stability to hard water, acids and alkalis. HART PRODUCTS CORP.

Tergit®. (*Supp.* I p. 238). Now a registered trademark. RIVERSIDE MFG. CO.

Tergolene Concentrate[NE]. An alkyl phenolethylene oxide condensate, with excellent detergent, emulsifying, and penetrating properties, used in scouring and dyeing operations. It is 100% active and stable to acids and alkalies. It is suitable for use on all fibers: COTTON, RAYON, ACETATE, SILK, WOOLENS, NYLON, and other synthetics. FABRIC CHEMICALS CO.

Terminix. A chemical termite control agent. Consists of a crystalline toxicant, of very low water solubility, dissolved in ortho-dichlorobenzene and volatile organic solvents. Applied only by licensed companies. TERMINIX DIV., E. L. BRUCE CO.

Termitkil. A chemical product for treating soil to kill termites, flying ants, and other similar insects. Used either full strength, or diluted with 3 parts of fuel oil. FAESY & BESTHOFF, INC.

Terne Plate△. Steel plate coated by the dip process with a relatively thin layer of an alloy of 20% tin and 80% lead, although other proportions of tin and lead are also used. TERNE PLATE is classified according to the thickness of the alloy coating: SHORT TERNES are steel plates of 14 to 30 gage in thickness, with coatings of 8 lb. or less; LONG TERNES have coatings of 8, 12 or 15 lb. The coating weight is measured in pounds per double base box containing approx. 436 sq. ft., or 112 sheets of 20 × 28 inches. *Uses:* As a construction material; for roofing; etc.

Terpex[NE]. A hydrocarbon oil of terpene origin which exhibits drying properties. Miscible with linseed oil, turpentine, aromatic and aliphatic solvents. Used in aluminum coatings, mastics and inks.
GLIDDEN CO.

Terraclor[NE]. Pentachloronitrobenzene, for use as a soil fungicide. OLIN MATHIESON CHEMICAL CORP.

Terra Cotta△. A term applied to various forms of burned clay used for decorative and structural purposes. They are molded from low-grade clays and are hard burned but not vitrified. It is used for roofing, floor tile, hollow building blocks, and in decorative construction work.

Terraflex®. A vinyl plastic-asbestos resilient floor tile, which is unaffected by grease, oil, alkaline moisture or mild acid solutions, and is highly fire resistant. Available in a number of different colors, in the standard size of 9″ × 9″, in $^1/_{16}$″ and $^1/_8$″ thicknesses.
JOHNS-MANVILLE SALES CORP.

Terra-New[NR]. A solvent-based sealer-finish for terrazzo floors, containing waxes and resins. This product functions both as a sealer and maintenance material. It will not discolor floors, is water-resistant, and slip-retardant. Can also be used on ceramic tile, slate, etc.
S. C. JOHNSON & SON

Tervan® 2735. A premium grade dairy wax for coating milk cartons. It is formulated with a special selected wax to which a tough plastic material has been added. This wax permits the application of a uniformly thin but tough wax film that produces cartons with high leakage resistance, minimum flaking, good bulge resistance and neat appearance.
ESSO STANDARD OIL CO.

Test Q. *See* OAKITE® TEST Q.

Testrolix[NR]. A male and female sex hormone preparation. A clear orange-red, currant-flavored liquid for oral administration. Each 4 cc. (approx. 1 teaspoonful) contains 0.02 mg. ethinyl estradiol and 10.0 mg. methyltestosterone in 17.5% alcohol. *Uses:* In the female, for treatment of disorders of the menstrual cycle, menopausal syndrome, functional uterine bleeding, amenorrhea, dysmenorrhea, menometrorrhagia, premenstrual tension, inhibition of lactation, and postpartum pains; in the male, for treatment of irritability, nervousness, diminished efficiency, and waning strength generally associated with the male climacteric.
CHICAGO PHARMACAL CO.

Tetronic®. A non-ionic surface-active agent used as a cold-water detergent and emulsifying and demulsifying agent; and in textile processing.
WYANDOTTE CHEMICALS CORP.,
MICHIGAN ALKALI DIV.

Texacoat. *See* TEXACO® TEXACOAT.

Texaco® Capella Oil. A lubricating oil for refrigeration service. Also available as TEXACO® CAPELLA OIL (WAXFREE), a specially refined low-temp. oil for compressor service. It will not wax out at temps. as low as —100°F., resists oxidation and foaming, is moisture free, is compatible with refrigerants, and retains its stability under severest conditions. TEXAS CO.

Texaco® Crater. A lubricant for wire rope and open gears. Its extra tough, adherent film penetrates and stays on, giving protection against wear and rust.
TEXAS CO.

Texaco® Crater X Fluid. A lubricant for wire rope and open gears. It has the same protective qualities as TEXACO® CRATER, but is in liquid form. TEXAS CO.

Texaco® Floatcoat. A rust-preventive oil that floats on oil without gelling or emulsifying; adheres to wet or dry metal; penetrates existing rust; and resists water washing after it is applied. *Use:* To prevent rust and corrosion inside ballast tanks, voids, coffer dams, and barge rakes; for inside protection of tail shaft tapers in propeller hubs and rudder voids; and for protection of chains in chain lockers and other places.
TEXAS CO.

Texaco® Multifax. A multi-purpose grease with excellent pumpability, for both anti-friction and sleeve-type bearings, eccentric straps, roller chains, and for lubricating other equipment where a grease is required.
TEXAS CO.

Texaco® Olympian Grease. A lubricant for plain, anti-friction, and cavity hub bearings of mine car wheels.
TEXAS CO.

Texaco® Paper Machine Oil HD. A lubricant for protecting heavily loaded roller bearings at temps. up to 300°F. or higher. It is exceptionally stable in the presence of water and heat; prevents rust and corrosion throughout the entire system; keeps lines and bearings free from accumulations of carbon, dust, and sludge; and separates readily from water.
TEXAS CO.

Texaco® Rustproof Compound. A petroleum product used to prevent rust on all exposed metal.
TEXAS CO.

Texaco® Soluble Oil CX. A cutting and grinding oil for the rust-free machining of metal parts to close tolerances. It forms stable emulsions with water.
TEXAS CO.

Texaco® Stazon. A lubricating grease which will not spatter, creep, or drip. Used for top roll and loom lubrication in textile plants. TEXAS CO.

Texaco® Texacoat. A petroleum product for protecting marine equipment. It is used to coat all topside equipment exposed to seas and weather with a tough protective film.
TEXAS CO.

Texaco® Texspray Compound. A fiber conditioner which is applied to seed cotton to improve gin production and lint quality; to permit lower dryer temps; to eliminate saw clogging; and to reduce static electricity. It can also be used on other fibers for reducing dust and lint to assure cleaner operations.
TEXAS CO.

Texapons®. A line of dispersing, wetting, emulsifying, and stabilizing agents for emulsion paints, pharmaceutical products, cosmetics, shampoos, detergents, etc. They are various lauryl sulfate sodium salts, ammonium compounds, and triethanolamine salts. Among the products are the following:

Designation	Composition	Appearance	Active ingredients, %
TEXAPON CS-PASTE	Mixture of inorganic and organic salts of a monoester of lauryl alcohol and sulfuric acid	White paste	56–58
TEXAPON EXTRACT A	Ammonium salt of a monolauryl ester of sulfuric acid	Slightly yellow viscous liquid	33–35

Designation	Composition	Appearance	Active ingredients, %
TEXAPON EXTRACT N 40	Anionic sodium lauryl sulfate	Crystal-clear viscous liquid	28
TEXAPON EXTRACT SPECIAL	Anionic sodium lauryl sulfate	Slightly yellow viscous liquid	46–48
TEXAPON EXTRACT T	Triethanolamine salt of a monolauryl ester of sulfuric acid	Yellow viscous liquid	52
TEXAPON HW-PASTE	Mixture of inorganic salts of a monoester of lauryl alcohol and sulfuric acid	White paste	30
TEXAPON K12	Fatty alcohol sulfate	White to slightly yellow powder	87–90
TEXAPON T-PASTE	Triethanolamine salt of saturated fatty alcohol sulfuric acid esters	Yellow to amber sticky paste	80–82
TEXAPON P	Mixture of special dispersing agents	Amber liquid	—
TEXAPON Z	Fatty alcohol sulfate	White powder	58–62
TEXAPON Z, HIGHLY CONC.	Fatty alcohol sulfate	White powder, and white needles	86–90

FALLEK PRODUCTS CO.

Texapret. A line of textile finishing agents. Included in the line are:

TEXAPRET C NEW. A highly viscous, yellow brown sizing and finishing agent that imparts a full and firm hand to all types of textiles.

TEXAPRET K POWDER. A white, water-soluble product that imparts a firm hand to textiles. Compatible with usual sizing and finishing agents.

TEXAPRET NA. A yellowish, low-viscosity liquid, soluble in hot or cold water, for finishing woven goods of all kinds, particularly various synthetic staple fiber and COTTON fabrics. It imparts a full, firm hand.

TEXAPRET WL CONC. NEW. A yellow, highly viscous liquid, soluble in hot or cold water. Unaffected by hard water, and compatible with many finishing and softening agents. It imparts excellent body without stiffening, and does not affect the shade of dyed goods. NOVA CHEMICAL CORP.

Texavon®. The trademark for a textile penetrant or scouring agent. AMERICAN CYANAMID CO.

Texbord®. Hardboard siding panels for use in building construction. CELOTEX CORP.

Texcor®. A deep oil-well cement that remains pumpable over a sufficiently long period to provide ample time to get the cement in the required place in deep hot wells of Louisiana and adjacent areas, and then hardens normally, providing a strong tight seal with high resistance to corrosive attack from sulfate waters. Composition, % by wt.: SiO_2, 22.6; Al_2O_3, 4.5; Fe_2O_3, 4.3; CaO, 64.3; MgO, 1.1; SO_2, 1.5; loss on ignition 0.9. LONE STAR CEMENT CO.

Texfoam®. (*HBMTN* p. 562). Now a product of B. F. GOODRICH SPONGE PRODUCTS DIV., B. F. GOODRICH CO., successor to SPONGE RUBBER PRODUCTS CO.

Texlite®. (*HBMTN* p. 562). Now a product of B. F. GOODRICH SPONGE PRODUCTS DIV., B. F. GOODRICH CO., successor to SPONGE RUBBER PRODUCTS CO.

Texodor®. A trademark for a series of fragrant additives for use in textile deodorization. SINDAR CORP.

Texoprint®. A registered trademark for a line of coated papers. KIMBERLY-CLARK CORP.

Texscour®. (*HBMTN* p. 563). Now a registered trademark. ARMOUR AND CO.

Texspray Compound. See TEXACO® TEXSPRAY COMPOUND.

Textarid®. (*HBMTN* p. 563). Now a registered trademark. L. SONNEBORN SONS, INC.

Textelle®. A linoleum flooring material, ⅛″ thick, for residential and commercial service. ARMSTRONG CORK CO.

Textilco®. (*HBMTN* p. 563). No longer available. TEXTILEATHER CORP.

Tex Top. See H-R TEX TOP[NE].

Text X. See OAKITE® TEST X.

Texzyme®. A standardized desizing solution containing proteolytic enzymes. *Use:* In the textile industry for removal of protein-base sizes from cloth. PABST BREWING CO.

T-Guard®. A sealer for terrazzo floors. J. I. HOLCOMB MFG. CO.

Thalivet®. (*Supp.* I p. 239). No longer available. SHARP & DOHME DIV., MERCK & CO.

The 2000 Mile Oil. See KENDALL, THE 2000 MILE OIL®.

Theelin R-P[NE]. (Trademark registration pending). An estrogen in water-soluble and water-insoluble forms, for rapid initial relief of menopausal symptoms and prolonged estrogenic effect. PARKE, DAVIS & CO.

T-H Emulsifiers[NE]. A series of emulsifiers designed especially for use in the preparation of insecticidal and herbicidal formulations. The following types are available:

C-I, for CHLORO IPC formulations.

D-I, which is suggested for DDT, BHC, METHOXYCHLOR, and RHOTHANE formulations, especially in hard water areas.

M-I, for LINDANE formulations.

MAL-1, which was developed specifically for MALATHION concentrates.

SW-1, for formulations of esters of 2,4-D, 2,4,5-T, and their combinations.

SW-4, for concentrates containing TOXAPHENE, CHLORDANE, PARATHION, methyl PARATHION, DDT, METHOXYCHLOR, and RHOTHANE.

W-I, for formulations of the esters of 2,4-D and 2,4,5-T when used in hard water areas.

Combinations of W-1 and M-1 are recommended for ALDRIN, DIELDRIN, ENDRIN, HEPTACHLOR, and BHC formulations.
THOMPSON-HAYWARD CHEMICAL CO.

Thenylene®. An antihistaminic, methapyrilene hydrochloride, in syrup and tablet forms. Used in the treatment of hay fever, nonseasonal allergic rhinitis, spasmodic allergic cough, etc. ABBOTT LABORATORIES

Theoglycinate®. A brand of theophylline-sodium glycinate, N.N.R., for the treatment of bronchial asthmas, Cheyne-Stokes breathing, congestive heart failure, and other conditions where theophylline therapy is indicated. Available in several dosage forms as follows:

THEOGLYCINATE® PLAIN TABLETS (uncoated). Each tablet contains the equivalent of 2½ grains theophylline, U.S.P.

THEOGLYCINATE® TABLETS WITH PHENOBARBITAL. Each tablet contains the equivalent of 2½ grains theophylline, U.S.P., and ¼ grain phenobarbitol.

THEOGLYCINATE® SYRUP. Each teaspoonful (4 cc.) contains the equivalent of 1 grain theophylline, U.S.P.

THEOGLYCINATE® SUPPOSITORIES (RECTAL). Each suppository contains the equivalent of 6 grains theophyllin, U.S.P.

THEOGLYCINATE® POWDER. Each grain is equivalent to ½ grain theophylline, U.S.P.
BRAYTEN PHARMACEUTICAL CO.

Thephorin® Tartrate. An antihistaminic agent for the treatment of allergic disorders, Parkinson's disease, dysmenorrhea, and cold symptoms. Chemically, it is a brand of pyridendene.
HOFFMAN-LA ROCHE INC.

Thera-Vita®. A potent multivitamin capsule containing balanced therapeutic amounts of all the nutritionally significant vitamins. Each capsule contains: 12,500 U.S.P. units VITAMIN A (synthetic vitamin A palmitate), 10 mg. VITAMIN B_1 (thiamine hydrochloride), 10 mg. VITAMIN B_2 (riboflavin); 100 mg. niocinamide, 1 mg. VITAMIN B_6 (pyridoxine hydrochloride); 10 mg. d-panthenol (equiv. to 11.5 mg. d-calcium pantothenate); 150 mg. VITAMIN C (ascorbic acid), 1,250 U.S.P. units VITAMIN D (activated ergosterol). WARNER-CHILCOTT LABORATORIES

The Red Writing Hood®. The trademark for a carbon paper. INTERCHEMICAL CORP.
AULT & WIBORG CARBON & RIBBON DIV.

Therlo®. A glass-to-metal sealing alloy, composed of 29% nickel, 17% cobalt, and the balance iron, used for sealing to hard or thermal shock-resistant glass. It matches such commercial hard glasses as CORNING #7052 and #7040 in expansivity from 80°C. to the annealing point. It produces permanent vacuum-tight seals, is resistant to mercury, and can be machined, welded, soldered, and brazed.
DRIVER-HARRIS CO.

Thermalite®. Formerly a product of TROPICAL PAINT & OIL CO.; now a product of TROPICAL PAINT CO.

Thermasil[NE]. A high-temp. pipe and block insulation for temps. up to 1,200°F. Consists of a hydrous calcium silicate compound reinforced with long asbestos fibers. Supplied as molded, sectional pipe insulation or block insulation.
EHRET MAGNESIA MFG. CO.

Thermatron[NE]. A selective gas-analysis instrument for industrial process control. *Uses:* To provide a simple, physical, accurate measurement of a single component in a complex mixture of gases.
MINE SAFETY APPLIANCES CO.

Thermax®. (*HBMTN* p. 565). Should have been listed as a registered trademark of THERMATOMIC CARBON CO.

Thermax-Stainless[NE]. A soft, semi-reinforcing carbon for rubber compounding, consisting of finely divided carbon obtained from gas. Sp.gr. 1.80; benzol extractable material, 0.25% max.
R. T. VANDERBILT CO.

Thermit®. A welding material consisting of a mechanical mixture of finely divided aluminum and iron oxide in the form of magnetic iron scale. Proportions are, roughly, three parts iron scale to one part aluminum. Reacts according to the reaction $8\ Al + 3\ Fe_3O_4 = 4\ Al_2O_3 + 9\ Fe$ to produce a superheated liquid filler metal used for the welding of heavy sections. *Uses:* For repairing heavy equipment, joining railroad rail into continuous lengths and fabricating machinery, equipment and parts.
METAL & THERMIT CORP.

Thermobonds. See STERLING® THERMOBONDS.

Thermoclad[NE]. A heat-resistant finish for steel.
SHERWIN-WILLIAMS CO.

Thermoglas Pipe Covering[NE]. An insulation for use on pipes having temps. up to 350°F. It "snaps in place." It weighs $1/10$ to ¼ as much as other insulations; it will not sag, rot, mold or otherwise decompose; it resists attack of most acids and alkalis; is not corrosive to metals; will not chip, flake, dent, break, or crumble; and is unaffected by water and insects. PHILIP CAREY MFG. CO.

Thermoglas R/F Insulation[NE]. A lightweight, fire-resistant thermal and acoustical insulation for use at temps. from sub-zero to 450°F. Available in a variety of thicknesses, densities, and roll widths; and either plain or with various facing materials adhered to the insulation. PHILIP CAREY MFG. CO.

Thermoil "A." (*HBMTN* p. 566). No longer available. VEGETABLE OIL PRODUCTS CO.

Thermoil "L." (*HBMTN* p. 566). No longer available. VEGETABLE OIL PRODUCTS CO.

Thermolite®. The trademark for a line of tin-based organic compounds used as stabilizers for polyvinyl chloride resins and other chlorinated materials.
METAL & THERMIT CORP.

Thermopoxy. See STERLING® T-653-LB THERMOPOXY.

Thermo Rod Packing[NE]. A heavy-duty packing for service only against high-temp, oils, gases and steam on reciprocating rods and plungers. It is made of asbestos yarn jackets braided over a center core of twisted asbestos-containing annealed iron wire. Between the jackets is a small amount of a heat-resisting compound. Furnished square or round, in coil or ring form, with or without lubricant and graphite finish. Available in sizes ¼″ and up.
JOHNS-MANVILLE SALES CORP.

ThermoTrode®. A DC arc-welding electrode for oxygenless preheating of steel joints. Available in ⅛″ × 3/16″ sizes. EUTECTIC WELDING ALLOYS CORP.

Thiazine®. A group of direct dyestuffs derived from Primuline and, therefore, containing a benzothiazole group. They are used to dye red shades on COTTON, WOOL, and SILK. GENERAL DYESTUFF CO.

Thiazol Yellow®. Direct yellow dyes containing benzothiazole radicals and used for dyeing COTTON and RAYON. GENERAL DYESTUFF CO.

Thick-Aid[NE]. A general-purpose, heat-stable, paint additive that imparts thixotropic body to paints and forms a gel structure of strong suspending power. When added in small amounts to paint, it increases the viscosity, which in turn eliminates sag, prevents pigment settling, and improves the brushing and leveling properties. It is a powder which is added to the paint system as part of the pigment grind.
ABCO CHEMICAL CO.

Thiochromogen®. A benzothiazole derivative which is used for dyeing COTTON. The color is subsequently developed by treatment with chlorine or by diazotization and coupling with a developer. Yellow, red, or brown shades of good wet fastness are obtained in this manner. GENERAL DYESTUFF CO.

Thiokol® TP-95. Incorrectly listed as TP-95 (*HBMTN* p. 576). THIOKOL CHEMICAL CORP.

Thionine®. A line of basic blue dyestuffs containing a thiazine ring. GENERAL DYESTUFF CO.

Thixo[NE]. A mixture of organic chemical additives for aqueous systems. It possesses thickening characteristics; suspending and film-forming properties; emulsifying, detergent and plasticizing properties and gelling, binding and stabilizing properties. Available in paste form at approx. 25% solids. Used in formulating printing inks, textile sizing compounds, pharmaceutical compounds, wood sealing compounds, etc.; for softening leather; etc. ABDO CHEMICAL CO.

Thixokon®. A thickened sodium acetrizoate solution for use as an X-ray contrast medium for retrograde and voiding urethrography.
MALLINCKRODT CHEMICAL WORKS

Thixon®. The trademark for a line of bonding agents for the adhesion of rubber and rubber-like materials to metal during vulcanization. The THIXON® bonding agents are available in four group types:
B-SERIES CEMENTS. A group of auxiliary bonding agents for promoting the adhesion of different polymers to various standard structural materials. Must be used over suitable primer or in some cases, brass plate. Bonds usually developed during application of heat and pressure. Available for NEOPRENE, natural rubber, S-type synthetics, THIOKOL, polyacrylates, HYPALON and BUTYL.
M-SERIES CEMENTS. A group of bonding agents for the adhesion of various polymers to the various structural metals in one-coat applications. Bonds are usually developed during application of heat and pressure, although some members of this series are also recommended for open steam cures. Available for NEOPRENE, natural rubber, S-type synthetics, N-type synthetics, THIOKOL and polyacrylates.
P-SERIES CEMENTS. A group of primers for developing adhesion between various polymers and the standard structural metals, using appropriate B-SERIES cements as a secondary coat. Available for NEOPRENE, natural rubber, S-type synthetics, N-type synthetics, THIOKOL, polyacrylates, HYPALON and BUTYL.
X-SERIES CEMENTS. A group of bonding agents for developing adhesion between unusual metal surfaces and hard-to-bond compounds of all standard polymers. Supplied from laboratory production on special specification.
Mfg'd by DAYTON CHEMICAL PRODUCTS LABORATORIES, INC.
Dist'd by HARWICK STANDARD CHEMICAL CO.

Thomas Soil-Rich Fertilizer®. The trademark for fertilizers and fertilizer materials.
PENNSYLVANIA SALT MFG. CO.

Thorobond®. A green-colored, liquid material that bonds all types of gypsum plaster and Portland cement to any structurally-sound surface. It is nonflammable, non-toxic, and is not affected by freezing and thawing cycles. Applied by spray or brush.
STANDARD DRY WALL PRODUCTS, INC.

Thorosheen® RW 7. A water-emulsion, acrylic resin masonry paint, designed as a finish coat to be applied over THOROSEAL (*HBMTN* p. 568), or as a color coat where it is desired to maintain the texture of the masonry surface over which it is to be applied. It is acid, alkali and mildew resistant; it dries in a very short time and can be recoated within an hour or two. Available in a number of colors.
STANDARD DRY WALL PRODUCTS, INC.

Thorotrase®. (*HBMTN* p. 568). Formerly mfg'd by HEYDEN CHEMICAL CORP.; now a product of TESTAGAR & CO.

Thorox[NE]. (*HBMTN* p. 568). No longer available.
STANDARD DRY WALL PRODUCTS, INC.

Thread-Tite®. (*HBMTN* p. 568). Now a registered trademark. ARMITE LABORATORIES

Thred-Gard. See "JOHN CRANE" THRED-GARD.

Three Sheep®. Food savoring powders comprising principally monosodium glutamate.
INTERNATIONAL MINERALS & CHEMICAL CORP.

Thrift®. The trademark for a line of inked ribbons.
INTERCHEMICAL CORP.,
AULT & WIBORG CARBON & RIBBON DIV.

Throway®. Mechanical, viscous-type, ventilating air filters of the disposable type.
AMERICAN AIR FILTER CO.

Thyracoids®. (*HBMTN* p. 568). No longer available.
REED & CARNRICK

Thyrocalx®. (*Supp.* I p. 242). No longer available.
SHARP & DOHME DIV., MERCK & CO.

T.I.A. See TROY T.I.A.

Tiger. See BOSTON TIGER.

Tiger® *or* **Tiger Brand®.** The trademark for a line of wire rope, slings, strands and wire rope fittings and cutters; and electrical wire and cable.
UNITED STATES STEEL CORP.

Tigerbraze®. The trademark for a line of rail bonds.
UNITED STATES STEEL CORP.

Tiger-Claw. See Fiege TIGER-CLAW®.

Tiger-Lube®. The trademark for a wire rope lubricant.
UNITED STATES STEEL CORP.

Tigerweld®. The trademark for a line of rail bonds.
UNITED STATES STEEL CORP.

Tilite®. A preparation for cleaning tile, porcelain, marble and terrazzo floors, and brass.
PENNSYLVANIA SALT MFG. CO.

Til Oil△. See SESAME OIL△.

Timbo. See LONCHOCARPUS△.

Tip Top[NE]. A fertilizer.
PENNSYLVANIA SALT MFG. CO.

Tissuglass. An ultra-thin and ultra-soft glass paper, available in thickness from 0.5 to 13 mils and widths to 40 in. Composed of microglass fibers to which a binder is added. It may be impregnated with various resins such as melamine, epoxy, silicone, polyvinyl chloride, polytetrafluorethylene, and polyester preparations. *Uses:* As a surfacing sheet for high- and low-pressure laminates; backing material for mica; etc.
AMERICAN MACHINE & FOUNDRY CO.

"T-1" Steel. See LUKENS "T-1" STEEL®.

Titan®. The trademark for a line of dynamite and detonating primers, specifically blasting caps and electric blasting caps.
HERCULES POWDER CO.

Tite-Lite®. An elastic glazing compound that produces a flexible, air-tight, and weather-tight joint.
TRUSCON LABORATORIES

Tite-Wall[NE]. (*HBMTN* p. 573). No longer available.
TRUSCON LABORATORIES

Titherm®. An exothermic mixture for use in metallurgy.
MALLINCKRODT CHEMICAL WORKS

TL-131[NE]. A water-soluble cutting fluid concentrate for use in grinding and machining of metals. Contains a blend of chemical ingredients that absorb and readily dissipate tool-consuming heat. Particularly effective in cutting and grinding hard steels and for high-speed machining.
S. C. JOHNSON & SON

T-Lock Amer-Plate®. Incorrectly listed as AMER-PLATE T-LOCK[NE] (*Supp.* I p. 14). AMERCOAT CORP.

Tobex®. A figured wire glass that diffuses light in all directions. One surface is plain, the other has thousands of rounded bosses that act like lenses in diffusing light that passes through the glass. It was designed especially for tobacco warehouses.
Mfg'd by BLUE RIDGE GLASS CORP.
Dist'd by LIBBEY-OWENS-FORD GLASS CO.

Toilex®. A powdered chemical compound that keeps toilet bowls clean and sanitary.
VESTAL, INC.

Tolad[NE]. A chemical additive for burning oils; designed to prevent the formation of insoluble sludge and to improve color stability.
TRETOLITE CO.

Toleron[NE]. Ferrous fumarate. A source of iron for oral administration, either alone or as a constituent of various drug preparations. It is well tolerated and exceptionally stable.
MALLINCKRODT CHEMICAL WORKS

Tolex®. See NYGEN® TOLEX®.

Tolgen®. (*Supp.* I p. 243). No longer available.
TEXTILEATHER DIV., GENERAL TIRE & RUBBER CO.

Toloxyn[NE]. 3-Orthotoloxy-1,2-propanediol (alpha-cresyl ortho glyceryl ether). A spasmolytic therapeutic agent affecting intraneural junctions.
SUMNER CHEMICAL CO.

Tolu Balsam△. A semi-solid, yellowish-brown gum obtained from the tree *Myroxylon balsamum,* or *Toluifera balsamum,* of Venezuela, Colombia, and Peru. It has a pleasant aromatic odor and taste. Used in cough syrups and other medicinals; and as a fixative in perfumes.

Tomato Fix®. (*Supp.* I p. 243). Should have been listed as a registered trademark.
THOMPSON CHEMICALS CORP.

Toolcast 1000 Resin. A liquid resin which can be cured with an accelerator to produce an ivory-colored, insoluble, highly solvent-resistant composition that is tough and resilient. Does not contain a solvent or diluent, has no volatile loss at curing temp., and requires no pressure for curing. A temp. of only 90°–180°F. is necessary to set the resin. Because of its low viscosity, the resin, when poured, produces castings that show the finest details, and when cured, can be machined, sawed, turned, drilled, tapped, sanded and buffed. The resin is non-flammable, has a low moisture absorption, and is resistant to most organic and inorganic solvents. Liquid, general-purpose ACCELERATOR 1033 is used with this resin when dimensional stability is not critical or when temps. do not exceed 250°F.; ACCELERATOR 1033-A, sometimes called "Hot Shot," is used for quick setting the resin without heat; and paste-type ACCELERATOR P-70 is recommended when dimensional stability is critical. *Uses:* For core boxes, checking fixtures, hydropress form blocks, nesting fixtures, master mock-ups, embossing dies, routing fixtures, printing plates, vacuum- and drape-forming dies, stretch-forming dies for plastics and sheet metals, laminating dies, etc.
AMERICAN RESIN CORP.

Toolplastik®. The trademark for a line of epoxy, phenolic and other plastics for tooling applications. Included are phenolic casting and foaming resins, and ethyl cellulose hot-melt casting resins.
REZOLIN, INC.

Topaz®. (*HBMTN* p. 575). Now a registered trademark. ARMOUR AND CO.

Top-bond. An air-drying spray for green sand cores and molds. It ties down the surface sand with a resin bond, thus keeping castings clean at the shakeout, and preventing sand pickup or sand inclusions in the castings. UNITED OIL MFG. CO.

Topitracin®. A medicinal consisting of 500 units bacitracin per gram. REED & CARNRICK

Topper®. A line of rubber sundries—fountain syringes and combination syringes—for sale by druggists. ARMSTRONG CORK CO.

Topper. A white, flat oil paint for interior walls and ceilings. It can be used over brick, concrete, wallboard, unsized plaster, non-bleeding wallpaper, calcimine, whitewash, and water-thinned wall paints. GILLESPIE VARNISH CO.

Tops-Gran. See TROY TOPS-GRAN.

Top-X[NR]. A blacktop sealer for surfacing and preserving blacktop pavement. Available in standard and oilproof grades. HALLEMITE MFG. CO.

Torch-O-Matic®. A name used to designate a line of automatic lighting air-acetylene torches. MINE SAFETY APPLIANCES CO.

Totrust® Instant Dry Metal Coat. A rust-inhibitive, chemical-resistant paint in red, olive green, light gray, machine gray, zinc chromate and stainless steel color, and black, white, and clear. Contains both primer and finish. Can be used on galvanized metal, aluminum, iron and steel, whether rusted or clear, damp or dry, painted or unpainted, interior or exterior. Heat resistant to 250°F.; does not become brittle at —50°F. WILBUR & WILLIAMS CO.

Town House[NR]. (Trademark registration pending.) A linoleum flooring material 0.090″ thick, for residential and light commercial service. ARMSTRONG CORK CO.

Toxaphene[△]. Chlorinated camphene. A powerful contact and stomach insecticide. Prepared by the chlorination of camphene to a chlorine content of 67–69%. It is a yellow, waxy solid with a mild terpene odor and a m.p. range of 65°–90°C. Insoluble in water; readily soluble in organic solvents, including petroleum. Effective against the cyclamen mite on ornamentals, and *Anoctus* spp. on mushrooms.

Toximul® 500. An all-purpose emulsifier for insecticides. It is effective in quantities of 3–4%, with over a dozen insecticides, and can be used in water of 50 to 1,000 ppm. hardness. NINOL LABORATORIES, INC.

Toximul® 600. An emulsifier for CHLORDANE, TOXAPHENE, DDT, LINDANE, and other insecticides. NINOL LABORATORIES, INC.

TP-95. (*HBMTN* p. 576). Should have been listed as THIOKOL® TP-95. THIOKOL CHEMICAL CORP.

TPN®. Mixture of tyrosine, pyridoxine hydrochloride, and niacinamide used in medicine for the treatment of allergic disorders. INTERNATIONAL MINERALS & CHEMICAL CORP.

Traffic-Cote®. An oleo-resinous sealer for wood, concrete, terrazzo and cork. It penetrates and seals the pores against dirt and moisture and prepares the surface for regular maintenance with a wax or floor finish. Keeps stains from penetrating and prevents undue wear. S. C. JOHNSON & SON

Traffic Top®. Asphalt-saturated fiberboard flooring and roof-deck units. CELOTEX CORP.

Traffic Wax[NR]. A solvent-type buffing wax in both liquid and paste forms. Contains a blend of hard vegetable waxes that provide a tough film which buffs to a rich luster and resists wear of heavy traffic. For use on wood, linoleum, cork and vinyl floors. (*See also* BEAUTIFLOOR TRAFFIC WAX®.) S. C. JOHNSON & SON

Tragacanth[△]. *Also known as* GUM TRAGACANTH[△]. The dried, gummy exudation of the shrub *Astragalus gummifer* and other Asiatic species of *Astragalus* found principally in Iran and also in Asia Minor and in Syria. The gum is obtained by making a small incision at the base of the shrub. The juice exudes from this incision and solidifies to an alteration product. The highest quality gum is obtained from the first incision. Unground TRAGACANTH is in the form of flattened, lamellated and curved pieces that are translucent, odorless, and white to yellow in color. In the ground form, it is generally white but often turns slightly yellow during storage. TRAGACANTH is acid in character; it is insoluble in alcohol but soluble in alkalies. Approx. 30–40% of the TRAGACANTH mass is soluble in water, forming a colloidal hydrosol solution, known as TRAGACANTHIN. The insoluble portion, consisting principally of bassorin, $(C_{11}H_{20}O_{10})_n$, swells in the water to form a gel. *Uses:* In pharmaceutical compounding as an excipient for tablets, for suspending heavy insoluble powders, etc.; as a general emulsifying agent; in foods and candies; in adhesives (mucilages and pastes); in textile sizing; in textile printing and general printing inks; in dyeing with insoluble color lakes; in leather dressings; etc.

Tragacanthin[△]. See TRAGACANTH[△].

Transfalt Strips[NR]. Preformed asphalt strips designed for flashings at various points on structures constructed with corrugated TRANSITE® sheets. Available in 3 types: TYPE O, for the upperside of the sheets; TYPE I, for the underside of the sheets; and TYPE R, for use between the ridge roll and the corrugated TRANSITE® roof sheets. JOHNS-MANVILLE SALES CORP.

Transfax®. (*HBMTN* p. 576). No longer available. EASTMAN KODAK CO.

Transflow M-32. A transparent, plastic sanitary tubing for the transmission of raw milk on the farm, in dairies, and to and from tank trucks. It is resistant to abrasion, erosion, water, steam, acids, alkalis, and cleaning solutions; and imparts neither taste nor odor to the milk. Sp.gr. 1.20; tensile strength, 1,875 lb./sq.in., brittle point, —43°C.; elongation, 340%. Available in sizes from ⅜″ i.d. × ¹¹⁄₁₆″ o.d. to 3″ i.d. × 4″ o.d. CHAMBERLAIN ENGINEERING CORP.

Transitone® Walls. A movable wall unit with integrally colored asbestos panels. This fireproof panel

is light in weight, rugged and sturdy. Available in light green and light tan.
JOHNS-MANVILLE SALES CORP.

Transitop[NB]. A structural building material that provides a hard, durable surface and an efficient insulating core in a single unit. It is composed of a core of ½" to 2" J-M insulating board, to which is veneered standard asbestos FLEXBOARD® on one or both sides. Standard sheets are 8' long and 48" wide. No protective painting is necessary, although the FLEXBOARD® veneer may be easily painted, if desired, for decorative effect. This board can be sawed, drilled or nailed. The overall heat transmission of the encased board, veneered both sides, in B.t.u.-ft./(hr. $\times$ sq.ft. $\times$ °F.), is 0.43 for the ½" core, 0.28 for the 1" core, and 0.20 for the 1½" core.
JOHNS-MANVILLE SALES CORP.

Transonic®. The trademark for an austenitic age-hardening stainless steel.
UNITED STATES STEEL CORP.

Transplant-Fix®. (*Supp.* I p. 244). Should have been listed as a registered trademark.
THOMPSON CHEMICAL CORP.

Transwall®. An accordion-type plastic curtain or wall.
BEMIS BROTHERS BAG CO.

Trasentine®-Phenobarbital. A potent antispasmodic and mild sedative. Used in the treatment of spastic conditions of abdominal viscera associated with hyperexcitability of the autonomic nervous system.
CIBA PHARMACEUTICAL PRODUCTS INC.

Tread-Grip®. A line of one-piece ELECTROFORGED® and welded steel stair treads that combine strength with safe, non-slip footing. They have an open construction to permit free water drainage and to eliminate accumulation of dust and dirt. The nosing is made of ALAN WOOD ALGRIP®, a strong, tough, abrasive-impregnated rolled steel plate.
HORACE T. POTTS CO.

Trepenol® ES. A paste detergent consisting of the sodium alkylsulfate of higher alcohols. It is very water soluble and stable. Used in the textile industry.
TREPLOW PRODUCTS, INC.

Trepenol® S-60. A sulfated ester of an alkyl phenoxy polyoxyethylene ethanol. It is an anionic, high-forming surfactant with excellent wetting, dispersing, emulsifying and detergent properties. Used in the textile industry where high, stable foam is desired in applications demanding good detergency, high wetting strength, easy emulsification, and low cost.
TREPLOW PRODUCTS, INC.

Trepenol® WA. A stable emulsifying agent with good detergency properties. Sodium laurylsulfate, supplied as a sodium chloride-free material or with sodium chloride. Used in the textile industry.
TREPLOW PRODUCTS, INC.

Trepolate® F-95. A light-colored, 95%-active sodium alkylarylsulfonate in powder or flake forms. It is a textile wetting agent and detergent that exhibits high calcium resistance and is very effective in high acid or alkaline baths.
TREPLOW PRODUCTS, INC.

Trepolate® T-60. Triethanolamine dodecyl benzene sulfonate having excellent detergency, foam, wetting speed, and surface tension reducing properties in aqueous solution. For use in the textile industry.
TREPLOW PRODUCTS, INC.

Tret-O-lite®. Chemical compounds for use in the chemical treatment of crude oils to remove salts, solids, and other impurities.
TRETOLITE CO.

Trex®. A line of emulsifiers for insecticidal materials.
NOPCO CHEMICAL CO.

Triazoline®. An antibacterial preparation containing sulfadiazine, sulfamerazine, and sulfathiazole. Available in the form of tablets.
ABBOTT LABORATORIES

Tribase E[NB]. A basic lead silicate sulfate containing 68% total PbO, of which 50.8% is safe and reactive. It is a fine white powder; insoluble in all common solvents; sp.gr. 5.55; refractive index, 2.1. *Use:* As a stabilizer for vinyl chloride resins, especially when used in the mfg. of insulation and dielectric material.
NATIONAL LEAD CO.

Tri-Basic Copper. *See* TENNESSEE TRI-BASIC® COPPER.

Tricainal®. A combination of PYRIBENZAMINE® hydrochloride and NUPERCAINE® base, for the treatment of hemorrhoidal pain, pruritis ani and pruritus vulvae. Supplied in the form of: (1) suppositories, each of which contains 10 mg. PYRIBENZAMINE® hydrochloride, 2.5 mg. NUPERCAINE® base, 100 mg. bismuth subgallate, 250 mg. zinc oxide, 1.0 mg. acetone sodium bisulfite, in a cocoa butter ointment base; and (2) ointment, each 100 g. of which contains 0.5 g. PYRIBENZAMINE® hydrochloride, and 0.125 g. NUPERCAINE® base, together with zinc oxide, bismuth subgallate lanolin and petrolatum, plus acetone sodium bisulfite as a preservative.
CIBA PHARMACEUTICAL PRODUCTS INC.

Triceratops (Design)®. Dicalcium phosphate, principally used as an animal and plant food supplement.
INTERNATIONAL MINERALS & CHEMICAL CORP.

Tridione®. An antispasmodic medicinal, trimethadione, in tablet and solution forms.
ABBOTT LABORATORIES

Trimix®. (*HBMTN* p. 580). Now a registered trademark.
L. SONNEBORN SONS, INC.

Trinesium®. A gastric antacid and adsorbent consisting of a bland, homogeneous, aqueous suspension of magnesium trisilicate in a dilute aluminum hydroxide gel.
ABBOTT LABORATORIES

Triple C Syrup[NB]. A medicinal for the relief of coughs due to simple colds and wherever a sedative expectorant is required. Each fluid oz. contains, 0.06 g. codeine phosphate, 2 minims chloroform, 0.52 g. potassium guaiacol sulfonate, 0.52 g. ammonium chloride, 5 mg. antimony and potassium tartrate, and wild cherry bark and white pine extractives in 3% alcohol.
AMERICAN PHARMACEUTICAL CO.

Triple Life[NB]. A non-flammable, water-emulsion finish that may be used on any type of flooring. It dries to a hard, lustrous, non-streaky, scuff-resistant finish.
FRANKLIN RESEARCH CO.

Triplematic®. A proportional mixing-metering pump for two-part resins. It mixes the resin and catalyst automatically in the proper proportions.
H. V. Hardman Co.

Tripoli△. *Also known as* Soft Silica△. A soft, porous, easily-crushed, highly absorbent silica formed by the alteration or decomposition of Chert or of highy siliceous sandstone. It consists of 96–99% SiO_2. It is used principally as a fine abrasive in cleaning and scouring preparations, and as a filler in paints and rubber; as an abrasive in "grease bricks" and "grease compounds," in which the abrasive is bonded with stearic acid, tallow, or paraffin; in metal polishes; and in foundry parting agents. Tripoli is quarried in Missouri, Illinois, eastern Tennessee, and Georgia.

Tri-Ten®. *See* U.S.S.® Tri-Ten®.

Tritex®. An ammonium nitrate nitrocarbonate blasting compound. Hercules Powder Co.

Tro-Mar® DX 130. An all-petroleum lubricant for marine diesel cylinders, formulated to eliminate the extreme corrosive wear generally associated with low-cost marine diesel fuels. Viscosity (S.U.S.) 1,778 at 100°F., and 129 to 210°F.
Esso Standard Oil Co.

Trona®. Trademark for industrial and agricultural chemicals, including borax, potash, soda ash, salt cake, and lithium chemicals mfg'd by the American Potash and Chemical Corp.

Tronolen®. A cosmetically pleasing, flesh-toned, antihistamine, antipruritic, anesthetic lotion. Contains 1% pramoxine hydrochloride and 2% diparalene hydrochloride. Used for relief of surface pain and itching in various dermatoses, etc.
Abbott Laboratories

Tronothane®. A surface anesthetic, pramoxine hydrochloride, in cream, jelly, lotion and solution forms. Used for the relief from discomfort and pain in hemorrhoids and rectal surgery, itching dermatoses, etc.
Abbott Laboratories

Trophonine®. (*HBMTN* p. 581). No longer available.
Reed & Carnrick

Trophonine X®. (*HBMTN* p. 581). No longer available.
Reed & Carnrick

Trophy® Gym Finish. A light-colored, abrasion-resistant gymnasium floor finish. Recommended for application over Trophy® Seal.
Hillyard Chemical Co.

Trophy® Seal. A penetrating seal for gym floors and other wood surfaces subject to heavy traffic, and for walls and woodwork. It is water-resistant, reduces absorption of grease and oil, prevents dirt from grinding in, and resists acid, alcohol, ink, and perspiration stains.
Hillyard Chemical Co.

Tropoxy^NB. An epoxy enamel for use on metal, wood, concrete and plaster. It resists severe chemical conditions such as alkalis, acids, oils and petroleum solvents. Available in two grades: Tropoxy #1 and Tropoxy #2. Where corrosive conditions are moderate, No. 1 is used. It can be obtained in white, gray, and black. No. 2, which is available only in gray, is used where highest resistance to chemicals and solvents is required.
Tropical Paint Co.

Troy-Brite®. (*HBMTN* p. 582). No longer available.
Troy Industrial Products,
Div. of Globe Sanitary Supply Co.

Troy Coco-Ster Compound. An odorless and tasteless quaternary ammonium compound. It is a disinfectant, germicide and deodorant, and sanitizing agent for use in restaurants and food-processing plants; locker rooms; swimming pools and pool runways; laundries, hospitals, schools, theaters; and on animal and poultry farms, dairies, etc.
Troy Industrial Products,
Div. of Globe Sanitary Supply Co.

Troy Compound 111. A steam-cleaning compound for meat trucks and other food trucks.
Troy Industrial Products,
Div. of Globe Sanitary Supply Co.

Troy Econo-Pine. A ready-to-use disinfectant for use on floors, utensils, equipment, walls, and in rest rooms.
Troy Industrial Products,
Div. of Globe Sanitary Supply Co.

Troy Fine Finish. A heavy-bodied, liquid steam-cleaning compound for use on interior or exterior aluminum or painted surfaces of automobiles, trucks, etc.
Troy Industrial Products,
Div. of Globe Sanitary Supply Co.

Troy Low-Dishwash. A high-alkalinity, non-caustic cleaner for washing and sanitizing dishes, glasses, silver, and utensils.
Troy Industrial Products,
Div. of Globe Sanitary Supply Co.

Troy Multi-Purpose. A cleaning compound, consisting of soap and synthetic detergents, for washing and sanitizing dishes, glasses, silver, and utensils.
Troy Industrial Products,
Div. of Globe Sanitary Supply Co.

Troy O & M Compound. A soapless hot-tank cleaner for removing grease, dirt, paint, and carbon from iron and steel.
Troy Industrial Products,
Div. of Globe Sanitary Supply Co.

Troy P.D.Q. Mechanics Soap. A lanolin-containing paste-type soap which cuts grease and grime rapidly, yet does not scratch the skin. May be used with or without water.
Troy Industrial Products,
Div. of Globe Sanitary Supply Co.

Troy Pine Emulso. A highly-concentrated disinfectant with a pine fragrance. Phenol coefficient, 5½. For use on floors, utensils, equipment, walls, and in rest rooms.
Troy Industrial Products,
Div. of Globe Sanitary Supply Co.

Troy Silken Suds Wash. An automobile-washing compound in concentrated liquid form. For use, 1 part is diluted with 16 parts water.
Troy Industrial Products,
Div. of Globe Sanitary Supply Co.

Troy Steam-O. A steam-cleaning, automotive, and industrial cleaner. It does not harm painted surfaces.
Troy Industrial Products,
Div. of Globe Sanitary Supply Co.

Troy Ster-L-Yzer. A formalin-base, strongly scented deodorant spray, particularly effective against burnt odors. TROY INDUSTRIAL PRODUCTS, DIV. OF GLOBE SANITARY SUPPLY CO.

Troy T.I.A. A heavy-duty, steam-cleaning compound for removing oil and grease from tractors, bulldozers and other heavy equipment. TROY INDUSTRIAL PRODUCTS, DIV. OF GLOBE SANITARY SUPPLY CO.

Troy Tops-Gran. A heavy-duty, hot-tank cleaner for removing grease, dirt, paint, carbon, etc. from fluid couplings, transmissions, etc. TROY INDUSTRIAL PRODUCTS, DIV. OF GLOBE SANITARY SUPPLY CO.

Troytuf® Dacron® Blanket. A DACRON® fabric for use in the mfg. of plastic laminates. Laminates made with TROYTUF DACRON have better abrasion resistance than those made with glass fibers, are more flexible, much lighter in weight, and have superior electrical properties, both wet and dry. Available in two weights: ½ oz./sq.ft. and 1 oz./sq.ft. (DACRON® is the registered trademark of E. I. DU PONT DE NEMOURS & CO.) TROY BLANKET MILLS

Trufect®. A registered trademark for book and printing papers. KIMBERLY-CLARK CORP.

Trumble®. The trademark for a line of gas traps. UNITED STATES STEEL CORP.

Tru-Nox. See SPRAYWAY® TRU-NOX.

Truo-Cillin®. A chemobiotic consisting of a combination of sulfonamides and PENICILLIN, in tablet form. ABBOTT LABORATORIES

Truozine®. A sulfonamide preparation containing sulfadiazine, sulfamerazine and sulfamethazine, in tablet and suspension forms. ABBOTT LABORATORIES

Tru-Rip®. A line of flexible, parallel-rip electric cords. Available in several styles with natural or synthetic rubber insulation. WHITNEY BLAKE CO.

Tru-Seal®. (*HBMTN* p. 582). No longer available. TRUSCON LABORATORIES

Tru-Sorb. See SUPER TRU-SORB®.

Tru-Vy-Kote[NR]. (Trademark registration pending). A chemical-resistant, vinyl-emulsion-type protective coating for interior and exterior use. It dries to a velvet-like finish. TRUSCON LABORATORIES

Trynazin®. A medicinal ointment containing atropine, butyn and sulfathiazole. ABBOTT LABORATORIES

Tubacide®. (*HBMTN* p. 583). Now a registered trademark. MILLER CHEMICAL & FERTILIZER CORP.

Tuba Root△. Same as DERRIS ROOT△.

Tubatoxin△. Same as ROTENONE△.

Tube-In-Strip®. Sheets of copper, brass, and aluminum with channels formed in them during molding. These channels can be inflated by air or hydraulic pressure to form heat-exchanger tubes with wall thicknesses of 0.0025″ or less depending on the inflation equipment available. REVERE COPPER AND BRASS, INC.

Tube Line®. A line of valves and fittings for pressures up to 4.000 lb./sq.in. Available for tubing sizes of ⅛″ to ½″ o.d. AUTOCLAVE ENGINEERS

Tucker's, Mrs., Salad Oil®. A winterized cottonseed oil. It remains clear and free-flowing longer at low temps. than ordinary salad oils. Does not separate when refrigerated. Used in salad dressings, mayonnaise, for seasoning and for frying. ANDERSON, CLAYTON & CO. FOODS DIV.

Tucker's, Mrs., Shortening®. An all-vegetable, fully hydrogenated shortening for use in baking, frying and pastry making. ANDERSON, CLAYTON & CO. FOODS DIV.

Tucks Coil Packing[NR]. A piston packing made from plies of heavy duck, bound together with a black rubber compound. Designed primarily as a cold-water packing for service on inside-packed pistons operating at medium pressure. Available in coil form only, ¼″ in diam. and up. JOHNS-MANVILLE SALES CORP.

Tufbak®. (*Supp.* I p. 247). Now a registered trademark. BEHR-MANNING CO.

Tuf-Bond[NR]. A plasticized polyvinyl chloride sheet material which is resistant to corrosion by most acids and alkalis at temps. up to 160°F. *Use:* As linings or coverings for chemical-process equipment. ELECTRO-CHEMICAL ENGINEERING & MFG. CO.

Tufcrete® All Purpose Sealer. A tough, elastic floor sealer that is resistant to oils, gasoline, grease, acids, etc. TUFCRETE CO.

Tufcrete® APS. A coal-tar pitch emulsion for application by squeegee to asphalt and concrete floors and pavements where the surface is exposed to the deteriorating and softening effects of oil, grease, petroleum solvents, acids, and other chemicals. It forms a durable seal, and greatly extends the life of the surface. TUFCRETE CO.

Tufcrete® Latex. A floor-surfacing and -patching material consisting of a powder and liquid which are mixed to troweling consistency and applied in a layer of $1/16$″ to ½″ thick. TUFCRETE CO.

Tufcrete® Resurfacer. A black, semi-plastic mastic which is mixed with sand and cement and trowelled to a thickness of ½″ on wood, concrete, brick, asphalt, or composition floors for industrial plants, warehouses, garages, foundries, etc., to form a durable, dustless fire resistant, vermin proof, and comfortable surface. TUFCRETE CO.

Tufcrete® Roof Resurfacers. A line of cold-applied products for repairing roofs.
TUFCRETE PLASTIC ROOF RESURFACER is used for touching up holes, joints, and parapets.
TUFCRETE PLASTIC ROOF RESURFACER PRIMER is used to prepare dried-out felt or paper for application of new material.
TUFCRETE LIQUID ROOF RESURFACER is used to provide a new wearing surface over a patch or entire roof. TUFCRETE CO.

Tufcrete® Underlay No. 3. A mastic, 1 part of which is mixed with ½ part Portland cement, 2½ parts sand, and sufficient water and spread on the base or old floor to form an underlayment for the floor surfacing. TUFCRETE Co.

Tufdek®. A non-skid floor coating available in 5 colors: gray, yellow, slate blue, tile green, and tile red. It is a cohesive, resinous plastic, containing wear-resistant, non-skid aggregates, and is resistant to oil, gasoline, alcohol, dilute acids, cleaning agents, and water. It can be applied by trowel to any clean surface; and it will not chip, crack or peel. *Use:* Around machinery; on pedals, steps and ladder treads; on ramps and platforms, floors and decks; around pools and tanks; in showers, mess halls, recreation rooms, patios, building entrances, etc. TUFCRETE Co.

Tufflex. *See* TURBO TUFFLEX®.

Tuf-On® #58-F, #58-M, *and* #74-F. (*HBMTN* p. 584). No longer available.
BROOKLYN VARNISH MFG. Co.

Tuf-On® 745-S *and* 747-S. Moisture- and fungus-resistant finishes for cables, cordage, wire, capacitors, coils, metal joints, paper labels, cans, sockets, potentiometers, and many other types of equipment. They meet specification MIL-V-173A: No. 745-S (Type I) and No. 747-S (Types I and II).
BROOKLYN PAINT & VARNISH Co.

Tuf-On Chlo-Dur. *See* TUF-ON® SELENIUM RECTIFIER COATINGS.

Tuf-On® Met-L-Brite Cleaner. A high-solids lacquer especially formulated to prevent tarnishing and corrosion of aluminum, brass, chrome, gold, silver, and steel. For either interior or exterior application. Available in two types: No. 220 for spray application; No. 240 for brush application. Dries quickly to a tough non-yellowing film, that has high abrasion and weathering resistance. *Uses:* For aluminum boats, trailer bodies, aircraft, stormdoors, sash, lighting fixtures, silverware, etc.
BROOKLYN PAINT & VARNISH Co.

Tuf-On® Selenium Rectifier Coatings. Coatings that are resistant to salt spray, moisture, fungus growth, and acid and alkali fumes. Used for coating rectifiers for military, industrial and commercial purposes. First, the rectifier is coated with TUF-ON CHLO-DUR RECTIFIER PRIMER; then with two coats of TUF-ON CHLO-DUR RECTIFIER ENAMEL, which may be thinned with TUF-ON #74 THINNER or xylol. The coatings are air dried for 15–30 min.; and then force dried at 140–175°F. for 30–60 min.
BROOKLYN PAINT & VARNISH Co.

Tumerol®. The trademark for a condiment, etc.
S. B. PENICK & Co.

Tung Oil△. *Also known as* CHINA WOOD OIL△. A drying oil obtained by pressing the seeds of the tree *Aleurites cordata* Steud., *Euphorbiacea*, which is indigenous to China and Japan but now also grown in Florida. Its color varies from a golden yellow to dark brown, depending upon the temp. used in the extraction. It has a pungent, disagreeable odor. On prolonged storage or on heating for a short time to 300°C., it polymerizes to a stiff jelly. The oil contains approx. 70% eleostearic acid. Sp.gr. 0.943–0.940; saponification no. 190; iodine no. 163; dries uniformily to a flat, non-glossy film; soluble in chloroform, ether, **carbon disulfide**, and oils; the polymerized product is practically insoluble in common organic solvents. *Uses:* In the mfg. of rapidly-drying enamels and varnishes, linoleum, floor cloth, brake linings, insulating compounds, etc.; for waterproofing paper, etc.

Tupco®. A mothproofing composition.
PENNSYLVANIA SALT MFG. Co.

Turbane®. A fuel for gas turbine engines. Gravity, A.P.I., 40.5°; color (Saybolt), 21.0 (min.); doctor test, sweet; sulfur, 0.130% (max.); flash point, 115°F. (min.); initial b.p., 330–370°F.; end point, 515°F. (max.). Marketed in service stations.
GASETERIA, INC.

Turbo®. An organic-coated COTTON or RAYON braided sleeving used as electrical insulation. Available in five grades: A-A-1, A-B-1, A-C-1, A-C-2, and A-C-3, conforming to A.S.T.M. specification D-372, NEMA standard VSI-1950, and Military Specification MIL-I-3190A. WILLIAM BRAND & Co.

Turbo 117®. A silicone-rubber-coated fibrous glass braided sleeving. Extremely flexible at temps. of from −100° to +500°F.; and fungus resistant. Conforms to Military Specifications MIL-I-3190A and MIL-I-18057. Available in 10 standard colors and natural tan. *Use:* For electrical insulation.
WILLIAM BRAND & Co

Turboglas®. A Class B electrical insulating tubing. It consists of a varnish coating over fibrous glass braid. Available in five standard grades meeting A.S.T.M., NEMA, and military specifications.
WILLIAM BRAND & Co.

Turbolene®. A polyethylene-type insulated wire and cable. Both standard and flame-retardant polyethylene types are available. For high-voltage, high-frequency, low-loss applications. Meets U/L and military requirements. WILLIAM BRAND & Co.

Turbolex®. A general-purpose plastic tubing for electrical insulation applications. Several types are available to meet A.S.T.M., D-922 and MIL-I-631B, Type F, Grade a, Class I, Category 1 requirements. Available in opaque colors and in transparent, in sizes of 0.022″ to 2.500″ i.d. WILLIAM BRAND & Co.

Turbosil®. A silicone-varnish-impregnated fibrous glass sleeving which meets Class H insulation requirements. Meets military specification MIL-I-3190A. Available in 5 standard grades.
WILLIAM BRAND & Co.

Turbotemp®. High-temp. wires and cables employing silicone rubber or TEFLON® insulation. Meets requirements of MIL-W-16878B Types E, EE and FF. Will operate at temps. of from −100° to +500°F. Resistant to water, oils, and chemicals.
WILLIAM BRAND & Co.

Turbotherm®. A plastic tubing or a plastic insulated wire, U/L approved. The plastic tubing, approved for 105°C. operation, is available in clear and opaque colors in sizes of 0.002″ to 2.500″ i.d. The wire is furnished in 300- and 600-volt ratings for operation at 80°, 90° or 105°C. with or without COTTON, RAYON, fibrous glass, or NYLON overbraids, with vinyl or

Nylon jackets, and with spiral or braided copper shields. WILLIAM BRAND & CO.

Turbotrans®. A plastic tubing or plastic-insulated wire for special high-temp applications. U/L approved for continuous 105°C. operation. Especially suitable for potting or baking applications. Tubing also meets the requirements of MIL-I-631B, Type F, Grade C. WILLIAM BRAND & CO.

Turbotuf®. A vinyl-coated, fibrous-glass braided sleeving which meets Class B insulation requirements. Extremely flexible and abrasion resistant. Available in all colors, in two grades, in sizes of 0.022" to 0.375" i.d. Meets military specification MIL-I-3190A. WILLIAM BRAND & CO.

Turbo Tufflex®. A semi-rigid vinyl-insulated hookup wire developed primarily for electronic business-machine applications. Flexible, yet tough, it eliminates the necessity for textile overbraids heretofore required to counteract cold flow and resist abrasion. Available in gauges #24 to #10, in all colors. U/L approved. WILLIAM BRAND & CO.

Turbozone®. A special low-temp., fungus-resistant vinyl tubing developed for aircraft applications. Meets Air Force Specification MIL-I-7444A (1). Available in amber or transparent (natural) and opaque colors. WILLIAM BRAND & CO.

Turkey Red Oil[△]**.** See CASTOR OIL[△].

Tu-Way[NR]**.** An asphalt-base aluminum roof paint that protects roof surfaces, and reduces under-roof temps. HALLEMITE MFG. CO.

Twecotan® Tanning Extracts. (*HBMTN* p. 586). No longer available. AMERICAN CYANAMID CO.

Tween®. (*Supp.* I p. 248). This product is also mfg'd in England and Germany. The trademark is registered in England but not in Germany.
ATLAS POWDER CO.
HONEYWILL-ATLAS, LTD.
ATLAS-GOLDSCHMIDT G.M.B.H.

TW-F®. A form of fibrous glass wool without binder, for use as an insulation for temps. up to 1,000°F. OWENS-CORNING FIBERGLAS CORP.

TwinLine[NR]**.** (*HBMTN* p. 587). No longer available. EASTERN EQUIPMENT CO.

Twin Weld[NR]**.** (*Supp.* I p. 249). This trade name for welding hose is a registered trademark in Canada. HEWITT-ROBINS, INC.

Tylac[NR]**.** A series of high-strength, film-forming latices. They are anionic in character and are supplied at a pH of 8 to 9. A non-staining antioxidant has been incorporated in all TYLAC latices. These latices yield soft, flexible films of high tensile strength without the addition of any compounding ingredients. Furthermore, no discoloring accelerators, sulfur or fine-particle-size reinforcing pigments are present in the latex or need to be added to develop optimum properties. INTERNATIONAL LATEX CORP.

Typhoon®. The trademark for an insect powder. S. B. PENICK & CO.

Ty-Ply® 3640. A non-tacky adhesive for bonding natural and synthetic RUBBER compounds to metals during vulcanization. It is a black, free-flowing liquid consisting of a specially developed resin in solution together with some dispersed solids. It is relatively insensitive to changing atmospheric conditions, and can be held for at least a month at normal room temp. in a dirt-free place without impairing the ultimate adhesion.
MARBON CHEMICAL DIV.,
BORG-WARNER CORP.

Ty-Ply® Q. A black, free-flowing liquid adhesive for bonding natural rubber, and GR-S and GR-I compounds to metal during vulcanization. It is similar to TY-PLY® 3640 but its variation in adhesion with high humidity is somewhat greater than for No. 3640. MARBON CHEMICAL DIV., BORG-WARNER CORP.

Tyron®. RAYON cord and fabric for the mfg. of tires. INDUSTRIAL RAYON CORP.

Tyroscabe®. (*Supp.* I p. 250). No longer available. SHARP & DOHME DIV., MERCK & CO.

U

U-A-S® "S" Solution. (*Supp.* I p. 250). No longer available.
NITROGEN DIV., ALLIED CHEMICAL & DYE CORP.

U-A-S® "W" Solution. (*Supp.* I p. 250). No longer available.
NITROGEN DIV., ALLIED CHEMICAL & DYE CORP.

Ubagrip®. (*Supp.* I p. 250). Now a registered trademark. A product of UBS CHEMICAL CORP., successor to UNION BAY STATE CHEMICAL CO.

Ubryco. An acid copper-plating process that deposits a thick copper plate as an undercoat for chromium, nickel-chromium, white brass-chromium, etc. It has excellent leveling and hiding properties. UDYLITE CORP.

Ucilon®. (*HBMTN* p. 589). Now a product of METAL & THERMIT CORP., successor to UNITED CHROMIUM, INC.

Udyguard. Plastic-coated guards for use with electroplating anode rods. UDYLITE CORP.

Ultimo®[Can.]**-4.** A machinery steel for applications requiring high strength in large sizes. Typical analysis, %: 0.45 carbon, 0.75 manganese, 0.030 phosphorus (max.), 0.030 sulfur (max.), 0.20 silicon, 0.75 chromium, 1.75 nickel, 0.40 molybdenum.
ATLAS STEELS LTD.

Ultracain® Ointment. (*HBMTN* p. 589). No longer available. CHATHAM PHARMACEUTICALS, INC.

Ultra-Filter[NR]**.** A name used to designate a mechanical filter respirator. *Use:* For protection against inhalation of radioactive dusts and particulates more toxic than lead. MINE SAFETY APPLIANCES CO.

Ultraflex[NR]**.** A microcrystalline wax, of the plastic type, used for paper and foil laminating, baking wrappers and cartons, sealing compounds, dental waxes, rust preventives, dairy package coatings, rubber compounding, fabric waterproofing, cosmetics, and other uses. M.p. 140–145°F.; penetration (100 g.) at 77°F. (ASTM D1321-54T), 25–30; color, amber, 2 (max.), and white. BARECO WAX CO.

Ultraflo®. A line of flow-coating enamels for the one-coat finishing of metal parts. They flow out to a minor-like finish free from sags, runs, or pinholes; and yet cling to sharp edges. Ultraflo primers are available for use with the Ultraflo enamels.
INTERCHEMICAL CORP., FINISHES DIV.

Ultramarine Blue△. A blue pigment that occurs naturally as the mineral lapis lazuli but is now made synthetically by calcining a mixture of kaolin, sodium carbonate, charcoal, quartz, sulfur, and a resin. It is a complex sodium silicate-sodium sulfide. A darker variety of this pigment is obtained by substituting sodium sulfate for the sodium carbonate in the mix. Available as blue lumps or powder; insoluble in water; readily decomposed by acid, including carbonic, with liberation of hydrogen sulfide. *Use:* As a pigment in calico printing, wall paper, mottled soap; for coloring tiles, cements, rubber, etc.; and as a laundry bluing to neutralize the yellowish tone in COTTON and LINEN fabrics.

Ultramin® B. A cationic textile softener consisting of a diamine condensate in paste form.
ULTRA CHEMICAL WORKS

Ultramin® SS. A cationic textile softener consisting of a fatty acid amine condensate in paste form.
ULTRA CHEMICAL WORKS

Ultrapole® DL. A liquid lauroyl diethanolamine amide. It is a 100% active, non-ionic emulsifier that is especially useful for oil-in-water systems. *Uses:* As an emulsifying agent; and as a dry cleaning detergent.
ULTRA CHEMICAL WORKS

Ultrapole® G Extra Conc. A fatty acid amide condensate. It is a non-ionic, surface active agent of 98–100% activity. It is especially useful as a detergent in textile processing.
ULTRA CHEMICAL WORKS

Ultrapole® S. A coconut oil amine condensate of 99–100% activity. It is a non-toxic, liquid detergent and emulsifier. *Uses:* As a general-purpose emulsifying agent for oil-in-water emulsions; as a wetting agent; and as a textile detergent and wetting agent.
ULTRA CHEMICAL WORKS

Ultrapole® S Liquid. A coconut oil-amine condensate of 99–100% activity. It is a non-ionic detergent-emulsifier.
ULTRA CHEMICAL WORKS

Ultravon® JF. A non-ionic detergent for washing greasy WOOL, washing spinning oils from WOOL, boiling-off COTTON, kier boiling, scouring RAYON, and afterwashing vat and naphthol dyeings. It is a pale yellow, slightly viscous liquid, completely soluble in warm water. Solutions have a neutral reaction and are stable in the presence of acids, alkalis, hard water, metallic salts, anionic and cationic materials.
CIBA CO.

Ultrox®. The trademark for prepared zirconium silicate ($ZrSiO_4$) in the form of a white crystalline powder. *Uses:* As an opacifier in glazes for vitreous sanitary ware, wall tile, stoneware, glazed brick, terra cotta, art ware, and special porcelains.
METAL & THERMIT CORP.

Umbrathor®. (*HBMTN* p. 590). Formerly mfg'd by HEYDEN CHEMICAL CORP.; now a product of TESTAGAR & CO.

Unaflo®. An oil-well cement made by intergrinding a special retarding agent with a sulfate-resistant type of portland cement in addition to the gypsum regularly used. This cement has a delayed, postponed, retarded set so that it remains fluid and pumpable under difficult cementing conditions or where high well temps. and pressures exist.
UNIVERSAL ATLAS CEMENT CO.

Underlay No. 3. See TUFCRETE® UNDERLAY No. 3.

Underlayment Board[NE]. (*Supp.* I p. 252). No longer available.
PHILIP CAREY MFG. CO.

Uncepac®. An automatic, molded packing material for reciprocating rods and plungers operating against steam, water, air, gas and oil where the rod is in line, true and not scored. It provides effective sealing with minimum packing depth. Designed so that each ring is a complete packing unit. Furnished in sets of endless or split rings.
JOHNS-MANVILLE SALES CORP.

Unibac®. A polymeric backing compound designed to impart strength and wear characteristics to all types of upholstery fabrics. Available for both pre-dye and post-dye product applications.
UBS CHEMICAL CORP.

Unichrome®. (*HBMTN* p. 591). Now a product of METAL & THERMIT CORP., successor to UNITED CHROMIUM, INC.

Uniflex[NE]. A bottlewashing additive with water conditioning and wetting properties. It speeds penetration; minimizes foam; reduces alkali carryover; promotes rapid rinsing; and controls scale.
WYANDOTTE CHEMICALS CORP., J. B. FORD DIV.

UniKool. An all-purpose, water-soluble cutting and grinding fluid and coolant. It forms a clear, transparent solution of pleasant odor; and has excellent rust-preventive and lubricating properties. Density, 8.4 lb./gal.; pH of working solution, 8.3; pour point, 20°F.
F. E. ANDERSON OIL CO.

Unipar. See PARKER UNIPAR®.

Uni-Pectin. A group of pectins for every purpose, obtained from the pulp of apples and the peel of lemons. Used in the mfg. of jams, jellies, preserves, and bakery and confectionery products; as stabilizers for ices and sherbets, dehydrated foods, drugs and other products; as emulsifiers for the oil and other industries; and as bases for many drugs.
COLYER CO.

Uniperal W. A dyeing assistant for use when dyeing wool with metal complex dyestuffs. It promotes level penetration and improve fastness to crocking. It is a viscous brown mass, easily soluble in water. Solutions are neutral, and stable to metal salts, acids and alkalis.
NOVA CHEMICAL CORP.

Unique®. A smokeless rifle powder.
HERCULES POWDER CO.

Unishade "NS"®. A scouring and leveling agent combined for the one-bath system of dyeing NYLON hosiery. Both the scouring and dyeing may be done at the same time in a one-bath operation. With UNISHADE "NS", hard-to-remove oils and stubborn soils are washed out of the hosiery easily; good welt-leg unions are maintained as the welt will not become lighter than the monofilament leg even under prolonged dyeing conditions; uniform shades between the welt and the leg, and from one stocking to another are produced consistently; over-dyed shades can be lightened uniformly by the addition of more UNISHADE "NS" to the dyebath. KALI MFG. CO.

Uni-Syn® Style No. 239. (*HBMTN* p. 593). No longer available. KEASBEY & MATTISON CO.

Unitex®. A centrifuged natural hevea latex. STEIN, HALL & CO.

Universal®. The trademark for a line of Portland and other hydraulic cements. UNIVERSAL ATLAS CEMENT CO.

Upson® Ceiling Tiles. (*Supp.* I p. 254). No longer available. UPSON CO.

Uranium "O"[NE]. The tradename for a uranium ore. STEWART RESEARCH LABORATORY

Uranium Oxide Yellow△. Same as URANIUM YELLOW△.

Uranium Yellow△. Also known as URANIUM OXIDE YELLOW△. Sodium diuranate. $Na_2U_2O_7 \cdot H_2O$; mol.wt. 652.15. A yellow, water-insoluble powder; soluble in acids. *Uses:* In the mfg. of yellowish-green fluorescent glass; for painting on porcelain; and in the mfg. of yellow and yellow-green glazing enamels.

Urethane Resins△. Same as ISOCYANATE RESINS△.

Uritone®. Elixir and tablets of methenamine, Parke-Davis, for treatment of infections of the urinary tract. PARKE, DAVIS & CO.

Urolitia®. (*Supp.* I p. 254). Now a registered trademark of the BORCHERDT CO., formerly BORCHERDT MALT EXTRACT CO.

Urosulfin®. A medicinal in tablet form. Each tablet contains 250 mg. sulfamethylthiadiazole and 50 mg. 2,6-diamino-3-phenylazopyridine HCl. *Uses:* For treatment of cystitis, pyelitis and many urinary tract infections accompanying pregnancy, prostatitis, malignancies, calculi, etc. NEPERA CHEMICAL CO.

Urosulfon®. A urinary tract antiseptic used for the treatment of infections of the urinary tract, such as pyelonephritis, etc. Also used in pre- and post-operative genito-urinary surgery. Supplied in the form of tablets, each of which contains 0.5 g. sulfacetamide. CONSOLIDATED MIDLAND CORP.

Urotropin®. A medicinal for the treatment of genitourinary infections including pyelitis, urethritis, cystitis, prostatitis and ureteritis; and as a precautionary measure before and after instrumentation of, or operation on, the urinary tract. It is a brand of methenamine (hexamethylenamine; hexamethylenetetramine). WARNER-CHILCOTT LABORATORIES

Urox®. A chemical herbicide, in granular form, for long term control of vegetation in non-crop areas such as railroad rights-of-way, highways, parking lots, drainage ditches, etc. It is effective against a wide range of annual and perennial grasses and broadleafed weeds. This herbicide is applied in its granular form at a rate of 100 to 400 lb. per acre. It is most effective when applied just as plant growth begins or shortly before it starts.
GENERAL CHEMICAL DIV., ALLIED CHEMICAL & DYE CORP.

"UR" Series. See CLAREMONT "UR" SERIES.

Ursulin®. (*HBMTN* p. 594). No longer available. AMERICAN CYANAMID CO.

Urucury Wax△. Same as OURICURY WAX△.

Usaphene 5[NE]. A disinfectant for general sanitation, for foot baths, and for disinfecting bathing suits, toilet rooms, sick-room utensils, and surgical instruments. Phenol coefficient, 5. Active ingredients: ortho-phenyl phenol, chloro-2 phenyl phenol, isopropyl alcohol, dodecyl benzene monosulfonate. Inert ingredient: 80% water.
U. S. SANITARY SPECIALTIES CORP.

Usaphene 10[NE]. Same as USAPHENE 5 except that it contains only 65% water. Phenol coefficient, 10.
U. S. SANITARY SPECIALTIES CORP.

USC. The trademark for a line of coating materials including:

A-35. A pure drying alkyd for floor, porch and deck concrete enamels, primers, sealers, and undercoats.

A 47-60. A pure drying alkyd-long oil vehicles for interior and exterior enamels, paints, and primers.

A-47% PURE DRYING ALKYD. A long soya oil alkyd, having excellent color retention and high gloss, for mfg. of finest architectural and mill white enamels, exterior and interior coatings.

A-73. A pure drying alkyd for low cost enamels and primers.

A-86. A pure drying alkyd for architectural enamels, pump enamels, and clear finishes.

A-374. A phenolated alkyd for floor, porch and deck enamels, primers, machinery enamels, 4-hr. enamels, and quick-drying enamels.

A-532. A pure drying alkyd for quick-drying primers, zone marking paints, and quick-drying enamels.

A-800. A pure drying alkyd for flats, primers, sealers, semi-gloss paints and undercoats.

A-900. A pure drying alkyd for one-coat self-sealing and self-priming flats, semi-gloss enamels, etc.

V-14. A 4-hr. quick-drying varnish for floor and deck paints, floor varnishes, concrete paints, touch-up enamels, and spar varnishes.

V-22. A liquid for quick-drying ready-mixed red lead paints, plastic, white lead pastes, and zinc oxide pastes.

V-75 ALUMINUM LIQUID. A vehicle for ready-mixed exterior and interior aluminum paints.
U. S. COATINGS CO.

U.S.I.® Chemicals. The trademark for a line of chemicals mfg'd by U. S. INDUSTRIAL CHEMICALS CO., DIV. OF NATIONAL DISTILLERS PRODUCTS CORP.

U.S.S.®. The trademark used to identify all of the products mfg'd by the UNITED STATES STEEL CORP.

U.S.S.® A-R Steel[NE]. A low-cost, abrasion-resisting steel developed particularly for the materials-handling industries. It is an intermediate carbon-manganese steel, with better workability than carbon steel of the same hardness level. Composition, %: carbon, 0.35–0.50; manganese, 1.50–2.00; phosphorus, 0.05 (max.); sulfur, 0.055 (max.); silicon, 0.15–0.35. *Uses:* For baffle plates, buckets, chutes, conveyors, cutter bars, hoppers, liners, screens, wearing plates, grinding mills, etc. UNITED STATES STEEL CORP.

U.S.S.® Carilloy®. The trademark for an extensive line of alloy steels. UNITED STATES STEEL CORP.

U.S.S.® Cor-Ten®. A high-strength, low-alloy steel that provides 50% higher effective strength than structural carbon steel and four to six times its resistance to atmospheric corrosion. It also has good workability and weldability. Composition, %: carbon, 0.12 (max.); manganese, 0.20–0.50; phosphorus, 0.07–0.15; sulfur, 0.05 (max.); silicon, 0.25–0.75; copper, 0.25–0.55; chromium, 0.30–1.25; nickel, 0.65 (max.). *Uses:* For air-conditioning equipment, agricultural equipment, material-handling equipment, mine equipment, tanks, trucks, tubing, wire, roofing, rivets, furnace parts, bolts and nuts, bins, etc. UNITED STATES STEEL CORP.

U.S.S.® Di-Lok®. The trademark for concrete reinforcing bars that fully meet the requirements of ASTM Specification A305-53T. UNITED STATES STEEL CORP.

U.S.S.® Freemax®. A free-machining plate steel. It is a high-sulfur, high-phosphorus, high-manganese, silicon-killed steel made by the open-hearth process. Composition, %: carbon, 0.12; manganese, 1.00; phosphorus, 0.09; sulfur, 0.25; silicon, 0.20. *Uses:* For rubber molds, plastic molds, steam platens, sprockets, gears, bushings, cams, machinery bases, die holders, etc. UNITED STATES STEEL CORP.

U.S.S.® Man-Ten®. A medium manganese-copper steel possessing high strength, good workability, and adequate weldability, together with high resistance to abrasion and fatigue. Its atmospheric corrosion is slightly better than that of copper steel. Composition, %: carbon, 0.25 (max.); manganese, 1.10–1.60; phosphorus, 0.045 (max.); sulfur, 0.05 (max.); silicon, 0.30 (max.); copper, 0.20 (min.). *Uses:* For asphalt mixers, booms, riveted bridges, power-shovel buckets, bulldozers, derricks, fan blades, tanks, hoisting drums, etc. UNITED STATES STEEL CORP.

U.S.S.® M-X®. A fast-cutting, free-machining, Bessemer screw stock. UNITED STATES STEEL CORP.

U.S.S.® T-1®. The trademark for a high-yield-strength heat-treated, constructional alloy steel. Composition %: carbon, 0.10–0.20; manganese, 0.60–1.00; phosphorus 0.40 (max.); sulfur, 0.050 (max.); silicon, 0.15–0.35; nickel, 0.70–1.00; chromium, 0.40–0.80; molybdenum, 0.40–0.60; vanadium, 0.30–0.10; copper, 0.15–0.50; boron, 0.002–0.006. Developed to meet the need for a steel, primarily in plate form, possessing a very high yield strength (90,000 lb./sq.in. or more) yet tough enough to withstand unusual stresses and pressure, as well as shock, either at low or high temps. UNITED STATES STEEL CORP.

U.S.S.® Tri-Ten®. A low-alloy, high-strength steel, formerly identified as U.S.S. MANGANESE-NICKEL-COPPER. It is a tonnage steel possessing relatively high strength and toughness, good weldability and workability, together with resistance to abrasion and fatigue. Its atmospheric corrosion resistance is somewhat better than that of copper steel. Composition, %: carbon 0.25 (max.); manganese, 1.30 (max.); phosphorus, 0.045 (max.); sulfur, 0.005 (max.); silicon, 0.10–0.30; copper, 0.30–0.60; nickel, 0.50–1.00. *Uses:* For booms, bridges, bulldozers, material-handling buckets, derricks, draglines, tractors, power shovels, scrapers, etc. UNITED STATES STEEL CORP.

U.S.S.® Vitrenamel®. A special-type of sheet steel designed for porcelain enameling. The sheets are finished with a special surface that forms a tenacious bond with the vitreous coating. UNITED STATES STEEL CORP.

Utility®. The trademark for a carbon paper. INTERCHEMICAL CORP., AULT & WIBORG CARBON & RIBBON DIV.

UV 9 Ultraviolet Absorber[NE]. 2-Hydroxy-4-methoxybenzophenone. A light stabilizer for polyesters, polystyrene, polyvinyl chloride, and other resins. Useful as a light-screening agent in a variety of film applications. AMERICAN CYANAMID CO.

Uvitex® P Conc. A water-soluble optical bleaching agent developed specifically for the whitening of paper. Used in concentrations of 0.02–0.05% by weight of the dry paper. Applied in the beater, with tub sizing, as a spray before calendering, or in casein-pigment coatings. CIBA CO.

Uvitex® RBS. An optical bleaching agent identical with UVITEX® RS (*HBMTN* p. 595) except that when applied in too heavy a concentration, it imparts a more neutral white in contrast to the reddish tint of UVITEX® RS. Under proper conditions, both give pure white effects. CIBA CO.

Uvitex® SI. (*HBMTN* p. 595). No longer available. CIBA CO.

Uvitex® TXS Conc. A water-soluble optical bleaching agent for whitening COTTON and RAYON. Applied from a neutral bath containing 0.01–0.10% UVITEX TXS CONC. CIBA CO.

Uvitex® U. A water-soluble optical brightener for use primarily on ORLON® and DACRON®, although it can be used on all textile fibers. It has good fastness to light, washing, and chlorine, and good resistance to heat. CIBA CO.

U. W. Grease. *See* KEYSTONE U. W. GREASE[NE].

V

V[NE]. (Trademark registration pending). A line of stabilizers for plastics. HARSHAW CHEMICAL CO.

Vaf®. A shortening made from modified meat fats and hydrogenated vegetable oils. Designed for general baking and cooking where a bland, neutral flavor and high creaming quality shortening is required. ANDERSON, CLAYTON & CO. FOODS DIV.

Vafet®. A modified meat fat-hydrogenated vegetable oil shortening, with mono and diglycerides added as

emulsifiers. It is a specialty shortening for use in cakes and icings.
ANDERSON, CLAYTON & CO. FOODS DIV.

Valite®. A line of industrial thermoplastic and thermosetting resins derived from agricultural products such as sugar cane BAGASSE. Most are available as solid resins, but VALITE RESIN 8123 is an alcohol-water solution of 60% solids conc., and VALITE RESIN 1366-I contains 45–50% solids in a water solution. *Uses:* As the sole resinous ingredient and as a replacement for shellac in phonograph records; as extenders for cellulose ethers; as wire coatings and protective coatings for metals; as plasticizers and extenders for vinyl resins and for ethyl cellulose; as binders for ceramics before firing; as laminating resins for cotton and glass fabrics, for paper, and for plywood lamination; and as extenders for phenol-formaldehyde resins in molding compounds, impregnating varnishes, and other products. VALITE CORP.

Valvoline All-Climate[NE]. A heavy-duty SAE 10W-30 motor oil for use at temps. from −10 to +110°F.
VALVOLINE OIL CO.

Vanade[NE]. A whipping and emulsifying ingredient of foods, consisting of a water dispersion of sorbitan monostearate and polyoxyethylene sorbitan monostearate. Its principal use is as an emulsifier in cakes that contain shortening. R. T. VANDERBILT CO.

Vancide® 26EC. A fungicide-bactericide. It is an emulsion concentrate formulation of the lauryl pyridinium salt of 5-chloro-2-mercaptobenzothiazole. *Use:* As a preservative for COTTON textiles.
R. T. VANDERBILT CO.

Vancide® 32. A non-toxic fungicide and bactericide composed principally of the beta-hydroxyethylpyridinium salt of 2-mercaptobenzothiazole. Available as a 40% solution. R. T. VANDERBILT CO.

Vancide® 50 Peps. A coating for the cut ends of banana stems to protect them during shipment and storage. R. T. VANDERBILT CO.

Vancide® 51. A fungicide-bactericide. A water solution (30% solids) of the sodium salts of dimethyl dithiocarbamic acid and 2-mercaptobenzothiazole. *Use:* As a preservative for starch paste, glue, cutting oils and the like; as a sanitizing spray or wash for surfaces of ships, freight cars, etc.; in agriculture, to preserve rose bushes in cold storage, and as a seed treatment for wheat, sorghum, and sweet potatoes; and as a textile preservative in conjunction with water-soluble zinc salts such as zinc sulfate.
R. T. VANDERBILT CO.

Vancide® 89 and Vancide® 89RE. N-trichloromethylmercapto-4-cyclohexene-1, 2-dicarboximide; tech. and purified. They are anti-fungal and anti-bacterial agents. *Uses:* For drug, cosmetic, and industrial applications; for the protection of vinyl film, paint and lacquer from damage by molds and bacteria.
R. T. VANDERBILT CO.

Van Cut®. A molybdenum (5.50%)-tungsten (6.00%) type of high-speed steel, combining ease of grinding with improved wear and heat resistance. It is a good general-purpose steel, performing exceptionally well on heavy and fine cuts. In addition, it is ideal for broaching, reaming, and finish machining. Because of this, it is used to mfg. hobs, chasers, form cutters, milling cutters, lathe and planer tools. Other constituents include: carbon 1.02%; silicon, 0.30%; manganese, 0.25%; chromium, 4.00%; vanadium, 2.50%.
VANADIUM-ALLOYS STEEL CO.

Vandrynilla®. The trademark for flavoring products, etc. S. B. PENICK & CO.

Vanesta[NE]. A polyoxyalkylene stearate product used in starch adhesives and starch sizes to minimize setback and gelling of the starch on cooling and aging.
R. T. VANDERBILT CO.

Vanette®. An imitation vanilla powder for use in baking and for pudding powders.
FLORASYNTH LABORATORIES, INC.

Vanfre[NE]. Materials developed to facilitate removal of rubber products after vulcanization. *Uses:* VANFRE is used as a release agent for lead-press-cured items; VANFRE CLEAR and VANFRE No. 3 are general-purpose releasing agents for molded goods and frame-cured sponge. R. T. VANDERBILT CO.

Vanillion C. See DIHYDRO VANILLION C®.

Vanlite[NE]. A whipping and emulsifying ingredient for foods, consisting of a water dispersion of polyoxyethylene sorbitan monostearate. Its principal use is as a whipping agent and tenderizer for sponge cakes. R. T. VANDERBILT CO.

Vanquin[NE]. (Trademark registration pending). A strawberry-flavored suspension of pyrrovinyquinium chloride, Parke-Davis, for treatment of pinworms in humans. PARKE, DAVIS & CO.

Vanstay-C73[NE]. A complex organic mixture of barium and zinc compounds. *Use:* As a heat stabilizer for mineral-filled vinyl tile other than asbestos filled. R. T. VANDERBILT CO.

Vanstay-HT[NE]. A complex coprecipitated organic mixture of barium and cadmium compounds. *Use:* As a heat stabilizer for all vinyl formulations.
R. T. VANDERBILT CO.

Vanstay-L[NE]. A phosphate-type light stabilizer for all but electrical grades of vinyl plastics.
R. T. VANDERBILT CO.

Vanstay-N[NE]. A complex mixture of barium and cadmium compounds. *Use:* As a heat stabilizer for vinyl plastics where roll plating is a problem.
R. T. VANDERBILT CO.

Vanstay-R[NE]. A mixture of organic compounds of barium and cadmium with chelating agents in selected solvents. *Use:* As a heat stabilizer for plastisols, and calendered and extruded vinyl plastics.
R. T. VANDERBILT CO.

Vanstay-S[NE]. A mixture of organic borate, phosphite and epoxy compounds in selected solvents. *Use:* As a booster for VANSTAY N, HT and other heat stabilizers. R. T. VANDERBILT CO.

Vanstay-Z[NE]. A mixture of organic zinc compounds in selected organic solvents. *Use:* As a heat stabilizer for all polyvinyl compounds.
R. T. VANDERBILT CO.

Vanwax[NE]. Low-cost, stable wax emulsions developed especially for the rubber industry. VANWAX may be applied by spraying, wiping, dipping, brushing, or tumbling with saturated rags.
R. T. VANDERBILT CO.

Vanzak[NE]. A lanolin concentrate in powder form. *Use:* In soaps, face powders, etc.
R. T. VANDERBILT CO.

Vanzyme[NE]. A starch-converting or amylolytic enzyme of the alpha amylase type. Available as a powder (VANZYME 31), and in the form of pre-weighted DISCS. *Uses:* To convert corn, tapioca or potato starches to produce starch sizes and adhesives.
R. T. VANDERBILT CO.

Vapolith®. The trademark for a line of heat-drying lithographic inks for web-fed presses.
INTERCHEMICAL CORP., PRINTING INK DIV.

Vaporin®. The trademark for a line of heat-drying letterpress inks for web-fed presses.
INTERCHEMICAL CORP., PRINTING INK DIV.

Vaporsphere®. A spherical steel shell containing a flexible hemispherical membrane, on the inside, which inflates, entraping the vaporized product vented from storage tanks. The VAPORSPHERE is a central storage unit interconnected to one or more fixed-roof tanks, forming a vaporsaving system.
CHICAGO BRIDGE & IRON CO.

Vaporstop. *See* SISALKRAFT VAPORSTOP®.

Vaportank. *See* HORTON® VAPORTANK.

Vaposet®. The trademark for a line of moisture-set printing inks.
INTERCHEMICAL CORP., PRINTING INK DIV.

Varee-Bryte XX[NE]. An extra-duty, water-resistant, slip-resistant floor finish for asphalt, linoleum, rubber, plastic, wood, composition, mastic and other floors. It contains DUPONT LUDOX®, a slip retardant.
U. S. SANITARY SPECIALTIES CORP.

Variamine®. A group of stabilized diazotized aminodiphenylamine bases used for the production of blues, and sometimes greens and browns, by coupling with an AS type of naphthol applied on COTTON or RAYON.
GENERAL DYESTUFF CO.

Vari/Phase[NE]. The trademark for a line of potentiometers, *i.e.* variable voltage dividers, not instruments.
CLAROSTAT MFG. CO.

Varisol®. A medicinal preparation, in injection form, used in the sclerosing treatment of varicose veins. Contains invert sugar, sodium chloride, and benzyl carbinol.
ABBOTT LABORATORIES

Vasco Supreme®. With its high carbon (1.57%) and high vanadium (5.00%), this T-15 steel (U. S. Patent No. 2,174,285) has proved itself unequalled for all tool steel applications involving wear or high cutting temps. It bridges the gap between high-speed steels and cemented carbides. It possesses higher hardness, higher hot hardness, higher wear resistance, and higher cutting efficiency than any other type of high-speed steel. It can be used at speeds 15% to 100% higher than normally used, and numerous tests have revealed that the performance life is 5 to 10 times superior to that of other high-speed steels. It is particularly valuable for machining high tensile materials such as heat-treated steels and abrasive materials, such as hard cast iron, cast steel, etc. It is useful as a tool bit, and for blanking dies, trimming dies, swaging dies, drills, milling cutters, form tools, punches, hobs, and wood-cutting knives. Other constituents include: silicon and manganese, 0.25% each; tungsten, 12.50%; chromium, 4.75%; cobalt, 5.00%.
VANADIUM-ALLOYS STEEL CO.

Vasoflavine®. (*Supp.* I p. 256). Now a registered trademark.
NATIONAL ANILINE DIV., ALLIED CHEMICAL & DYE CORP.

Vatsol® **OT-B Wetting Agent.** A free-flowing white powder containing 85% VATSOL OT and 15% sodium benzoate. Used in the mfg. of wettable powders.
AMERICAN CYANAMID CO.

Vatsol® **Wetting Agents.** A line of wetting agents supplied in the following types:

Designation	Description
OS	A powder (sodium isopropyl naphthalene sulfonate) designed expressly for improving insecticide and fungicide dusts.
OT	One of the most powerful wetting agents available; supplied in pellet, paste, liquid and aqueous forms; used in oil sprays, liquid and dust insecticides, and fruit and vegetable washes.
OTB	A free-flowing white powder containing 85% VASTOL OT and 15% sodium benzoate. Used in the mfg. of wettable powders.

AMERICAN CYANAMID CO.

"VC" Series. *See* CLAREMONT "VC" SERIES.

VD Glaze[NE]. (*HBMTN* p. 600). No longer available.
TRUSCON LABORATORIES

Veegum[NE]. A complex magnesium-aluminum silicate which forms gels with water. *Uses:* As a protective colloid, thickener and suspender, and emulsion stabilizer for drug, cosmetic and industrial applications.
R. T. VANDERBILT CO.

Veegum "T"[NE]. A magnesium-aluminum silicate used as a bonding and hardening agent in ceramic bodies and glazes.
R. T. VANDERBILT CO.

Vegetable Parchment△. *See* PARCHMENT△.

Vegetaromes[NE]. (1) An oak bark extraction for use as a blender in liquors, and (2) a St. John's Bread extraction for use as a fixative for fruit flavors and imitation vanilla.
FLORASYNTH LABORATORIES, INC.

Vegetol[NE]. A defoamer consisting of a sulfonated tallow base.
HERCULES POWDER CO.

Vegicod®. (*HBMTN* p. 600). No longer available.
NOPCO CHEMICAL CO.

Vegicut®. (*HBMTN* p. 600). No longer available.
NOPCO CHEMICAL CO.

Vegisol®. (*HBMTN* p. 600). No longer available.
NOPCO CHEMICAL CO.

Vegisulph®. (*HBMTN* p. 600). No longer available.
NOPCO CHEMICAL CO.

Veg-Oil Soap Cleanser. A semi-solid neutral soap, of approx. 45% soap solids, for use as a floor cleaner.
J. I. HOLCOMB MFG. CO.

Veg-Ro-Sul®. (*Supp.* I p. 256). No longer available.
GENERAL CHEMICAL DIV.,
ALLIED CHEMICAL & DYE CORP.

Vehicol®. The trademark for an aromatic elixir used as a base for medicinal preparations.
ABBOTT LABORATORIES

Velon®. The trademark for a group of plastic materials which at present includes vinyl sheetings in light and heavy gauges, and extruded vinylidene chloride monofilaments. These products are known as:
  VELON® FLEX, a heavy gauge all-plastic vinyl- or fabric-backed vinyl sheeting. The all-plastic sheeting is available in a wide variety of colors, in several thicknesses, and in smooth or textured finishes either plain or printed. The fabric-backed sheeting is also available in a variety of colors, smooth or textured finishes, either plain or printed. VELON® FLEX is widely used as an upholstery fabric, for wall panels, hassocks, luggage, commercial furniture, automobile seat covers, etc.
  VELON® FILM, a light-gauge vinyl sheeting, in thickness of 0.004″ to 0.012″. Available in translucent, semi-translucent, or opaque forms, in a wide range of colors, in smooth, embossed or printed surfaces. It is used as a decorative fabric for draperies, bedspreads, table cloths, shower curtains, etc.; for wearing apparel; for various protective coatings in industry; etc.
  VELON® FILAMENT, an extrusion of polyvinylidene chloride in the form of a solid plastic monofilament yarn. Available in gauges from 0.008″ to 0.030″. It is a smooth and lustrous yarn, made in a wide range of colors, both translucent or opaque. The filament can be woven, knitted, braided, or twisted. The resulting fabrics or cords have many uses where strength, resistance to abrasion, elasticity, and non-absorbence are desirable features. Some of these uses are upholstery fabrics woven of all plastic yarn and mixed fibers, window screening, agricultural shade cloth, etc.
FIRESTONE PLASTICS CO.

Velsicol AL-5. (*HBMTN* p. 601). No longer available.
VELSICOL CHEMICAL CORP.

Velsicol Resin EC-70. A paint and varnish resin. Sp.gr. 1.094; m.p. (ball & ring), 235–245°F.; cloud point (Nujol), 70–80°C.; color (Barrett), 3–4; iodine no. 80; soluble in aromatic solvents; insoluble in naphthas, alcohols, ketones, and esters; compatible with unbodied drying oil. VELSICOL CHEMICAL CORP.

Velsicol Resin X-30. A thermoplastic paint and varnish resin. Sp.gr. (60°F.), 1.03–1.06; m.p. (ball & ring), 200–220°F.; color (Gardner), 11 (max.); iodine no. 150 (max.); acid no. 0–2; saponification no. 0–2; soluble in esters, aromatic and aliphatic naphthas; insoluble in ketones and alcohols; compatible with drying, semi-drying, and non-drying oils and marine oils.
VELSICOL CHEMICAL CORP.

Velvasil® Silicone Fluid. A selected series of organopolysiloxane fluids available in viscosities ranging from 40 to 100,000 centistokes. These fluids are physiologically inert; have excellent water repellency and low surface tension; have excellent thermal, chemical and physical stability; are essentially colorless, odorless, and tasteless; have no tendency to become rancid in storage; and can be readily emulsified. VELVASIL fluids are readily soluble in aliphatic and aromatic hydrocarbons, chlorinated hydrocarbons and higher alcohols. They have limited compatability with most of the commonly used ingredients for cosmetic applications. *Uses:* As a base for medicinal ingredients; as an ointment base, and lipstick base; in the formulation of protective skin creams and lotions, baby lotions and creams, sun tan lotions and creams, hairdressings, lip pomade, cold creams, emollient creams, vanishing creams, etc.
GENERAL ELECTRIC CO.

Velvet®. An all-vegetable, hydrogenated shortening of highest quality and stability. It has high creaming quality and good plasticity which gives it excellent performance in cakes, cookies, pies and for frying.
ANDERSON, CLAYTON & CO. FOODS DIV.

Velvet B®. An all-vegetable, fully hydrogenated shortening for use in baking, frying and pastry making.
ANDERSON, CLAYTON & CO. FOODS DIV.

Velvet M®. A hydrogenated vegetable oil product scientifically developed for use in Mellorine and other frozen desserts. It is a sharp-melting fat with a bland flavor that produces Mellorine with a quick "get-away," fine melt-down and delicious eating quality.
ANDERSON, CLAYTON & CO. FOODS DIV.

Velvet Oil®. The trademark for a cottonseed salad oil and liquid shortening.
ANDERSON, CLAYTON & CO. FOODS DIV.

Velvorene®. A special formula, emulsifier-type hydrogenated vegetable oil, specially developed for fillings in biscuits and cookies, and for use in cakes, icings and other baked products. Specially suited for sandwich-type cookies and wafer fillings.
ANDERSON, CLAYTON & CO. FOODS DIV.

Veniturp®. The trademark for selected Veratrum Viride Alkaloids.
S. B. PENICK & CO.

Venopak®. The trademark for a disposable venoclysis unit for administration of intravenous fluids.
ABBOTT LABORATORIES

Venoset®. The trademark for a universal venoclysis unit for administration of intravenous fluids.
ABBOTT LABORATORIES

Venotube®. The trademark for a disposable set for syringe administration of medicinals.
ABBOTT LABORATORIES

Verabore®. Selected amorphous alkaloids of Veratrum Viride. *Uses:* For the treatment of high blood presure and toxemia of pregnancy.
S. B. PENICK & CO.

Veratridine△. *See* SABADILLA△.

Veratrine△. *See* SABADILLA△.

Veratrone®. (*HBMTN* p. 602). No longer available. PARKE, DAVIS & CO.

Verclysyl®. An invert sugar solution with B-complex factors for intravenous administration to patients who are unable to take nourishment by mouth. ABBOTT LABORATORIES

Verel®. A modified acrylic textile fiber having a very soft hand, good dyeability, high moisture regain, white color, and excellent flame, chemical and weather resistance, in addition to the normally good properties of acrylic fibers. Physical properties: tenacity, 2.5–2.8 G/D; elongation, 33–35%; sp.gr. 1.37%; moisture regain, 3.5–4.0%. *Uses:* For sweaters, knit dresses, draperies; work clothing and industrial fabrics; man-made fur for coats, jacket liners, and trim; and in blends with cotton, wool, silk and rayon for men's and women's wear and knit goods. EASTMAN CHEMICAL PRODUCTS, INC.

Verible®. (*Supp.* I p. 257). No longer available. SHARP & DOHME DIV., MERCK & CO.

Verifax®. Photocopying apparatus and photographic processing chemicals for use in office photocopying apparatus. EASTMAN KODAK CO.

Vermiculite△. A foliated mineral consisting of an alteration product of biotite and other micas. It occurs in masses of crystalline plates that have a sp.gr. of about 2.3 and a hardness of 1.5 on Moh's scale. Upon being calcined at a temp. of approx. 1,800°F., VERMICULITE expands as much as 16 times its original volume and its color turns to a silvery or golden hue. It is ground into pellet form and used as an insulating fill, as an aggregate in plasters, in the mfg. of plastic mortars and refractory concrete, as a filler in caulking compounds, in the mfg. of thermal and acoustical insulation board, etc.

Vermizine®. (*Supp.* I p. 257). Now a registered trademark. CHICAGO PHARMACAL CO.

Versene® 9. A powdered form of the trisodium salt of ethylenediaminetetraacetic acid, technical. $C_{10}H_{13}O_8N_2Na_3$; mol.wt. 358.2. Bulk density, 4.8 lb./gal.; pH (1% aqueous solution), 9.3; readily soluble in water. *Use:* As a chelating agent for polyvalent metallic ions. Used primarily in the soap industry. DOW CHEMICAL CO.

Versene® 67. A dilute, light straw-colored, aqueous solution of the tetrasodium salt of ethylenediaminetetraacetic acid, technical. $C_{10}H_{12}O_8N_2Na_4$; mol.wt. 380.2. Sp.gr. (25/25°C), 1.20; wt. per gal. (25°C), 10.0; pH (1% aqueous solution), 11.8; completely soluble in water. *Uses:* As an efficient chelating agent for polyvalent metallic ions. Used in textile finishing, soap and detergent mfg., etc. DOW CHEMICAL CO.

Versene® 100. A concentrated, straw-colored, aqueous solution of a technical grade of tetrasodium salt of ethylenediaminetetraacetic acid. $C_{10}H_{12}O_8N_2Na_4$; mol.wt. 380.2. Sp.gr. (25/25°C.), 1.31; wt. per gal. (25°C.), 10.9 lb.; pH (1% aqueous solution), 11.8. *Uses:* As an efficient chelating agent for divalent and polyvalent metallic ions in aqueous solutions. Widely used in textile processing, detergent formulations, and metal cleaning. DOW CHEMICAL CO.

Versene® Acid. Technical grade of ethylenediaminetetraacetic acid. $C_{10}H_{16}O_8N_2$; mol.wt. 292.2. It is a dry, white powder having a bulk density of 5 lb./gal. Solubility in water at 25°C. is under 0.5%. *Uses:* As an efficient chelating agent for the inactivation of polyvalent metallic ions; widely used as a raw material for the preparations of various derivatives, such as metal chelates, salts (K, NH$_4$), esters, etc. DOW CHEMICAL CO.

Versene® Beads. White, spray-dried beads of the tetrasodium salt of ethylenediaminetetraacetic acid, technical. $C_{10}H_{12}O_8N_2Na_4$; mol.wt. 380.2. Bulk density, 2.0 lb./gal.; pH (1% aqueous solution), 11.8; solubility in water (25°C.), 150 g./100 cc. *Uses:* As an efficient chelating agent for the inactivation of divalent and polyvalent metallic ions. Widely used in detergent formulations. DOW CHEMICAL CO.

Versene® Fe-3 Beads. An off-white, spray-dried bead consisting of approx. 90% tetrasodium salt of ethylenediaminetetraacetic acid, technical; and 10% of the monosodium salt of N,N-di(2-hydroxyethyl) glycine, technical. Bulk density, 3.8 lb./gal.; pH (1% aqueous solution), 11.8; readily soluble in water. *Uses:* As an efficient chelating agent for polyvalent metallic ions; exhibits stronger specific chelation for ferric iron in the mildly alkaline range than does VERSENE®. Used in textile processing, liquid detergent formulations, and in the polymerization of synthetic rubber. DOW CHEMICAL CO.

Versene® Fe-3 Liquid. A concentrated, light straw-colored, aqueous solution obtained by mixing 93% VERSENE® 67 with 7% VERSENE FE-3 SPECIFIC®. Sp.gr. (25/25°C.), 1.20; wt. per gal. (25°C.), 10.0 lb.; pH (1% aqueous solution), 11.8; completely soluble in water. *Uses:* As a chelating agent for polyvalent metallic ions; exhibits a stronger specific chelation for ferric iron in the mildly alkaline range than does VERSENE®. Used in textile processing, liquid detergent formulations, and in the polymerization of synthetic rubber. DOW CHEMICAL CO.

Versene® Fe-3 Powder. An off-white, slightly dusty powder consisting of approx. 90% tetrasodium salt of ethylenediaminetetraacetic acid, technical, and 10% monosodium salt of N,N-di(2-hydroxyethyl) glycine, technical. Bulk density, 7.1 lb./gal.; pH (1% aqueous solution), 11.8; readily soluble in water. *Uses:* As a chelating agent for polyvalent metallic ions; exhibits a stronger specific chelation for ferric iron in the mildly alkaline range than does VERSENE®. Used in textile processing, liquid detergent formulations, and in the polymerization of synthetic rubber. DOW CHEMICAL CO.

Versene Fe-3 Specific®. A concentrated, straw-colored, aqueous solution of the monosodium salt of N,N-di(2-hydroxyethyl)glycine, technical. $C_6H_{12}O_4NNa$; mol.wt. 185.2. Sp.gr. (25/25°C.), 1.20; wt. per gal. (25°C.), 10.0; pH (1% aqueous solution), 12.0; completely soluble in water. *Uses:* As a specific chelating agent for the inactivation of ferric iron in an alkaline medium. Used in textile, rubber, and detergent applications. DOW CHEMICAL CO.

Versene® Powder. A powder form of the tetrasodium salt of ethylenediaminetetraacetic acid, technical. It is an off-white, slightly dusty powder having a bulk density of 5 lb./gal.; solubility in water

(25°C.), 150 g./100 cc.; pH (1% aqueous solution), 11.8. *Uses:* As an efficient chelating agent for the inactivation of divalent and polyvalent metallic ions. Widely used in textile processing, detergent formulations, and metal cleaning. Dow CHEMICAL CO.

Versene® S. A liquid chelating agent specifically designed for the control of iron in aqueous systems containing free caustic. It is a concentrated, straw-colored aqueous solution; sp.gr. (25/25°C.), 1.19; wt. per gal. (25°C.), 9.9; pH (1% aqueous solution), 12.0; completely soluble in water. It is used to chelate free iron in the presence of free caustic. It will not chelate alkaline earth ions under these conditions. Widely used in COTTON-finishing operations. Dow CHEMICAL CO.

Versene® T. A liquid chelating agent for the control of iron and alkaline earth metals in aqueous systems containing free caustic. It is a concentrated, clear, light straw-colored, aqueous solution. Sp.gr. (25/25°C.), 1.19; wt. per gal. (25°C.), 9.9; pH (1% aqueous solution), 12.0; completely soluble in water. *Uses:* For chelating iron in the presence of free caustic. It will also chelate alkaline earth ions under these conditions. Widely used in COTTON-finishing operations, and in scale-removing applications. Dow CHEMICAL CO.

Versenol® 120. A concentrated solution of the trisodium salt of N-hydroxyethylethylenediaminetriacetic acid, technical. $C_{10}H_{15}O_7N_2Na_3$; mol.wt. 344.2. Sp.gr. (25/25°C.), 1.31; wt. per gal. (25°C.), 10.9 lb.; pH (1% aqueous solution), 11.8; completely soluble in water. *Uses:* As an efficient chelating agent for polyvalent metallic ions, especially for ferric ions in an alkaline pH range of 7 to 12. Widely used in textile processing, detergent formulations, and metal cleaning. Dow CHEMICAL CO.

Versenol® Beads. A spray-dried form of the trisodium salt of N-hydroxyethylethylenediaminetriacetic acid, technical. $C_{10}H_{15}O_7N_2Na_3$; mol.wt. 344.2. Bulk density, 2.0 lb./gal.; pH (1% aqueous solution), 11.8; solubility in water (25°C.), 150 g./100 cc. *Uses:* As an efficient chelating agent for polyvalent metallic ions, especially for ferric ions in the alkaline range of 7 to 12. Widely used in the textile industry, in detergent formulations, and in metal cleaning. Dow CHEMICAL CO.

Versenol® Powder. A powdered form of the trisodium salt of N-hydroxyethylethylenediaminetriacetic acid, technical. $C_{10}H_{15}O_7N_2Na_3$; mol.wt. 344.2. It is a white, slightly dusty powder; bulk density, 5.0 lb./gal.; pH (1% aqueous solution), 11.8; solubility in water (25°C.), 150 g./100 cc. *Uses:* As an efficient chelating agent for polyvalent metallic ions, especially for ferric ions in the alkaline range of 7 to 12. Widely used in the textile industry, in detergent formulations, and in metal cleaning. Dow CHEMICAL CO.

Versilube®. Organopolysiloxane compositions which are employed in lubricating and hydraulic applications. These compositions may take the form of fluids or greases and are capable of lubricating at extremes in temp. GENERAL ELECTRIC CO.

Vertelectric[NE]. *See* PETRECO® ELECTROSPHERE[NE] DE-SALTING PROCESS.

Verti-Groove®. (*Supp.* I p. 258). Should have been listed as a registered trademark. CELOTEX CORP.

Ves-Phene®. A germicidal detergent for cleansing and disinfecting floors, sick rooms, operating rooms, shower and locker rooms, and all areas where soil and bacterial contamination are high. VESTAL, INC.

Vespray®. An air sanitizer and deodorizer intended to reduce temporarily the hazard of infection by air-borne micro-organisms and to alleviate obnoxious odors in sick rooms, meeting rooms, kitchens, baths, and other enclosed areas. VESTAL, INC.

Vetrophin®. The trademark for pituitary gonadotrophin, veterinary, for intravenous use.
ABBOTT LABORATORIES

Vez®. A surface tension depressant used to prevent foaming. TRETOLITE CO.

VHPF®. (*HBMTN* p. 603). Now a registered trademark. MILLER CHEMICAL & FERTILIZER CORP.

Vialon®. A line of metallized dyestuffs for the dyeing of polyamide (NYLON, PERLON, etc.) fibers from a neutral bath with ammonium sulfate. They are level dyeing colors with excellent all-around fastness.
Mfg'd by BADISCHE ANILIN-U. SODA-FABRIK AG.
Dist'd by NOVA CHEMICAL CORP.

Vianol® Antioxidant. An antioxidant for use in poultry and animal feeds to preserve vitamins and protect against rancidity. SHELL CHEMICAL CORP.

Vibalt[NE]. (*Supp.* I p. 258). No longer available.
J. B. ROERIG & CO.

Vibresist®[Can.]. *See* ATLAS VIBRESIST®[Can.].

Vibrocap®. Electric blasting caps particularly adapted for seismograph firing circuits.
HERCULES POWDER CO.

Victalube 5810[NE]. Formerly known as 5810[NE] (*Supp.* I p. 271). VICTOR CHEMICAL WORKS

Victawet®. (*HBMTN* p. 604). No longer available.
VICTOR CHEMICAL WORKS

Victawet® 24C. (*Supp.* I p. 259). No longer available. VICTOR CHEMICAL WORKS

Victor Antistatic Agent[NE] A, PCO, 8, 12, 20 *and* 27. Formerly known as ANTISTATIC AGENT[NE] A, PCO, 8, 12, 20 *and* 27 (*Supp.* I p. 17).
VICTOR CHEMICAL WORKS

Victor Stabilizers[NE] 21, 53, 85, 85X *and* 6162X. Formerly known as STABILIZERS[NE] 21, 53, 85, 85X *and* 6162X (*Supp.* I p. 223). VICTOR CHEMICAL WORKS

Victory® Wax. (*HBMTN* p. 604). Should have been listed as a registered trademark.
BARECO WAX CO.

Vi-Daylin®. The trademark for a homogenized mixture of multi-vitamins especially suitable for infants and children. ABBOTT LABORATORIES

Vidine[△]. Same as CHOLINE[△].

Vigoramin®. A multivitamin preparation used in the treatment of multiple vitamin deficiencies. Supplied in the form of spheres.
CONSOLIDATED MIDLAND CORP.

Vike Water Seal[NE]. A soft, plastic, pipe-joint compound for equipment handling water, air, steam, gas, and ammonia. KEYSTONE LUBRICATING CO.

Vikon FPB[NE]. A 55% thermoplastic copolymer emulsion which produces a clear, flexible, slightly elastic film which has high stability to light and heat, remaining essentially unaffected below its softening point. This textile finishing agent increases the tear and tensile strength when used at low conc. in resin finishes. It reacts with the resin and is not removed by washing. It is also a suitable backing for many types of upholstery fabrics. VIKON CHEMICAL CO.

Vikon RL[NE]. A high stability, 55% polyvinyl acetate emulsion which produces a film of relatively high clarity. It was developed especially for textile finishing where it shows unusually good stability in the pad-mangle and during drying on cans. It can also be used successfully for hot calendered finishes. It is especially suited for use on printed fabrics because it does not cause mark-off of the dyestuffs. VIKON CHEMICAL CO.

Vim. See BOSTON VIM.

Vinac. The trade name for a line of polyvinyl acetate resin products. VINAC emulsions are available in various grades, and are used in the formulation of adhesives for wood, fiber, cork, paper, ceramics, leather, metals, and cloth; as binders for paper, pulp, leather, asbestos, ground cork, textile fibers, etc.; for mfg. of coatings for metal, wood, paper, and ceramics; and as bases for emulsion-type paints, primers, and sealers. VINAC beads are used in the formulation of adhesives, inks, coatings, saturants, hot melts, heat seals, chewing gum, plastic bubbles, paints, and other products. Available in low, medium and high polymer grades. COLTON CHEMICAL CO.

Vinactane®. An adjunct in the treatment of tuberculosis. A potent antibiotic produced by an actinomycete, *Act. vinaceus*. Effective against streptomycin-resistant strains of tubercle bacilli. Supplied as VINACTANE® sulfate, a sterile powder to be dissolved in water or isotonic sodium chloride solution. CIBA PHARMACEUTICAL PRODUCTS INC.

Vinalube R-100[NE]. An emulsion of lubricants which is an economical finish for raw stock dyed viscose staple. VIKON CHEMICAL CO.

Vinaplas-Lac. An air-dry coating developed specifically for use on flexible vinyls, plastisols, plastigels, and other highly plasticized casting resins. Applied by spray or brush. It has very little adhesion to smooth metal surfaces and it may be readily stripped from spray masks. Available in clear and pigmented colors. SCHWARTZ CHEMICAL CO.

Vincul[NE]. (*HBMTN* p. 605). No longer available. PROTECTIVE COATINGS, INC.

Vinethene®. An inhalation anesthetic for operations of short duration. Principally vinyl ether ($CH_2=CH-O-CH=CH_2$) a clear, almost colorless liquid with a characteristic odor, boiling at 28.3°C. VINETHENE® is actually approx. 96% vinyl ether, 3.5% alcohol and 0.01% oxidation inhibitor. MERCK SHARP & DOHME

Vinobel®. A medicinal, in tablet form, designed to improve the control of postencephalitic Parkinsonism. Each red-coated tablet contains 0.4 mg. and each orange-coated tablet contains 0.8 mg. of the total alkaloids of belladonna root obtained by extraction with wine. WM. S. MERRELL CO.

Vinol. A line of polyvinyl alcohols available in two general series: PA (partially acetylated), and FH (fully hydrolized). The PA series is available in low, medium, and high viscosities; and the FH in low, medium, medium-high and high viscosities. *Uses:* In the formulation of high wet-strength adhesives for paper; as binders for ceramic bodies to improve green strength and extrusion properties; as binders for non-woven fabrics and felts; as textile sizes and in textile finishes; as paper sizes and for paper coatings; as protective coatings; as cast films for packaging and wrapping purposes; and as emulsifying agents for making oil-in-water emulsions. COLTON CHEMICAL CO.

Vinylairé®. A cellular polyvinyl chloride available in standard sheets, 26″ x 52″, in thicknesses from ⅛″ to 2″; and in larger sheets on special order. Density, 7 lb./cu.ft.; thermal conductivity, 0.23 B.t.u.-inch/hr. x sp.ft. x °F.; resistant to water, body acids, fruit juices, dilute acids, mineral oil, dilute alkalis; not resistant to gasoline, and carbon tetrachloride. *Use:* As a protective padding in sporting goods equipment for football, baseball, hockey, boxing, rugby, auto and boat racing, etc. It is a "slow memory" material, *i.e.*, it gives way slowly under impact, and absorbs the force of the blow. DURA FLEX CO.

Vinyl-Cote[NE]. Corrosion-resistant vinyl resin coatings for industrial maintenance, marine, and railway finishes. GLIDDEN CO.

Vinylfoam. A vinyl plastic foam material for use as a cushioning and padding in furniture, bedding, transportation seating, etc. It is also used for numerous other applications and products including gaskets, filters, shock mountings, cleaning sponges, brassiere shapes, toys, wall coverings, laminated structures, clothing and apparel padding, and automotive crash fronts. It does not oxidize, harden, or dry out; has high tear strength and dimensional stability, good fire resistance, and excellent moisture, mildew, and chemical resistance. Available in white and in colors, in sheets up to 72″ wide and 5″ thick. ELASTOMER CHEMICAL CORP.

Vinylith®. The trademark for a line of vinyl-base finishes. FIDELITY CHEMICAL PRODUCTS CORP.

Violamine®. A group of red-violet acid dyestuffs for coloring WOOL and leather. GENERAL DYESTUFF CO.

Virbonite®. A nitro-carbo-nitrate explosive especially adapted for use in seismographic exploration. HERCULES POWDER CO.

Virgo® Descaling Salt. A mixture of salts, which, when fused, has the property of chemically removing scale and other impurities on metal surfaces. The impurities can then be very readily removed with no measurable attack on the base metal. Supplied as light blue flakes with a m.p. of approx. 600°F. HOOKER ELECTROCHEMICAL CO.

Virgo® Molten Cleaner. A salt designed to desand, degraphitize, and de-enamel and perform other miscellaneous salt-bath operations on metals. Supplied in the form of a green flake material.
HOOKER ELECTROCHEMICAL CO.

Viscasil®. Organopolysiloxane fluids of varying viscosities which can be used as damping and hydraulic media. Such fluids are also used in polishes and other coating compositions. GENERAL ELECTRIC CO.

Visco 77. (*HBMTN* p. 607). Now a product of INDIANA COMMERCIAL FILTERS CORP., successor to HONAN-CRANE CORP.

Viscolan 14[NE]. An oil that is used in viscose RAYON mfg. to improve the chemical and physical properties of the fibers. It is especially recommended for use in tire-cord mfg. since it increases the tensile strength of the fibers appreciably.
PIONEER CHEMICAL WORKS, INC.

Viscolan C[NE]. An oil used in the mfg. of viscose RAYON and CELLOPHANE, to improve physical and chemical properties. With this oil, the ripening time of viscose can be shortened by 12 to 20 hr.
PIONEER CHEMICAL WORKS, INC.

Viscosine®. Oily and non-oily viscous liquids for use on dust-control surfaces for dust-retention purposes. AMERICAN AIR FILTER CO.

Visionaire®. The trademark for a line of prefabricated homes. UNITED STATES STEEL HOMES, INC.

Vistex® with Teflon®. A chemically resistant and stable, high-strength, resilient sheet gasket stock of tetrafluoroethylene resin reinforced with polyester fiber felt. It is characterized by exceptional resistance to lateral deformation or "cold flow" under high bolt torque or line pressures. Suitable for use with ASA flat face pipe flanges under severe corrosive chemical conditions from −100°F. to +400°F. Type NES is rated Class I stable for high-test hydrogen peroxide service. VISTEX® is a registered trademark of AMERICAN FELT CO.; TEFLON® is a registered trademark of E. I. DUPONT DE NEMOURS & CO.
AMERICAN FELT CO.

Vistone®. The trademark for a line of oiliness agents used in industrial oils. ENJAY CO.

Vitab B-Complex Extract. A vitamin compound composed of B-complex vitamins from yeast and rice bran in a malt extract base. Sp.gr. 1.3–1.33; pH of 2% solution in distilled water, 4.0–4.5; total solids, 60–62%. Contains per ml., 0.15–0.20 mg. THIAMIN, 0.01–0.02 mg. RIBOFLAVIN, 2.0–2.5 mg. NIACIN, 0.15–0.20 mg. VITAMIN B_6, 0.275–0.300 mg. PANTOTHENIC acid, 8.0–9.0 mg. choline, 6.0–7.5 mg. inositol, and 1.2–3.5 mcg. biotin. CHARLES BOWMAN & CO.

Vita-Dulcet®. The trademark for a multi-vitamin preparation in the form of brown, oblong-shaped sugar tablets with a modified cocoa flavor.
ABBOTT LABORATORIES

Vita-Fresh®. (*HBMTN* p. 608). Formerly mfg'd by U. S. FINISHING CO.; now a product of USF-ASPINOOK FINISHING DIV., GERA CORP.

Vita-Kaps®. The trademark for multi-vitamin tablets used as a dietary supplement.
ABBOTT LABORATORIES

Vita-King®. The trademark for a vitamin supplement for animal diets. ABBOTT LABORATORIES

Vitalized®. (*HBMTN* p. 608). Formerly mfg'd by U. S. FINISHING CO.; now a product of USF-ASPINOOK FINISHING DIV., GERA CORP.

Vitalized Cleaner. A high-sudsing liquid soap cleanser for use on floors and walls. It is particularly useful for removing tough, built-up dirt and grease from concrete floors. J. I. HOLCOMB MFG. CO.

Vital Sugar. (*HBMTN* p. 608). No longer available. VITAMIN PRODUCTS CO.

Vitamin H△. *Same as* BIOTIN△.

Vita-Pine. A soap-base cleaner for use on any floors except rubber. It contains pine oil which readily dissolves and removes rubber burns.
J. I. HOLCOMB MFG. CO.

Vita-Proof®. (*HBMTN* p. 610). Formerly mfg'd by U. S. FINISHING CO.; now a product of USF-ASPINOOK FINISHING DIV., GERA CORP.

VitaStain. 2,3,5-Triphenyltetrazolium chloride. $(C_6H_5)_3N_4Cl$; mol. wt. 322.5; m.p. 245°C.; color, white to pale yellow; form, crystalline powder. A reagent for the determination of germinability of seeds; for staining the cambrium layer of living twigs; for staining yeasts, bacteria, and a wide variety of living tissue. ARAPAHOE CHEMICALS INC.

Viterra® Tastitabs®. A vitamin-mineral preparation containing VITAMINS A, B_1, B_2, B_6, B_{12}, C, D, NIACINAMIDE, calcium pantothenate, cobalt, copper, iodine, iron, potassium, molybdenum, manganese, magnesium, and zinc. J. B. ROERIG & CO.

Vitex®. A dry, alkaline detergent, in granular form, used to neutralize the acid components of dirt. It thus acts as a soap builder by increasing the detergent value of the soap. PENNSYLVANIA SALT MFG. CO.

Vi-Thyro®. A thyroid preparation, each soluble capsule of which contains 60 mg. thyroid, together with VITAMINS A, B_1, B_2, B_{12}, C, D, E, NIACINAMIDE, calcium pantothenate, choline, inositol, methionine, cobalt, iodine, magnesium and manganese. Used in the treatment of hypothyroidism; and menstrual menopausal disorders, infertility, mental depressive states, and other conditions where thyroid is indicated. J. B. ROERIG & CO.

Vitrafros®. (*Supp.* I p. 260). Now a registered trademark. VICTOR CHEMICAL WORKS

Vitrenamel®. *See* U.S.S.® VITRENAMEL®.

Vitreosil®. (*HBMTN* p. 610). Now mfg'd by THERMAL AMERICAN FUSED QUARTZ CO., successor to THERMAL SYNDICATE, LTD.

Vitron® Roving. A glass fiber reinforcement material for use with epoxy and silicone resins. This roving material is treated with a special sizing material known as VITRON® SIZING. The roving possesses excellent adhesion when used with these resins for the production of such products as reinforced plastic pipe, pipe couplings and other items which require strong glass-to-resin adhesion. It may also be used with polyester resins to produce rod stock of very high translucency. L.O.F. GLASS FIBERS CO.

Vitrosol®. An alkaline compound with a high pH, designed for use in soak cleaning operations prior to vitreous enameling. DIVERSEY CORP.

VPI®. (*HBMTN* p. 611). No longer available.
SHELL CHEMICAL CORP.

Vulcanex®. (*HBMTN* p. 615). No longer available.
E. I. DU PONT DE NEMOURS & CO.

Vulcan® Gage and Die Steel. An air-hardening tool and die steel possessing good abrasion resistance. It is a deep hardening steel which has excellent nondeforming properties. Typical analysis: 1.00% carbon, 5.25% chromium, 1.15% molybdenum, and 0.25% vanadium. VULCAN CRUCIBLE STEEL CO.

Vulcosal[NR]. An industrial grade of salicylic acid that has been treated to prevent dusting. Used as a retarder in the vulcanization of rubber.
DOW CHEMICAL CO.

Vulkene®. Filled, cross-linked polyolefin compositions, such as polyethylene, useful in molding applications and in other industrial arts. Carbon black filled, cross-linked polyethylene identified by this name can be used in pipe mfg. to give products which are heat-resistant and resistant to stress cracking in environments causing such cracking.
GENERAL ELECTRIC CO.

Vultac®. (*HBMTN* p. 616). Now a product of PENNSYLVANIA SALT MFG. CO., which has absorbed SHARPLES CHEMICALS, INC.

Vultra C®. Organic chemicals which are sulfides of phenols and substituted phenols, and are useful as plasticizers, vulcanizing agents, and age resisters in the mfg. of rubber and rubber products.
PENNSYLVANIA SALT MFG. CO.

Vyflex® L-10 Lining. A plastic lining material for tanks. It is resistant to most acids, including chromic, hydrobromic, hydrochloride, hydrofluoric, nitric, phosphoric, and sulfuric; ammonium, calcium, potassium, and sodium hydroxides; electroplating solutions and salts; and many solvents. It is not recommended for use with acetone, ketones, ethers, esters, and aromatic and chlorinated hydrocarbons.
KAYKOR INDUSTRIES, INC.

Vygen® 100. A general-purpose vinyl resin for calendering, extruding, and molding operations. It has excellent heat and light stability. Sp.gr. 1.4; bulk density, 21 lb./cu.ft.; loss in wt. on heating, 0.5%.
GENERAL TIRE & RUBBER CO.

Vynafoam®. The trademark for an expandable vinyl plastisol. INTERCHEMICAL CORP., FINISHES DIV.

Vysheen®. (*HBMTN* p. 616). No longer available.
GOODALL FABRICS, INC.

W

W[NR]. The trade name for a line of stainless steel.
UNITED STATES STEEL CORP.

W4X. A chromium-molybdenum-tungsten-vanadium hot-work die steel furnished in both annealed and heat-treated conditions. A. FINKL & SONS CO.

W-13 Stabilizer®. (*HBMTN* p. 616). Should have been listed as a registered trademark.
AMERICAN MAIZE PRODUCTS CO.

W-167. A pressure-sensitive-type adhesive designed specifically for bonding polyethylene to a wide variety of surfaces. Can also be used to bond vinyl film to various surfaces but it is not satisfactory for use with vinyl containing migratory plasticizers. Consists of a rubber-resin complex in a low boiling aliphatic petroleum solvent. Applied by brush, dip, spray, or roller coat. Has excellent water resistance.
WILROSS PRODUCTS CO.

W.A. 58[NR]. (*HBMTN* p. 616). No longer available.
VICTOR CHEMICAL WORKS

Wall Mate. A polyvinyl emulsion paint for interior and exterior walls—plaster, brick, stucco, concrete, cement block, adobe, asbestos board and shingles, stone, magnesite, asphalt, creosoted or tarred surfaces, wood, and metal. It is practically odorless; and the dry film is washable.
KLEE WATERPROOFING CORP.

Wall-Tex®. (*HBMTN* p. 616). Should have been listed as a registered trademark.
COLUMBUS COATED FABRICS CORP.

Warrior. See BOSTON WARRIOR.

Wascofilm[NR]. A pure polyethylene moisture barrier supplied in rolls. Waterproof, lightweight, and air resistant; flexible at low temps.
WASCO PRODUCTS, INC.

Wascolite Showerwall[NR]. A prefabricated tub enclosure with sliding panels of corrugated ACRYLITE. Available in four sizes as a tub enclosure or stall shower. WASCO PRODUCTS, INC.

Wascoseal[NR]. A plastic vapor barrier for concealed flashing purposes. Resistant to acids, alkalis and caustics. Applied dry by simple spot bonding to the structure. WASCO PRODUCTS, INC.

Washita Oilstone[△]. See OILSTONE[△].

Water Airlube No. 50. (*HBMTN* p. 618). No longer available. PARKER APPLIANCE CO.

Waterleaf[△]. See PARCHMENT[△].

Water-Skipper®. A water repellent, in an aerosol spray can, for the treatment of natural or synthetic fabrics, protective clothing, shoes, felt, paper, metal, or wood. It renders porous materials water repellent and nonporous materials waterproof. Used for the treatment of workman's clothing, industrial equipment, electrical wiring, and equipment exposed to rain or snow. It reduces or eliminates rust on metal equipment due to excessive moisture. It is also used as a special surface treatment for calender, embossing rolls, and curing cans to prevent sticking. It contains high melt waxes and silicones and a new tung oil derivative plus FREON. Available in 12-oz. and 3-lb. containers. TEXTILE ADJUNCTS CORP.

Watersphere®. A modern elevated water tank of welded construction used to provide gravity water pressure for general service and fire protection in municipal and private water systems. Installations for municipal service are built in accordance with the

American Water Works Association Specifications, and those for automatic sprinkler service meet Fire Insurance Underwriter's requirements.

CHICAGO BRIDGE & IRON CO.

Water-Wonder[NB]. A flutterboard of expanded polyvinyl chloride (SPONGEX® PLASTIC) for swimming instruction and as water safety aid.

B. F. GOODRICH SPONGE PRODUCTS DIV.

Waukegan®. The trademark for a galvanized 4-point (half-round point) barbed wire, with barbs spaced 5" apart.

UNITED STATES STEEL CORP.

Wax-Cool, #130®. A water-dispersible coolant consisting of a blend of waxes in aqueous emulsion form. Designed for machining and grinding of non-ferrous metals such as aluminum, copper and brass, and the more ductile series of stainless steel. It is supplied as a concentrate, and can be diluted with 10 to 30 parts of water.

S. C. JOHNSON & SON

Wax-Cut®. A metal-cutting lubricant consisting of a blend of waxes suspended in clear oil. The material is added to cutting oils to provide better lubrication. For use in automatic screw machines, milling machines, broach grinders, gear machines, turret lathes, and all other machines where cutting oils are used.

S. C. JOHNSON & SON

Wax-Draw®. An all-purpose metal-working lubricant containing specially processed waxes. Available in wet- and dry-film types, and both can be applied by spraying, brushing, dipping or roller coating. Can be used on ferrous metals, stainless steel, and non-ferrous metals. For use in all press-working operations, drawing and forming tube drawing, impact extrusion, stretch forming, cold heading, coining and swaging, tapping, drilling and reaming.

S. C. JOHNSON & SON

Wax Emulsion WB[NB]. (*Supp.* I p. 262). No longer available.

LAUREL SOAP MFG. CO.

Wax Emulsion WG[NB]. A stable wax emulsion used on COTTON yarns to increase lubricity and softness.

LAUREL SOAP MFG. CO.

Wax-Shine®. Wax dispersions designed to reduce shrinkage and provide an attractive, natural shine on fruits and vegetables. They can be applied to either wet or dry fruit and vegetables. For use on tomatoes, cucumbers, peppers, squash, watermelons, apples, pears and other fruits and vegetables.

S. C. JOHNSON & SON

Wax-Strip®. A liquid, concentrated cleaner which, when mixed with hot water, effectively softens and removes old waxes, finishes and dirt from floors. Composed of neutral soaps and detergents, and designed especially for removal of the highly water-resistant floor finishes. Safe to use on all floors, including rubber and asphalt tile.

S. C. JOHNSON & SON

Waxtra®. A self-polishing floor finish composed of hard vegetable waxes, resins and volatile ingredients. It dries to a high luster, has slip-retardant properties, excellent dirt and water-spotting resistance, and can withstand repeated damp moppings and buffing without diminishing gloss. Recommended for use on asphalt, rubber and vinyl tile, linoleum, terrazzo and sealed wood and cork.

S. C. JOHNSON & SON

WCC[NB]. A hot-work die steel containing 4.25% each of tungsten, chromium, and cobalt, and 2.10% vanadium. This unusual steel outperforms standard 9.50% tungsten hot-work die steels on most applications, especially at elevated temps. Its high vanadium content contributes to its hot hardness properties and materially increases its resistance to wear and thermal fatigue. WCC steel is more resistant to heat checking than any of the standard tungsten hot-work die steels. Typical uses are for hot extrusion dies; steel, copper or brass, permanent molds for brass casting; hot forging die inserts; and hotpress dies for both steel and brass.

VANADIUM-ALLOYS STEEL CO.

Wear-Arc® 3-IP, 6-IP, and 12-IP. A line of iron powder, low-hydrogen, hard surfacing and build-up welding alloys. The three grades have the following composition:

Wear-Arc Grade	Elements other than iron, %				
	C	Mn	Cr	Si	Mo
3-IP	0.30–0.40	1.10–1.40	1.75–2.25	—	—
6-IP	2.25–2.50	0.75–1.00	6.50–8.00	1.00–1.25	—
12-IP	3.25–3.50	2.50–3.00	12.50–13.50	1.25–1.50	0.90–1.00

ALLOY RODS CO.

Wear-Arc Super WH®. An arc welding electrode for making superior wear resistance welds on manganese and carbon steel parts subjected to severe impact and abrasion. Hardness (Rockwell C), 35.

ALLOY RODS CO.

Wear-Arc WH®. An arc welding electrode for build-up and high-strength welding of manganese and carbon steel parts subjected to severe impact, abrasion, and compression. Tensile strength, 95,000–100,000 lb./sq.in.; yield strength, 75,000–79,500 lb./sq.in.; hardness (Rockwell C), 25–32.

ALLOY RODS CO.

Weatherite® Sheating. A combination insulating and structural sheathing board that is integrally impregnated throughout with an asphaltic compound. It provides a high degree of protection against wind and water penetration, although it is not a vapor barrier. For horizontal application, it is furnished with a "V-Tite" joint, which is designed to provide max. resistance to the infiltration of dirt and moisture.

JOHNS-MANVILLE SALES CORP.

Weedmaster[NB]. (*HBMTN* p. 620). No longer available.

MICHIGAN CHEMICAL CO.

Weednix[NE]. A selective contact weedkiller especially suitable for use in nurseries and on vegetable crops. LARVACIDE PRODUCTS, INC.

Weedrench[NE]. A concentrate for preparing a drench to kill weed seeds before planting of crops.
LARVACIDE PRODUCTS, INC.

Wehrbest[NE]. A type of steel casting that is very suitable for abrasion-resisting applications, such as bucket teeth or parts, crusher liners, conveyor links, etc. WEHR STEEL CO.

Weld-Crete®. A liquid agent for permanently bonding new concrete to old concrete or directly to brick, wood, MASONITE, gypsum block, metal, ceramic tile, or many other surfaces. It eliminates the need for chipping, drilling, roughening. and working or scarifying of the concrete base. One gal. covers 250–400 sq.ft. of surface. LARSEN PRODUCTS CORP.

Weldfast®. (*Supp*. I p. 263). This product is manufactured by the FIBERCAST CORP., owner of the trademark. It is distributed by the YOUNGSTOWN STEEL PRODUCTS CO.; the YOUNGSTOWN STEEL PRODUCTS CO. OF CALIFORNIA; and the CONTINENTAL SUPPLY CO.

Weld-O-Bond[NE]. An agent for bonding cement or plaster to any surface—marble, glass, stone, brick, concrete, wood, MASONITE®, asbestos, etc. Applied by brush or spray, it dries in 40 min. The bond is non-toxic; will not oxidize, crack or craze; and is unaffected by humidity or alkalinity of lime, cement, or plaster. Bond strength, over 20 tons per sq.ft.
CALIFORNIA STUCCO PRODUCTS OF N. E., INC.

Weldron[NE]. A vinyl plastic resembling leather. It is used as an upholstery material.
UNITED STATES PLYWOOD CORP.

Westerner®. The trademark for a line of prefabricated homes. UNITED STATES STEEL HOMES, INC.

Wet-Tex®. (*HBMTN* p. 622). No longer available.
NIAGARA CHEMICAL DIV.,
FOOD MACHINERY & CHEMICAL CORP.

Weytone F P[NE]. A concentrated, liquid flame-retarding and weighting agent. It produces excellent flame-retardance on cellulosic fibers and SILK, imparts a desirable weighted hand, and does not cause harshness. It is anionic and compatible with most common types of anionic finishing agents.
TEX-CHEM CO.

White Beauty®. A registered trademark for flaked hydrogenated cottonseed oil used in shortening and oleomargarine. ANDERSON, CLAYTON & CO. FOODS DIV.

White "B.V.M." Wax[NE]. A wax suitable for cosmetic and other applications. M.p. 154°F.; acid no. 29; saponification no. 79.
INTERNATIONAL WAX REFINING CO.

White Dammar△. *See* COPAL△.

White Gum△. *Same as* SANDARAC△.

White Magic®. (*HBMTN* p. 409). Now a registered trademark. OIL BASE, INC.

White Streak. A powdered chemical abrasive cleanser for use on painted walls, woodwork, floors, porcelain, tile, marble, granite, and mosaic.
J. I. HOLCOMB MFG. CO.

Whitetan® **B**. (*HBMTN* p. 623). No longer available. AMERICAN CYANAMID CO.

Wilson-Snyder®. The trademark for a line of reciprocating and centrifugal pumps for oil-field and industrial use. UNITED STATES STEEL CORP.,
OIL WELL SUPPLY DIV.

Windsor Cutting Oil 910[NE]; **Windsor Cutting Oil 6150**[NE]; **Windsor Special Base**[NE]; *and* **Windsor T-G Grinding Oil**[NE]. (*HBMTN* p. 623). Should have been listed as WINSOR® CUTTING OIL 910, WINSOR® CUTTING OIL 6150, WINSOR® SPECIAL BASE, *and* WINSOR® T-G GRINDING OIL.
F. E. ANDERSON OIL CO.

Winsor® **Cutting Oil 910, Winsor**® **Cutting Oil 6150, Winsor**® **Special Base,** *and* **Winsor**® **T-G Grinding Oil**. Incorrectly listed as WINDSOR CUTTING OIL 910[NE]; WINDSOR CUTTING OIL 6150[NE]; WINDSOR SPECIAL BASE[NE]; *and* WINDSOR T-G GRINDING OIL[NE] (*HBMTN* p. 623).
F. E. ANDERSON OIL CO.

Wintergreen Oil△. *Same as* SWEET BIRCH OIL△.

Witcizer®. The trademark name for a line of esters of fatty acids and dibasic acids used principally as plasticizers for thermoplastic resins and lacquers, and as textile lubricants, metal-drawing compounds and mold-release agents. Included in the line are:

Witcizers No.	Chemical name	Formula	Mol. wt.	Description	Boiling point, °C.	Sp. gr.	Flash point (COC), °F.	Refractive index
100	Butyl oleate (tech.)	$C_{15}H_{33}COOC_4H_9$	338	Clear, oily liquid, with mild odor	220–225 (15 mm. Hg)	0.865	350	1.429
101	Butyl oleate (premium grade)	$C_{15}H_{33}COOC_4H_9$	338	Clear, oily odorless liquid	210–220 (15 mm. Hg)	0.865	350	1.429
200	Butyl stearate (tech.)	$C_{17}H_{35}COOC_4H_9$	340	Clear, oily liquid with mild odor	220–225 (25 mm. Hg)	0.860	370	1.442

Witcizers No.	Chemical name	Formula	Mol. wt.	Description	Boiling point °C.	Sp. gr.	Flash point (COC), °F.	Refractive index
201	Butyl stearate (cosmetic grade)	$C_{17}H_{35}COOC_4H_9$	340	Clear, oily liquid with faint odor	220–225 (25 mm. Hg)	0.860	370	1.442
300	Dibutyl phthalate	$C_6H_4(COOC_4H_9)_2$	278	Clear, colorless liquid	206 (20 mm. Hg)	1.045	352	1.491
312	Di-2-ethylhexyl phthalate	$C_6H_4(COOC_8H_{17})_2$	390	Clear, colorless liquid	229 (5 mm. Hg)	0.986	425	1.486
313	Di-isooctyl phthalate	$C_6H_4(COOC_8H_{17})_2$	390	Clear, colorless liquid	234 (4 mm. Hg)	0.984	430	1.486

WITCO CHEMICAL CO.

Witco®. The trademark of WITCO CHEMICAL CO. for their line of industrial chemicals.

Witco® Blancal. (*HBMTN* p. 625). No longer available. WITCO CHEMICAL CO.

Witcogum®. (*HBMTN* p. 625). No longer available. WITCO CHEMICAL CO.

Witcolac®. (*HBMTN* p. 625). No longer available. WITCO CHEMICAL CO.

Witco Stabilizers #40 and #70[NE]. (*HBMTN* p. 625). No longer available. WITCO CHEMICAL CO.

Witcote #4[NE]. A non-toxic, bituminous mastic compound for automobile undercoating. Prevents rust and corrosion, acts as a sound deadener, seals cracks and seams, and insulates the floor. WITCOTE #4 is applied with standard spray equipment, and is approved by the Underwriters Laboratories.
WITCOTE CHEMICAL CO.

Witcote® #100. (*HBMTN* p. 625). No longer available. WITCO CHEMICAL CO.

Witcote® #202. (*HBMTN* p. 625). *Now known as* PIONEER #202[NE]. WITCO CHEMICAL CO.

Witcote® #301. (*HBMTN* p. 625). *Now known as* PIONEER #301[NE]. WITCO CHEMICAL CO.

Witcote® #500. (*HBMTN* p. 625). *Now known as* PIONEER #500[NE]. WITCO CHEMICAL CO.

Witcote® #501. (*HBMTN* p. 626). No longer available. WITCO CHEMICAL CO.

Witcote® #601. (*HBMTN* p. 626). No longer available. WITCO CHEMICAL CO.

Witcote® #602. (*HBMTN* p. 626). No longer available. WITCO CHEMICAL CO.

Witcote® #607 and #609. (*HBMTN* p. 626). *Now known as* PIONEER #607 *and* #609[NE].
WITCO CHEMICAL CO.

Witcote® #700. (*HBMTN* p. 626). No longer available. WITCO CHEMICAL CO.

Witte®. The trademark for a line of internal-combustion engines and electrical generating units powered by internal-combustion engines.
UNITED STATES STEEL CORP., OIL WELL SUPPLY DIV.

Wittox®. A line of naphthenate fungicides and preservatives including:
8% WITTOX C. A solution of copper soap of naphthenic acid in mineral spirits. A dark-green, viscous liquid; completely soluble in petroleum solvents; insoluble in water. Used as a fungicide and preservative for wood and fabric; and as an ingredient of anti-fouling ship paints. Metal content, 8%.
2.2% WITTOX C. Same as 8% WITTOX C but with lower metal content.
8% WITTOX Z. A yellow solution of zinc naphthenate in mineral spirits. Metal content, 8%. Used as a fungicide and water-repellent for wood, textiles, and cordage to render them rot resistant and mildew resistant. WITCO CHEMICAL CO.

Wizard®. An all-vegetable, fully hydrogenated shortening for use in baking, frying and pastry making.
ANDERSON, CLAYTON & CO. FOODS DIV.

Wood Oil[△]. Same as GURJUN BALSAM[△].

Wood Particle Board[△]. Same as PARTICLE BOARD[△].

Wood Rosin[△]. See ROSIN[△].

Woodside Rapid Carburizers. A line of carburizing compounds for case-hardening steel. They are of two general types: charcoal base, and non-burning. The charcoal-base compounds are made by coating hardwood charcoal and coke granules with the carbonates of barium, sodium and calcium. These coatings are bound to the granules with organic, oil, or water binders. The non-burning carburizers are made by coking a mixture of energizing chemicals, such as barium and calcium carbonate, and low-ash, low-sulfur coal, then crushing and screening the coke in size. PARK CHEMICAL CO.

Wood-Trim[NE]. A thin veneer backed by paper or fabric for edging plywood and other panels.
UNITED STATES PLYWOOD CORP.

Wool△. The fine, soft, curly hair or fleece of sheep and other animals. It is composed principally of a complex protein, keratin, that is characterized by its relatively high sulfur content of 2–4%. Dilute mineral acids do not affect Wool, but caustic soda solutions, even in such dilute concentrations as 3% or less, rapidly destroy it at boiling and lower temps. Sheeps Wool is one of the most important commercial fibers available. *Uses:* For the production of a variety of Wool fabrics, and carpets; as an insulation material; as a packing material; etc.

Wool Grease△. *See* Degras△.

Wormol®. (*Supp.* I p. 265). No longer available.
General Chemical Div.,
Allied Chemical & Dye Corp.

WP-134. A general-purpose, solvent-type adhesive that is characterized by its outstanding resistance to water, alkali, and aliphatic solvents. Applied by brush, dip or spray; five min. of heating at 200°F. and a pressure of 300 lb./sq.in. is sufficient to remove most of the solvent and give a strong bond. *Uses:* For bonding fiberglass to boilers, vinyl to wood and metal, felt to wood, metal, cement-asbestos board and innumerable other items that require a heat-, water-, and alkali-resistant bond. Wilross Products Co.

WP-758. A two-part adhesive consisting of a liquid and a filler containing vulcanizing agents. The liquid portion is a latex-type elastomer modified with synthetic resinous materials that are converted when mixed with the vulcanizing agents. The resulting plastic mass cures in about 24 hr. to a tough, flexible, black, waterproof adhesive mass that adheres to practically all types of surfaces even when moist or damp. *Uses:* For bonding metal, glass, cloth, wood, rubber, plastics, etc. to themselves and to each other.
Wilross Products Co.

WP-861. A water-base, synthetic resin-rubber complex, emulsion adhesive. A brown-colored material, the adhesive viscosity of which can be varied from a thick mush to a thin liquid without affecting the adhesive bond. It can be applied by brush, spray, dip, or roller-coat methods; both surfaces to be bonded should be coated with this adhesive; one of the surfaces to be bonded should be porous to permit absorption and subsequent evaporation of the water. *Uses:* For bonding a wide variety of materials including vinyl film to paper, wood, Masonite®, fiberglass, Celotex®, etc. It can also be used to bond metal and metal foils to these materials.
Wilross Products Co.

WW Hotwork[NR]. This steel was developed to give maximum resistance to heat checking combined with good wear-resisting qualities at high temps. In attaining these qualities, it was necessary to sacrifice the ability to attain high strength levels at low temp. Thus, application is limited to operations where relatively low levels of stress are encountered. WW Hotwork has good resistance to tempering at high temp. It has also been employed successfully for holders to contain carbide and cast alloy extrusion-die inserts. It has proved exceptional in aluminum die-casting dies, but its economic justification in this application is limited to extremely long runs and the die design. It has also given excellent runs on zinc die-casting nozzles. Vanadium-Alloys Steel Co.

Wyandotte 85[NR]. An acid-type cleaner specifically developed for fulfilling railroad requirements. It is a brownish, dustless, granular product, 100% soluble in water. Contains acid salts, inhibitors, wetting and emulsifying agents. *Use:* For exterior maintenance cleaning of passenger cars—painted surfaces, glass, and stainless steel. Wyandotte Chemicals Corp.,
J. B. Ford Div.

Wyandotte 397[NR]. An inhibited low-foaming, alkaline cleaner for use in spray washers or steam guns. Contains silicates, phosphates, carbonates, and synthetic detergents. It is non-corrosive to steel, aluminum, magnesium, copper, brass, and other metals. *Use:* For cleaning aluminum and other aircraft parts. Often used in aircraft engine overhaul cleaning and carbon removal. Wyandotte Chemicals Corp.,
J. B. Ford Div.

Wyandotte 418[NR]. A soluble, heavy-soil detergent for laundries. Wyandotte Chemicals Corp.,
J. B. Ford Div.

Wyandotte 453[NR]. A dry powdered and granular alkaline steam cleaning compound for removing all types of soils encountered on aircraft exteriors, engines, decks, etc. Contains alkaline silicates, phosphates, and carbonates, plus a synthetic wetting agent. Total silicates (as SiO_2), 12%; total phosphates (as P_2O_5), 2%. Wyandotte Chemicals Corp.,
J. B. Ford Div.

Wyandotte 548[NR]. An all-soluble, mild alkaline cleaner for painted and other surfaces of passenger cars and diesel locomotives.
Wyandotte Chemicals Corp.,
J. B. Ford Div.

Wyandotte 608[NR]. A corrosion-inhibiting buffer used in the precleaning of buffed zinc die castings and other metals to control pH and prevent staining. It is a pale buff, granular powder that contains phosphate buffering salts and chromate-type corrosion inhibitors.
Wyandotte Chemicals Corp.,
J. B. Ford Div.

Wyandotte 979[NR]. A rust remover and metal conditioner. Wyandotte Chemicals Corp.,
J. B. Ford Div.

Wyandotte Better Blend Soda®. A U.S.P. grade of powdered bicarbonate of soda, that has been treated with food-grade tri-calcium phosphate to provide easy flowability. *Uses:* As an important ingredient in self-rising flours, baking powders, and bakery products; and as a blowing agent in sponge rubber.
Wyandotte Chemicals Corp.,
Michigan Alkali Div.

X

X-Cell Super X[NR]. A solder similar in properties to "50–50" solder yet lower in cost. *Use:* For copper roofing and flashings, tanks, fire-protection equipment, electrical equipment, motors, generators, radio and television equipment, food-processing equipment, etc. It also finds use in the soldering of stainless steel, since it resembles stainless steel in color more closely than ordinary solder. Hewitt Metals Corp.

X-Cide[NE]. An organic industrial bactericide for treating waters used in water-flood secondary recovery operations in crude oil production.
TRETOLITE CO.

XLO Die Blocks®[Can.]. A line of chromium-nickel-molybdenum die blocks designed especially for the drop-forge industry. Available in a wide range of sizes and tempers.
ATLAS STEELS LTD.

X-Trude®. (*Supp.* I p. 267). This product is mfg'd by the FIBERCAST CORP., owner of the trademark. It is dist'd by the YOUNGSTOWN STEEL PRODUCTS CO.; the YOUNGSTOWN STEEL PRODUCTS CO. OF CALIFORNIA; and the CONTINENTAL SUPPLY CO.

X-Var®. A chemical-type insulation and spot stripper, designed to remove the insulation from wires coated with enamels, FORMVAR, FORMEX, NYLON, etc. The wire is merely dipped into the appropriate type of X-VAR, depending on the type of coating to be removed, allowed to stand in the air for a few seconds after withdrawal, and then wiped clean.
FIDELITY CHEMICAL PRODUCTS CORP.

XXX-1[NE], **XXX-35**[NE], *and* **XXX-317 Oil**[NE]. (*HBMTN* p. 630). No longer available.
BAKER CASTOR OIL CO.

Y

Yacca Gum△. Same as ACAROID RESIN△.

Yamtox[NE]. (*HBMTN* p. 630). No longer available.
PLANT PRODUCTS CORP.

Yarmor®. The trademark for a pine oil.
HERCULES POWDER CO.

Yellow for Green[NE]. A chrome yellow pigment especially designed for use with blue pigments in paints, enamels, printing inks, and plastics to make green products. Chrome greens made with it and iron blue have better durability and are less expensive than those made with conventional chrome yellow.
SHERWIN-WILLIAMS CO.

Yellow Protopet® **No. 2.** (*HBMTN* p. 631). Now a registered trademark.
L. SONNEBORN SONS, INC.

Yellow Resin△. Same as ROSIN△.

Yerbine. See MALTO® YERBINE.

Ylang-Ylang Oil△. *Also known as* CANANGA OIL△. An essential oil distilled from the flowers of *Canangium adorata*, a tree cultivated in the East Indies, Madagascar, and the Philippines. Contains geraniol and linalool esters of acetic and benzoic acids; p-cresol methyl ether, cadinene; a phenol; and a sesquiterpene. It is a light-yellow, very fragrant liquid and is used in delicate perfumes and in soaps.

Yucatan Sisal△. *See* SISAL△.

Z

ZAC® Electrocast®. (*HBMTN* p. 631). Should have been listed as CORHART® ZAC® ELECTROCAST®.
CORHART REFRACTORIES CO.

Zanzibar Copal△. *See* COPAL△.

Zanzibar Gum△. *See* ANIMI GUM△.

Zen®. A liquid for cleaning, sanitizing, and deodorizing toilets, urinals, and other vitreous ware. It contains acid and detergent; and quickly removes stains.
J. I. HOLCOMB MFG. CO.

Zerewitinoff Reagent△. A solution of methyl magnesium iodide in purified n-butyl ether. It is a clear, light-colored liquid containing a small amount of sediment which has no effect on its principal use as an analytical reagent for the determination of the number of active hydrogen atoms present in organic compounds. It may also be used to determine water, alcohols, and amines in inert solvents.

Zerogloss®. A moisture-resistant compound of ground asbestos fiber and asphalt which is used to give a bright black protective finish to pipe insulation.
JOHNS-MANVILLE SALES CORP.

Zerokote®. A job-mixed, plaster-finish coating that is applied over ROCK CORK® or other insulation sheets where abrasion or rubbing against the walls may be expected. The coating is made by mixing 1 lb. ZEROKOTE® EMULSION, 1 lb. plasterer's sand, and 1 lb. J-M No. 302 INSULATING CEMENT with about 4 gal. (33 lb.) of water. The sand and cement are mixed dry, and to this is added a mixture of ZERKOTE® EMULSION and 2½ gal. of water. More of the water is then added slowly until good troweling consistency is obtained. ZEROKOTE® should not be used when the temp. is likely to exceed 100°F. or for a finish on insulation exposed to the direct action of the weather.
JOHNS-MANVILLE SALES CORP.

Zero-Mist. A stable surface-active additive for chromium plating baths. It is designed to eliminate spray and mist from chromium baths. Supplied in the form of easily-handled, small pellets which form a thin foam blanket when the bath is in operation.
UDYLITE CORP.

Zero Perm. A vapor barrier consisting of a 1-mil sheet of aluminum laminated between two ½-mil sheets of MYLAR® polyester film. It is flexible, strong, and tough. It can be used on pipe insulation to eliminate condensation and to provide moisture vapor-proof protection under exposure to salt air, corrosive fumes, oils, and acids; and it can be used for lining floors, walls, and ceilings to control extreme humidity conditions.
ALUMISEAL CORP.

Zeroseal®. A special, heavy-bodied plastic cement, composed of asbestos fiber, asphalt and other mineral ingredients, used to seal all joints of ZEROTEX® pipe insulation, and to close all pores in the sealing membrane of ZEROTAPE®, which is applied over ZEROTEX® on fittings. It affords thorough water-tightness.
JOHNS-MANVILLE SALES CORP.

Zerospot[NE]. A rinse additive for machine dishwashing. A small quantity of this material added to the dishwashing water greatly increases the free-rinsability of the cleaner.
DIVERSEY CORP.

Zerotape®. A high-grade, waterproof fabric used as a sealing membrane over ZEROTEX® on fittings and over end joints on pipe insulation.
JOHNS-MANVILLE SALES CORP.

Zerotex®. A felted mineral wool, held together with a water-resistant binder, and surface-coated to increase handling strength and flexibility. It is used to insulate fittings on cold pipe lines. Furnished in blankets 20" wide by 48" in length, with a normal thickness of 2". JOHNS-MANVILLE SALES CORP.

Zertan[NE]. The brand name for a linear-type polyethylene. DOW CHEMICAL CO.

Zest®. The trademark for monosodium glutamate, used extensively in soups and in meat products, including prepared meats, canned meats and frozen products; and also in canned and frozen sea foods and in canned and frozen vegetables.
A. E. STALEY MFG. CO.

Zinc Shield[NE]. A cold galvanizing preparation for application by brush, spray or dip. The dry film consists of 95% zinc and 5% polymerized binder. It provides an excellent weather-protecting coating for structural steel, tanks, bridges, metal roofs, television towers and other structures. WILBUR & WILLIAMS CO.

Zinc Toning Salts[NE]. (*HBMTN* p. 633). No longer available. HANSON-VAN WINKLE-MUNNING CO.

Zinodine®. (*HBMTN* p. 633). No longer available. AMERICAN CHEMICAL PAINT CO.

Zinsol[NE]. An inorganic pretreatment for zinc and zinc-coated metals, that improves the adhesion of organic coatings. MAAS & WALDSTEIN CO.

Zintox®. (*HBMTN* p. 633). No longer available.
GENERAL CHEMICAL DIV.,
ALLIED CHEMICAL & DYE CORP.

Zipsol Dishbrite. (*HBMTN* p. 634). No longer mfg'd by FIDELITY CHEMICAL PRODUCTS CORP.

Zipsol Glasbrite. (*HBMTN* p. 634). No longer mfg'd by FIDELITY CHEMICAL PRODUCTS CORP.

Zipsol® Metal Cleaner #74. A safe, efficient and economical degreasing solvent used to remove heavy deposits of grease, oil and buffing compounds. Can be diluted with kerosene or mineral spirits. Used at room temp. in a tank or applied by spray.
FIDELITY CHEMICAL PRODUCTS CORP.

Ziradryl® Cream, Lotion. BENADRYL® HYDROCHLORIDE (diphenhydramine hydrochloride, Parke-Davis) with zirconium carbonate, for relief, prevention, or protection against poison ivy or poison oak dermatitis. PARKE, DAVIS & CO.

Zirco®. A non-toxic paint drier catalyst. It is a zirconium organic complex containing 6% zirconium metal. Color (Gardner-Holdt), 4 (max.); viscosity (Gardner), A-; solvent, odorless mineral spirits. It can replace lead and other driers, either entirely or in part, in various types of paint systems with an improvement in the drying properties of the paint.
ADVANCE SOLVENTS & CHEMICAL

Zircono Core & Mold Wash[NE]. A core and mold wash similar in composition to HI-RESIST CORE & MOLD WASH except that it contains an oil-type binder instead of a synthetic resin. M. A. BELL CO.

Zirnox®. A non-greasy, soothing lotion combining the antihistamine BRISTAMIN® dihydrogen citrate (1%) with zirconium oxide (4%). *Uses:* For the prophylaxis and symptomatic treatment of poison ivy, poison oak and sumac dermatitis, and for the relief of minor skin irritations.
BRISTOL LABORATORIES INC.

Zyljectin®. The trademark for a peri-anal anesthetic that is administered by injection.
ABBOTT LABORATORIES

Zymocide®. (*HBMTN* p. 634). No longer available.
REED & CARNRICK

NUMBERS

No. 1 Ice Machine Oil[NE]. An oil for the lubrication of external or internal bearings of refrigerators employing ammonia, carbon dioxide, ethane, FREON, methyl chloride, propane, and sulfur dioxide. Viscosity (Saybolt Universal), 110 sec. at 100°F.; cold test, −20°F. *Use:* For compressors operating at evaporating coil temps. down to −20°F., and discharge gas temps. as high as 300°F.
KEYSTONE LUBRICATING CO.

2,3,6®. (*Supp.* I p. 269). Should have been listed as COUPLER 2,3,6®. NATIONAL ANILINE DIV.,
ALLIED CHEMICAL & DYE CORP.

2,4,5-T△. (2,4,5-Trichlorophenoxy) acetic acid. $C_8H_5Cl_3O_3$; mol.wt. 255.50. Crystals from benzene melt at 153°C.; practically insoluble in water; soluble in alcohol; forms water-soluble sodium and alkanolamine salts. It is a plant hormone possessing herbicidal properties; especially valuable in brush control.

2-4 Dow®. (*HBMTN* p. 636). Now a registered trademark. DOW CHEMICAL CO.

2-AN Light Stain Oil®. (*HBMTN* p. 635). No longer available. NEVILLE CHEMICAL CO.

3B® Mercaptan. (*HBMTN* p. 636). *Now known as* 3B® MERCAPTAN #174, and marketed by PENNSYLVANIA SALT MFG. CO., which has absorbed SHARPLES CHEMICALS, INC.

3-C Calcium Chloride®. (*HBMTN* p. 636). Now marketed as COLUMBIA® CALCIUM CHLORIDE.
COLUMBIA-SOUTHERN CHEMICAL CORP.

3-R®. The trademark for a line of inked ribbons.
INTERCHEMICAL CORP.,
AULT & WIBORG CARBON & RIBBON DIV.

No. 4 Silkos. *See* SILKOS.

No. 8 Silkos. *See* SILKOS.

10-39. *See* AIRKEM 10-39®.

No. 10 Mineral Spirits[NE]. (*HBMTN* p. 636). Incorrectly listed as a registered trademark.
ANDERSON-PRICHARD OIL CORP.

No. 12 Alsibronz. *See* ALSIBRONZ®.

No. 16. A water-ground mica for use as a tire-lubricant. FRANKLIN MINERAL PRODUCTS CO.

No. 18. A water-ground mica for use as a bearing lubricant. FRANKLIN MINERAL PRODUCTS CO.

18% Normal® Superphosphate. A superphosphate fertilizer made by mixing carefully controlled proportions of finely-ground phosphate rock and sulfuric acid. Supplies phosphorus, calcium and sulfur to the

soil, and is used as a topdress for pastures and hay fields, in re-seeding legume grass, as a plow-down ahead of corn, potatoes, tobacco and other crops, etc.
AMERICAN AGRICULTURAL CHEMICAL CO.

19/Up®. A brand of roll roofing.
CELOTEX CORP.

No. 20 Alsibronz. See ALSIBRONZ®.

20/FOS®. Defluorinated phosphate for use as plant and animal food supplements.
INTERNATIONAL MINERALS & CHEMICAL CORP.

No. 21 Leafy Alsibronz. See ALSIBRONZ®.

30 Alloy[NE]. An electrical resistance alloy of 2.25% nickel and the balance copper. Resistance, 30 ohms/circular mil-ft.; sp.gr. 8.9; m.p. 1,100°C.; specific heat, 0.092 calories/g. × °C.; temp. coefficient of resistance, 0.0015 ohms/°C.   DRIVER-HARRIS CO.

No. 30 Alsibronz. See ALSIBRONZ®.

33 Alloy[NE]. An electrical resistance alloy of 3% silicon, and balance nickel. Resistance, 162 ohms/circular mil-ft.; sp.gr. 8.60; m.p. 1,420°C.; specific heat, 0.128 calories/g. × °C.; temp. coefficient of resistance, 0.0024 ohms/°C.   DRIVER-HARRIS CO.

#38 M.R. (Hard Hydrocarbon)[NE]. (*HBMTN* p. 637). No longer available.   WITCO CHEMICAL CO.

No. 40 Alsibronz. See ALSIBRONZ®.

No. 43 Core & Mold Wash[NE]. A white, refractory, powdered-type core and mold wash that is especially suitable for use with brass, aluminum and light gray iron work. It is mixed with water prior to use, forming a smooth, creamy wash. The refractory particles are tiny flakes which give a fine, velvety feeling to the dry core. Cores may be dipped, swabbed or sprayed, whichever is most convenient.
M. A. BELL CO.

No. 44 and No. 45 Greases. See KEYSTONE® No. 44 and No. 45 Greases.

No. 45 Alsibronz. See ALSIBRONZ®.

No. 46 Alsibronz. See ALSIBRONZ®.

No. 50 Alsibronz. See ALSIBRONZ®.

"50" Oil[NE]. An industrial soybean oil, break-free and light in color. It is offered in two grades: regular and bleached. Both grades have outstanding heat bleach characteristics. The max. specifications for the regular grade are: acid no. 2.5; free fatty acids, 1.25; color (Gardner), 12; heat bleach color (600°F.), 5. Bleached "50" OIL has a max. color of 8 and a max. heat bleach color of 3. Physical and chemical data: iodine value (Wijs), 128–136; saponification value, 186–196; viscosity (Gardner-Holdt), A; refractive index at 25°C., 1.4728–1.4734; unsaponifiable matter, 0.5–1.5%. *Uses:* Both grades of "50" OIL are economical, general-purpose, industrial oils. Their high acidity promotes resin solubility and makes them especially suitable for varnishes and enamels and also as grinding vehicles.
A. E. STALEY MFG. CO.

"66" Drawing Inks. See CRAFTINT "6" DRAWING INKS.

"70" Dustcop®. (*HBMTN* p. 638). No longer available.   GENERAL CHEMICAL DIV.,
ALLIED CHEMICAL & DYE CORP.

"76" Motor Tune Up. A gasoline-engine cleaner which removes gum, softens and removes carbon, frees rings and sticking valves, and cleans spark plugs. Twelve oz. of "76" are added slowly through the carburetor while the engine is idling. The gums and carbon are discharged with the exhaust.
BELL LABORATORY, INC.

No. 91 Solid Alkali[NE]. A silicated and phosphated alkali, in the form of white flakes. Total alkalinity, 70–71% Na_2O. *Use:* For bottlewashing in dairies, beverage plants, and breweries.
WYANDOTTE CHEMICALS CORP.,
J. B. FORD DIV.

95 Alloy[NE]. An electrical resistance alloy of 11% nickel, and the balance copper. Resistance, 90 ohms/circular mil-ft.; sp.gr. 8.9; m.p. 1,100°C.; specific heat, 0.092 calories/g. × °C.; temp. coefficient of resistance, 0.00049 ohms/°C.   DRIVER-HARRIS CO.

99®. A weed killing composition containing propylene glycol butyl ether esters of 2,4-D.
DOW CHEMICAL CO.

99 Alloy[NE]. An extremely pure grade of nickel—99.8%. It has a high temp. coefficient of electrical resistance—0.0060—and is used as a standard alloy for resistance thermometers.   DRIVER-HARRIS CO.

No. 100 Plum Core Wash[NE]. A powdered core wash having a Mexican GRAPHITE base. It is mixed with water prior to use as a finished wash. It is highly refractory, which makes it suitable for use in producing any size casting. Works exceedingly well as a shake-on facing.   M. A. BELL CO.

105® Catalyst and 205® Catalyst. Two dehydrogenation catalysts which are very efficient in the selective dehydrogenation of olefins and of ethyl-substituted aromatic compounds to the corresponding di-olefins. They are used primarily in the dehydrogenation of butene to butadiene and ethyl benzene to styrene. Their use permits continuous process operation without need of cyclic catalyst regeneration. SHELL-205 CATALYST is widely used as a catalyst in synthetic rubber production. SHELL-105 CATALYST is used primarily in the dehydrogenation of ethyl benzene; 105 also continues to be used in butadiene mfg. and the desulfurization of natural gas. Both SHELL-105 and 205 CATALYSTS are iron oxide catalysts promoted with potassium carbonate and chromium oxide, the basic difference being the greater potassium carbonate content of SHELL-205 which allows the dehydrogenation process to operate at lower steam dilution ratios. SHELL CHEMICAL CORP.

106 Acids[NE]. (*HBMTN* p. 638). No longer available.   BAKER CASTOR OIL CO.

#123 J-Cut[NE]. A cutting oil concentrate composed of a blend of specially processed waxes and extreme-pressure ingredients suspended in oil. Effectively lubricates over a broad range of heat and pressure found in difficult cutting operations. It blends readily with any clear oil. *Uses:* In automatic screw machines, pipe threading machines, tapping machines, turret lathes, and all other machines in which extreme-pressure cutting oils are used. S. C. JOHNSON & SON

#140 Stik-Wax[NE]. A metal-working lubricant in stick form, which contains a special blend of solid waxes. It will lubricate all types of metal work. *Uses:* For drilling, tapping, sawing, grinding, etc.
S. C. JOHNSON & SON

142 Alloy[NE]. An alloy of 41% nickel and the balance iron, with approx. the same coefficient of expansion as that of 7050 glass, used with a borated copper coating for sealing in glass. Also used as a thermostatic metal, and for terminal caps of automotive sealed beam lamps. DRIVER-HARRIS CO.

146 Alloy[NE]. An alloy of 46% nickel and the balance iron. Coefficient of linear expansion, 9.5×10^{-6}. *Use:* For terminals of vitreous enamelled resistors.
DRIVER-HARRIS CO.

#188 Core Paste[NE]. A dextrin-base core paste. Its white color provides a desirable contrast where dark cores are used, aiding materially in the finishing operations. It air dries very rapidly; however, oven drying is recommended where high speed is essential.
M. A. BELL CO.

189 Acids[NE]. (*HBMTN* p. 639). No longer available. BAKER CASTOR OIL CO.

No. 210 Ice Machine Oil[NE]. Similar to No. 1 ICE MACHINE OIL but of higher viscosity—320 S.U.S. at 100°F. *Use:* For old and worn compressors.
KEYSTONE LUBRICATING CO.

#230 J-Cool[NE]. A water-dispersable cutting fluid concentrate that serves both as a coolant and lubricant. Contains special ingredients that absorb and dissipate both frictional and work heat. It has a bactericide that combats odors, dermatitis, and corrosion caused by bacteria. For use in lathes, drills, mills, or wherever a water-dispersable coolant is used.
S. C. JOHNSON & SON

No. 302 Insulating Cement. *See* J-M No. 302 INSULATING CEMENT[NE].

385®. *See* MYCALEX® 385.

400®. *See* MYCALEX® 400.

410®. *See* MYCALEX® 410®.

410X®. *See* MYCALEX® 410X.

#422 Synthetic Detergent. (*HBMTN* p. 640). No longer available. ARMOUR AND CO.

531 Basic Laboratory Kit[NE]. A kit consisting of a number of several different types of electrically conductive paints, three solvents for the paints, a printed-circuit design manual, and instruction sheets.
MICRO-CIRCUITS CO.

2000 Mile Oil. *See* KENDALL, THE 2000 MILE OIL®.

5810[NE]. (*Supp.* I p. 271). Now known as VICTALUBE 5810[NE]. VICTOR CHEMICAL WORKS

PRODUCTS WITHDRAWN FROM THE MARKET

Products Withdrawn from the Market

These products were listed in the 1953 Edition of Handbook of Material Trade Names or Supplement I but have since been withdrawn from the market. The page numbers preceded by (*H*) refer to product descriptions in the 1953 Edition; page numbers preceded by (*S*) refer to product descriptions in Supplement I. (*See also* Supp. I, pages 275–278).

A

ACCO^{NE} Calcium Caseinate ......(*H*) 2
Acele® ....(*H*) 2
Acidogen® ......(*H*) 3
Acme® Grade 4-L-10 ....(*H*) 3
Acoustolight ....(*H*) 4
Acrol® ....(*H*) 5
Adrephine® ......(*H*) 8
Adsol^{NE} ....(*H*) 8
Advawet® NA-6 .(*H*) 10
Aeroflo® 40......(*H*) 11
Aeropan SR-1^{NE}..(*H*) 12
Aeroseal® Q .....(*H*) 13
Aero Soap T^{NE}..(*H*) 13
Aero Sodium Cyanamid, Dust^{NE} .... (*H*) 13
Aerosol® AS.....(*H*) 13
Aerosol® IB.....(*H*) 13
Aerotex Accelerator T^{NE}.....(*H*) 14
Aerotex Resins 140, 160, 301, 625^{NE}..........(*H*) 14
Ahcobase Oil W-200^{NE} ....(*H*) 17
Ahcofix® 134 *and* Ahcofix® S.....(*S*) 6
Air Dryette, Jr. ....(*H*) 18;(*S*) 7
Ajax #2^{NE}.......(*H*) 9
Albaloy® Plating Process ....(*S*) 8
Alcolube ....(*H*) 26
Aldarsone® ......(*H*) 26
Alkabar® ....(*H*) 29
Alk-Li-Pruf Cement® ....(*H*) 30
Aluminoid^{NE} .....(*H*) 40
Amdelate® ....(*H*) 41
Aminonat® ......(*H*) 43
Aminovite® .....(*H*) 43
Amisate® ....(*H*) 44
Ampave® ....(*S*) 14
Ampulbex® ......(*H*) 45
Aneskreme^{NE} ...(*H*) 46
Anespray^{NE} .....(*H*) 46
Anti-Seize^{NE} ....(*H*) 50
Apco-Sol 42^{NE} ..(*H*) 51
Apex^{NE} (BETHLEHEM STEEL CO.) .... (*H*) 53
Apex Rich Hardeners ....(*H*) 53
Apolarthron ......(*H*) 53
Aquaresin GB^{NE} (*H*) 55

Arcodol® ....(*S*) 19
Argyn® ....(*H*) 57
Arosol ....(*H*) 65
Arrolime^{NE} .....(*H*) 66
Asbestoboard^{NE} .(*H*) 66
Asbestol Filler^{NE} (*H*) 66
Asbesto-Sorb® ..(*H*) 67
A-SEE® ....(*S*) 22
Aseptoforms® ...(*H*) 67
Atrinal® ....(*S*) 22

B

Bacigro® ....(*S*) 24
Bancroft Clay®..(*H*) 74
Bardamp ....(*H*) 75
Beaver Clay^{NE}...(*H*) 78
Beechwood® .....(*S*) 25
Belgrade Glue^{NE} (*H*) 80
Bennett Clay^{NE}..(*H*) 81
Benzylets® ......(*S*) 26
Be-Tabs^{NE} ......(*H*) 83
BHC Base ......(*H*) 84
Bismarsen® .....(*H*) 85
Bismol® ....(*H*) 85
Blancal® ....(*H*) 87
Blandets^{NE} ......(*S*) 29
Bleachette® Laundry Blue......(*H*) 88
Blowing Agent No. 15^{NE}......(*H*) 88
Blu-Chek® ......(*S*) 29
Braddock Clay ..(*H*) 91
Brunswick Clay^{NE} ....(*H*) 94
BSZ-300® Process (*S*) 33
Buderma Ointment® ....(*H*) 95
Burton Clay^{NE}...(*S*) 33
Busan® ....(*H*) 97

C

C-4^{NE} ....(*H*)101
Cactus^{NE} ....(*H*)102
Cadux® Brightener ....(*H*)102
Cadux® HS Process ....(*S*) 35
Cadux® Salts....(*H*)102
Calcilact® ......(*H*)103
Calcium Cyanamid 6-16^{NE} ....(*H*)103
Calfast® ....(*S*) 35
Calsoma® ....(*H*)106
Camphacidol^{NE} ..(*H*)106
Carbose 53^{NE}.....(*S*) 37

Carnauba Wax #352^{NE} ....(*H*)112
Cartun^{NE} ....(*H*)116
Catiosan^{NE} .....(*H*)118
Cemco Floor Enamel^{NE} .....(*S*) 41
Cementseal Exterior ....(*H*)122
Cementseal Interior ....(*H*)122
Cercon "A" Wax (*H*)123
Chase Wexford^{NE} (*H*)126
Chlorazene® ....(*H*)130
Chobeline® .....(*H*)131
CI-104^{NE} ....(*S*) 44
Cimcut® Base Additive ....(*S*) 45
Clar-Apel® Cellulose Film ......(*H*)135
Coalkote ....(*H*)137
Colloresin .....(*H*)139
Colorex® ....(*H*)140
Compreg^{NE} (EARLEY & LOETSCHER MFG. CO.) (*H*) 49
Conserv Wax ...(*H*)144
Copar® ....(*H*)146
Copofilm® .....(*H*)146
Copoloid^{NE} .....(*H*)146
Coprote® Dust ....(*H*)147; (*S*) 50
Cordfil® ....(*H*)148
Cream Softener^{NE} (AMERICAN CYANAMID CO.)...(*H*)151
Crystallose® ...(*H*)155
Crystle® ....(*H*)155
Cumberland Clay® ....(*H*)156
Cutrilin® ......(*H*)157
Cyacor^{NE} ....(*H*)158
Cykel 70 ....(*S*) 55
Cykelsoy® .....(*H*)159

D

Daintex® ....(*H*)161
Deltacortone^{NE} ..(*S*) 59
Demal 14^{NE} .....(*H*)167
Dentabest® .....(*S*) 59
Descotone® .....(*S*) 59
Detergent D^{NE} (CIBA CO.) ....(*H*)168
Digipoten^{NE} .....(*H*)172
Dippo Silver Cleaner^{NE} .....(*S*) 62
Dormasol® ......(*S*) 63
Dormatone® ....(*H*)177
Double Brand ...(*H*)178

Drex "8"® ....(*H*)183; (*S*) 63
Drillalloy^{NE} .....(*H*)184
Drillyfe^{NE} ....(*H*)184
Dus-Cop® ....(*S*) 67
Dux® Primer ...(*H*)195
Dux® Putties ...(*H*)195
Dysco® ....(*H*)196

E

E-D-E® ....(*S*) 69
Emcol E607-L^{NE} (*H*)207
Emcol MS-16^{NE} (*H*)208
Emersol® 300 Series ....(*H*)209
E.M.E. Syrup^{NE} .(*H*)209
Empire^{NE} (HANSON-VAN WINKLE-MUNNING CO.) .....(*S*) 73
Emulsept® ......(*H*)209
Emulsion 63^{NE} ..(*H*)210
Emulsoblack® ..(*H*)210
Ephetal® ....(*H*)215
Ep. Kote® ......(*S*) 76
Ergotole® ......(*S*) 77
Erusto® Dry Spotter ....(*H*)216
Erusto® Pre-Spotter ....(*H*)216
Essex^{NE} (HANSON-VAN WINKLE-MUNNING CO.) (*S*) 78
Estacod® ....(*H*)217
Eternit® ....(*H*)217
Ethacreo® ......(*S*) 79
Excelsior Oil A ..(*H*)222
Ex-O-Wax® .....(*H*)222
Extender 600^{NE} ..(*H*)222

F

Farlwood^{NE} ......(*H*)225
Fel-Pro No. 131^{NE} (*H*)228
Feltone^{NE} ....(*H*)228
Ferdico Aviation No. 30 ....(*S*) 83
Ferophos^{NE} ......(*H*)229
Feroxolene^{NE} ....(*H*)229
Ferritex® ....(*H*)230
Ferrox Yellow® (*H*)231
Ferti-Lux® ......(*S*) 84
Fixateur ....(*H*)235
Fleet Wing® .....(*S*) 86
Flexoresin B1^{NE} (*H*)237
Florene® (*H*)239; (*S*) 87
Flor-Sho^{NE} ......(*S*) 88

251

Products Withdrawn from the Market

Fluer-O-Plas K^{NE} (H)240
Folbexii^{NE} ...... (H)242
Fonate ....(H)242
Fruitex Dust® ..(H)246
Fume-Saf White® (H)247
Fungidust® ......(S) 92

G

Gar-Vor® Compound ....(S) 95
Gelobarin^{NE} .....(S) 95
Generalime^{NE} ...(H)251
Genicide® and Genicide®-A ..(H)252
Genidust® ......(H)252
Geniphene® ....(H)252; (S) 96
Genisul® ....(H)252; (S) 96
Glazetex ....(H)257
Glov-Cote ......(H)258
Glycox® 1300 ....(H)259
Glycox® 1400 ...(H)259

H

Halletone^{NE} ......(S)101
Hammond's® Horicum ......(S)101
Hamp Waxes^{NE} .(H)266
Hc Hc^{NE} ....(H)271
Hepasol^{NE} ....(H)273
Hepatone® ......(S)102
Hercose® AP and Hercose® C ..(H)274
Hi-Cyan® ....(H)276; (S)103
Hinj® ....(H)278
Hi-Temp Teflinings^{NE} ....(H)278
Hob-A-Form^{NE} ..(H)279
Hospital V^{NE} ...(S)105
Houdrane ....(H)281
Hydrimix^{NE} .....(S)106
Hydromagma® ...(S)107
Hydrotex (Beacon Co.) ......(H)288
Hysol® Concrete Floor Enamels (H)290
Hysol® Rack Coating ......(H)290
Hyzin^{NE} ....(H)291

I

I. C. Degreaser^{NE} (S)108
Implenal^{NE} ......(H)293
Imulary^{NE} ....(H)293
Indulin® A and C (H)296
Infazyme® (Temporarily withdrawn) ......(H)298
Insurok® T-725 ......(H)300; (S)112
Invadine B® and Invadine N Conc.® ....(H)301
Ionex® ....(H)301
Isco Bohemia Montan Wax^{NE} (H)303
Isohalant® ....(H)305
Iversine^{NE} ....(S)113

J

Japtox® ....(S)114
Jelliff Alloy "1000"® ....(S)114
J-M Weather-Protected® Insulation ....(S)115

K

Kalinex® Dust ..(H)309
Kalista® ....(H)309
Kap XX^{NE} ......(H)310
Kayquinone® ....(H)311
K-Cemo® ....(H)312
KEM® ....(H)313
KEM® #222 ....(H)313
Kem® Rayon Super-Size VC and V-10 ...(H)314
Kem® Rol ......(H)314
KEM®ulsion .....(H)314
Kerodor® ....(S)118
Kerozone® ....(H)316; (S)118
Keystone Clay^{NE} (H)317
Klinch^{NE} ....(H)318
Knight® ....(H)318
Knox-Out® Moths ....(H)319
Kodalak® ....(H)319
K Oil^{NE} ....(H)319
Komyrj® ....(H)320
Kostico® ....(H)322
Kote-Aid® ......(H)322
Kote-Rax® Grade M ....(S)121
Kot-Masq^{NE} .....(H)322
KP-120^{NE} ......(H)322
KP-150^{NE} ......(H)323
Kresola ....(H)324
Kriegr-O-Dip Universal^{NE} ....(H)324
Kriegr-O-Dip V^{NE} ....(H)324
Kriegr-O-Tex^{NE} .(H)324

L

L-30 ....(H)327
Lacet Resin^{NE} ...(H)328
Lanum® ....(S)124
Lariat® ....(S)124
Larvonil^{NE} ......(H)329
Leader Flakes ..(H)331
Lentin® ....(S)125
Liquid C.H.Q.® (S)130
Logolube^{NE} ......(H)338
Lonco #42 ......(S)131
Loosol® ....(H)339
Lumisol ....(S)132
Lusterlite® ....(H)344; (S)132

M

M-58 Dust^{NE} ...(H)345
Magca^{NE} ....(S)133
Maglite® ....(S)133
Magnel^{NE} ....(H)347
Magno® ....(H)347
Maintinets® .....(S)133
Majestic^{NE} ......(S)133
Master of Flame® (S)138

Mattolin ....(H)352
Mazic® No. 2 Anodes ....(H)352
Mazic® Brightener ....(H)352
Mearlin® ....(H)354
Mechling® ......(H)354
Mermix^{NE} ......(S)140
Metalweld Plasticote^{NE} ...(S)141
Michigan Metal. (H)365
Mico Spreader^{NE} (H)365
Microwood ......(S)144
Mil-Du-Rid® ....(S)144
Miramesh^{NE} .....(H)370
Molding Wax #583 ....(H)373
Monolate® ......(H)375
M. T. Emery^{NE} .(H)377
Mulsafact® .....(S)150
Mulsolv^{NE} ......(H)378

N

Nabor^{NE} ....(S)152
Naremide® ......(S)154
National^{NE} (Delaware Tool Steel Corp.) ....(H)384
National® Anhydrous Ammonia (S)155
Neopon^{NE} ....(S)156
Nephritin® ......(H)389
Nerva-Seal® ....(H)389
Nevasota® ......(H)390
Nevillac OA, RT, RX and ZC® .(H)391
Neville "G" Resin® ....(H)391
Nevoll® ....(H)392
Nevtar® ....(H)392
Nilstain C-20® ...(S)159
Nopco 75^{NE} .....(H)401
Nopco 99® ......(H)401
Nopco 800® .....(H)401
Nopco FM® ....(H)402; (S)161
Nopcol MDP® ....(H)402; (S)161
Nopcovar® ....(H)402; (S)161
Novusol® ....(H)403
Nurex® ....(H)407
Nuva B^{NE} ......(H)408

O

Odo-Kakes® .....(H)409
Oleacid® ....(H)411
Onyx 10® ....(H)412
Opaltone® ......(H)413
Optimus® Electric Cleaner ...(H)413
Ora-Lutin® .....(H)413
Ornatox® ....(S)166
Ortar® Emulsion —Type P.C. ...(S)166
Ovalclene® ......(H)416
Oxyseal® ....(H)416

P

Padrina® ....(S)169
Padrophyll® .....(S)169
Palm Wax #1 ...(H)419

Parez® Resins 605, 609, 610 ....(H)423
Parical® Dust ...(H)423
Parisul® Dust ...(H)423
Pathex® ....(S)172
Pax® No. 11 ....(S)174
Pax® No. 31 ....(S)174
Paxcide^{NE} ......(S)175
Pax® Liquid Antiseptic Hand Soap with Emollient ....(S)175
Pax® Liquid Hand Soap Regular (with Emollient) ....(S)176
Pax® Stock #70 ..(S)176
P-D Tungsten^{NE} (H)426
Penasoid® Suspension ....(S)177
Penesolve 901^{NE} (S)178
Pen Hob^{NE} .....(H)430
Peninsular Black Label^{NE}, Gray Label^{NE}, and Green Label^{NE} (H)430
Pennant® ....(H)431
Penofen® ....(H)432
Pentergent® .....(H)434
Perabeta® ......(H)435
Petrofac ....(H)439
Phenac® ....(H)439
Phe-Ni-Met® ...(H)439
Plasticizer #239 (General Chemical Div.) ....(H) 447
Plasticizers VA^{NE} (H)447
Plastoid® Plastic Rope ....(H)450
Plastolein® 9110, 9114, and 9128..(H)450
Por-Lox® ....(H)460
Poro-Cel® (Minnesota Mining & Mfg. Co.) ...(H)460
Porofos® ....(H)460; (S)191
Potentox® ......(S)192
Product G. L. ...(H)463
Produral® ......(S)193
Prohexinol® .....(S)193
Protektuss® .....(S)194
Protex® ....(S)194
Protex Gel W® ..(H)465
Purtone® ....(H)468
Pyoktanin® .....(S)195
Pyrasteel® ......(H)468
Pyrasteel® ......(H)468
Pyroset® D and N.D. ....(H)470
Pyrote® ....(H)470

R

R-313 ....(H)472
Radul D® ......(H)473
Ratmaster^{NE} ....(H)474
Red-E-To-Use® ..(S)199
Redigram® ......(S)199
Redilev® ....(S)199
Red-Skin ....(H)476
Red Tiger^{NE} ....(H)477
Refined Vegetable Wax #717^{NE} ...(H)478
Refined Wax #648A^{NE} ......(H)478

Re-juv-nal® .....(H)479
Rest-Ore-Nap® ..(H)484
Roachmaster® ...(H)491
Roboline® ......(H)491
Roco Wall Size ..(S)203
Rosetone® ......(H)492
RS^NR ....(S)206
RS 12 Conductive Shielding Micropaint^NR ....(S)206
Rubberlith® .....(H)495
Rubber Red^NR ..(H)495
Rust-Oleum® Mer-Q-Ree ....(S)208

S

S-32 ....(H)497
Sadler Clay^NR ..(H)498
Sagrotan® ......(H)498
Sapamine A® ...(H)503
Scotch-Top^NR ...(H)506
Sealed Lok-Joint Lath® ....(H)507
Seal-tite® ......(H)507
Secal^NR ....(H)508
Seed-Less-Set® ..(H)508
Sellogen® AS ....(S)212
Sellogen® P .....(S)212
Setamol® WSN ..(H)510
Sheerset® Resin .(H)511
Shelf-X® ....(H)511
Silkoat^NR ....(S)216
Skat® ....(H)517
Skiabaryt® .....(S)218
Snofos® ....(H)519; (S)218
Sodan® Solution .(S)219
Soilox® ....(S)219
Solbrol M & P ..(H)521
Soligens® ......(H)521
Solinox® ....(H)521
Solomides® .....(S)219
Solutized® .....(H)522
Sparta 80^NR ....(H)525
Special Flexible Fyrex® ....(H)527
Specification® ...(H)527
Spor-Go® ....(S)222
Spraysoy^NR .....(H)530

Stabilizers No. 1 and No. D-17^NR ......(H)531; (S)223
Stabilizers JCX, SN, and V-1-N^NR ....(H)531
Stanolex® Furnace Oil ....(H)534
Steelyfe® ......(H)538
Ster-O-Mint® ...(H)538
Steropes^NR ......(H)538
Stim-Root® .....(H)539
StoneTex® ......(H)539
StrapLbond^NR ...(S)224
Stratalets® ......(S)227
Subrote® ....(S)228
Sulfast® ....(S)229
Superflo Boiled Oil^NR ....(H)546
Superheat^NR .....(S)231
Superoxol® .....(S)231
Syntex L-852 ....(S)234
Synthabond® ....(S)234

T

Tallowene^NR ....(H)555
Tando® ....(H)556; (S)236
Teal® ....(H)557
Teca® ....(H)557
Teco Polychrome Rabake ....(H)557
Tecosteel ......(H)557
Teglac® Resins (H)558
Tempro (Formula CI-103)^NR .....(S)237
Textilco® ......(H)563
Thalivet® ....(S)239
Thermoil "A" ...(H)566
Thermoil "L" ...(H)566
Thorox^NR ....(H)568
Thyracoids® ....(H)568
Thyrocalx® ......(S)242
Tite-Wall^NR .....(H)573
Tolgen® ....(S)243
Transfax® ......(H)576
Trophonine® ....(H)581
Trophonine X® ..(H)581
Troy-Brite® .....(H)582

Tru-Seal® ....(H)582
Tuf-On® #58-F, #58-M, and #74-F ....(H)584
Twecotan® Tanning Extracts ..(H)586
TwinLine^NR .....(H)587
Tyroscabe® ......(S)250

U

U-A-S® "S" Solution ....(S)250
U-A-S® "W" Solution ....(S)250
Ultracain® Ointment ....(H)589
Underlayment Board^NR ....(S)252
Uni-Syn® Style No. 239 ....(H)593
Upson® Ceiling Tiles ....(S)254
Ursulin® ....(H)594
Uvitex® SI ......(H)595

V

VD-Glaze^NR .....(H)600
Vegicod® ....(H)600
Vegicut® ....(H)600
Vegisol® ....(H)600
Vegisulph® .....(H)600
Veg-Ro-Sul® ....(S)256
Velsicol AL-5 ...(H)601
Veratrone® ......(H)602
Veribile® ....(S)257
Vibalt^NR ....(S)258
Victawet® ....(H)604
Victawet® 24C ...(S)259
Vincul^NR ....(H)605
Vital Sugar .....(H)608
VPI® ....(H)611
Vulcanex® ......(H)615
Vysheen® ......(H)616

W

W.A. 58^NR .....(H)616
Water-Airlube No. 50^NR ......(H)618

Wax Emulsion WB^NR ....(S)262
Weedmaster^NR ..(H)620
Wet-Tex® ......(H)622
Whitetan® B ....(H)623
Witco® Blancal ..(H)625
Witcogum® .....(H)625
Witcolac® ....(H)625
Witco Stabilizers #40 and #70^NR (H)625
Witcote® #100 ..(H)625
Witcote® #501 ..(H)626
Witcote® #601 ..(H)626
Witcote® #602 ..(H)626
Witcote® #700 ..(H)626
Wormol® ....(S)265

X

XXX-1^NR, XXX-35^NR, and XXX-317 Oil^NR .....(H)630

Y

Yamtox^NR ......(H)630

Z

Zinc Toning Salts^NR ....(H)633
Zinodine® ......(H)633
Zintox® ....(H)633
Zipsol Dishbrite^NR ....(H)634
Zipsol Glasbrite^NR ....(H)634
Zymocide® .....(H)634

Numbers

2-AN Light Stain Oil® ....(H)635
#38 M.R. (Hard Hydrocarbon)^NR ....(H)637
"70" Dustcop® ..(H)638
106 Acids^NR .....(H)638
189 Acids^NR .....(H)639
#422 Synthetic Detergent .....(H)640

CLASSIFICATION SECTION

Classification Section

A

ABRASION-RESISTING ALLOYS
Allisite
U.S.S A-R Steel
Wehrbest

ABRASIVES
Attasorb
Behr-Disker
Blue Flash
Buffem
Bufrite
Carbicon
Corundum
Crocus Cloth
Cuttle Bone
Double XX
Edg-R-Discs
Emery
Fibrex
Flint
Fut-Sure
Garnet
Green-Bak
Gritcloth
Iron Shot
Kon-Toor Wheel
Lionblast
Litholite
Lundite
No-Fil
Oilstone
Pumice
Rottenstone
Rouge
Satin Rouge
Screen-Bak
Simex
Snow Floss
Soapstone
Spirapoint
Super Floss
Super-Lap
Tripoli

ABSORBENT COTTON, SURGICAL PADS & GAUZE, ETC. (See also Dressings, Surgical)
Cotton

ABSORBENTS, CARBON DIOXIDE
Cardioxide
Soda Lime

ABSORBENTS, OIL & GREASE (FOR FLOORS)
Pennsorb
Sol-Speedi-Dri
Super Tru-Sorb

ACCELERATORS, CONCRETE & MORTAR
Concretite

ACCELERATORS, RUBBER
Dipac
Dithac-W
Ethylac #650
Kenmix Dispersions
Lecithin
Merac #225
Michigan No. 40
NOBS No. 1 Accelerator
Setsit-9
Sharples Accelerator 52
Sharples Accelerator 57
Sharples Accelerator 62
Sharples Accelerator 66
Sharples Accelerator 67
Sharples Accelerator 77

ACCORDIAN-TYPE CURTAINS. See Curtains, Accordian Type

ACID-, ALKALI-, AND CORROSION-RESISTING ALLOYS
Corex
Speculum Metal
Tenelon
Transonic
W

ACID-BASE INDICATORS. See Indicators, Acid-Base

ACID-RESISTING CEMENTS. See Cements, Acid-Resisting

ACID-RESISTING PAINTS. See Paints, Etc., Acid-, Alkali-, and Corrosion-Resisting

ACIDS
Pennsalt LF-42
Pickling Acids
Sorbistat
TCA
Versene Acid

ACOUSTICAL MATERIALS
Acousti-Lux
Akoustikos Felt
Alumitee
Banacoustic Blankets
BX-4M Insulation
Crestone
Forestone
Fresco Acoustical Tile
Full Random
Gold Bond Sprayolite
Hewitex
L.O.F. Super-Fine
Lumicel
Microlite
Microtex
Noisemaster
Noise-Stop Baffles
Panelcoustic
Perfolite
Perforated Fibretex
Simpson
Sonocor
Sonofaced Acoustical Tile
Steelacoustic
Striatone
Thermoglas R/F Insulation
Vermiculite

ACRYLIC RESINS & PLASTICS. See Resins & Plastics, Acrylic

ACTIVATED CARBONS
Adsorbit
Black Magic
Clack Activated Carbon (High Capacity)
Deodorite
Oilex

ACTIVATORS, RUBBER ACCELERATOR
Ozide

ADHESIVE EXTENDERS. See Extenders, Adhesive

ADHESIVE FILM PRIMERS. See Primers, Adhesive Film

ADHESIVE FILMS
Tackmaster

ADHESIVE TAPES
Able-Stick

ADHESIVES, AIR FILTER
Viscosine

ADHESIVES FOR BELTS. See Belt Adhesives & Couplings

ADHESIVES, BRUSH & BRISTLE
Eposet

ADHESIVES, CARTON- & CASE-SEALING
Cart-N-Seel

ADHESIVES, CELLOPHANE
Accobond 3900, Cellulosic Film Resin

ADHESIVES, FLOOR & WALL TILE, ETC.
Armstrong F-1402 Wall Tile Cement
Dexcel
J-1190
P-179
P-323
Pioneer #610 Adhesive

ADHESIVES, GENERAL PURPOSE & MISC.
Canada Balsam
Cyanamer 370, Acrylic Polymer
Dexcel
Eclipse
P-360
WP-134

ADHESIVES, GLASS

Bloomingdale Adhesive FM-47
Bloomingdale Adhesive FM-47 Film
CD Cement 203
ChemoTec
Duron #90
Helix Bonding Agents
Resiweld Adhesives

ADHESIVES, LABELING

Adhesive 701
Kleen-Grip
Polygriptex

ADHESIVES, LAMINATING

A-M 6701
A-M 6712
A-M 6720
Amres 118
Amres 250
Amres 1400
Amres 2612
Amres 2620
Bloomingdale Adhesive FM-47
Bloomingdale Adhesive FM-47 Film
P-297
Simplex
Staclipse

ADHESIVES, LEATHER

Bloomingdale Adhesive FM-47
Bloomingdale Adhesive FM-47 Film
CD Cement 24
Helix Bonding Agents
Prestix Contact Cement
Resiweld Adhesives
Rhoads JE-538 Waterproof and Oil-Resistant Cement
Stadex
Tanamer Product 370
Vinac

ADHESIVES, METAL

Acraglas
Bloomingdale Adhesive FM-47
Bloomingdale Adhesive FM-47 Film
CD Cement 203
CD Cement 400
ChemoTec
Duron #90
Helix Bonding Agents
P-297
P-360
Resiweld Adhesives
Vinac
WP-134
WP-758
WP-861

ADHESIVES, PAPER

Amres 3710B
Amres 3910
Baktak Gum
Bondcor
CD Cement 203
CD Cement 204
Econoflex
Hero
P-297
P-323
P-354
Prestix Contact Cement
Prosein
Res-N-Dex
Res-N-Seal
Simplex
Stadex
Sta-Thik
Staybind
Superseal
Vinac
Vinol

ADHESIVES, PLASTIC

Acraglas
Bloomingdale Adhesive FM-47
Bloomingdale Adhesive FM-47 Film
CD Cement 2
CD Cement 18
CD Cement 24
CD Cement 26
CD Cement 32
CD Cement 33
CD Cement 94
CD Cement 114
CD Cement 125
CD Cement 200
CD Cement 201
CD Cement 202
CD Cement 203
CD Cement 204
CD Cement 400
CD Cement 1508
CD Cement 1509
CD Cement 1516
CD Cement PS-7
Helix Bonding Agents
Kleen-Grip
Metagrip
P-179
P-222
P-268
P-297
P-323
P-380
Polygriptex
Prestix Contact Cement
Resiweld Adhesives
Styrad 205
W-167
WP-134
WP-758
WP-861

ADHESIVES, PLYWOOD

A-M 14
A-M 188
A-M 302
A-M 414-T
A-M 604
A-M 6701
A-M AP 30
A-M AP 30R
Amres 54
Amres 136, 580, 4565, 5531, 5570 and 5580
Amres 250
Amres 1910
Amres 1920
Valite

ADHESIVES, RUBBER (See also Bonding Agents, Rubber-Metal & Plastic-Metal)

Helix Bonding Agents
P-297
P-360
Resiweld Adhesives
WP-758

ADHESIVES, SYNTHETIC-RESIN BASE

Acraglas
Amres 118
Amres 136, 580, 4565, 5531, 5570 and 5580
Amres 250
Amres 255
Amres 275
Amres 1400
Amres 1910
Amres 1920
Amres 2670 and Amres 2670B
Amres 3710B
Amres 3910
Amres 4050C
Amres 4070A
Amres 4511
Amres 6120 and 6120A
Amres 6121
Amres 6130
Amres 6131
CD Cement 2
CD Cement 18
CD Cement 24
CD Cement 26
CD Cement 32
CD Cement 33
CD Cement 94
CD Cement 114
CD Cement 125
CD Cement 200
CD Cement 201
CD Cement 202
CD Cement 203
CD Cement 204
CD Cement 400
CD Cement 1508
CD Cement 1509
CD Cement 1516
CD Cement PS-7
Hewhold
Kleen-Grip
Metagrip
P-179
P-222
P-268
P-269
P-297
P-323
P-354
P-360
P-380
Polygriptex
Resiweld Adhesives
Styrad 205
Valite
WP-758
WP-861

ADHESIVES, TEXTILE

Amres 3910
Bloomingdale Adhesive FM-47
Bloomingdale Adhesive FM-47 Film
CD Cement 26
CD Cement 200
CD Cement 203
CD Cement 1508
Hero
P-297
P-323
P-354
Prestix Contact Cement
Vinac
Vinol
WP-134
WP-758

ADHESIVES, THERMAL INSULATION

Amres 4050C
Amres 4070A

ADHESIVES, WOOD

Acraglas
A-M 6712
A-M 6720
Amres 250
Amres 275
Amres 1400
Amres 1910
Amres 1920
Amres 2612
Amres 2620
Amres 2670 and Amres 2670B
Amres 4511
Bloomingdale Adhesive FM-47
Bloomingdale Adhesive FM-47 Film
CD Cement 26
CD Cement 200
CD Cement 204
CD Cement 1508
Duron #90
Helix Bonding Agents
Hero
Hewhold
P-179
P-269
P-297
P-323
P-360
Resiweld Adhesives
Vinac
WP-134
WP-758

ADSORBENTS (See also Activated Carbons)
Clack Activated Carbon (High Capacity)
Fuller's Earth
Oilex

AGGREGATES, ANTI-SLIP
Emeritex
Fut-Sure

AGGREGATES, LIGHTWEIGHT
Colfoam
Microballoon Spheres
Strata-Seal
Vermiculite

AGRICULTURAL DUSTING POWDERS. See Dusting Powders, Agricultural

AGRICULTURAL FUNGICIDES. See Fungicides, Agricultural

AGRICULTURAL INSECTICIDES. See Insecticides, Agricultural

AGRICULTURAL SPRAYS. See Sprays, Agricultural

AGRICULTURAL SPRAY SPREADERS & STICKERS. See Spreaders & Stickers, Agricultural Spray

AIR-CONDITIONING EQUIPMENT & SYSTEMS. See Heating, Cooling, Ventilating, & Air-Conditioning Equipment, Systems, etc.

AIR-ENTRAINING AGENTS, CONCRETE
Sulfonate WS

AIR FILTER ADHESIVES. See Adhesives, Air Filter

AIR FILTER OILS
Airfil

AIR FILTERS. See Filters, Air

AIR POLLUTION DETECTORS. See Detectors, Air Pollution

ALCOHOL, ETHYL
Filmcol Proprietary Solvent

ALCOHOL, RUBBING
Alcolo
Petrohol

ALCOHOLS, MISC.
Abitol
Alcolo
Naxol
Pentasol #26
Pentasol #27
Pentasol #258
Pentasol Frother #124
Petrohol

ALGAECIDES
Delrad
Pittabs
Sol-Vet

ALGINS & ALGIN DERIVATIVES
Kelube

ALKALIS
Greenwich Lye
Nialk
Penbrite
Pennex, Pennex A, and Pennex B

ALKALI-RESISTING ALLOYS. See Acid-, Alkali-, & Corrosion-Resisting Alloys

ALKALI-RESISTING COATINGS. See Coatings Acid-, Alkali-, and Corrosion-Resisting

ALKALI-RESISTING PAINTS, ETC. See Paints, Etc., Acid-, Alkali-, and Corrosion-Resisting

ALKYD RESINS & PLASTICS. See Resins & Plastics, Alkyd

ALLYL RESINS & PLASTICS. See Resins & Plastics, Allyl

ALUMINUM & ALUMINUM-BASE ALLOYS
Apex 417

ALUMINUM PAINTS
Alumicone
Kemplate
Reflex-Sol
Silverbrite
Tu-Way

AMINO ACIDS & SALTS
Hydrolyzed Vegetable Proteins 43-A and 52-A
Protein Insecticide Baits #2 and #7
Special Nutrient 22 and Special Nutrient 114
Sta-Mino

AMMONIUM CARBONATE & BICARBONATE
Keystone Ammonium Carbonate

ANALYTICAL REAGENTS
Arapahoe
Cupferron
Keystone Ammonium Carbonate
Soda Ash
Stansol
VitaStain
Zerewitinoff Reagent

ANALYZERS, GAS & LIQUID
Lira
Samplair
Smokescope
Thermatron

ANESTHETICS
A-C
Butesin
Butyn
Combuthal
Heavy Solution Nupercaine
Nupercaine
Nupercaine In Oil
Nuporals
Pentothal
Surital
Tronothane
Vinethene
Zyljectin

ANIMAL DEWORMING AGENTS. See Deworming Agents, Animal

ANIMAL FEEDSTUFFS. See Feedstuffs, Animal, Poultry, etc.

ANIMAL INSECTICIDES. See Insecticides, Animal & Livestock

ANIMAL REPELLENTS. See Repellents, Animal & Bird

ANODES, CATHODIC PROTECTION
Galvomag

ANTI-ADHESIVE & ANTI-TACK AGENTS, RUBBER
Sliprite
Vanwax

ANTI-BLOCKING AGENTS, TEXTILE
Anti-Block QP
Attasorb

ANTI-CARBURIZING & ANTI-NITRIDING COMPOUNDS
Anti-Cementite
Metlseel

ANTI-FOAMING AGENTS
A-M 5602
A-M P.O.E.
Anti-Foam 60
Anti-Foam Extra S
Cyanatex Anti-foam
Cynol Rewetting, Softening & Defoaming Agents
Defoamer F-947
Defoamer H-450
Ecco Defoamer PD
Ecco Defoamer PL
Edsoy
Emka Defoam Concentrate
Foamicide 581
(continued)

ANTI-FOAMING AGENTS (continued)
Foamicide 581B
Foamicide S
Fomout
Hydrosperse Foam Depressant
Naxol
Naxol D
Nopco KFC
Orco Antifoam AF
Silicones
Superior Foam Killer
Uniflex
Vegetol
Vez

ANTI-NITRIDING COMPOUNDS. See Anti-Carburizing & Anti-Nitriding Compounds

ANTI-OXIDANTS, COSMETIC, DRUG, DYE, PAINT, PLASTIC & SOAP
Sta-Sol

ANTI-OXIDANTS, OIL, FAT, ETC.
Ionol C.P.
Sta-Sol
Suconox
Tenox
Vianol Antioxidant

ANTI-OXIDANTS, RUBBER
Antioxidant 2246
Delpac
Nevastain A and B
Sunoco Anti-Check
Tenamene 30
Tenamene 31
Vultra C

ANTI-PITTING AGENTS, ELECTROPLATING
Alkontrol

ANTI-SCALING AGENTS, HEAT-TREATING
Kasenit Keepbryte
Metlseel

ANTISEPTIC SOAPS. See Soaps, Antiseptic, Germicidal & Deodorant

ANTISEPTICS
Enterosulfon
Germicin
Isodine
Sprayway First Aid
Urosulfon
TCA

ANTI-SETTLING AGENTS, PAINT
Metasap
M-P-A
Thick-Aid

ANTI-SKINNING AGENTS, PAINT & PRINTING INK
Ink-Sav
Nevillac 10°
Orthophen #278
Paint-Sav
Sunaptic Acids

ANTI-SLIP AGENTS, TEXTILE
Rexoslip
Rexoslip Concentrate
Rexowax CNN
Siligen A

ANTI-SLIP AGGREGATES. See Aggregates, Anti-Slip

ANTI-SLIP FLOOR PLATES, STAIR TREADS, ETC.
Tread-Grip

ANTI-STATIC AGENTS, PLASTIC & TEXTILE
Aerotex Antistatic
Aerotex Softener H
Anstac 2-M
Anstac CA
Anstac CN
Anstac M
Anstac N
Anstac P
Anstac P-1
Anstac V
Antistat
Bradsyn J Softener
Bradtone B
Ceraloid 356
Ceraloid 356WD
Delectrol 379
Drapetex 35
Emkastat K
Emkatex N-25
Hygrolized Oil 221
Merix Stabilite
Merix Stabilite A
Nopcostat
Parko Static-Stop

ANTI-STRIP AGENTS, ASPHALT, TAR, ETC.
Pave

ANTI-TACK AGENTS, RUBBER. See Anti-Adhesive & Anti-Tack Agents, Rubber

ANTI-TRANSPIRANTS, NURSERY
Plantex

ARTISTS' PAINTS. See Paints, Etc., Artists'

ARTISTS' SUPPLIES
Craftint Color-Vu Papers
Craftint Doubletone
Craftint Singletone

ASBESTOS-CEMENT CONDUIT, PIPE, FITTINGS, ETC.
Ring-Tite Coupling

ASBESTOS SHEETS, FELTS, BOARDS, ETC.
Asbestos Roll Fire-Felt
Ceilinite
Electrobestos
Niagrite
Pal-lite
Powminco Asbestos

ASBESTOS-CEMENT SHEETS, BOARDS, SHINGLES, ETC.
Asbestone "Economy 250"
Asbestone Standard "400"
Chroma-Tone
Flexboard
Ohmstone
Pal-lite

ASPHALT ANTI-STRIP AGENTS. See Anti-Strip Agents, Asphalt, Tar, Etc.

ASPHALT PRODUCTS
Penncoat

ASPHALT-SURFACE SEALERS. See Sealers, Asphalt-Surface

ASPHALTS, TARS & PITCHES
Gilsonite
Gilsulate
Pigmentar
Stearin Pitch

ASSISTANTS, BLEACHING. See Bleaching Assistants

ASSISTANTS, DYEING. See Dyeing Assistants

ASSISTANTS, KIER-BOILING. See Kier-Boiling Assistants

AUTOMATIC TRANSMISSION FLUIDS. See Fluids, Automatic Transmission

AUTOMOBILE CLEANERS & DETERGENTS. See Cleaners & Detergents, Automobile, Bus, Truck, Railroad Equipment, Etc.

AUTOMOBILE PAINTS. See Paints, Etc., Automobile

AUTOMOBILE POLISHES & WAXES. See Polishes & Waxes, Automobile

AUTOMOBILE RADIATOR CLEANERS. See Cleaners & Detergents, Automobile Radiator

AUTOMOBILE UNDERCOATINGS. See Undercoatings, Automobile

B

BAGS & SACKS
Bemis Rip-Tabb
Resistal-Weld
Rezlok
Ripp-Nipp
Ruf-Grip

BAITS, INSECT
Protein Insecticide Baits #2 and #7

BAKING-PAN LUBRICANTS. See Lubricants, Baking-Pan

BAKING POWDER INGREDIENTS
Keystone Ammonium Carbonate
Wyandotte Better Blend Soda

BAR IRON & STEEL. See Steel & Iron Bars & Rods

BAR SOAPS. See Soaps, Bar

BARBED WIRES
American
Baker Perfect
Glidden
Iowa
Lyman
Waukegan

BARN INSECTICIDES. See Insecticides, Poultry House, Barn, Etc.

BARRIERS, VAPOR. See Vapor Barriers

BATES, LEATHER TANNING
Takabate

BATTERY BOXES & SEPARATORS
Ace-Sil

BATTING MATERIALS. See also Upholstery Padding & Stuffing Materials
Quilticel

BEAMS, ROOF & FLOOR
AmBridge
Porete Prestressed Beams

BEARING MATERIALS, PLASTIC & OTHER NON-METALLIC
Amethyst
Garnet

BEARING & BUSHING METALS
Bunting
Hewitt Copper-Hard
Hewitt Mill Bearing-Metal
Hewmet
Mocar

BEARINGS
Durex

BEDDING COMPOUNDS, MARINE
Dolfinite

BEDDING MATERIALS, GUN STOCK
Acraglas

BELT ADHESIVES & COUPLINGS
Metalweld Joints
Moran's
Rhoads JE-538 Waterproof and Oil-Resistant Cement

BELTS, CONVEYOR
Boston Bay State
Boston Bull Dog
Boston Bull Dog Neoprene
Boston Bull Dog Rotocord
Boston Colliery King
Boston Damascus
Boston Flameout
Boston Granger
Boston Haul King
Boston Heat King
Boston Herringbone
Boston High Load
Boston Iron Clad
Boston Mucker
Boston New Utah
Boston Rough Top
Boston Service
Boston Silver King
Boston Silver King Rotocord
Boston Speed-Lite
Boston Tiger
Cyclone
Flex-Deck
Flex-Grid
Red Tag

BELTS, POWER TRANSMISSION
Boston Bull Dog Cord
Boston Bull Dog Gold Edge
Boston Cyclops
Boston Perfection Cord
Boston Speed-Lite
Boston Warrior
Gilt Edge
Gripotan
Power
Stronghold
Tannate

BENTONITES
Ben-A-Gel

BEVERAGE CLOUDING AGENTS. See Clouding Agents, Beverage

BINDERS, BOX BOARD
Amres 225
Amres 255
Amres 6120 and 6120A
Amres 6121
Amres 6130
Amres 6131

BINDERS, BRIQUETTING
Eclipse
Sta-Thik

BINDERS, CERAMIC & CLAY (See also Binders, Refractory)
Bloomingdale Adhesive FM-47
Bloomingdale Adhesive FM-47 Film
CD Cement 203
ChemoTec
Cyanamer 370, Acrylic Polymer
Glu-Beeds
Hyform Emulsion
Palconate
Palcotan
Stadex
Sta-Thik
Stayco
Valite
Veegum "T"
Vinac
Vinol

BINDERS, CORE. See Core Binders & Pastes

BINDERS, FOUNDRY MOLD (See also Core Binders & Pastes)
Durez
Top-bond

BINDERS, GENERAL PURPOSE & MISC.
Eclipse
Lo-Fat
Staclipse
Stadex

BINDERS, GRINDING WHEEL
Durez

BINDERS, PAPER COATING
Amres 225
Glu-Beeds
Rhoplex B-15
Staclipse
Staysize
Stazyme

BINDERS, PIGMENT
Aerotex Resin 180
Aerotex Resin 390
Aerotex Resin P-114
Aerotex Resin P-116
Aerotex Resin P-117
Aerotex Resin P-200
Metagel-811, 811-32, 820, 860
Metaglow-303
Parez Resins
Staclipse

BINDERS, TABLET
Burtonite #7
Tragacanth

BINDERS, TEXTILE PRINTING. See Textile Printing Binders

BIOLOGICAL STAINS. See Stains, Biological

BIRD POISONS. See Poisons, Rat, Bird, Fish, Etc.

BIRD REPELLENTS. See Repellents, Animal & Bird

BLACKENING TREATMENTS, COPPER
Ebonol "C" and "C" Special

BLACKENING TREATMENTS, STEEL
Du-Lite Oxiblak Oxynate No. 7

BLAST CLEANING GRITS. See Grits, Blast Cleaning

BLASTING CAPS
Gyrocoil Primatube
Herco Tube Titan
No-Vent Vibrocap

BLEACHES, OPTICAL. See Optical Bleaches

BLEACHING AGENT STABILIZERS. See Stabilizers, Bleaching Agent

BLEACHING AGENTS
Ad-Dri Dri-Clor
Becco Emkaron
Bleachit I Pennex, Pennex A, and
Bleachit IA Pennex B
CCH Spot-Clor
Clor

BLEACHING ASSISTANTS
B-Tex Speco Bleach Assist
Exol-K145 Speco Sodium Chlorite

BLEMISH REMOVERS, FURNITURE
Blem Decto-Stick

BLOWING AGENTS, RUBBER & PLASTIC
Wyandotte Better Blend Soda

BLUINGS, LAUNDRY. See Laundry Bluings

BOARDS, ASBESTOS. See Asbestos Sheets, Felts, Boards, Etc.

BOARDS, ASBESTOS-CEMENT. See Asbestos-Cement Sheets, Boards, Shingles, Etc.

BOARDS, BUILDING. See Building Boards

BOARDS, BULLETIN. See Bulletin Boards

BOARDS, GYPSUM. See Gypsum Lath, Boards, Tile, Etc.

BOILER CLEANERS. See Cleaners & Detergents, Boiler & Furnace

BOILER COMPOUNDS
Ke-Tone Palcotan
Palconate Sol-Vet

BONDING AGENTS, CONCRETE, PLASTER, ETC. (See also Plaster Bonds)
Lok-Crete Thorobond
P-297 Weld-Crete
Pennprime Well-O-Bond

BONDING AGENTS, FLOOR-SURFACING
Emeri-Bond

BONDING AGENTS, PREPAINT. See also Primers, Metal
Alumiprep Galvaprep
Chromicoat Lyfanite
CrysCoat Ospho
Divobond Phosteem
Divobond ST Prep-N-Cote
Fosclean Surtreat Process
Fosdraw

BONDING AGENTS, RUBBER-METAL & PLASTIC-METAL
Braze Thixon
Braze Cover Cements Ty-Ply 3640
Dura Cement Ty-Ply Q
P-297 WP-758

BOTANICAL DRUGS. See Drugs, Botanical

BOTTLE SEALS. See Seals, Bottle

BOTTLES
Cleaneasy Ovale
Label-Rite Phenix

BOTTLE-WASHING CLEANERS. See Cleaners & Detergents, Bottle-Washing

BOX BOARD BINDERS. See Binders, Box Board

BRAZING FLUXES. See Fluxes, Brazing, Soldering, Tinning & Welding

BRAZING PASTES
Handy Hi-Temp

BRICKS
Emeri-Brick

BRIGHTENING AGENTS, METAL
Korox #1

BRIQUETTES, CHARCOAL. See Charcoal & Charcoal Briquettes

BRIQUETTING BINDERS. See Binders, Briquetting

BROMINATING AGENTS
NBA NBS

BRONZES
Bunting Speculum Metal

BRUSH & BRISTLE ADHESIVES. See Adhesives, Brush & Bristle

BUFFERS, MISC.
Aerotex Buffer 190-A Wyandotte 608
Aerotex Buffer DCY

BUFFING COMPOUNDS & BASES
Bufrite Lundite
Cuttle Bone

BUILDERS, SOAP. See Soap Builders.

BUILDING BOARDS (See also Building Panels; and Wallboards)
Acousti Lock Board Novocore
Asbestone "Economy 250" Novowall
Asbestone Standard "400" Panelply
Celo-Siding Particle Board
Celotex Perforated Fibretex
Colony Presdwood
Flexboard ShadowGrain
Kimsul Simpson
Leatherwood Transitop
Nevamar Weatherite Sheating

BUILDING MATERIALS, MISC.
Basalt Wascolite Showerwall
Spectra-Glaze

BUILDING PANELS (See also Building Boards; and Wallboards)

Acousti-Lux
Acrylite
Filon
Huetex
Leatherwood
Light/Stop
Lumicel
Maxlite
Novocore
Novowall
Panelcoustic
Panelply
Perforall
Presdwood
PyroPanl
Resolite
Resolite Fire-Snuf
Screwlock
Steelacoustic
Striatone
Sullvyne-Clad
Texbord

BUILDING PAPERS
Kimsul

BULLETIN BOARDS
Tell-Board

BUOYANCY PRODUCTS
Aer-O-Buoy
Agilene-F
Balsa Wood
'n icer
Spongex Handi-Floats
Spongex Ring Life Buoys
Water-Wonder

BURNISHING COMPOUNDS
Burnek 452
Burnishing Compound No. 321
Enthone Compound B-102

BUS CLEANERS. See Cleaners & Detergents, Automobile, Bus, Truck, Railroad Equipment, Etc.

BUSHING METALS. See Bearing & Bushing Metals

BUSINESS MACHINE RIBBONS, ETC. See Ribbons, Typewriter, Business Machine, Etc.

BUSINESS MACHINE ROLLS, ETC. See Rolls, Typewriter, Business Machine, Etc.

C

CABLES, ELECTRIC
Amarine
Amerbestos
Amerbus
Amerclad
Amerglass
Amergraph
American
Americore
Amerite
Amerprene
Amerseal
Amersheath
Amersteel
Amerzone
Ametallic
Amperox
Ampolene
Ampyrol
Armorlokt
Dynaprene
Firefite
Reliance
Tiger or Tiger Brand
Tru-Rip

CABLES, STEEL
Amergard
Amerstrand
Hyco-Span
Multisafty
Tiger or Tiger Brand

CALCIUM CARBONATES
Coral

CALCIUM CYANIDES
Aero Cyanide

CALCIUM PHOSPHATES
20/FOS
Phos-Feed
Triceratops (Design)

CAPS, BLASTING. See Blasting Caps

CARBIDES, CAST & CEMENTED
Kenface

CARBON BLACKS
Continex CF
Continex FEF
Continex HAF
Continex ISAF
Continex SRF-NS
Cosmic Black
Elftex
Excelsior
Micronex
Neo Spectra
Philblack A
Philblack O
Thermax-Stainless

CARBON DIOXIDE ABSORBENTS. See Absorbents, Carbon Dioxide

CARBON PAPER
Aristocrat
Aulta
A & W
Capitol
Crest
Filigree
Finesse
The Red Writing Hood
Utility

CARBONS, ACTIVATED. See Activated Carbons

CARRIERS & DILUENTS, INSECTICIDE & FUNGICIDE
Continental Clay
Phosphodust

CARTON- & CASE-SEALING ADHESIVES. See Adhesives, Carton- & Case-Sealing

CASE HARDENING MATERIALS & PROCESSES
Carbo-Fluid "H"
Nitrocycle
R-Mor-Plate
Woodside Rapid Carburizers

CAST CARBIDES. See Carbides, Cast & Cemented

CAST IRONS
Refax

CASTING RESINS. See Resins, Casting

CASTINGS, NON-FERROUS
Stoody Wear-Resistant Castings

CASTINGS, STEEL. See Steel Castings & Forgings

CASTOR OILS
AN-10
Castor Oil
Dehydrol

CATALYST SUPPORTS
Celite Mineral Fillers
Houdry Hard Alumina
Pumice

CATALYSTS, HYDROGENATION
Houdry Platinum Hydrogenation Catalyst
Rufert

CATALYSTS, MISC.
Adsorbit
Aero Specialty Catalysts
A-M 620
Hopcalite

CATALYSTS, PETROLEUM PROCESSING
105 Catalyst & 205 Catalyst
Aerocat
Aeroform
Aero HDS Catalyst
Aero Specialty Catalysts
Houdry Chrome Alumina Catalyst
Houdry Cobalt Molybdate Catalyst
Houdry Mineral Kaolin Cracking Catalyst
Houdry Platinum Hydrogenation Catalyst
Houndry Silica Alumina Catalyst
Houdry Type 3-D Platinum Catalyst

CATALYSTS, POLYMERIZATION
Aerotex Accelerator 187	Becco
Aerotex Accelerator AS	Di-Cup
Aerotex Accelerator MX	Epon Curing Agent
Aerotex Accelerator NF	Mona Catalyst M
Aerotex Accelerator S	Nacconate 310
Aerotex Accelerator UTX	Nacconate 1080-H

CATHODIC PROTECTION ANODES. See Anodes, Cathodic Protection

CAULKING-COMPOUND OILS
Panarez

CAULKING COMPOUNDS, ETC. (See also Putties, Luttings, Glazing Compounds, Mastics, Etc.)
Arco Non-Shrinking Dum	Oakum
Dum Calk	Pakseal
Dolfinite	Plastic-Calk
Kapco	

CELLOPHANE ADHESIVES. See Adhesives, Cellophane

CELLULAR & FOAM PLASTICS. See Resins & Plastics, Cellular & Foam

CELLULAR RUBBERS. See Rubbers, Cellular & Foam

CELLULOSE, CHEMICAL
Cellunier-F

CELLULOSE ACETATE PLASTICS. See Plastics, Cellulose Acetate

CELLULOSE ACETATE-BUTYRATE PLASTICS. See Plastics, Cellulose Acetate-Butyrate

CELLULOSE BUTYRATE PLASTICS. See Plastics, Cellulose Butyrate

CELLULOSE NITRATE PLASTICS. See Plastics, Cellulose Nitrate

CELLULOSE PULP, FIBER, FILM, SHEET & FLOCK (See also Wood Pulp & Fiber)
Coir	Cotton

CEMENT DISPERSING AGENTS. See Dispersing Agents, Cement

CEMENTED CARBIDES. See Carbides, Cast & Cemented

CEMENTS, ACID-RESISTING
Acidsil Cement	Knight No. 2 Cement
Coresite Cement	Knightbond #6 Cement
Corobond	Knightbond #7
Duron #90	Knight Super XX Cement

CEMENTS, ELECTRICAL-INSULATING (See also Insulating Materials, Electrical)
Asbestoment S

CEMENTS, GROUTING
Chempoint	Stonfil

CEMENTS, HYDRAULIC
Atlas	Strata-Lite
Duraplastic	Texcor
Luminite	Unaflo
Starcor	Universal

CEMENTS, INSULATING. See Cements, Electrical-Insulating; and Cements, Thermal-Insulating

CEMENTS, OIL-WELL
Starcor	Texcor
Strata-Lite	Unaflo

CEMENTS, PATCHING & REPAIR
Caspro	El-tex
Duron #90	Stonfil

CEMENTS, REFRACTORY
Asbestoment S	R & I Hot Moldit
Hy-Temp Refracto	R & I Moldit-D
Knight Super XX Cement	R & I Plastic Chrome
Luminite	Superline
R & I Aluminacrete	

CEMENTS, SILICATE & SILICA
Acidsil Cement	Knight No. 2 Cement
Corlok	Penchlor FCC

CEMENTS, SULFUR-BASE
Knightbond #6 Cement	Knightbond #7

CEMENTS, SYNTHETIC-RESIN BASE
Corobond	Duron #90

CEMENTS, THERMAL-INSULATING
Caspro	J-M No. 302

CERAMIC BINDERS. See Binders, Ceramic & Clay

CERAMIC CLAYS. See Clays, Ceramic

CERAMIC COATINGS. See Coatings, Ceramic

CERAMIC COLORING AGENTS. See Coloring Agents, Glass & Ceramic

CERAMIC GLAZES. See Glazes, Ceramic

CERAMIC-MOLD LUBRICANTS. See Lubricants, Ceramic- & Glass-Mold

CERAMIC OPACIFIERS. See Opacifiers, Ceramic

CERAMIC PAINTS See Paints, Etc., Ceramic

CERAMIC RAW MATERIALS
Flint	Potter's Flint
Kaolin	Talc

CERAMICS
Knight-Ware	Terra Cotta

CHARCOAL & CHARCOAL BRIQUETTES
Black Magic	Mr. Charcoal
King O' Chef's	

CHELATING AGENTS (See also Complexing Agents; and Sequestering Agents)
Agron	Versene 100
Calmasene T	Versene Acid
Kalex Cul	Versene Beads
Kalex G	Versene Fe-3 Beads
Kalex V	Versene Fe-3 Liquid
Mark C	Versene Fe-3 Powder
Monitor A	Versene Fe-3 Specific
Novanol AO and B Powders	Versene Powder
	Versene S
Quadrol	Versene T
Seqlene	Versenol 120
Solon F	Versenol Beads
Versene 9	Versenol Powder
Versene 67	

CHEMICAL CELLULOSE. See Cellulose, Chemical

CHEMICAL STONEWARE
Knight-Ware

CHEMICALS, INORGANIC, MISC.
Aero Cyanide
Becco
Columbia-Southern
Keystone Ammonium Carbonate
Kodak
Mono-Man
Nialk
Penbrom
Pennex, Pennex A, and Pennex B
Sugar
Tret-O-lite
Trona
U.S.I. Chemicals

CHEMICALS, ORGANIC, MISC.
Amoco
Arapahoe
B-B-L
Columbia-Southern
Commerce
DPi
Jaylene
Keryl
Kodak
MpT
Plastamine
Sharsol
Staley's
Tret-O-lite
U.S.I. Chemicals

CHEMICALS, PHOTOGRAPHIC. See Photographic Chemicals

CHEMICALS, REAGENT
Cupferron
NIS
Penbrom

CHLORINATED HYDROCARBONS. See Hydrocarbons, Chlorinated

CHLORINATED RUBBER. See Rubbers, Chlorinated

CHLORINATING AGENTS
NCS
Pittabs

CLAD-METALS, NON-FERROUS
Mallory Millosil Process

CLAD STEELS. See Steels, Clad

CLARIFYING AGENTS
Fuller's Earth
Talc

CLAY BINDERS. See Binders, Ceramic & Clay

CLAY DISPERSING AGENTS. See Dispersing Agents, Clay

CLAYS (See also Fillers, Clay & Shale)

CLAYS, CERAMIC
Albion
Kaolin
Peerless Kaolin

CLAYS, MISC.
Albion
Continental Clay
Fuller's Earth
H. T.
Klondyke
No Karb
Peerless Clay
Spray-Satin
Steller

CLEANERS, SILVER. See Silver Cleaners & Polishes

CLEANERS & DETERGENTS, AUTOMOBILE, BUS, TRUCK, RAILROAD EQUIPMENT, ETC.
Afta
Deep Gloss Carnu
J-Wax
Lecton Car-Care
Lecton Easy-Care
Lecton Solvent
Ninex 21
O-B
Okemco
Parko
Parko-Beauty Coat
Parko Eze Cleaner
Parko K-R Hand Rubbing Compound
Parko Kwik Wash
Parko Silcoseal
Pendit WA Cosmetic
Pen-Glo
Rantier
Saturol
Troy Compound 111
Troy Fine Finish
Troy Silken Suds Wash
Troy Steam-O
Wyandotte 85
Wyandotte 453
Wyandotte 548

CLEANERS & DETERGENTS, AUTOMOBILE RADIATOR
Ahcowet SDS
Parko

CLEANERS & DETERGENTS, BOILER & FURNACE
Soot-Solv

CLEANERS & DETERGENTS, BOTTLE-WASHING
No. 91 Solid Alkali
Alcotabs
Aquet
Aseptisil
B-Kleer
Divobrite
Limelite
MCC Flake Bottle Wash
Oakite Bottle-Soak
Penso
Relion
Spec-Tak

CLEANERS & DETERGENTS, CONCRETE & MASONRY
Bull Frog Saf-T-Klenz
Flushol
Greasolve
Kem-O-Kleen
Kleen Floor
Tilite
Vitalized Cleaner
White Streak

CLEANERS & DETERGENTS, DAIRY
Canrite
CF-10
Dari-Kleen
Dicoloid
Divo
MC-3
MCC Flake Bottle Wash
New Diokem
Novex
Penso
Peptex
Phos-Kleen
Raydex
Rub-R-Kleen
SR-10
Tembrite

CLEANERS & DETERGENTS, DISHWASHING
Alcojet
Ampolite
CF-10
Daisy
DCM
Dishine
Divo-Dip
Lustral
Nami-Lo
Ninex 21
Ninox BJO
O-B
Pax Chlorinated Dish Wash
Pax Liquid Dish Wash
Pendit WA Cosmetic
Peptex
SR-10
Troy Low-Dishwash
Troy Multi-Purpose
Zerospot

CLEANERS & DETERGENTS, DRAIN PIPE, TOILET, URINAL, ETC.
Bowlette
Expello
F & B
Kem-O-Kleen
Patterson's Pine Oil Disinfectant
Pennsalt EC-7
Pennsalt EC-51
Pennsalt Whirlaway
San-A-Jon-Liquid
Sani-Tate
Toilex
Zen

CLEANERS & DETERGENTS, DRY-CLEANING
Fil-Trolax
Flo
Ken-Olax
Pensuds
Pet-Rolax
Power-Pak
Sol-U-Soap
Sunolax
Ultrapole DL

CLEANERS & DETERGENTS, ELECTROLYTIC
Enbond "Z" Process
Enthone Cleaner 99
Gilron
Gilronco

CLEANERS & DETERGENTS, FLOOR
Aftalene
Aftite
Airkem a-3
Airkem Deoterge
Beautiflor
Beautiflor Traffic Wax
Dipak
Emerel
Floats Off
Formula 900
Greasolve
Kleen Floor
Korex
Krylon Cleaner and Degreaser
(continued)

CLEANERS & DETERGENTS, FLOOR (continued)

Minit Cleaner
Ninol 1281
Oakite Penetrant
Octo-Solve
Patterson's Pine Oil Disinfectant
Pax Formula TL-13 Floor Cleaner
Puritine
Rep
Snydex
Tilite
Veg-Oil Soap Cleanser
Vitalized Cleaner
Vita-Pine
Wax-Strip
White Streak

CLEANERS & DETERGENTS, FOOD-PROCESSING PLANTS

Airkem Deoterge
Dipak
Diversol CX
Divobrite
Heavy Duty
Kontrex
Oakite Bactericide
Oakite General Cleaner
Penso
Phos-Kleen
Raydex
Spray Flo
Tembrite

CLEANERS & DETERGENTS, FURNITURE (See also Polishes & Waxes, Furniture)

Afta
Johnson's Cream Wax
Pride
Rub-Once

CLEANERS & DETERGENTS, GENERAL PURPOSE & MISC.

Aerosol 18
Amoco
Chlor-Tergent
Dippo Suds
Dumore
Emcol 4155
Emcol 4400A
Emcol 5120
Emcol 5130
Emcol 5137
Emcol 5138
Emcol 6020
Emcol P10-59
Flaxoap
Hyonic
Johnson's
Liqui-Det
Lonco Copperbrite #48
MC-1
Nonic #300
Oakite Di-Sanite
Oakite Penetrant
Oakite Test X
Orthosil
Penphate
Pensal Cleans All
Plyokem
Poly-Tergent
Quillaja
Saponaria
Sul-Fon-Ate
Sulfonate OS
Sunaptic Acids
Ultrapole S Liquid
Vitex

CLEANERS & DETERGENTS, GERMICIDAL (See also Soaps, Antiseptic, Germicidal, & Deodorant)

Airkem a-3
Aseptisil
Clor
Korex
Oakite Sanitizer No. 1
Patterson's Pine Oil Disinfectant
Phos-Kleen
Ves-Phene

CLEANERS & DETERGENTS, GLASS, TILE, ETC. (See also Cleaners & Detergents, Bottle-Washing)

Ahcowet SDS
Alcotabs
Aquet
Daisy
Floats Off
Gleme
Jubilee
Nami-Lo
Ninox BJO
O-B
Pax Formula TL-13 Floor Cleaner
Peptex
Perfon
Puritine
SR-10
Troy Low-Dishwash
Troy Multi-Purpose
White Streak
Wyandotte 85

CLEANERS & DETERGENTS, HAIR & SKIN (See also Hand Creams, Protective; and Shampoos & Shampoo Bases)

Go-Jo Hand Cleaner
Jumbo Junior
Ninex 21
Oakite Hand Cleaner
O-B
Patterson's Hand Cleaner and Conditioner
Pax No. 119
Pax C. M. 118
Pax Deodorant Cream Soap
Pax Dictator Special
Pax Hand Cleaning Lotion
Pax Repeater Hand Cleanser
Skin-Cote
Soaperior
Soapure

CLEANERS & DETERGENTS, HAND

Go-Jo Hand Cleaner
Patterson's Hand Cleaner and Conditioner
Pax No. 119
Pax C. M. 118
Pax Deodorant Cream Soap
Pax Dictator Special
Pax Hand Cleaning Lotion
Pax Repeater Hand Cleanser
Rogette
Skin-Cote

CLEANERS & DETERGENTS, HOUSEHOLD

Alcotabs
MC-3
Nonic #218
O-B

CLEANERS & DETERGENTS, INDUSTRIAL

Airkem a-3
Brulinsolv
Dipak
Diversey No. 16
Korex
Oakite Test X
Pennsalt A-27
Pennsalt EC-54
Pennsalt SC-25
Safety-Solv

CLEANERS & DETERGENTS, INSTITUTIONAL

Airkem a-3
Airkem Deoterge
Korex

CLEANERS & DETERGENTS, INTERNAL-COMBUSTION ENGINE

"76" Motor Tune Up
Krylon Cleaner and Degreaser
Nox-Carbon
Pennsalt SC-25

CLEANERS & DETERGENTS, LAUNDRY

CF-10
Dynahue
Namiglo
Nami-Lo
Neopone LO Beads
Pax Liquid Dish Wash
Teko
Wyandotte 418

CLEANERS & DETERGENTS, LEATHER

Aftite
Lecton Leather-Care
Lecton Plastic & Leather Cleaner

CLEANERS & DETERGENTS, METAL (See also Solvents, Metal-Cleaning)

Aftite
Aldox
Aluminum Brightener I-2767-C
Alumiprep
Alutone
AMS 35
B-Kleer
Brulinsolv
Bull Frog Saf-T-Klenz
Canrite
CF-10
Chlorothene
Dicoloid
Ditran
Diversey No. 16
Diversey No. 519
Diversey No. 808
Divobond
Divolume
Dow-Tri
Enbond "Z" Process
Enthone Cleaner 99
Expray 541
Fairtex
Flushol
Fosclean
Fosdraw
Gilron
Gilronco
Globe Kold Dip Metal Cleaner
Greasolve
Henrox #8
Highlite
Industrial No. 39
Industrial "S"
Jet Cleaners
Kem-O-Kleen
Kleen-Flush
Krylon Cleaner and Degreaser
Lume-Brite
Mersoclean 540
Metal Luster
Metalprep
M.F. Acid
MSS 32
Novex
Oakite Aviation Cleaner
Oakite Bactericide
Oakite LSD
Oakite Penetrant
Oakite Platers' "A" Special
(continued)

CLEANERS & DETERGENTS, METAL (*continued*)

Oakite Railroad Cleaner
Oakite Test Q
Oakite Test X
O-B
Okemco
Painticator
Par-Kem Cleaners
Parko
Parko Tank-O-Lene
Parko Tank-Solv
Pax Formula TL-13 Floor Cleaner
Pen-Gleam
Pennsalt AE-16
Pennsalt EC-7
Pennsalt EC-51
Pennsalt Scale Remover 4
Peptex
Perfon
Phos-It
Phosphosil
Phosteem
Pickling Acids
Prep-N-Cote
Prep-Pik-L
Puritine
Renovator
Rustripper
Safety-Solv
Saturol
Solvent Degreaser
Supersolve
Tilite
Troy O & M Compound
Troy Steam-O
Troy T.I.A.
Troy Tops-Gran
Virgo Descaling Salt
Virgo Molten Cleaner
Vitrosol
Wyandotte 85
Wyandotte 397
Wyandotte 453
Zipsol Metal Cleaner #74

CLEANERS & DETERGENTS, PAINT-BRUSH

Rinse-Kleen

CLEANERS & DETERGENTS, PAINT-SPRAY BOOTH

Deterge
Hydropurge
Pennsalt PB-1
Strip-Eze

CLEANERS & DETERGENTS, PAINTED SURFACE

Johnson's Cream Wax
Krylon Cleaner and Degreaser
Nami-Lo
Pen-Gleam
Pennsalt EC-7
Pennsalt EC-51
Renovator
White Streak
Wyandotte 85
Wyandotte 548

CLEANERS & DETERGENTS, PLASTIC

Acra-Kleen
Anstac 2-M
Anstac CA
Anstac CN
Anstac M
Anstac N
Anstac V
CD Cleaner 27
CD Dip Polish 231
Divo-Dip
Lecton Plastic & Leather Cleaner
Parko Static-Stop
Pennsalt EC-7
Pennsalt EC-51

CLEANERS & DETERGENTS, POT & PAN

Daisy
Dico
Kontrex
Protex Metallum
SR-10
Troy Low-Dishwash
Troy Multi-Purpose

CLEANERS & DETERGENTS, RUBBER & RUBBER MOLD

Parko
Pax White Wall Tire Cleaner
Speedee White Sidewall Tire Cleaner

CLEANERS & DETERGENTS, RUG & UPHOLSTERY

Aftite
Krylon Cleaner and Degreaser
O-B
Parko
Parko Blue Foam Upholstery Cleaner

CLEANERS & DETERGENTS, TEXTILE

Aftalene
Aftite
Alcophate Paste
Basopal NH Conc. Powder
Bradsol OR
Chloral
Clarapent Neutrascour
Depcogel 3X
Dispersal 955
Eccoclean RPW
Eccosyn
Emkagen 49
Emkagen Concentrate
Emkagen RS
Emkalite
Emkalite MS
Emkapon K
Emkaterge A and B
Emkaterge NA-2
Emkatex A-1
Emkatex F-2
Exsol
Fancosol
Felanol Powder
Fultex A
Kaliscour
Korex
Moropon LC
Nekanil
Nekanil AC Special
Neopone LO Beads
Nonic #218
Nonic #234
Novanol AO *and* B Powders
Novanol R
Novapon A
Nyapon FP
Orcoboil #15
Orcoceylene #30
Orcopal #18
Orco Scour 48
Orcquesol LHN
Parko
Reginol HNP
Rexobase
Rexobase GA
Rexobase TR-3
Rexoclean
Rexopon E
Rexopon V
Rexoscour
Rexosolve
Rexosolve 150
Rexosolve CR
Rexosolve EP
Rexosolve HP
Rexosolve TR
Sandopan DTC
Scourlon-Pentalon
Soda Ash
Speco Pal EO 33
Spotticator
Sulfanone A
Synterge 748
Synterge 750
Tacanols
Talamine M. A.
Tergenol S Liquid Conc.
Tergolene Concentrate
Tetronic
Texavon
Trepenol ES
Trepenol S-60
Trepolate F-95
Trepolate T-60
Ultrapole G Extra Conc.
Ultrapole S
Ultrapole S Liquid
Ultravon JF
Unishade "NS"

CLEANERS & DETERGENTS, WALL

Afta
Aftalene
Airkem a-3
Airkem Deoterge
Floats off
Jubilee
Korex
Minit Cleaner
Ninol 1281
Puritine
Renovator
Vitalized Cleaner
White Streak

CLEANERS & DETERGENTS, WOODWORK

Aftalene
Emerel
Flushol
Jubilee
Nu-Finish
Pax Formula TL-13 Floor Cleaner
Renovator

CLOSURES, CONTAINER. See **Container Closures**

CLOTHS, FILTER. See **Filter Cloths**

CLOUDING AGENTS, BEVERAGE

Cloudinol N
Entrapped Powdered Clouding Flavors
Entrapped Powdered Cloudinol

COAGULANTS, MISC.

Separan 2610

COATED FABRICS. See **Fabrics, Coated & Impregnated**

COATED PAPER. See **Papers, Coated**

COATED WIRES. See **Wires, Coated**

COATINGS, ACID-, ALKALI-, & CORROSION RESISTING (See *also* Paints, *Etc.*, Acid-, Alkali-, & Corrosion-Resisting)

Acme Polyfluoron Liquid Dispersion
Agilon
Apco Vaportite No. 100
Armorhide
Carbomastic Series
Ceilcrete
Ceil-Por
Coverlac
(*continued*)

COATINGS, ACID-, ALKALI-, & CORROSION RESISTING (continued)

Ensign 345 Chromogard
Enthone Black Wax Emulsion No. 19
Enthone Clear Wax Emulsion No. 18
Enthowax Q-524
EverLube 1329
Gilsulate
Glaskote
Lastiglas
Neoprene W
Nitro-Dur
Nox-Sound
O. B. Well Pack
PDO-40
Penncoat
Pioneer #202
Pioneer #216
Pioneer #507 Aluminum Mastic
Pioneer #607 and #609
Pioneer #820 Cork Insulation
Pioneer #1008 Vapor Seal
Polyprene
Pyrocote-AC (Anti-Corrosive)
Pyrocote-CR (Chemical Resistant)
Pyrothene
Sprayway Plastic Spray
Synhibit "AQ"
Witcote #4
Zinc Shield

COATINGS, CERAMIC
Pyroceramik

COATINGS, CONCRETE-FORM
Form-Saver

COATINGS, CONCRETE & MASONRY (See also Paints, Etc., Concrete & Masonry)
Apco Vaportite No. 100
Ceilcrete
Ceil-Por
Pioneer #202
Pioneer #630 Primer
Pioneer #1008 Vapor Seal

COATINGS, FIREPROOF
Asbestoment S
Niagrite

COATINGS, FRUIT, VEGETABLE, FLOWER, ETC.
Brytene
Clearfresh
Colorfresh
Primafresh
Wax-Shine

COATINGS, IGNITION-SYSTEM. See Ignition-System Coatings

COATINGS, LEATHER
Sprayway Plastic Spray

COATINGS, METAL (See also Paints, Etc., Metal; and Coatings, Refractory, For Metals)
Acme Polyfluoron Liquid Dispersion
Agilon
Aluma Block
Apco Vaportite No. 100
Armorhide
Carbomastic Series
Ceilcrete
Ceil-Por
Chem-o-sol
Corogard
Coverlac
Denflex Plastisol Primers
Ebonol "C" and "C" Special
Ensign 345 Chromogard
Enthone Black Wax Emulsion No. 19
Enthone Clear Wax Emulsion No. 18
Enthowax Q-524
EverLube 1329
Gilsulate
Glaskote
Neoprene W
Nitro-Dur
Nox-Sound
PDO-40
Pearson
Penncoat
Pioneer #202
Pioneer #214
Pioneer #216
Pioneer #507 Aluminum Mastic
Pioneer #607 and #609
Pioneer #820 Cork Insulation
Pioneer #1008 Vapor Seal
Polyprene
Pyroceramik
Pyrocote-AC (Anti-Corrosive)
Pyrocote-CR (Chemical Resistant)
Pyrometalik
Pyrothene
Sprayway Plastic Spray
Synhibit "AQ"
Valite
Witcote #4
Zinc Shield

COATINGS, OXIDE METAL. See Oxide Metal Coatings

COATINGS, PAPER
Acrylic Resin
Amres 6110
Aquacal
Bilt-Rex
Chem-o-sol
Cypel Resin
Cyzac
Epolene E
Epolene N
H. T.
Nopco ESI
Nopcote
Parez Resins
Prosein
Silkos
Spray-Satin
Starwax
Steller
Sunoco Polyseal
Tervan 2735
Ultraflex

COATINGS, PLASTIC (See also Paints, Etc., Plastic)
Metalplex
Plastiplex
Polyplex
Sprayway Plastic Spray
Vinaplas-Lac

COATINGS, REFRACTORY, FOR METALS
Pyroceramik

COATINGS, ROOF. See Roof Coatings

COATINGS, SPRAY-BOOTH. See Spray-Booth Coatings

COATINGS, SYNTHETIC-RESIN BASE
Agilon
Lastiglas
Nitro-Dur
PDO-40
Pyrothene

COATINGS, TANK (See also Coatings, Metal; and Tank Linings)
Pioneer #202
Pioneer #607 and #609

COATINGS, TEXTILE
Ceil-Por
Chem-o-sol
Unibac

COATINGS, THERMAL INSULATION
Apco Vaportite No. 100
Insulation Seal 820
Insul-Master Vaporseal
Monoplast
Pioneer #202
Pioneer #401-P
Rain-Shield
Zerogloss
Zerokote
Zero Perm
Zerotape

COATINGS, WOOD (See also Paints, Etc., Wood)
Ceilcrete
Ceil-Por

COLD SOLDERS
Flawmaster
Parko
Parko Miracle Metal

COLLOIDS, PROTECTIVE
Euvon ASN
Felcolloid W
Keystone Gelatin
Novanol WS Powder
Veegum

COLORING AGENTS. See also Dyes; Paints, Etc.; and Pigments

COLORING AGENTS, CONCRETE, MORTAR, ETC.
Dragon's Blood
Duromit

COLORING AGENTS, GLASS & CERAMIC
Chromoveil
Mono-Man
Redium Selenium
Uranium Yellow

COLORING AGENTS, GRASS, SHRUB, BUSH, ETC.
Instant Evergreen

COLORING AGENTS, PAINT, ETC., MISC. (*See also* Pigments & Fillers)
Britone Red
Dragon's Blood
Graphic Red
Illini Red
Orion Red

COLORING AGENTS, PAPER
Permansa
Solar

COLORING AGENTS, PRINTING INK
Anthosine
Arcturus Red
Brilliant Toning Red
Britone Red
Fanal
Graphic Red
Hansa
Illini Red
Orion Red
Permansa
Plasticone Red
Polaris Red
Rhoduline
Royal Purple
Rubanox Red
Serene Green
Solfast
Superior Red
Yellow for Green

COLORING AGENTS, RESIN & PLASTIC (*See also* Dyes, Plastic; Paints, Etc., Plastic; *and* Pigments)
Anthosine
Arcturus Red
Brilliant Toning Red
Claremont "PE" Series
Claremont "RP" Series
Claremont "UR" Series
Claremont "VC" Series
Cyan
Drycol
Nacrosol
Orion Red
Phenoform
Plasticone Red
Polaris Red
Pyrolux Maroon
R-B-H Fast Yellow
Resoform
Rubanox Red
Serene Green
Shamrock Green
Solfast
S-t-r-e-t-c-h
Yellow for Green

COLORING AGENTS, RUBBER
Anthosine
Arcturus
Brilliant Toning Red
Britone Red
Graphic Red
Illini Red
Nacrosol
Plasticone Red
Polaris Red
Rubanox Red
Serene Green
Solfast

COLORING AGENTS, WAX
Alkanet
Ceres

COMMUNICATION EQUIPMENT
Hoistphone
Maskfone
MinePhone
Telecrane

COMPLEXING AGENTS (*See also* Chelating Agents; *and* Sequestering Agents)
Monitor A

CONCRETE ACCELERATORS. See Accelerators, Concrete & Mortar

CONCRETE AIR-ENTRAINING AGENTS. See Air-Entraining Agents, Concrete

CONCRETE BONDING AGENTS. See Bonding Agents, Concrete, Plaster, Etc.

CONCRETE CLEANERS. See Cleaners & Detergents, Concrete & Masonry

CONCRETE COATINGS. See Coatings, Concrete & Masonry; *and* Paints, Etc., Concrete & Masonry

CONCRETE COLORING AGENTS. See Coloring Agents, Concrete, Mortar, Etc.

CONCRETE-CURING MEMBRANES
Ger-Pak

CONCRETE-FORM COATINGS. See Coatings, Concrete-Form

CONCRETE HARDENERS. See Hardeners, Concrete & Masonry-Integral; *and* Hardeners, Concrete & Masonry-Surface

CONCRETE PAINTS, ETC. See Paints, Etc., Concrete & Masonry

CONCRETE PLASTICIZERS. See Plasticizers, Concrete & Mortar

CONCRETE WATERPROOFING AGENTS. See Waterproofing & Dampproofing Agents, Concrete & Masonry

CONCRETE SURFACE SEALERS. See Sealers, Concrete & Masonry Surface

CONDIMENTS
Aji-Ac'cent
Mei-Wei-Fen
Shirayuki
Tasti
Three Sheep
Tumerol
Zest

CONDITIONERS, SOIL. See Soil Conditioners & Stabilizers

CONDUCTORS, ELECTRICAL. See Electrical Conductors

CONDUIT, ASBESTOS-CEMENT. See Asbestos-Cement Conduit

CONTAINER CLOSURES
Crown (in design)
Ezytite
Hi-Speed

CONTAINERS, MISC. (*See also* Bottles)
Abbo-Liter
Abbo-Vac
Boyco
Cyclone
Handi-Pack
Lable-Rite
Opalite
Pourite
Red Tag
Saftepak
Saf-T-Pak Torpedo Tube

CONTRAST MEDIA, X-RAY. See X-Ray Contrast Media

CONVEYOR BELTS. See Belts, Conveyor

CONVEYORS
Cupolinor

COOLING EQUIPMENT & SYSTEMS. See Heating, Cooling, Ventilating, & Air-Conditioning Equipment & Systems.

COPPER & COPPER-BASE ALLOYS
30 Alloy
95 Alloy
Nicuar
Speculum Metal

COPPER-BEARING STEELS. See Steels, Copper-Bearing

COPPER BLACKENING TREATMENTS. See Blackening Treatments, Copper

CORE BINDERS & PASTES
#188 Core Paste
Chemcore
Durez
Eureka Core Paste
Fastdry Core Paste
Kuik Kore Kompound
Mabco Core Oils
Mabco Quality Pitch Core Compound
Pennsalt MS-1
Perilla Oil
Reddy Core Paste
Stadex
Top-bond

CORE MATERIALS, STRUCTURAL
Agilene-F
Aircomb

CORE & MOLD WASHES
No. 43 Core & Mold Wash
No. 100 Plum Core Wash
AP Core and Mold Wash
Atlas Core Wash
D & S Core & Mold Wash
Hi-Resist Core & Mold Wash
Karbko Core & Mold Wash
Koreline Core Wash
Sandseal Core & Mold Wash
Zircono Core & Mold Wash

CORROSION PREVENTIVES. See Rustproofing Agents & Corrosion Preventives

CORROSION-RESISTING ALLOYS. See Acid-, Alkali-, & Corrosion-Resisting Alloys
Greek Ascoloy

COSMETIC ANTI-OXIDANTS. See Anti-Oxidants, Cosmetic, Drug, Dye, Paint, Plastic, & Soap

COSMETIC DYES. See Dyes, Food, Drug, Soap, Cosmetic, Etc.

COSMETIC EMULSIFYING AGENTS. See Emulsifying Agents, Cosmetic

COSMETIC PRESERVATIVES. See Preservatives, Fat, Oil, Drug, Cosmetic, Etc.

COSMETIC SOLVENTS. See Solvents, Cosmetic

COSMETIC THICKENING AGENTS. See Thickening Agents, Food, Cosmetic, Drug, Etc.

COSMETICS & COSMETIC BASES
Deoleated
Fijoline
Golden Lavender
Hydra-Magic
Pendit WA-D
Pendit WA-T
Spermacetti
Velvasil Silicone Fluid

COTTON, ABSORBENT. See Absorbent Cotton, Surgical Pads & Gauze, Etc.

COUNTER & TABLE TOPS
Corlex
Decaboard
Decarlite
Granette
Railite

COUPLINGS FOR BELTS. See Belt Adhesives & Couplings

COVERINGS, ROLL. See Roll Coverings

COVERS, FLOATING, FOR OIL TANKS
Colfoam Microballoon Spheres

CRACK & JOINT SEALERS, CONCRETE & MASONRY. See Sealers, Concrete & Masonry Crack & Joint

CRASH PADDING MATERIALS
Hewitex

CREASE & CRUSHPROOFING AGENTS, TEXTILE
Aerotex Resin 133
Aerotex Resin 134
Aerotex Resin 802
Aerotex Resin EU
Aerotex Resin M-3
Aerotex Resin MW
Aerotex Resin UM
Cyana Permel Plus Finish
Cyana Silicone Plus Finish
Cyana Superset Finish
Depcoset RI
Emboset BM
Emboset NR
Emboset Z
Hartoset E
Monares Paste
Monaset
Resin 300
Stansets

CRYOLITE
Kryoflux

CULTURE MEDIA
Agar-Agar   B-B-L

CURTAINS, ACCORDIAN-TYPE
Transwall

CUSHIONING MATERIALS, MISC. (See also Vibration Dampeners; Crash Padding Materials; and Batting Materials)
Cel-Fibe   Microflex

CUTTING & GRINDING OILS & COOLANTS (See also Lubricants, Metal-Working & Finishing)
#123 J-Cut
#230 J-Cool
Black Fish Oil
DoAll
Hamikleer 1391
K-7
Kem-Cut
Kem-Grind
Kleen-Kool
Oakite Soluble Oil
Park-Cut M.P.
Power-Cut
Shamrock
Sunicut 11-S
Sunicut 85
Sunicut 102-S and Sunicut 110-S
Sunicut 105
Sunicut 171
Sunicut 209-S
Sunicut 216
Sunicut 793
Sunicut 5534
Sunicut "W" Series Cutting Oils
Sunoco Emulsifying Cutting Oil HD "F"
Sunoco Emulsifying Cutting Oils
Texaco Soluble Oil CX
TL-131
UniKool
Wax-Cool, #130
Wax-Cut

D

DAIRY CLEANERS. See Cleaners & Detergents, Dairy

DAMPENERS, VIBRATION. See Vibration Dampeners

DECKS, ROOF. See Roof Decks

DECOLORIZING AGENTS (See also Absorbents; and Activated Carbons)
Fuller's Earth   Rez

DEFOAMING AGENTS. See Anti-Foaming Agents

DEFLOCCULANTS
Clay Deflocculants No. 2 and 5
Metafos
Palconate
Palcotan

DEFOLIANTS
Aero Cyanamid
Aminotriazole
De-Fol-Ate
Shed-A-Leaf

DEHAIRING AGENTS
Oakite Scald-Aid   Sebacol

DE-ICING AGENTS & ICE PREVENTIVES
Calsalt   Paradyne

DELUSTRANTS, TEXTILE
Emka Permadul DS-2
Emka Permadul O
Lumattin SL
Rexodull DK
Rexodull M
Rexodull XX

DEODORANT SOAPS. See Soaps, Antiseptic, Germicidal & Deodorant

DEODORANTS, INDUSTRIAL PRODUCT (*See also* Perfumes & Perfume Bases)
Betula Oil
Chlorophyll
Deodall
Odrene
Resodor
Texodor

DEODORANTS, SANITIZING
Airkem 10-39
Airkem a-3
Airkem Deoterge
Bactine
Chlorophyll
Freshettes
Korex
Multi-Chlor
Odor Crystals
Patterson's Creosote Dip and Disinfectant
Pine-Ola
Sani-Tate
Vespray
Zen

DEODORANTS, SPACE-TYPE
Aeromatic De-Odor Mist
Airkem Blue Label
Airkem Green Label
Airkem Red Label
Airkem Red Label Mist
DSX-11
Glade (Aerosol)
Glade (Wick)
O-B
Pine Air
Spice Air
Spring Aire
Troy Ster-L-Yzer
Vespray

DEPILATORIES. *See* Dehairing Agents

DESIZING AGENTS, TEXTILE
Diazyme
Dry Exsize-T
Emkazyme
Exsize-T
Exzyme
Super Exsize-T
Texzyme

DETECTORS, AIR POLLUTION
Colorimetric
Explosimeter
Gascope

DEVELOPING AGENTS, DYESTUFF
Becco

DEWORMING AGENTS, ANIMAL
A-B-C Phenothiazine
Flavor-Feen
Livestock Self Dewormer
Patterson Phenothiazine, Drench Grade

DEXTRINS
Stadex

DIAGNOSTIC AIDS, MEDICAL
Acetest
Bumintest
Clinistix
Clinitest
Dextrotest
Hematest
Ictotest
Occultest
Rachromate
Radiocaps
Regitine
Risa

DIATOMACEOUS EARTHS
Celite
Celite Filter-Aids
Celite Mineral Fillers
Filter-Cel
Hyflo Super-Cel
Infusorial Earth
Snow Floss
Standard Super-Cel
Super Floss

DIE-CASTING DIE ALLOYS
Hodi
MC (Mold and Cavity Steel)
Speed Cut
WCC
WW Hotwork

DIE STEELS. *See* Steels, Tool & Die

DIPS & SPRAYS, LIVESTOCK
Bone Oil
Patterson's Creosote Dip and Disinfectant
Tall Oil

DISHWASHING CLEANERS. *See* Cleaners & Detergents, Dishwashing

DISINFECTANTS
Becco
Birch Oil
Bone Oil
Clor
Clorital
Diversol CX
Korex
Multi-Chlor
Oakite Bactericide
O-B
Patterson's Creosote Dip and Disinfectant
Patterson's Pine Oil Disinfectant
Pine-Ola
Riz
Sani-Tate
Troy Coco-Ster Compound
Troy Econo-Pine
Troy Pine Emulso
Usaphene 5
Usaphene 10

DISINFECTANTS, SEED. *See* Seed Disinfectants

DISINFECTANTS, SOIL. *See* Soil Disinfectants, Fungicides & Fumigants

DISINFECTING PAINTS. *See* Paints, Etc., Fungus-Resisting, Disinfecting, Etc.

DISPERSING AGENTS, CEMENT
Palconate
Palcotan

DISPERSING AGENTS, CLAY
Clay Deflocculants No. 2 and 5

DISPERSING AGENTS, DYE
Alkylene A
Dispersol
Emkatard
Emkatex N-25
Emkatex NE
Penetrant Y
Penetron Conc.

DISPERSING AGENTS, GENERAL PURPOSE & MISC.
Aerosol 18
Aerosol 22
Ben-A-Gel
Bentone 18-C
Cyanamer 370, Acrylic Polymer
Metafos
Palconate
Palcotan
Poly-Tergent
Specon #33
Surfonic Adducts
Texapons
Tragacanth
Veegum

DISPERSING AGENTS, PAINT & PIGMENT
Aerosol C-61
Dispersol
Kelube
Levelon
Metasap
Permagel
Sulfonate WS
Texapons
Thixo

DISPERSING AGENTS, RUBBER & RUBBER LATEX
Emcol K-8300
Palconate
Palcotan

DISPERSING AGENTS, TEXTILE-PROCESSING
Mulsoid 815M
Solasol
Solasol USP Extra
Synterge 748
Synterge 750
Tragacanth

DISPERSING AGENTS, WAX & RESIN
Dispersol
Levelon

DISPERSIONS, RESIN. *See* Resin Dispersions & Emulsions

DOORS
Securit Interior Glass Doors

DRAIN PIPE CLEANERS. *See* Cleaners & Detergents, Drain Pipe, Toilet, Urinal, Etc.

DRAWING INKS. *See* Inks, Drawing

DRAWING PAPERS
Craftint Color-Vu Papers   Craftint Singletone
Craftint Doubletone

DRESSINGS, SURGICAL
Parresine

DRIERS, PAINT
Activ-8   Zirco

DRILL RODS
Commando Drill Rod

DRIPLESS PIPE COATINGS. See Pipe Coatings & Coverings, Dripless

DRUG ANTI-OXIDANTS. See Anti-Oxidants, Cosmetic, Drug, Dye, Paint, Plastic & Soap

DRUG DYES. See Dyes, Food, Drug, Soap, Cosmetic, Etc.

DRUG PRESERVATIVES. See Preservatives, Fat, Oil, Drug, Cosmetic, Etc.

DRUG STABILIZERS. See Stabilizers, Drug & Pharmaceutical

DRUG THICKENING AGENTS. See Thickening Agents, Food, Cosmetic, Drug, Etc.

DRUGS, BOTANICAL
Evenized   Rajah Brand
Initial Line   Regal
Octagon (Hippocrates)

DRY-CLEANING DETERGENTS. See Cleaners & Detergents, Dry-Cleaning

DRY-CLEANING SOLVENTS. See Solvents, Dry-Cleaning

DRY-FILM LUBRICANTS. See Lubricants, Dry-Film

DRYING AGENTS, GAS & LIQUID
Driocel S   Parko Super-Dri

DUCT LININGS
Armaglas

DUCTS, HOODS, TANKS, ETC., PLASTIC
Airtron   Glastic Channel-Duct

DUPLICATING FLUIDS, STENCILS, ETC.
Aristoclean   Finespirit
Aristomaster   Finessemaster
Aulta   Gloria
Aulta Clean   Gloriamaster
Aultamaster   Gloriaspirit
A & W

DUST COLLECTING EQUIPMENT, SYSTEMS, ETC.
AAF   Electro-KLEAN
AMER-clone   Electro-MATIC
Cycoil   Electro-PL
Electro-AIRMAT   Roto-Clone

DUST COLLECTORS & SAMPLERS
Cascade Impactor   Midget Impinger
Drildust

DUSTING POWDERS, AGRICULTURAL
Garden Duster   Pratt's Shot Gun Spray or Dust
Liberty
Mystikil Rose Duster   Tennessee Tri-Basic Copper

DUSTPROOFING AGENTS, COAL, ROAD, MINING, ETC.
Ahcowet SDS

DYE ANTI-OXIDANTS. See Anti-Oxidants, Cosmetic, Drug, Dye, Paint, Plastic & Soap

DYE DISPERSANTS. See Dispersing Agents, Dye

DYE FIXATIVES
Bellefix CN and Bellefix VS   Gambier
Bellefix N-100   Glycinal HD_2
Deepset Salt L   Lyofix EW Conc.
Depco Fix N   Novafix CA
Emkafix R   Novafix CU
Felcofix   Novafix WW
Felcofix CM   Pilate Fast Salt O Solution
Felcofix O

DYEING ASSISTANTS
Cibalan Salt H   Metafos
Cibalan Salt N   Neolan Salt P
Cibalan Salt S   Neovadine AL
Cyanatex Dyeing Assistant EM   Neovadine AN
Depcolin   Novanol Nap
Dispersing Agent N.F.L.   Novanol WS Powder
Dissolving Salt B   Novapon A
Emkafol D   Novapon NE
Emkagen RS   Orco Ferrosol Powder WS and Orco Ferrosol Liquid
Emkalane MF
Emkanyl 85   Orcolana Strip NA
Emkapene RW   Penetrant Y
Emkaron   Pilate Fast Salt O Solution
Emkatex 49-P
Euvon ASN   Scourlon-Pentalon
Fancosol   Solasol
Fancosol P   Solpon KD
Felcomine VAB   Specon X 13
Felsyn 61   Synthramine A 50% Paste
Felsyn 187
Felsyn MS   Talamine M. A.
Glycinal HD_2 Uniperal W
Lanazine Tip

DYE SOLVENTS. See Solvents, Dye

DYE STABILIZERS
Harofix CP

DYE STRIPPERS
Albigen A   Stripping Agent Soluble Conc.
Oroxalyde Liquid

DYES, FLUORESCENT
Calcofluor Dyes

DYES, FOOD, DRUG, SOAP, COSMETIC, ETC.
Alkanet   Litmus
Annatto   Safflower
Chlorophyll   Saffron
Florasynth

DYES, LAKE COLOR
Calco Lake Dyes

DYES, OIL-SOLUBLE
Alkanet   Irisol
Dual Dye   Resoform
Fugitints   Rhoduline

DYES, PAPER
Benzo Black
Benzo Black Blue
Benzo Brown
Benzo Grey
Calcoloid Dyes
Fastusol
Flavazine
Hansa
Litmus
Oxamine
Pheno Direct Color Dyes
Rhoduline

DYES, PLASTIC
Anthosine
Phenoform
Resoform

DYES, TEXTILE, LEATHER, ETC.
Algol
Algosol
Alphanol
Annatto
Anthracyanine
Anthrasol
Aquaprint
Aridye
Arigen
Arilan
Arilite
Astrol
Atlantic Neutrazoic Dyestuffs
Azo Acid
Azo Fuchine
Azonine
Azo Phloxine
Azophor
BASF
Basolan
Belamine Fast Blue Bluc
Bellefast Colors
Benzo Black
Benzo Black Blue
Benzo Brown
Benzofix
Benzoform
Benzo Grey
Buffalo
Calcofluor Dyes
Calcoloid Dyes
Calcosol Dyes
Calcosyn Dyes
Calcozoic Dyes
Catechu
Cellit
Cellitazol
Celliton
Chromindigen
Chromogene
Chromoglaucine
Cochineal
Coelestol
Cyper
Dianil
Diazanil
Duralene
Eastofix
Emeraldol
Erganil
Eukesol
Fastusol
Flavazine
Flavophosphine
Fugitints
Fustic
Gambier
Genacryl
Genalan
Gendyco
Geranol
Helizaron
Hydron
Immedial
Indo Carbon
Indoine
Infra
Interchem
Irisol
Litmus
Lumatex
Melanogen
Metalan
Neopilate Dyestuffs
Neutranyl Colors
Nile
Novagen Black II BN
Novalan
Novanthrene Brilliant Green 3B
Nyagene Black 3B Conc.
Nyalite Fast Blue NPC
Nyanthrene
Orcochrome Black P New
Orcolon Black #55 Paste
Orco Metallan
Orcomine Black RBM Conc.
Ortol
Ortolan
Oxamine
Palanthrene Brown LG Double Paste
Palatine
Para
Parnol
Pilate
Radio
Rapidogen
Resoform
Rhoduline
Ronagen Black IL
Ronagen Black IL Powder
Rubinol
Safflower
Sapphirol
Sulphon Azurine
Suprafix
Supralan
Thiazine
Thiazol Yellow
Thiochromogen
Thionine
Variamine
Vialon
Violamine

DYES, WATER-SOLUBLE
Saffron

DYESTUFF DEVELOPERS. See Developing Agents, Dyestuff

DYESTUFF INTERMEDIATES
Anthosine
MpT

E

ELECTRIC CABLES. See Cables, Electric

ELECTRIC FURNACES. See Furnaces, Electric

ELECTRICAL-CONDUCTING PAINTS. See Paints, Etc., Electrical-Conducting

ELECTRICAL CONDUCTORS
Amarine
Amerbestos
Amerbus
Amerclad
Amercord
Amerductor
Amerglass
Amergraph
American
Americore
Amerprene
Amerseal
Amersheath
Amersteel
Amerstrand
Amertel
Amerzone
Ametallic
Amperox
Ampolene
Ampyrol
Armorlokt
Dynaprene
Firefite
Reliance
Tiger or Tiger Brand
Tru-Rip
Turbolene
Turbotemp
Turbotherm
Turbotrans
Turbo Tufflex

ELECTRICAL EQUIPMENT & PARTS
Ad-A-Switch
Claro
Clarostat
Clarostat (in Symbol)
C Line
Fixtohm
Flexohm
Fuzohm
Glasohm
Greenohm
Greenohm Jr.
House of Resistors, The
Humdinger
Pick-A-Shaft
Potpot
R T V
Standee
Vari/Phase

ELECTRICAL GENERATING EQUIPMENT
Witte

ELECTRICAL HEATING ELEMENTS
Briskeat
Heat Sheets
Jelliff Alloy "C"

ELECTRICAL HEATING PANELS. See Heating Panels, Electrical

ELECTRICAL INSULATING MATERIALS. See Insulating Materials, Electrical; and Cements, Electrical-Insulating

ELECTRICAL INSULATING TAPES & SEALANTS. See Tapes & Sealants, Electrical Insulating

ELECTRICAL INSULATION (See also Insulating Materials, Electrical)
Acme Polyfluoron Liquid Dispersion
Acme Polyfluoron Molding Powder
Biwax
Ceil-Por
Cymel
Epoxy Resins
Fiberfilm
Helix Bonding Agents
Helix Potting Compounds
IPI-Isofoam
Isomica
Mica
Poly-A9 Cast Film
Samica
Starwax
Synthamica
Tissuglass
Turbo
Turbo 117
Turboglas
Turbolex
Turbosil
Turbotherm
Turbotrans
Turbotuf
Turbozone

ELECTRICAL-RESISTANCE ALLOYS
30 Alloy
33 Alloy
95 Alloy
99 Alloy
Jelliff Alloy "30"
Jelliff Alloy "45"
Jelliff Alloy "60"
Jelliff Alloy "A"
Jelliff Alloy "C"
Karma

ELECTRICAL WIRING EQUIPMENT & SUPPLIES
Amerite
Turbolene
Turbotemp
Turbotherm
Turbotrans
Turbo Tufflex

ELECTRICALLY-CONDUCTIVE FLOOR-SURFACING MATERIALS. See Floor-Surfacing Materials, Electrically-Conductive

ELECTRICALLY-CONDUCTIVE GLASS. See Glass, Electrically-Conductive

ELECTRODES, BRAZING & WELDING. See Welding & Brazing Rods & Electrodes

ELECTROLYTIC CLEANERS & DETERGENTS. See Cleaners & Detergents, Electrolytic

ELECTRONIC ALLOYS. See Radio & Electronic Alloys

ELECTROPLATING ANTI-PITTING AGENTS. See Anti-Pitting Agents, Electroplating

ELECTROPLATING BATH ADDITIVES
Alkontrol
Sta-Mino
Sweetose
Zero-Mist

ELECTROPLATING COMPOUNDS
Cad-Sol
SRHS

ELECTROPLATING EQUIPMENT
Udyguard

ELECTROPLATING FOAM BLANKET MATERIALS. See Foam Blanket Materials, Electroplating

ELECTROPLATING PROCESSES
Bry-Cad
Hi-C
Mallory Millosil Process
Ubryco

ELECTROPLATING STOP-OFF LACQUERS & TAPES. See Stop-Off Lacquers, Tapes, Etc., Electroplating

EMULSIFYING AGENTS, COSMETIC
Sta-Sol
Texapons

EMULSIFYING AGENTS, FATS & OILS
Degalol

EMULSIFYING AGENTS, FOOD-PRODUCT
D-6
D-7
DM-30
DPi
Emargol
Lecithin
Myvatex
Sta-Sol
Super-G
Uni-Pectin
Vanade
Vanlite

EMULSIFYING AGENTS, GENERAL PURPOSE & MISC.
Aerosol 18
Aerosol 22
Aerosol AY
Aerosol MA-80%
Aerosol OS
Aerosol OT-75%
Aerosol OT-100%
Algin or Alginic Acid
Ceramol
Emcol 5138
Emcol 6020
Emcol H-31A
Emcol H-35A
Emcol H-52
Emcol P10-59
Emkabase
Emulsarin
Factolac
Gammanol
Ninate 411
Nonic #261
Nonic #300
Permagel
Polyrad
Poly-Tergent
Rexobase XX
Sunaptic Acids
Teko
Texapons
Tragacanth
Vinol

EMULSIFYING AGENTS, INSECTICIDE, FUNGICIDE, & HERBICIDE
Emcol H-83T
Emcol H-85T
Emcol H-300X and Emcol H-500X
Emcol H-A and Emcol H-B
Specon #33
T-H Emulsifiers
Toximul 500
Toximul 600
Trex

EMULSIFYING AGENTS, PHARMACEUTICAL
Texapons
Uni-Pectin

EMULSIFYING AGENTS, TEXTILE PROCESSING
Dispersal 955
Dispersal 1278
Felcobase Sal
Novapon A
Novulphor A Oil-Soluble
Novulphor EL
Orcowet #33
Reginol HNP
Rexobase GA
Specon #33
Specon X 13
Sta-Sol
Synterge 750
Tacanols
Tergolene Concentrate
Tetronic
Trepenol S-60
Trepenol WA
Ultrapole DL
Ultrapole G Extra Conc
Ultrapole S

EMULSION BREAKERS
Polyrad

EMULSION STABILIZERS. See Stabilizers, Emulsion

EMULSIONS, RESIN. See Resin Dispersions & Emulsions

ENAMELS, PORCELAIN. See Porcelain Enamels

ENGINE CLEANERS, INTERNAL COMBUSTION. See Cleaners & Detergents, Internal-Combustion Engine

ENGINES, INTERNAL COMBUSTION
Witte

ENZYMES
Alase
Amizyme
Dextrinase
Diazyme
Dry Exsize-T
Emkazyme
Exsize-T
Exzyme
Fermex
Hyazyme
Mylase
Papain
Resizet
Super Exsize-T
Surprise
Takabate
Texzyme
Vanzyme

EPOXY RESINS & PLASTICS. See Resins & Plastics, Epoxy

EQUIPMENT LUBRICANTS. See Lubricants, Equipment & Machinery, Misc.

EQUIPMENT PAINTS. See Paints, Etc., Machinery & Equipment

ESSENTIAL OILS
Anise Oil
Betula Oil
Bromvegol
Cajeput Oil
Duval
Guaiacum Oil
Lemongrass Oil
Petitgrain
Safflower
Sandalwood Oil
Sesame Oil
Sweet Birch Oil
Ylang-Ylang Oil

ETCHING AGENTS, METAL
Alumiprep
Mil-Etch
Pennsalt AE-16

ETHYL ALCOHOL. See Alcohol, Ethyl

ETHYL CELLULOSE RESINS & PLASTICS. See Resins & Plastics, Ethyl Cellulose

EXOTHERMIC MIXTURES
Thermit
Titherm

EXPANDABLE RESINS & PLASTICS. See Resins & Plastics, Expandable

EXPLOSIVES, INDUSTRIAL
Amex
Champion
Contractors
Cyamite
Cyamon
Cyamon Primers
Cyanxe
Hercoal
Hercogel
Herculite
Methanite
Permigels
Red H
Saf-T-Pak Torpedo Tube
Spiralok
Tamptite
Tritex
Virbonite

EXTENDERS, ADHESIVE
A-M 150
A-M 160
A-M 580
A-M 620
A-M 3720
A-M 4620
A-M 5531
Amres 225

EXTENDERS, RESIN & PLASTIC
Extelite

EXTENDERS, RUBBER & RUBBER LATEX
Resin 529

EXTERIOR PAINTS. See Paints, Etc., Exterior.

EXTRACTION SOLVENTS. See Solvents, Extraction

EXTREME-PRESSURE LUBRICANTS. See Lubricants, Extreme-Pressure

EXTRUSIONS, METAL. See Metal Extrusions

F

FABRIC CLEANERS & DETERGENTS. See Cleaners & Detergents, Textile; Cleaners & Detergents, Laundry; and Spot & Stain Removers, Fabric-Cleaning

FABRIC PRESERVATIVES. See Preservatives, Textile; and Mildewproofing Agents & Mildewicides

FABRICS, COATED & IMPREGNATED
Chi-lon
Coflex
Cohyde
Filmtex
Syntilon

FABRICS & ROVINGS, GLASS
Coronized
Garan Roving
Micro-Quartz
Pennply
Tissuglass
Vitron Roving

FABRICS, MISC.
Bemibrite
Bolting Cloth
Felt
Mechbond Felts
Nygen Tolex
Troytuf Dacron Blanket

FABRICS, TEXTILE
Alluracel
Balloon Cloth
Beachanese
Buckram
Bunting
Burlap
Cambric
Celafaille
Celallure
Celaloom
Celaspun
Celbrook
Celsheer
Chifonese
Clairanese
Crepenese
Duranap
Hawkskin
Heritage
Jersanese
Lanese
Luracel
Lustrocel
Multicord
Plush
Prospector
Serenacel
Tyron

FARM TOOLS & EQUIPMENT. See Tools & Equipment, Farm & Garden

FASTENERS, WALLBOARD
Alumitee
Perf-A-Bead

FAT ANTI-OXIDANTS. See Anti-Oxidants, Oil, Fat, Etc.

FAT EMULSIFIERS. See Emulsifying Agents Fats & Oils

FAT LIQUORS
Tanoyl HDF

FAT PRESERVATIVES. See Preservatives, Fat, Oil, Drug, Cosmetic, Etc.

FAT STABILIZERS. See Stabilizers, Fat, Oil, Etc.

FATS & OILS (See also Paint & Varnish Oils & Vehicles)
Black Fish Oil
Borneo Tallow
Degras
Nylene

FATTY ACID DERIVATIVES
Myvacet
Myverol

FATTY ACIDS
Pamak

FEED SUPPLEMENTS
20/FOS
Agron
Cal-Cofron
Calpan Free-Flo
Choline
Corn Steep Liquor
DPi
Fortracin
Hicratized
Klotogen F
Myvamix
Nopcaine
Nopcom
Nopco-Pak
Nopcosol
Penicel
Phos-Feed
Pro-Gen
Sta-Mino
Super Drex
Super Nopdex
Triceratops (Design)
Vita-King

FEEDSTUFFS, ANIMAL, POULTRY, ETC.
Canary Seed

FELTS. See Tar Papers & Felts

FELTS, ASBESTOS. See Asbestos Sheets, Felts, Boards, Etc.

FENCING, METAL
American
Cyclone
Diamond
Monitor
Prairie
Protector
Red Tag
Sno Gard

FERTILIZERS
18% Normal Superphosphate
AA Quality Fertilizers
AA Quality Phosphate Rock
"Aero" Ammonium Sulfate
Aero Cyanamid
Agrico
Agrinite
Amanol Nitrogen Solutions
Crackerjack
F & B
F & B Starter Grower 15-30-15
Ferti-Liquid 10-20-10
Fertilis
Four Leaf
Four Leaf Clover (Design)
Fur-Ag
Gran-Form
Herpoco
Hynite
Liqua-Leaf
Mello-Green
Multi-Super
N-dure
Nu-Iron
Nu-M
Nu-Manese
Or-Fer-Gro
Poly-Po-Nitro
Premium Producer
Rainbow
Satisfaction at Harvest Time
Tecmangam
Tennessee Tri-Basic Copper
Thomas Soil-Rich Fertilizer
Tip Top

FIBERBOARDS & FIBERBOARD PRODUCTS
Celopad
Celopak
Celo-Roof
Celotex
Leatheroid Fibre
Taylor Vulcanized Fibre

FIBERS, GLASS
Decra-Brite
Garan Roving

FIBERS, NATURAL
Asbestos
Bagasse
Broomcorn
Caroa
Catgut
Cotton
Hemp
Kapok
Ramie
Rattan
Silk
Sisal
Wool

FIBERS, SYNTHETIC
Belastraw
Creslan
Estron
Kylan
Troytuf Dacron Blanket
Velon
Verel

FIBERS, TEXTILE. *See* **Threads, Yarns, & Fibers, Textile**

FIBERS, WOOD. *See* **Wood Pulp & Fibers**

FILLERS, CLAY & SHALE
Albion
Kaolin
Klondyke
No Karb
Rottenstone

FILLERS, FIBER & FLOCK
Palco Industrial Fibers

FILLERS, WOOD. *See* **Sealers & Fillers, Wood**

FILM, PHOTOGRAPHIC. *See* **Photographic Paper & Film**

FILMS, ADHESIVE. *See* **Adhesive Films**

FILMS, PLASTIC. *See* **Plastic Sheets & Films**

FILTER AIDS
AnthraAid
Celite
Celite Filter-Aids
Dicalite 7
Dicalite Speedflow, Speedex, Speedplus, Superaid, *and* 4200
Filter-Cel
Hyflo Super-Cel
Infusorial Earth
Nerofil
Rez
Standard Super-Cel

FILTER CLOTHS
Mechbond Felts
Shurflo

FILTER MEDIA
Anthrafilt
Dust-Stop
Filter Sand
Palco Industrial Fibers
Paterson
Powminco Asbestos
Shurflo
Vinylfoam

FILTERS, AIR
AAF
Absolute Filters
Aerosolve Filters
Airmat
All-Dust
AMER-glas
AMERjet
Auto-AIRMAT
Clear-Vue
Dust-Stop
Electro-AIRMAT
Electro-KLEAN
Electro-MATIC
Electro-PL
Filterdown
Multi-Duty
Roll-O-MAT
Roll-O-MATIC
Roto-Clone
Throway
Ultra-Filter

FINISHING AGENTS, LEATHER
Black Fish Oil
Duralene
Herring Oil
Leather Product 612
Leather Product UF
Neatsfoot Oil

FINISHING AGENTS, TEXTILE
Aerotex Cream 450
Aerotex Fire Retardant NDC
Aerotex Fire Retardant NDS
Aerotex Purifying Agent No. 1
Aerotex Resin 110
Aerotex Resin 120
Aerotex Resin 121
Aerotex Resin 133
Aerotex Resin 134
Aerotex Resin 159
Aerotex Resin 801
Aerotex Resin 802
Aerotex Resin 803
Aerotex Resin 7513
Aerotex Resin EU
Aerotex Resin M-3
Aerotex Resin MW
Aerotex Resin UM
Aerotex Syrup 55
Aerotex Syrup 250 Conc.
Aerotex Thickener 37
Atco GS-14
Atco Rezsoft JA
Bellefix CN *and* Bellefix VS
Bradsyn J Softener
Bradsyn Lining Softener
Bradsyn N Softener
Bradsyn Plasticizer A-2
Bradtone B
Calen-Aid
Caustic Gum
Clarofin R-40
Cyana
Cyana Permel Finish
Cyana Permel Plus Finish
Cyana Purifying Finish
Cyana Shrinkage Control Finish
Cyana Silicone Finish
Cyana Silicone Plus Finish
Cyana Superset Finish
Cyanatex
Cyanatex 3119 Softener
Cyanatex Cream Softener
Cyanatex SB 100 Softener
Depcoset RI
Eccowax UL-100
Emboset BM
Emboset NR
Emboset Z
Emka Finish A
Emkalon BT
Emkanet B
Emka Non-Snag BD
Emkapruf AFP
Emkapruf FL
Emka Ribbon Finish
Emkawate
Emkawate OB
Fel
Felcolloid W
Felcotex
Felcowhite 174
Felcowhite 180
Harto-Resin PCS
Hartoset E
Hartuwet S
Kylan
Lanaset Resin
Lanaset Resin MW
Lanoseal
Macco Finish 6000
Monabond
Monabond C
(continued)

FINISHING AGENTS, TEXTILE (continued)

Monares Paste	Rexobond N-8
Monaset	Rexodull CNY
Monatose	Rexogel
Moropol 600	Rexole CJ
Moropol 700	Rexole ESC
Nopcotex	Rexoloid
Penford Finishing Gum 3XL and 3XP	Rexonite D
	Rexoslip
Perapret AX 45	Rexoslip Concentrate
Perapret LN 25	Rexowax CNN
Perapret PN	Rexowax DR
Permaloid 155	Scotchgard Stain Repeller
Permaloid 170V20	Siligen A
Permel Resin B	Spermacetti
Poly-Coupler	Staclipse
Pyroset DO Fire Retardant	Stadex
	Sta-Gel
Pyroset Fire Retardant N-2	Stansets
	Sta-Thik
Raygomm	Stayco
Resiloid B	Stazyme
Resin 107	Sweetose
Resin 300	Tanoyl HDF
Resin RF *and* Resin 112	Texapret
Resin Syrup J S	Vikon FPB
Resizet	Vikon RL
Reslube	Vinol
Rexobond	Viscolan 14
Rexobond 46 Concentrate	Viscolan C
Rexobond E-12	Wax Emulsion WG
Rexobond E-36, E-48, E-60 and E-72	Weytone F P

FIRE-EXTINGUISHING CHEMICALS
Parko

FIRE- & FLAMEPROOFING AGENTS, TEXTILE, WOOD, ETC.

Aerotex Fire Retardant NDC	Pyrosan A
	Pyroset DO Fire Retardant
Aerotex Fire Retardant NDS	
	Pyroset Fire Retardant N-2
Emkapruf AFP	
Emkapruf FL	Weytone F P
Flame Retardant Base	

FIREPROOF COATINGS. See **Coatings, Fireproof**

FIRE-RETARDANT PAINTS. See **Paints, Etc., Fire-Retardant & Thermal Insulating**

FIRST AID SUPPLIES & KITS
All-Weather

FISH POISONS. See **Poisons, Rat, Bird, Fish, Etc.**

FISH & SPERM OILS
Herring Oil   Sperm Oil

FITTINGS. See **Pipes, Tubes & Fittings, Non-Ferrous; Pipes, Tubes & Fittings, Steel;** *and* **Plastic Pipe & Fittings**

FITTINGS, ASBESTOS-CEMENT. See **Asbestos Cement Conduit, Pipe, Fittings, Etc.**

FIXATIVES, DYE. See **Dye Fixatives**

FIXATIVES, PERFUME. See **Perfume Fixatives**

FLASHING MATERIALS, BUILDING

Nervastral Seal-Pruf H-D	Transfalt Strips
Nervastral Seal-Pruf Tape 30 *and* 60	

FLATTING AGENTS, PAINT

Cab-o-sil	Permagel
Metasap	Quso

FLAVORING MATERIALS

Aldex	Mapleagenda
Anise Oil	Maplearome
Anise Seed	Planifoline
Betula Oil	Presto Flavor Bases
Caligrape	Protovan
Caramellone	Protovanol "C"
Chocolatone	Protovanol "C" Powdered
Cinnamon	Solo Brand
Citrosynth Oils	Spicearomes
Cloves	Storax
Concordal	Suganilla
Dihydro Vanillion C	Sweet Birch Oil
Emulsaromes	Syntharome Flavors
Entrapped Powdered Clouding Flavors	Syntharome Oils
	Syntharome Oils (Imitation)
Entrapped Powdered Flavors	
	Synthofruit Oils (Imitation)
Flavan	
Florasynth	Tamarix
Floravanol "C" #30	Vandrynilla
Fruitosynth Flavors	Vanette
Graposynth	Vegetaromes
Kiss-O'-Flavor	

FLEXIBLE MOLD-MAKING MATERIALS. See **Mold-Making Materials, Flexible**

FLOCCULATING AGENTS

"Aerofloc" Reagents	Separan 2610
Cyanamer 370, Acrylic Polymer	

FLOOR BEAMS. See **Beams, Roof & Floor**

FLOOR CLEANERS. See **Cleaners & Detergents, Floor**

FLOOR-COVERING MATERIALS

Carpetone	Install-it-Yourself
Decoray	Moderntred
Estate	Newray
Excelon	Sunland
Granette	Terraflex
Hydrocord	Textelle
Imperial	Town House

FLOOR PAINTS. See **Paints, Etc., Floor**

FLOOR-PATCHING MATERIALS

Acobyte	Stonfast
El-tex	Stonfil
Grip-Dek	Stonpach
Kapco	Super-Bondsit
Permamix	Tufcrete Latex
Quick-Set	

FLOOR PLATES, ANTI-SLIP. See **Anti-Slip Floor Plates, Stair Treads, Etc.**

FLOOR PRESERVATIVES. See **Sealers & Preservatives, Floor**

FLOOR SEALERS. See **Sealers & Preservatives, Floor**

FLOOR-SURFACING BONDING AGENTS. See **Bonding Agents, Floor-Surfacing**

FLOOR-SURFACING MATERIALS. See **Flooring & Floor-Surfacing Materials**

FLOOR-SWEEPING COMPOUNDS
O-B

Classification Section

FLOOR TILE ADHESIVES. See Adhesives, Floor & Wall Tile, Etc.

FLOOR TILES
Novotile
Terraflex

FLOOR WAXERS & POLISHERS
Beautiflor Waxer
Glo-Coater
Super-12
Super-16

FLOOR WAXES. See Waxes, Floor; and Waxes, Self-Polishing

FLOORING & FLOOR-SURFACING MATERIALS
(See also Floor-Patching Materials)
Acobyte
Amazite
Certified Styrroid
Certified Styrroidite
El-tex
Emeri-Brick
Grip
I-Beam-Lok
Multigrip
Skimkote
Sono-Grip
Stonpach
Traffic Top
Tufcrete Latex
Tufcrete Resurfacer
Tufdek

FLOORING MATERIALS, NON-SKID
Certified Styrroid
Certified Styrroidite
Grip
Grip-Dek
Sono-Grip
Sure-Foot
Tufdek

FLOORING UNDERLAYMENTS
Tufcrete Underlay No. 3

FLOTATION REAGENTS
Aero Depressants
Aerofloat Promoter 211
Aerofloat Promoter 249
Aerofroth Frothers
"Aeromine" Promoters
Aero Promoter 404
Aero Promoter 708
Aero Promoter 712
Aero Promoters 801 and 825
Aero Xanthate 301
Aero Xanthate 350
Aero Xanthates 322, 325, and 343
Burtonite #7
Mono-Man
Palconate
Palcotan
Pentasol #27
Pentasol Frother #124
Sulfonate WS
Sunaptic Acids
Tall Oil

FLOWER COATINGS. See Coatings, Fruit, Vegetable, Flower, Etc.

FLUIDS, AUTOMATIC TRANSMISSION
Kendall Automatic Transmission Fluid
Parko

FLUORESCENT DYES. See Dyes, Fluorescent

FLUORETHYLENE RESINS & PLASTICS. See Resins & Plastics, Fluorethylene

FLUXES, BRAZING, SOLDERING, TINNING & WELDING
Salamac
ST-760, 780, 781, and 840

FLUXES, METAL-REFINING & MELTING
Fluxing Stone
Mabco Aluminum Flux

FOAM BLANKET MATERIALS, ELECTROPLATING
Zero-Mist

FOAMING AGENTS
Aerofroth Frothers
Aerosol 18
Aerosol C-61
Becco
Entrapped Plantarome Foam Producer
Ninex 21
Quillaja
Sulfonate WS

FOAM PLASTICS. See Resins & Plastics, Cellular & Foam

FOAM RUBBER. See Rubbers, Cellular & Foam

FOAM STABILIZERS
Hyonic
Ninol AA62

FOOD DYES. See Dyes, Food, Drug, Soap, Cosmetic, Etc.

FOOD PRESERVATIVES. See Preservatives, Food

FOOD-PROCESSING PLANT CLEANERS. See Cleaners & Detergents, Food-Processing Plant

FOOD PRODUCTS
Accolade Oleomargarine
Amaizo 721A Starch
Anise Seed
Casein
Colac
Cottonseed Oil
Dixie
Finesse
Flair Shortening
Flo
Fribase
Fry-Base
Gleam
Glen Eden Margarine
Golden Capri
Golden Mist Margarine
Gold'n:Wedge Margarine
Granular Frodex
Grayson Margarine
Hibase
Hollandale Margarine
Hrdflakes
Hy-Base
Hy-Chill Salad Oil
Insta-Sol
Jack Rabbit
Jaxmor
Kerba
Kiss-O'-Flavor
Lik-Wid
Liqui-Fry
Lite
Log Cabin
Log Cabin Margarine
Meadolake Margarine
Meva
Mix-Ezy
Nylene
Octagon (Hippocrates)
Par-T-Kreme
Pream
PSM-35
Py-Eze
Pylex
Shine
Southern Queen
Staley's
Sta-Mino
Sweetose
Ten-B-Low
Mrs. Tucker's Salad Oil
Mrs. Tucker's Shortening
Vaf
Vafet
Velvet
Velvet B
Velvet-M
Velvet Oil
Velvorene
Wizard

FOOD STABILIZERS. See Stabilizers, Food

FOOD SUPPLEMENTS
20/FOS
Abdec Drops
Abdec Kapseals
Betalco V-P 728
Betaris V-P 727
Bi-Cap
Biost Tablets V-P 733
Biost V-P 730
Calci-Phade V-P 724
Calciplex V-P 725
Calcisalin
Cataplex E₂ V-P 732
Cerodyn V-P 723
Dicaldimin
Dicalets
Doh-Tone
Eldec Kapseals
Ferroplus V-P 722
Forticon
Gantrex
Gerix
Hydrolyzed Vegetable Proteins 43-A and 52-A
Hyotole-12
Livitol
Maxilets
Micratized
Minaplex V-P 721
Minerovit
Myva-Dry
Myvapack
Myvax
Nopcaine
Nopcom
Nopco-Pak
Nualets
Patheba Tablets
Prenasup
Protedyn V-P 726
RG Soya Lecithin
Rutaplex A V-P 729A
Rutaplex V P 729
Staley's
Super Drex
Super Nopdex
Toleron
Triceratops (Design)
Verclysyl
Vitab B-Complex Extract
Vita-Kaps

FOOD THICKENING AGENTS. *See* Thickening Agents, Food, Cosmetic, Drug, Etc.

FORGINGS, STEEL. *See* Steel Castings & Forgings

FOSSIL RESINS. *See* Resins, Fossil

FOUNDRY MOLD BINDERS. *See* Binders, Foundry Mold

FRICTION TAPES. *See* Tapes, Friction

FRUIT COATINGS. *See* Coatings, Fruit, Vegetable, Flower, Etc.

FUEL-OIL ADDITIVES
Deisel Gumout
Fuelgard
Oil-Solv
Paradyne
Tenamene 60
Tolad

FUELS, MOTOR. *See* Motor Fuels

FULLER'S EARTH
Fuller's Earth

FUMIGANTS, GRAIN
Larva-Tectant
Serafume

FUMIGANTS, SOIL. *See* Soil Disinfectants, Fungicides & Fumigants

FUNGICIDE CARRIERS & DILUENTS. *See* Carriers & Diluents, Insecticide & Fungicide

FUNGICIDE EMULSIFERS. *See* Emulsifying Agents, Insecticide, Fungicide & Herbicide

FUNGICIDES, AGRICULTURAL
Aero Cyanamid
Bell's Atom-Ix
Bone Oil
Bordeaux Mixture
Gallotox
Gallotox 51
Isotox PMA Seed Treater
Larvacide
Liberty
Lime Sulfur
Micro Nu-Cop
Mildex
Mystikil Rose Duster
Nicotine Pyrox
Patterson's Copper Carbonate, 20%
Puradrin
Puraseed
Sharples Accelerator 52
Sharples Accelerator 62
Tennessee Tri-Basic Copper

FUNGICIDES, INDUSTRIAL
Advacide
Ferox
Gallicide
Gallosan
Germocid
Merfenel 51
Merfenel PMA
RADA
Rosin Amine D
Sterozol
Vancide 32
Vancide 50 Peps
Vancide 51
Vancide 89 *and* Vancide 89RE
Wittox

FUNGICIDES, MEDICINAL
Bactine
Formula 44

FUNGICIDES, PAINT
Advacide
Vancide 89 *and* Vancide 89RE

FUNGICIDES, SEWER-TREATMENT
Rooticate

FUNGICIDES, SOIL. *See* Soil Disinfectants, Fungicides & Fumigants

FUNGICIDES, TEXTILES (*See also* Preservatives, Textile)
Vancide 26EC
Vancide 51
Wittox

FUNGUS-RESISTING PAINTS. *See* Paints, Etc., Fungus-Resisting, Disinfecting, Etc.

FURANE RESINS & PLASTICS. *See* Resins & Plastics, Furane

FURNACE CLEANERS. *See* Cleaners & Detergents, Boiler & Furnace

FURNACE WALLS
Bi-Met

FURNACES, ELECTRIC
Heroult

FURNITURE
Birchcraft
Ethan Allen
Restocrat
Roomates

FURNITURE BLEMISH REMOVERS. *See* Blemish Removers, Furniture

FURNITURE CLEANERS. *See* Cleaners & Detergents, Furniture

FURNITURE POLISHES & WAXES. *See* Polishes & Waxes, Furniture

G

GALVANIZED STEELS. *See* Steels, Galvanized

GALVANIZING COMPOUNDS
Aladdin Galvanizing Compound
Drygalv

GARDEN TOOLS & EQUIPMENT. *See* Tools & Equipment, Farm & Garden

GARMENTS, PROTECTIVE
Acidpruf
Chemgard
Chemklos
Chempruf
Cool Cap
Earsaver
M-S-A
MSA Comfo Cap
Shockgard
Skullgard

GAS ANALYZERS. *See* Analyzers, Gas & Liquid

GAS-DRYING AGENTS. *See* Drying Agents, Gas & Liquid

GAS- & LIGHT-FADING INHIBITORS
Emkacide GFI-40
Emkafume S
GFN Inhibitor Base
Hartofume C
Inhibitex

GAS GENERANTS, OXYGEN & HYDROGEN
Becco

GAS ODORANTS. *See* Odorants, Gas

GAS PURIFICATION MATERIALS, EQUIPMENT, ETC.
Black Magic

GAS TRAPS. *See* Traps, Gas, Steam, Etc.

GASKETING & PACKING MATERIALS
Acme Polyfluoron Molding Powder
Agilene-F
Bistex with Teflon
Cardinal
Clipper Seal Packing
Combat
Cork
Cumpac
"John Crane" Chemlon
Kearsarge Gaskets
Kearsarge Sheet Packing
Klinger-Acidit
Klingerit
Klingerit-1000
Klinger-Oilit
Liberty Red Rubber Sheet Packing
Mobilene
Palmetto G-T Ring
Parker Unipar
Runwel
Sea Ring Packing
Service Sheet Packing and Cut Gaskets
Spirotallic
Tadpole Gasketing Tape
Thermo Rod Packing
Tucks Coil Packing
Uneepac
Vinylfoam

GELATINES & GLUES
Econoflex
Glu-Beeds
Hero
Isinglass
Keystone Gelatin

GELLING AGENTS (See also Thickening Agents)
Ben-A-Gel
Bentone
Bentone 18-C
Bentone 34
Bentone 38

GELLING AGENTS, INDUSTRIAL PRODUCT
Abco-Gel

GEMS
Amethyst
Corundum
Garnet

GENERATING EQUIPMENT, ELECTRICAL. See Electrical Generating Equipment

GERMICIDAL CLEANERS. See Cleaners & Detergents, Germicidal

GERMICIDAL SOAPS. See Soaps, Antiseptic, Germicidal, & Deodorant

GERMICIDES
ACCO Streptomycin D
Amerse
Bactine
Becco
Biostat
Biostat-PA
B-K Bacili-Kil
Diversol CX
Fortracin
Gallicide
Gallosan
Germicin
Merfenel 51
Merfenel PMA
Multi-Chlor
Phytomycin
Pittabs
Staphene
Sterozol
Troy Coco-Ster Compound
Vancide 26EC
Vancide 32
Vancide 50 Peps
Vancide 51
Vancide 89 and Vancide 89RE
X-Cide

GLARE ELIMINATORS
Krylon Dulling Spray

GLASS ADHESIVES. See Adhesives, Glass

GLASS CLEANERS. See Cleaners & Detergents Glass, Tile, Etc.

GLASS COLORING AGENTS. See Coloring Agents, Glass

GLASS, ELECTRICALLY-CONDUCTIVE
Ra-Grid Heater Plates

GLASS FABRICS. See Fabrics & Rovings, Glass

GLASS FIBERS. See Fibers, Glass

GLASS-MOLD LUBRICANTS. See Lubricant Ceramic & Glass Molds

GLASS, PLATE & WINDOW
Fine-Tex
Huewhite
Lustracrystal
Lustragray
Lustrakool
Lustrawhite
Parallel-O-Plate
Satinol Finish
Securit Glass
Tobex

GLASS POLISHING AGENTS. See Polishing Agents, Glass

GLASS PRODUCTS, MISC.
Cleaneasy
Huetex
Label-Rite
Ovale
Phenix
Securit Interior Glass Doors

GLASS RAW MATERIALS
Flint
Kyanite

GLASS-TO-METAL SEALING ALLOYS
142 Alloy
Therlo

GLAZES, CERAMIC
Chromoveil
Fleckel

GLAZING COMPOUNDS. See Putties, Lutings, Glazing Compounds, Mastics, Etc.

GLAZING MATERIALS, PLASTIC-TYPE
Acrylic Resin
Filon
Maxlite
Resolite
Resolite Fire-Snuf

GLUE PRESERVATIVES. See Preservatives, Gum, Starch, Glue, Etc.

GLUES. See Gelatines & Glues; and Adhesives

GOGGLES. See Spectacles & Goggles; and Lenses, Safety

GRAIN FUMIGANTS. See Fumigants, Grain

GRAIN INSECTICIDES. See Insecticides, Grain

GRANULATED SOAPS. See Soaps, Granulated & Powdered

GRAPHITE-CONTAINING LUBRICANTS. See Lubricants, Graphite-Containing

GRASS COLORING AGENTS. See Coloring Agents, Grass, Shrub, Bush, Etc.

GREASE BASES
Metasap
Metavis 540
Metavis 543

GREASES, LUBRICATING. See Lubricating Greases

GRINDING AIDS
Attasorb

GRINDING WHEEL BINDERS. See Binders, Grinding Wheel

GRITS, BLAST-CLEANING
Lionblast

GROUTING CEMENT ADDITIVES
Intraplast

GROUTING CEMENTS. See Cements, Grouting

GUM FORMATION INHIBITORS FOR GASOLINE. See Inhibitors, Gum Formation (Petroleum Products)

GUMMED PAPERS. See Papers, Gummed

GUM PLASTICIZERS. See Plasticizers, Gum, Starch, Etc.

GUM PRESERVATIVES. See Preservatives, Gum, Starch, Glue, Etc.

GUM SOLVENTS. See Solvents, Gum, Resin, Plastic, Wax, Etc.

GUMS & GUM SUBSTITUTES
Burtonite #7
Chicle
Ethylex
Gum Arabic
Gutta Percha
Pontianak
Sandarac
Stacolloid
Staley's
Starguar
Storax
Tolu Balsam
Tragacanth

GUNPOWDERS (See also Explosives)

Bear
Bullseye
E. C.
Herco
Hercules 2400
Hercules Red Dot
Hitemp
Hi Vel
Infallible
Lightning
Sharpshooter
Unique

GUN STOCK BEDDING MATERIALS. See Bedding Materials, Gun Stock

GYPSUM LATH, BOARDS, TILE, ETC. (See also Building Boards; and Wallboards)

Acousti Lock Board
Celotex
Screwlock

H

HAIR CLEANERS. See Cleaners & Detergents, Hair & Skin; and Shampoos and Shampoo Bases

HAMMERS AND MALLETS

Basa
Empire

HAND CLEANERS & DETERGENTS. See Cleaners & Detergents, Hand

HAND CREAMS & LOTIONS

Donovo
Fend-X
Hydra-Magic
Lubritine
Pax Hand Cleaning Lotion

HAND CREAMS, PROTECTIVE

Covicone
Fend-A
Fend-E
Fend-F
Fend-I
Fend-I Special
Fend-L
Fend-O
Fend-PC
Fend-Silicone
Fend-U
Fend-X
Go-Jo Protective Hand Cream
Kerodex
Stanley Hand Save

HAND SOAPS. See Soaps, Hand

HARDENERS, CONCRETE & MASONRY—INTEGRAL

Concretite
Emeritex

HARD RUBBERS. See Rubbers, Hard

HARDENERS, CONCRETE & MASONRY—SURFACE

Colored Metalsium
Durocrete
Duromit
Emeri-Topcrete
Silicotite
Sonotard
Super Metalsium

HARDWARE, MISC.

Superior Curtain Rods
Superior Metal Mouldings
Superlok

HEATING, COOLING, VENTILATING & AIR-CONDITIONING EQUIPMENT, SYSTEMS, ETC.

Amervent
Draft/Stop
Herman Nelson
Lamb Air Mover
Selectotherm

HEATING ELEMENTS, ELECTRICAL. See Electrical Heating Elements

HEATING PANELS, ELECTRICAL

Ra-Grid Heater Plates

HEAT-RESISTING ALLOYS

Greek Ascoloy

HEAT-TRANSFER MEDIA

Circo Heat Transfer Oils

HEAT-TREATING ANTI-SCALING AGENTS. See Anti-Scaling Agents, Heat-Treating

HEAT-TREATING OILS, SALTS, ETC.

Aeroheat 1100
Aeroheat 1200R
Draw-Bright 600
Draw-Bright 750
Herring Oil
Sperm Oil
Sunquench 78
Sun Quenching Oil No. 11
Sun Quenching Oil Light

HECTOGRAPHS

Aristoclean
Aristomaster
Aulta Clean
Aultamaster
Finespirit
Finessemaster
Gloriamaster
Gloriaspirit

HERBICIDE EMULSIFERS. See Emulsifying Agents, Insecticide, Fungicide, & Herbicide

HIGH-TEMPERATURE LUBRICANTS. See Lubricants, High-Temperature

HOODS, PLASTIC. See Ducts, Hoods, Tanks, Etc., Plastic

HORMONES, PLANT

CIPC
Nu-Set

HOSE, RUBBER. See Rubber Hose

HOUSEHOLD CLEANERS. See Cleaners & Detergents, Household

HOUSEHOLD INSECTICIDES. See Insecticides, Household

HOUSES, PREFABRICATED

Catalina
Champion
Coronado
Talisman
Visionaire
Westerner

HUMECTANTS

Poly-G
Quadrol
Sweetose

HYDRAULIC CEMENTS. See Cements, Hydraulic

HYDRAULIC FLUIDS

Castor Oil
Circo Hydraulic Oils
Houghto-Safe
Kendall Automatic Transmission Fluid
Kendall Lemon Oil
Lubeway
Park-Cut M.P.
Parko
Pentasol #27
Silicones
Sunvis 700 Oils
Sunvis 900 Oils
Viscasil

HYDROCARBONS, CHLORINATED

Isotron
Nialk

HYDROGEN GENERANTS. See Gas Generants, Oxygen & Hydrogen

HYDROGEN PEROXIDE

Becco

I

ICE PREVENTIVES. See De-Icing Agents & Ice Preventives

IGNITION SYSTEM COATINGS

Sprayway Plastic Spray

IMBEDDING MATERIALS, MICROSCOPY

Storax

IMPREGNATED FABRICS. See **Fabrics, Coated & Impregnated**

IMPREGNATING RESINS. See **Resins, Impregnating**

INCENSE
Fum-Aromas   S. B. Penick & Company

INDICATORS, ACID-BASE
Alkanet   Litmus

INDUSTRIAL CLEANERS. See **Cleaners & Detergents, Industrial**

INDUSTRIAL EXPLOSIVES. See **Explosives, Industrial**

INDUSTRIAL FUNGICIDES. See **Fungicides, Industrial**

INDUSTRIAL INSECTICIDES. See **Insecticides Industrial**

INDUSTRIAL PAINTS. See **Paints, Etc., Industrial**

INHIBITORS, GAS- & LIGHT-FADING. See **Gas- & Light-Fading Inhibitors**

INHIBITORS, GUM FORMATION (FOR PETROLEUM PRODUCTS)
Tenamene 60

INHIBITORS, PICKLING BATH
Inhibitor 250   Oakite Pickle Control No. 5

INHIBITORS, POLYMERIZATION
Sulfole

INKS, DRAWING
Craftint "66" Drawing Inks

INKS, PRINTING. See **Printing Inks**

INKS, STENCIL
Krylon Stencil Ink Sprays

INKS, TEXTILE
Long Reach

INNERSOLES. See **Shoe Soles, Innersoles, Linings, Etc.**

INORGANIC CHEMICALS, MISC. See **Chemicals, Inorganic, Misc.**

INSECT BAITS. See **Baits, Insect**

INSECTICIDE CARRIERS & DILUENTS. See **Carriers & Diluents, Insecticide & Fungicide**

INSECTICIDE EMULSIFIERS. See **Emulsifying Agents, Insecticide, Fungicide & Herbicide**

INSECT REPELLENTS. See **Repellents, Insect**

INSECTICIDE SOLVENTS. See **Solvents, Insecticide**

INSECTICIDE SYNERGISTS. See **Synergists, Insecticide**

INSECTICIDE WETTING AGENTS. See **Wetting Agents, Insecticide**

INSECTICIDES, AGRICULTURAL
Actophene
Anabasine
Aratron
Bayol N-300
BHC
Borerkil
DCPM
DDD
Dee-T-Cide
Deracloud
Deramist
Derris Root
DFDT
Dieldrin
Dimite
Dinoseb
DNC
Endrin
Garden Duster
Heptachlor
Hy-Gam
Hy-Tox Insect Dust
Isodrin
Isotox PMA Seed Treater
Liberty
Lonchocarpus
Malathion
Mergamma
Methoxychlor
Mystikil Rose Duster
Mystikil Termite Emulsion
Nicotine Pyrox
Parathion
Paris Green
Pencal
Penclor
Penco
Penfluor
Penphene
Pestroy
Pratt's Shot Gun Spray *or* Dust
Pyrethrum
Pyrox
Raid
Rotenone
Ryania
Sabadilla
Scale-Tox
Schradan
Sharples Accelerator 52
Sharples Accelerator 62
Strobane
Superior Nu-Oil
Swedish Green
Tall Oil
T.E.P.
Toxaphene

INSECTICIDES, ANIMAL & LIVESTOCK (See also **Dips & Sprays, Livestock**)
Curex Flea Duster
Deracloud
Deramist
Derrilox
Fly-Away Dairy Spray
Fly-Away Dairy Spray Concentrate
Hy-Tox Insect Dust
Kil-O-Mist
Methoxychlor
MGK Repellent 11
Patterson's Creosote Dip and Disinfectant
Patterson's Livestock Fly Spray with Crag Fly Repellent
Sabadilla
Tall Oil

INSECTICIDES, GRAIN
Isotox Spray No. 200
Larva-Tectant
L-P Industrial Spray

INSECTICIDES, HOUSEHOLD
Aerosol Insekil
Airkem Aerosol Insecticide
Airkem Non-Toxic Insecticide
Arresto-Moth
Cedar Breeze
Crown Brand
Dead Easy
Derris Root
DFDT
Erustomoth
Fast-Kill
Fly-A-Way Aerosol
Furethrin
Insecote
Insekil 100
Isotox Spray No. 200
Kil-O-Mist
Larvacide
Lonchocarpus
Magikil Ant and Roach Duster
Magikil Jelly Ant Bait
Malathion
Mistofume
Mysterious Roach Killer Outfit
O-B
Pamisc
Parathion
Penclor
S. B. Penick & Company
Penphene
Pestroy
Pyrethrum
Pyropo
Raid
Rotenone
Sabadilla
Scotch'em
Servacide
Smo-Cloud
Sprayway Tru-Nox
Terminix
Typhoon

INSECTICIDES, INDUSTRIAL
Airkem Aerosol Insecticide
Bone Oil
Ferox
Insekil E.C.
(continued)

INSECTICIDES, INDUSTRIAL (continued)
Kil-O-Mist
Larvacide
L-P Industrial Spray
Malikil
Servacide

INSECTICIDES, POULTRY HOUSE, BARN, ETC.
Fly-A-Way Aerosol
Fly-Away Dairy Spray Concentrate
Hy-Tox Insect Dust
Methoxychlor
Patterson's Livestock Fly Spray with Crag Fly Repellent

INSTITUTIONAL CLEANERS. See Cleaners & Detergents, Institutional

INSULATING MATERIALS, ELECTRICAL (See also Cements, Electrical-Insulating; and Electrical Insulation
Alkanex
Armaturo Asbestos Tape
Asbestoment S
Isolastane
Isoplex
Micro-Quartz
Mycalex 385
Mycalex 400
Mycalex 410
Mycalex 410X
Mycalex K and KM
Plastite
Quinorgo
Silicones
Soapstone
Sterling T-653-LB Thermopoxy
Sterling Thermobonds

INSULATING MATERIALS, THERMAL
Aer-O-Buoy
Aerowrap
Armaflex
Armaglas
Armalite
Armstrong LT Cork Coverings
Asbestos Roll Fire-Felt
Balsa Wood
Bi-Met
BX-4M Insulation
BX-18 Block
Cardinal
Caspro
Cellamite
Celo-Roof
Celotex
ChemoTec
Colfoam
Colony
Combat
Cork
Dolfinite
Felt
Fibrocel
Fibrofil
Gilsulate
Hairinsul
Hewitex
Hylo
IPI-Isofoam
Kapok
L.O.F. Super-Fine
Microlite
Micro-Quartz
Microtex
Mobil-Roll
Ohmstone
Ozite
Palco Industrial Fibers
Perforated Fibretex
Perimsul
P-F
Pioneer #507 Aluminum Mastic
Pioneer #820 Cork Insulation
Poly-Cell
Prasco High Temperature SC
ShadowGrain
Simpson
Talc
Thermasil
Thermoglas Pipe Covering
Thermoglas R/F Insulation
TW-F
Vermiculite
Weatherite Sheating
Zerotex

INSULATION JOINT SEALERS. See Sealers, Insulation Joint

INSULATORS, ELECTRICAL. See Electrical Insulators

INTERIOR PAINTS. See Paints, Etc., Interior

INTERMEDIATES, DYESTUFF. See Dyestuff Intermediates

INTERMEDIATES, ORGANIC SYNTHESIS
Abitol
Arapahoe
MpT
Camphor
Jaylene
Nacconate
Naxol
Naxol D
Pentalene #95
Pentalene #195
Pentaphen #67
Pentasol #26
Pentasol #27
Phosgene
Poly-G
Poly-Solv
Quadrol
Sunaptic Acids
Surfonic Adducts
Versene Acid

INTERMEDIATES, PLASTIC, RESIN, ETC.
Buramine
Casein
Nacconate
Nacconate 1300-50
Palconate
Pentaphen #67

INTERNAL-COMBUSTION-ENGINE CLEANERS. See Cleaners & Detergents, Internal-Combustion-Engine

INTERNAL COMBUSTION ENGINES. See Engines, Internal Combustion

IRON, CAST. See Cast Irons

IRON, MALLEABLE. See Malleable Irons

IRON WIRE. See Wires, Steel & Iron

J

JACKETING, THERMAL INSULATION
Asbestos Firetard Jacket
Fireclad

JET-ENGINE FUELS. See Fuels, Jet-Engine

JET-ENGINE OILS. See Lubricating Oils, Jet-Engine

JOINT-COVERING MATERIALS, WALLBOARD
Perf-A-Tape

JOINT SEALERS, CONCRETE & MASONRY. See Sealers, Concrete & Masonry, Crack & Joint

JOINT SEALERS, METAL. See Sealers, Metal Crack & Joint

JOINTING COMPOUNDS, WATER & SEWER PIPE
Pioneer #301

K

KIER-BOILING ASSISTANTS
Hartex PN

L

LABELING ADHESIVES. See Adhesives, Labeling

LABELS, SELF-STICKING
Able-Stick
E-Z Code
Tel-A-Pipe

LABORATORY TABLE TOPS, SINKS, ETC.
Soapstone

LACQUERS, STOP-OFF. See Stop-Off Lacquers Tapes, Etc., Electroplating

LADLE ADDITIVES, METALLURGICAL
Aeromet

LAKE COLOR DYES. See Dyes, Lake Color

LAKES & TONERS
Britone Red
Fanal
Graphic Red
Illini Red
Solar

LAMINATED FABRICS. See Fabrics, Laminated

LAMINATED METALS
Sullvyne-Clad

LAMINATED PLASTICS. See Plastics, Laminated

LAMINATING ADHESIVES. See Adhesives, Laminating

LAMINATING RESINS. See Resins, Impregnating & Laminating

LANOLIN & LANOLIN DERIVATIVES
Mellisol
Vanzak

LAPPING COMPOUNDS
Super-Lap

LATEX, RUBBER. See Rubber Latex

LATH. See Gypsum Lath, Board, Tile, Etc.

LAUNDRY BLUINGS
Erustohue
Ultramarine Blue

LAUNDRY CLEANERS. See Cleaners & Detergents, Laundry

LAUNDRY SOURS
Dyeset
Erustohue
Erusto-Max
Erusto-Ray
Erustosol

LEAD & LEAD-BASE ALLOYS
Halloy
Hewitt - Detroit Body Solder
Mocar
X-Cell Super X

LEATHER
Suede

LEATHER ADHESIVES. See Adhesives, Leather

LEATHER CLEANERS. See Cleaners & Detergents, Leather

LEATHER COATINGS. See Coatings, Leather

LEATHER DYES. See Dyes, Textile, Leather, Etc.

LEATHER FINISHING AGENTS. See Finishing Agents, Leather

LEATHER LUBRICANTS. See Lubricants, Leather

LEATHER TANNING BATES. See Bates, Leather Tanning

LEATHER WATERPROOFING AGENTS. See Waterproofing Agents, Leather

LEATHER WETTING AGENTS. See Wetting Agents, Leather

LECITHINS
Emultex
Gliddol Lecithin
RG Soya Lecithin
Sta-Sol

LENSES, SAFETY
ANP
Enduron
Optilite

LEVELING AGENTS, PAINT
Levelon
Rheotol
Thick-Aid

LEVELING AGENTS, TEXTILE DYEING
Alkylene A
Atlasol Ag
Dissolving Salt B
Emkalane MF
Emkanyl 85
Emkapene RW
Emkapon K
Emka Supertex
Emkatard
Emkatex 49-P
Emkatex NE
Felco Retarder V
Lunetzol A
Mulsoid 815M
Nekanil
Penetrant Y
Rexopene
Scourlon-Pentalon
Specon X 13
Sulfanone A
Synterge 750
Tergenol S Liquid Conc.
Unishade "NS"

LIGHT-FADING INHIBITORS. See Gas- & Light-Fading Inhibitors

LIGHTWEIGHT AGGREGATES. See Aggregates, Lightweight

LIGHTWEIGHT PLASTERS. See Plasters, Lightweight

LIMESTONE
Coral

LININGS, DUCT. See Duct Linings

LININGS, PIPE. See Pipe Linings

LININGS, SHOE. See Shoe Soles, Innersoles, Linings, Etc.

LININGS, TANK. See Tank Linings; and Rubber Linings, Tank, Etc.

LINOLEUM
Decoray
Install-it-Yourself
Newray
Textelle
Town House

LIQUID ANALYZERS. See Analyzers, Gas & Liquid

LIQUID DRYING AGENTS. See Drying Agents, Gas & Liquid

LIQUID SOAP. See Soaps, Liquid

LIVESTOCK DIPS & SPRAYS. See Dips & Sprays, Livestock

LIVESTOCK INSECTICIDES. See Insecticides, Animal & Livestock

LOW-TEMPERATURE LUBRICANTS. See Lubricants, Low-Temperature

LOW-THERMAL-EXPANSION ALLOYS
146 Alloy

LUBRICANTS, BAKING-PAN, ETC.
Dri-Bake
Edsoy

LUBRICANTS, CERAMIC-, & GLASS-MOLD
CWAB
Hyform Emulsion
Partex

LUBRICANTS, DRY-FILM
No. 16
No. 18
Grafon
Lock-Ease

LUBRICANTS, EQUIPMENT & MACHINERY, MISC.
No. 1 Ice Machine Oil
No. 210 Ice Machine Oil
All Purpose Gear Lubricant
Cat Roll Grease
Circo Lubricating Oils
Condensed Oil No. 50
C. P. Grease
DoAll
Door-Ease Stainless Stick Lubricant
Enthowax Q-524
Gearteck
Grafon
Kendall All-Oil Gear Lube
Kendall Multi-Purpose Hypoid Gear Lube, SCL
Kendall Outboard Gear Grease
Kendall Outboard Hypoid Gear Lube
Keystone No. 29 Cartridged Grease
Keystone No. 44 and No. 45 Greases
(continued)

LUBRICANTS, EQUIPMENT & MACHINERY, MISC. (continued)

Keystone No. 122 Grease
Keystone All Purpose Hypoid Lubricant
Keystone U. W. Grease
K. L. C. Oil
K. O. Grease
KR Lubricant
Krylon-Houghton Tenac Open Gear and Cable Lubricant
Lubeway
New Solnus Oils
Nu Aero Chain Life
O-B
Saw Eez
Spray-Lube
SR Lubricants
S. T. O. Lubricant
Sun 1300 and 1301 Greases
Sun 1893 and 1897 Greases
Sun C-850 EP Greases
Sun C-891T Grease
Sunep Oils
Suniso Refrigeration Oils
Sun N-52X Grease
Sunoco Way Lubricant
Sunotex Machine Oil
Sunotex Machine Oil Light
Sun Prestige 40 Greases
Suntac Oils
Sunvis 700 Oils
Sunvis 900 Oils
Sunvis Oils
Surett
Surett Fluid
Texaco Capella Oil
Texaco Crater
Texaco Crater X Fluid
Texaco Multifax
Texaco Olympian Grease
Texaco Paper Machine Oil HD
Texaco Stazon

LUBRICANTS, EXTREME-PRESSURE

Kendall Multi-Purpose Hypoid Gear Lube, SCL
Kendall Outboard Hypoid Gear Lube
Spray-Lube
Sunep Oils

LUBRICANTS, GRAPHITE-CONTAINING

Grafon
Lock-Ease
Saw Eez

LUBRICANTS, HIGH-TEMPERATURE

Resin Release N
Silicones
Versilube

LUBRICANTS, LEATHER

Kendall Lemon Oil

LUBRICANTS, LOW-TEMPERATURE

No. 1 Ice Machine Oil
No. 210 Ice Machine Oil
Suniso Refrigeration Oils
Texaco Capella Oil
Versilube

LUBRICANTS, METAL-CASTING MOLD (See also Parting Agents, Metal Casting)

Kor-Flo
Liberty Liquid Parting
Metasap
Talc

LUBRICANTS, METAL-WORKING & FINISHING (See also Cutting & Grinding Oils & Coolants)

#140 Stik-Wax
DoAll
Drawax 930 and 931
Drawcote
Durpon
Hamicote D-20
Hamicote D-20-500
Kleen-Kool
Metasap
Oakite Special Drawing Compound
Power-Cut
Rapeseed Oil
Saw Eez
SR Lubricants
Wax-Cut
Wax-Draw
Witcizer

LUBRICANTS, PLASTIC & PLASTIC MOLD

CD Mold Release A
Celite Mineral Fillers
Door-Ease Stainless Stick Lubricant
Drawax 930 and 931
DS-207
Kantstik
Leadstar
Release Agent "G"
Resin Release N.
Silicones
Super King Bomb-Lube
Witcizer

LUBRICANTS, PLUG VALVE

Q Cock Lubricant

LUBRICANTS, RUBBER

No. 16
Door-Ease Stainless Stick Lubricant
Drawax 930 and 931
Lubritine
Parker O-Lube
Ru Glide

LUBRICANTS, RUBBER-MOLD

Drawax 930 and 931
Vanfre

LUBRICANTS, SURGICAL

Lubritine

LUBRICANTS, TEXTILE

Aerotex Softener W
Bradsyn Softener S
Bradtone B
CD Lubricant 105
Ceraloid 356
Ceraloid 356WD
Ceraloid X497702
Cyanatex SB 100 Softener
Dispersal 1278
Drawax 936
Emka Konetex
Emkasize CT Concentrate
Emkatan K
Fancoseal
Felcolan GL
Felcolube K
Hygrolized Oil 221
Lanaseal
Lanoseal
Moretex Napping Softener A
Nopcolube
Rapeseed Oil
Rexolube
Rexowax W-19
Rexowax WS
Texaco Texspray Compound
Vinalube R-100
Wax Emulsion WG
Witcizer

LUBRICANTS, WIRE ROPE

Krylon-Houghton Tenac Open Gear and Cable Lubricant
Surett
Surett Fluid
Texaco Crater
Texaco Crater X Fluid
Tiger-Lube

LUBRICATING GREASES

Carum
Cat Roll Grease
Commerce
C. P. Grease
Degras
Kendall Multi-Purpose Hypoid Gear Lube, SCL
Kendall Outboard Gear Grease
Keystone No. 29 Cartridged Grease
Keystone No. 44 and No. 45 Greases
Keystone No. 122 Grease
Keystone U. W. Grease
K. O. Grease
Petrolatum
Sun 1300 and 1301 Greases
Sun 1893 and 1897 Greases
Sun C-850 EP Greases
Sun C-891T Grease
Sun N-52X Grease
Sun Prestige 40 Greases
Surett
Surett Fluid
Texaco Crater
Texaco Crater X Fluid
Texaco Multifax
Texaco Olympian Grease
Texaco Stazon
Versilube

LUBRICATING GREASE THICKENING AGENTS. See Thickening Agents, Lubricating Grease

LUBRICATING OIL & GREASE ADDITIVES

Aeronox
Com-Plus
Ethylac #650
Or-Lo
Sharples Accelerator 52
Sharples Accelerator 62
Sharples Accelerator 77
Sulfonate OS
Vistone

LUBRICATING OILS (See also Motor Oils)

Ben Oil
Black Fish Oil
Castor Oil
Circo Lubricating Oils
Commerce
Condensed Oil No. 50
Door-Ease Dripless Oil
Dowlube
Dynavis Oils
Estor HD
Kendall, The 2000 Mile Oil
Kendall All-Oil Gear Lube
Kendall Lemon Oil
Kendall Motor Oil Non-Detergent
Kendall Outboard Motor Oil
Kendall Super-D Oil
K. L. C. Oil
Kodak
Lock-Ease
Neatsfoot Oil
(continued)

LUBRICATING OILS (continued)

New Solnus Oils
Park-Cut M.P.
Rapeseed Oil
Sperm Oil
Suniso Refrigeration Oils
Sunoco Way Lubricant
Sunotex Machine Oil
Sunotex Machine Oil Light
Suntac Oils
Sunvis 700 Oils
Sunvis 900 Oils
Sunvis Oils
Texaco Capella Oil
Texaco Paper Machine Oil HD
The 2000 Mile Oil
Tro-Mar DX 130
Valvoline All-Climate
Versilube

LUBRICATING OILS, STEAM-CYLINDER

D-25 Cylinder Oil
D-50 Cylinder Oil
Esso-Mar EP56
Esso-Mar EP65

LUTINGS. See **Putties, Lutings, Glazing Compounds, Mastics, Etc.**

M

MACHINERY LUBRICANTS. See **Lubricants, Equipment & Machinery, Misc.**

MACHINERY PAINTS. See **Paints, Etc., Machinery & Equipment**

MACHINERY STEELS. See **Steels, Machinery**

MAGNESIUM & MAGNESIUM-BASE ALLOYS

Corosex
Galvomag

MAGNET WIRES

Amvar

MALLEABLE IRONS

H. T. M.

MALLETS. See **Hammers & Mallets**

MARINE BEDDING COMPOUNDS. See **Bedding Compounds, Marine**

MARINE PAINTS, ETC. See **Paints, Etc., Marine**

MASKING MATERIALS, PAINT

CD Spray Mask A
Coverlac
Dursign
Parko
Parko Protex-It

MASKING MATERIALS, SOLDERING

Lonco PC #33 Solder Resist

MASONRY CLEANERS. See **Cleaners & Detergents, Concrete & Masonry**

MASONRY COATINGS. See **Coatings, Concrete & Masonry;** and **Paints, Etc., Concrete & Masonry**

MASONRY CRACK & JOINT SEALERS. See **Sealers, Concrete & Masonry Crack & Joint**

MASONRY PAINTS. See **Paints, Etc., Concrete & Masonry**

MASONRY SEALERS, SURFACE. See **Sealers, Concrete & Masonry Surface**

MASONRY WATERPROOFING AGENTS. See **Waterproofing & Dampproofing Agents, Concrete & Masonry**

MASTICS. See **Putties, Lutings, Glazing Compounds, Mastics, Etc.**

MEAT TENDERIZERS

Papain

MEDICAL APPLIANCES

Abboject
Abbo-Liter
Abbo-Vac
Aerohalor
Cly-Q-Pak
Donopak
Donopak-Ette
Manolator
Non-Vac
Phantocube
Pliapak
Powdalator
Venopak
Venoset

MEDICAL DIAGNOSTIC AIDS. See **Diagnostic Aids, Medical**

MEDICINAL FUNGICIDES. See **Fungicides, Medicinal**

MEDICINALS

Abbocillin
A-C
Acaroid Resin
Acetycol
Acidoride
Actaloy
ACTH
Afko-Carb
Afko Ear Oil
Afko-Hist
Afko Rub
Afko-Sal
Akfo Syrup
Afko-Thricin Cream
Afko-Thricin Lozenges
Agoral
Alcophobin
Algin or Alginic Acid
Alglyn Tablets
Alka-Seltzer
Alka-Zane
Alminate Tablets
Americaine with Neomycin
Aminet
Aminosol
Amo-Dex
Amoebicon
Anayodin
Angitet
Anise Oil
Antistine-Privine
Antrenyl
Anusol
Apamide
Apamide-Vess
A-P-N
Apresoline
Apromal
Aquestrol
Atarox
Atophan
Atrobar-M
Aurocoloid
Auroseed
Azo Gantrisin
Azonamide
Bacillets
Bactine
Barbonate Tablets
Becco
Beclysyl
Bejectal
Belglyn Tablets
Betamene
Betasyamine
Bevidox
Biomydrin
Black Balsam
Blutene
Bristalin
Bristiamin APC Tablets
Bristamin Tablets
Bristapen 200
B.S.P. Tablets
Cajeput Oil
Cal-Bis-Ma
Calcidrine
Camoform
Carbogen
Carmethose
Carmethose-Trasentine
Catechu
Cathomycin
Cel-U-Bee Tablets
Centrine
Cevicetyl
Chlorogiene
Chlorostrep Kapseals
Choledyl
Cholmodin
Choline
Cibalgine
Cinchona
Citrex Syrup
Citrisan
Cobenzil
Cochise
Co-Deltra
Co-Hydeltra
Colpotab
Compocillin-V
Consol
Consolets
Coramine
Coryban
C.S.A. Tablets, Improved
Cumopyran
Darthronol
Decholin
Degalol
Desbutal
Desoxets
Diace
Dial
Diasone
Diatussin
Dibistine
Digifortis
Di-Paralene
Doriden
Doxol
Duozine
Eldec Kapseals
Elkosin
Enterab
Enterosulfon
Entero-Vioform Tablets
Ephynal Acetate
Erythrocin
Erythromid
Eticylol
Femandren Linguets
(*continued*)

MEDICINALS (continued)

Ferro-Desicol Kapseals
Ferronord
Filmtab
Gantricillin (100)
Gantricillin 300
Gantrisin Cream
Gantrisin Ear Solution
Gantrisin Nasal Solution
Gantrisin Ophthalmic
Gelusil
Gentamine Tablets
Germicin
Gemonil
Glutazyme
Gray's Compound
Gynestrol
Hepta-Desicol Kapseals
H.M.C.
Hyazyme
Hydeltra
Hydeltracin
Hydro-Bilein
Hydrocortone-T.B.A.
Hydrodyne
Hydrozets
Hypertencin and Hypertencin Mild
Hyprophen
Hytrophen
Iberol
Ichthyamer
Immunovac
Infatabs
Inositol
Inversine
Ionosol
Ion-O-Trate
Iradogen
Isadoxol
Isocrin
Isodine
Isopacin
Itrumil Sodium
Kectil Suspension
Kwell
Lipo Gantrisin
Lipoiodine
Lissephen
Lorfan Tartrate
Lullamin Drops
Malglyn Compound Tablets
Malto Yerbine
Manartal
Medinal
Mepherin
Merlenate
Meta Cine Douche Powder
Metasert Inserts
Methionine
Methium
Methium with Reserpine
Microsulfon
Moebiquin
Monitan
Mucotin
My-B-Den
Mytinic
Nembudeine
Nembu-Donna
Nembu-Fedrin
Nembu-Gesic
Nembu-Serpin
Nembutal
Neobon
Neobon Liquid
neo Bromth Tablets
Neohetramine
Neuro-Centrine
Nicamin
Niconyl
Norisodrine
Nostyn
Nuporals
NYQ
Old Dr. Stork's
Palapent
Panbiotic
Papain
Paradione
Para-Syllium
Parsidol
Patheba Tablets
Peausan
Peganone
Pen-Aqua
Penicillin
Penitracin
Peralga
Peritrate
Phenurone
Phylladrine
Phytin
Pinealco
Placidyl
Plestran
Plimasin
Polycycline
Polycycline Aqueous '250'
Polycycline Intramuscular
Polycycline Intravenous
Polycycline Ointment
Polycycline Ophthalmic Ointment
Pre-mens
Prenasup
Proketuss
Promacetin
Protobore
Prulose Complex
Pyribenzamine-Ephedrine Tablets
Pyribenzamine Expectorant
Pyribenzamine Injectable Solution
Pyribenzamine Ointment and Cream
Pyricidin
Quelicin
Quertine
Racobal
Radiocaps
Rauwicon
Reditrin
Regitine
Restolic
Rhatany
Rimifon
Ritalin
Roxel *and* Roxel Forte
Salihexin
Sandalwood Oil
Sanicyl
Sebb
Seed-O-Lax
Seleen
Selsun
Senokap
Senokot
Serpasil
Serpasil-Apresoline
Serphedrine
Serphylline
Serpicon
Sesame Oil
Silicote Skin Protectant Ointment
Sinker
Sippyplex
Somatovite
Sorlate
Sterilope
Sterisil
Stigmonene
Stilphostrol
Stimavate Tastitabs
Storax
Storcavite
Streptoconin
Strocillin
Sulestrex
Sulfastrep
Sulfa-Ter Tablets
Sulfedex
Sulfedexan
Sulf-Opto
Sulvetil
Sulvetil-Es
Swedish Green
Tabcin
Tarcortin
Tashan Cream
TCA
Teebacin
Teebacin Acid
Teebaconin
Teebazone
Tempogen Forte
Testrolex
Theelin R-P
Thenylene
Theoglycinate
Theophorin Tartrate
Toleron
Toloxyn
Tolu Balsam
Topitracin
TPN
Trasentine-Phenobarbital
Triazoline
Tricainal
Tridione
Trinesium
Triple C Syrup
Tronolen
Tronothane
Truo-Cillin
Truozine
Trynazin
Uritone
Urosulfin
Urosulfon
Urotropin
Vanquin
Varisol
Veniturp
Venotube
Verabore
Vinactane
Vinobel
Viterra Tastitabs
Vi-Thyro
Ziradryl Cream, Lotion
Zirnox

MEDICINALS, VETERINARY

A-B-C Phenothiazine
Antilepto
Bovigen
Caparsolate
Delvinal
Dornavac
Eramide
Erysipogen
Erythrotil
Flavor-Feen
Forvecil
Gallimycin
Hypobeta-20
Livestock Self Dewormer
Nemazene
Nembusen
Patterson Phenothiazine, Drench Grade
Pro-Stat
Vetrophin

MELAMINE RESINS & PLASTICS. See **Resins & Plastics, Melamine**

MEMBRANES, CONCRETE-CURING. See **Concrete-Curing Membranes**

MEMBRANES, WATERPROOFING. See **Waterproofing Membranes**

METAL ADHESIVES. See **Adhesives, Metal**

METAL BRIGHTENING AGENTS. See **Brightening Agents, Metal**

METAL-CASTING MOLD-FACING MATERIALS. See **Mold-Facing Materials, Metal-Casting**

METAL-CASTING MOLD LUBRICANTS. See **Lubricants, Metal-Casting Mold**

METAL-CASTING MOLD-MAKING MATERIALS. See **Mold-Making Materials, Metal-Casting**

METAL-CASTING PARTING AGENTS. See **Parting Agents, Metal-Casting**

METAL-CASTING PROCESSES, EQUIPMENT, & MATERIALS, MISC.

Durabutton	Mabco Pattern Paint
Durarod	Mabcotherm 23IS
Durastrip	Mabcotherm Pipe Eliminator
Duratube	
Flexigate	Microcast
Glascast	Release Agent "G"

METAL-CASTING SEALERS. See Sealers, Metal-Casting

METAL CLEANERS. See Cleaners & Detergents, Metal; and Solvents, Metal-Cleaning

METAL-CLEANING SOLVENTS. See Solvents, Metal-Cleaning; and Cleaners & Detergents, Metal

METAL COATINGS. See Coatings, Metal; and Paints, Etc., Metal

METAL CRACK & JOINT SEALERS. See Sealers, Metal Crack & Joint

METAL ETCHING AGENTS. See Etching Agents, Metal

METAL EXTRUSIONS

Superior Curtain Rods   Superior Metal Mouldings

METAL FENCING. See Fencing, Metal

METAL FOILS

Flouro-Foil

METAL MOLDINGS. See Molding, Metal, Wood Plastic, Etc.

METAL PAINTS. See Paints, Etc., Metal

METAL PICKLING AGENTS. See Pickling Agents, Metal

METAL POLISHES. See Polishes, Metal

METAL POWDERS

Speedex

METAL PRIMERS. See Primers, Metal; and Paints, Etc., Metal

METAL REFINING & MELTING FLUXES. See Fluxes, Metal Refining & Melting

METAL-WORKING & -FINISHING LUBRICANTS. See Lubricants, Metal-Working & -Finishing

METALLIC SOAPS. See Soaps, Metallic

METALLIZING COMPOUNDS

Pyrometalik

METALLURGICAL LADEL ADDITIVES. See Ladel Additives, Metallurgical

METALS & ALLOYS. See:

Abrasion-Resisting Alloys	Clad Metals, Non-Ferrous
Acid-, Alkali-, & Corrosion-Resisting Alloys	Copper & Copper-Base Alloys
Aluminum & Aluminum-Base Alloys	Die-Casting Die Alloys
	Electrical Conductors
Bearing & Bushing Metals	Electrical Heating Elements
Bronzes	Electrical-Resistance Alloys
Carbides, Cast & Cemented	Electrodes, Brazing & Welding
Cast Irons	
Glass-to-Metal Sealing Alloys	Steel Castings & Forgings
Ladle Additives, Metallurgical	Steel & Iron, Bar & Rod
Laminated Metals	Steel & Iron, Sheet, Roll, Strip & Plate
Lead & Lead-Base Alloys	Steels, Case-Hardening
Low-Thermal-Expansion Alloys	Clad
Magnesium & Magnesium-Base Alloys	Equipment
	Galvanized
Magnet Wires	Machinery
Malleable Irons	Rails, Etc.
Metal Extrusions	Reinforcing
Metal Foils	Spring
Metal Powders	Stainless
Nickel & Nickel-Base Alloys	Tool & Die
	Terne Plate
Pipes, Tubes, & Fittings	Thermocouples & Accessories
Plastic Mold & Die Alloys	Tin & Tin-Base Alloys
Poles & Posts, Steel	Tungsten & Tungsten-Base Alloys
Porous Metals & Alloys	Wear-Resisting Alloys
Radio & Electronic Alloys	Welding & Brazing Rods & Electrodes
Rare Earth Alloys & Oxides	Wire Rope
Selenium	Wires, Non-Ferrous
Sintered Metal Products	Wires, Steel & Iron
Solders	

METERING PUMPS. See Pumps, Metering

METERS, SOUND. See Sound Meters

MICAS

No. 16	Mycalex 410
No. 18	Mycalex 410X
Alsibronz	Mycalex K and KM
Dragon's Blood	"R"
Isomica	Samica
Kalsitex	Silkos
Mica	Synthamica
Mycalex 385	Vermiculite
Mycalex 400	

MICROBIOLOGICAL NUTRIENTS. See Nutrients, Microbiological

MICROCRYSTALLINE WAXES. See Waxes, Microcrystalline

MICROPROJECTORS

Dust-Vue Microprojector

MICROSCOPY IMBEDDING MATERIALS. See Imbedding Materials, Microscopy

MILDEWPROOFING AGENTS & MILDEWICIDES (See also Fungicides, Industrial)

Advacide	Emkacide MP
Atco GS-14	Interchem

MILITARY GASES. See Poison Gases, Military

MINERAL OILS, WHITE

Commerce

MODIFIERS, WAX. See Wax Modifiers

MOISTURE-RESISTANT PAINTS, ETC. See Paints, Etc., Moisture-Resistant

MOLD WASHES. See Core & Mold Washes

MOLDED PLASTICS. See Plastics, Molded

MOLDING COMPOUNDS, SYNTHETIC-RESIN & PLASTIC

- Ace Parene
- Ace Parith
- Ace Parlan
- Ace Parnal
- Ace Parsan
- Ace-Tuf
- Acme Polyfluoron Molding Powder
- Alkyd Resins
- CD Spray Mask A
- Cordopreg
- Cymac
- Cymel
- Dur-Ace
- Durez
- Exon
- Fiberite
- Fortiflex
- Fostarene
- Hercocel
- Lexan
- Nixon
- Plenco
- Pleogen
- Polymix
- Riji-Tuf
- Styromix
- Tempron
- Tenite Acetate
- Tenite Butyrate
- Tenite Polyethylene
- Valite
- Vulkene
- Vygen 100

MOLDINGS, METAL, WOOD, PLASTIC, ETC.

- Silvatrim

MOLD-FACING MATERIALS, METAL CASTING

- Mabco Mineral Facing
- Mabco Seacoal Facing
- Star Facing

MOLD-MAKING MATERIALS, FLEXIBLE

- Flexible Mold Compound #201
- Poly-Flex 100

MOLD-MAKING MATERIALS & PROCESSES, METAL-CASTING

- Plasti Sand Process

MONOSODIUM GLUTAMATE

- Aji-Ac'cent
- Mei-Wei-Fen
- Shirayuki
- Tasti
- Three Sheep
- Zest

MOP OILS & DRESSINGS

- Cling
- Dustnox
- Nu-Finish

MORDANTS

- Keystone Ammonium Carbonate
- Orcochromate Mordant

MORTAR ACCELERATORS. See Accelerators, Concrete & Mortar

MORTAR COLORING AGENTS. See Coloring Agents, Concrete, Mortar, Etc.

MORTAR PLASTICIZERS. See Plasticizers, Concrete & Mortar

MORTARS

- Coresite Cement
- Knight No. 2 Cement

MOTHICIDES

- Arresto-Moth
- Cedar Breeze
- Erustomoth
- Insekil 100
- Raid

MOTHPROOFING AGENTS

- Raid
- Sterilair
- Tupco

MOTOR FUELS

- Sky Chief Marine Gasoline
- Turbane

MOTOR OIL ADDITIVES

- Com-Plus
- Dee-Zol
- Dowlube
- Mix-I-Go
- Paradyne
- Parko Super-Dri
- Petrox

MOTOR OILS (See also Lubricating Oils)

- Commerce
- Dowlube
- Dynavis Oils
- Estor HD
- Kendall, The 2000 Mile Oil
- Kendall Motor Oil Non-Detergent
- Kendall Outboard Motor Oil
- Kendall Super-D Oil
- The 2000 Mile Oil
- Tro-Mar DX 130
- Valvoline All-Climate

MULTI-COLOR PAINTS. See Paints, Etc., Multi-Color

N

NAILS

- American
- Amering
- Cooler
- Corker
- Griptite
- Ideal
- Kupred
- Lock-Seal
- Red Hoop
- T

NATURAL FIBERS. See Fibers, Natural

NATURAL RESINS. See Resins, Natural

NATURAL RUBBERS. See Rubbers, Natural

NATURAL WAXES. See Waxes, Natural

NICKEL & NICKEL-BASE ALLOYS

- 33 Alloy
- 99 Alloy
- Cathaloy
- Monar
- Permagrid

NON-FERROUS CASTINGS. See Castings, Non-Ferrous

NON-FERROUS CLAD METALS. See Clad Metals, Non-Ferrous

NON-FERROUS PIPES, TUBES & FITTINGS. See Pipes, Tubes & Fittings, Non-Ferrous

NON-SKID FLOORING MATERIALS. See Flooring Materials, Non-Skid

NON-SKID PAINTS. See Paints, Etc., Non-Skid

NON-SKID RUGS & CARPETING. See Rugs & Carpeting, Non-Skid

NURSERY ANTI-TRANSPIRANTS. See Anti-Transpirants, Nursery

NUTRIENTS, MICROBIOLOGICAL

- Corn Steep Liquor
- Special Nutrient 4-S
- Special Nutrient 22 and Special Nutrient 114
- Sta-Mino

NYLON RESINS & PLASTICS. See Resins & Plastics, Nylon

O

ODORANTS, GAS

- Pentalarm "A"
- Stopleak #1008
- Stopleak #1009

OIL ABSORBENTS (FOR FLOORS). See Absorbents, Oil & Grease (For Floors)

OIL ANTI-OXIDANTS. See Anti-Oxidants, Oil, Fat, Etc.

OIL EMULSIFIERS. See Emulsifying Agents, Fat & Oils

OIL PRESERVATIVES. See Preservatives, Fat, Oil, Drug, Cosmetic, Etc.

OIL SOLUBLE DYES. *See* **Dyes, Oil Soluble**

OIL STABILIZERS. *See* **Stabilizers, Fat, Oil, Etc.**

OIL TANK FLOATING COVERS

OIL-WELL CEMENTS. *See* **Cements, Oil Well**

OIL-WELL DRILLING-MUD ADDITIVES

Adomite	Palco Seal
Black Magic "Supermit"	Palcotan
Burtonite #7	Peptomagic
Cypan	Quebracho
Economagic No-Glo Oil	Strata-Fiber
Palco Industrial Fibers	Strata-Seal
Palconate	

OIL-WELL DRILLING & PRODUCTION EQUIPMENT

Oilwell

OILS. *See:*

Air Filter Oils	Mop Oils & Dressings
Castor Oils	Motor Oils
Essential Oils	Oils, Misc.
Fish & Sperm Oils	Paint & Varnish Oils & Vehicles
Heat-Treating Oils	
Hydraulic Fluids	Penetrating Oils
Lubricating Oils	Pine Oils
Lubricating Oils, Steam-Cylinder	Tall Oils
	Transformer Oils
Lubricating Oils, Steam Turbine	Vegetable Oils & Vegetable Oil Products
Mineral Oils, White	

OILS, MISC.

Bone Oil	Poppy Oil
Neatsfoot Oil	Rapeseed Oil

OPACIFIERS, CERAMICS

Ultrox

OPTICAL BLEACHES

Bleachit IA	Orco Synthrowite FWN
B-Tex	Orco Synthrowite GNW
Cellu-Brite	Uvitex P Conc.
Felcowhite 174	Uvitex RBS
Felcowhite 180	Uvitex TXS Conc.
Orco Synthrowite FWN	Uvitex U

ORGANIC CHEMICALS, MISC. *See* **Chemicals, Organic, Misc.**

ORGANIC SYNTHESIS INTERMEDIATES. *See* **Intermediates, Organic Synthesis**

ORGANOSOLS (*See also* **Plastisols**)

Polyprene

OXIDE-METAL COATINGS

Du-Lite Oxiblak	Ebonol "C"

OXIDES, RARE EARTH. *See* **Rare Earth Alloys & Oxides**

OXIDIZING AGENTS

Becco	Novatol
NCS	Pennex,

OXYGEN GENERANTS. *See* **Gas Generants, Oxygen & Hydrogen**

P

PACKAGING & PACKAGE WRAPPING MATERIALS (*See also* **Bags & Sacks**)

Bemibrite	Cel-Fibe
Bemis Ripp-Tabb	Celopad
Celopak	Patapar
Combat	Printable "TS" Ger-Pak
Craftint Foilcraft	Resistal-Weld
Ger-Pak	Rezlok
Handi-Pack	Ripp-Nipp
Long Reach	Ruf-Grip
Palco Industrial Fibers	Saf-T-Pak Torpedo Tube
Parchment	

PACKING MATERIALS. *See* **Gasketing & Packing Materials**

PACKINGS, TOWER. *See* **Tower Packings**

PADDING MATERIALS, CRASH. *See* **Crash Padding Materials**

PADDINGS, UPHOLSTERY. *See* **Upholstery Padding & Stuffing Materials**

PAINT ADDITIVES, MISC. (*See also* **Anti-Skinning Agents, Paint**)

Drawlene	Rincontroller
M-P-A	Thick-Aid
Rheotol	

PAINT ANTI-OXIDANTS. *See* **Anti-Oxidants, Cosmetic, Drug, Dye, Paint, Plastic & Soap**

PAINT ANTI-SETTLING AGENTS. *See* **Anti-Settling Agents, Paint**

PAINT ANTI-SKINNING AGENTS. *See* **Anti-Skinning Agents, Paint**

PAINT-BRUSH CLEANERS. *See* **Cleaners & Detergents, Paint-Brush**

PAINT DISPERSANTS. *See* **Dispersing Agents, Paint & Pigment**

PAINT DRIERS. *See* **Driers, Paint**

PAINT FLATTING AGENTS. *See* **Flatting Agents, Paint**

PAINT FUNGICIDES. *See* **Fungicides, Paint**

PAINT LEVELLING AGENTS. *See* **Levelling Agents, Paint**

PAINT MASKING MATERIALS. *See* **Masking Materials, Paint**

PAINT OILS. *See* **Paint & Varnish Oils & Vehicles**

PAINT PRESERVATIVES. *See* **Preservatives, Paint**

PAINT RESINS. *See* **Resins, Paint, Varnish, Etc.**

PAINT-SPRAY-BOOTH CLEANERS. *See* **Cleaners & Detergents, Paint-Spray Booth**

PAINT-SPRAY-BOOTH COATINGS. *See* **Spray-Booth Coatings**

PAINT STABILIZERS. *See* **Stabilizers, Paint, Etc.**

PAINT STRIPPERS. *See* **Paint & Varnish Oils & Vehicles**

PAINT THICKENING AGENTS. *See* **Thickening Agents, Paint**

PAINT THINNERS. *See* **Solvents & Thinners, Paint, Varnish, Etc.**

PAINT TINTING AGENTS. *See* **Tinting Agents, Paint**

PAINT WETTING AGENTS. See Wetting Agents, Paint & Pigment

PAINT & VARNISH OILS & VEHICLES

"50" Oil
Amber Oil
"AR" Soy Bean Oil
Burnok
BV
Chemlin
Chempol EP-1
Chempol EP-2
Chempol EP-3
Chempol M-2410
Chempol M-2803
Chempol M-3009
Chempol M-3423
Chempol M-4000
Chempol M-4501
Chempol O-2211
Chempol O-2321
Chempol O-2512
Chempol O-2518
Chempol O-3222
Chempol O-3316
Chempol P-2400
Chempol P-2405
Chempol P-2420
Chempol P-2426
Chempol P-2901
Chempol P-2907
Chempol P-3002
Chempol P-3004
Chempol P-3034
Chempol P-3303
Chempol P-3400
Chempol P-3401
Chempol P-3427
Chempol P-3511
Chempol P-3514
Chempol P-3600
Chempol P-3620
Chempol P-4000
Chempol P-4006
Chempol P-4010
Chempol P-4101
Chempol P-4151
Chempol P-4154
Chempol P-4300
Chempol P-4321
Chempol P-4400
Chempol P-4723
Chempol S-2200
Chempol S-2401
Chempol S-2403
Chempol S-2407
Chempol S-2600
Chia-seed Oil
Cottonseed Oil
Dehydrol
Flexbond 800
Gen-Flo
Grapeseed Oil
Oiticica Oil
Panapol
Perilla Oil
Poppy Oil
Rezamul
Rosin Oil
Stillingia Oil
Tall Oil
Terpex
Tung Oil
USC

PAINT & VARNISH REMOVERS

Diversey No. 16
Enthone Enamel Stripper "P"
Enthone Stripper S-300
Hydropurge
Oakite Stripper Additive
Oakite Stripper, Stripper M-3, Stripper R-6, Stripper No. 110, and Stripper S-A.
Rinse-Away
Rinse-Off
Rustripper
Striprite
Striptex
X-Var

PAINTED-SURFACE CLEANERS. See Cleaners & Detergents, Painted-Surface

PAINTS, ETC., ABRASION-RESISTING

EverLube 1329

PAINTS, ETC., ACIDS-, ALKALI-, & CORROSION-RESISTING

Acme Polyfluoron Liquid Dispersion
Acolite
Apco
Armorhide
BV
Carbomastic Series
Chemfast
Chempol O-2512
Chemtred
Corogard
Epoxin
EverLube 1329
Gripclad
Griplate
Hallephane
Kem Cati-Coat
Neoprene W
Nipoxin
Pioneer #607 and #609
Pioneer #622 Asphalt Paint
Protective Coating #621
Rubber-Coat Liquid Neoprene
Rub-R-Lon
Speed-Rex
Sterling T-653-LB Thermopoxy
Sterling Thermobonds
Stoncote
Tank Clad
Totrust Instant Dry Metal Coat
Tropoxy
Tuf-On Selenium Rectifier Coatings
Vinyl-Cote

PAINTS, ETC., ALUMINUM. See Aluminum Paints

PAINTS, ETC., ARTISTS'

Craftint Super White "37"
Kodak

PAINTS, ETC., AUTOMOBILE

BV
Exlon
OK

PAINTS, ETC., CERAMIC

Apco

PAINTS, ETC., CONCRETE & MASONRY

Acrylastic
Arcopel
Arcotone
BV
Chemtred
Kem Cati-Coat
Kem-Krete
PDO-40
Plexicolor
Rayotint
Reflex-Sol
Rubber-Coat Liquid Neoprene
Sher-Gide
Spectrum
Stoncote
Sure-Foot
Thorosheen RW 7
Topper
Tropoxy
Wall Mate

PAINTS, ETC., ELECTRICAL-CONDUCTING

531 Basic Laboratory Kit
RS14 Shielding Micropaint
RS17 Polyshield Micropaint
SC12 and SC13 Silver Micropaints
SS12-B Silver Shielding Micropaint

PAINTS, ETC., EXTERIOR

Acrylastic
Arcopel
Aulspar
BV
Kem
Kem-O-Lite
Kemplate
Krylon Spray Enamels
Painter Craft
Protective Coating #621
Rub-R-Lon
Silverbrite
Spectrum
S W P
Totrust Instant Dry Metal Coat
Tru-Vy-Kote
Wall Mate

PAINTS, ETC., FIRE-RETARDANT & THERMAL INSULATING

Duo-Tex

PAINTS, ETC., FLOOR

BV
Chempol O-2211
Chemtred
Clearkote
Diamond Floor Finish
Kladak
Neoprene W
Saf-T-Dek
Sure-Foot
Trophy Gym Finish

PAINTS, ETC., FUNGUS-RESISTING, DISINFECTING, ETC.

Arcopel
Ruf-On 745-S and 747-S
Tuf-On Selenium Rectifier Coatings

PAINTS, ETC., HEAT-RESISTING

Alumicone
Durheat
Thermoclad

PAINTS, ETC., INDUSTRIAL

Eye Comfort
Kem
Kem Cati-Coat
Speed-Rex

PAINTS, ETC., INTERIOR

Acrylastic
Allwall
Arcotone
Aulspar
Beauty-Lok
BV
"Dutch Boy" Nalplex
Est-R-Lux
Eye Comfort
Kem
Kemplate
Krylon Spray Enamels

(continued)

PAINTS, ETC., INTERIOR (continued)
Monolux Supreme White Enamel
Opal-Glo
Painter Craft
Quali-Kote
Raylite
Rayotint
Rub-R-Lon
Silverbrite
Spectrum
Super-Kem-Tone
Topper
Totrust Instant Dry Metal Coat
Tru-Vy-Kote

PAINTS, ETC., MACHINERY & EQUIPMENT
Acolite
Adelphi Met-L-Kote Machinery Enamel
Carbomastic Series
Carclad
Dolfinite
Epoxin
Kem
Kemak
Kem-Kold-Bild
Kem Transport
Krylon Spray Enamels
Neoprene W
Nigron
Nipoxin
Speed-Rex
Ultraflo
Vinyl-Cote

PAINTS, ETC., MARINE
BV
Dolfinite
Ensign 714 Epcovar
Neoprene W

PAINTS, ETC., METAL
Acme Polyfluoron Liquid Dispersion
Acolite
Alumicone
Apco
Arcotone
Armorhide
Art Lace
Bar-Ox
Bayflex
Bombay Black
Carbomastic Series
Carclad
Checklac
Chemfast
Chempol O-2518
Cocell
Corogard
Dolfinite
Duracel
Elixirin
Epoxin
EverLube 1329
Ferro-cide
Ferrolox
Galustre
Glidair
Gripclad
Griplate
Hammerguild
IC
Kem
Kemak
Kem Cati-Coat
Kem-Kold-Bild
Kemplate
Kem Transport
Laqua
Lithocrome
Mabco Pattern Paint
Metalguild
Motletone
Neoprene W
Neoprime A
Neoprime B
Nigron
Nipoxin
Peerless
Pioneer #607 and #609
Pioneer #622 Asphalt Paint
Ponkote
Protective Coating #621
Reflex-Sol
Rubber-Coat Liquid Neoprene
Ruf-On Selenium Rectifier Coatings
Speed-Rex
Stoncote
Strepltex
Sure-Foot
Syntemp
Tank Clad
Thermoclad
Totrust Instant Dry Metal Coat
Tropoxy
Tuf-On 745-S and 747-S
Tuf-On Met-L-Brite Clear
Ultraflo
Vinyl-Cote
Wall Mate
Zinc Shield

PAINTS, ETC., MISC.
Aerosyn
Chemvar
Climatic Paints
Crystolux
Glidair
Heath and Milligan Paints
IC
Mawco
Mound City Paints
Nilustre
PC&C
Royal Paints

PAINTS, ETC., MOISTURE-RESISTANT
Arcopel

PAINTS, ETC., MULTICOLOR
Multicolor

PAINTS, ETC., NON-SKID
Rub-R-Lon
Saf-T-Dek
Sono-Grip
Sure-Foot

PAINTS, ETC., PAPER
Tuf-On 745-S and 747-S

PAINTS, ETC., PLASTIC
Acrylic Frosting Lacquer 158A
Corrucote
Duraprem
Polysty-Lac

PAINTS, ETC., PRINTED-CIRCUIT. See Printed-Circuit Paints

PAINTS, ETC., ROOFING (See also Roof Coatings)
Reflex-Sol
Tu-Way

PAINTS, ETC., RUBBER
Parko

PAINTS, ETC., RUBBER-BASE
Apco
Arcopel
BV
Chemtred
Neoprene W
Neoprime A
Neoprime B
Raylite
Rubber-Coat Liquid Neoprene
Rub-R-Lon
Synpra

PAINTS, ETC., SYNTHETIC-RESIN BASE
Acolite
Acrylastic
Acrylic Frosting Lacquer 158A
Adelphi Met-L-Kote Machinery Enamel
Aerosyn
Allwall
Arcotone
Armorhide
Art Lace
Auflex
Aultone
Bar-Ox
Carbomastic Series
Chemfast
Chempol O-2211
Chempol O-2321
Chempol O-2512
Duflex
Ecomul
Epoxin
Est-R-Lux
Flexcel
Galustre
Hallephane
IC
Metalace
Motletone
Nipoxin
OK
PDO-40
Plexicolor
Polyprene
Ponkote
Protective Coating #621
Rayotint
Spectrum
Speed-Rex
Sterling T-653-LB Thermopoxy
Sterling Thermobonds
Stoncote
Synpex
Thorosheen RW 7
Tropoxy
Tru-Vy-Kote
Vinaplas-Lac
Vinyl-Cote
Vinylith
Wall Mate

PAINTS, ETC., WALL
Allwall
"Dutch Boy" Nalplex
Monolux Supreme White Enamel
Opal-Glo
Quali-Kote
Raylite
Spectrum
Super-Kem-Tone
Topper
Wall Mate

PAINTS, ETC., WATER-MIX
Acrylastic
Allwall
"Dutch Boy" Nalplex
Plexicolor
Raylite
Rayotint
Spectrum
Super-Kem-Tone
Thorosheen RW 7
Tru-Vy-Kote
Wall Mate

PAINTS, ETC., WOOD
Apco
Arcotone
Aulspar
(continued)

PAINTS, ETC., WOOD *continued*)

Beauty-Lok
BV
Chempol O-2211
Chempol O-2512
Chempol O-3316
Deco
Diamond Floor Finish
Dolfinite
Glidkote
Kem
Kem Cati-Coat
Krylon Hide-a-Mark
Krylon Spray Enamels
Mabco Pattern Paint
Monolac
Monolac Varnish Stain
Monolux Supreme White Enamel
Neoprime A
Neoprime B
Painter Craft
P.A.R.
Plexicolor
Ponkote
Protective Coating #621
Spectrum
Stoncote
Sure-Foot
SWP
Tech-Var
Trophy Gym Finish
Tropoxy
Wall Mate

PAN CLEANERS. *See* **Cleaners & Detergents, Pot & Pan**

PAPER ADHESIVES. *See* **Adhesives, Paper**

PAPER COATING BINDERS. *See* **Binders, Paper Coating**

PAPER-COATING WAXES. *See* **Waxes, Paper-Coating**

PAPER COATINGS. *See* **Coatings Paper**

PAPER COLORING AGENTS. *See* **Coloring Agents, Paper**

PAPER DYES. *See* **Dyes, Paper**

PAPER PAINTS. *See* **Paints, Etc., Paper**

PAPER PLASTICIZERS. *See* **Plasticizers, Paper**

PAPER SIZES. *See* **Sizing Agents, Paper**

PAPER WATERPROOFING AGENTS. *See* **Waterproofing Agents, Paper, Etc.**

PAPER WETTING AGENTS. *See* **Wetting Agents, Paper**

PAPER WHITENING AGENTS. *See* **Whitening Agents, Paper**

PAPER & PAPER PRODUCTS, MISC. (*See also* **Building Papers; Drawing Papers;** *and* **Photographic Paper & Film**)

Bidco
Conseco
Craftint Foilcraft
Delsey
Duo-Dustin
Hifect
Kimpak
Kleenex
K-Lens-M Tissue
Lumifect
Marvalon
Multifect
Munising
Neenah
Parchment
Proco
Rotofect
Ruf-Grip
Sanek
Simpson
Trufect

PAPERS, BUILDING. *See* **Building Papers**

PAPERS, COATED

Craftint Foilcraft
Crandon
Flash Gloss
Foiltone
Fontana
Kimfect
Lithofect
Marvalon
Prentice
Shorewood
Texoprint

PAPERS, DRAWING. *See* **Drawing Papers**

PAPERS, GUMMED
Devac

PAPERS, PHOTOGRAPHIC. *See* **Photographic Paper & Film**

PAPERS, WAXED
Munising   Patax

PARCHMENT
Durapak   Patapar
Parchkin

PARTING AGENTS, METAL CASTING
Liberty Liquid Parting

PARTING AGENTS, PLASTER MOLD
Partex

PATCHING CEMENTS. *See* **Cements, Patching & Repair**

PATCHING MATERIALS, FLOOR. *See* **Floor Patching Materials**

PATCHING MATERIALS, ROAD. *See* **Road-Patching Materials**

PATCHING MATERIALS, ROOF. *See* **Roof-Patching Materials**

PAVING MATERIALS
Basalt

PEARL ESSENCE
Mearlmaid

PECTINS
Uni-Pectin

PENCILS
Aladdin Soapstone Pencil

PENETRATING OILS
Door-Ease Dripless Oil
Krylon Rust Release
Nu Aero
Parko
Penetrating Oils No. 1 and No. 1A

PERFUME FIXATIVES
Astrotone BR
Black Balsam
Petitgrain
Storax
Tolu Balsam

PERFUMES & PERFUME BASES (*See also* **Deodorants, Industrial Product**)

Anise Oil
Betula Oil
Cajeput Oil
Dorisyl
Duval
Florasynth
Flowerols
Jasmonene
Lavamenthe
Lemongrass Oil
Mellitone
Odrene
Openteine
Penthanco
Penval
Prentalin
Resodor
Rogepel
Rosaryl
Rose Marrakesh
Rosottone
Rosottone Savon
Sandalwood Oil
Sweet Birch Oil
Synalol E
Synalyl D
Tabatonka
Tarophen
Texodor

PEROXIDE, HYDROGEN. *See* **Hydrogen Peroxide**

PETROLATUMS
Commerce   Petrolatum

PETROLEUM-PROCESSING CATALYSTS. *See* **Catalysts, Petroleum-Processing**

PETROLEUM REFINING PROCESSES
Bender Process
Houdresid
Houdriflow
Houdriforming
Houdry Dehydrogenation
Iso-Plus Houdriforming
Petreco
Petreco Electrofining
Petreco Electrosphere Desalting Process

PETROLEUM RESINS. See Resins, Petroleum

PETROLEUM SOLVENTS. See Solvents, Petroleum

PETROLEUM WAXES. See Waxes, Petroleum

PHARMACEUTICAL EMULSIFIERS. See Emulsifying Agents, Pharmaceutical

PHARMACEUTICAL SPECIALTIES
Art Weave
Baby Jumbo
Cleaneasy
Fold-Spray
Gold Leaf
Label-Rite
Opalite
Ovale
Phenix
Quilt
Topper

PHARMACEUTICAL STABILIZERS. See Stabilizers, Drug & Pharmaceutical

PHARMACEUTICALS & PHARMACEUTICAL BASES (See also Medicinals)
Alka-Seltzer
Camphor
Initial Line
Lotocreme
Nostyn
Octagon (Hippocrates)
Old Dr. Stork's
Penresina
Petrolatum
Pinealco
Sebb
Spermacetti
Talc
Uni-Pectin
Vehicol
Velvasil Silicone Fluid

PHENOLIC RESINS & PLASTICS. See Resins & Plastics, Phenolic

PHOTOGRAPHIC CHEMICALS
Dektomat
Duomat
Ektachrome
Ektagraph
Ektonol
Fixomat
Flexichrome
Kodafix
Kodak
Kodalk
KPR
Stopomat

PHOTOGRAPHIC MATERIALS & EQUIPMENT, MISC.
Dry-Developer
Flexichrome
Kodak
Microverter
Slip-Screen
Technicolor
Technirama
Techniscope
Technivision
Verifax

PHOTOGRAPHIC PAPER & FILM
Kodachrome

PHOTOGRAPHIC PRINTS
Kodachrome

PICKLING AGENTS, METAL
Aldox
Pickling Acids

PICKLING-BATH ADDITIVES
Alkontrol

PICKLING-BATH INHIBITORS. See Inhibitors, Pickling-Bath

PIGMENT BINDERS. See Binders, Pigments

PIGMENT DISPERSANTS. See Dispersing Agents, Paint & Pigment

PIGMENT WETTING AGENTS. See Wetting Agents, Paint & Pigment

PIGMENTS, COLORED, MISC. (See also Coloring Agents)
Aquaprint
Arcturus Red
Aridye
Bonadur
Brilliant Toning Red
Britone Red
Ceres
Cyan
Dearborn Red
Eukesol
Graphic Red
Hansa
Harmon Colors
Illini Red
Micro-Fast
Micro-Tex
Nacrosol
Orion Red
Paris Green
PC&C
Permachlor Red
Permachrom Red
Permansa
Plasticone Red
Polaris Red
Pyrolus Maroon
Resoform
Royal Purple
Rubanox Red
Sepia
Serene Green
Shamrock Green
Solar
Solfast
Superior Red
Swedish Green
Ultramarine Blue
Uranium Yellow

PIGMENTS & FILLERS, ALUMINUM COMPOUNDS
ASP

PIGMENTS & FILLERS, CALCIUM COMPOUNDS
Fibrous Filler

PIGMENTS & FILLERS, CLAY
Peerless Clay

PIGMENTS & FILLERS, METALLIC
Midas Gold

PIGMENTS & FILLERS, MICA
Alsibronz
Kalsitex
Mica
"R"
Silkos
Vermiculite

PIGMENTS & FILLERS, MISC.
Accosperse
Colfoam Microballoon Spheres
Nacromer Pearl Pigments
Solar

PIGMENTS & FILLERS, SILICA
Cab-o-sil
Celite
Celite Mineral Fillers
Infusorial Earth
Quso
Tripoli

PIGMENTS & FILLERS, TALC
Meerschaum
Nytal
Soapstone
Talc

PIGMENTS & FILLERS, ZINC COMPOUNDS, MISC.
Ozark

PIGMENTS & FILLERS, ZINC OXIDE
Ozide
Ozlo

PINE OILS
Yarmor

PIPE, ASBESTOS-CEMENT. See Asbestos-Cement Conduit, Pipe, Fittings, etc.

PIPE COATINGS & COVERINGS, DRIPLESS
Dolfinite

PIPE COVERINGS (See also Insulating Materials, Thermal)
Aerowrap
Armaflex
Armstrong LT Cork Coverings
Fibrocel
Prasco High Temperature Thermasil
Thermoglas Pipe Covering

PIPE LININGS (See also Coatings, Metal; and Tank Linings)

Acme Polyfluoron Liquid Dispersion
Carbomastic Series
Lastiglas
Luminite

PIPE-THREAD COMPOUNDS

"John Crane" Chemlon
"John Crane" PLS (Plastic Lead Seal)
"John Crane" Thred-Gard
Key Graphite Paste
Key Tite
No-Glo Thread Lubricant
Parker Unipar
Vike Water Seal

PIPE-WRAP MATERIALS

Blue Flag
Duramat
Duramesh
Glaskote
Nervastral Seal-Pruf H-D

PIPES & FITTINGS, PLASTIC. See Plastic Pipe & Fittings

PIPES, TUBES, & FITTINGS, NON-FERROUS

Alpha
Tube-In-Strip

PIPES, TUBES & FITTINGS, STEEL

B (in diamond)
Boston
National
Scale Free
Shelby
Silverline
Speedline
Spellerized
Tube Line

PITCHES. See Asphalts, Tars & Pitches

PLANT HORMONES. See Hormones, Plant

PLASTER BONDS

Caspro
Kapco
Plaster-Weld
Thorobond
Well-O-Bond

PLASTER HARDENERS. See Hardeners, Concrete & Plaster—Integral

PLASTER-MOLD PARTING AGENTS. See Parting Agent, Plaster-Mold

PLASTER SEALERS. See Sealers, Plaster; and Sizing Agents, Wall

PLASTERS, LIGHTWEIGHT

Gold Bond Sprayolite
Perfolite

PLASTERS, WALL

Caspro
Celotex
Gold Bond Sprayolite
Gray Stone
Perfolite

PLASTIC ADHESIVES See Adhesives, Plastic

PLASTIC ANTI-OXIDANTS. See Anti-Oxidants, Cosmetic, Drug, Paint, Plastic & Soap

PLASTIC ANTI-STATIC AGENTS. See Anti-Static Agents, Plastic & Textile

PLASTIC CLEANERS & DETERGENTS. See Cleaners & Detergents, Plastic

PLASTIC COATINGS. See Coatings, Plastic; and Paints, Etc., Plastic

PLASTIC COLORING AGENTS. See Coloring Agents, Resin & Plastic; Dyes, Plastic; Paints, Plastic; and Pigments

PLASTIC DUCTS. See Ducts, Hoods, Tanks, Etc., Plastic

PLASTIC DYES. See Dyes, Plastic

PLASTIC HOODS. See Ducts, Hoods, Tanks, Etc., Plastic

PLASTIC INTERMEDIATES. See Intermediates, Plastic, Resin, Etc.

PLASTIC-METAL BONDING AGENTS. See Bonding Agents, Rubber-Metal & Plastic-Metal

PLASTIC MOLD & DIE ALLOYS

MC (Mold and Cavity Steel)
Speed Cut
U.S.S. Freemax

PLASTIC & PLASTIC MOLD LUBRICANTS. See Lubricants Plastic & Plastic Mold

PLASTIC MOLDINGS. See Moldings, Metal, Wood, Plastic, Etc.

PLASTIC PAINTS. See Paints, Etc., Plastic

PLASTIC PIPE & FITTINGS

Ace Parian
Ace Riviclor
Dur-Ace
National
Reflin Pipe

PLASTIC POLISHES. See Polishes, Plastic

PLASTIC RODS & TUBES

Ace Parian
Ace Parlan
Ace Riviclor
Acme Polyfluoron Molding Powder
Cadco
Dur-Ace
Ger-Flex.
Ger-Pak
Ger-Tube
Lami-Rock
Nixon
Transflow M-32
Turbolex
Turbotherm
Turbotrans
Turbozone

PLASTIC SEALERS. See Sealers, Plastic

PLASTIC SHEETS & FILMS

Ace Parian
Ace Riviclor
Acme Polyfluoron Molding Powder
Acrylic Resin
Acrylite
Beautafilm
Bosfilm
Cadco
Decaboard
Decaflex
Decaform
Decarlite
Dur-Ace
Enduron
Filon
Foiltone
Genuwood
Gerlite
Ger-Pak
Krene
Larvacover
Masland Duran Clad
Maxlite
Nevamar
Nixon
Nygen Tolex
Plexiglas R
Poly-A9 Cast Film
Printable "TS" Ger-Pak
PyroPanl
Resin-Glas
Resolite
Resolite Fire-Snuf
Saran Wrap
Tuf-Bond
Velon
Wascofilm
Wascoseal

PLASTIC SOLVENTS. See Solvents, Gum, Resin, Plastic, Wax, Etc.

PLASTIC STABILIZERS. See Stabilizers, Resin & Plastic

PLASTIC TANKS. See Ducts, Hoods, Tanks, etc., Plastic

PLASTICS, CELLULAR & FOAM. See Resins & Plastics, Cellular & Foam

PLASTICS, CELLULOSE ACETATE

Ace Parnal
Cadco
CCA
Nixon
Tenite Acetate

PLASTICS, CELLULOSE ACETATE-BUTYRATE

Ace Parlan

PLASTICS, CELLULOSE BUTYRATE
Nixon
Tenite Butyrate

PLASTICS, CELLULOSE NITRATE
Yellow for Green
Herculoid
Nixon

PLASTICS, ETHYL CELLULOSE. See Resins & Plastics, Ethyl Cellulose

PLASTICS, LAMINATED
Corlex
Decaboard
Decaflex
Decaform
Decarlite
Genuwood
Lami-Rock
Masland Duran Clad
Nevamar
Raiflex
Railite
Sullvyne-Clad
Sunform
Taylor Laminated Plastics

PLASTICS, METAL-COATED
Foiltone

PLASTICS, MOLDED (See also Molding Compounds, Synthetic-Resin & Plastic)
Saftepak

PLASTICIZERS, CONCRETE & MORTAR
Plastolith
Sonotard

PLASTICIZERS, GUM, STARCH, ETC.
EC and ECT Stabilizers
Rexole GR
Rexole MC-2
Sweetose
Vanesta

PLASTICIZERS, PAPER
Rexole TW

PLASTICIZERS, RUBBER
Dyal
Dymal
Kenflex A, B, L, N
KP-220
KP-550
Metasap
Plasticizer LP and Plasticizer MP
Polycizer DBP
Polycizer DBS
Polycizer DOS
Polymel C-130
Polymel DX
Polymel DX-111 Powder
RC Plasticizer BD-8
RC Plasticizer O-16
RC Plasticizer TG-8
RC Plasticizer TG-9
Resin 529
Rosin Oil
Rucoam
Sundex-170
Vultra C

PLASTICIZERS, SYNTHETIC-RESIN & PLASTIC
Abitol
Aerotex Softener W
Cabflex
Camphor
Celluphos
Chempol P-3504
Citroflex 2
Citroflex 4
Citroflex A-2
Conoco H-300
Drapex 4.4
Dyal
Dymal
Eldoplast 45
Epoxidol
Harflex 300
Harflex 325
Hercoflex
Kenflex A, B, L, N
KP-220
KP-550
Metasap
Monapolene A
Monapolene Concentrates
Monapolene N
MPS-500 Plasticizer
Nevillac 10°
NP-10
Panaflex
Plasticizer LP and Plasticizer MP
Polycizer 532
Polycizer 562
Polycizer 632
Polycizer 662
Polycizer DBS
Polycizer DOS
Polycizer DBP
Quadrol
RC Plasticizer BD-8
RC Plasticizer E-S
RC Plasticizer O-16
Resoflex R-296
RC Plasticizer TG-8
RC Plasticizer TG-9
RC Polymeric BGA
Rucoam
Staflex
Sundex-170
Witcizer

PLASTISOLS
Chem-o-sol

PLATE GLASS. See Glass, Plate & Window

PLATES, IRON & STEEL. See Steel & Iron Sheet, Roll, Strip, & Plate

PLUG VALVE LUBRICANTS. See Lubricants, Plug Valve

PLYWOOD ADHESIVES. See Adhesives, Plywood

PLYWOODS (See also Building Boards)
African Honeywood

POISON GASES, MILITARY
Phosgene

POISONS, RAT, BIRD, FISH, ETC.
Derris Root
Dethdiet
Larvacide
Magitrack Mouse Duster
Patterson's Water Soluble
Pivalyn
Rat-A-Way Bait
Rat-A-Way Concentrate
Redratsquill
Red Squill

POLES & POSTS, STEEL
Gide-Rite
Sno Gard

POLISHERS, FLOOR. See Floor Waxers & Polishers

POLISHES & WAXES, AUTOMOBILE
Car-Plate
Deep Gloss Carnu
Johnson's Cream Wax
J-Wax
Lecton Car-Care
Lecton Easy-Care
Lecton Super-Care
Legsure
Parko-Beauty Coat
Parko Eze-Wax
Parko Silcoseal

POLISHES & WAXES, FURNITURE
Lecton Furniture-Care
Liquid Shineze
Lustre-N-Dure
Nu-Finish
O-B
Pride
Rub-Once
Speed-Wax

POLISHES, METAL (See also Buffing Compounds; and Burnishing Compounds)
A-O-K
Metal Luster
O-B

POLISHES, PLASTIC
CD Dip Polish 231
Celite Mineral Fillers

POLISHES, SILVER. See Silver Cleaners & Polishes

POLISHES, WOOD
Liquid Shineze
Lusture-N-Dure
Nu-Finish

POLISHING AGENTS, GLASS
Celite Mineral Fillers

POLISHING WHEELS
Kon-Toor Wheel

POLYCARBONATE RESINS & PLASTICS. See Resins & Plastics, Polycarbonate

POLYESTER RESINS & PLASTICS. See Resins & Plastics, Polyester

POLYETHER RESINS & PLASTICS. See Resins & Plastics, Polyether

POLYETHYLENE RESINS & PLASTICS. See Resins & Plastics, Polyethylene

POLYMERIZATION CATALYSTS. See Catalysts, Polymerization

POLYMERIZATION INHIBITORS. See Inhibitors, Polymerization

POLYSTYRENE RESINS & PLASTICS. See Resins & Plastics, Polystyrene

POLYURETHANE RESINS & PLASTICS. See Resins & Plastics, Polyurethane

POLYVINYL RESINS & PLASTICS. See Resins & Plastics, Polyvinyl

POLYVINYLIDENE RESINS & PLASTICS. See Resins & Plastics, Polyvinylidene

PORCELAIN ENAMELS
Neowite #10

POROUS METALS & ALLOYS
Deva-Metal

POT CLEANERS. See Cleaners & Detergents, Pot & Pan

POTTING RESINS. See Resins, Potting

POULTRY FEEDSTUFFS. See Feedstuffs, Animal, Poultry, Etc.

POULTRY HOUSE INSECTICIDES. See Insecticides, Poultry House, Barn, Etc.

POWDERED SOAPS. See Soaps, Granulated & Powdered

POWDERS, METAL. See Metal Powders

POWER-TRANSMISSION BELTS. See Belts, Power-Transmission

PREFABRICATED HOUSES. See Houses, Prefabricated

PREPAINT BONDING AGENTS. See Bonding Agents, Prepaint

PRESERVATIVES, FABRIC
Germocid

PRESERVATIVES, FAT, OIL, DRUG, COSMETIC, ETC.
Ionol C.P.
Vancide 89 and Vancide 89RE

PRESERVATIVES, FLOOR. See Sealers & Preservatives, Floor

PRESERVATIVES, FOOD
A*C*M
Biostat
Ionol C.P.
Lecithin
Sorbistat
Sta-Sol
Tenox
Vancide 50 Peps
Vianol Antioxidant

PRESERVATIVES, GUM, STARCH, GLUE, ETC.
Vancide 51

PRESERVATIVES, PAINT
Vancide 89 and Vancide 89RE

PRESERVATIVES, TEXTILE
Vancide 26EC
Vancide 51
Wittox

PRESERVATIVES, WOOD
Cellu-San
Dura-wood
Paris Green
Wittox

PRESSURE VESSELS
NT (in circle)

PRIMERS, ADHESIVE-FILM
P-204

PRIMERS, METAL (See also Paints, Etc., Metal)
Chem-Bond
Chempol EP-1
Chempol M-2410
Corogard
Divobond ST
Gripclad
Griplate
Krylon Metal Primer
Lyfanite
Ospho
PDO-40
Pennprime
Stanley 40X-610
Surtreat Process
Synhibit "AQ"
Zinsol

PRINTED-CIRCUIT PAINTS
531 Basic Laboratory Kit
SC12 and SC13 Silver Micropaints

PRINTING INK ANTI-SKINNING AGENTS. See Anti-Skinning Agents, Paint & Printing Ink

PRINTING INK COLORING AGENTS. See Coloring Agents, Printing Ink

PRINTING INKS
Anilox
Aqualox
Claremont "RP" Series
Claremont "VC" Series
Duraprem
Everyday
Flexogem
Flexotuf
Gemglo
Gemtone
Glo-Ray
Holdfast
In-tag
IPI
Lithoday
Lithogem
Match Box
Vapolith
Vaporin
Vaposet

PROTECTIVE COLLOIDS. See Colloids, Protective

PROTECTIVE GARMENTS. See Garments, Protective

PROTECTIVE HAND CREAMS See Hand Creams, Protective

PROTEINS
"Alpha" Protein
Beta Protein
Casein
Gliddol
Hydrolyzed Vegetable Proteins 43-A and 52-A
Protein Insecticide Baits #2 and #7
Staley's
Sta-Mino

PUBLICATIONS
Drugology

PULLEYS
Lorig-Aligner

PULP, WOOD. See Wood Pulp & Fiber

PUMPS & PUMP PARTS
Di-Hard
Hi-Brin
Hi-Hard
NPD (in monogram)
Silverline
Wilson-Snyder

PUMPS, METERING
Triplematic

PUTTIES, LUTINGS, GLAZING COMPOUNDS, MASTICS, ETC. (See also Caulking Compounds; and Sealers)
Apco Vaportite No. 100
CD Spray Mask A
Corrumastic
Dolfinite
Kapco
Nox-Sound
Tite-Lite

Q

QUATERNARY AMMONIUM COMPOUNDS
Troy Coco-Ster Compound

R

RADIATOR STOP-LEAK MATERIALS
Parko

RADIO & ELECTRONIC ALLOYS
Cathaloy
Cuprochrome
Permagrid

RAILROAD EQUIPMENT CLEANERS. See Cleaners & Detergents, Automobile, Bus, Truck, Railroad Equipment, Etc.

RAILS, STEEL. See Steel Rails

RARE EARTH ALLOYS & OXIDES
Remox

RAT POISONS. See Poisons, Rat, Bird, Fish, Etc.

REAGENT CHEMICALS. See Chemicals, Reagent

REAGENTS, ANALYTICAL. See Analytical Reagents

REAGENTS, FLOTATION. See Flotation Reagents

REDUCING AGENTS
Oroxalyde Liquid
Sweetose
T-C Hydro

REFRACTORIES (See also Cements, Refractory)
Cuplopax
Electrobestos
Fibro-Cel
Hyline
Kaolin
Kyanite
R & I Aluminacrete
R & I Hot Top Moldit
R & I Moldit-D
R & I Plastic Chrome
Superline

REFRACTORY CEMENTS. See Cements, Refractory

REFRACTORY COATINGS FOR METALS. See Coatings, Refractory, for Metals

REINFORCING STEELS. See Steels, Reinforcing

REPAIR CEMENTS. See Cements, Patching & Repair

REPELLENTS, ANIMAL & BIRD
F & B

REPELLENTS, INSECT
MGK Repellent 11   Off!

REPELLENTS, WATER. See Water Repellents; and Waterproofing Agents

RESIN COLORING AGENTS. See Coloring Agents, Resin & Plastic; Dyes, Plastic; Paints, Plastic; and Pigments

RESIN DISPERSING AGENTS. See Dispersing Agents, Wax & Resin

RESIN DISPERSIONS & EMULSIONS
Accobond 3900, Cellulosic Film Resin
Acme Polyfluoron Liquid Dispersion
Aerotex Resin 110
Aerotex Resin 120
Aerotex Resin 121
Aerotex Resin 159
Aerotex Resin 7513
Aerotex Resin P-114
Aerotex Resin P-116
Aerotex Resin P-117
Cyanamer 380, Acrylic Polymer
Cymel
Cypel Resin
Durez
Exon
Flexbond 800
Griffco
Harto-Resin PCS
Hewhold
Norvan
Parez Resins
Plantex
Polymul
Vikon FPB
Vikon RL
Vinac

RESIN EXTENDERS. See Extenders, Resin & Plastic

RESIN INTERMEDIATES. See Intermediates, Plastic, Resin, Etc.

RESIN SOLUTIONS
Durez

RESIN SOLVENTS. See Solvents, Gum, Resin, Plastic, Wax, Etc.

RESIN STABILIZERS. See Stabilizers, Resin & Plastic

RESINS (See also Resins & Plastics)

RESINS, CASTING (See also Resins, Potting)
Allyl Plastics
Chem-o-sol
ChemoTec
Epoxy Resins
Formula 3117
Helix Potting Compounds
Maraset
MR
Pleogen
Polyester Resins
Toolcast 1000 Resin

RESINS, FOSSIL
Amber
Amberoid
Animi Gum
Kauri Gum

RESINS, IMPREGNATING & LAMINATING
Acme Polyfluoron Molding Powder
Alkanex
Binder P-812
Cymel
Durez
Epoxy Resins
Formula 3117
Hetron
Maraset
MR
Paraplex P-444
Pleogen

RESINS, NATURAL
Acaroid Resin
Amber
Amberoid
Animi Gum
Black Boy Resin
Camphor
Canada Balsam
Dammar
Dragon's Blood
Elemi
Galex Pellets
Gurjun Balsam
Red Acaroid
Resin 529
Rosin
Sandarac
Shellac

RESINS, PAINT, VARNISH, ETC.
Abrac Resins 22 and 22A
Acaroid Resin
Acrylic Resin
Alkyd Resins
Amber
Amberoid
Animi Gum
Black Boy Resin
BV
Chempol EP-1
Chempol EP-2
Chempol EP-3
Chempol M-2410
Chempol M-2803
Chempol M-3009
Chempol M-3423
Chempol M-4000
Chempol M-4501
Chempol P-2400
Chempol P-2405
Chempol P-2420
Chempol P-2426
Chempol P-3034
Chempol P-3303
Chempol P-3400
Chempol P-3401
Chempol P-3427
(continued)

RESINS, PAINT, VARNISH, ETC. (continued)

Chempol P-3504	Dymerex
Chempol P-3511	Dyphene
Chempol P-3514	Dyphenite
Chempol P-3600	Elemi
Chempol P-3620	Epoxy Resins
Chempol P-4000	Gurjun Balsam
Chempol P-4006	Isocyanate Resins
Chempol P-4010	Kauri Gum
Chempol P-4101	Kino Resin
Chempol P-4151	Krumbhaar Resins
Chempol P-4154	Lexan
Chempol P-4300	Norvan
Chempol P-4321	Opticleer
Chempol P-4400	Organosol
Chempol P-4723	Panarez
Chempol S-2200	Plastisol
Chempol S-2401	Red Acaroid
Chempol S-2403	Resin MS2
Chempol S-2407	Rosin
Chempol S-2600	Sandarac
Chemrez	Shellac
Copal	Super-Beckamine
Cyzac	USC
Dammar	Valite
Devran	Velsicol Resin EC-70
Durez	Velsicol Resin X-30
Dyal	Vinac
Dymal	

RESINS, PETROLEUM
Kenflex A, B, L, N

RESINS, POTTING (See also Resins, Casting)

Alkyd Resins	IPI-Isofoam
Eposet	MR
Helix Potting Compounds	

RESINS & PLASTICS, ACRYLIC

Ace Parene	Formez No. 50
Acrylic Resin	Gerlite
Acrylite	Paraplex P-444
Acrysol G-110	Plexiglas R
Alkyd Resins	Resin-Glas
Binder P-812	Rhoplex B-15
Cadco	Sprayway Plastic Spray
Cyanamer 370, Acrylic Polymer	

RESINS & PLASTICS, ALKYD

Chemrez	Dymal
Dyal	Resin RF and Resin 112

RESINS & PLASTICS, ALLYL

Allyl Plastics	Enduron
Durez	

RESINS & PLASTICS, CELLULAR & FOAM

Aer-O-Buoy	Nopcofoam
Agilene-F	Poly-Cell
Armaflex	Polyester Resins
Armalite	Resthane
Boscel	Spongex Handi-Floats
CCA	Spongex Ring Life Buoys
Formez No. 50	Vinylairé
Hewitex	Vynafoam
IPI-Isofoam	Vinylfoam
Isocyanate Resins	Water-Wonder
'n icer	

RESINS & PLASTICS, EPOXY

Devran	Helix Potting Compounds
Eposet	Maraset
Epoxy Resins	Sterling T-653-LB Thermopoxy
Helix Bonding Agents	

RESINS & PLASTICS, ETHYL CELLULOSE

Ace Parith	Nixon
Hercocel	

RESINS & PLASTICS, EXPANDABLE (See also Resins & Plastics, Cellular & Foam)
Vynafoam

RESINS & PLASTICS, FLUORETHYLENE
Acme Polyfluoron Liquid Dispersion
Acme Polyfluoron Molding Powder

RESINS & PLASTICS, FURANE
Furane Resins

RESINS & PLASTICS, MELAMINE

Accobond 3900, Cellulosic Film Resin	Lanaset Resin MW
Aerotex Cyrup 55	Melostrength Resin
Cymel	Parez Resins
Fiberite	Raiflex
Lanaset Resin	Railite
	Super-Beckamine

RESINS & PLASTICS, MISC.

Hydramine	Plastamine
Kymene	

RESINS, & PLASTICS, NYLON
Agilon

RESINS & PLASTICS, PHENOLIC

Amres 118	Amres 3910
Amres 136, 580, 4565, 5531, 5570 and 5580	Amres 6110
	Durez
Amres 1420	Dyphene
Amres 1430	Dyphenite
Amres 2612	Fiberite
Amres 2620	Mastolyn
Amres 3710B	Plenco

RESINS & PLASTICS, POLYCARBONATE
Lexan

RESINS & PLASTICS, POLYESTER

Alkanex	Polychem
Dypol	Polyester Resins
Formula 3117	Reflin Pipe
Glastic Channel-Duct	Resolite
Hetron	Resolite Fire-Snuf
MR	Sunform
Pleogen	

RESINS & PLASTICS, POLYETHER
Penton

RESINS & PLASTICS, POLYETHYLENE

Ace Parian	Polymix
Agilene-F	Printable "TS" Ger-Pak
Cadco	Tellerette
Fortiflex	Tenite Polyethylene
Ger-Pak	Vulkene
Ger-Tube	Wascofilm
Hi-Fax	Zertan

RESINS & PLASTICS, POLYSTYRENE

Ace Parsan	Fostarene
Bilt-Rex	Handi-Pack
Cadco	Poly-A9 Cast Film
Cymac	Styromix
Dowpac	

RESINS & PLASTICS, POLYURETHANE

Boscel	Isocyanate Resins
Formez No. 50	Nopcofoam
Hewitex	Poly-Cell
IPI-Isofoam	Resthane

RESINS & PLASTICS, POLYVINYL

Ace-Flex
Ace Riviclor
Aer-O-Buoy
Beautafilm
Bosfilm
Chem-o-sol
Estate
Exon
Ger-Flex
Granette
Griffco
Harto-Resin PCS
Imperial
Krene
Lemac 7, 15, 40, 150, 1,000 and 6,000
Lemac WD
Lemol 65-98
Masland Duran Clad
Monabond
Monabond C
'n icer
Nixon
Norvan
Organosol
Plantex
Plastisol
Plastite
Polyprene
Resin 107
Spongex Handi-Floats
Spongex Ring Life Buoys
Tuf-Bond
Turbozone
Velon
Vikon RL
Vinac
Vinol
Vinylairé
Vinylfoam
Vygen 100
Vynafoam
Water-Wonder
Weldron

RESINS & PLASTICS, POLYVINYLIDENE

Saran Wrap

RESINS & PLASTICS, UREA

Aerotex Cream 450
Aerotex Syrup 250 Conc.
Amres 200
Amres 210
Amres 225
Amres 255
Amres 275
Colfoam Microballoon Spheres
Emboset BM
Emboset NR
Emboset Z
Leather Product UF
Monares Paste
Monaset
Parez Resins
Resin 300
Resin Syrup J S

RESISTANCE WELDING ELECTRODES. See Electrodes, Resistance Welding

RESPIRATORS

Air-Cub
Air-Mask
All-Dust
All-Service
Chemox
Clear-Vue
Comfo
H-H Inhalator
McCaa
Mersorb
MSA Self-Rescuer
O_2 Cub
O_2 Mask
Pneolator
Pneophone
Ultra-Filter

RETARDERS, RUBBER ACCELERATOR

Retarder PD
Sharples Accelerator 52
Sharples Accelerator 62
Sharstop 204
Sharstop 268
Vulcosal

RIBBONS, TYPEWRITER, BUSINESS MACHINE, ETC.

3-R
Aristocrat
Aulta
Aultalith
Aulta Special
A & W
Capitol
College
Crest
Thrift

ROAD-PATCHING MATERIALS

Stonfast

RODS, PLASTIC. See Plastic Rods & Tubes

RODS, STEEL. See Steel & Iron, Bars & Rods

RODS, WELDING & BRAZING. See Welding & Brazing Rods & Electrodes

ROLL COVERINGS

Cork

ROLLS, TYPEWRITER, BUSINESS MACHINE, ETC.

Aulta
Crest

ROOF BEAMS. See Beams, Roof & Floor

ROOF COATINGS (See also Roofing Materials; and Paints, Etc., Roofing)

Halco-Lume
Pioneer #406
Pioneer #630 Primer
Regal Roof Coating
Tufcrete Roof Resurfacers

ROOF DECKS

Traffic Top

ROOF-PATCHING MATERIALS

Special A. R. Roof Putty
Tufcrete Roof Resurfacers

ROOF-TYPE VENTILATING UNITS. See Ventilating Units, Roof-Type

ROOFING MATERIALS

19/Up
Celo-Roof
Celotex
Corotop
Modernedge Slatekote
Perma-Ply
Ranch Style
Regal Cap Sheet
Slatekote
Slatekote Duplex
Storm Seal
Syphon Seal

ROOFING PAINTS. See Paints, Etc., Roofing

ROOT ERADICATORS

Rooticate

ROSIN DERIVATIVES, MISC.

Abitol
Dymerex

ROSINS

Galex Pellets

ROVINGS, GLASS. See Fabrics & Rovings, Glass

RUBBER ACCELERATOR ACTIVATORS. See Activators, Rubber Accelerator

RUBBER ACCELERATOR RETARDERS. See Retarders, Rubber Accelerator

RUBBER ACCELERATORS. See Accelerators, Rubber

RUBBER ADHESIVES. See Adhesives, Rubber

RUBBER ANTI-ADHESIVES & ANTI-TACK AGENTS. See Anti-Adhesives & Anti-Tack Agents, Rubber

RUBBER ANTI-OXIDANTS. See Anti-Oxidants Rubber

RUBBER-BASE PAINTS. See Paints, Etc., Rubber-Base

RUBBER CLEANERS & DETERGENTS. See Cleaners & Detergents, Rubber

RUBBER COLORING AGENTS. See Coloring Agents, Rubber

RUBBER DISPERSANTS. See Dispersing Agents, Rubber & Rubber-Latex

RUBBER EXTENDERS. See Extenders, Rubber & Rubber Latex

RUBBER HOSE

Boston All-Purpose
Boston Bay State
Boston Bull Dog Acid Discharge
Boston Bull Dog Acid Suction
Boston Concord Yellow Jack
Boston Flexer
Boston Tiger
Boston Vim

RUBBER LATEX
Gen-Flo
Rucoam
Tylac
Unitex

RUBBER LATEX DISPERSANTS. *See* **Dispersing Agents, Rubber & Rubber Latex**

RUBBER LATEX EXTENDERS. *See* **Extenders, Rubber & Rubber Latex**

RUBBER LATEX THICKENING AGENTS. *See* **Thickening Agents, Rubber Latex**

RUBBER LUBRICANTS. *See* **Lubricants, Rubber**

RUBBER-METAL BONDING AGENTS. *See* **Bonding Agents, Rubber-Metal & Plastic-Metal**

RUBBER MOLD CLEANERS & DETERGENTS. *See* **Cleaners & Detergents, Rubber & Rubber Mold**

RUBBER-MOLD LUBRICANTS. *See* **Lubricants Rubber-Mold**

RUBBER PAINTS. *See* **Paints, Etc., Rubber**

RUBBER PLASTICIZERS. *See* **Plasticizers, Rubber**

RUBBER PRODUCTS, MISC.
Hard Rubber

RUBBER-RECLAIMING COMPOUNDS
PDO-40

RUBBER & RUBBER LATEX STABILIZERS. *See* **Stabilizers, Rubber & Rubber Latex**

RUBBER SOFTENERS. *See* **Softeners, Rubber**

RUBBER SOLVENTS. *See* **Solvents, Rubber**

RUBBER SUNDRIES
Art Weave
Baby Jumbo
Fold-Spray
Gold Leaf
Quilt
Topper

RUBBER TACKIFIERS. *See* **Tackifiers, Rubber**

RUBBER VULCANIZING AGENTS. *See* **Vulcanizing Agents, Rubber**

RUBBERS, CELLULAR & FOAM
H-R Tex Top
Restfoam

RUBBERS, CHLORINATED
Chlorinated Rubber

RUBBERS, HARD
Ace-Hide
Ace-Sil
Ace-Tuf
Riji-Tuf
Tempron

RUBBERS, NATURAL
Balata
Cryptostegia Rubber
Dandelion Rubber
Guayule
Gutta Percha

RUBBERS, SYNTHETIC, & RUBBER SUBSTITUTES
Isocyanate Resins
Silicones

RUBBING ALCOHOL. *See* **Alcohol, Rubbing**

RUG CLEANERS. *See* **Cleaners & Detergents, Rug & Upholstery**

RUG UNDERLAYS
Cardinal
Castle
Hewitex
H-R Tex Top
Isocyanate Resins
Ozite

RUGS & CARPETING, NON-SKID
Sunland

RUST & SCALE REMOVERS
Drycid
Ke-Tone
Metalprep
M. F. Acid
Phos-It
Pickling Acids
Prep-Pik-L
Rustripper
Wyandotte 979

RUSTPROOFING AGENTS & CORROSION PREVENTIVES
Akrode
A. V. S. Rust Preventive
Chem-Bond
Coverlac
Diversey No. 16
Ensign 345 Chromogard
Enthobrite CU-55
Enthone Black Wax Emulsion No. 19
Enthone Clear Wax Emulsion No. 18
Enthowax Q-524
Fosclean
Fosdraw
Galvomag
Gilronex
Hydrin
Kasenite Keepbryte
Krylon-Houghton Rust Veto Spray
Laqua
Monox
Na-Sul
N. V. Medium
Oakite Soluble Oil
Oakite Special Protective Oil
Oakite Steel Preserver
Ospho
Parko
Polyrad
Prep-N-Cote
Rinsite
Spradri
Sunkote A
Surett P-65
Surtreat Process
Synhibit "AQ"
Texaco Floatcoat
Texaco Rustproof Compound
Texaco Texacoat
Ultraflex
Water-Skipper

S

SACKS. *See* **Bags & Sacks**

SAFETY EQUIPMENT
Air-Cub
Air Curtain
Air-Mask
All-Dust
All-Service
All-Vision
Burns Valve
Chemox
Cleartone
Clear-Vue
Colorimetric
Comfo
Coolband
Cool Cap
Ear Defenders
Earsaver
H-H Inhalator
Maskfone
McCaa
Mersorb
M-S-A
MSA Comfo Cap
MSA Self-Rescuer
Noisefoe
O_2 Cub
O_2 Mask
Persorb
Saf-Drive
Shockgard
Skullgard
Speedframe
Supergard

SAFETY LENSES. *See* **Lenses, Safety**

SANDWICH CONSTRUCTION CORE MATERIALS. *See* **Core Materials, Structural**

SANITIZING AGENTS
Airkem 10-39
Airkem a-3
Amerse
Bactine
Bull Frog Saf-T-Klenz
Chlor-Tergent
Diversol CX
Formula 44
Korex
Multi-Chlor
New Diokem
Oakite Bactericide
Oakite Di-Sanite
Oakite Sanitizer No. 1
O-B
Patterson's Pine Oil Disinfectant
Phos-Kleen
Pine-Ola
Pittabs
Riz
Sani-Tate
Staphene
Toilex
Troy Coco-Ster Compound
Usaphene 5
(continued)

SANITIZING AGENTS (continued)
Usaphene 10
Vancide 51
Ves-Phene
Vespray
Zen

SANITIZING DEODORANTS. See Deodorants, Sanitizing

SCALE REMOVERS. See Rust & Scale Removers

SCREENS
American
Bolting Cloth
Cyclone
Red Tag

SEALERS, ASPHALT-SURFACE
Plexichrome
Stontstreet
Top-X

SEALERS, CONCRETE & MASONRY CRACK & JOINT
Arco Non-Shrinking Dum
Dum Calk
Blok-Joint
Pioneer #301

SEALERS, CONCRETE & MASONRY SURFACE
Arcotone
Conq-R-Dust
Granitex
Kapco
Nervastral J. R. Joint Sealer
Plastergrip
Quickwall Primer
SonNoMar
Tufcrete All Purpose Sealer
Tufcrete APS

SEALERS & PRESERVATIVES, FLOOR
BV
Conq-R-Dust
Granitex
K-99
Kendall Lemon Oil
Red Label Gym Finish
Safe-T-Sheen
SonNoMar
Style
Terra-New
T-Guard
Traffic-Cote
Trophy Seal
Tufcrete All Purpose Sealer
Varee-Bryte XX

SEALERS, INSULATION-JOINT
Laptite
Zeroseal
Zerotape

SEALERS, METAL-CASTING
Mabco Iron Filler

SEALERS, METAL CRACK & JOINT
Asbestos Roll Fire-Felt
Fibro-Cel
Flawmaster
Flintseal JFR
KopeSeal

SEALERS, PLASTER (See also Sizing Agents, Wall)
Quickwall Primer

SEALERS, PLASTIC
Plastergrip

SEALERS & FILLERS, WOOD
Deco
Decto-Stick
Dolfinite
Homoclad
Pen-Wood 176
SFC
Trophy Seal

SEALING ALLOYS, GLASS-TO-METAL. See Glass-to-Metal Sealing Alloys

SEALS, BOTTLE
Lacacap

SEED DISINFECTANTS
Agrox
Gallotox
Gallotox 51
Isotox PMA Seed Treater
Mergamma
Patterson's Copper Carbonate, 20%
Pentrete
Puradrin
Puraseed
Vancide 51

SELENIUM
Redium Selenium

SELF-EMULSIFYING WAXES. See Waxes, Self-Emulsifying

SELF-POLISHING WAXES. See Waxes, Self-Polishing

SELF-STICKING LABELS. See Labels, Self-Sticking

SEQUESTERING AGENTS (See also Chelating Agents; and Complexing Agents)
Calmasene T
Hy-Phos
Kalex Cul
Kalex G
Kalex V
Metafos
Monaquest E
Monitor A
Orco Ferrosol Powder WS and Orco Ferrosol Liquid
Seqlene
Solon F

SEWER-PIPE JOINTING COMPOUNDS. See Jointing Compounds, Water and Sewer Pipe

SEWER-TREATMENT, FUNGICIDES. See Fungicides, Sewer-Treatment

SHALES. See Fillers, Clay & Shale

SHAMPOOS & SHAMPOO BASES
Derrilox
Pendit WA Cosmetic

SHEATHINGS (See also Building Boards)
Celotex
Particle Board
Weatherite Sheating

SHEET IRON & STEEL. See Steel & Iron Sheet, Roll, Strip & Plate

SHEETS, ASBESTOS. See Asbestos Sheets, Felts, Boards, Etc.

SHEETS, ASBESTOS-CEMENT. See Asbestos-Cement Sheets, Felts, Boards, Etc.

SHEETS, PLASTIC. See Plastic Sheets & Films

SHINGLES
Aristocrat
Celo-Lok
El Rey
Inselock
Ranch Style
Shadow Crest

SHINGLES, ASBESTOS-CEMENT. See Asbestos-Cement Sheets, Boards, Shingles, Etc.

SHOE SOLES, INNERSOLES, LININGS, ETC.
Hewitex
Isocyanate Resins
Ozite

SHORTENINGS, VEGETABLE
Accolade Oleomargarine
Dixie
Edsoy
Finesse
Flair Shortening
Flo
Fry-Base
Gleam
Glen Eden Margarine
Golden Mist Margarine
Gold'n:Wedge Margarine
Grayson Margarine
Hollandale Margarine
Hy-Base
Jack Rabbit
Jaxmor
Kerba
Log Cabin
Log Cabin Margarine
Meadolake Margarine
Meva
Mix-Ezy
PSM-35
Py-Eze
Shine
Southern Queen
Vaf
Vafet
Velvet
Velvet B
Velvet-M
Velvet Oil
Valvorene
White Beauty
Wizard

SHRINKPROOFING AGENTS, PROCESSES, ETC., TEXTILE
Aerotex Resin 801
Aerotex Resin M-3
Aerotex Resin MW
Aerotex Resin UM
Cyana Shrinkage Control Finish
Emboset BM
Emboset NR
Emboset Z
Hartoset E
Kylan
Lanaset Resin
Lanaset Resin MW
Monabond
Monabond C
Sanforized
Sanforlan
Stansets

SHRUB COLORING AGENTS. See Coloring Agents, Grass, Shrub, Bush, Etc.

SIDING MATERIALS, BUILDING
Celo-Siding
Celotex
Colony
Grain-Tex
Home-Tex
Rock-Tex
ShadowGrain
Storm Seal
Texbord

SILICA PIGMENTS & FILLERS. See Pigments & Fillers, Silica

SILICA & SILICATE CEMENTS. See Cements, Silica & Silicate

SILICONES
Anti-Foam 60
Dri-Bake
Hartuwet S
Ranedare
SC-50
Silicones
Silicones
Velvasil Silicone Fluid
Versilube
Viscasil

SILVER CLEANERS & POLISHES
Satin Rouge
Speed-Glos

SINKS, LABORATORY. See Laboratory Table Tops, Sinks, Etc.

SINTERED METAL PRODUCTS
Bunting

SIZING AGENTS, PAPER
ACCO Rosin Sizes
Amres 200
Amres 210
Amres 1420
Amres 1430
Aquapel
Bilt-Wax
Caladex
Casein
Corrugating Starch #1
Corrugating Starch #5
Cyfor Fortified Rosin Sizes
Cyron Chemical Size
Eclipse
Ethylex
Glu-Beeds
Kymene
Lycoid
Melostrength Resin
Parez Resins
Pexol
Rosin
Staclipse
Stayco
Stacolloid
Stadex
Staycal
Staysize
Stazyme
Vinol

SIZING AGENTS, TEXTILE
Amasize
Casein
Eclipse
Emkasize CT Concentrate
Ethylex
Gransize
Kelube
Keystone Gelatin
Kylan
Neo Size
Penford Finishing Gum 3XL and 3XP
Penprim
Sperse
Nopcosize
Permaloid 155
Resiloid 250
Sago Flour
Stacolloid
Sta-Gel
Staybind
Stayco
Stazyme
Supranyl
Tragacanth
Vinol

SKIN CLEANERS. See Cleaners & Detergents, Hair & Skin; and Hand Creams, Protective

SLIME CONTROL AGENTS
Gallicide
Gallosan
Oakite Sanitizer No. 1

SOAP ANTIOXIDANTS. See Anti-Oxidants, Cosmetic, Drug, Paint, Plastic & Soap

SOAP BUILDERS
Penbrite
Vitex

SOAP DYES. See Dyes, Food, Drug, Soap, Cosmetic, Etc.

SOAPS, ANTISEPTIC, GERMICIDAL & DEODORANT
Pax Deodorant Cream Soap
Soapure

SOAPS, BAR
Eiderdown

SOAPS, GRANULATED & POWDERED
Eiderdown
O-B

SOAPS, HAND (See also Cleaners & Detergents, Hair & Skin)
O-B
Soaperior
Soapure
Troy P.D.Q. Mechanics Soap

SOAPS, LIQUID
Detergol
Soaperior
Soapure

SOAPS, METALLIC
Aquacal
Calstar
Disperso
DS-207
Leadstar
Mark WS
Metasap
Metavis 540
Metavis 543

SOAPS, MISC.
Flaxoap

SOAPS, POWDERED. See Soaps Granulated & Powdered

SODIUM CARBONATES & BICARBONATES
Natrona Brand Bicarbonate of Soda
Soda Ash
Trona
Wyandotte Better Blend Soda

SODIUM PHOSPHATES
Metafos

SOFTENERS, RUBBER (See also Plasticizers, Rubber)
Circo Light Process Aid
Circomar-5AA
Circomar-25
Circomar-110
Circosol-2XH
Degras
Naxol
Panarez
Petrolatum
Pigmentar
PT Pine Tar Products
Sundex-41
Sundex-53
Sundex-85
Sundex-170
Sun Process Oil 515
Tall Oil

SOFTENERS, TEXTILE
Aerotex Softener H
Aerotex Softener W
Atco Rezsoft JA
Bradsyn J Softener
Bradsyn Lining Softener
Bradsyn N Softener
Bradsyn Plasticizer A-2
Bradsyn Softener S
Bradtone B
Catamine SF
Ceraloid X497702
Cyanatex
Cyanatex 3119 Softener
(continued)

SOFTENERS, TEXTILE (continued)

Cyanatex Cream Softener
Cyanatex SB 100 Softener
Decolon RU
Drapetex 35
Ecco-847
Emka Finishing Oil
Emkalon AX
Emkalon BT
Emkalon C-50
Emkalon CX
Emkalon H-460
Emkalon N Base
Emkalon OS
Emkatan K
Fancoseal
Felcolube 121
Felcolube 146
Felcolan GL
Fultex A
Lanaseal
Lanoseal
Maccowax Softener
Monapolene A
Monapolene Concentrates
Monapolene N
Monasoft S
Moropol 600
Moropol 700
Novasoft A
Papain
Sapamine OC
Softex Y
Ultramin B
Ultramine SS
Viscolan 14
Viscolan C
Wax Emulsion WG

SOIL CONDITIONERS & STABILIZERS

Fur-Ag
Palco Industrial Fibers

SOIL DISINFECTANTS, FUNGICIDES & FUMIGANTS

BHC
Bromex
D-D Soil Fumigant
Dorlone
Fumazone
Larvacide
Nemagon Soil Fumigant
Nemex
Termitkil
Terraclor

SOLDERING FLUXES. See Fluxes, Brazing, Soldering, Tinning & Welding

SOLDERING MASKING MATERIALS. See Masking Materials, Soldering

SOLDERS

Halloy
Hewitt-Detroit Body Solder
X-Cell Super X

SOLDERS, COLD. See Cold Solders

SOLVENTS, COSMETIC

Naxol
Petrohol

SOLVENTS, DRY-CLEANING

Afta
Aftalene
Kleen-It
Roly-Poly Dry Cleaner
Spotticator
Super Stod-Sol

SOLVENTS, DYE

Naxol
Naxol D
Poly-Solv

SOLVENTS, EXTRACTION

Pent-Acetate #28
Pent-Acetate #29
Petrohol

SOLVENTS, GUM, RESIN, PLASTIC, WAX, ETC.

Naxol
Naxol D
Pentasol #27
Petrohol
Poly-Solv
Solvent 101

SOLVENTS, INSECTICIDE

Panasol

SOLVENTS, METAL-CLEANING (See also Cleaners & Detergents, Metal)

Ahcowet SDS
Chlorothene
Dow-Tri
Krylon Cleaner and Degreaser
Painticator
Parko Tank-O-Lene
Parko Tank-Solv
Saturol
Solvent Degreaser
Zipsol Metal Cleaner #74

SOLVENTS, MISC.

Arapahoe
Filmcol Proprietary Solvent
Jaysol
Nialk
Painticator
Panalene
Pent-Acetate #28
Pentasol Frother #124
Poly-Solv
Rosin Oil
Tecsol

SOLVENTS & THINNERS, PAINT, VARNISH, ETC.

Apco 360
Canada Balsam
Dipentene
Flexichrome
Lacquer-Flo
Naxol
Naxol D
Panasol
Penetrell
Pentasol #27
Pent-Acetate #28
Pent-Acetate #29
Pentasol #258
Petrohol

SOLVENTS, PETROLEUM

Apco 360
Panalene
Panasol
Super Stod-Sol

SOLVENTS, RUBBER

Naxol D
PT Pine Tar Products

SOUND-ABSORPTION MATERIALS. See Acoustical Materials

SOUND DEADENERS (See also Acoustical Materials)

Pioneer #202
Pioneer #214
Pioneer #216
Witcote #4

SOUND METERS

Soundscope

SOURS, LAUNDRY. See Laundry Sours

SPACE-TYPE DEODORANTS. See Deodorants, Space-Type

SPATCHLING COMPOUNDS

Spred Patch

SPECTACLES & GOGGLES (See also Lenses, Safety)

Amco-Goggle
ANP
Spec-Pro-Tector
Specti-Goggle

SPERM OIL. See Fish & Sperm Oils

SPICES

Cinnamon
Cloves

SPOT AND STAIN REMOVERS, FABRIC-CLEANING (See also Cleaners & Detergents, Textile)

Afta
Aftite
Mist
Sol-U-Lube
Spot-Clor

SPRAY-BOOTH COATINGS

Oakite Shield
Spra-Gard

SPRAYING EQUIPMENT FOR INSECTICIDES, FUNGICIDES, HERBICIDES, FUMIGANTS, ETC.

Fumigun
Larvacover

SPRAYS, AGRICULTURAL

Nicotine Pyrox
Pratt's Shot Gun Spray or Dust
Scale-Tox
Superior Nu-Oil

SPREADERS & STICKERS, AGRICULTURAL SPRAY

Lo-Fat
Tenlo

SPRING WIRE. *See* **Wires, Spring**

STABILIZERS, BLEACHING AGENT
Depco Bleach Assist   Speco Bleach Assist

STABILIZERS, DRUG & PHARMACEUTICAL
(*See also* Preservatives, Fat, Oil, Drug, Cosmetic, Etc.)
Algin *or* Alginic Acid   Lo-Fat

STABILIZERS, DYE. *See* **Dye Stabilizers**

STABILIZERS, EMULSION
Attasorb
Ben-A-Gel
Brominol
Cab-o-sil
Lo-Fat
Naxol
Naxol D
Permagel
Prosein
Texapons
Veegum

STABILIZERS, FOAM. *See* **Foam Stabilizers**

STABILIZERS, FOOD (*See also* **Preservatives Food**)
Algin *or* Alginic Acid
Burtonite V-31-E
Densitol
DM-30
Doh-Tone
Gravinol
Lo-Fat
Uni-Pectin

STABILIZERS, OIL, FAT, ETC. (*See also* Preservatives, Fat, Oil, Drug, Cosmetic, Etc.)
Agar-Agar   Kelube
Algin *or* Alginic Acid   Uni-Pectin

STABILIZERS, PAINT, VARNISH, ETC.
Emultex
Ethylex
Lo-Fat
Stayco
Texapons

STABILIZERS, RESIN & PLASTIC
Advastab
Barca 10
Calstar
Clarite
CS-137
Drapex 4.4
DS-207
Dyphos
Dythal
Flomax 25
Leadstar
Lectro "60"
Mark C
Mark WS
Merix Stabilite
Merix Stabilite A
Metasap
Nalzin
Normasal
Provinite
Stabelan
Staflex
Stayrite
Thermolite
Tribase E
UV 9 Ultraviolet Absorber
V
Vanstay-C73
Vanstay-HT
Vanstay-L
Vanstay-N
Vanstay-R
Vanstay-S
Vanstay-Z

STABILIZERS, RUBBER & RUBBER LATEX
Cyanamer 370, Acrylic Polymer   Emcol K-8300

STABILIZERS, SOIL. *See* **Soil Conditioners & Stabilizers**

STAIN REMOVERS, FABRIC. *See* **Spot & Stain Removers, Fabric-Cleaning**

STAINLESS STEELS. *See* **Steels, Stainless;** *and* **Acid-, Alkali-, & Corrosion-Resisting Alloys**

STAINS, BIOLOGICAL
VitaStain

STAINS, WOOD
Annatto
Artistain
Ligno-sote
Monolac Varnish Stain
Rich Tone Oil Stain
SFC

STAIR TREADS, ANTI-SLIP. *See* **Anti-Slip Floor Plates, Stair Treads, Etc.**

STARCH PLASTICIZERS. *See* **Plasticizers, Gum, Starch, Glue, Etc.**

STARCH PRESERVATIVES. *See* **Preservatives, Gum, Starch, Glue, Etc.**

STARCHES & STARCH DERIVATIVES
Amaizo 721A Starch
Bondcor
Caladex
Corrugating Starch #1
Corrugating Starch #5
Eclipse
Ethylex
Freezist
Gransize
Hydrolyzed Vegetable Proteins 43-A and 52-A
Monatose
Penford Finishing Gum 3XL and 3XP
Raygomm
Sago Flour
Simplex
Staclipse
Stacolloid
Sta-Crem
Stadex
Sta-Gel
Staley's
Stargum
Sta-Rx
Sta-Thik
Staybind
Staycal
Stayco
Staysize
Stazyme

STEAM-CYLINDER LUBRICATING OILS. *See* **Lubricating Oils, Steam-Cylinder**

STEAM TRAPS. *See* **Traps, Gas, Steam, Etc.**

STEEL & IRON, BARS & RODS
Amercut
Bamboosteel
C (in diamond)
Carnegie
Illinois
T

STEEL BLACKENING TREATMENTS. *See* **Blackening Treatments, Steel**

STEEL CABLES. *See* **Cables, Steel**

STEEL CASTINGS & FORGINGS
E (in shield)

STEEL POLES & POSTS. *See* **Poles & Posts, Steel**

STEEL RAILS, ETC.
Carnegie
Illinois
Taylor
Tigerbraze
Tigerweld

STEEL & IRON SHEET, ROLL, STRIP & PLATE
Amerstrip
Arrow
Eagle
Keystone
Lectro-Clad
Star
Storm Seal
Superdraw
Terne Plate
U.S.S. Carilloy
U.S.S. Vitrenamel

STEEL TANKS. *See* **Tanks, Steel**

STEEL WIRE. *See* **Wires, Steel & Iron**

STEELS, CLAD
Lectro-Clad   Terne Plate
Lukens Clad Steels

STEELS, COPPER-BEARING
Keystone   Star

STEELS, EQUIPMENT
Amerled
Atlas Chippewa
Atlas Nushank
Atlas Ottawa
Atlas Vibresist
Lukens "T-1" Steel
Par-Ten
Superkore
U.S.S. Carilloy
(*continued*)

STEELS, EQUIPMENT (continued)
U.S.S. Cor-Ten
U.S.S. Freemax
U.S.S. Man-Ten
U.S.S. T-1
U.S.S. Tri-Ten
Wehrbest

STEELS, GALVANIZED
Amgal
Arrow
Blue Bonnet

STEELS, MACHINERY
AHT-28
Atlas CM
Atlas KK
FCC No. 1
FCC 5X1-V
FCC CV
Hardy Nickel Iron
Lukens "T-1" Steel
Par-Ten
SPS-245
Ultimo-4
U.S.S. Carilloy
U.S.S. Cor-Ten
U.S.S. Freemax
U.S.S. Man-Ten
U.S.S. M-X
U.S.S. T-1
U.S.S. Tri-Ten
Wehrbest

STEELS, REINFORCING
C (in diamond)
T
U.S.S. Di-Lok

STEELS, STAINLESS (See also Acid-, Alkali-, & Corrosion-Resisting Alloys)
Chromar
Corex
Greek Ascoloy
Tenelon
Transonic
W

STEELS, STRUCTURAL
Geneva
U.S.S. Tri-Ten

STEEL, TIN-COATED
Ferrostan
Superdraw

STEELS, TOOL & DIE
Atlas HW-7
Atlas Ottawa
Atlas Vibresist
Chromewear
Commando Drill Rod
Cuprodie
Durodi
FCC No. 1
FCC 5X1 Special
FCC 5X1-V
FCC ALX
FCC CTS
FCC EZ
FCC Fernite 24
FCC Flamhard
FCC Roloy
FCC Roloy No. 2
FS
FX
Graph-Air
Hodi
MC (Mold and Cavity Steel)
MM 6 & 6
Mo-Max
Shelldie
Speed Cut
TCI Tool Steel
Tenneseal
Tennessee
Van Cut
Vasco Supreme
Vulcan Gage & Die Steel
W4X
WCC
WW Hotwork
XLO Die Blocks

STENCIL DUPLICATING FLUIDS, ETC. See Duplicating Fluids, Stencils, Etc.

STENCIL INKS. See Inks, Glassware, Ceramic, Stencil, Etc.

STERILIZING AGENTS (See also Disinfectants; and Germicides)
Pittabs

STONEWARE, CHEMICAL. See Chemical Stoneware

STOP-LEAK MATERIALS, RADIATOR. See Radiator Stop-Leak Materials

STOP-OFF LACQUERS, TAPE, ETC., ELECTRO-PLATING
Corac

STRAPPING MATERIALS & EQUIPMENT
Gerrard
SGS

STRIP-COATING MATERIALS
CD Strip A
CD Strip B
Coverlac
Dip-Pak
Narliner Type 5018
Peel-Pak
Plastic Peel No. 3601
Spra-Gard
Spraylat SC-1071B

STRIP IRON & STEEL. See Steel & Iron Sheet, Roll, Strip & Plate

STRIPPERS, DYE. See Dye Strippers

STRUCTURAL STEELS. See Steels, Structural

STUFFINGS, UPHOLSTERY. See Upholstery Padding & Stuffing Materials

SUGARS & OTHER SWEETENING AGENTS
Dulcet
Invert Sugar
Sweetose

SULFUR
Blackbird
Devil
Lily
Mule
Red Wing
Spider
Star

SULFUR-BASE CEMENTS. See Cements, Sulfur-Base

SUNBURN PREVENTIVES, SUN-SCREEN AGENTS, ETC.
Fend-L
Suconox
UV 9 Ultraviolet Absorber

SUNDRIES, RUBBER. See Rubber Sundries

SUN-SCREEN AGENTS, ETC. See Sunburn Preventives, Sun-Screen Agents, Etc.

SUPPORTS, CATALYST. See Catalyst Supports

SURGICAL DRESSINGS. See Dressings, Surgical

SURGICAL LUBRICANTS. See Lubricants, Surgical

SURGICAL PADS & GAUZE. See Absorbent Cotton, Surgical Pads & Gauze, Etc.

SWEETENING AGENTS. See Sugars & Other Sweetening Agents

SYNERGISTS, INSECTICIDE
Sesamin

SYNTHETIC FIBERS. See Fibers, Synthetic

SYNTHETIC-RESIN BASE ADHESIVES. See Adhesives, Synthetic-Resin Base

SYNTHETIC-RESIN BASE CEMENTS. See Cements, Synthetic-Resin Base

SYNTHETIC-RESIN BASE COATINGS. See Coatings, Synthetic-Resin Base

SYNTHETIC-RESIN BASE PAINTS. See Paints, Etc., Synthetic-Resin Base

SYNTHETIC-RESIN MOLDING COMPOUNDS. See Molding Compounds, Synthetic-Resin & Plastic

SYNTHETIC-RESIN & PLASTIC PLASTICIZERS. See Plasticizers, Synthetic-Resin & Plastic

SYNTHETIC RUBBERS. *See* Rubbers, Synthetic, & Rubber Substitutes

SYNTHETIC WAXES. *See* Waxes, Synthetic

T

TABLE TOPS. *See* Counter & Table Tops

TABLE TOPS, LABORATORY. *See* Laboratory Table Tops, Sinks, Etc.

TABLET BINDERS. *See* Binders, Tables

TACKIFIERS, RUBBERS
Rosin Oil

TALL OILS
Metalyn
Pamak
Tall Oil

TANK COATINGS. *See* Coatings, Tank

TANK LININGS
Acme Polyfluoron Liquid Dispersion
Carbomastic Series
Lastiglas
Narliner Type 5018
Vyflex L-10 Lining

TANKS, PLASTIC. *See* Ducts, Hoods, Tanks, Etc., Plastic

TANKS, STEEL
Hortondome Roof
Hortonsphere
Hortonspheroid
Horton Vaportank
Vaporsphere
Watersphere

TANNING AGENTS
Canaigre
Catechu
Divi-divi
Galls
Gambier
Leather Product 612
Leather Product UF
Mangrove
Nacconate
Nacconate 310
Palconate
Palcotan
Quebracho
Rhatany
Sumac
Suprak Tanning Agents

TAPES, ADHESIVE. *See* Adhesive Tapes

TAPES & SEALANTS, ELECTRICAL-INSULATING (*See also* Insulating Materials, Electrical; *and* Tapes, Friction)
Acme Polyfluoron Molding Powder
Alexall Tape
Bull Dog Plastic Electrical Tape
Bull Dog Splicing Compound

TAPES, FRICTION
Bull Dog Friction Tape

TAPES, STOP-OFF. *See* Stop-Off Lacquers, Tapes, Etc., Electroplating

TAR ANTI-STRIP AGENTS. *See* Anti-Strip Agents, Asphalt, Tar, Etc.

TAR PAPERS & FELTS
Cardinal
Combat
Ozite

TARS. *See* Asphalts, Tars & Pitches

TENDERIZERS, MEAT. *See* Meat Tenderizers

TERNE PLATE
Terne Plate

TEXTILE ADHESIVES. *See* Adhesives, Textile

TEXTILE ANTI-BLOCKING AGENTS. *See* Anti-Blocking Agents, Textile

TEXTILE ANTI-SLIP AGENTS. *See* Anti-Slip Agents, Textile

TEXTILE ANTI-STATIC AGENTS. *See* Anti-Static Agents, Plastic & Textile

TEXTILE CLEANERS & DETERGENTS. *See* Cleaners & Detergents, Textile

TEXTILE COATINGS. *See* Coatings, Textile

TEXTILE CREASE- & CRUSHPROOFING AGENTS. *See* Crease- & Crushproofing Agents, Textile

TEXTILE DELUSTRANTS. *See* Delustrants, Textile

TEXTILE DESIZING AGENTS. *See* Desizing Agents, Textile

TEXTILE DYEING LEVELING AGENTS. *See* Leveling Agents, Textile Dyeing

TEXTILE DYEING & PRINTING THICKENING AGENTS. *See* Thickening Agents, Textile Dyeing & Printing

TEXTILE DYES. *See* Dyes, Textile, Leather, Etc.

TEXTILE FABRICS. *See* Fabrics, Textile

TEXTILE-FINISHING AGENTS. *See* Finishing Agents, Textile

TEXTILE FINISHING PROCESSES
Lektroset

TEXTILE FIRE- & FLAMEPROOFING COMPOUNDS. *See* Fire- & Flameproofing Compounds, Textile, Wood, Etc.

TEXTILE FUNGICIDES. *See* Fungicides, Textile; *and* Preservatives, Textile

TEXTILE INKS. *See* Inks, Textile

TEXTILE LUBRICANTS. *See* Lubricants, Textile

TEXTILE MACHINERY & EQUIPMENT
Run-Rite

TEXTILE PRESERVATIVES. *See* Preservatives, Textile; *and* Mildewproofing Agents

TEXTILE PRINTING BINDERS
Bondrez
Caustic Gum
Lumatex Binder F
Metagel-811, 811–32, 820, 860
Metaglow-303
Perapret A
Perapret AX 45

TEXTILE PRINTING COLORS
Aquaprint
Aridye
Kemprint
Sherdye

TEXTILE PROCESSING DISPERSANTS. *See* Dispersing Agents, Textile Processing

TEXTILE PROCESSING EMULSIFYING AGENTS. *See* Emulsifying Agents, Textile Processing

TEXTILE SHRINKPROOFING AGENTS, PROCESSES, ETC. *See* Shrinkproofing Agents, Processes, Etc., Textile

TEXTILE SIZING AGENTS. *See* Sizing Agents, Textile

TEXTILE SOFTENERS. *See* Softeners, Textile

TEXTILE THREADS, YARNS & FIBERS. *See* Threads, Yarns & Fibers, Textile

TEXTILE WATERPROOFING AGENTS. *See* Waterproofing Agents, Textile

TEXTILE WEIGHTING AGENTS. *See* Weighting Agents, Textile

TEXTILE WETTING AGENTS. *See* Wetting Agents, Textile

TEXTILE WHITENING AGENTS. *See* Whitening Agents, Textile; *and* Optical Bleaches

THERMAL INSULATION ADHESIVES. *See* Adhesives, Thermal Insulation

THERMAL INSULATION COATINGS. *See* Coatings, Thermal Insulation

THERMAL INSULATION JACKETING. *See* Jacketing, Thermal Insulation

THERMAL-INSULATING CEMENTS. *See* Cements, Thermal-Insulating

THERMAL-INSULATING MATERIALS. *See* Insulating-Materials, Thermal

THERMAL-INSULATING PAINTS. *See* Paints, Etc., Fire-Retardant & Thermal-Insulating

THERMOCOUPLES & ACCESSORIES
Conax

THICKENING AGENTS, FOOD, COSMETIC, DRUG, ETC.
Abco-Gel
Agar-Agar
Algin or Alginic Acid
Ben-A-Gel
Bentone 38
Biost Tablets V-P 730
Burtonite #7
D-6
D-7
Eclipse
Elemi
Freezist
Irish Moss
Kelube
Quso
Sta-Crem
Starguar
Thixo
Uni-Pectin
Vanlite
Veegum

THICKENING AGENTS, LUBRICATING GREASE
Abco-Gel

THICKENING AGENTS, MISC.
Attasorb
Bentone
Bentone 18-C
Bentone 34
Bentone 38
Cab-o-sil
Cyanamer 370, Acrylic Polymer
Ethylex
Permagel
Sperse

THICKENING AGENTS, PAINT
Algin or Alginic Acid
Ben-A-Gel
Bentone 18-C
Bentone 34
Lecithin
M-P-A
Quso
Stayco

THICKENING AGENTS, RUBBER LATEX
Acrysol G-110

THICKENING AGENTS, TEXTILE DYEING & PRINTING
Algin or Alginic Acid
Ben-A-Gel
Stadex

THINNERS, PAINT & VARNISH. *See* Solvents & Thinners, Paint, Varnish, Etc.

THIXOTROPIC AGENTS
Attasorb
Cab-o-sil
M-P-A
Permagel
Thick-Aid

THREADS, YARNS & FIBERS, TEXTILE
Belastraw
Celaspun
Celatow
Coir
Cotton
Estron
Fortecel
Fortenese
Silk
Tyron
Velon
Verel

TILE CLEANERS. *See* Cleaners & Detergents, Glass, Tile, Etc.

TILE, GYPSUM. *See* Gypsum Lath, Board, Tile, Etc.

TILES, FLOOR. *See* Floor Tiles

TILES, WALL. *See* Wall Tiles

TIN & TIN-BASE ALLOYS
Hewitt Copper-Hard
Hewitt Mill Bearing-Metal
Hewmet

TIN-COATED STEEL. *See* Steels, Tin-Coated

TINNING FLUXES. *See* Fluxes, Brazing, Soldering, Tinning & Welding

TINTING AGENTS, PAINT
Anthosine
Hansa
Rhoduline

TOILET CLEANERS. *See* Cleaners & Detergents, Drain Pipe, Toilet, Urinal, Etc.

TONERS. *See* Lakes & Toners

TOOLS & EQUIPMENT, FARM & GARDEN
Boyco
Poppy

TOOL STEELS. *See* Steels, Tool & Die

TOWER PACKINGS
Dowpac
Intalox Saddle Packing
Tellerette

TRANSFORMER OILS
Chlorextol

TRAPS, GAS, STEAM, ETC.
Trumble

TRUCK CLEANERS. *See* Cleaners & Detergents, Automobile, Bus, Truck, Railroad Equipment, Etc.

TUBES, NON-FERROUS. *See* Pipes, Tubes & Fittings, Non-Ferrous

TUBES, PLASTIC. *See* Plastic Rods & Tubes

TUBES, STEEL. *See* Pipes, Tubes & Fittings, Steel

TUNGSTEN & TUNGSTEN-BASE ALLOYS
Mallory 1000
Mallory 1000 Gyromet

TYPEWRITER RIBBONS. *See* Ribbons, Typewriter, Business Machine, etc.

TYPEWRITER ROLLS. *See* Rolls, Typewriter, Business Machine, Etc.

U

UNDERCOATINGS, AUTOMOBILE
Nox-Sound
Pioneer #216
Witcote #4

UNDERLAYMENTS, FLOORING. See Flooring Underlayments

UNDERLAYS, RUG. See Rug Underlays

UPHOLSTERY CLEANERS. See Cleaners & Detergents, Rug & Upholstery

UPHOLSTERY MATERIALS
Coflex
Filmtex
Nygen Tolex
Plush
Velon
Vinylfoam
Weldron

UPHOLSTERY PADDING & STUFFING MATERIALS (See also Batting Materials)
Cardinal
Celacloud
Combat
Cotton
Hewitex
Ozite
Restfoam
Vinylfoam

URANIUM ORE
Uranium "O"

UREA RESINS & PLASTICS. See Resins & Plastics, Urea

URINAL CLEANERS. See Cleaners & Detergents, Drain Pipe, Toilet, Urinal, Etc.

V

VACUUM PUMP FLUIDS
Narcoil 10
Narcoil 40
Narescoil
Silicones

VAPOR BARRIERS
Apco Vaportite No. 100
Ger-Pak
Pioneer #202
Pioneer #401-P
Pioneer #1008 Vapor Seal
Sisalkraft Moistop
Sisalkraft Vaporstop
Wascofilm
Wascoseal
Zero Perm

VARNISH REMOVERS. See Paint & Varnish Removers

VARNISH RESINS. See Resins, Paint, Varnish, Etc.

VARNISH STABILIZERS. See Stabilizers, Paint, Varnish, Etc.

VARNISH THINNERS. See Solvents & Thinners, Paint, Varnish, Etc.

VEGETABLE COATINGS. See Coatings, Fruit, Vegetable, Flower, Etc.

VEGETABLE OIL PRODUCTS
Accolade Olemargarine
Dixie
Emultex
Finesse
Flair Shortening
Flo
Fribase
Fry-Base
Gleam
Glen Eden Margarine
Golden Mist Margarine
Gold'n:Wedge Margarine
Grayson Margarine
Hibase
Hollandale Margarine
Hy-Base
Jack Rabbit
Jaxmor
Kerba
Log Cabin
Log Cabin Margarine
Meadolake Margarine
Meva
Mix-Ezy
PSM-35
Py-Eze
Pylex
Shine
Southern Queen
Mrs. Tucker's Shortening
Vaf
Vafet
Velvet
Velvet B
Velvet M
Velvorene
White Beauty
Wizard

VEGETABLE OILS
"50" Oil
"AR" Soy Bean Oil
Babassu Oil
Ben Oil
Chemlin
Chia-seed Oil
Coconut Oil
Copra
Cottonseed Oil
Edsoy
Golden Capri
Grapeseed Oil
Hrdflakes
Hy-Chill Salad Oil
Lik-Wid
Liqui-Fry
Lite
Perilla Oil
Rapeseed Oil
Sesame Oil
Staley's
Mrs. Tucker's Salad Oil
Velvet Oil

VEGETABLE SHORTENINGS. See Shortenings, Vegetable

VENEERS, WOOD. See Wood Veneers

VENTILATING EQUIPMENT & SYSTEMS. See Heating, Cooling, Ventilating, & Air-Conditioning Equipment & Systems

VENTILATING UNITS, ROOF-TYPE
American
Amervent
Draft/Stop

VETERINARY MEDICINALS. See Medicinals Veterinary

VIBRATION DAMPENERS
Cork
Felt
Kil-Klatter
Microflex
Pioneer #214
Vinylfoam

VITAMINS & VITAMIN PREPARATIONS
Abdec Drops
Abdec Kapseals
Acterol-D
Ascorbacaine
Beclysyl
Beesix
Bejectal
Bevidox
Calcisalin
Catalyn V-P 710
Cataplex
Cataplex E₂ V-P 732
Cerol V-P 719
Convalets
Darthronol
Dayalets
DPi
Eff-Plus V-P 731
Eflex V-P 720
Ephynal Acetate
Forticon
Glutazyme
Haliver
Hemosules
Hyotole-12
Hypobeta-20
Iberol
Infantovit Drops
Infantovit and Infantovit Chewable
Infantovit Plus
Libeplex
Livitol
Livitol Syrup
Livrex
Lixa-Beta
Maxilets
Micratized
Minerovit
Multi-B-Plex
Mulvitol and Mulvitol Strong
Mytinic
Myva-Dry
Myvamix
Myvapack
Myvax
Natopherol
Nicothiamin
Nopco Chemical Co.
Nopcosol
Nopvite
NYQ
Omni-Beta
One-A-Day
Optilets
Pre-Daylin
Resiston
Rutaplex A V-P 729A
Rutaplex V-P 729
Stimavite Tastitabs
Storcavite
Sur-Bex
Super Nopdex
Surplex
Thera-Vita
Vi-Daylin
Vigoramin
Vitab B-Complex Extract
Vita-Dulcet
Vita-Kaps
Vita-King
Viterra Tastitabs

VULCANIZING AGENTS, RUBBER
Blackbird
Devil
Di-Cup
Vultra C
Spider
Star

W

WALLBOARD FASTENERS. See **Fasteners, Wallboard**

WALLBOARD JOINT-COVERING MATERIALS. See **Joint-Covering Materials, Wallboard**

WALLBOARDS (See also Building Boards)
Leatherwood
Lok-Bevel
Novocore
Novowall
Particle Board
Perforated Fibretex
Presdwood

WALL CLEANERS. See **Cleaners & Detergents, Wall**

WALL COVERINGS (See also Wallboards; and Wall Tiles)
Budget
Filmtex
Krene
Vinylfoam

WALL PAINTS. See **Paints, Etc., Wall**

WALL PLASTERS. See **Plasters, Wall**

WALL-TILE ADHESIVES. See **Adhesives, Floor & Wall Tile, Etc.**

WALL TILES
Celotex
Fresco Acoustical Tile
Sonofaced Acoustical Tile

WALL UNITS. (See also Curtains, Accordian-Type)
Gold Bond Holostud
Transitone Walls

WALLS, FURNACE. See **Furnace Walls**

WATER COLORS
Flexichrome
Kodak

WATER-DISPLACING AGENTS
Spradri

WATER-MIX PAINTS. See **Paints, Etc., Water-Mix**

WATER-PIPE JOINTING COMPOUNDS. See **Jointing Compounds, Water & Sewer Pipe**

WATERPROOFING & DAMPPROOFING AGENTS, CONCRETE & MASONRY—INTEGRAL
Metasap
Stontite
Super-Bondsit

WATERPROOFING & DAMPPROOFING AGENTS, CONCRETE & MASONRY—SURFACE
Caspro
Kapco
Metasap
Pioneer #1008 Vapor Seal
Silicones

WATERPROOFING AGENTS, LEATHER
Kendall Lemon Oil
Water-Skipper

WATERPROOFING AGENTS, PAPER, PACKING MATERIAL, ETC.
Metasap
SC-50
Water-Skipper

WATERPROOFING AGENTS, TEXTILE
Aerotex Water Repellent S
"Cravenette"
Cyana Permel Finish
Cyana Silicone Finish
Cyana Silicone Plus Finish
Dryette
Eccopel
Emkapel C
Fabripel
Hartuwet C and B
Hartuwet S
Kylan
Life for Fabrics
Morepel RW
Paramul Repellent 115
Paramul Repellent DC-1 and DC-2
Penprim.
Permel Resin B
SC-50
Silicones
Water-Skipper

WATERPROOFING AGENTS, WOOD
Cellu-Pel
Metasap
P.A.R.
Pioneer #500
SC-50
Water-Skipper

WATERPROOFING MEMBRANE
Nervastral Seal-Pruf H-D

WATER PURIFICATION & TREATMENT MATERIALS (See also Activated Carbons; Boiler Compounds; Filter Media; Water Softening Agents)
Clack Activated Carbon (High Capacity)
Corosex
Globaline
Ke-Tone
NCS
Sol-Vet

WATER REPELLENTS (See also Waterproofing Agents)
Ranedare

WATERSOFTENING AGENTS
Hy-Phos
Orco Ferrosol Powder WS and Orco Ferrosol Liquid
Rexofos
Soda Ash
Sol-Vet

WATER SOFTENING & TREATING EQUIPMENT, CONTROLS, VALVES, ETC.
Duomatic
Manumatic

WATER-SOLUBLE DYES. See **Dyes, Water-Soluble**

WAX-COLORING AGENTS. See **Coloring Agents, Wax**

WAX DISPERSING AGENTS. See **Dispersing Agents, Wax & Resin**

WAX MODIFIERS
Abitol
Acaroid Resin
Epolene N
Krumbhaar Resins

WAX SOLVENTS. See **Solvents, Gum, Resin, Plastic, Wax, Etc.**

WAXED PAPER. See **Papers, Waxed**

WAXERS, FLOOR. See **Floor Waxers & Polishers**

WAXES, FLOOR (See also Waxes, Self-Polishing)
Award
Beautiflor
Beautiflor Traffic Wax
Brown Label No-Buff
Clad
Emulsacera
Flourish
Glaze
Hard Gloss Glo-Coat
Heavy-Duty Hard Gloss
Hy-Sheen
Johnson's
Liquid Shineze
Lustre-N-Dure
O-B
Plyowax
Shur-Tred
Solvacera
Stride
Traffic Wax
Triple Life
Waxtra

WAXES, GENERAL PURPOSE & MISC.
Biwax
Emulsacera
Montan Wax
Octagon (Hippocrates)
Ozokerite
Solvacera
White "B.V.M." Wax

WAXES, MICROCRYSTALLINE
Bilt-Wax
Petrolite
Starwax
Sunoco Waxes
Ultraflex

WAXES, NATURAL
Beeswax
Candelilla Wax
Carnauba Wax
Japan Wax
Jojoba Wax
Ouricury Wax
Spermacetti

WAXES, PAPER-COATING
Tervan 2735

WAXES, PETROLEUM
Bilt-Wax
Micris
Petrolite
Starwax
Sunoco Anti-Check
Sunoco Waxes
Ultraflex

WAXES, SELF-EMULSIFYING
Defoamer H-450

WAXES, SELF-POLISHING
Brown Label No-Buff
Brulin Bright
Clad
Contact Wax
Flourish
Glaze
Hard Gloss Glo-Coat
Heavy-Duty Hard Gloss
Hy-Sheen
Johnson's
O-B
Plyowax
Shur-Tred
Stride
Triple Life
Waxtra

WAXES, SYNTHETIC
Drawax 936
Epolene E
Epolene N
Nopcowax

WEAR-RESISTING ALLOYS
Chromewear
FCC Nitri-Cast-Iron
Mantalloy
U.S.S. A-R Steel
Wehrbest

WEATHERSTRIPPING & WEATHERPROOFING MATERIALS, BUILDING
Corrumastic

WEED KILLERS
2,4,5-T
99
Aero Cyanamid
Aminotriazole
Baron
Chlorax "40"
Chlor-Bor
Chlorea
CIPC
Dinoseb
Dowpon
F & B
Ivy-Kil
Kill-All
MCPA
Mema
Mystikil Termite Emulsion
Novon
Penco
Penite
Radapon
Reddon
STCA
TCA
Ten-Ten
Urox
Weednix
Weedrench

WEIGHTING AGENTS, TEXTILES
Emkawate
Macco Finish 6000
Resizet
Rexobond
Rexogum
Rexoslip
Weytone F P

WELDING COMPOUNDS
Thermit

WELDING ELECTRODES, RESISTANCE. See Electrodes, Resistance Welding
Chromar

WELDING EQUIPMENT
Amco-Goggle
Amcohood
ANP
Pro-Tecto-Cape
Spec-Pro-Tector
Specti-Goggle
Torch-O-Matic

WELDING FLUXES. See Fluxes, Brazing, Soldering, Tinning & Welding

WELDING & BRAZING RODS & ELECTRODES
Atom-Arc
Bronze-Arc C
Bronze-Arc Mn
Eutec-CopWeld
Eutectic Low Temperature Welding Alloys
Handy Hi-Temp
L-60, L-61, L-70, L-18-8 and L-201
LowAmp
LowTemp
Mang-Arc
McKay Tube-Alloy
Monar
Nicuar
NiTectic
Premier
Speedex
Stoody Automatic and Semi-Automatic Wires
Stoody Build-Up
ThermoTrode
Wear Arc 3-IP, 6-IP, and 12-IP
Wear-Arc Super WH
Wear-Arc WH

WETTING AGENTS, GENERAL PURPOSE & MISC.
Aerosol 22
Aerosol AY
Aerosol C-61
Aerosol MA-80%
Aerosol OS
Aerosol OT-75%
Aerosol OT-100%
Aerosol OT-B
Dowfax
Emcol H-31A
Gammanol
Glend-Eze
Hyonic
Hy-Phos
Lecithin
Ninex 303
Nonic #218
Nonic #259
Nonic #260
Nonic #261
Nonic #300
Nopcosulf
Nopcotal
Penphate
Polyrad
Poly-Tergent
Reginol HNP
Specon #33
Sul-Fon-Ate
Sulfonate OS
Sulfonate WS
Sunaptic Acids
Surfonic Adducts
Texapons
Ultrapole S
Ultrapole S Liquid
Uniflex
Vatsol OT-B Wetting Agent

WETTING AGENTS, INSECTICIDE
Sulfonate WS
Tenlo
Vatsol Wetting Agents

WETTING AGENTS, LEATHER
Detergol

WETTING AGENTS, PAINT & PIGMENT
Sta-Sol
Texapons

WETTING AGENTS, PAPER
Cynol Rewetting, Softening & Deforming Agents

WETTING AGENTS, TEXTILE
Ahcowet SDS
BASF
B-Tex
Carbose 55
Depcogel 3X
Dispersal 1278
Dispersing Agent N.F.L.
Ecco-W-88
Eccowet LF
Emka Finish A
Emkafol D
Emkanol MA
Emkapon K
Emka Supertex
Emkatex 49-P
Euvon ASN
Fancosol
Felcomine SX
Fultex A
Glycinal HD$_2$
Hartex PN
(continued)

WETTING AGENTS, TEXTILE (continued)

Inferol H-138
Kaliscour
Lunetzol A
Monapal T
Nekanil
Nonic #218
Nonic #234
Nopcotal
Novapon A
Orcoboil #15
Orco Pentro PS
Orcowet #33
Penetron Conc.
Pentex 44
Reginol HNP
Rexopene
Rexowet A Concentrate, Rexowet A, and Rexowet A-25
Rexowet CR
Rexowet GR
Rexowet MS
Rexowet RW
Solasol
Solasol USP Extra
Speco Pal EO 33
Sulfanone A
Synterge 750
Tacanols
Talamine M. A.
Tergenol S Liquid Conc.
Tergolene Concentrate
Texavon
Trepenol S-60
Trepolate F-95
Trepolate T-60
Ultrapole S

WHEELS, POLISHING. See Polishing Wheels

WHITENING AGENTS, PAPER
Uvitex P Conc.

WHITENING AGENTS, TEXTILE
Bleachit IA
B-Tex
Calcofluor Dyes
Cellu-Brite
Felcowhite 174
Felcowhite 180
Neowhite D Liquid
Orco Synthrowite FWN
Orco Synthrowite GNW
Uvitex RBS
Uvitex TXS Conc.
Uvitex U

WINDOW GLASS. See Glass, Plate & Window

WIRE-ROPE LUBRICANTS. See Lubricants, Wire-Rope

WIRE ROPES & FITTINGS
American
Excellay
Fiege Tiger-Claw
Hyco-Span
Monitor
Tiger or Tiger Brand

WIRES, BARBED. See Barbed Wires

WIRES, COATED
Amerlum
Amgal
Blue Bonnet

WIRES, MAGNET. See Magnet Wires

WIRES, SPRING
Acme
American
Amerloy
Crown
Premier

WIRES, STEEL & IRON
Acme
Amer-Construction
Amerfine
Amerhead
American
Amerstitch
Amertel
Amgal
Blue Bonnet
Crown
Rival
Super-Tens

WIRING EQUIPMENT & SUPPLIES. See Electrical Wiring Equipment & Supplies

WOOD ADHESIVES. See Adhesives, Wood

WOOD COATINGS. See Coatings, Wood; and Paints, Etc., Wood

WOOD FIRE- AND FLAMEPROOFING AGENTS. See Fire- & Flameproofing Agents, Textile, Wood, Etc.

WOOD MOLDINGS. See Moldings, Metal, Wood, Plastic, Etc.

WOOD PAINTS. See Paints, Etc., Wood

WOOD POLISHES. See Polishes, Wood

WOOD PRESERVATIVES. See Preservatives, Wood

WOOD PRODUCTS, MISC.
Simpson

WOOD PULP & FIBER
Palco Industrial Fibers

WOOD SEALERS. See Sealers, Wood

WOOD STAINS. See Stains, Wood

WOOD VENEERS
Microveer
Wood-Trim

WOOD WATERPROOFING AGENTS. See Waterproofing Agents, Wood

WOODS
Balsa Wood
Cocobola
Ebony
Fustic
Greenheart
Lignum Vitae
Quassia
Quebracho

WOODWORK CLEANERS. See Cleaners & Detergents, Woodwork

WRENCHES
Favorite

X

X-RAY CONTRAST MEDIA
Pantopaque
Thixokon

Y

YARNS, TEXTILE. See Threads, Yarns & Fibers, Textile

Z

ZINC OXIDE FILLERS & PIGMENTS. See Fillers & Pigments, Zinc Oxide

DIRECTORY SECTION

Directory Section

A

ABBOTT LABORATORIES
North Chicago, Ill.

Abbocillin®
Abboject®
Abbo-Liter®
Abbo-Vac®
A-C®
Acidoride®
Actaloy®
Aerohalor®
Alcolo®
Aminosol®
Anesthesin®
Aurocoloid[NR]
Auroseed®
Bacillets®
Beclysyl®
Bejectal®
Bevidox®
Blutene®
Brominol®
Butesin®
Butyn®
Calcidrine®
Cal-Cofron[NR]
Calpan Free-Flo[NR]
Caparsolate®
Citrex Syrup®
Cly-Q-Pak®
Cobenzil®
Combuthal®
Compocillin-V[NR]
Convalets®
Covicone®
Cumopyran®
Dayalets®
Densitol®
Desbutal®
Desoxets®
Diasone®
Dicaldimin®
Dicalets®
Di-Paralene®
Donopak®
Donopak-Ette®
Dulcet®
Duozine®
Enterab®
Eramide®
Erythrocin®
Erythromid[NR]
Erythrotil®
Filmtab®
Forvecil®
Gallimycin[NR]
Gemonil®
Gerix®
Gravinol®
Haliver®
H.M.C.®
Hvazyme®
Hydro-Bilein®
Iberol®
Ionosol®
Ion-O-Trate®
Klotogen F®
Lissephen®
Lotocreme®
Lubritine[NR]
Manartal®
Manolator®
Maxilets[NR]
Natopherol®
Nembudeine®
Nembu-Donna®
Nembu-Fedrin®
Nembu-Gesic®
Nembusen®
Nembu-Serpin®
Nembutal®
Nicamin®
Nicothiamin®
Non-Vac[NR]
Norisodrine®
Nualets®
Optilets®
Paradione®
Para-Syllium®
Parresine®
Peganone®
Penicel®
Pentothal®
Phantocube®
Phenurone®
Phylladrine®
Placidyl®
Pliapak[NR]
Powdalator®
Pre-Daylin®
Pro-Gen®
Pro-Stat[NR]
Quelicin®
Quertine®
Rachromate®
Racobal[NR]
Radiocaps®
Risa®
Salihexin®
Seleen®
Selsun®
Sorlate®
Sterilope®
Strocillin®
Sulestrex®
Sulfedex®
Sulfedexan®
Sulf-Opto®
Sulvetil®
Sulvetil-Es[NR]
Sur-Bex®
Surplex®
Thenylene®
Thiazoline®
Tridione®
Trinesium®
Tronolen®
Tronothane®
Truo-Cillin®
Truozine®
Trynazin®
Varisol®
Vehicol®
Venopak®
Venoset®
Venotube®
Verclysyl®
Vetrophin®
Vi-Daylin®
Vita-Dulcet®
Vita-Kaps®
Vita-King®
Zyljectin®

ABCO CHEMICAL CO.
2316 Atlantic Ave., Brooklyn 33, N. Y.

Abco-Gel[NR]
Dispersol[NR]
Levelon[NR]
Thick-Aid[NR]
Thixo[NR]

ABESTO MFG. CORP.
131 Wabash St., Michigan City, Ind.

Abesto® Fibrated
Abesto® Liquid
Abesto® Lumiclad®
Abesto® Quick-Setting Plastic
Abesto® Sealer
Abesto® Semi-Plastic

ACETO CHEMICAL CO., INC.
40–40 Lawrence St., Flushing 54, N. Y.

Ceramol[NR]
Solasol[NR]
Solasol USP Extra[NR]

ACF INDUSTRIES, INC.
30 Church St., New York 8, N. Y.
(*See also* W-K-M Mfg. Co., Inc., Key Products Div.)

Refax®

ACME RESIN CORP.
1401 Circle Ave., Forest Park, Ill.

Acme Polyfluoron® Liquid Dispersion
Acme Polyfluoron® Molding Powder
Plasti Sand Process®

ACME SCIENTIFIC CO.
1450 W. Randolph St., Chicago 7, Ill.

Super-Lap

ACME WIRE CO.
New Haven 14, Conn.

Acme-Stick®
Formbond®
Hyfilm®

ACORN REFINING CO., THE
8001 Franklin Blvd., Cleveland 2, Ohio

Acobyte
Acolite
Est-R-Lux
Quick-Set
Rub-R-Lon

ADELPHIA PAINT & COLOR WORKS, INC.
86-00 Dumont Ave., Ozone Park 17, N. Y.

Adelphia Met-L-Kote Machinery Enamel[NR]

ADHESIVE PRODUCTS CORP.
1660 Boone Ave., New York 60, N. Y.

Apco
Kleen-Grip
Metagrip
Plastic Peel No. 3601
Polygriptex
Prestix Contact Cement
Stix-Grip[NR]

ADVANCE SOLVENTS & CHEMICAL
(*Division of* Carlisle Chemical Works, Inc.)
New Brunswick, N. J.

Advacide®
Advastab®
Zirco®

315

AFTA SOLVENTS CORP.
470 W. 128th St., New York 27, N. Y.
Afta   Aftite
Aftalene

AGKEM, INC.
(*Division of* The Kalo Co.)
506 Main St., Quincy, Ill.)
Garden Duster[NE]

AGRASHELL, INC.
640 N. 13th St., Easton, Pa.
Extelite®   Sliprite®

AIRKEM, INC.
241 E 44th St., New York 17, N. Y.
Airkem 10-39®   Airkem® Green Label
Airkem a-3®   Airkem Non-Toxic Insec-
Airkem Aerosol Insecti-   ticide[NE]
  cide[NE]   Airkem® Red Label
Airkem® Blue Label   Airkem® Red Label Mist
Airkem Deoterge®

AKRON CHEMICAL CO.
255 Fountain St., Akron 4, Ohio
Plasticizer LP *and* Plasticizer MP[NE]

ALADDIN ROD & FLUX MFG. CO.
1300 Burton St. S. E., Grand Rapids 7, Mich.
Aladdin® Galvanizing   Aladdin® Soapstone
  Compound   Pencil

ALCONOX, INC.
853 Broadway, New York 3, N. Y.
Alcojet®   Alcotabs®

ALLEGHENY LUDLUM STEEL CORP.
532 Oliver Bldg., Pittsburgh 22, Pa.
(*See also* Allegheny Ludlum Steel Corp., Forgings & Castings Div.)
Allegheny Ludlum® 47-   Allegheny Ludlum® Nu-
  50, 88X, *and* Magnet   metal®, Ohmaloy®,
  Steels   Sealmet®, *and* Silicon
Allegheny Ludlum® Clad   Steels
  Steel, Corrosion Re-
  sisting Castings, *and*
  Stainless Steel Alloys

ALLEGHENY LUDLUM STEEL CORP., FORGINGS & CASTINGS DIV.
Ferndale 20, Detroit, Mich.
FCC® No. 1   FCC® EZ
FCC® 5X1 Special   FCC® Fernite® 24
FCC® 5X1-V   FCC® Flamhard
FCC® ALX   FCC® Nitri-Cast-Iron
FCC® CTS   FCC® Roloy
FCC® CV   FCC® Roloy No. 2

ALLIED CHEMICAL & DYE CORP.
61 Broadway, New York 6, N. Y.
See General Chemical Div.; National Aniline Div.; Nitrogen Div.; *and* Solvay Process Div.

ALLIS-CHALMERS MFG. CO.
1127 S. 70th St., Milwaukee 1, Wisc.
Allis-Chalmers®   Chlorextol®
Allisite®   Mantalloy®

ALLOY RODS CO.
3100 W. Market St., York, Pa.
Atom-Arc®   Wear-Arc® 3-IP, 6-IP,
Bronze-Arc C®   *and* 12-IP
Bronze-Arc Mn®   Wear-Arc Super WH®
Mang-Arc®   Wear-Arc WH®

ALUMISEAL CORP.
385 Madison Ave., New York 17, N. Y.
Zero Perm

AMERCOAT CORP.
4809 Firestone Blvd., South Gate, Calif.
Amer-Plate® Plain   T-Lock Amer-Plate®

AMERICAN AGILE CORP.
P. O. Box 168, Bedford, Ohio
Agilene®-F   Agilon[NE]

AMERICAN AGRICULTURAL CHEMICAL CO.
50 Church St., New York 7, N. Y.
18% Normal® Super-   Keystone® Ammonium
  phosphate   Carbonate
AA Quality® Fertilizers Keystone® Gelatin
AA Quality® Phosphate   Nicotine Pyrox®
  Rock   Phos-Feed®
Agrico®   Phosphodust®
Agrinite®   Pyrox®
Cosmic® Black

AMERICAN AIR FILTER CO.
Louisville 8, Ky.
AAF®   Electro-PL®
Airmat®   Filterdown®
AMER-clone®   Herman Nelson®
AMER-glas®   Light/Stop®
AMERjet®   Multi-Duty®
Amervent®   Roll-O-MAT®
Auto-AIRMAT®   Roll-O-MATIC®
Cycoil®   Roto-Clone®
Draft/Stop®   Selectotherm®
Electro-AIRMAT®   Throway®
Electro-KLEAN®   Viscosine®
Electro-MATIC®

AMERICAN CELCURE WOOD PRESERVING CORP.
(*Formerly* Celcure Southern Corp.)
P. O. Box 3262, Jacksonville 6, Fla.
Celcure®

AMERICAN CYANAMID CO.
30 Rockefeller Plaza, New York 20, N. Y.
Accobond® 3900 Cellu-   Aerosol® 18
  losic Film Resin   Aerosol® 22
ACCO® Rosin Sizes   Aerosol® AY
Accosperse®   Aerosol® C-61
ACCO® Streptomycin   Aerosol® MA-80%
  D[NE]   Aerosol® OS
"Aero"® Ammonium Sul-   Aerosol® OT-75%
  fate   Aerosol® OT-100%
Aerocat®   Aerosol® OT-B
Aero® Cyanamid   Aerotex Accelerator
Aero® Cyanide   187[NE]
Aero® Depressants   Aerotex Accelerator
Aerofloat® Promoter 211   AS[NE]
Aerofloat® Promoter 249 Aerotex Accelerator
Aerofloat® Promoters   MX[NE]
"Aerofloc"® Reagents   Aerotex Accelerator
Aeroform®   NF[NE]
Aerofroth® Frothers   Aerotex Accelerator S[NE]
Aero® HDS Catalyst   Aerotex Accelerator
Aeroheat® 1100   UTX[NE]
Aeroheat® 1200R   Aerotex Antistatic[NE]
Aeromet®   Aerotex Buffer 190-A[NE]
"Aeromine"® Promoters   Aerotex Buffer DCY[NE]
Aeronox®   Aerotex Cream 450[NE]
Aero® Promoter 404   Aerotex Fire Retardant
Aero® Promoter 708   NDC[NE]
Aero® Promoter 712   Aerotex Fire Retardant
Aero® Promoters 801 *and* NDS[NE]
  825   Aerotex Purifying Agent
Aero® Specialty Cata-   No. 1[NE]
  lysts   (*continued*)

American Cyanamid Co. *(continued)*
Aerotex Resin 110[NR]
Aerotex Resin 120[NR]
Aerotex Resin 121[NR]
Aerotex Resin 133[NR]
Aerotex Resin 134[NR]
Aerotex Resin 159[NR]
Aerotex Resin 180[NR]
Aerotex Resin 390[NR]
Aerotex Resin 801[NR]
Aerotex Resin 802[NR]
Aerotex Resin 803[NR]
Aerotex Resin 7513[NR]
Aerotex Resin EU[NR]
Aerotex Resin M-3[NR]
Aerotex Resin MW[NR]
Aerotex Resin P-114[NR]
Aerotex Resin P-116[NR]
Aerotex Resin P-117[NR]
Aerotex Resin P-200[NR]
Aerotex Resin UM[NR]
Aerotex Softener H[NR]
Aerotex Softener W[NR]
Aerotex Syrup 55[NR]
Aerotex Syrup 250 Conc.[NR]
Aerotex Thickener 37[NR]
Aerotex Water Repellent S[NR]
Aero® Xanthate 301
Aero® Xanthates 322, 325, *and* 343
Aero® Xanthate 350
Amanol® Nitrogen Solutions
Amex®
Aminotriazole[NR]
Antioxidant 2246®
Bonadur[NR]
Calcofluor® Dyes
Calco Lake® Dyes
Calcoloid Dyes[NR]
Calcosol® Dyes
Calcosyn® Dyes
Calcozoic® Dyes
Creslan®
Cyamite®
Cyamon®
Cyamon® Primers
Cyan[NR]
Cyana®
Cyanamer® 370, Acrylic Polymer
Cyana® Permel® Finish
Cyana® Permel Plus® Finish
Cyana® Purifying Finish
Cyana® Shrinkage Control Finish
Cyana® Silicone Finish
Cyana® Silicone Plus Finish
Cyana® Superset® Finish
Cyanatex®
Cyanatex® 3119 Softener
Cyanatex® Anti-foam
Cyanatex® Cream Softener
Cyanatex® Dyeing Assistant EM
Cyanatex® SB 100 Softener
Cyanex®
Cyfor® Fortified Rosin Sizes
Cymac®
Cymel®
Cynol® Rewetting, Softening & Defoaming Agents
Cypan®
Cypel® Resin
Cyron® Chemical Size
Cyzac®
Hyform® Emulsion
Lanaset® Resin
Lanaset® Resin MW
Leather Product 612[NR]
Leather Product UF[NR]
Melostrength® Resin
NOBS No. 1 Accelerator®
Paramul® Repellent 115
Paramul® Repellent DC-1, *and* DC-2
Parez® Resins
Permel® Resin B
Permigels®
Pheno® Direct Color Dyes
Pyroset® DO Fire Retardant
Pyroset® Fire Retardant N-2
Retarder PD[NR]
Saf-T-Pak® Torpedo Tube
Suprak® Tanning Agents
Tanamer® Product 370
Texavon®
UV 9 Ultraviolet Absorber[NR]
Vatsol® OT-B Wetting Agent
Vatsol® Wetting Agents

AMERICAN FELT CO.
  Glenville, Conn.
Vistex® with Teflon®

AMERICAN GILSONITE CO.
  134 W. Broadway, Salt Lake City 1, Utah
Gilsulate®

AMERICAN GREASE STICK CO.
  2651 Hoyt St., Muskegon, Mich.
Door-Ease® Dripless Oil
Door-Ease® Stainless Steel Lubricant
Lock-Ease®
Ru Glide®

AMERICAN HAIR & FELT CO.
  Merchandise Mart, Chicago 54, Ill.
Cardinal®
Castle®
Combat®
Hairinsul®
Kil-Klatter®
Ozite®
Sunland®

AMERICAN HARD RUBBER CO.
  93 Worth St., New York 13, N. Y.
Ace-Flex®
Ace-Hide®
Ace® Parene®
Ace® Parian®
Ace® Parith®
Ace® Parlan®
Ace® Parnal®
Ace® Parsan®
Ace® Riviclor®
Ace-Sil®
Ace-Tuf®
Dur-Ace[NR]
Riji-Tuf®
Tempron®

AMERICAN HOME PRODUCTS CORP. See Ives-Cameron Co.

AMERICAN LAFRANCE CORP.
  (*Formerly* American LaFrance Foamite Corp.)
  100 E. La France St., Elmira, N. Y.
American LaFrance® Crystals

AMERICAN MACHINE & FOUNDRY CO.
  5502 2nd Ave., Brooklyn 20, N. Y.
Fiberfilm
Tissuglass

AMERICAN MAIZE PRODUCTS CO.
  250 Park Ave., New York 17, N. Y.
Amaizo® "400" Stabilizer
Amaizo® 721A Starch
Amioca®
Flufftex®
Frodex®
Gelex®
Granular Frodex®
Salicoa®
W-13 Stabilizer®

AMERICAN-MARIETTA CO., ADHESIVE RESIN & CHEMICAL DIV.
  3400—13th Ave. S. W., Seattle 4, Wash.
  (*See also* Presstite-Keystone Engineering Products Co.)
A-M 14
A-M 150
A-M 160
A-M 188
A-M 302
A-M 414T
A-M 580
A-M 604
A-M 620
A-M 3720
A-M 4620
A-M 5531
A-M 5602
A-M 6701
A-M 6712
A-M 6720
A-M AP 30
A-M AP 30R
A-M P.O.E.
Amres 54
Amres 118
Amres 136, 580, 4565, 5531, 5570 *and* 5580
Amres 200
Amres 210
Amres 225
Amres 250
Amres 255
Amres 275
Amres 1400
Amres 1420
Amres 1430
Amres 1910
Amres 1920
Amres 2612
Amres 2620
Amres 2670 *and* Amres 2670B
Amres 3710B
Amres 3910
Amres 4050C
Amres 4070A
Amres 4511
Amres 6110
Amres 6120 *and* 6120A
Amres 6121
Amres 6130
Amres 6131

AMERICAN MONOMER CORP.
  511 Lancaster St., Loeminster, Mass.
Lemac 7, 15, 40, 150, 1,000 *and* 6,000[NR]
Lemac WD[NR]
Lemol 65-98[NR]

AMERICAN PETROCHEMICAL CORP. See Mol-Rez Div.

AMERICAN PHARMACEUTICAL CO.
  120 Bruckner Blvd., New York 54, N. Y.
Afko-Carb[NR]
Afko Ear Oil[NR]
Afko-Hist[NR]
Afko Rub[NR]
Afko-Sal[NR]
Afko Syrup[NR]
Afko-Thricin Cream[NR]
(*continued*)

AMERICAN PHARMACEUTICAL CO. (continued)
Afko-Thricin Lozenges^{NR}
B.S.P. Tablets^{NR}
Cel-U-Bee Tablets^{NR}
C.S.A. Tablets, Improved^{NR}
Gentamine Tablets^{NR}
Ichthyamer^{NR}
Old Dr. Stork's^{NR}
Seed-O-Lax®
Sulfa-Ter Tablets^{NR}
Triple C Syrup^{NR}

AMERICAN POTASH & CHEMICAL CORP.
3030 W. Sixth St., Los Angeles 54, Calif.

Aratron®   Trona®

AMERICAN RESIN CORP.
3215 N. Sheffield Ave., Chicago 13, Ill.

Toolcast 1000 Resin

AMERICAN SISALKRAFT CORP.
55 Starkey Ave., Attleboro, Mass.

Sisalkraft Moistop®   Sisalkraft Vaporstop®

AMERICAN SOLDER & FLUX CO.
19th & Willard Sts., Philadelphia 40, Pa.

Drygalv^{NR}

AMERICAN STEEL & WIRE DIV. See United States Steel Corp.

AMERICAN URN BAG CO.
2432 Grand Concourse, New York 58, N. Y.

Shurflo®

AMERICAN WINDOW GLASS CO.
9 W. Park Way, Pittsburgh 12, Pa.

Lustracrystal®
Lustragray®
Lustrakool®
Lustrawhite®

AMES CO., INC.
(*Division of* Miles Laboratories, Inc.)
1127 Myrtle St., Elkhart, Ind.

Acetest®
Aminet®
Anayodin®
Apamide®
Apamide-Vess®
Apromal®
Bumintest®
Cholmodin®
Clinitest®
Clinistix®
Decholin®
Degalol®
Dextrotest®
Diatussin®
Hematest®
Ictotest®
My-B-Den®
Nostyn®
Occultest®
Stilphostrol®

AMES LABORATORIES, INC., THE
132 Water St., S. Norwalk, Conn.

Ink-Sav   Paint-Sav

AMOCO CHEMICALS CORP.
910 S. Michigan Ave., Chicago 80, Ill.

Amoco®
Indoil®
Indoil® Detergent Alkylate
Indoil® Isooctyl Alcohol
Indoil® Sulfonates
Indopol®
Panaflex®
Panalene^{NR}
Panapol®
Panarez®
Panasol®

ANDERSON, CLAYTON & CO.
P. O. Box 2538, Houston 1, Tex.
(*See also* Anderson, Clayton & Co. Foods Div.)

Long Reach®

ANDERSON, CLAYTON & CO. FOODS DIV.
(*Formerly* Mrs. Tucker's Foods, Inc.)
Gibralter Life Bldg., (P. O. Box 35), Dallas 21, Tex.

Accolade Oleomargarine^{NR}
Dixie®
Finesse®
Flair Shortening^{NR}
Flo®
Fribase®
Fry-Base®
Gleam®
Glen Eden® Margarine
Golden Capri^{NR}
Golden Mist Margarine^{NR}
Gold'n:Wedge® Margarine
Grayson® Margarine
Hibase®
Hollandale Margarine^{NR}
Hrdflakes®
Hy-Base®
Hy-Chill Salad Oil®
Jack Rabbit®
Jaxmor®
Kerba®
Lik-Wid®
Liqui-Fry®
Lite®
Log Cabin®
Log Cabin® Margarine
Meadolake® Margarine
Meva^{NR}
Mix-Ezy®
Nylene®
PSM-35®
Py-Eze®
Pylex®
Shine®
Southern Queen®
Super-G®
Tuckers, Mrs., Salad Oil®
Tuckers, Mrs., Shortening®
Vaf®
Vafet®
Velvet®
Velvet B®
Velvet M®
Velvet Oil®
Velvorene®
White Beauty®
Wizard®

ANDERSON, F. E., OIL CO., INC.
543 Brownstone Ave., Portland, Conn.

K-7
Shamrock
UniKool
Winsor® Cutting Oil 910
Winsor® Cutting Oil 6150
Winsor® Special Base
Winsor® T-G Grinding Oil

ANDERSON-PRICHARD OIL CORP.
Liberty Bank Bldg., Oklahoma City 2, Okla.

No. 10 Mineral Spirits^{NR}
Apco 360^{NR}
Apco Vaportite No. 100®
Super Stod-Sol®

ANDERSON-STOLZ CORP.
1727–33 Walnut St., Kansas City 8, Mo.

Oil-Solv
Sol-Vet
Soot-Solv

ANSUL CHEMICAL CO.
1 Stanton St., Marinette, Wisc.

Saf-Drive®

ANTHRACITE EQUIPMENT CORP.
Anthracite Institute Bldg., Wilkes-Barre, Pa.

AnthraAid   Anthrafilt®

APEX SMELTING CO.
2537 W. Taylor St., Chicago 12, Ill.

Apex 417

APOTHECARIES HALL CO.
28 Benedict St., Waterbury, Conn.

Liberty®

AQUABAR CO., THE
607–9 Commercial Trust Bldg., Philadelphia 2, Pa.

Emeritex^{NR}

ARAPAHOE CHEMICALS, INC.
2800 Pearl St., Boulder, Colo.

Arapahoe®
Globaline
VitaStain

ARCO CO.
7301 Bessemer Ave., Cleveland 27, Ohio

Arco Flex®
Arco Non-Shrinking Dum Dum Calk^{NR}
Arcopel^{NR}
Arco Rays®
Arcotone^{NR}
Arco Top®
Arco Zon®
Optonic®
Synite®, Synite® Aluminum Paint, *and* Synite® Enamels

ARCOS CORP.
1500 S. 50th St., Philadelphia 43, Pa.

Chromar
Monar
Nicuar

ARGUS CHEMICAL CORP.
633 Court St., Brooklyn 31, N. Y.

Drapex 4.4®
Mark C®
Mark WS®

ARMITAGE, JOHN L., & CO.
245 Thomas St., Newark 5, N. J.

Armorhide

ARMITE LABORATORIES
6609 Broad St., Los Angeles 1, Calif.

Armite® Anti-Seize Compound
Armite® Joint-Seal Compound No. 411
Led-Plate® Anti Seize Compound No. 250
Sealmore®
Thread-Tite®

ARMOUR AND CO.
1355 W. 31st St., Chicago 9, Ill.

Energetic®
Flint®
Formula #99®
Giant®
Industrial®
Texscour®
Topaz®

ARMSTRONG CORK CO
Lancaster, Pa.

Armaflex®
Armaglas®
Armalite[NE]
Armstrong F-1402 Wall Tile Cement[NE]
Armstrong LT Cork Coverings
Art Weave®
Baby Jumbo®
Budget[NE]
Carpetone®
Chempoint®
Cleaneasy®
Corlex®
Crestone®
Decoray®
Estate[NE]
Excelon®
Fold-Spray®
Full Random[NE]
Gold Leaf®
Granette®
Handi-Pack®
Hi-Speed®
Hydrocord[NE]
Imperial[NE]
Install-it-Yourself[NE]
J-1190[NE]
K-99®
Label-Rite®
Lok-Bevel®
Mobile-Roll[NE]
Moderntred[NE]
Monoplast®
Newray®
Opalite®
Ovale®
Phenix®
Quilt®
Rain-Shield®
Textelle®
Topper®
Town House[NE]

ARMSTRONG PRODUCTS CO.
P. O. Box 1, Warsaw, Ind.

Armstrong Epoxy Resin Adhesives[NE]

ARNAR-STONE LABORATORIES, INC
(*Formerly* Americaine, Inc.)
225 E. Prospect Ave., Mount Prospect, Ill.

Americaine®
Americaine with Neomycin®
Amerotol®
Silicote Skin Protectant Ointment®

ARNOLD, HOFFMAN & CO.
55 Canal St., Providence 1, R. I.

Ahcowet® SDS
Synthramine® A 50% Paste
Synthrapol® NX

ARROWHEAD RUBBER CO.
(*Division of* National Motor Bearing Co.)
2350 Curry St., Long Beach 5, Calif.

Airtron®

ARVEY CORP.
3462 N. Kimball Ave., Chicago 18, Ill.
(*See also* Velsicol Chemical Corp.)

Cel-O-Glass®

ASHLAND OIL & REFINING CO. See Valvoline Oil Co.

ATECH, INC.
3840 Lagrange St., Toledo 12, Ohio

Alumicone

ATHELSTAN PRODUCTS CO.
4700 Aldrich Ave. So., Minneapolis 9, Minn.

Ded-N-Dun®

ATLANTIC CHEMICAL CORP.
153 Prospect St., Passaic, N. J.

Atlantic Neutrazoic® Dyestuffs

ATLAS COLOR & CHEMICAL CO., INC.
60 K St., King Terminal, South Boston 27, Mass.

Atlasol Ag[NE]
Clarapent® Neutrascour

ATLAS-GOLDSCHMIDT G.m.b.H.
Postliessfach 17, Essen I, Germany

Arlacel®Ger.
Atlox®Ger.
Atpet®Ger.
Brij®Ger.
Myrj®Ger.
NNO®[NE]Ger.
NNOR[NE]Ger.
Span®Ger.
Tween[NE]Ger.

ATLAS POWDER CO.
Wilmington 99, Del.

Arlacel®
Atlox®
Atmos®
Atmul®
Atpet®
Brij®
Myrj®
NNO®
NNOR®
Renex®
Span®
Tween®

ATLAS POWDER CO., CANADA, LTD.
Brantford, Ont., Canada

Arlacel®Can.
Atmos®Can.
Atmul®Can.
Atpet®Can.
NNO®Can.
Span®Can.

ATLAS STEELS LTD.
E. Main St., Welland, Ontario, Canada

AHT-28®Can.
Atlas Chippewa®Can.
Atlas®Can.CM
Atlas HW-7[NE]
Atlas®Can. KK (Sioux)
Atlas Nushank[NE]
Atlas Ottawa®Can.
Atlas Vibresist®Can.
Commando Drill Rod®Can.
Hardy Nickel Iron[NE]
Hodi[NE]
SPS-245®Can.
Ultimo®Can.-4
XLO Die Blocks®Can.

ATOMIC BASIC CHEMICAL CORP.
90 Clairton Blvd., Pittsburgh 36, Pa.

A-B-C Phenothiazine[NE] Flavor-Feen®
Livestock Self Dewormer®

AUSTENAL, INC.
224 E. 39th St., New York 16, N. Y.

Microcast®

AUTOCLAVE ENGINEERS
2930 W. 22nd St., Erie, Pa.

Tube Line®

AYERST LABORATORIES
22 E. 40th St., New York 16, N. Y.

Kerodex®

B

BADISCHE ANILIN-U. SODA-FABRIK AG.
Friesenheimer Strasse 38, Ludwigshafen (Rhein), Germany
(*See also* Nova Chemical Corp.)

Albigen® A
BASF
Basolan
Lumatex®
Lumatex® Binder F
Palathrene® Brown LG Double Paste
Vialon®

BAIRD CHEMICAL CORP.
  10 W. 33rd St., New York 1, N. Y.
  [See also: Howards of Ilford Ltd., and Howards & Sons (Canada) Ltd.]
Abrac Resins 22 and 22A   Resin MS2
Akrode[NR]

BAKELITE COMPANY
  (Division of Union Carbide Corp.)
  30 E. 42nd St., New York 17, N. Y.
Krene®

BAKER CASTOR OIL CO.
  120 Broadway, New York 5, N. Y.
AN-10[NR]   M-P-A[NR]
Estynox®   Opalwax®

BALDWIN-HILL CO.
  500 Breunig Ave., Trenton, N. J.
Perimsul®

BALTIMORE BIOLOGICAL LABORATORY, INC.
  (Division of Becton, Dickinson and Co.)
  1640 Gorsuch Ave., Baltimore 18, Maryland
B-B-L

BARECO WAX CO.
  (Division of Petrolite Corp.)
  P. O. Box 2009, Tulsa 2, Okla.
Be Square® Special   Starwax®
Waxes   Ultraflex®
Petrolite®   Victory® Wax

BARNEBEY-CHENEY CO.
  Cassady at 8th Aves., Columbus 19, Ohio
Adsorbit®   Deodorite®
Black Magic®

BAROID DIV., NATIONAL LEAD CO.
  111 Broadway, New York 6, N. Y.
Ben-A-Gel®   Bentone® 34
Bentone®   Bentone® 38
Bentone® 18-C

BARRELED SUNLIGHT PAINT CO.
  Providence 1, Rhode Island
Quickwall Primer   Spectrum

BASIC VARNISH AND RESEARCH CORP.
  215 N. Tenth St., Brooklyn 11, N. Y.
BV

BAUMRITTER, T., CO.
  171 Madison Ave., New York 18, N. Y.
Birchcraft®   Restocraft®
Ethan Allen®   Roomates®

BAY STATE ABRASIVE PRODUCTS CO.
  Westboro, Mass.
Blue Flash®   Gritcloth®

B. B. CHEMICAL CO.
  784 Memorial Drive, Cambridge 39, Mass.
Boscel[NR]   Duralene®
Bosfilm®   Duranap®

BEACON CHEMICAL INDUSTRIES, INC.
  (Formerly Beacon Co.)
  33 Richdale Ave., Cambridge 40, Mass.
Aquacal®

BECCO CHEMICAL DIV., FOOD MACHINERY & CHEMICAL CORP.
  Station B, Buffalo 7, N. Y.
Becco®

BECTON, DICKINSON AND CO.   See Baltimore Biological Laboratory, Inc.

BEHR-MANNING CO.
  (Division of Norton Co.)
  2756 Howe St., Troy, N. Y.
Behr-Disker®   Metalweld® Joints
Buffem®   No-Fil®
Carbicon®   Screen-Bak®
Edg-R-Discs[NR]   Spirapoint®
Green-Bak[NR]   Tufbak®
Kon-Toor® Wheel

BELLE CHEMICAL CO., INC.
  Reading, Pa.
Belamine Fast Blue   Bellefix N-100[NR]
  Bluc[NR]   Calmasene T[NR]
Bellefast Colors[NR]   Neutranyl Colors[NR]
Bellefix CN[NR] and Bellefix VS[NR]

BELL LABORATORY, INC.
  2421 Kilgore Ave., Orlando, Fla.
"76" Motor Tune Up   Mix-I-Go
Bell's Atom-Ix   Or-Lo
Dee-Zol

BELL, M. A., CO.
  217 Lombard St., St. Louis 2, Mo.
No. 43 Core & Mold   Liberty Liquid Parting[NR]
  Wash[NR]   Mabco Aluminum Flux[NR]
No. 100 Plum Core   Mabco Core Oils[NR]
  Wash[NR]   Mabco Iron Filler[NR]
#188 Core Paste[NR]   Mabco Mineral Facing[NR]
AP Core and Mold   Mabco Pattern Paint[NR]
  Wash[NR]   Mabco Quality Pitch
Atlas Core Wash[NR]   Core Compound[NR]
D & S Core & Mold   Mabco Seacoal Facing[NR]
  Wash[NR]   Mabcotherm 23 IS[NR]
Eureka Core Paste[NR]   Mabcotherm Pipe Eliminator[NR]
Fastdry Core Paste[NR]
Flexigate®   Release Agent "G"[NR]
Hi-Resist Core & Mold   Reddy Core Paste[NR]
  Wash[NR]   Sandseal Core & Mold
Karbko Core & Mold   Wash[NR]
  Wash[NR]   Star Facing[NR]
Koreline Core Wash[NR]   Zircono Core & Mold
Kuik Kore Kompound[NR]   Wash[NR]

BELL-RAY CHEMICAL CORP.
  3132 W. Garfield Ave., Milwaukee 8, Wisc.
Chem-Bond   Kem-O-Kleen

BEMIS BROTHERS BAG CO.
  601 S. 4th St., St. Louis 2, Mo.
Bemibrite®   Ripp-Nipp®
Bemis Ripp-Tabb®   Ruf-Grip®
Resistal-Weld®   Transwall®
Rezlok®

BERMAN CHEMICAL CO.
  712 Superior St., Toledo 4, Ohio
Bull Frog® Saf-T®Klenz

BETHLEHEM STEEL CO.
  701 E. Third St., Bethlehem, Pa.
Bethlehem Superalloy
  Hollow Drill®

BIGELOW-LIPTAK CORP.
  13300 Puritan Ave., Detroit 27, Mich.
Bi-Met

BIGGS, CARL H., CO., INC.
  2255 Barry Ave., W. Los Angeles 64, Calif.
Adhesive 701   Helix Bonding Agents
Flawmaster   Helix Potting Compounds
Flexible Mold Compound   Protective Coating #621
  #201   Solvent 101

BIRCHWOOD CHEMICAL CO.
4500 W. 44th St., Minneapolis, Minn.
Aluma Block®

BISHOPRIC PRODUCTS CO., THE
4413 Este Ave., Cincinnati 32, Ohio
Lastiglas®

BIWAX CORP.
Skokie, Ill.
Biwax

BLAIR LABORATORIES, INC.
87 Woodland Rd., Short Hills, N. J.
Diace[NR]
Doxol[NR]
Isadoxol[NR]
Serphedrine®
Serphylline®

BLANCHARD BRO. & LANE
408 Frelinghuysen Ave., Newark, N. J.
Blanchardized®

BLOOMINGDALE RUBBER CO.
Delaware Ave. & Flower St., Chester, Pa.
Bloomingdale Adhesive FM-47
Bloomingdale Adhesive FM-47 Film

BLUE RIDGE GLASS CORP.
Kingsport, Tenn.
Fine-Tex®
Huetex®
Huewhite®
Parallel-O-Plate®
Ra-Grid® Heater Plates
Satinol® Finish
Securit® Glass
Securit® Interior Glass Doors
Tobex®

BORCHERDT CO.
(*Formerly* Borcherdt Malt Extract Co.)
217 N. Wolcott Ave., Chicago 12, Ill.
Urolitia®

BORDEN CO., THE, CHEMICAL DIV.
350 Madison Ave., New York 17, N. Y.
A-118[NR]
Cure-Set Adhesive[NR]
Hydrocure[NR]
K-87 Asphalt Tile Cement[NR]
M6[NR]
M-75[NR]
M-F-21[NR]
New Plastic Mix[NR]
Placco[NR]
R-66[NR]
Super-Crete-X[NR]

BORG-WARNER CORP. See Marbon Chemical Div.

BOSTON WOVEN HOSE & RUBBER CO.
P. O. Box 1071, Boston 3, Mass.
Alexall Tape
Boston All-Purpose
Boston Bay State
Boston Bull Dog
Boston Bull Dog Acid Discharge
Boston Bull Dog Acid Suction
Boston Bull Dog Cord
Boston Bull Dog Gold Edge
Boston Bull Dog Neoprene
Boston Bull Dog Rotocord
Boston Colliery King
Boston Concord Yellow Jack
Boston Cyclops
Boston Damascus
Boston Flexer
Boston Flameout
Boston Granger
Boston Haul King
Boston Heat King
Boston Herringbone
Boston High Load
Boston Iron Clad
Boston Mucker
Boston New Utah
Boston Perfection Cord
Boston Rough Top
Boston Service
Boston Silver King
Boston Silver King Rotocord
Boston Speed-Lite
Boston Tiger
Boston Vim
Boston Warrior
Bull Dog Friction Tape
Bull Dog Plastic Electrical Tape
Bull Dog Splicing Compound

BOWMAN, CHARLES, & CO.
220 E. 42nd St., New York 17, N. Y.
Vitab B-Complex Extract

BOYER-CAMPBELL CO., THE
6540 St. Antoine, Detroit 2, Mich.
Skin-Cote

BRAND, WILLIAM, & CO., INC., THE
North & Valley Sts., Willimantic, Conn.
Turbo®
Turbo 117®
Turboglas®
Turbolene®
Turbolex®
Turbosil®
Turbotemp®
Turbotherm®
Turbotrans®
Turbotuf®
Turbo Tufflex®
Turbozone®

BRAYTEN PHARMACEUTICAL CO.
Chattanooga 9, Tenn.
Alglyn® Tablets
Belglyn® Tablets
Malglyn® Compound Tablets
Meta Cine® Douche Powder
Metasert® Inserts
neo Bromth® Tablets
Patheba® Tablets
Theoglycinate®

BRISCOE MFG. CO.
1055 Gibbard Ave., Columbus 3, Ohio
Briskeat®

BRISTOL LABORATORIES INC.
630 Fifth Ave., New York 20, N. Y.
Alminate® Tablets
Barbonate® Tablets
Bristalin®
Bristamin® APC Tablets
Bristamin® Tablets
Bristapen® 200
Centrine®
Kectil® Suspension
Mytinic®
Neuro-Centrine®
Palapent®
Panbiotic®
Pen-Aqua®
Polycycline®
Polycycline® Aqueous '250'
Polycycline® Intramuscular
Polycycline® Intravenous
Polycycline® Ointment
Polycycline® Ophthalmic Ointment
Zirnox®

BROOKLYN PAINT & VARNISH CO.
(*Formerly* Brooklyn Varnish Mfg. Co., Inc.)
50 Jay St., Brooklyn 1, N. Y.
Tuf-On® 745-S *and* 747-S
Tuf-On® Met-L-Brite Clear
Tuf-On® Selenium Rectifier Coatings

BROSITES PRODUCTS CORP.
50 Church St., New York 7, N. Y.
Mechbond Felts[NR]

BROWNELL'S, BOB
(*Formerly* Brownell Industries, Inc.)
Corner Main & Third, Montezuma, Iowa
Acraglas®
Oxynate No. 7

BRUCE, E. L., CO. See Terminix Div.

BRULIN & CO., INC.
2939-45 Columbia Ave., Indianapolis 7, Ind.
1793 W. 12th St., Oakland 7, Calif.
Bowlette[NR]
Brulin Bright[NR]
Brulinsolv[NR]
Clearkote[NR]
Contact Wax[NR]
Lume-Brite[NR]
Octo-Solve®
Safety-Solv[NR]
Solvent Degreaser[NR]
Syndex[NR]

BUNTING BRASS & BRONZE CO.
Toledo 1, Ohio
Bunting®

BURGESS, FOBES CO.
P. O. Box 106, Portland 6, Maine
Crystolux[NR]
Deco[NR]
Ferro-cide[NR]
Ligno-Sote[NR]
Pen-Wood 176[NR]

BURNS & RUSSELL CO.
Bayard & Severn Sts., Baltimore 30, Md.
Spectra-Glaze®

BURTONITE CO., THE
Nutley 10, N. J.
Burtonite® #7
Burtonite® V-31-E
Glu-Beeds®

C

CABOT, GODFREY L., INC.
77 Franklin St., Boston 10, Mass.
Black Pearls®
Cabflex®
Cab-o-sil®
Elftex®
PT Pine Tar Products[NR]
Supercarbovar®

CADILLAC PLASTIC CO.
15111 Second Blvd., Detroit 3, Mich.
Cadco®

CALIFORNIA SPRAY-CHEMICAL CORP.
Richmond, Calif.
Cherry Coposil®
Isotox® PMA Seed Treater
Isotox® Spray No. 200

CALIFORNIA STUCCO PRODUCTS OF N. E., INC.
169 Waverly St., Cambridge 39, Mass.
Allwall[NR]
Caspro®
Plexichrome[NR]
Plexicolor[NR]
Raylite[NR]
Rayotint[NR]
Weld-O-Bond[NR]

CAMBRIDGE FILTER CORP.
725 E. Water St., Syracuse 3, N. Y.
Absolute Filters
Aerosolve Filters

CAMBRIDGE INDUSTRIES CO.
101 Potter St., Cambridge 42, Mass.
Resoflex® R-296

CAMPBELL INDUSTRIES, INC.
(*Subsidiary of* Clarostat Mfg. Co.)
North Aurora, Ill.
Fixtohm®

CANADA ROOF PRODUCTS LTD.
2627 Arbutus St., Vancouver 9, B. C., Canada
Ace-Tex®[Can.]
Plasti-Gum®[Can.]
Plasti-Seal®[Can.]

CANNON CHEMICAL CO.
179 Portland St., Cambridge 41, Mass.
Lecton® Car-Care
Lecton® Easy-Care
Lecton® Furniture-Care
Lecton Leather-Care
Lecton® Plastic & Leather Cleaner
Lecton® Solvent
Lecton® Super-Care

CARBOLINE CO.
331 Thornton Ave., St. Louis 19, Mo.
Carbomastic Series
Neoprene W

CAREY, PHILIP, MFG. CO.
Lockland, Cincinnati 5, Ohio
Fireclad[NR]
Insulation Seal 820[NR]
Thermoglas Pipe Covering[NR]
Thermoglas R/F Insulation[NR]

CARLISLE CHEMICAL WORKS, INC.
West St., Reading, Ohio
(*See also* Advance Solvents & Chemical Div.)
Cellu-Brite[NR]
Fuelguard[NR]
Pave[NR]

CARNEGIE-ILLINOIS STEEL CORP. *See* United States Steel Corp.

CARTER-WATERS CORP.
2440 Pennway, Kansas City 8, Mo.
Blok-Joint[NR]

CEILCOTE CO., THE
4832 Ridge Rd., Cleveland 9, Ohio
Ceilcrete®
Ceil-Por®
Corobond®

CELANESE CORP. OF AMERICA
180 Madison Ave., New York 16, N. Y.
Alluracel[NR]
Beachanese®
Celacloud[NR]
Celafaille®
Celallure®
Celaloom®
Celaspun®
Celatow®
Celbrook®
Celluphos®
Celsheer®
Chifonese®
Clairanese®
Crepenese®
Fortecel®
Fortenese®
Fortiflex®
Hawkskin®
Heritage®
Jersanese®
Lanese®
Luracel®
Lustrocel®
MR®
Multicord®
Prospector®
Quilticel®
Serenacel®

CELLU-SAN DIV., DARWORTH INC.
Simsbury, Conn.
Cellu-Pel®
Cellu-Quin®
Cellu-San®

CELOTEX CORP.
120 S. La Salle St., Chicago 3, Ill.
19/Up®
Acousti-Celotex® Varitex®
Acousti Lock Board®
Acousti-Lux®
Alumitee®
Aristocrat®
Celo-Lok[NR]
Celopad®
Celopak®
Celo-Roof®
Celo-Siding®
Celotex®
Channel-Lap®
Colony[NR]
Duo-Tex®
El Rey®
Ferox®
Gray Stone®
Lumicel®
Plastolite®
SC[NR]
Screwlock®
Shadow Crest[NR]
ShadowGrain®
Steelacoustic®
Straitone[NR]
Texbord®
Traffic Top®
Verti-Groove®

CENTRAL O-B PRODUCTS CO.
1230-40 Genesee St., Buffalo 11, N. Y.
A-O-K[NR]
Kil-O-Mist[NR]
O-B®
San-A-Jon Liquid[NR]

CERESIT WATERPROOFING CORP.
3227 S. Shields Ave., Chicago 16, Ill.
Colored Metalsium[NR]
Craxment[NR]
Metalsium[NR]
Silcotite
Super Metalsium[NR]

CHAMBERLAIN ENGINEERING CORP.
5005 Brimfield Rd., Akron 9, Ohio
Transflow M-32

CHARCOAL CORP. OF AMERICA
726 Fairmont Ave., Fairmont, W. Va.
Black Magic[NR]
King O' Chef's[NR]
Mr. Charcoal[NR]

CHASE BRASS & COPPER CO.
236 Grand St., Waterbury 20, Conn.
Alpha®

CHASE CHEMICAL CO.
1374 E. 170th St., Cleveland 10, Ohio
Donovo

CHATHAM PHARMACAL
P. O. Box 951, Bisbee, Ariz.
Cochise®

CHEMICAL OIL & RESIN CO.
(*Formerly* Chemical Oil Processing Co.)
84 Peter St., Toronto 2, Ontario, Canada
Chemcore
Chemlin
Chemrez
Chemvar
Polychem

CHEMICAL PRODUCTS CORP.
King Philip Rd., E. Providence 14, R. I.
Chem-o-sol®

CHEMO PURO MFG. CORP.
150 Doremus Ave., Newark 5, N. J.
Chlorophenesin®
Salnide®

CHICAGO APPARATUS CO.
1735 N. Ashland Ave., Chicago 22, Ill.
Stansol®

CHICAGO BRIDGE & IRON CO.
322 S. Michigan Ave., Chicago 4, Ill.
Chi-lon®
Hortondome Roof[NR]
Hortonsphere®
Hortonspheroid®
Horton® Vaportank
Vaporsphere®
Watersphere®

CHICAGO PHARMACAL CO.
5547 N. Ravenswood Ave., Chicago 40, Ill.
Barbita®
Cevicetyl®
Citrisan[NR]
Hytrophen[NR]
Merlenate[NR]
Peausan®
Prenasup®
Textrolix[NR]
Vermizine®

CHIPMAN CHEMICALS CO., INC.
P. O. Box 309, Bound Brook, N. J.
Agrox®
Chlorax® "40"
Chlorea®
Mema®
Mergamma®
Shed-A-Leaf®

CIBA CO., INC.
627 Greenwich St., New York 14, N. Y.
Albatex® POK
Cibalan® Salt H
Cibalan® Salt N
Cibalan® Salt S
Lyofix® EW Conc.
Neolan® Salt P
Neovadine® AL
Neovadine® AN
Sapamine® FLK
Sapamine® OC
Ultravon® JF
Uvitex® P Conc.
Uvitex® RBS
Uvitex® TXS Conc.
Uvitex® U

CIBA PHARMACEUTICAL PRODUCTS INC.
Summit, N. J.
Antistine®-Privine®
Antrenyl®
Apresoline®
Carmethose®
Carmethose®-Trasentine®
Cibalgine®
Coramine®
Dial®
Dibistine®
Doriden®
Elkosin®
Entero-Vioform® Tablets
Eticylol®
Femandren® Linguets®
Heavy Solution Nupercaine®
Itrumil® Sodium
Lipoiodine®
Nupercaine®
Nupercaine® In Oil
Nuporals®
Phytin®
Plimasin®
Pyribenzamine®-Ephedrine Tablets
Pyribenzamine® Expectorant
Pyribenzamine® Injectable Solution
Pyribenzamine® Ointment and Cream
Regitine®
Ritalin®
Serpasil®
Serpasil®-Apresoline®
Trasentine®-Phenobarbital
Tricainal®
Vinactane®

CLACK WATER TREATMENT, INC.
(*Formerly* Clack Water Treatment Service)
949 Applegate Rd., P. O. Box 2046, Madison 5, Wis.
Clack Activated Carbon (High Capacity)
Corsex®
Duomatic®
Manumatic®
Oilex

CLAIRE MFG. CO.
7640 Vincennes Ave., Chicago 20, Ill.
Fast-Kill
Gleme
Pine Air
Spice Air
Spring Aire

CLAREMONT PIGMENT DISPERSION CORP.
39 Powerhouse Rd., Roslyn Heights, N. Y.
Claremont "PE" Series
Claremont "RP" Series
Claremont "UR" Series
Claremont "VC" Series

CLARK, ROBERT H., CO.
9330 Santa Monica Blvd., Beverly Hills, Calif.
Jumbo Junior

CLAROSTAT MFG. CO.
Dover, N. H.
(*See also* Campbell Industries, Inc.)
Ad-A-Switch®
Claro®
Clarostat®
Clarostat (in Symbol)®
C Line®
Flexohm®
Fuzohm®
Glasohm®
Greenohm®
Greenohm Jr.®
House of Resistors, The®
Humdinger®
Pick-A-Shaft®
Potpot®
R T V®
Standee®
Vari/Phase[NR]

CLAYMONT STEEL PRODUCTS DEPT. See Colorado Fuel & Iron Corp., Claymont Steel Products Dept.

CLAYTON, ANDERSON, & CO. FOODS DIV. See Anderson, Clayton & Co. Foods Div.

CLEVELAND TWIST DRILL CO.
1242 E. 49th St., Cleveland 14, Ohio
Mo-Max®

CLOVER CHEMICAL CO.
Eighty Four, Pa.
Ferti-Liquid® 10-20-10

CLUETT, PEABODY & CO., INC.
10 E. 40th St., New York 16, N. Y.
Sanforized®
Sanforlan®

COLLOIDS, INC.
394-8 Frelinghuysen Ave., Newark 5, N. J.
Anti-Block QP[NR]
Ceraloid 356[NR]
Ceraloid 356WD[NR]
Ceraloid X4977D2[NR]
Dispersal 995[NR]
Dispersal 1278[NR]
Drawax 930[NR] *and* 931[NR]
Drawax 936[NR]
Delectrol 379[NR]
Foamicide 581[NR]
Foamicide 581B[NR]
Hygrolized Oil 221[NR]
Mulsoid 815M[NR]
Pentex 44[NR]
Permaloid 155[NR]
Permaloid 170V20[NR]
Resiloid 250[NR]
Resiloid B[NR]
Synterge 748[NR]
Synterge 750[NR]

COLONIAL STEEL CO. DIV. See Vanadium-Alloys Steel Co.

COLORADO FUEL & IRON CORP., CLAYMONT STEEL PRODUCTS DEPT.
813 West St., Wilmington 99, Del.
Lectro-Clad®

COLTON CHEMICAL CO.
(*Division of* Air Reduction Co.)
1747 Chester Ave., Cleveland 14, Ohio
Colfoam®   Flexbond 800
Colfoam® Microballoon®   Vinac
Spheres   Vinol

COLUMBIA-GENEVA STEEL DIV. See United States Steel Corp.

COLUMBIAN CARBON CO.
380 Madison Ave., New York 17, N. Y.
Excelsior®   Neo Spectra®
Micronex®

COLUMBIA-SOUTHERN CHEMICAL CORP.
(*Subsidiary of* Pittsburgh Plate Glass Co.)
1 Gateway Center, Pittsburgh 22, Pa.
Calsalt®   Columbia-Southern®
Columbia® Calcium   Phosflake®
Chloride   Pittabs®

COLUMBUS COATED FABRICS CORP.
Seventh & Grant Aves., Columbus 16, Ohio
Wall-Tex®

COLYER CO.
10 W. 47th St., New York 36, N. Y.
Uni-Pectin

COMMERCE CHEMICAL CORP.
Warren, Pa.
Commerce®   Com-Plus®

COMMERCE OIL CORP.
Warren, Pa.
Commerce®   Micris[NR]

COMMERCIAL SOLVENTS CORP. See Thermatomic Carbon Co.

CONAX CORP.
7811 Sheridan Dr., Buffalo 21, N. Y.
Conax®

CONSOLIDATED COVER CO.
15 Williams Ave., San Francisco 24, Calif.
Bidco®   Proco®
Conseco®

CONSOLIDATED MIDLAND CORP.
15 Parkway, Katonah, N. Y.
Alcophobin[NR]   Methionine[NR]
Amoebicon®   Microsulfon[NR]
Enterosulfon®   Minerovit®
Forticon®   Moebiquin®
Germicin[NR]   Mulvitol® *and* Mulvitol®
Hypertencin[NR] *and* Hy-   Strong
pertencin Mild[NR]   Rauwicon[NR]
Infantovit® *and* Infanto-   Resiston[NR]
vit® Chewable   Serpicon[NR]
Infantovit® Drops   Streptoconin®
Infantovit® Plus   Teebacin®
Isopacin®   Teebacin Acid®
Libeplex®   Teebaconin®
Livitol®   Teebazone®
Livitol® Syrup   Urosulfon®
Livrex[NR]   Vigoramin®

CONSOLIDATED WESTERN STEEL DIV. See United States Steel Corp.

CONSOWELD CORP.
(*Formerly* Consolidated Water Power & Paper Co.)
P. O. Box 50, Wisconsin Rapids, Wisconsin
Consoweld®   Flash Gloss®

CONTINENTAL CHEMISTE CO.
2256 W. Ogden Ave., Chicago 12, Ill.
Smo-Cloud

CONTINENTAL OIL CO.
P. O. Box 2197, Houston 1, Texas
Admite®   Conoco H-300[NR]

CONTINENTAL SPECIALTIES CO.
3215-17 S. Lombard Ave., Cicero 50, Ill.
Kiss-O'-Flavor®

CORDO MOLDING PRODUCTS, INC.
230 Park Ave., N. Y. 17, N. Y.
Cordopreg®

CORHART REFRACTORIES CO.
1600 W. Lee St., Louisville 10, Ky.
Corhart® ZAC® Electrocast®

CORNING GLASS WORKS
P. O. Box 544, Corning, N. Y.
Glascast

CORRULUX DIV., L-O-F GLASS FIBERS CO.
See L-O-F Glass Fibers Co., Corrulux Div.

CRAFTINT MFG. CO.
1615 Collamer Ave., Cleveland 10, Ohio
Craftint "66" Drawing   Craftint Foilcraft[NR]
Inks[NR]   Craftint Singletone[NR]
Craftint Color-Vu   Craftint Super White
Papers[NR]   "37"[NR]
Craftint Doubletone[NR]   Draw-Kleen®

CRANE PACKING CO.
6400 W. Oakton St., Morton Grove, Ill.
"John Crane" Chemlon®   "John Crane" Thred-
"John Crane" PLS (Plas-   Gard
tic Lead Seal)

CRAVENETTE CO., U. S. A., THE
(*Formerly* Cravenette Corp.)
729 Madison St., Hoboken, N. J.
"Cravenette"®   Dryette®

CROWN CORK & SEAL CO.
Eastern Ave. & Kresson St., Baltimore 24, Md.
Crown (in design)®   Pourite®

CROWN ZELLERBACH CORP., CHEMICAL PRODUCTS DIV.
Camas, Wash.
Orzan® AH-3

CUPRINOL DIV., DARWORTH INC.
Simsbury, Conn.
Cuprinol® Sav-It®   Dura-wood®

CUTLER-HAMMER, INC.
315 N. 12th St., Milwaukee 1, Wisc.
Hydrone®

CYCLONE FENCE DEPT., AMERICAN STEEL & WIRE DIV. See United States Steel Corp.

D

DACAR CHEMICAL PRODUCTS CO.
1077 McCartney St., Pittsburgh 20, Pa.
Dexcel®

DARWORTH INC. *See* **Cellu-San Div.,** *and* **Cuprinol Div.**

DAUBERT CHEMICAL CO.
333 N. Michigan Ave., Chicago 1, Ill.
Cedar Breeze®
Hydrin®
Nox-Carbon®
Nox-Sound®

DAYTON CHEMICAL PRODUCTS LABORATORIES, INC.
P. O. Box 27, West Alexandria, Ohio
Thixon®

DECAR PLASTIC CORP.
1212 N. Central Park Ave., Chicago 51, Ill.
Decaboard
Decaflex
Decaform
Decarlite

DECTO PRODUCTS CO.
54 Broadway, Salem, Mass.
Decto-Stick®

DEECY PRODUCTS CO.
120 Potter St., Cambridge 42, Mass.
Barca® 10
Staflex®

DELAWARE TOOL STEEL CORP.
East Wilmington 99, Del.
Delsteel® Alloy

DENNIS CHEMICAL CO.
2701 Papin St., St. Louis 3, Mo.
Denflex Plastisol
Primers[NR]

DE PAUL CHEMICAL CO., INC.
44-27 Purvis St., Long Island City 1, N. Y.
Decolon® RU
Depco® Bleach Assist
Depco® Fix N
Depcogel® 3X
Depcolin®
Depcoset® RI

DEVA-METAL CORP.
P. O. Box 146, Ridgewood, N. J.
Deva-Metal[NR]

DEVCON CORP.
(*Formerly* Chemical Development Corp.)
19 Endicott St. (P. O. Box 2), Danvers, Mass.
Acrylic Frosting Lacquer 158A
Anstac 2-M
Anstac CA
Anstac CN
Anstac M
Anstac N
Anstac P
Anstac P-1
Anstac V
CD Cement 2
CD Cement 18
CD Cement 24
CD Cement 26
CD Cement 32
CD Cement 33
CD Cement 94
CD Cement 114
CD Cement 125
CD Cement 200
CD Cement 201
CD Cement 202
CD Cement 203
CD Cement 204
CD Cement 300
CD Cement 400
CD Cement 1508
CD Cement 1509
CD Cement 1516
CD Cement PS-7
CD Cleaner 27
CD Dip Polish 231
CD Lubricant 105
CD Mold Release A
CD Mold Release B
CD Mold Release B-2
CD Spray Mask A
CD Strip 100
CD Strip A
CD Strip B
Devcon®

DEVOE & RAYNOLDS CO., INC. *See* **Truscon Laboratories Div.**

DIELECT INC.
P. O. Box 369, Fords, New Jersey
Poly-A9 Cast Film

DISTILLATION PRODUCTS INDUSTRIES, DIV. OF EASTMAN KODAK CO.
Rochester 3, N. Y.
DPi®
EKC®
Myvacet®
Myva-Dry®
Myvamix®
Myvapack®
Myvatex®
Myvax®
Myverol®
Pantopaque®

DIVERSEY CORP., THE
1820 Roscoe St., Chicago 13, Ill.
Ampolite®
Canrite®
Dico®
Dicoloid®
Dipak®
Ditran®
Diversey No. 16[NR]
Diversey No. 519[NR]
Diversey No. 808[NR]
Diversol® CX
Divo®
Divobond®
Divobond® ST
Divobrite®
Divo-Dip®
Divolume®
Dumore®
Heavy Duty®
Kontrex®
Lustral®
New Diokem®
Novex®
Peptex®
Perfon®
Plyokem®
Plyowax®
Protex Metallum®
Relion®
Rub-R-Kleen®
Spec-Tak®
Striptex®
Tembrite®
Vitrosol®
Zerospot[NR]

DoALL CO., THE
Des Plaines, Ill.
DoAll®
Kleen-Flush
Kleen-Kool
Power Cut®
Saw Eez

DOLPHIN PAINT & VARNISH CO.
P. O. Box 1594, Central Sta., Toledo 3, Ohio
Dolfinite®

DORAN CHEMICAL CORP.
5415-17-19 St. John Ave., Kansas City 23, Mo.
Speedee White Sidewall Tire Cleaner

DOUGLAS AIRCRAFT CO., INC.
3000 Ocean Park Blvd., Santa Monica, Calif.
Aircomb®

DOW CHEMICAL CO.
Midland, Mich.
2-4 Dow®
99®
Baron®
Chlorothene®
Dorisyl[NR]
Dorlone[NR]
Dowfax[NR]
Dowlube®
Dowpac[NR]
Dowpon[NR]
Dow-Tri[NR]
Fumazone[NR]
Galvomag[NR]
Lavamenthe[NR]
Mellitone[NR]
Novon[NR]
Prentalin[NR]
Radapon[NR]
Reddon[NR]
Rogepel[NR]
Rosaryl[NR]
Rose Marrakesh[NR]
Rosottone[NR]
Rosottone Savon[NR]
Saran Wrap[NR]
Separan 2610®
Serafume[NR]
Synalol E[NR]
Synalyl D[NR]
Tabatonka[NR]
Tarophen[NR]
Ten-Ten®
Versene® 9
Versene® 67
Versene® 100
Versene® Acid
Versene® Beads
Versene® Fe-3 Beads
Versene® Fe-3 Liquid
Versene® Fe-3 Powder
Versene Fe-3 Specific®
Versene® Powder
Versene® S
Versene® T
Versenol® 120
Versenol® Beads
Versenol® Powder
Vulcosa[NR]
Zertan[NR]

DRIVER-HARRIS CO.
P. O. Drawer 31, Harrison, N. J.

30 Alloy[NR]	142 Alloy[NR]
33 Alloy[NR]	146 Alloy[NR]
95 Alloy[NR]	Karma®
99 Alloy[NR]	Therlo®

DRIVER, WILBUR B., CO.
1875 McCarter Highway, Newark 4, N. J.

Cuprochrome[NR]   Permagrid[NR]

DU-LITE CHEMICAL CORP., THE
River Rd., Middletown, Conn.

Du-Lite®   Oxiblak®

DU PONT DE NEMOURS, E. I., & CO.
Wilmington 98, Del.

Hylene® M-50 Organic Isocyante	Ondal® A Oxidizing Agent
Hylene® M Organic Isocyante	Orel® Rubber Lubricant

DURA FLEX CO.
2043 Colorado, Santa Monica, Calif.

Vinylairé®

DUREZ PLASTICS DIV., HOOKER ELECTRO-CHEMICAL CO.
(*Formerly* Durez Plastics & Chemicals, Inc.)
500 Walck Rd., North Tonawanda, N. Y.

Durez®   Hetron®

E

EAGLE-PICHER CO., THE
900 American Bldg., Cincinnati 1, Ohio

Hylo®

EASTERN COLOR & CHEMICAL CO.
137-139 Canal St., Providence 3, R. I.

Ecco-847[NR]	Eccowax UL-100[NR]
Eccoclean RPW[NR]	Eccowet LF[NR]
Ecco Defoamer PD[NR]	Metagel-811, 811-32, 820, 860[NR]
Ecco Defoamer PL[NR]	
Eccopel[NR]	Metaglow-303[NR]
Eccosyn[NR]	Solon F[NR]
Ecco-W-88[NR]	

EASTERN EQUIPMENT CO., INC.
P. O. Box 897, Willow Grove, Pa.

Amco-Goggle[NR]	Pro-Tecto-Cape®
Amcohood[NR]	Spec-Pro-Tector®
ANP®	Specti-Goggle[NR]

EASTMAN CHEMICAL PRODUCTS, INC.
(*Division of* Eastman Kodak Co.)
Kingsport, Tenn.

Eastofix®	Tenamene® 30
Epolene® E	Tenamene® 31
Epolene® N	Tenamene® 60
Estrobond®	Tenite® Acetate
Estron®	Tenite® Butyrate
NP-10[NR]	Tenite® Polyethylene
Tecmangam®	Tenox®
Tecsol®	Verel®

EASTMAN KODAK CO.
343 State St., Rochester 4, N. Y.
(*See also* Distillation Products Div., *and* Eastman Chemical Products, Inc.)

Dektomat®	Kodachrome®
Duomat®	Kodafix®
Ektachrome®	Kodak®
Ektagraph®	Kodalk®
Ektonol®	KPR®
Fixomat®	Stopomat®
Flexichrome®	Verifax®

EHRET MAGNESIA MFG. CO.
Valley Forge, Pa.

Thermasil[NR]

ELASTOMER CHEMICAL CORP.
212 Wright St., Newark 5, N. J.

Vinylfoam

ELECTRICAL COATINGS, INC.
11 Rantaul St., Beverly, Mass.

Heat Sheets

ELECTRO-CHEMICAL ENGINEERING & MFG. Co.
(*Formerly* Electro-Chemical Supply & Engineering Co.)
750 Broad St., Emmaus, Pa.

Duron #90[NR]	Nitro-Dur[NR]
El-tex[NR]	Tuf-Bond[NR]
Flouro-Foil[NR]	

ELECTRO-TECHNICAL PRODUCTS DIV., SUN CHEMICAL CORP.
113 E. Centre St., Nutley 10, N. J.

Sunform®

ELM COATED FABRICS CO., INC.
261 Fifth Ave., New York 16, N. Y.

Filmtex®

EMERY INDUSTRIES, INC.
Carew Tower, Cincinnati 2, Ohio

Emerox® 1110 Azelaic Acid	Emersoft® 7000
	Emolein® 2957 *and* 2958

EMKAY CHEMICAL CO.
319-325 Second St., Elizabeth, N. J.

Emkabase[NR]	Emka Supertex[NR]
Emkacide GFI-40[NR]	Emkatan K[NR]
Emkacide MP[NR]	Emkatard[NR]
Emka Defoam Concentrate[NR]	Emkaterge A *and* B[NR]
	Emkaterge NA-2[NR]
Emka Finish A[NR]	Emkatex 49-P[NR]
Emka Finishing Oil[NR]	Emkatex A-1[NR]
Emkafix R[NR]	Emkatex F-2[NR]
Emkafol D[NR]	Emkatex N-25[NR]
Emkafume S[NR]	Emkatex NE[NR]
Emkagen 49[NR]	Emkawate[NR]
Emkagen Concentrate[NR]	Emkawate OB[NR]
Emkagen RS[NR]	Emkazyme[NR]
Emka Konetex[NR]	Rexobase[NR]
Emkalane MF[NR]	Rexobase TR-3[NR]
Emkalite[NR]	Rexobase XX[NR]
Emkalite MS[NR]	Rexobond[NR]
Emkalon AX[NR]	Rexobond 46 Concentrate[NR]
Emkalon BT[NR]	
Emkalon C-50[NR]	Rexobond E-12[NR]
Emkalon CX[NR]	Rexobond E-24, E-36, E-48, E-60 *and* E-72[NR]
Emkalon H-460[NR]	
Emkalon N Base[NR]	Rexobond N-8[NR]
Emkalon OS[NR]	Rexoclean[NR]
Emkanet B[NR]	Rexodull CNY[NR]
Emkanol MA[NR]	Rexodull DK[NR]
Emka Non-Snag BD[NR]	Rexodull M[NR]
Emkanyl 85[NR]	Rexodull XX[NR]
Emkapel C[NR]	Rexofos[NR]
Emkapene RW[NR]	Rexogel[NR]
Emka Permadul DS-2[NR]	Rexogum[NR]
Emka Permadul O[NR]	Rexole CJ[NR]
Emkapon K[NR]	Rexole ESC[NR]
Emkapruf AFP[NR]	Rexole GR[NR]
Emkapruf FL[NR]	Rexole MC-2[NR]
Emka Ribbon Finish[NR]	Rexole TW[NR]
Emkaron[NR]	Rexoloid[NR]
Emkasize CT Concentrate[NR]	Rexolube[NR]
	Rexonite D[NR]
Emkastat K[NR]	(*continued*)

EMKAY CHEMICAL CO. (continued)

Rexopene[NR]
Rexopon E[NR]
Rexopon V[NR]
Rexoscour[NR]
Rexoslip[NR]
Rexoslip Concentrate[NR]
Rexosolve[NR]
Rexosolve 150[NR]
Rexosolve CR[NR]
Rexosolve HP[NR]
Rexosolve TR[NR]
Rexowax CNN[NR]
Rexowax DR[NR]
Rexowax W-19[NR]
Rexowax WS[NR]
Rexowet A Concentrate, Rexowet A and Rexowet A-25[NR]
Rexowet CR[NR]
Rexowet GR[NR]
Rexowet MS[NR]
Rexowet RW[NR]

EMULSOL CHEMICAL CORP.
(Division of Witco Chemical Co.)
59 E. Madison St., Chicago 3, Ill.

Emargol®
Emcol 4155[NR]
Emcol 4400A[NR]
Emcol 5120[NR]
Emcol 5130[NR]
Emcol 5137[NR]
Emcol 5138[NR]
Emcol 6020[NR]
Emcol H-31A[NR]
Emcol H-35A[NR]
Emcol H-52[NR]
Emcol H-83T[NR]
Emcol H-85T[NR]
Emcol H-300X[NR] and Emcol H-500X[NR]
Emcol H-A and Emcol H-B[NR]
Emcol K-8300[NR]
Emcol P10-59[NR]

ENDRISS CHEMICALS
940 N. Delaware Ave., Philadelphia 23, Pa.

Chromotex®
Neutrotone®
Super Mafos®
Super Nufos®

ENJAY CO., INC.
(Affiliate of Esso Standard Oil Co.)
15 W. 51st St., New York 19, N. Y.

Deenax®
Jaylene®
Jaysol®
Paradyne®
Paraflow®
Paranox®
Parapoid®
Parapol®
Paratac®
Paratone®
Petrohol®
Vistone®

ENSIGN PRODUCTS CO.
3528 E. 76th St., Cleveland 5, Ohio

Ensign 345 Chromogard[NR]   Ensign 803 Epcostrip[NR]
Ensign 714 Epcovar[NR]

ENTHONE, INC.
442 Elm St., New Haven 2, Conn.

Ebonol® "C" and "C" Special
Enbond "Z' Process[NR]
Enthobrite CU-55[NR]
Enthone Black Wax Emulsion No. 19[NR]
Enthone Cleaner 99[NR]
Enthone Clear Wax Emulsion No. 18[NR]
Enthone Compound B-102[NR]
Enthone Enamel Stripper "P"[NR]
Enthone Stripper S-300[NR]
Enthowax Q-524[NR]
Etchalume® 14

ESSO STANDARD OIL CO.
15 W. 51st St., New York 19, N. Y.
(See also Enjay Co., Inc.)

Airfil®
Bayol® N-300
Carum®
Esso-Mar EP56
Esso-Mar EP65
Estor HD®
Surett®
Surett® Fluid
Surett® P-65
Tervan® 2735
Tro-Mar® DX 130

EUTECTIC WELDING ALLOYS CORP.
40-40—172nd St., Flushing 58, N. Y.

Eutec-CopWeld®
Eutectic Low Temperature Welding Alloys®
LowAmp®
LowTemp®
NiTectic®
ThermoTrode®

EVERLUBE CORP. OF AMERICA
6940 Farmdale Ave., N. Hollywood, Calif.

EverLube 1329

F

FABRIC CHEMICALS CO.
61-63 Cornelison Ave., Jersey City 4, N. J.

Fabripel®
Reslube[NR]
Tergolene Concentrate[NR]

FACTOR, MAX, & CO.
1655 N. McCadden Place, Hollywood 28, Calif.

Golden Lavender®
Hydra-Magic®
Sebb®

FAESY & BESTHOFF, INC.
25 E. 26th St., New York 10, N. Y.

F & B
F & B Starter Grower 15-30-15
Micro Nu-Cop
Rooticate
Termitkil

FALLEK PRODUCTS CO., INC.
165 Broadway, New York 6, N. Y.

Texapons®

FANCOURT, W. F., CO.
516 S. Delaware Ave., Philadelphia 47, Pa.

Antistat[NR]
B-Tex[NR]
Exsol[NR]
Fancoseal[NR]
Fancosol[NR]
Fancosol P[NR]
Fel[NR]
Fultex A[NR]
Lanaseal[NR]
Lanoseal[NR]
Penetrant Y[NR]
Scourlon-Pentalon[NR]
Softex Y[NR]

FEELEY, E. C., CO.
650 State St., Charlotte, N. C.

Felanol Powder[NR]
Felcobase Sal[NR]
Felcofix[NR]
Felcofix CM[NR]
Felcofix O[NR]
Felcolan GL[NR]
Felcolloid W[NR]
Felcolube 121[NR]
Felcolube 146[NR]
Felcolube K[NR]
Felcomine SX[NR]
Felcomine VAB[NR]
Felco Retarder V[NR]
Felcotex[NR]
Felcowhite 174[NR]
Felcowhite 180[NR]
Felsyn 61[NR]
Felsyn 187[NR]
Felsyn MS[NR]

FELDMAN, DAVID, & ASSOCIATES
Calle Barranquitas 51, Santurce, Puerto Rico

Microveer

FIBERCAST CORP.
Box 326, Sand Springs, Okla.

Fibercast®
Lami-Rock®
Weldfast®
X-Trude®

FIBER CHEMICAL CORP.
P. O. Box 218, Matawan, N. J.

Neowhite D Liquid[NR]

FIBERITE CORP., THE
512-528 W. 4th St., Winona, Minn.

Fiberite®

FIBREBOARD PAPER PRODUCTS CORP., PABCO INDUSTRIAL INSULATIONS DIV.
475 Brannan St., San Francisco 19, Calif.

Caltemp®
Grip-Dek[NR]
Prasco® High Temperature

FIDELITY CHEMICAL PRODUCTS CORP.
470 Frelinghuysen Ave., Newark 12, N. J.

Aerosyn®
Dip-Pak®
Hammerguild®
Hydropurge®
Hydrosperse® Foam Depressant
Laqua®
Metalguild®
Peel-Pak®
Spra-Gard®
Synpra®
Syntemp®
Vinylith®
X-Var®
Zipsol® Metal Cleaner #74

FILON PLASTICS CORP.
2051 E. Maple Ave., El Segundo, Calif.
Filon®

FINKL, A., & SONS CO.
2001 Southport Ave., Chicago 14, Ill.

Cuprodie	FX
Durodi	Shelldie
FS	W4X

FIRESTONE PLASTICS CO.
(*Division of* The Firestone Tire & Rubber Co.)
Box 690, Pottstown, Pa.

Beautafilm	Velon®
Exon®	

FIRESTONE TIRE & RUBBER CO., THE. *See* Firestone Plastics Co.

FLINTKOTE CO.
30 Rockefeller Plaza, New York 20, N. Y.

Flintseal® JFR

FLORASYNTH LABORATORIES, INC.
900 Van Nest Ave., P. O. Box 12, New York 62, N. Y.

Caligrape[NR]	Fruitosynth Flavors®
Caramellone®	Graposynth®
Chocolatone®	Mapleagenda[NR]
Citrosynth Oils[NR]	Maplearome[NR]
Cloudinol N[NR]	Planifoline[NR]
Concordal[NR]	Presto Flavor Bases[NR]
Dihydri Vanillion C®	Protovan®
Emulsaromes[NR]	Provotanol "C"[NR]
Entrapped® Plantarome®	Protovanol "C"
Foam Producer	Powdered[NR]
Entrapped® Powdered	Solo Brand[NR]
Clouding Flavors	Spicearomes[NR]
Entrapped® Powdered	Syntharome Flavors®
Cloudinol	Syntharome Oils®
Entrapped® Powdered	Syntharome Oils®
Flavors	(Imitation)
Flavan[NR]	Synthofruit Oils®
Florasynth®	(Imitation)
Floravanol "C" #30[NR]	Vanette®
Flowerols[NR]	Vegetaromes[NR]

FOOD MACHINERY AND CHEMICAL CORP.
See Becco Chemical Div.; *and* Ohio Apex Div.

FOOTE MINERAL CO.
18 W. Chelten Ave., Philadelphia 44, Pa.
Calgran®

FOREMOST FOOD & CHEMICAL CO., EL DORADO DIV.
P. O. Box 599, Oakland 4, Calif.
Eldoplast 45®

FORT PITT CHEMICAL CO.
26th and Smallman Sts., Pittsburgh 22, Pa.
Plastolith®

FOSTER-GRANT CO., INC.
Leominster, Mass.
Fostarene®

FRANKLIN MINERAL PRODUCTS CO.
Franklin, N. C.

No. 10	Kalsitex
No. 18	"R"
Alsibronz®	Silkos

FRANKLIN RESEARCH CO.
5134 Lancaster Ave., Philadelphia 31, Pa.

Ammoniated Speedsope®	Formula 900[NR]
Award[NR]	Life® for Fabrics
Brytene®	Speed·Glos®
Chekit®	Speed·Wax®
Dustchek®	Triple Life[NR]

FREDERICK, PURDUE, CO. *See* Purdue Frederick Co.

FREEMAN CHEMICAL CORP.
Port Washington, Wisc.

Chempol® EP-1	Chempol® P-3303
Chempol® EP-2	Chempol® P-3400
Chempol® EP-3	Chempol® P-3401
Chempol® M-2410	Chempol® P-3427
Chempol® M-2803	Chempol® P-3504
Chempol® M-3009	Chempol® P-3511
Chempol® M-3423	Chempol® P-3514
Chempol® M-4000	Chempol® P-3600
Chempol® M-4501	Chempol® P-3620
Chempol® O-2211	Chempol® P-4000
Chempol® O-2321	Chempol® P-4006
Chempol® O-2512	Chempol® P-4010
Chempol® O-2518	Chempol® P-4101
Chempol® O-3222	Chempol® P-4151
Chempol® O-3316	Chempol® P-4154
Chempol® P-2400	Chempol® P-4300
Chempol® P-2405	Chempol® P-4321
Chempol® P-2420	Chempol® P-4400
Chempol® P-2426	Chempol® P-4723
Chempol® P-2901	Chempol® S-2200
Chempol® P-2907	Chempol® S-2401
Chempol® P-3002	Chempol® S-2403
Chempol® P-3004	Chempol® S-2407
Chempol® P-3034	Chempol® S-2600

FROST PAINT & OIL CORP.
1209 Northeast Tyler, Minneapolis 13, Minn.
Sure-Foot[NR]

FULLER, H. B., CO.
181 W. Kellogg Blvd., St. Paul 2, Minn.
Resiweld Adhesives

G

G & A LABORATORIES, INC.
P. O. Box 1217, Savannah, Ga.
Galex® Pellets

GALLOWHUR CHEMICAL CORP.
N. Water St., Ossining, N. Y.

Gallicide®	Gallotox® 51
Gallosan®	Puradrin®
Gallotox®	Puraseed®

GASETERIA, INC.
1031 E. Washington St., Indianapolis 2, Ind.
Turbane®

GENERAL ABRASIVE CO., INC.
College Ave. & Hyde Park Blvd., Niagara Falls, N. Y.

Bufrite®	Litholite®
Fut-Sure®	Lundite®
Lionblast®	

GENERAL ANILINE & FIM CORP. *See* General Dyestuff Co.

GENERAL CHEMICAL DIV., ALLIED CHEMICAL & DYE CORP.
40 Rector St., New York 6, N. Y.

Saftepak®	Urox®

GENERAL DYESTUFF CO.
(*Division of* General Aniline & Film Corp.)
435 Hudson St., New York 14, N. Y.

Algol®	Anthrasol®
Algosol®	Astrol®
Alphanol®	Azo Acid®
Anthosine®	Azo Fuchsine®
Anthracyanine®	(*continued*)

GENERAL DYESTUFF CO. (continued)

Azonine®
Azo Phloxine®
Azophor®
Benzo Black®
Benzo Black Blue®
Benzo Brown®
Benzofix®
Benzoform®
Benzo Grey®
Cellit®
Cellitazol®
Celliton®
Ceres®
Chromindigen®
Chromogene®
Chromoglaucine®
Coelestol®
Cyper®
Dianil®
Diazanil®
Emeraldol®
Erganil®
Eukesol®
Fanal®
Fastusol®
Flavazine®
Flavophosphine®
Fugitints®
Genacryl®
Genalan®
Gendyco®
Geranol®
Hansa®
Hydron®
Immedial®
Indo Carbon®
Indoine®
Infra®
Irisol®
Melanogen®
Metalan®
Nile®
Oxamine®
Palatine®
Phenoform®
Radio®
Rapidogen®
Resoform®
Rhoduline®
Rubinol®
Sapphirol®
Solar®
Sulphon Azurine®
Suprafix®
Supralan®
Thiazine®
Thiazol Yellow®
Thiochromogen®
Thionine®
Variamine®
Violamine®

GENERAL ELECTRIC COMPANY
Schenectady 5, N. Y.

Alkanex®
Anti-Foam 60[NR]
Dri-Bake®
Lexan®
SC-50[NR]
Velvasil® Silicone Fluid
Versilube®
Viscasil®
Vulkene®

GENERAL MOTORS CORP. See Moraine Products Div.

GENERAL TIRE & RUBBER CO.
Akron 9, Ohio
(See also Textileather Div.)

Gen-Flo®
Vygen® 100

GERA CORP. See USF-Aspinook Finishing Div.

GERING PRODUCTS INC.
N. 7th St. & Monroe Ave., Kenilworth, N. J.

Drycol®
Blend-Eze®
Gerlite®
Ger-Flex®
Ger-Pak®
Ger-Tube®
Polymix®
Printable "TS" Ger-Pak®
S-t-r-e-t-c-h®
Styromix®

GERRARD STEEL STRAPPING DIV. See United States Steel Corp.

GILLESPIE VARNISH CO.
131–159 Dey St., Jersey City 6, N. J.

Monolac
Monolac Varnish Stain
Monolux Supreme White Enamel
Plastergrip
Rich Tone Oil Stain
Rinse-Away
Topper

GLASS LABORATORIES, INC.
65th St. at 9th Ave., Brooklyn 20, N. Y.

Silvatrim®

GLASTIC CORP., THE
4321 Glenridge Rd., Cleveland 21, Ohio

Glastic® Channel-Duct®

GLIDDEN CO., THE
900 Union Commerce Bldg., Cleveland 14, Ohio

"Alpha"® Protein
Beta® Protein
Bombay Black®
Climatic Paints[NR]
Glidair[NR]
Gliddencoat®
Gliddol®
Glidkote®
Health and Milligan® Paints
Mound City Paints[NR]
Penetrell[NR]
Pigmentar®
Prosein®
RG® Soya Lecithin
Royal® Paints
Spred® Patch
Terpex[NR]
Vinyl-Cote[NR]

GLOBE COMPOUND CO., INC.
Waterbury-Bristol Rd., Waterbury 12, Conn.

Monitor A[NR]

GLOBE SANITARY SUPPLY CO. See Troy Industrial Products Div.

GOJER, INC.
Box 991, Akron 9, Ohio

Go-Jo® Hand Cleaner
Go-Jo® Protective Hand Cream

GOODALL-SANFORD, INC.
1430 Broadway, New York 18, N. Y.

Goodallite®
Redo®
Super Redo®

GOODRICH, B. F., CHEMICAL CO.
(Division of B. F. Goodrich Co.)
3135 Euclid Ave., Cleveland 15, Ohio

Harmon® Colors

GOODRICH, B. F., SPONGE PRODUCTS DIV., B. F. GOODRICH CO.
(Formerly Sponge Rubber Products Co.)
Howe Ave., Shelton, Conn.

Cell-Tite®
'n icer®
Spongex®
Spongex® Handi-Floats[NR]
Spongex® Plastic
Spongex® Ring Life Buoys
Texfoam®
Texlite®
Water-Wonder[NR]

GOODRICH-GULF CHEMICALS, INC.
3121 Euclid Ave., Cleveland 15, Ohio

Ameripol®

GRAFO COLLOIDS CORP.
310 Wilkes Place, Sharon, Pa.

Grafon[NR]

GRANT, FOSTER, CO. See Foster-Grant Co.

GREAT LAKES CARBON CORP.
18 E. 48th St., New York 17, N. Y.
612 S. Flower St., Los Angeles 17, Calif.

Dicalite® 7
Dicalite® Speedflow, Speedex, Speedplus, Superaid, and 4200
Nerofil®
Strata-Fiber®
Strata-Lite®
Strata-Seal

GREAT LAKES STEEL CORP.
Ecorse, Detroit 29, Mich.

N-A-X®

GREENE, TWEED & CO.
N. Wales, Pa.

Basa®
Empire®
Favorite®
Moran's®
Palmetto G-T® Ring
Runwel®

GREINER, EMIL, CO., THE
20–26 N. Moore St., New York 13, N. Y.

Aquet[NR]

H

HALLEMITE MFG. CO., THE
2446 W. 25th St., Cleveland 13, Ohio
Amazite[NR]
Chemtred[NR]
Ferrolox[NR]
Flushol[NR]
Grip[NR]
Halco-Lume[NR]
Hallephane[NR]
Lok-Crete[NR]
Skimkote[NR]
Top-X[NR]
Tu-Way[NR]

HANDY & HARMAN
82 Fulton St., New York 7, N. Y.
Handy Hi-Temp.[NR]

HARCHEM DIV., WALLACE & TIERNAN INC.
(*Formerly* Hardesty Chemical Co., Inc.)
25 Main St., Belleville 9, N. J.
Harflex® 300
Harflex® 325
Harflex® 500

HARDMAN, H. V., CO., INC.
571 Cortlandt St., Belleville 9, N. J.
Eposet®
Triplematic®

HARSHAW CHEMICAL CO.
1945 E. 97th St., Cleveland 6, Ohio
Harshaw®
Rufert®
Tellerette®
V[NR]

HART PRODUCTS CORP., THE
1440 Broadway, New York 18, N. Y.
Alkylene A[NR]
Drapetex 35[NR]
Hartex PN[NR]
Harofix CP[NR]
Hartofume C[NR]
Harto-Resin PCS[NR]
Hartoset E[NR]
Hartuwet C *and* B[NR]
Hartuwet S[NR]
Kalex Cul[NR]
Kalex G
Kalex V[NR]
Penetron Conc.[NR]
Reginol HNP[NR]
Sulfanone A[NR]
Tergenol S Liquid Conc.[NR]

HARVEY, G. F., CO., THE
Saratoga Springs, N. Y.
Angitet
Azonamide
Mepherin

HARWICK STANDARD CHEMICAL CO.
60 S. Seiberling St., Akron 5, Ohio
Polycizer® 532
Polycizer® 562
Polycizer® 632
Polycizer® 662
Polycizer® DBP
Polycizer® DBS
Polycizer® DOS

HEATBATH CORP.
P. O. Box 78, Springfield 1, Mass.
Duracoat®
Sheen®

HENRY, J. F., CHEMICAL CO., INC.
4 Station Square, Rutherford, N. J.
AMS 35
Henrox #8
Korox #1
MSS 32
Salamac

HERCULES POWDER CO.
900 Market St., Wilmington 99, Del.
Abitol®
Actophene[NR]
Aquapel®
Bear®
Bullseye®
Champion®
Contractors®
Delpac[NR]
Delrad®
Di-Cup[NR]
Dipentene®
Dymerex®
E. C.®
Gyrocoil®
Herco®
Hercoal®
Hercocel®
Hercoflex®
Hercogel®
Herco Tube®
Hercules®
Hercules 2400®
Hercules Red Dot®
Herculite®
Herculoid®
Herpoco®
Hi-Fax[NR]
Hitemp®
Hi Vel®
Infallible®
Kymene®
Lightning®
Mastolyn®
Metalyn®
Methanite®
MpT[NR]
No-Vent®
Pamak[NR]
Penton[NR]
Pexol®
Polyrad®
Primatube®
RADA[NR]
Red H®
Rosin Amine D[NR]
Sharpshooter®
Sperse[NR]
Spiralok®
Superior® Foam Killer
Tamptite®
Titan®
Tritex®
Unique®
Vegetol[NR]
Vibrocap®
Virbonite®
Yarmor®

HERMAN NELSON DIV. See American Air Filter Co., Inc.

HEWITT, C. B., & BROTHERS, INC.
23–25 Greene St., New York 13, N. Y.
Hewhold

HEWITT METALS CORP.
1918 Stanley at 12th St., Detroit 8, Mich.
Halloy[NR]
Hewitt Copper-Hard[NR]
Hewitt-Detroit Body Solder[NR]
Hewitt Mill Bearing-Metal[NR]
Hewmet[NR]
Mocar[NR]
X-Cell Super X[NR]

HEWITT-ROBINS, INC.
Glenbrook P. O., Stamford, Conn.
Foam'n Fabric *and* Foam-on-Fabric[NR]
Hewitex[NR]
H-R Tex Top[NR]
Maltese Cross®
Monarch[NR]
Restfoam®
Resthane[NR]
Twin Weld[NR]

HILLYARD CHEMICAL CO.
P. O. Box 909, St. Joseph 1, Mo.
Diamond® Floor Finish
Trophy® Gym Finish
Trophy® Seal

HOFFMAN, ARNOLD, & CO. See Arnold, Hoffman & Co.

HOFFMANN-LA ROCHE INC.
Roche Park, Nutley 10, N. J.
Azo Gantrisin®
Ephynal® Acetate
Gantricillin® (100)
Gantricillin® 300
Gantrisin® Cream
Gantrisin® Ear Solution
Gantrisin® Nasal Solution
Gantrisin® Ophthalmic
Lipo Gantrisin®
Lorfan Tartrate[NR]
Rimifon®
Tashan Cream[NR]
Theophorin® Tartrate

HOLCOMB, J. I., MFG. CO., INC.
1601 Barth Ave., Indianapolis 7, Ind.
Aeromatic De-Odor Mist
Aerosol Insekil®
Clad®
Cling®
Dishine
DSX-11®
Floats Off®
Formula 44
Freshettes®
Glaze
Greasolve
Hy-Sheen
Insecote®
Insekil 100®
Insekil E.C.®
Liquid Shineze
Malikil®
Metal Luster
Minit Cleaner®
Nu-Finish
Odor-Crystals
Pine-Ola
Puritine®
Rep®
Riz®
Rogette®
Rub-Once
Safe-T-Sheen®
T-Guard®
Veg-Oil-Soap Cleanser
Vitalized Cleaner
Vita-Pine
White Streak
Zen®

HOLLANDER, ALLEN, CO., THE
  385 Gerard Ave., New York 51, N. Y.
Able-Stick

HONEYWILL-ATLAS, LTD.
  Devonshire House, Mayfair Place, Picadilly, London W-1, England
Arlacel®Brit.
Atlox®Brit.
Atpet®Brit.
Brij®Brit.
Myrj®Brit.
NNO®NE Brit.
NNOR®NE Brit.
Renex®Brit.
Span®Brit.
Tween®Brit.

HOOKER ELECTROCHEMICAL CO.
  P. O. Box 344, Niagara Falls, N. Y.
MPS-500® Plasticizer
Niagathal®
Nialk®
Virgo® Descaling Salt
Virgo® Molten Cleaner

HORN, A. C., CO.
  10th St. & 44th Ave., Long Island City 1, N. Y.
Super-Bondsit®

HOSKINS MFG. CO.
  4445 Lawton Ave., Detroit 8, Mich.
Alumel®
Copel®
Hoskins® Alloy 502

HOUDRY PROCESS CORP.
  1528 Walnut St., Philadelphia 2, Pa.
Houdresid[NE]
Houdriflow[NE]
Houdriforming[NE]
Houdry Chrome Alumina Catalyst[NE]
Houdry Cobalt Molybdate Catalyst[NE]
Houdry Dehydrogenation[NE]
Houdry Hard Alumina[NE]
Houdry Mineral Kaolin Cracking Catalyst[NE]
Houdry Platinum Hydrogenation Catalyst[NE]
Houdry Silica Alumina Catalyst[NE]
Houdry Type 3-D Platinum Catalyst[NE]
Iso-Plus Houdriforming[NE]

HOUGHTON, E. F., CO.
  303 W. Lehigh Ave., Philadelphia 33, Pa.
Houghto-Safe®

HOWARDS OF ILFORD LTD.
  Ilford near London, England
Akrode[NE]

HOWARDS & SONS (CANADA) LTD.
  247 Dunbar Ave., Town of Mount Royal, Montreal, Quebec
Resin MS2

HULL, R. O., & CO., INC.
  1302 Parsons Court, Rocky River 16, Ohio
Cad-Sol[NE]

HUNTINGTON LABORATORIES, INC.
  900–970 E. Tipton St., Huntington, Ind.
Korex®
Sani-Tate[NE]
Sol-U-Lube[NE]
Sol-U-Soap[NE]

HUNT-SPILLER MFG. CORP.
  383 Dorchester Ave., Boston 27, Mass.
Hunt-Spiller® Gun Iron

I

INDEPENDENT CHEMICAL CORP.
  70-30 79th Place, Glendale, Brooklyn 27, N. Y.
Specon #33[NE]
Specon X 13[NE]
Speco Bleach Assist[NE]
Speco Pal EO 33[NE]
Speco Sodium Chlorite[NE]

INDIANA COMMERCIAL FILTERS CORP.
  (*Formerly* Honan-Crane Corp.)
  508-12 Indianapolis Ave., Lebanon, Ind.
Visco 77

INDUSTRIAL RAYON CORP.
  Union Commerce Bldg., Cleveland 1, Ohio
Lektroset®
Tyron®

INERTOL CO., INC.
  480–490 Frelinghuysen Ave., Newark 12, N. J.
Ponkote®

INSUL-MASTIC CORP. OF AMERICA
  7750 W. 61st Pl., Summit, Ill.
Insul-Master Vaporseal
Poly-Cell®

INTERCHEMICAL CORP. *See* Interchemical Corp., Albion Kaolin Div.; Interchemical Corp., Ault & Wiborg Carbon & Ribbon Div.; Interchemical Corp., Cotan Div.; Interchemical Corp., Finishes Div.; Interchemical Corp., In-tag Div.; Interchemical Corp., Printing Ink Div.; Interchemical Corp., Textile Colors Div.; *and* R-B-H Dispersions

INTERCHEMICAL CORP., ALBION KAOLIN DIV.
  67 W. 44th St., New York 36, N. Y.
Albion®

INTERCHEMICAL CORP., AULT & WIBORG CARBON & RIBBON DIV.
  417 E. 7th St. (P. O. Box 58), Cincinnati 1, Ohio
3-R®
Aristoclean®
Aristocrat®
Aristomaster®
Aulta®
Aulta Clean®
Aultalith®
Aultamaster®
Aulta Special®
A & W®
Capitol®
College®
Crest®
Filigree®
Finespirit®
Finesse®
Finessemaster®
Gloria®
Gloriamaster®
Gloriaspirit®
The Red Writing Hood®
Thrift®
Utility®

INTERCHEMICAL CORP., COTAN DIV.
  341 Oliver St., Newark 5, N. J.
Coflex®
Cohyde®

INTERCHEMICAL CORP., FINISHES DIV.
  P. O. Box 659, Newark 1, N. J.
Auflex®
Aulspar®
Aultone®
Bayflex®
Drawlene®
Elixirin®
Epoxin®
Hammerlin® Enamels
IC®
Lithocrome®
Monopeen®
Nigron®
Nipoxin®
Polyfax® Process
Polymerin®
Polyprene®
Polytherm®
Protektol®
Rincontroller®
SFC®
Ultraflo®
Vynafoam®

INTERCHEMICAL CORP., IN-TAG DIV.
  67 W. 44th St., New York 36, N. Y.
In-tag®
Interchem®

INTERCHEMICAL CORP., PRINTING INK DIV.
  67 W. 44th St., New York 36, N. Y.
Anilox®
Aqualox®
Everyday®
Flexogem®
Flexotuf®
Gemglo®
Gemtone®
Glo-Ray®
Holdfast®
IPI®
Lithoday®
Lithogem®
Match Box®
Vapolith®
Vaporin®
Vaposet®

INTERCHEMICAL CORP., TEXTILE COLORS DIV.
150 Wagaraw Rd., Hawthorne, N. J.
Aquaprint®
Aridye®
Arigen®
Arilan[NR]
Arilite[NR]
Interchem®

INTERNATIONAL LATEX CORP.
Playtex Park, Dover, Delaware
(*See also* Isodine Pharmacal Corp.)
Tylac[NR]

INTERNATIONAL MINERALS & CHEMICAL CORP.
20 N. Wacker Drive, Chicago 6, Ill.
20/FOS®
Aji-Ac'cent[NR]
Betamene®
Betasyamine®
Crackerjack®
Cuplopax®
Cupolinor®
Durabutton®
Dura Cement®
Durarod®
Durastrip®
Duratube®
Fertilis®
Four Leaf®
Four Leaf Clover (Design)®
Hyline®
Hy-Temp Refracto[NR]
Kor-Flo®
Mei-Wei-Fen[NR]
Mello-Green®
Multi-Super®
Poly-Po-Nitro®
Premium Producer®
Rainbow®
Rez[NR]
Satisfaction at Harvest Time®
Shirayuki®
Superline®
Tasti[NR]
Three Sheep®
TPN®
Triceratops (Design)®

INTERNATIONAL NICKEL CO., INC., THE
67 Wall St., New York 5, N. Y.
Inco-Rod "A"®

INTERNATIONAL WAX REFINING CO.
E. Hawthorne Ave. & L. I. R. R., Valley Stream, N. Y.
Emulsacera[NR]
Solvacera[NR]
White "B.V.M." Wax[NR]

ISOCYANATE PRODUCTS, INC.
P. O. Box 1681, Wilmington, Del.
IPI-Isofoam

ISODINE PHARMACAL CORP.
(*Subsidiary of* International Latex Corp.)
Dover, Delaware
Isodine®

IVES-CAMERON CO.
(*Division of* American Home Products Corp.)
Box 8299, Philadelphia 1, Pa.
Monitan®

J

JEFFERSON CHEMICAL CO.
1106 Prudential Bldg. (Box 303), Houston 1, Texas
Surfonic® Adducts

JELLIFF, C. O., MFG. CORP., THE
Southport, Conn.
Jelliff Alloy "30"®
Jelliff Alloy "45"®
Jelliff Alloy "60"®
Jelliff Alloy "A"®
Jelliff Alloy "C"®

JERSEY STATE CHEMICAL CO.
59 Lee Ave., Halendon, N. J.
Resin 107[NR]
Resin 300[NR]
Resin RF[NR] *and* Resin 112[NR]
Resin Syrup J S[NR]

JOHNS-MANVILLE SALES CORP.
22 E. 40th St., New York 16, N. Y.
Akoustikos Felt[NR]
Armaturo Asbestos Tape[NR]
Asbestoment S[NR]
Asbestos Firetard Jacket[NR]
Asbestos Roll Fire-Felt®
Banacoustic Blankets[NR]
Besta-Monia[NR]
BX-4M Insulation[NR]
BX-18 Block[NR]
Ceilinite[NR]
Celite®
Celite® Filter-Aids
Celite® Mineral Fillers
Cellamite®
Clipper Seal Packing[NR]
Cumpac®
Electrobestos[NR]
Fibrocel®
Fibro-Cel®
Fibrofil®
Filter-Cel®
Flexboard®
Hyflo® Super-Cel
Jewett®
J-M No. 302 Insulating Cement[NR]
Kearsarge® Gaskets
Kearsarge® Sheet Packing
Laptite[NR]
Liberty Red Rubber Sheet Packing[NR]
Mobilene®
Modernedge Slatekote[NR]
Navalon®
Niagrite[NR]
Ohmstone®
Pakseal[NR]
Pal-lite[NR]
Perforated Fibretex[NR]
Quinorgo®
Regal® Cap Sheet
Regal® Roof Coating
Ring-Tite® Coupling
Sea Ring Packing[NR]
Service® Sheet Packing and Cut Gaskets
Slatekote[NR]
Slatekote Duplex[NR]
Snow Floss[NR]
Special A. R. Roof Putty[NR]
Spirotallic®
Standard Super-Cel[NR]
Super Floss[NR]
Tadpole Gasketing Tape[NR]
Terraflex®
Thermo Rod Packing[NR]
Transfalt Strips[NR]
Transitone® Walls
Transitop[NR]
Tucks Coil Packing[NR]
Uneepac®
Weatherite® Sheating
Zerogloss®
Zerokote®
Zeroseal®
Zerotape®
Zerotex®

JOHNSON & JOHNSON. *See* Personal Products Corp.

JOHNSON, S. C., & SON, INC.
Racine, Wis.
#123 J-Cut[NR]
#140 Stik-Wax[NR]
#230 J-Cool[NR]
Beautiflor®
Beautiflor Traffic Wax®
Beautiflor Waxer®
Blem®
Brown Label® No-Buff®
Car-Plate®
Clearfresh[NR]
Colorfresh®
Conq-R-Dust[NR]
Deep Gloss® Carnu®
Emerel®
Glade® (Aerosol)
Glade® (Wick)
Glo-Coater®
Hard Gloss® Glo-Coat®
Heavy-Duty Hard Gloss®
Johnson's®
J-Wax®
Johnson's Cream Wax®
Jubilee®
Kleen Floor®
Off![NR]
Pride®
Primafresh®
Raid®
Red Label Gym Finish[NR]
Shur-Tred®
Stride®
Super-12®
Super-16®
Terra-New[NR]
TL-131[NR]
Traffic-Cote®
Traffic Wax[NR]
Wax-Cool, #130®
Wax-Cut®
Wax-Draw®
Wax-Shine®
Wax-Strip®
Waxtra®

K

KALI MFG. CO.
427 Moyer St., Philadelphia 25, Pa.
Kaliscour®
Unishade "NS"®

KALO CO., THE. *See* Agkem, Inc.

KASENIT CO.
3 King St., Mahwah, N. J.
Anti-Chementite
Kasenit Keepbryte[NR]

Directory Section

KAYE-TEX MFG. CORP. *See* **Kaykor Industries, Inc.**

KAYKOR INDUSTRIES
(*Division of* Kaye-Tex Mfg. Corp.)
Yardville, N. J.
Vyflex® L-10 Lining

KEASBEY & MATTISON CO.
Ambler, Pa.
Non-Sweat®

KELCO CO.
120 Broadway, New York 5, N. Y.
Kelube®

KENDALL REFINING CO.
77 N. Kendall Ave., Bradford, Pa.
Kendall All-Oil Gear Lube[NR]
Kendall Automatic Transmission Fluid[NR]
Kendall Lemon Oil[NR]
Kendall Motor Oil Non-Detergent[NR]
Kendall Multi-Purpose Hypoid Gear Lube, SCL[NR]
Kendall Outboard Gear Grease[NR]
Kendall Outboard Hypoid Gear Lube[NR]
Kendall Outboard Motor Oil[NR]
Kendall Super-D Oil[NR]
Kendall, The 2000 Mile Oil®
The 2000 Mile Oil®

KENNAMETAL INC.
Lloyd Ave., Latrobe, Pa.
Kenface®

KENRICH CORP.
57-02 48th St., Maspeth 78, N. Y.
Kenflex® A, B, L, N
Kenmix® Dispersions

KEYSTONE LUBRICATING CO.
21st, Clearfield and Lippincott Sts., Philadelphia 32, Pa.
No. 1 Ice Machine Oil[NR]
No. 210 Ice Machine Oil[NR]
All Purpose Gear Lubricant[NR]
A. V. A. Rust Preventive[NR]
Cat Roll Grease[NR]
Condensed Oil No. 50[NR]
C. P. Grease[NR]
D-25 Cylinder Oil[NR]
D-50 Cylinder Oil[NR]
Keystone No. 29 Cartridged Grease[NR]
Keystone® No. 44 *and* No. 45 Greases
Keystone No. 122 Grease[NR]
Keystone All Purpose Hypoid Lubricant[NR]
Keystone U. W. Grease[NR]
K. L. C. Oil[NR]
K. O. Grease[NR]
KR Lubricant[NR]
N. V. Medium[NR]
Penetrating Oils No. 1 *and* 1A[NR]
Q Cock Lubricant[NR]
SR Lubricants[NR]
S. T. O. Lubricant[NR]
Vike Water Seal[NR]

KIMBERLY-CLARK CORP.
Neenah, Wis.
Crandon[NR]
Delsey®
Duo-Dustin®
Fontana[NR]
Hifect®
Kimfect[NR]
Kimpak®
Kimsul®
Kleenex®
Lithofect[NR]
Lumifect®
Marvalon®
Multifect®
Munising®
Neenah®
Prentice[NR]
Rotofect®
Sanek®
Shorewood[NR]
Texoprint®
Trufect®

KLEE WATERPROOFING CORP.
(*Formerly* American Fluresit Co.)
4011 Red Bank Rd., Cincinnati 27, Ohio
Acrylastic
Durocrete
Duromit
Wall Mate

KLINGER, RICHARD, LTD.
Sidcup, Kent, England
Klinger-Acidit®[Brit.]
Klingerit®[Brit.]
Klingerit-1000®[Brit.]
Klinger-Oilit®[Brit.]

KNIGHT, MAURICE A.
Kelley Ave., Akron 9, Ohio
Acidsil Cement[NR]
Coresite Cement[NR]
Knight No. 2 Cement[NR]
Knightbond #6 Cement[NR]
Knightbond #7[NR]
Knight Super XX Cement[NR]
Knight-Ware®
Permanite® *and* Permanite® Resin Cement
Pyroflex® *and* Pyroflex® Lacquer
Sealon[NR]

KRIEGER COLOR & CHEMICAL CO., INC.
6531 Santa Monica Blvd., Hollywood 38, Calif.
Instant Evergreen[NR]

KRUMBHAAR CHEMICALS, INC.
24–30 Jacobus Ave., South Kearny, N. J.
Krumbhaar Resins

KRYLON, INC.
Ford & Washington Sts., Norristown, Pa.
Krylon® Cleaner and Degreaser
Krylon® Dulling Spray
Krylon® Hide-a-Mark®
Krylon-Houghton® Rust Veto Spray
Krylon-Houghton® Tenac Open Gear and Cable Lubricant
Krylon® Metal Primer
Krylon® Rust Release
Krylon® Spray Enamels
Krylon® Stencil Ink Sprays

L

LARSEN PRODUCTS CORP.
4934 Elm St., Bethesda, Md.
Plaster-Weld®
Weld-Crete®

LARVACIDE PRODUCTS, INC.
117 Liberty St., New York 6, N. Y.
Bromex[NR]
Fumigun[NR]
Larvacide®
Larvacover[NR]
Larva-Tectant[NR]
L-P Industrial Spray[NR]
Mildex[NR]
Nemex[NR]
Plantex[NR]
Servacide[NR]
Weednix[NR]
Weedrench[NR]

LAUREL SOAP MFG. CO., INC.
Tioga, Thompson and Almond Sts., Philadelphia 34, Pa.
Catamine SF[NR]
Pyrosan A[NR]
Wax Emulsion WG[NR]

LEA MFG. CO., THE
16 Cherry Ave., Waterbury 20, Conn.
Learok®

LEGGE, WALTER G., CO.
101 Park Ave., New York 17, N. Y.
Legsure®

LETHELIN PRODUCTS CO., INC.
15 Mac Questen Parkway, South, Mount Vernon, N. Y.
Borekil®
Curex® Flea Duster
Ivy-Kil[NR]
Magikil® Ant and Roach Duster
Magikil® Jelly Ant Bait
Magitrack Mouse Duster[NR]
Mysterious Roach Killer Outfit[NR]
Mystikil® Rose Duster
Mystilki® Termite Emulsion

LIBBEY-OWENS-FORD GLASS CO.
Nicholas Bldg., Toledo 3, Ohio
(*See also* L. O. F. Glass Fibers Co.; *and* L. O. F. Glass Fibers Co., Corrulux Div.)

Fine-Tex®	Satinol® Finish
Huetex®	Securit® Glass
Huewhite®	Securit® Interior Glass Doors
Parallel-O-Plate®	
Ra-Grid® Heater Plates	Tobex®

LINCOLN ELECTRIC CO.
22801 St. Clair Ave., Cleveland 17, Ohio
L-60, L-61, L-70, L-18-8, and L-201[NR]   ST-760, 780, 781, *and* 840[NR]

L.O.F. GLASS FIBERS CO.
1810 Madison Ave., Toledo 1, Ohio

Blue Flag[NR]	Microflex®
Decra-Brite[NR]	Microlite®
Duramat®	Micro-Quartz[NR]
Duramesh[NR]	Microtex[NR]
Garan® Roving	Super-Fine[NR]
L.O.F. Super-Fine[NR]	Vitron® Roving

L-O-F GLASS FIBERS CO., CORRULUX DIV.
(*Formerly* Corrulux Corp.)
P. O. Box 20026, Houston 25, Tex.

Corrucote®	Maxlite®
Corrulux®	PyroPanl®
Corrumastic®	

LONDON CHEMICAL CO., INC.
1535 N. 31st Ave., Melrose Park, Ill.
Lonco Copperbrite #48
Lonco PC #33 Solder Resist

LONE STAR CEMENT CORP.
100 Park Ave., New York 17, N. Y.
Starcor®   Texcor®

LUKENS STEEL CO.
Coatesville, Pa.
Lukens Clad Steels[NR]   Lukens "T-1" Steel®

M

MAAS & WALDSTEIN CO.
2121 McCarter Highway, Newark 4, N. J.

Art Lace[NR]	Lacacap[NR]
Checklac[NR]	Mawco[NR]
Cocell[NR]	Metalace[NR]
Corac[NR]	Motletone[NR]
Duflex[NR]	Nilustre®
Duracel®	Opticleer®
Duraprem[NR]	Peerless[NR]
Durheat[NR]	Plasti-Calk[NR]
Dursign[NR]	Polysty-Lac®
Ecomul[NR]	Stripltex®
Flexcel[NR]	Synpex[NR]
Galustre[NR]	Zinsol[NR]

MAC CHEMICAL CO.
5113 Kingston Pike, P. O. Box 10001, Knoxville, Tenn.

Alcophate Paste[NR]	Macco Finish 6000[NR]
Chloral[NR]	Maccowax Softener[NR]
Clarofin R-40[NR]	Talamine M. A.[NR]
Dispersing Agent N.F.L.[NR]	

MAGUIRE, WALTER, CO.
Lincoln Bldg., 60 E. 42nd St., New York 17, N. Y.
Emeri-Bond[NR]   Emeri-Topcrete®
Emeri-Brick[NR]

MAJESTIC RAYON CORP.
116 W. 23rd St., New York 11, N. Y.
Belastraw®

MALLINCKRODT CHEMICAL WORKS
2nd & Mallinckrodt Sts., St. Louis 7, Mo.

Cryogel®	Thixokon®
Miokon® Sodium	Titherm®
Remox®	Toleron[NR]
SL®	

MALLORY, P. R., & CO.
Indianapolis 6, Ind.
Mallory 1000®   Mallory Millosil® Process
Mallory 1000 Gyromet®

MARBLETTE CORP., THE
37-21 Thirtieth St., Long Island City 1, N. Y.
Maraset®

MARBON CHEMICAL DIV., BORG-WARNER CORP.
1926 W. Tenth Ave., Gary, Ind.
Ty-Ply® 3640   Ty-Ply® Q

MASLAND DURALEATHER CO.
Amber and Willard Sts., Philadelphia 34, Pa.
Masland Duran®   Masland Durasol®
Masland Duran® Clad

MASONITE CORP.
111 W. Washington St., Chicago 2, Ill.

Leatherwood®	Ridgeline[NR]
Panelply[NR]	Shadowvent® Siding
Presdwood®	

MASTIC ASPHALT CORP.
131 S. Taylor St. (P. O. Box 65), South Bend 24, Ind.

Grain-Tex®	Inselock®
Home-Tex®	Rock-Tex®

MAX FACTOR & CO. *See* Factor, Max, & Co.

McKAY CO., THE
McKay Bldg., 1005 Liberty Ave., Pittsburgh 22, Pa.
McKay Tube-Alloy®

McLAUGHLIN GORMLEY KING CO.
1715 Fifth St., S. E., Minneapolis 14, Minn.
MGK® Repellent 11

MEARL CORP.
153 Waverly Pl., New York 14, N. Y.
Mearlmaid
Nacromer® Pearl Pigments

MERCK SHARP & DOHME
(*Division of* Merck & Co., Inc.)
640 N. Broad St., Philadelphia 1, Pa.

Antilepto[NR]	Hydrozets
Bovigen®	Hyotole®-12
Cathomycin®	Hypobeta®-20
Co-Deltra[NR]	Inversine[NR]
Co-Hydeltra[NR]	Methajade®
Delvinal®	Pipizan®
Dornavac®	Proketuss®
Erysipogen[NR]	Reditrin[NR]
Hydeltra®	Restolic[NR]
Hydeltracin®	Roxel[NR] *and* Roxel Forte[NR]
Hydrocortone®-T.B.A.	
Hydroderm®	Sulfastrep®
Hydrodyne[NR]	Tempogen® Forte
Hydroptic®	Vinethene®
Hydrospray®	

MERIX CHEMICAL CO.
1021 E. 55th St., Chicago 15, Ill.
Merix® Stabilite   Merix® Stabilite A

MERRELL, WM. S., CO., THE
Cincinnati 15, Ohio
Consol®   Gantrex®
Consolets®   Vinobel®

METALS & CONTROLS CORP., GENERAL PLATE DIV.
Attleboro, Mass.
Bronco®

METAL & THERMIT CORP.
Rahway, N. J.
Anozinc®   Ucilon®
Stannochlor®   Ultrox®
Thermit®   Unichrome®
Thermolite®

METASAP CHEMICAL CO.
(*Subsidiary of* Nopco Chemical Co., Inc.)
Logan & Davis Sts., Harrison, N. J.
Metasap®   Metavis® 543
Metavis® 540   Stabelan®

METRO-ATLANTIC INC.
Centredale 11, R. I.
Atco GS-14[NR]   Emboset NR®
Atco Rezsoft JA[NR] Emboset Z®
Emboset BM®   Ranedare®

MICA INSULATOR CO.
(*Subsidiary of* Minnesota Mining & Mfg. Co.)
P. O. Box 1076, Schenectady 1, N. Y.
Isomica®   Samica®

MICHIGAN CHEMICAL CORP.
St. Louis, Mich.
Michigan No. 40

MICHIGAN CHROME AND CHEMICAL CO.
8615 Grinnell Ave., Detroit 13, Mich.
Miccroloid®   Miccro Supreme® Layout
Miccromask®   and Identification Dye
Miccropeel®   Miccro Supreme®
Miccrosol®   Spatterproof
Miccrosol® E-1003   Miccrotex®
Miccro Supreme® Better Miccrotube®
   Seal Compound   Miccrowax®

MICRO-CIRCUITS CO.
New Buffalo, Mich.
531 Basic Laboratory   SC12 *and* SC13 Silver
   Kit[NR]   Micropaints[NR]
RS14 Shielding Micro-   SS12-B Silver Shielding
   paint[NR]   Micropaint[NR]
RS17 Polyshield Micro-
   paint[NR]

MILES LABORATORIES, INC.
1127 Myrtle St., Elkhart, Ind.
(*See also* Ames Co., Inc.; Sumner Chemical Co., Inc.; *and* Takamine Laboratories, Inc.)
Alka-Seltzer®   One-A-Day®
A-P-N®   Tabcin®
Bactine®

MILLER CHEMICAL & FERTILIZER CORP.
2226 N. Howard St., Baltimore 18, Md.
Fly-A-Way Aerosol[NR] Liqua-Leaf[NR]
Fly-Away Dairy Spray   Mico® Sulphur
Fly-Away Dairy Spray   Nu-Film®
   Concentrate   Nu-Set[NR]
Hy-Tox Insect Dust   Ortazol® *and* Ortazol®
Kill-All[NR]   Powder

Rat-A-Way Bait[NR]   Superior Nu-Oil®
Rat-A-Way Concen-   Tubacide®
   trate[NR]   VHPF®
Scale-Tox

MILLER, HARRY, CORP.
(*Formerly* Haas-Miller Corp.)
4th & Bristol Sts., Philadelphia 40, Pa.
Hamicote® D-20   Hamikleer® 1391
Hamicote® D-20-500

MILNE, A., & CO.
741-3-5 Washington St., New York 14, N. Y.
Milne AMC[NR]   MM 6 & 6[NR]

MINERALS & CHEMICALS CORP. OF AMERICA
(*Formerly* Attapulgus Clay Co.)
Menlo Park, N. J.
ASP®   Klondyke®
Attaclay®   No Karb®
Attasol®   Permagel®
Attasorb®   Porocel®
Cyclocel®   Sol-Speedi-Dri®
Driocel®   Spray-Satin®
Driocel S®   Steller®
H. T.®

MINE SAFETY APPLIANCES CO.
201 N. Braddock Ave., Pittsburgh 8, Pa.
Acidpruf[NR]   Fend-U®
Air-Cub[NR]   Fend-X®
Air Curtain[NR]   Fend-Silicone[NR]
Air-Mask[NR]   Gascope®
All-Dust®   H-H Inhalator[NR]
All-Service®   Hoistphone[NR]
All-Vision®   Hopcalite®
All-Weather[NR]   Lamb Air Mover[NR]
Burns Valve®   Lira[NR]
Carbogen®   Maskfone[NR]
Cardoxide®   McCaa®
Cascade Impactor[NR] Mersorb®
Chemgard[NR]   Midget Impinger[NR]
Chemklos[NR]   MinePhone[NR]
Chemox®   M-S-A®
Chempruf[NR]   MSA Comfo Cap®
Cleartone[NR]   MSA Self-Rescuer®
Clear-Vue[NR]   Noisefoe[NR]
Colorimetric[NR]   O₂ Cub[NR]
Comfo®   O₂ Mask[NR]
Coolband®   Persorb®
Cool Cap[NR]   Pneolator®
Drildust[NR]   Pneophone[NR]
Dust-Vue Microprojec- Samplair®
   tor[NR]   Shockgard[NR]
Ear Defenders[NR]   Skullgard[NR]
Earsaver[NR]   Smokescope®
Explosimeter®   Soundscope[NR]
Fend-A®   Speedframe[NR]
Fend-E®   Supergard[NR]
Fend-F®   Telecrane®
Fend-I®   Tell-Board[NR]
Fend-I Special®   Thermatron[NR]
Fend-L®   Torch-O-Matic®
Fend-O®   Ultra-Filter[NR]
Fend-PC®

MINNESOTA MINING & MFG. CO.
900 Fauquier Ave., St. Paul 6, Minn.
(*See also* Mica Insulator Co.)
Aggrecoat®   Kel-F®

MOL-REZ DIV., AMERICAN PETROCHEMICAL CORP.
3134 California St., N. E., Minneapolis 18, Minn.
Pleogen®

MONA INDUSTRIES, INC.
65-75 E. Twenty-third St., Paterson 17, N. J.
Monabond[NR]
Monabond C[NR]
Mona® Catalyst M
Monapal T[NR]
Monapolene A[NR]
Monapolene Concentrates[NR]
Monapolene N[NR]
Monaquest E[NR]
Monares Paste[NR]
Monaset[NR]
Monasoft S[NR]
Monatose[NR]

MORAINE PRODUCTS DIV. OF GENERAL MOTORS CORP.
1420 Wisconsin Blvd., Dayton 1, Ohio
Durex®
Moraine Porous Metal®

MORETEX CHEMICAL PRODUCTS, INC.
314 W. Henry St., Spartanburg, S. C.
Kylan[NR]
Morepel RW[NR]
Moretex Napping Softener A[NR]
Moropol 600[NR]
Moropol 700[NR]
Moropon LC[NR]

MORNINGSTAR, NICOL, INC. See Paisley Products Inc.

M & R DIETETIC LABORATORIES, INC.
625 Cleveland Ave., Columbus 16, Ohio
Colac
Insta-Sol
Par-T-Kreme
Pream®
Ten-B-Low

MYCALEX CORP. OF AMERICA
125 Clifton Blvd., Clifton, N. J.
(See also Synthetic Mica Corp.)
Mycalex® 385
Mycalex® 400®
Mycalex® 410®
Mycalex® 410X®
Mycalex® K and KM

N

NARMCO RESINS & COATINGS CO.
600 Victoria St., Costa Mesa, Calif.
Formula 3117[NR]

NASHUA CORP.
Nashua, N. H.
Davac®

NATIONAL ANILINE DIV., ALLIED CHEMICAL & DYE CORP.
40 Rector St., New York 6, N. Y.
Buffalo®
Caprolan®
Caprolan® Deep-Dye Nylon
Caprolan® Tensile-Tough
Coupler 2, 3, 6®
Deepset[NR] Salt L
Lathanol® LAL
Nacconate®
Nacconate® 65
Nacconate® 80
Nacconate® 100
Nacconate® 200
Nacconate® 300
Nacconate® 310
Nacconate® 1080-H
Nacconate® 1300-50
Nacrosol[NR]
Naxol[NR]
Naxol D[NR]
Para[NR]
Vasoflavine®

NATIONAL GYPSUM CO.
325 Delaware Ave., Buffalo 2, N. Y.
Asbestone®
Asbestone® "Economy 250"
Asbestone® Standard "400"
Chroma-Tone[NR]
Gold Bond® Holostud
Gold Bond® Sprayolite
Panelcoustic[NR]
Perfolite[NR]
Ranch Style[NR]

NATIONAL LEAD CO.
111 Broadway, New York 6, N. Y.
(See also Baroid Div.)
Calstar[NR]
Clarite[NR]
CS-137[NR]
DS-207®
"Dutch Boy" Nalplex®
Dyphos®
Dythal®
Flomax 25[NR]
Leadstar[NR]
Lectro "60"[NR]
Nalzin[NR]
Normasal®
Provinite[NR]
Tribase E[NR]

NATIONAL MALLEABLE & STEEL CASTINGS CO.
10600 Quincy Ave., Cleveland 6, Ohio
H. T. M.[NR]

NATIONAL MILLING & CHEMICAL CO.
4601 Flat Rock Rd., Philadelphia 27, Pa.
Namiglo
Nami-Lo®

NATIONAL MOTOR BEARING CO. See Arrowhead Rubber Co.

NATIONAL PLASTIC PRODUCTS CO.
Odenton, Md.
Nevamar®

NATIONAL PLASTICS INC.
P. O. Box 152, Knoxville, Tenn.
Run-Rite®

NATIONAL RESEARCH & CHEMICAL CO.
12520 Cerise Ave., Hawthorne, Calif.
Deterge
Strip-Eze
Striprite

NATIONAL RESEARCH CORP.
70 Memorial Drive, Cambridge 42, Mass.
Foiltone[NR]
Narcoil® 10
Narcoil® 40
Narescoil®
Narliner® Type 5018

NATIONAL STARCH PRODUCTS INC.
270 Madison Ave., New York 16, N. Y.
Instant-Jel®
Nalex®
Nu-Film®

NATIONAL VULCANIZED FIBRE CO.
P. O. Box 311, Wilmington 99, Del.
Leatheroid® Fibre

NATVAR CORP.
211 Randolph Ave., Woodbridge, N. J.
Isolastane®
Isoplex®

NEILSON CHEMICAL CO.
6564 Benson St., Detroit 7, Mich.
Alumiprep®
Galvaprep®
Lyfanite®
Metalprep®
Phosteem®
Prep-N-Cote®
Prep-Pik-L®

NEPERA CHEMICAL CO., INC.
21 Gray Oaks Ave., Yonkers 2, N. Y.
Biomydrin®
Choledyl®
Neohetramine®
Pyricidin®
Urosulfin®

NEVILLE CHEMICAL CO.
Neville Island, Pittsburgh 25, Pa.
Nevastain A and B
Nevillac 10°®

NEW YORK QUININE AND CHEMICAL WORKS, INC.
50 Church St., New York 8, N. Y.
NYQ (in design)®

NINOL LABORATORIES
Prudential Plaza, Chicago 1, Ill.
Ninate 411
Ninex 21
Ninex 303
Ninol 1281
Ninol AA62
Ninox BJO
Toximul® 500
Toximul® 600

NITROGEN DIV., ALLIED CHEMICAL & DYE CORP.
40 Rector St., New York 6, N. Y.
N-dure[NR]

NIXON NITRATION WORKS
Nixon, N. J.
Nixon

NOPCO CHEMICAL CO., INC.
Logan & Davis Sts., Harrison, N. J.
(*See also* Metasap Chemical Co.)

Dual Dye®	Nopcosol®
Durpon®	Nopcostat®
Gammanol®	Nopcosulf[NR]
Griffco®	Nopcotal®
Hyonic[NR]	Nopcote®
Micratized®	Nopcotex®
Nopcaine®	Nopcowax®
Nopco ESI[NR]	Nopvite®
Nopcofoam[NR]	Polymul[NR]
Nopco KFC[NR]	Super Drex®
Nopcolube[NR]	Super Nopdex®
Nopcom®	Tanoyl HDF®
Nopco-Pak®	Tenlo®
Nopcosize[NR]	Trex®

NORDMARK PHARMACEUTICAL LABORATORIES, INC.
35A Ellis Ave., Irvington, N. J.
Ferronord®

NORTON CO. *See* **Behr-Manning Co.**
Alkontrol[NR]   Jet Cleaners[NR]

NOVA CHEMICAL CORP.
153 Waverly Place, New York 14, N. Y.
(*See also* Badische Anilin -u. Soda-Fabrik AG. and Rohner, Ltd.)

NORTHWEST CHEMICAL CO.
9310 Roselawn Ave., Detroit 4, Mich.

Albigen® A	Novanol R
BASF	Novanol WS Powder Green 3B
Basolan	Novapon A
Basopal NH Conc. Powder	Novapon NE
Bleachit I	Novasoft A
Bleachit IA	Novatol
Dissolving Salt B	Novulphor A Oil-Soluble
Euvon ASN	Novulphor EL
Flame Retardant Base	Ortol
Germocid	Ortolan®
GFN Inhibitor Base	Palathrene® Brown LG Double Paste
Glycinal HD2	Perapret A
Helizaron	Perapret AX 45
Lumatex®	Perapret LN 25
Lumatex® Binder F	Perapret PN
Lumattin SL	Pilate
Lunetzol A	Pilate Fast Salt O Solution
Nekanil	
Nekanil AC Special	Ronagen Black IL
Neopilate Dyestuffs	Siligen A
Novafix CA	Stripping Agent Soluble Conc.
Novafix CU	
Novafix WW	Texapret
Novagen Black II BN	Uniperal W
Novalan	Vialon
Novanol AO *and* B Powders	
Novanol Nap	

NYANZA COLOR & CHEMICAL CO., INC.
109 Worth St., New York 13, N. Y.

Nyagene Black 3B Conc[NR]	Nyanthrene[NR]
	Nyapon FP[NR]
Nyalite Fast Blue NPC[NR]	Parnol[NR]

O

OAKITE PRODUCTS, INC.
19 Rector St., New York 6, N. Y.

Chlor-Tergent®	Oakite® Platers' "A" Special
Chromicoat®	
CrysCoat®	Oakite® Railroad Cleaner
DCM	Oakite® Sanitizer No. 1
Drycid®	Oakite® Scald-Aid
Highlite	Oakite® Shield
Limelite	Oakite® Soluble Oil
Liqui-Det	Oakite® Special Drawing Compound
Oakite®	
Oakite® Aviation Cleaner	Oakite® Special Protective Oil
Oakite® Bactericide	
Oakite® Bottle-Soak	Oakite® Steel Preserver
Oakite® Composition No. 97	Oakite® Stripper Additive
	Oakite® Stripper, Stripper M-3, Stripper R-6, Stripper No. 110
Oakite® Composition No. 98	
Oakite® Composition No. 99	Oakite® Test Q
	Oakite® Test X
Oakite® Di-Sanite	Okemco®
Oakite® General Cleaner	Renovator
Oakite® Hand Cleaner	Rinsite
Oakite® ISD	Rustripper®
Oakite® Penetrant®	Saturol
Oakite® Pickle Control No. 5	

OHIO-APEX DIV., FOOD MACHINERY AND CHEMICAL CORP.
Nitro, W. Va.
KP-220[NR]   KP-550[NR]

OIL BASE, INC.
130 Oris St., Compton, Calif.

Black Magic®	OB Gel®
Black Magic "Supermix"®	OB Gen®
	OB Hevywate®
Chemical "V"®	OB Mix Fix®
Chemical "X"®	OB Wate®
Economagic®	OB Well Pack[NR]
No-Glo Oil®	OB Zero®
No-Glo Thread Lubricant®	Peptomagic®
	White Magic®

OIL WELL SUPPLY DIV. *See* **United States Steel Corp.**

OLD AMERICAN ROOFING MILLS, DIV. OF THE RUBBEROID CO.
(*Formerly* American Asphalt Roof Corp.)
7600 Truman Rd., Kansas City 26, Mo.
Old American®

OLIN MATHIESON CHEMICAL CORP.
Mathieson Bldg., Baltimore 3, Md.

Ad-Dri®	Phytomycin[NR]
Blackbird®	Poly-G®
CCH®	Poly Solv®
Devil®	Poly-Tergent[NR]
Lily®	Red Wing®
MCC® Flake Bottle Wash	Spider®
	Star[NR]
Mule®	Terraclor[NR]

ORGANIC CHEMICAL CORP.
P. O. Box 432, Providence 1, R. I.

Lanazine Tip[NR]	Orco Ferrosol Powder
Orco Antifoam AF[NR]	WS *and* Orco Ferrosol Liquid[NR]
Orcoboil #15[NR]	
Orcoceylene #30[NR]	Orcolana Strip NA[NR]
Orcochromate Mordant[NR]	Orcolon Black #55 Paste[NR]
Orcochrome Black P New[NR]	
	(*continued*)

ORGANIC CHEMICAL CORP. (continued)
Orco Metallan[NR]
Orcomine Black RBM Conc[NR]
Orcopal #18[NR]
Orco Pentro PS[NR]
Orco Scour 48[NR]
Orco Synthrowite FWN[NR]
Orco Synthrowite GNW[NR]
Orcowet #33[NR]
Orcquesol LHN[NR]
Oroxalyde Liquid[NR]

ORIGINAL BRADFORD SOAP WORKS, INC.
West Warwick, R. I.
Bradsol OR[NR]
Bradsyn J Softener[NR]
Bradsyn Lining Softener[NR]
Bradsyn N Softener[NR]
Bradsyn Plasticizer A-2[NR]
Bradsyn Softener S[NR]
Bradtone B[NR]

OSBORN, C. J., CO.
1301 W. Blancke St., Linden, N. J.
Miravar[NR]

OSMOSE WOOD PRESERVING CO. OF AMERICA, INC.
980 Ellicott St., Buffalo 9, N. Y.
Cop-R-Nap®
Osmoplastic®
Osmosalts®
Preserv-A-Post®

O'SULLIVAN RUBBER CORP., PLASTICS DIV.
Winchester, Pa.
Sullvyne-Clad®

OWENS-CORNING FIBERGLAS CORP.
National Bank Bldg., Toledo 1, Ohio
AE® Board
AE-F® Board
Aerowrap®
Coronized®
Corotop®
Dust-Stop®
Fresco Acoustical Tile[NR]
Noise-Stop Baffles[NR]
Perma-Ply®
P-F®
Sonocor®
Sonofaced® Acoustical Tile
TW-F®

P

PABCO INDUSTRIAL INSULATIONS DIV. See Fibreboard Paper Products Corp.

PABST BREWING CO., INDUSTRIAL PRODUCTS DIV.
Merchandise Mart, Chicago 54, Ill.
Amizyme®
Dry Exsize-T®
Exsize-T®
Exzyme®
Super Exsize-T®
Texzyme®

PACIFIC LUMBER CO.
100 Bush St., San Francisco 4, Calif.
Palco® Industrial Fibers
Palconate®
Palco Seal®
Palcotan®

PACKWOOD, G. H., MFG. CO.
1545 Tower Grove Ave., St. Louis 10, Mo.
Pax® No. 119
Pax® Chlorinated Dish Wash
Pax® C. M. 118
Pax® Deodorant Cream Soap
Pax® Dictator Special
Pax® Formula TL-13 Floor Cleaner
Pax® Hand Cleaning Lotion
Pax® Liquid Dish Wash
Pax® Repeator Hand Cleanser
Pax® White Wall Tire Cleaner

PAISLEY PRODUCTS INC.
(Division of Morningstar, Nichol, Inc.)
630 W. 51st St., New York 19, N. Y.
Freezist[NR]
Hero[NR]
Res-N-Dex[NR]
Res-N-Seal[NR]
Starguar[NR]
Stargum®

PARK CHEMICAL CO.
8074 Military Ave., Detroit 4, Mich.
Carbo-Fluid "H"[NR]
Draw-Bright 600[NR]
Draw-Bright 750[NR]
Kem-Cut[NR]
Kem-Grind[NR]
Park-Cut M.P.[NR]
Par-Kem Cleaners[NR]
Parko®
Parko® Beauty Coat
Parko® Blue Foam Upholstery Cleaner
Parko® Eze Cleaner
Parko® Eze-Wax
Parko® K-R Hand Rubbing Compound
Parko® Kwik Wash
Parko® Miracle Metal
Parko® Protex-It
Parko® Silcoseal
Parko® Static-Stop
Parko® Super-Dri
Parko® Tank-O-Lene
Parko® Tank-Solv
Woodside Rapid Carburizers

PARKE, DAVIS & CO.
P. O. Box 118, R. P. Annex, Detroit, 32, Mich.
Abdec® Drops
Abdec® Kapseals®
Camoform®
Chlorostrep® Kapseals®
Digifortis®
Eldec® Kapseals®
Ferro-Desicol® Kapseals®
Hepa-Desicol® Kapseals®
Immunovac®
Infatabs®
Iradogen®
Nemazene®
Niconyl®
Promacetin®
Sanicyl®
Surital®
Theelin R-P[NR]
Uritone®
Vanquin[NR]
Ziradryl® Cream, Lotion

PARKER APPLIANCE CO., THE
17325 Euclid Ave., Cleveland 12, Ohio
Parker O-Lube[NR]
Parker Unipar®

PARKER RUST PROOF CO. See Tropical Paint Co.

PARKWOOD LAMINATES, INC.
24 Water St., Wakefield, Mass.
Genuwood®
Hi-den®

PATERSON PARCHMENT PAPER CO.
Bristol, Pa.
Durapak®
Parchkin®
Patapar®
Patax®
Paterson®

PEARSON-FERGUSON CHEMICAL CO., INC.
1400 Union Ave., Kansas City 1, Mo.
Patterson Phenothiazine, Drench Grade[NR]
Patterson's Copper Carbonate, 20%[NR]
Patterson's Creosote Dip and Disinfectant[NR]
Patterson's Hand Cleaner and Conditioner[NR]
Patterson's Livestock Fly Spray with Crag® Fly Repellent
Patterson's Pine Oil Disinfectant
Patterson's Water Soluble Pivalyn[NR]

PEMCO CORP.
5601 Eastern Ave., Baltimore 24, Md.
Chromoveil[NR]
Fleckel[NR]
Lectraseal[NR]
Metlsteel®
Neowite #10

PENICK & FORD LTD.
420 Lexington Ave., New York 17, N. Y.
Penford Finishing Gum 3XL and 3XP[NR]

PENICK, S. B., & CO.
50 Church St., New York 7, N. Y.
Aldex®
Aquestrol®
Bromvegol®
Crown Brand®
Dead Easy®
Deoleated®
Deracloud®
Deramist®
Derrilox®
Dethdiet®
Drugology®
Duval®
Eiderdown®
(continued)

PENICK, S. B., & CO. (*continued*)
Emulsarin®
Evenized®
Factolac®
Fijoline®
Fortracin®
Fum-Aromas®
Gynestrol®
Initial Line®
Jasmonene®
Mistofume®
Octagon (Hippocrates)®
Openteine®
Penitracin®
Pinealco®
S. B. Penick & Company®
Penresina®
Penthanco®
Penval®
Protobore®
Pyropo®
Rajah Brand®
Redratsquill®
Regal®
Suganilla®
Tamarix®
Tumerol®
Typhoon®
Vandrynilla®
Veniturp®
Verabore®

PENNSYLVANIA REFINING CO.
Butler, Pa.
Diesel Gumont®
Gearteck[NR]

PENNSYLVANIA SALT MFG. CO.
3 Penn Center Plaza, Philadelphia 2, Pa.
3-B® Mercaptan
Aldox®
Arresto-Moth®
Aseptisil®
B-K Bacili-Kil®
B-Kleer®
Buramine®
Chlor-Bor®
Clor®
Clorital®
Corlok[NR]
Dari-Kleen®
Dee-T-Cide®
De-Fol-Ate®
Dipac[NR]
Dithac-W®
Doh-Tone®
Drawcote®
Dri-Clor®
Dyeset®
Dynahue®
Erustohue®
Erusto-Max®
Erustomoth®
Erusto-Ray[NR]
Erustosol®
Ethylac® #650
Expello®
Ezytite®
Fil-Trolax®
Flo®
Fosclean®
Fosdraw®
Gilron®
Gilronco®
Gilronex®
Gran-Form[NR]
Greenwich Lye®
Hi-Gam®
Hydramine®
Hy-Phos®
Inhibitor 225[NR] and Inhibitor 226[NR]
Inhibitor 250[NR]
Isotron[NR]
Keryl®
Klen-Olax®
Kryoflux®
MC-1®
MC-3®
Merac® #225
Mist[NR]
Natrona Brand® Bicarbonate of Soda
Neoprime A®
Neoprime B®
Nonic® #218, #234, #259, #260, #261 and #300
Or-Fer-Gro[NR]
Orthophen® #278
Orthosil®
Painticator®
Pamisc®
Penbrite®
Penbrom®
Pencal®
Penchlor FCC®
Penclor®
Penco
Penflour®
Pen-Gleam®
Pen-Glo®
Penite®
Penncoat®
Pennex®, Pennex A®; and Pennex B®
Pennply®
Pennprime®
Pennsalt A-27®
Pennsalt AE-16®
Pennsalt EC-7®
Pennsalt EC-51®
Pennsalt EC-54®
Pennsalt LF-42®
Pennsalt MS-1®
Pennsalt PB-1®
Pennsalt SC-25[NR]
Pennsalt Scale Remover 4®
Pennsalt Whirlaway®
Pennsorb®
Penphate®
Penphene®
Penprim[NR]
Pensal Cleans All®
Penso®
Pensuds®
Pent-Acetate® #28, and #29
Pentalarm "A"®
Pentalene® #95 and #195
Pentaphen® #67
Pentasol® #26, #27, and #258
Pentasol® Frother #124
Pentrete®
Pet-Rolax®
Phos-Kleen®
Phosphosil®
Plastamine®
Power-Pak[NR]
Raydex®
Scotch'em[NR]
Sharples Accelerator[NR] 52, 57, 62, 66, 67, and 77
Sharsol®
Sharstop® 204 and 268
Spot-Clor®
Spotticator®
Spray Flo®
Sterilair®
Stopleak® #1008 and #1009
Sunolax®
Thomas Soil-Rich Fertilizer®
Tilite®
Tip Top[NR]
Tupco®
Vitex®
Vultac®
Vultra C®

PERFECTING SERVICE CO., CHEMICAL DIV.
See Spradri Co.

PERMAMIX CORP.
228 N. LaSalle St., Chicago 1, Ill.
Permamix®

PERSONAL PRODUCTS CORP.
(*Subsidiary of* Johnson & Johnson)
Milltown, N. J.
Cel-Fibe[NR]

PETRECO
(*Division of* Petrolite Corp.)
P. O. Box 2546, Houston 1, Texas
Bender Process[NR]
Petreco®
Petreco® Electrofining[NR]
Petreco® Electrophere[NR] Desalting Process

PETROLITE CORP. See Bareco Wax Co.; Petreco; *and* Tretolite Co.

PFANSTIEHL LABORATORIES, INC.
104 Lakeview Ave., Waukegan, Ill.
Agron®
Seqlene®

PFIZER, CHAS., & CO., INC.
11 Bartlett St., Brooklyn 6, N. Y.
A*C*M®
Bi-Cap®
Biostat®
Biostat®-PA
Citroflex® 2
Citroflex® 4
Citroflex® A-2
Sorbistat[NR]

PHILADELPHIA QUARTZ CO.
Public Ledger Bldg., Independence Sq., Philadelphia 6, Pa.
Quso

PHILLIPS CHEMICAL CO., RUBBER CHEMICALS DIV.
318 Water St., Akron 8, Ohio
Philblack® A
Philblack® O
Sulfole®

PIONEER CHEMICAL WORKS, INC.
940 N. Delaware Ave., Philadelphia 23, Pa.
Defoamer F-947[NR]
Defoamer H-450[NR]
Inferol H-138[NR]
Solpon KD[NR]
Viscolan 14[NR]
Viscolan C[NR]

PIONEER SCIENTIFIC CORP.
161 Great Neck Rd., Great Neck, N. Y.
Enduron[NR]

PITTSBURGH PLATE GLASS CO. See Columbia-Southern Chemical Corp.

PLASTIC FILM CORP.
475 Fifth Ave., New York 17, N. Y.
Syntilon®

PLASTICS ENGINEERING CO.
1607 Geele Ave., Sheboygan, Wisc.
Plenco

PLEXON CORP.
116 W. 23rd St., New York 11, N. Y.
Plexon® Pigtail

POLYMEL CORP., THE
2238 Eastern Ave., Baltimore 31, Md.
Polymel® 6, 7, C-128, D, and H-2
Polmel® C-130
Polymel® D-Tac
Polymel® DX
Polymel® DX-111 Powder

POLYMER INDUSTRIES, INC.
Springdale, Conn.
ChemoTec®

PORETE MFG. CO.
Porete Ave., North Arlington, N. J.
Porete® Prestressed Beams

PORTER, H. K., CO., INC. See Vulcan Crucible Steel Co.

POTTS, HORACE T., CO.
Erie Ave. and D St., Philadelphia 34, Pa.
Speedline®
Tread-Grip®

POWHATAN MINING CO.
Woodlawn, Baltimore 7, Md.
Powminco Asbestos

PRATT, B. G., CO.
204 Twenty-First Ave., Paterson, N. J.
Pratt's Shot Gun Spray or Dust

PRESSTITE-KEYSTONE ENGINEERING PRODUCTS CO.
(*Division of* American-Marietta Co.)
3900 Chouteau Ave., St. Louis 10, Mo.
Kapco[NR]
KopeSeal®

PRESSURE PRODUCTS CO.
P. O. Box 342, West Chester, Pa.
Nu Aero®
Nu Aero® Chain Life
Spray-Lube[NR]

PRICE-DRISCOLL CORP.
520 Fifth Ave., New York 36, N. Y.
Super King Bomb-Lube

PROTECTION PRODUCTS MFG. CO.
P. O. Box 747, 2305 Superior Ave., Kalamazoo 99, Mich.
P.A.R.®

PURDUE FREDERICK CO.
135 Christopher St., New York 14, N. Y.
Chlorogiene®
Colpotab®
Glutazyme®
Gray's Compound®
Pre-mens®
Senokap®
Senokot®
Sippyplex®
Somatovite®

PYROCOTE CHEMICALS, INC.
229-05 Sixty-nineth Ave., Bayside 64, N. Y.
Pyroceramik®
Pyrocote-AC® (Anti-Corrosive)
Pyrocote-CR® (Chemical Resistant)
Pyrometalik®
Pyrothene[NR]

Q

QUAKER OATS CO., THE, CHEMICALS DEPT.
Merchandise Mart Plaza, Chicago 54, Ill.
Fur-Ag®

QUIGLEY CO.
415 Madison Ave., New York 17, N. Y.
Plastic Insulcrete®

R

RAYMOND LABORATORIES, INC.
261 E. Fifth St., St. Paul 1, Minn.
Penidt® WA Cosmetic
Pendit® WA-D
Pendit® WA-T

RAYONIER, INC.
161 E. 42nd St., New York 17, N. Y.
Cellunier®-F

R-B-H DISPERSIONS DIV. OF INTERCHEMICAL CORP.
Factory Lane, Bound Brook, N. J.
Midas Gold®
R-B-H Fast Yellow[NR]
Resin 529®

REED & CARNRICK
155 Van Wagenen Ave., Jersey City 6, N. J.
Alracompt®
Analeptone®
Kwell®
Lullamin® Drops
Tarcortin®
Topitracin®

REFLIN CO.
5730 Kearney Villa Rd., San Diego 11, Calif.
Reflin Pipe

REFRACTORY & INSULATION CORP.
120 Wall St., New York 5, N. Y.
R & I Aluminacrete®
R & I Hot Top Moldit®
R & I Moldit Chrome Castable Refractory®
R & I Moldit-D®
R & I Plastic Chrome®

REICHHOLD CHEMICALS, INC.
525 N. Broadway, White Plains, N. Y.
Epoxidol®
Plyacien®
Rezamul®
Super-Beckamine®

REISS ASSOCIATES INC., PLASTICS DIV.
Reiss Ave., Lowell, Mass.
Raiflex
Railite

RESOLITE CORP.
Zelienople, Pa.
Resolite
Resolite Fire-Snuf®

REVERE COPPER & BRASS, INC.
New York Central Bldg., 230 Park Ave., New York 17, N. Y.

REX CORP., THE
Hayward Rd., West Action, Mass.
Resin-Glas
Tube-In-Strip®

REZOLIN, INC.
5736 W. 96th St., Los Angeles 45, Calif.
Corfoam
Dyform
PrEpoxy Partingkote No. 832
Toolplastik®

RHOADS, J. E., & SONS
2100 W. 11th St., Wilmington 99, Del.
Gilt Edge
Gripotan
Power
Rhoads JE-538 Waterproof and Oil-resistant Cement
Stronghold
Tannate

RHODIA, INC.
  60 E. 56th St., New York 22, N. Y.
Astrotone® BR

RIVERSIDE MFG. CO.
  4919 Connecticut St., St. Louis 9, Mo.
Ree-Drape®   Tergit®

ROBINSON MOULDED PRODUCTS LIMITED
  183 George St., Toronto 2, Ont., Canada
Aer-O-Buoy[NR]

ROERIG, J. B., & CO.
  536 Lake Shore Dr., Chicago 11, Ill.
Atarax®   Stimavite® Tastitabs®
Coryban®   Storcavite®
Darthronol   Viterra® Tastitabs®
Neobon®   Vi-Thyro®
Neobon® Liquid

ROHM & HAAS CO.
  Washington Square, Philadelphia 5, Pa.
Acrysol® G-110   Paraplex® P-444
Binder P-812[NR]   Plexiglas® R
CF-10   Rhoplex® B-15

ROHNER LTD.
  Pratteln, Switzerland
  (*See also* Nova Chemical Corp.)
Ronagen Black IL
  Powder

RUBBA, INC.
  1015 E. 173rd St., New York 60, N. Y.
Liquizinc[NR]   Rubbakote[NR]

RUBBER AND ASBESTOS CORP.
  225 Belleville Ave., Bloomfield, N. J.
Tackmaster®

RUBBER CORP. OF AMERICA
  (*Formerly* Revertex Corp. of America)
  225 Broadway, New York 7, N. Y.
RC Plasticizer BD-8[NR]   RC Plasticizer TG-9[NR]
RC Plasticizer E-S[NR]   RC Polymeric BGA[NR]
RC Plasticizer O-16[NR]   Rucoam®
RC Plasticizer TG-8[NR]

RUBBEROID CO. *See* Old American Roofing Mills, Div. of The Rubberoid Co.

RUBBER & PLASTICS COMPOUND CO., INC.
  30 Rockefeller Plaza, New York 20, N. Y.
Nerva-Kote®   Nervastral Seal-Pruf®
Nervastral J. R. Joint   Tape 30 *and* 60
  Sealer[NR]   Nervatape®
Nervastral Seal-Pruf®   Nervatape® #7
  H-D

RUMFORD CHEMICAL WORKS
  Rumford 16, R. I.
Metafos®

RUSTICIDE PRODUCTS CO.
  3125 Perkins Ave., Cleveland 14, Ohio
Ospho®

S

SANDOZ CHEMICAL WORKS, INC.
  61-63 Van Dam St., New York 13, N. Y.
Sandopan® DTC

SAYLES FINISHING PLANTS, INC.
  70 W. 40th St., New York 18, N. Y.
Storm King

SCHWARTZ CHEMICAL CO.
  326 W. 70th St., New York 23, N. Y.
Acra-Kleen[NR]   Vinaplas-Lac

SELBY, BATTERSBY & CO.
  5220 Whitby Ave., Philadelphia 43, Pa.
Selbalith®

SERVICE INDUSTRIES, CHEMICAL PRODUCTS DIV.
  2107 E. Somerset St., Philadelphia 34, Pa.
Acidulum®   R-Mor-Plate®
Cezit®

SHELL CHEMICAL CORP.
  50 W. 50th St., New York 20, N. Y.
105® Catalyst *and* 205®   Ional®, C.P.
  Catalyst   Nemagon[NR] Soil Fumi-
D-D® Soil Fumigant   gant
Epon Curing Agent®   Neosol® Proprietary Sol-
Filmcol® Proprietary   vent
  Solvent   Nitrogation Ammonia[NR]
Ionol® Antioxidant   Vianol® Antioxidant

SHERWIN-WILLIAMS CO., THE
  11541 S. Champlain Ave., Chicago 28, Ill.
Arcturus Red®   Micro-Fast[NR]
Artistain[NR]   Micro-Tex[NR]
Beauty-Lok[NR]   Multicolor[NR]
Brilliant Toning Red[NR]   OK®
Britone Red[NR]   Opal-Glo®
Carclad[NR]   Orion Red[NR]
Dearborn Red[NR]   Ozark[NR]
Dehydrol®   Ozide[NR]
Dyal®   Ozlo[NR]
Dymal®   Painter Craft[NR]
Dyphene®   PC&C[NR]
Dyphenite®   Permachlor Red[NR]
Dypol[NR]   Permachrom Red[NR]
Exlon[NR]   Permansa®
Flaxoap[NR]   Pestroy®
Graphic Red[NR]   Plasticone Red®
Gripclad[NR]   Polaris Red[NR]
Griplate[NR]   Pyrolux Maroon[NR]
Heetclad®   Quali-Kote®
Homoclad[NR]   Royal Purple[NR]
Illini Red[NR]   Rubanox Red[NR]
Kem®   Serene Green[NR]
Kemak[NR]   Shamrock Green[NR]
Kem Cati-Coat[NR]   Sherdye®
Kem-Kold-Bild®   Sher-Gide[NR]
Kem-Krete®   Silverbrite[NR]
Kem-Namel® Snow   Solfast®
  White   Superior Red[NR]
Kem-O-Lite[NR]   Super-Kem-Tone®
Kemplate®   S W P®
Kemprint[NR]   Tank Clad®
Kem Transport[NR]   Tech-Var®
Lacquer-Flo®   Thermoclad[NR]
Lustre-N-Dure[NR]   Yellow for Green[NR]

SIGMA CHEMICAL CO.
  3500 DeKalb St., St. Louis 18, Mo.
Buck Buffer®   Shu-Glo®

SIKA CHEMICAL CORP.
  35 Gregory Ave., Passaic, N. J.
Intraplast[NR]   Sikacrete®

SIMONDS ABRASIVE CO.
  Tacony & Fraley Sts., Philadelphia 37, Pa.
Double XX®   Simex®
Fibrex®

SIMPSON TIMBER CO.
  1010 White Bldg., Seattle 1, Wash.
  Including Simpson Logging Co., Shelton, Wash.;
  Simpson Redwood Co., Arcata, Calif.; *and*
  Simpson Paper Co., Everett, Wash.
Forestone®   Simpson®
Noisemaster®

SINDAR CORP.
  330 W. 42nd St., New York 6, N. Y.
Deodall®   Resodor®
Odrene®   Texodor®

SLOMONS LABORATORIES, INC.
  31-27 Thomson Ave., Long Island City 1, N. Y.
Kleen-It   Sobo® Adhesive
Roly-Poly Dry Cleaner

SMOOTH-ON MFG. CO.
  568-574 Communipaw Ave., Jersey City 4, N. J.
Poly-Flex 100[NE]

SOLUOL CHEMICAL CO., INC.
  Natick, R. I.
Exol-K145®

SOLVAY PROCESS DIV., ALLIED CHEMICAL & DYE CORP.
  61 Broadway, New York 6, N. Y.
Ozene®

SONNEBORN, L., SONS, INC.
  404 Fourth Ave., New York 16, N. Y.
Cemcoat® Filler and   Mulsivon®
  Dustproofer   Penequick®
Cordurol®   Penetralene®
Deo-Base®   Petronate®
Form-Saver[NE]   Sonaquol®
Fybrol®   SonNoMar®
Hydrocide®   Sono-Grip[NE]
Hydrocide® No. 633   Sono-Jell®
Hydrocide® Paste   Sonotard[NE]
Hydrocide® Powder   S.R.P.®
Kaukit®   Sulphopet®
Lapidolith®   Textarid®
Lignophol®   Trimix®
Lignophol® Quick-Drying   Yellow Protopet® No. 2

SPECIALTY PRODUCTS CO.
  190 Warren St., Jersey City 2, N. J.
Kantstik   Resin Release N.

SPRADRI CO.
  (Chemical Div. of Perfecting Service Co.)
  332 Atando Ave., Charlotte 6, N. C.
Spradri®

SPRAYLAT CORP.
  1 Park Ave., New York 16, N. Y.
Coverlac®   Spraylat® SC-1071B

SPRAYWAY, INC.
  (*Formerly* Tru-Pine Co.)
  7638 Vincennes Ave., Chicago 20, Ill.
Sprayway® First Aid   Sprayway® Tru-Nox
Sprayway® Plastic Spray

STALEY, A. E., MFG. CO.
  Box 151, Decatur, Ill.
"50" Oil[NE]   Ethylex[NE]
"AR" Soybean Oil[NE]   Gransize®
Caladex®   Hydrolyzed Vegetable
Corrugating Starch #1[NE]   Proteins 43-A *and*
Corrugating Starch #5[NE]   52-A[NE]
Eclipse®   Lo-Fat®
Edsoy®   Protein Insecticide Baits
Emultex®   #2 *and* #7[NE]

Simplex®   Sta-Rx®
Special Nutrient 4-S®   Sta-Sol®
Special Nutrient 22® *and* Sta-Thik®
  Special Nutrient 114®   Staybind®
Staclipse®   Staycal®
Stacolloid®   Stayco®
Sta-Crem[NE]   Staysize®
Stadex®   Stazyme®
Sta-Gel®   Sweetose®
Staley's®   Zest®
Sta-Mino®

STANDARD CHEMICAL PRODUCTS, INC.
  1301 Jefferson St., Hoboken, N. J.
  (*Plant:* Sugaw Creek Rd. & Raleigh St., Charlotte, N. C.)
Stansets[NE]   Stantone[NE]

STANDARD DRY WALL PRODUCTS, INC.
  Box X, New Eagle, Pa.
Thorobond®   Thorosheen® RW 7

STANDARD SOLUTION CO., INC.
  Box 548, Route 2, Menasha, Wisc.
Stansol®

STANDARD ULTRAMARINE AND COLOR CO.
  Box 2166, Huntington 18, W. Va.
Bahama Blues®

STANLEY CHEMICAL CO.
  E. Berlin, Conn.
Stanley 40X-610[NE]   Stanley Hand Save[NE]

STEIN, HALL & CO.
  285 Madison Ave., New York 17, N. Y.
Amasize®   EC *and* ECT Stabil-
Baktak Gum[NE]   izers[NE]
Bondcor®   Lycoid®
Bondrez[NE]   Raygomm®
Cart-N-Seel[NE]   Superseal®
Caustic Gum[NE]   Supranyl[NE]
Cetosols®   Unitex®

STERLING QUALITY PRODUCTS, INC.
  (*Formerly* Sterling Paint & Varnish Co.)
  184 Commercial St., Malden 8, Mass.
Rinse-Kleen   Rinse-Off

STERLING VARNISH CO., THE
  Haysville Borough, Sewickley, Pa.
Sterling® T-653-LB   Sterling® Thermobonds
Thermopoxy

STEWART RESEARCH LABORATORY
  2930 N. E. 21st Terrace, Coral Shores, Fort Lauderdale, Fla.
Uranium "O"[NE]

STONHARD CO., INC.
  1306 Spring Garden St., Philadelphia 23, Pa.
Concretite®   Stonpach®
Stoncote[NE]   Stontite®
Stonfast®   Stontreet[NE]
Stonfil[NE]

STOODY CO.
  11928 E. Slauson Ave., Whittier, Calif.
Stoody Automatic and   Stoody Build-Up[NE]
  Semi-Automatic   Stoody Wear-Resistant
  Wires[NE]   Castings[NE]

SULLIVAN CHEMICALS DIV., SULLIVAN VARNISH CO.
  420 Hart St., Chicago 22, Ill.
Metalplex   Polyplex
Plastiplex

SUMNER CHEMICAL CO., INC.
(*Division of* Miles Laboratories, Inc.)
1127 Myrtle St., Elkhart, Ind.

Hyprophen[NR] Toloxyn[NR]
Suconox[NR]

SUN CHEMICAL CORP. *See* Electro-Technical Products Div.

SUN OIL CO.
1608 Walnut St., Philadelphia 3, Pa.

Circo® Heat Transfer Oils
Circo® Hydraulic Oils
Circo® Light Process Aid
Circo® Lubricating Oils
Circomar®-5AA
Circomar®-25
Circomar®-110
Circosol®-2XH
Dynavis® Oils
Lubeway®
New Solnus® Oils
PDO-40[NR]
Sulfonate OS[NR]
Sulfonate WS[NR]
Sun® 1300 *and* 1301 Greases
Sun® 1893 *and* 1897 Greases
Sunaptic® Acids
Sun® C-850 EP Greases
Sun® C-891T Grease
Sundex® 41
Sundex®-53
Sundex®-85
Sundex®-170
Sunep® Oils
Sunicut® 11-S
Sunicut® 85
Sunicut® 102-S *and* Sunicut® 110-S
Sunicut® 105
Sunicut® 171
Sunicut® 209-S
Sunicut® 216
Sunicut® 793
Sunicut® 5534
Sunicut® "W" Series Cutting Oils
Sunisco® Refrigeration Oils
Sunkote A
Sun® N-52X Grease
Sunoco® Anti-Check
Sunoco® Emulsifying Cutting Oil HD "F"
Sunoco® Emulsifying Cutting Oils
Sunoco Polyseal®
Sunoco® Waxes
Sunoco Way® Lubricant
Sunotex® Machine Oil
Sunotex® Machine Oil Light
Sun® Prestige 40 Greases
Sun® Process Oil 515
Sunquench 78
Sun® Quenching Oil No. 11
Sun® Quenching Oil Light
Suntac® Oils
Sunvis 700 Oils[NR]
Sunvis 900 Oils[NR]
Sunvis Oils[NR]

SUPERIOR TUBE CO.
Norristown, Pa.

Cathaloy®

SWIFT & CO., GENERAL ADHESIVE PRODUCTS DEPT.
4115 Packers Ave., Chicago 9, Ill.

Econoflex

SYNTHETIC MICA CORP.
(*Subsidiary of* Mycalex Corp. of America)
Beverly Rd. and Passaic Ave., Caldwell Township, N. J.

Synthamica®

T

TAKAMINE LABORATORIES
(*Division of* Miles Laboratories, Inc.)
193 Arlington Ave., Clifton, N. J.

Alase® Resizet®
Dextrinase® Superise®
Diazyme® Takabate®

TAYLOR FIBRE CO.
Norristown, Penna.

Taylor Laminated Plastics[NR] Taylor Vulcanized Fibre[NR]

TECHNICOLOR CORP.
6311 Romaine St., Hollywood 38, Calif.

Technicolor® Techniscope®
Technirama® Technivision®

TECNIFAX CORP.
195 Appleton St., Holyoke, Mass.

Dry-Developer[NR] Slip-Screens®
Microverter®

TENNESSEE Coal & Iron Div. *See* United States Steel Corp.

TENNESSEE CORP.
617–29 Grant Bldg., P. O. Box 2205, Atlanta 1, Ga.

Mono-Man® Sul-Fon-Ate®
Nu-Iron® T-C Hydro®
Nu-M® Tennessee Tri-Basic® Copper
Nu-Manese®

TERMINIX DIV., E. L. BRUCE CO.
1648 Thomas St., Memphis, Tenn.

Terminix

TESTAGAR & CO., INC.
1354 W. Lafayette, Detroit 26, Mich.

Acterol-D Beesix
Amo-Dex Multi-B-Plex
Ascorbacaine Thorotrase®
Atrobar-M Umbrathor®

TEXAS CO., THE
135 E. 42nd St., New York 17, N. Y.

Petrox®
Sky Chief® Marine Gasoline
Texaco® Capella Oil
Texaco® Crater
Texaco® Crater X Fluid
Texaco® Floatcoat
Texaco® Multifax
Texaco® Olympian Grease
Texaco® Paper Machine Oil HD
Texaco® Rustproof Compound
Texaco® Soluble Oil CX
Texaco® Stazon
Texaco® Texacoat
Texaco® Texspray Compound

TEX-CHEM CO.
20–21 Wagaraw Rd., Fair Lawn, N. J.

Anti Foam Extra S[NR] Neo Size[NR]
Inhibitex[NR] Weytone F P[NR]

TEXTILE ADJUNCTS CORP.
876 Pacific St., Brooklyn 38, N. Y.

Calen-Aid® Tacanols®
Poly-Coupler® Water-Skipper®

TEXTILEATHER DIV., THE GENERAL TIRE & RUBBER CO.
607 Madison Ave., Toledo 3, Ohio

Nygen® Tolex®

THERMAL AMERICAN FUSED QUARTZ CO.
(*Formerly* Thermal Syndicate, Inc.)
18–20 Salem St., Dover, N. J.

Vitreosil®

THERMATOMIC CARBON CO.
(*Division of* Commercial Solvents Corp.)
260 Madison Ave., New York 16, N. Y.

P-33® Thermax®

THIOKOL CHEMICAL CORP.
Trenton 7, N. J.

Thiokol® TP-95

THOMPSON CHEMICALS CORP.
3600 Monon St., Los Angeles 27, Calif.

Bramblcide® 4 *and* 5
Bramble-Weedicide® 4, 5, *and* 32
Color Fix® No. 128 *and* No. 384
Fruit Fix® 133, 200 *and* 800
Lincide 20
Neothren Spray
Potato Fix®
Tomato Fix®
Transplant-Fix®

THOMPSON & CO.
1018 Edward St., Oakmont, Pa.
Synhibit "AQ"

THOMPSON-HAYWARD CHEMICAL CO.
2915 Southwest Blvd., Kansas City 8, Mo.
T-H Emulsifiers[NR]

TIMKEN ROLLER BEARING CO., THE, STEEL AND TUBE DIV.
Canton 6, Ohio
Graph-Air®

TREPLOW PRODUCTS, INC.
59 Camden St., Paterson, N. J.
Trepenol® ES
Trepenol® S-60
Trepenol® WA
Trepolate® F-95
Trepolate® T-60

TRETOLITE CO.
(*Division of* Petrolite Corp.)
369 Marshall Ave., St. Louis 19, Mo.
Monox®
Tolad[NR]
Tret-O-Lite®
Vez®
X-Cide[NR]

TROPICAL PAINT CO.
(*Subsidiary of* Parker Rust Proof Co.)
1246 W. 70th St., Cleveland 2, Ohio
Thermalite®
Tropoxy

TROY BLANKET MILLS
200 Madison Ave., New York 16, N. Y.
Troytuf® Dacron Blanket

TROY INDUSTRIAL PRODUCTS, DIV. OF GLOBE SANITARY SUPPLY CO.
2249 E. 38th St., Los Angeles 58, Calif.
Daisy
Globe Kold Dip Metal Cleaner
Troy Coco-Ster Compound
Troy Compound 111
Troy Econo-Pine
Troy Fine Finish
Troy Low-Dishwash
Troy Multi-Purpose
Troy O & M Compound
Troy P.D.Q. Mechanics Soap
Troy Pine Emulso
Troy Silken Suds Wash
Troy Steam-O
Troy Ster-L-Yzer
Troy T.I.A.
Troy Tops-Gran

TRUSCON LABORATORIES
(*Division of* Devoe & Raynolds Co., Inc.)
Box 69, Milwaukee Junction P. O., Detroit 11, Mich.
Bar-Ox®
Chemfast[NR]
Devran®
Eye Comfort®
Granitex[NR]
Saf-T-Dek[NR]
Speed-Rex®
Tite-Lite®
Tru-Vy-Kote[NR]

TRU-SORB CORP.
22 Cross St., Bridgeport 1, Conn.
Super Tru-Sorb®

TUFCRETE CO., INC.
502 E. Locust St., Des Moines 9, Iowa
Tufcrete® All Purpose Sealer
Tufcrete® APS
Tufcrete® Latex
Tufcrete® Resurfacer
Tufcrete® Roof Resurfacers
Tufcrete® Underlay No. 3
Tufdek®

TWINSBURG-MILLER CORP.
P. O. Box 207, Twinsburg, Ohio
Glaskote[NR]

U

UBS CHEMICAL CORP.
(*Formerly* Union Bay State Chemical Co., Inc.)
491 Main St., Cambridge 42, Mass.
Bondrite®
Lustreflex®
Ubagrip®
Unibac®

UDYLITE CORP., THE
1651 E. Grand Blvd., Detroit 11, Mich.
Bry-Cad
Hi-C
Surtreat Process
Ubryco
Udyguard
Zero-Mist

ULTRA CHEMICAL WORKS
Wood and Shady Sts., Paterson, N. J.
Detergol®
Dippo Suds®
Neopone LO Beads®
Ultramin® B
Ultramin® SS
Ultrapole® DL
Ultrapole® G Extra Conc.
Ultrapole® S
Ultrapole® S Liquid

UNION CARBIDE CORP. See Bakelite Co.

UNITED CHEMICAL CORP. OF NEW MEXICO
Hobbs, New Mexico
Ke-Tone®

UNITED FERTILIZER CO.
Carrollville, Milwaukee County, Wisc.
Hynite®

UNITED LABORATORIES, INC.
16803 Euclid Ave., Cleveland 12, Ohio
Certified Styrroid®
Certified Styrroidite®

UNITED OIL MFG. CO.
1429 Walnut St., Erie, Pa.
Top-bond

U. S. COATINGS CO.
225 Manida St., Bronx 59, N. Y.
USC

UNITED STATES GYPSUM CO.
300 W. Adams St., Chicago 6, Ill.
Perf-A-Bead®
Perf-A-Tape®

U. S. INDUSTRIAL CHEMICALS CO.
(*Division of* National Distillers Products Corp.)
99 Park Ave., New York 16, N. Y.
Petrothene®
U.S.I.® Chemicals

UNITED STATES PLYWOOD CORP.
55 W. 44th St., New York 18, N. Y.
African Honeywood[NR]
Novocore®
Novotile®
Novowall[NR]
Weldron[NR]
Wood-Trim[NR]

UNITED STATES SAFETY SERVICE CO.
1215 McGee St., Kansas City 6, Mo.
Optilite®

U. S. SANITARY SPECIALTIES CORP
1001 S. California Ave., Chicago 12, Ill.
Dustnox[NR]
Flourish®
Mellisol®
Soaperior®
Soapure[NR]
Usaphene 5[NR]
Usaphene 10[NR]
Varee-Bryte XX[NR]

UNITED STATES STEEL CORP.
525 Wm. Penn Place, Pittsburgh 30, Pa.
Including American Steel & Wire Div., Rockefeller Building, Cleveland 13, Ohio; Carnegie-Illinois Steel Corp., 525 Wm. Penn Place, Pittsburgh 30, Pa.; Columbia-Geneva Steel Div., 120 Montgomery St., San Francisco 6,
(*continued*)

UNITED STATES STEEL CORP. (*continued*)
Calif.; Consolidated Western Steel Div., P. O. Box 2015, Terminal Annex, Los Angeles 54, Calif.; Cyclone Fence Dept., American Steel & Wire Div., Waukegan, Ill.; Gerrard Steel Strapping Div., 2915 W. 47th St., Chicago 32, Ill.; Oil Well Supply Div., 2001 N. Lamar St., Dallas 2, Texas; Tennessee Coal & Iron Div., P. O. Box 599, Fairfield, Ala.; United States Steel Products Div., 30 Rockefeller Plaza, New York 20, N. Y.; *and* United States Steel Supply Div., 208 S. LaSalle St., Chicago 4, Ill.
(*See also* Universal Atlas Cement Co.; *and* United States Steel Homes, Inc.)

Acme®
Amarine®
AmBridge®
Amerbestos®
Amerbus[NR]
Amerclad®
Amer-Construction[NR]
Amercord[NR]
Amercut®
Amerductor®
Amerfine[NR]
Amergard®
Amerglass®
Amergraph®
Amerhead®
American®
Americore®
Amering®
Amerite®
Amerled®
Amerloy[NR]
Amerlum®
Amerprene[NR]
Amerseal®
Amersheath®
Amersteel®
Amerstitch®
Amerstrand®
Amerstrip®
Amertel®
Amerzone®
Ametallic®
Amgal®
Amperox®
Ampolene®
Ampyrol®
Amvar®
Armorlokt[NR]
Arrow®
B (in diamond)®
Baker Perfect®
Bamboosteel®
Blue Bonnet®
Boston®
Boyco®
C (in diamond)®
Carnegie®
Cooler®
Corex[NR]
Corker®
Crown®
Cyclone®
Diamond®
Di-Hard®
Eagle®
Excellay®
F (in shield)®
Ferrostan®
Fiege Tiger-Claw®
Firefite®
Flex-Deck[NR]
Flex-Grid[NR]
Geneva®
Gerrard®
Gide-Rite®
Glidden®
Griptite[NR]
Heroult®
Hi-Brin®
Hi-Hard®
Hyco-Span[NR]
I-Beam-Lok®
Ideal®
Illinois®
Iowa®
Keystone®
Kupred®
Lock-Seal®
Lorig-Aligner®
Lyman®
Monitor®
Multigrip[NR]
Multisafty[NR]
National®
Nitrocycle[NR]
NPD (in monogram)®
NT (in circle)®
Oilwell®
Par-Ten®
Pearson®
Poppy®
Prairie®
Premier®
Protector®
Red Hoop®
Red Tag®
Reliance®
Rival®
Scale Free®
SGS®
Shelby®
Silverline®
Sinker®
Sno Gard®
Spellerized®
Star®
Storm Seal®
Sugar®
Superdraw®
Superkore®
Super-Tens®
Syphon Seal[NR]
T®
Taylor[NR]
TCI Tool Steel®
Tenelon[NR]
Tenneseal®
Tennessee®
Tiger® *or* Tiger Brand®
Tigerbraze®
Tiger-Lube®
Tigerweld®
Transonic®
Trumble®
U.S.S.®
U.S.S.® A-R Steel[NR]
U.S.S.® Carilloy®
U.S.S.® Cor-Ten®
U.S.S.® Di-Lok®
U.S.S.® Freemax®
U.S.S.® Man-Ten®
U.S.S.® M-X®
U.S.S.® T-1®
U.S.S.® Tri-Ten®
U.S.S.® Vitrenamel®
W[NR]
Waukegan®
Wilson-Snyder®
Witte®

UNITED STATES STEEL HOMES, INC.
(*Subsidiary of* United States Steel Corp.)
Charlestown Rd., New Albany, Ind.

Catalina®
Champion®
Coronado®
Talisman®
Visionaire®
Westerner®

UNITED STATES STEEL PRODUCTS DIV. *See* United States Steel Corp.

UNITED STATES STEEL SUPPLY DIV. *See* United States Steel Corp.

UNITED STATES STONEWARE CO.
Akron 9, Ohio

Intalox Saddle Packing

UNIVERSAL ATLAS CEMENT CO.
(*Subsidiary of* United States Steel Corp.)
100 Park Ave., New York 17, N. Y.

Atlas®
Duraplastic®
Luminite®
Unaflo®
Universal®

UPCO CO., THE
4805 Lexington Ave., Cleveland 3, Ohio

Reflex-Sol[NR]

USF-ASPINOOK FINISHING DIV., GERA CORP.
(*Formerly* U. S. Finishing Co.)
261 Fifth Ave., New York 16, N. Y.

Finish 3-164
Stabilized®
Vita-Fresh®
Vitalized®
Vita-Proof®

V

VALITE CORP.
Box 3207, Bywater Station, New Orleans 17, La.

Valite®

VALOLINE OIL CO.
(*Division of* Ashland Oil & Refining Co.)
Freedom, Pa.

Valvoline All-Climate[NR]

VANADIUM-ALLOYS STEEL CO., COLONIAL STEEL CO. DIV.
Latrobe, Pa.

Chromewear®
Colonial No. 6 Non-Shrinkable®
Greek Ascoloy®
MC (Mold and Cavity Steel)[NR]
Speed Cut®
Van Cut®
Vasco Supreme®
WCC[NR]
WW Hotwork[NR]

VANDERBILT, R. T., CO., INC.
230 Park Ave., New York 17, N. Y.

Activ-8[NR]
Bilt-Rex[NR]
Bilt-Wax[NR]
Braze[NR]
Braze Cover Cements[NR]
Clay Deflocculants No. 2 *and* 5[NR]
Continental Clay[NR]
CWAB[NR]
D-6[NR]
D-7[NR]
DM-30[NR]
Fibrous Filler[NR]
Fomont[NR]
Merfenel 51[NR]
Merfenel PMA[NR]
Na-Sul[NR]
Norvan[NR]
Nytal[NR]
(*continued*)

VANDERBILT, R. T., INC. (continued)
Partex[NE]
Peerless Clay[NE]
Peerless Kaolin[NE]
Redium Selenium[NE]
Rheotol[NE]
Setsit-9[NE]
Thermax-Stainless[NE]
Vanade[NE]
Vancide® 26EC
Vancide® 32
Vancide® 50 Peps
Vancide® 51
Vancide® 89 and Vancide® 89RE
Vanesta[NE]
Vanfre[NE]
Vanlite[NE]
Vanstay-C73[NE]
Vanstay-HT[NE]
Vanstay-L[NE]
Vanstay-N[NE]
Vanstay-R[NE]
Vanstay-S[NE]
Vanstay-Z[NE]
Vanwax[NE]
Vanzak[NE]
Vanzyme[NE]
Veegum[NE]
Veegum "T"[NE]

VELSICOL CHEMICAL CORP.
(*Subsidiary of* Arvey Corp.)
330 S. Grand Ave., Chicago 11, Ill.
Velsicol Resin EC-70
Velsicol Resin X-30

VESTAL, INC.
4963 Manchester Ave., St. Louis 10, Mo.
Amerse®
Staphene®
Style®
Toilex®
Ves-Phene®
Vesspray®

VICTOR CHEMICAL WORKS
155 N. Wacker Dr., Chicago 6, Ill.
Natox[NE]
Victalube 5810[NE]
Victor Antistatic Agent[NE] A, PCO, 8, 12, 20 *and* 27
Victor Stabilizers[NE] 21, 53, 85, 85X *and* 6162X
Vitrafos®

VIKON CHEMICAL CO.
1384 Massachusetts Ave., Cambridge 38, Mass.
Vikon FPB[NE]
Vikon RL[NE]
Vinalube R-100[NE]

VITAMIN PRODUCTS CO.
2023 W. Wisconsin Ave., Milwaukee 3, Wisc.
Betalco V-P 728
Betaris V-P 727
Biost Tablets V-P 733
Biost V-P 730
Calciplex V-P 725
Calci-Phade V-P 724
Catalyn V-P 710
Cataplex
Cataplex E₂ V-P 732
Cerodyn V-P 723
Cerol V-P 719
Eff-Plus V-P 731
Eflex V-P 720
Ferroplus V-P 722
Minaplex V-P 721
Protedyn V-P 726
Rutaplex A V-P 729A
Rutaplex V-P 729

VULCAN CRUCIBLE STEEL CO.
(*Division of* H. K. Porter Co., Inc.)
Aliquippa, Pa.
Vulcan® Gage and Die Steel

W

WALLACE & TIERNAN, INC. *See* Harchem Div., Wallace & Tiernan, Inc.

WALLERSTEIN CO., INC.
180 Madison Ave., New York 16, N. Y.
Fermex®
Mylase®
Sebacol®
Sterozol®

WARNER-CHILCOTT LABORATORIES
(*Division of* Warner-Lambert Pharmaceutical Co.)
Morris Plains, N. J.
Acetycol®
Agoral®
Alka-Zane®
Anusol®
Atophan®
Cal-Bis-Ma®
Calcisalin®
Cellothyl®
Depancol®
Gelusil®
Hemosules®
Hetoxin®
Isocrin®
Lixa-Beta®
Maltine®
Malto® Yerbine
Medinal®
Methium®
Methium® with Reserpine
Mucigel®
Mucotin®
Neoferrum®
Nitramac® Tablets
Omni-Beta®
Parsidol®
Peralga®
Peritrate®
Plestran®
Proloid®
Prulose® Complex
Sterisil[NE]
Stigmonene®
Tedral®
Thera-Vita®
Urotropin®

WARNER-LAMBERT PHARMACEUTICAL CO.
See Warner-Chilcott Laboratories

WASCO PRODUCTS, INC.
Bay State Rd., Cambridge 38, Mass.
Acrylite[NE]
Wascofilm[NE]
Wascolite Showerwall[NE]
Wascoseal[NE]

WASHBURN CO., T. F.
2244 Elston Ave., Chicago 14, Ill.
Burnok®

WEHR STEEL CO.
2100 S. 54th St., Milwaukee 46, Wisc.
Wehrbest[NE]

WESTERN LITHOGRAPH CO., WESTLINE PRODUCTS DIV.
600 E. Second St., Los Angeles 54, Calif.
E-Z Code
Tel-A-Pipe

WESTLINE PRODUCTS DIV. *See* Western Lithograph Co.

WHITFIELD CHEMICAL CO.
14225 Schaefer Highway (P. O. Box 3956), Detroit 27, Mich.
Alk-A-Sol®

WHITNEY BLAKE CO.
New Haven 14, Conn.
Dynaprene®
Plastite®
Tru-Rip®

WILBUR & WILLIAMS CO., THE
130 Lincoln St., Brighton 35, Mass.
Rubber-Coat® Liquid Neoprene
Totrust ® Instant Dry Metal Coat
Zinc Shield[NE]

WILKINS CO., INC., THE
P. O. Box 628, Cortland, N. Y.
K-Lens-M® Tissue

WILROSS PRODUCTS CO.
Hawthorne, N. J.
P-179
P-204
P-222
P-268
P-269
P-297
P-323
P-354
P-360
P-380
Styrad 205
W-167
WP-134
WP-758
WP-861

WITCO CHEMICAL CO.
122 E. 42nd St., New York 17, N. Y.
(*See also* Emulsol Chemical Corp.)
Continex® CF
Continex® FEF
Continex® HAF
Continex® ISAF
Continex® SRF-NS
Disperso®
Formez No. 50®
Pioneer #202[NE]
Pioneer #214[NE]
(*continued*)

WITCO CHEMICAL CO. (*continued*)
Pioneer #216[NR]
Pioneer #301[NR]
Pioneer #401-P[NR]
Pioneer #406[NR]
Pioneer #500[NR]
Pioneer #507 Aluminum Mastic[NR]
Pioneer #607 *and* #609[NR]
Pioneer #610 Adhesive[NR]
Pioneer #622 Asphalt Paint[NR]
Pioneer #630 Primer[NR]
Pioneer #820 Cork Insulation[NR]
Pioneer #1008 Vapor Seal[NR]
Stayrite®
Witcizer®
Witco®
Witcote #4[NR]
Wittox®

W-K-M MFG. CO., INC., KEY PRODUCTS DIV.
(*A subsidiary of* acf Industries Inc.)
P. O. Box 2117, Houston 1, Tex.
Key Abso-Lute®
Key Graphite Paste®
Key Tite®

WOLF, JACQUES, & CO.
350 Lexington Ave., Passaic, N. J.
Compressive Shrinkage Oil S-261-C[NR]
Desmer O-112®

WOODALL INDUSTRIES INC.
7565 E. McNichols Rd., Detroit 34, Mich.
Perforall®

WURDACK CHEMICAL CO.
4977 Fyler Ave., St. Louis 9, Mo.
Kladak[NR]

WYANDOTTE CHEMICALS CORP., J. B. FORD DIV.
Wyandotte, Mich.
No. 91 Solid Alkali[NR]
Aluminum Brightener I-2767-C[NR]
Alutone®
Burnek 452[NR]
Burnishing Compound No. 321[NR]
Carbose 55[NR]
Expray 541[NR]
Fairtex[NR]
Foamicide S[NR]
Industrial No. 39[NR]
Industrial "S"[NR]
Mersoclean 540[NR]
M.F. Acid[NR]
Mil-Etch[NR]
Multi-Chlor®
Phos-It®
Rantier[NR]
SR-10[NR]
Supersolve[NR]
Teko[NR]
Uniflex[NR]
Wyandotte 85[NR]
Wyandotte 397[NR]
Wyandotte 418[NR]
Wyandotte 453[NR]
Wyandotte 548[NR]
Wyandotte 608[NR]
Wyandotte 979[NR]

WYANDOTTE CHEMICALS CORP., MICHIGAN ALKALI DIV.
Wyandotte, Mich.
Quadrol®
Tetronic®
Wyandotte Better Blend Soda®

Y

YOUNGSTOWN MFG., INC.
66–76 S. Prospect St., Youngstown 6, Ohio
Superior Curtain Rods[NR]
Superior Metal Mouldings®
Superlok®

COMPANY NAME OR ADDRESS CHANGES

Company Name or Address Changes

A number of companies whose products were described in the 1953 Edition of Handbook of Material Trade Names or in Supplement I have changed their names or addresses.

A

Advance Solvents & Chemical Corp., 245 Fifth Ave., New York 16, N. Y.
Now Advance Solvents & Chemical, Div. of Carlisle Chemical Works, Inc., New Brunswick, N. J.

Air Reduction Chemical Co., Div. of Air Reduction Co., Inc., 60 E. 42nd St., New York 17, N. Y.
Now at 150 East 42nd St., New York 17, N. Y.

Alconox, Inc., Jersey City 4, N. J.
Now at 853 Broadway, New York 3, N. Y.

Alpha Corp., The
Now The Alpha-Molykote Corp., 65 Harvard Ave., Stamford, Conn.

Aluminum Co. of America, 801 Gulf Bldg., Pittsburgh 19, Pa.
Now at 1501 Alcoa Bldg., Pittsburgh 19, Pa.

Aluminum Industries, Inc., 2438 Beekman St., Cincinnati 25, Ohio.
Now at 3670 Werk Rd., Cincinnati 11, Ohio.

Americaine, Inc., 1316 Sherman Ave., Evanston, Ill.
Now Arnar-Stone Laboratories, Inc., 225 E. Prospect Ave., Mount Prospect, Ill.

American Asphalt Roof Corp., 15th St. & Blue River, Kansas City 3, Mo.
Now Old American Roofing Mills, Div. of The Ruberoid Co., 7600 Truman Rd., Kansas City 26, Mo.

American Celcure Wood Preserving Corp., P. O. Box 3262, Jacksonville 6, Fla.
Formerly Celcure Southern Corp.

American Cholesterol Products, Inc., Milltown, N. J.
Now at Amerchol Park, Edison, N. J.

American Fluresit Co.
Now Klee Waterproofing Corp., 4011 Red Bank Rd., Cincinnati 27, Ohio.

American LaFrance Foamite Corp.
Now American LaFrance Corp., 100 E. La France St., Elmira, N. Y.

American Maize Products Co., 100 E. 42nd St., New York 17, N. Y.
Now at 250 Park Ave., New York 17, N. Y.

American-Marietta Co., Valdura Div., 43 E. Ohio St., Chicago 11, Ill.
Now at 101 E. Ontario St., Chicago 11, Ill.

American Mineral Spirits Co., 155 E. 44th St., New York 17, N. Y.
Now at Mountain Ave., Murray Hill, N. J.

American Window Glass Co., Farmers Bank Bldg., Pittsburgh 22, Pa.
Now at 9 W. Park Way, Pittsburgh 12, Pa.

Amoco Chemicals Corp., 910 S. Michigan Ave., Chicago 80, Ill.
This company was formed on Jan. 31, 1957 by merger of Pan American Chemicals Corp., 557 Fifth Ave., New York 17, N. Y., and Indoil Chemical Co., 910 S. Michigan Ave., Chicago 80, Ill.

Andersen Specialty Mfg. Corp., 5618 S. Harper Ave., Chicago 37, Ill.
Now at 10412 Corliss Ave., Chicago 28, Ill.

Anderson Clayton & Co. Foods Div., Gibraltar Life Bldg., P. O. Box 35, Dallas 21, Tex.
Formerly Mrs. Tucker's Foods, Inc., Sherman, Tex.

Apex Specialties Co., 50 Valley St., Providence 9, R. I.
Now at 1115 Douglas Ave., Providence 4, R. I.

Arnar-Stone Laboratories, Inc., 225 E. Prospect Ave., Mount Prospect, Ill.
Formerly Americaine, Inc., 1316 Sherman Ave., Evanston, Ill.

Asbestone Corp., P. O. Box 5257-B, New Orleans 15, La.
Now part of National Gypsum Co., 325 Delaware Ave., Buffalo 2, N. Y.

Attapulgas Clay Co., 210 W. Washington Square, Philadelphia 5, Pa.
Now Minerals & Chemicals Corp. of America, Menlo Park, N. J.

B

Bareco Oil Co., Wax Div.
Now Bareco Wax Co., A Div. of Petrolite Corp., P. O. Box 2009, Tulsa 2, Okla.

Beacon Co., 97 Bickford St., Boston 30, Mass.
Now Beacon Chemical Industries, Inc., 33 Richdale Ave., Cambridge 40, Mass.

Bearium Metals Corp., 268 State St., Rochester 4, N. Y.
Now at Mill & Commercial Sts., Rochester 14, N. Y.

Bee Chemical Co.
Now Logo Inc., Div. of Bee Chemical Co., 13799 S. Avenue "O", Chicago 33, Ill.

Behr-Manning Corp.
Now Div. of Norton Co., 2756 Howe St., Troy, N. Y.

Bigelow-Liptak Corp., 2842 W. Grand Blvd., Detroit 2, Mich.
Now at 13300 Puritan Ave., Detroit 27, Mich.

Bitucote Products Co., 1411 Central Industrial Drive, St. Louis 10, Mo.
Now at 1337 S. Kingshighway, St. Louis 10, Mo.

Borcherdt Malt Extract Co.
  Now Borchert Co., 217 N. Wolcott Ave., Chicago 12, Ill.

Brand, William, & Co., 272 Fourth Ave., New York 10, N. Y.
  Now William Brand & Co., Inc., North & Valley Sts., Willimantic, Conn.

Brooklyn Varnish Mfg. Co., Inc.
  Now Brooklyn Paint & Varnish Co., 50 Jay St., Brooklyn 1, N. Y.

Brownell Industries, Inc., Montezuma, Iowa.
  Now Bob Brownell's, Corner Main & Third, Montezuma, Iowa.

Bunker Hill Co., The, Sales and Fabrication Div., 2700—16th Ave., S. W., Seattle 4, Wash.
  Formerly Northwest Lead Co.

C

Carboloy Dept., General Electric Co.
  Now Metallurgical Products Dept., General Electric Co., Box 237, Roosevelt Park P. O., Detroit 32, Mich.

Capac Plastics, Inc.
  Now Capac Industries, Inc., Capac, Mich.

Carbide and Carbon Chemicals Co., A Div. of Union Carbide and Carbon Corp.
  Now Union Carbide Chemicals Co., A Div. of Union Carbide Corp., 30 E. 42nd St., New York 17, N. Y.

Carbisulphoil Co., 3114–22 Swiss Ave., Dallas 1, Texas.
  Now at 2917 Swiss Ave., Dallas 4, Texas.

Case Hardening Service Co., 3091 Mayfield Rd., Cleveland 18, Ohio.
  The mailing address now is P. O. Box 4586, Cleveland 24, Ohio.

Celcure Southern Corp., Graham Bldg., Jacksonville 6, Fla.
  Now American Celcure Wood Preserving Corp., P. O. Box 3262, Jacksonville 6, Fla.

Cerophyl Laboratories, Inc., Div. of National Chlorophyll and Chemical Co., 63 Southwest Blvd., Kansas City 3, Kansas.
  Now at 1125 Board of Trade Bldg., Kansas City, Mo.

Chain Belt Co. of Milwaukee, 1600 W. Bruce St., Milwaukee 4, Wisc.
  Now Chain Belt Co., 5701 W. Greenfield Ave., Milwaukee 1, Wisc.

Chapman Chemical Co., 707 Dermon Bldg., Memphis 3, Tenn.
  Now at 60 N. Third St., Memphis 1, Tenn.

Chemical Development Corp., Danvers, Mass.
  Now Devcon Corp., 19 Endicott St. (P. O. Box 2), Danvers, Mass.

Chemical Oil Processing Co., 1460 Dupont St., Toronto 9, Ontario, Canada.
  Now Chemical Oil & Resin Co., 84 Peter Street, Toronto 2, Ontario, Canada.

Chicago Steel Foundry Co., 3720 South Kedzie Ave., Chicago 32, Ill.
  Company out of business.

Chilcott Laboratories, Morris Plains, N. J.
  Now a part of Warner-Chilcott Laboratories, Morris Plains, N. J.

Chippewa Paper Products Co., 3313 W. 48th Place, Chicago 38, Ill.
  Now Chippewa Paper Products Co., Inc., 2425 South Rockwell St., Chicago 8, Ill.

Clack Water Treatment Service.
  Now Clack Water Treatment, Inc., 949 Applegate Rd., Madison, Wisc.

Claremont Pigment Dispersion Corp., 110 Wallabout St., Brooklyn 11, N. Y.
  Now at 39 Powerhouse Rd., Roslyn Heights, N. Y.

Cliffs Dow Chemical Co., P. O. Drawer 28, Marquette, Mich.
  The mailing address now is P. O. Drawer 298, Marquette, Mich.

Cluett, Peabody Co., 40 Worth St., New York 13, N. Y.
  Now Cluett, Peabody & Co., Inc., 10 E. 40th St., New York 16, N. Y.

Colgate-Palmolive-Peet Co.
  Now Colgate-Palmolive Co., 105 Hudson St., Jersey City 2, N. J.

Columbia Southern Chemical Co., Subsidiary of Pittsburgh Plate Glass Co., Fifth Ave. at Bellefield, Pittsburgh 13, Pa.
  Now at One Gateway Center, Pittsburgh 22, Pa.

Consolidated Water Power & Paper Co.
  Now Consoweld Corp., P. O. Box 50, Wisconsin Rapids, Wisc.

Continental Can Co., Inc., Shellmar-Betner Div., Mt. Vernon, Ohio.
  Formerly Shellmar Products Corp.

Continental-Diamond Fibre Co.
  Now Continental-Diamond Fibre Div. of The Budd Co., Inc., Newark, Del.

Corrulux Corp., P. O. Box 6524, Houston 5, Tex.
  Now L-O-F Glass Fibers Co., Corrulux Div., P. O. Box 20026, Houston 25, Tex.

Cravenette Corp.
  Now The Cravenette Company, U.S.A., 8th & Madison Sts., Hoboken, N. J.

Crucible Steel Co. of America, Oliver Bldg., Pittsburgh 30, Pa.
  Now at Henry W. Oliver Bldg., Mellon Sq., Pittsburgh 22, Pa.

D

Desitin Chemical Co., 70 Ship St., Providence 2, R. I.
  Now at 812 Branch Ave., Providence 4, R. I.

Devcon Corp., 19 Endicott St. (P. O. Box 2), Danvers, Mass.
  Formerly Chemical Development Corp.

Dixon Lubricating Saddle Co.
  Now Dixon Corporation, Bristol, R. I.

Doran Chemical Co., 1701 Westport Rd., Kansas City 11, Mo.
  Now at 5415–17–19 St. John Ave., Kansas City 23, Mo.

Durez Plastics & Chemicals, Inc.
  Now Durez Plastics Div., Hooker Electrochemical Co., 500 Walck Road, North Tonawanda, N. Y.

E

Eagle-Picher Co., The.
  See Fabricon Products Div.

Eastman Chemical Products, Inc., Kingsport, Tenn.
Sales division of Eastman Kodak Co. for products manufactured by Tennessee Eastman Co.

Electro-Chemical Supply & Engineering Co.
Now Electro-Chemical Engineering & Mfg. Co., 750 Broad St., Emmaus, Pa.

Emulsol Chemical Corp., 50 E. Madison St., Chicago 3, Ill.
Now Div. of Witco Chemical Co.

F

Fabricon Products, Inc., Plastics Div.
Now Fabricon Products, Div. of The Eagle-Picher Co., 1721 Pleasant Ave., River Rouge 18, Mich.

Fairfield Chemical Div., Food Machinery & Chemical Corp., P. O. Box 1616, Baltimore 3, Md.
Now at 441 Lexington Ave., New York 17, N. Y.

Federal Leather Co., The
Now Federal Industries, A Div. of Textron Inc., 681 Main St., Belleville 9, N. J.

Feldman, David, & Associates, 523–27 Walnut St., Cincinnati 2, Ohio.
Now at Calle Barranquitas 51, Santruce, Puerto Rico.

Felt Products Mfg. Co., 1523 Carroll Ave., Chicago 7, Ill.
Now at 1504–14 Carroll Ave., Chicago 7, Ill.

Fibreboard Paper Products Corp., 475 Brannan St., San Francisco 19, Calif.
Formerly Paraffin Companies.

Fibreboard Paper Products Corp., Pabco Industrial Insulations Div., 475 Brannan St., San Francisco 19, Calif.
Formerly Pabco Products Inc.

Forest Products Chemical Co., Box 6756 Hollywood P. O., Memphis 8, Tenn.
The mailing address now is Box 6745 Hollywood P. O., Memphis 8, Tenn.

Fries Bros., Inc., 271 Church St., New York 13, N. Y.
Now at Box 8, Carlstadt, N. J.

Fry Plastics Co., 7606 S. Vermont Ave., Los Angeles 44, Calif.
Now at 7826 S. Vermont Ave., Los Angeles 8, Calif.

G

Gallowhur Chemical Corp., 801 Second Ave., New York 17, N. Y.
Now at North Water St., Ossining, N. Y.

Gelvatex Coatings Corp., 93 N. Arroyo Parkway, Pasadena, Calif.
Now at 901 E. Vermont, Anaheim, Calif.

General Drug Co., 170 Varick St., New York 13, N. Y.
Company liquidated as of October 1, 1955.

General Dyestuff Corp.
Now General Dyestuff Co., Div. of General Aniline & Film Corp., 435 Hudson St., New York 14, N. Y.

Glass Fibers, Inc., Waterville, Ohio.
Now L.O.F. Glass Fibers Co., 1810 Madison Ave., Toledo 1, Ohio.

Glidden Co., The, 11001 Madison Ave., Cleveland 2, Ohio.
Now at 900 Union Commerce Bldg., Cleveland 14, Ohio.

Goodall Fabrics, Inc., 625 Madison Ave., New York 22, N. Y.
Now Goodall-Sanford, Inc., 1430 Broadway, New York 18, N. Y.

Goodrich, B. F., Sponge Products Div., B. F. Goodrich Co., Howe Ave., Shelton, Conn.
Formerly Sponge Rubber Co.

H

Hammond Paint & Chemical Co., 29–31 Farnsworth St., Boston 10, Mass.
Now Hammond Paint & Chemical Co., Inc., 108 Dudley St., Boston 19, Mass.

Harchem Div., Wallace & Tiernan, Inc., 25 Main St., Belleville 9, N. J.
Formerly Hardesty Chemical Co., Inc., 41 E. 42nd St., New York 17, N. Y.

Hardesty Chemical Co., Inc., 41 E. 42nd St., New York 17, N. Y.
Now Harchem Div., Wallace & Tiernan, Inc., 25 Main St., Belleville 9, N. J.

Haas-Miller Corp.
Now Harry Miller Corp., 4th & Bristol Sts., Philadelphia 40, Pa.

Holcomb, J. I., Mfg. Co., 44th St. & Cold Spring Rd., Indianapolis 44, Ind.
Now at 1601 Barth Ave., Indianapolis 7, Indiana.

Honan-Crane Corp.
Now Indiana Commercial Filters Corp., 508–12 Indianapolis Ave., Lebanon, Ind.

Houghton Laboratories, Inc., 322 Bush St., Olean, N. Y.
Now at 322 Houghton Ave., Olean, N. Y.

Hunnewell Soap Co., 114–116 W. Second St., Cincinnati 2, Ohio.
Now at 1136 Harrison Ave., Cincinnati 14, Ohio.

I

Illium Corp., Freeport, Ill.
No longer in business. The physical assets and ownership of the registered trademark Illium® were purchased in 1953 by Stainless Foundry & Engineering, Inc., 5132 N. 35th St., Milwaukee 9, Wisc.

Indiana Commercial Filters Corp., 508–12 Indianapolis Ave., Lebanon, Ind.
Formerly Honan-Crane Corp.

Indoil Chemical Co.
Now a part of Amoco Chemicals Corp., 910 S. Michigan Ave., Chicago 80, Ill.

Industrial Research Laboratories, Ltd.
Now Industrial Research Laboratories, Div. of Honolulu Oil Corp., 961 E. Slauson Ave., Los Angeles 11, Calif.

Innis, Speiden & Co., 117 Liberty St., New York 6, N. Y.
Now Innis, Speiden & Co., Inc., Div. of Berkshire Chemicals Inc., 420 Lexington Ave., New York 17, N. Y.

J

Johnson Plastic Corp., 3 Brown Rd., Chagrin Falls, Ohio.
The mailing address now is Box 312, Chagrin Falls, Ohio.

K

Kasenit Co., 3 King St., Mahwah, N. J.
Now at 799 Greenwich St., New York 14, N. Y.

Kelco Co., 31 Nassau St., New York 5, N. Y.
Now at 120 Broadway, New York 5, N. Y.

Kem Products Co., 229 High St., Newark 2, N. J.
Company no longer in business.

Key Co., P. O. Box 494, East St. Louis, Ill.
Now W-K-M Mfg. Co., Inc., Key Products Div. (A subsidiary of *acf* Industries Inc.), P. O. Box 1117, Houston 1, Texas.

Klee Waterproofing Corp., 4011 Red Bank Rd., Cincinnati 27, Ohio.
Formerly American Fluresit Co.

Koppers Co., Inc., Chemical Div., Penacol Plant, Petrolia, Pa.
Formerly Pennsylvania Coal Products Co.

Krylon, Inc., 2038 Washington Ave., Philadelphia 46, Pa.
Now at Ford and Washington Sts., Norristown, Pa.

L

LaMotte Chemical Products Co., Towson, Baltimore 4, Md.
Now at Chestertown, Md.

Landau, J., Co., 200 Wooster St., New York 12, N. Y.
Mailing address now P. O. Box 135, Carlstadt, N. J.

Lastik Products Co., Inc., Keenan Bldg., Pittsburgh 22, Pa.
Now at Iroquois Bldg., Pittsburgh 13, Pa.

Lewis, Harry R., Co., The, Warren, Pa.
The business of this company has been taken over by the Commerce Oil Corp. *and* the Commerce Chemical Co., Warren, Pa.

Link-Belt Co., 307 N. Michigan Ave., Chicago 1, Ill.
Now at Prudential Plaza, Chicago 1, Ill.

Lithgow, James, Co., Inc., 1313 W. Sepulveda Blvd. (P. O. Box 338), Norwalk, Calif.
Now at 13701 S. Carmenita Rd. (P. O. Box 565), Norwalk, Calif.

L-O-F Glass Fibers Co., 1810 Madison Ave., Toledo 1, Ohio.
Formerly Glass Fibers, Inc., Waterville, Ohio.

L-O-F Glass Fibers Co., Corrulux Div., P. O. Box 20026, Houston 25, Tex.
Formerly Corrulux Corp.

Logo Inc., Div. of Bee Chemical Co., 13799 S. Avenue "O", Chicago 33, Ill.
Formerly Bee Chemical Co.

Louisville Cement Co., 315 Guthrie St., Louisville 2, Ky.
Now at 501 S. Second St., Louisville 2, Ky.

Lucidol Div., Novadel-Agene Corp.
Now Lucidol Div., Wallace & Tiernan Inc., 1740 Military Rd., Buffalo 5, N. Y.

M

Maltine Co., The
Now a part of Warner-Chilcott Laboratories, Div. of Warner-Lambert Pharmaceutical Co., Morris Plains, N. J.

Metal & Thermit Corp., 100 E. 42nd St., New York 17, N. Y.
Now at Rahway, N. J.

Metallurgical Products Dept., General Electric Co., Box 237 Roosevelt Park P. O., Detroit 32, Mich.
Formerly Carboloy Dept., General Electric Co.

Micronizer Processing Co., Inc.
Now a part of Pittsburgh Plate Glass Co., Corona Chemical Div., New Albany Rd., Moorestown, N. J.

Miller, Harry, Corp., 4th & Bristol Sts., Philadelphia 40, Pa.
Formerly Haas-Miller Corp.

Milwaukee Chemical Co., P. O. Box 100, Cedarburg, Wisc.
The mailing address now is P. O. Box 5, Cedarburg, Wisc.

Minerals & Chemicals Corp. of America, Menlo Park, N. J.
Formerly Attapulgus Clay Co., 210 W. Washington Square, Philadelphia 5, Pa.

Mystik Adhesive Products Co., a Div. of Chicago Show Printing Co., 2635 N. Kildare Ave., Chicago 39, Ill.
The name of this company was incorrectly listed as Mystic Adhesive Products Co.

N

National Gypsum Co., Western Div., 742 Grayson St., Berkeley, Calif.
Formerly Wesco Waterpaint Co.

National Milling & Chemical Co., 4601 Nixon St., Philadelphia 27, Pa.
Now at 4601 Flat Rock Rd., Philadelphia 27, Pa.

Niagara Alkali Co., 60 E. 42nd St., New York 17, N. Y.
Now an integrated part of Hooker Electrochemical Co., P. O. Box 344, Niagara Falls, N. Y.

Northwest Lead Co.
Now The Bunker Hill Co., Sales and Fabrication Div., 2700—16th Ave. S. W., Seattle 4, Wash.

O

Oakite Products, Inc., 116-A Thames St., New York 6, N. Y.
Now at 19 Rector St., New York 6, N. Y.

Old American Roofing Mills, Div. of The Ruberoid Co., 7600 Truman Rd., Kansas City 26, Mo.
Formerly American Asphalt Roof Corp., 15th St. & Blue River, Kansas City 3, Mo.

Owens-Corning Fiberglas Corp., Nicholas Bldg., Toledo 1, Ohio.
Now at National Bank Bldg., Toledo 1, Ohio.

P

Pabco Products Inc.
Now Fibreboard Paper Products Corp., Pabco Industrial Insulations Div., 475 Brannan St., San Francisco 19, Calif.

Pacific Coast Borax Co., Div. of Borax Consolidated, Ltd.
Now United States Borax & Chemical Corp., Pacific Coast Borax Co. Div., 100 Park Ave., New York 17, N. Y.

Pacific Mills, Industrial Fabrics Dept., 1407 Broadway, New York 18, N. Y.
Now Pacific Mills Industrial Fabrics, Div. of Pacific Mills Domestics Corp., 1430 Broadway, New York 18, N. Y.

Paispearl Products, Inc., 65 Nassau St., New York 7, N. Y.
Now at 24 Aqueduct Lane, Hastings-on-Hudson, N. Y.

Pall Mall Mfg. Co., 12–19 Jackson Ave., Long Island City 1, N. Y.
Now at 11–07 43rd Rd., Long Island City 1, N. Y.

Pan American Chemicals Corp., 557 Fifth Ave., New York 17, N. Y.
Now a part of Amoco Chemicals Corp., 910 S. Michigan Ave., Chicago 80, Ill.

Pantasote Co., The, 444 Madison Ave., New York 22, N. Y.
Now at 415 Madison Ave., New York 17, N. Y.

Paraffin Companies.
Now Fibreboard Paper Products Corp., 475 Brannan St., San Francisco 19, Calif.

Pennsylvania Coal Products Co.
Now a part of Koppers Co., Inc., Chemical Div., Penacol Plant, Petrolia, Pa.

Pioneer Latex and Chemical Co., Lincoln Blvd., Middlesex, N. J.
Now a part of The Borden Co., Chemical Div., 350 Madison Ave., New York 17, N. Y.

Pioneer Scientific Corp., 295 Lafayette St., New York 12, N. Y.
Now at 161 Great Neck Rd., Great Neck, N. Y.

Pittsburgh Coke & Chemical Co., Grant Bldg., Pittsburgh 19, Pa.
The mailing address is now P. O. Box 1645, Pittsburgh 30, Pa.

Pittsburgh Corning Corp., 307 Fourth Ave., Pittsburgh 22, Pa.
Now at One Gateway Center, Pittsburgh 22, Pa.

Plastic Metals Div., The National Radiator Co., 153 Bridge St., Johnstown, Pa.
Now Plastic Metals Div., National-U. S. Radiator Corp., 342 Madison Ave., New York 17, N. Y.

Pla-Tank, Inc.
Now Pla-Tank Div., Haveg Industries, Inc., West Warren, Mass.

Plexon, Inc., 212 Fifth Ave., New York 10, N. Y.
Now Plexon Corp., 116 W. 23rd St., New York 11, N. Y.

Polymel Corp., The, 1502 Fidelity Bldg., Baltimore 1, Md.
Now The Polymel Corp., 2238 Eastern Avenue, Baltimore 31, Md.

Pope & Gray, Inc., 95 Morton St., New York 14, N. Y.
Now at Industrial West, Allwood, Clifton, N. J.

Presstite Engineering Co.
Now Presstite-Keystone Engineering Products Co., Div. of American-Marietta Co., 3900 Chouteau Ave., St. Louis 10, Mo.

Q

Quigley Co., Inc., 527 Fifth Ave., New York 17, N. Y.
Now at 415 Madison Ave., New York 17, N. Y.

R

Ranetite Mfg. Co., 1915 S. Broadway, St. Louis 4, Mo.
Now Ranetite Mfg. Co., Inc., Div. of Ranetite Waterproofing Corp., 1917 S. Broadway, St. Louis 4, Mo.

Ranetite Waterproofing Corp.
See Ranetite Mfg. Co.

Revertex Corp. of America, 274 Ten Eyek St., Brooklyn 6, N. Y.
Now Rubber Corp. of America, 225 Broadway, New York 7, N. Y.

Rex Corp., The, 51 Landsdowne St., Cambridge 39, Mass.
Now at Hayward Rd., West Acton, Mass.

Rezolin, Inc., 4823 W. Jefferson Blvd., Los Angeles 16, California.
Now at 5736 W. 96th St., Los Angeles 45, California.

Robeson Process Co., 500 Fifth Ave. at 42nd St., New York 36, N. Y.
Mailing address now P. O. Box 960, Erie, Pa.

Ross & Rowe, Inc., 50 Broadway, New York 4, N. Y.
Now at 50 Church St., New York 7, N. Y.

Rubber Corp. of America, 225 Broadway, New York 7, N. Y.
Formerly Revertex Corp. of America, 274 Ten Eyek St., Brooklyn 6, N. Y.

S

St. Regis Paper Co., Panelyte Div., 230 Park Ave., New York 17, N. Y.
Now at 150 E. 42nd St., New York 17, N. Y.

Sayles Finishing Co., 72 Leonard, New York 13, N. Y.
Now Sayles Finishing Plants, Inc., 70 West 40th St., New York 18, N. Y.

Sheffield Chemical Co.
Now Sheffield Chemical Div., Sheffield Farms Co., Inc., Norwich, Conn.

Sheffield Farms Co.
See Sheffield Chemical Div.

Shellmar Products Corp.
Now Continental Can Co., Inc., Shellmar-Betner Div., Mt. Vernon, Ohio.

Sigma Chemical Co., 4648 Easton Ave., St. Louis 13, Mo.
Now at 3500 DeKalb St., St. Louis 18, Mo.

Sonneborn, L., Sons, Inc., 300 Fourth Ave., New York 10, N. Y.
Now at 404 Fourth Ave., New York 16, N. Y.

Southern Acid & Sulphur Co., Inc., Rialto Bldg., St. Louis 2, Mo.
The business of this company has been purchased by Olin Mathieson Chemical Corp., Mathieson Bldg., Baltimore 3, Md.

Special Chemicals Corp., 30 Irving Pl., 6th Floor, New York 3, N. Y.
Now at 100 S. Water St., Ossining, N. Y.

Sponge Rubber Products Co.
Now B. F. Goodrich Sponge Products Div., B. F. Goodrich Co., Howe Ave., Shelton, Conn.

Sprayway, Inc., 7638 Vincennes Ave., Chicago 20, Ill.
Formerly Tru-Pine Co.

Stange, Wm. J., Co., 2536 W. Monroe St., Chicago 12, Ill.
Now at 342 N. Western Ave., Chicago 12, Ill.

Sterling Paint & Varnish Co., 184 Commercial St., Malden 8, Mass.
Now Sterling Quality Products, Inc., 184 Commercial St., Malden 8, Mass.

Stewart Research Laboratory, Franconia, Alexandria, Va.
Now at 2930 N. E. 21st Terrace, Coral Shores, Ft. Lauderdale, Fla.

Stupakoff Ceramic & Mfg. Co.
Now Stupakoff Div. of The Carborundum Co., Latrobe, Pa.

Synvar Corp., P. O. Box 1768, Wilmington 99, Del.
The mailing address now is P. O. Box 1752, Wilmington 99, Del.

T

Takamine Laboratory, Inc., Clifton, N. J.
Now Takamine Laboratories, Div. of Miles Laboratories, Inc.

Tanner Chemical Co., 1250 Wordsworth Ave., Ferndale, Detroit 20, Mich.
This Company has gone out of business.

Tennessee Eastman Co., Kingsport, Tenn.
Products manufactured by this Company, a division of Eastman Kodak Co., are now sold through Eastman Chemical Products, Inc., Kingsport, Tenn.

Thermal Syndicate, Ltd., 12 E. 46th St., New York 17, N. Y.
Now Thermal American Fused Quartz Co., 18–20 Salem St., Dover, N. J.

Thompson, H. I., Co.
Now H. I. Thompson Fiber Glass Co., 1733 Cordova St., Los Angeles 7, Calif.

Traver Corp., 350–360 W. Ontario St., Chicago 10, Ill.
The business of this corp. has been purchased by the Container Corporation of America, 358 W. Ontario St., Chicago 10, Ill.

Tropical Paint & Oil Co., The
Now Tropical Paint, Subsidiary of Parker Rust Proof Co., 1246 W. 70th St., Cleveland 2, Ohio.

Tru-Pine Co.
Now Sprayway, Inc., 7638 Vincennes Ave., Chicago 20, Ill.

Tucker's, Mrs., Foods, Inc., Sherman, Tex.
Now Anderson, Clayton & Co., Foods Div., Gibralter Life Bldg. (P. O. Box 35), Dallas 21, Tex.

U

UBS Chemical Corp., 491 Main St., Cambridge 42, Mass.
Formerly Union Bay State Chemical Co., Inc.

Union Bay State Chemical Co., Inc.
Now UBS Chemical Corp., 491 Main St., Cambridge 42, Mass.

Union Carbide & Carbon Corp.
Now Union Carbide Corp., 30 E. 42nd St., New York 17, N. Y.

United States Borax & Chemical Corp., Pacific Coast Borax Co. Div., 100 Park Ave., New York 17, N. Y.
Formerly Pacific Coast Borax Co., Div. of Borax Consolidated, Ltd.

United States Graphite Co.
Now The United States Graphite Co., Div. of The Wickes Corp., 1621 Holland Ave., Saginaw, Mich.

U. S. Finishing Co., 40 Worth St., New York 13, N. Y.
Now USF-Aspinook Finishing Div., Gera Corp., 261 Fifth Ave., New York 16, N. Y.

USF-Aspinook Finishing Div., Gera Corp., 261 Fifth Ave., New York 16, N. Y.
Formerly U. S. Finishing Co., 40 Worth St., New York 13, N. Y.

W

Welding Equipment & Supply Co., 223 Leib St., Detroit 7, Mich.
Now at 5225 E. Davison, Detroit 12, Mich.

Wesco Waterpaint Co., Div. of National Gypsum Co.
Now National Gypsum Co., Western Div., 742 Grayson St., Berkeley, Calif.

Wickes Corp.
See United States Graphite Co.

Witco Chemical Co., 295 Madison Ave., New York 17, N. Y.
Now at 122 E. 42nd St., New York 17, N. Y.

W-K-M Mfg. Co., Inc., Key Products Div. (A subsidiary of *acf* Industries Inc.), P. O. Box 1117, Houston 1, Texas.
Formerly Key Co., P. O. Box 494, East St. Louis, Ill.

Woodall Industries Inc., 3500 Oakton St., Skokie, Ill.
Now at 7565 E. McNichols Rd., Detroit 34, Mich.

DATE DUE

Demco, Inc. 38-293